Features and Benefits
Merrill Geometry: Applications and Connections

1. **NCTM Standards**   As the correlation on pages T4-T5 shows, strict attention was paid to the *NCTM Standards* in developing this program.

2. **Applications**   Because the ability to grasp concepts and skills is enhanced when they are tied to applications, most lessons open with an application. This is strengthened by including *Applications* in every set of exercises (pages 153-154), as well as in examples (page 171).

3. **Connections**   Connections to interdisciplinary areas (page 70) and to other math areas, such as algebra (page 8), number theory (page 198), trigonometry (page 376), statistics (page 417), and probability (page 507) enhance learning and increase student interest.

4. **Problem Solving**   Most Problem-Solving Strategy lessons relate a strategy to a real-world situation (page 95). The strategy presented in Lesson 4-6 will help students write a proof (page 199, Example 2).

5. **Proof**   Formal proof is introduced in Chapter 2 with the first proof relating to algebra (pages 88-90). The reasoning and *logic* needed to understand proof is presented in the first three lessons of Chapter 2. You will find a balance in the treatment of two-column proof and paragraph proof (page 193).

6. **Algebra**   Algebra is integrated in various ways: as lessons (page 8), proof (page 89), graphing (page 166), connections (page 254), and coordinate proof (page 595). This integration is supplemented by the *Algebra Review* that is included at the end of the odd-numbered chapters (page 66).

7. **Investigations**   These hands-on activities give students the opportunity to discover geometric relationships by using inductive reasoning (pages 170, A1)

8. **Constructions**   Geometric constructions are integrated with the related content (page 149). This type of hands-on activity helps to improve the students' understanding of the geometric concepts presented in the lesson.

9. **Technology**   The integration of technology opens the students' world to the powerful applications of mathematics: scientific calculator (page 377), graphing calculator (page 155), Geometric Supposer (page 75), LOGO (page 49), spreadsheets (page 501), and BASIC (page 147).

10. **Mixed Review**   To help students maintain previously-taught skills and concepts, a *Mixed Review* is included in every set of exercises (page 154). Students are able to find the necessary help because each problem is referenced to the related lesson.

11. **Projects**   The *Extended Projects* appendix offers ways for your students to work together on intriguing long-term projects (page B1).

12. **Portfolios/Journals**   The *Portfolio* suggestion asks students to select items from their work that represent different aspects of their mathematical knowledge (page 550).

    The *Journal* entry gives students the opportunity to keep a log of their thoughts and ideas about the mathematics they are studying (page 12).

13. **Teacher's Support**   The *Teacher's Wraparound Edition* makes it easy for you to organize, present, and enhance the content. The extensive set of resource materials helps you increase each student's chance for success. See pages 12-15 in the brochure that follows.

YOUR STUDENTS ARE ABOUT TO SEE GEOMETRY IN A WHOLE NEW LIGHT

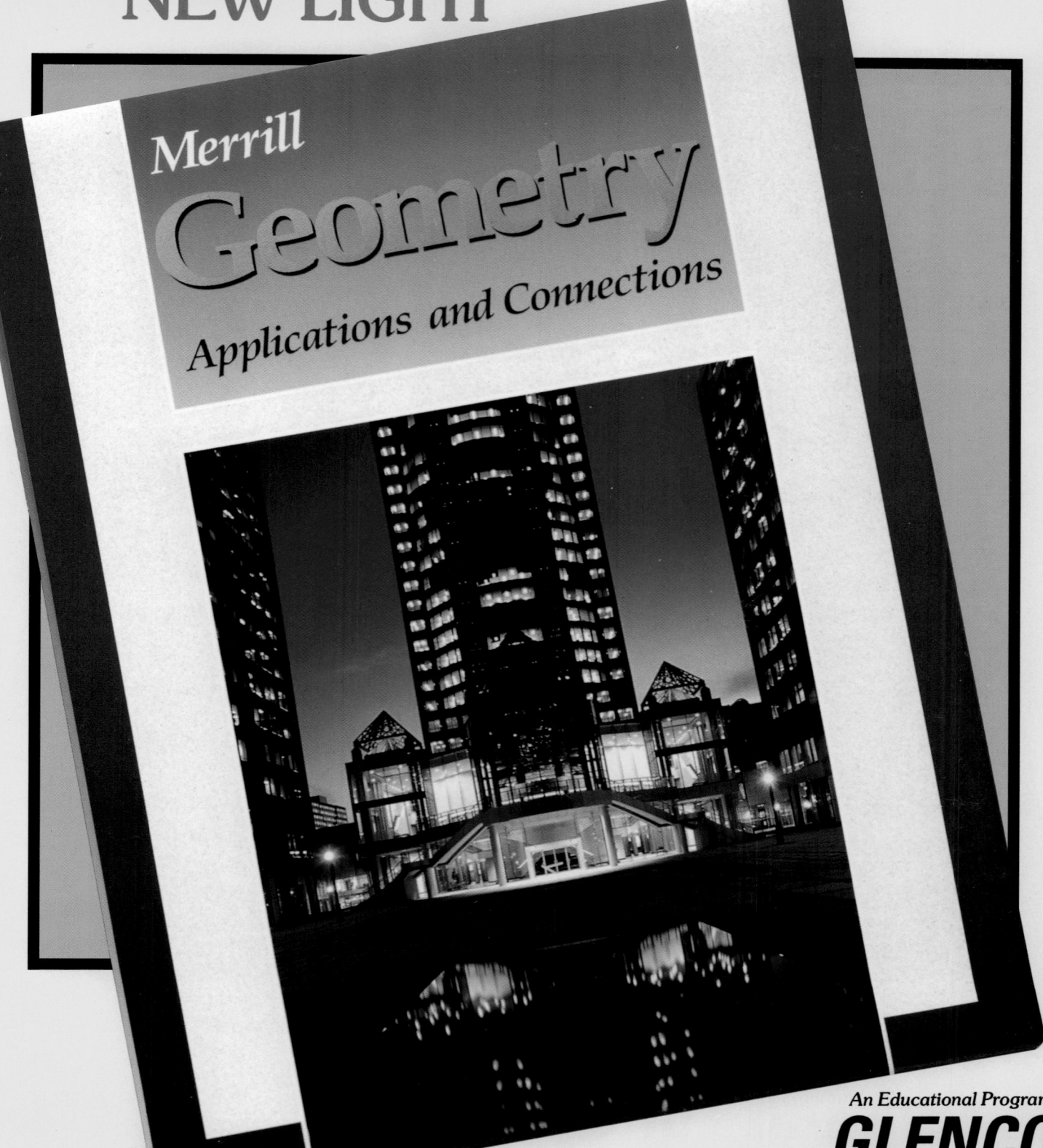

Merrill

Geometry

Applications and Connections

An Educational Program from

GLENCOE

ANNOUNCING A NEW
GEOMETRY: Applica

A geometry program
that brings life to geometry
the continuous use of real world applications

All too often students never quite understand the reason for learning geometry. Many students think of geometry as an abstract mathematical subject that has no place in their everyday world.

GEOMETRY: Applications and Connections will change the way high school students view geometry. Real-life applications, mathematical connections, interdisciplinary connections, and multicultural connections are integrated throughout in order to teach students that succeeding in geometry will help them to succeed later in life...as logical thinkers and confident problem solvers in society.

The textbook offers a vast array of lesson features, challenging activities, and thought-provoking applications that correlate with the four main NCTM standards:

- Problem Solving
- Communication
- Reasoning
- Connections

The content represents the leading edge in geometry instruction because of its focus on these four standards.

This is a geometry program that integrates and maintains algebraic skills and concepts and makes geometric concepts relevant to everyday life. It truly is the perfect course for all your high school students.

"When Am I Ever Going To Use This?"

GEOMETRY: Applications and Connections will help you answer that question. With content that continuously applies and connects geometry principles with other areas of mathematics, other disciplines, and real-world applications, your students will come to understand the importance of geometry and its relevance to their future lives and careers.

The theme on each Chapter Opener features **Geometry Around The World**. This multicultural feature helps students appreciate the wide range of applications of geometry in various world cultures.

CHAPTER 2

Reasoning and Introduction to Proof

CHAPTER OBJECTIVES
In this chapter, you will:
- make conjectures,
- use the laws of logic to make conclusions, and
- write proofs involving segment and angle theorems.

GEOMETRY AROUND THE WORLD
United States

What rectangle filled with three circles helps keep you safe every day? Give up? The answer is a traffic light, developed in 1923 by an African American inventor named Garrett Morgan.

Born in Tennessee in 1875, Morgan moved to Cleveland, Ohio, when he was 18. There, he found work repairing sewing machines and soon invented a belt fastener to make the machines operate more efficiently. Later, he invented a gas mask to protect fire fighters inside smoke-filled buildings. The patented device won a gold medal from the International Exposition for Sanitation and Safety. Morgan and three others wore the masks when they entered a gas-filled tunnel to save workers trapped by an explosion. During World War I, Morgan's invention protected Allied soldiers from breathing the deadly gases their enemies used in battle.

Concern for safety also motivated Morgan, at age 48, to invent a three-way automatic electric traffic light. At the time, he was said to be the only African American in Cleveland who owned a car. Morgan patented his device and later sold the rights to market it to the General Electric Company. He died in 1963.

GEOMETRY IN ACTION

Garrett Morgan systematically went about developing his inventions. First, he identified the problem to be solved. How can sewing machines be made to operate more efficiently? How can people be protected from breathing deadly fumes? How can traffic be regulated to protect pedestrians and drivers?

What do you suppose Morgan did after he identified the problem? Write the steps you think he might have gone through to invent the traffic light.

◄ *"Park Avenue in New ... Inset: Garrett Morgan*

This modern traffic light looks different from Garrett Morgan's original invention, but the purpose is the same — saving lives.

69

Real-World Applications, supported by stimulating photographs and graphics, introduce the content of most lessons. These applications help students see the relevance of geometry. This helps prepare students to apply geometric principles to real-world situations.

2-7 Two-Column Proof with Angles

Objective
After studying this lesson, you should be able to:
- complete proofs involving angle theorems.

Application

The Leaning Tower of Pisa, the famous bell tower in Pisa, Italy, is considered to be one of the seven wonders of the modern world. The tower has leaned ever since the ground beneath the tower began to shift after the first three stories were built. Today, the tower stands about 17 feet off the perpendicular. Its lean increases about $\frac{1}{20}$ of an inch per year.

FYI
According to legend, in 1589, Galileo made his famous experiments with falling weights from the top of the Leaning Tower of Pisa.

The angle that the tower makes with the ground is about 84° on one side and 96° on the other. If you look at the Leaning Tower of Pisa as a ray and the ground as a line, then the angles the tower forms with the ground form a linear pair. Theorem 2-2 states that if two angles form a linear pair, the angles are supplementary.

Theorem 2-2 Supplement Theorem
If two angles form a linear pair, then they are supplementary angles.

You will be asked to prove Theorem 2-2 in Exercise 15.

Example 1

APPLICATION Construction

The flagpole shown at the right forms an angle of 54° with the wall. Find the measure, x, of the larger angle formed by the flagpole and the wall.

The angles form a linear pair. Using Theorem 2-2, the angles must be supplementary. Since the measures of supplementary angles have a sum of 180, we can write this equation.

$$x + 54 = 180$$
$$x + 54 - 54 = 180 - 54 \quad \text{Subtract 54 from each side.}$$
$$x = 126$$

The larger angle measures 126.

LESSON 2-7 TWO-COLUMN PROOF WITH ANGLES   105

4

Mathematical Connections are a big part of the program. The content of every lesson is motivated by a connection or a real-world application. Throughout the text, the student is presented with examples and problems that connect geometry to algebra, coordinate geometry, and statistics. Algebra is also used to introduce students to geometric concepts. When students see a geometric concept is a familiar algebraic setting, they can more easily understand the concept.

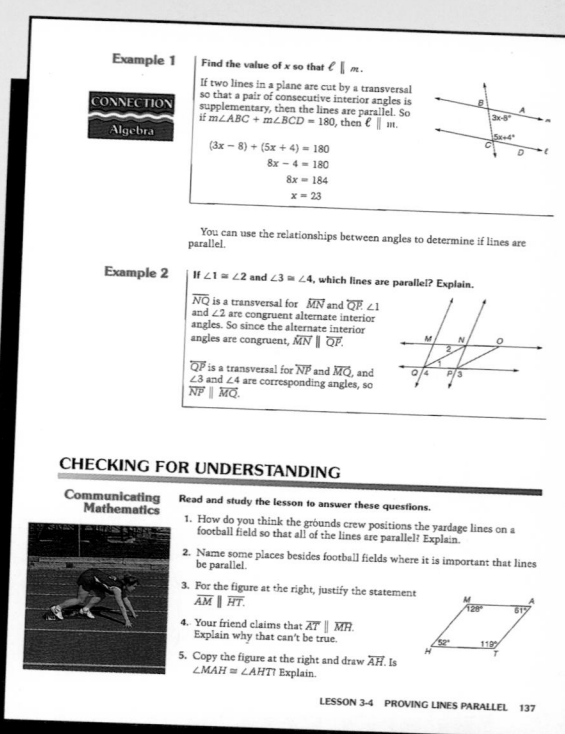

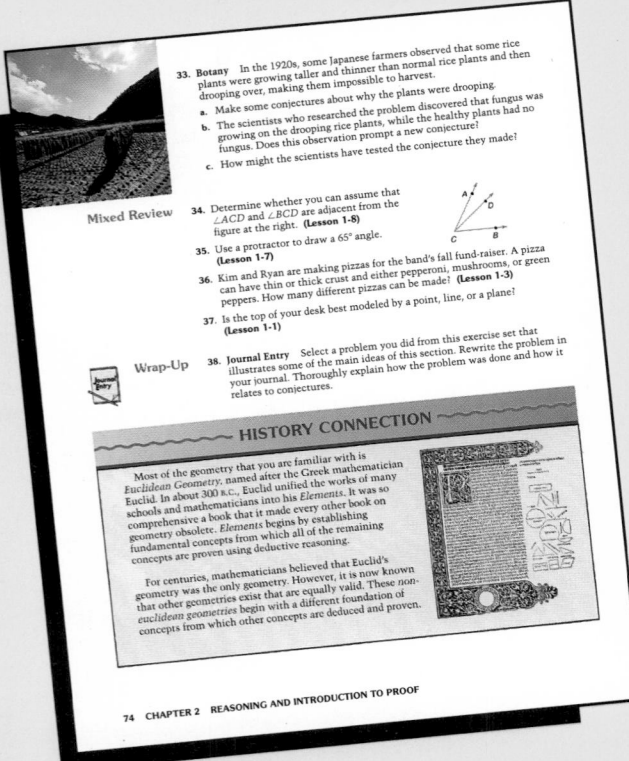

"This standard emphasizes the importance of ... modeling connections between problem situations that may arise in the real world or in disciplines other than mathematics; and mathematical connections between two equivalent representations ..."
–NCTM Standards

In addition to connections between geometry and other areas of mathematics, students are exposed to connections with other disciplines. The **History Connection** introduces students to men and women of various cultures who make contributions to their field thanks to their understanding and application of geometry.

A Unique Approach To Problem Solving

STUDENT EDITION

GEOMETRY: Applications and Connections takes a unique approach to problem solving. The lesson format uses examples from algebra to introduce and apply problem solving strategies to geometry. This integration of algebra not only makes it easier for your students to understand geometric concepts, it also maintains important algebra skills they will need in the future.

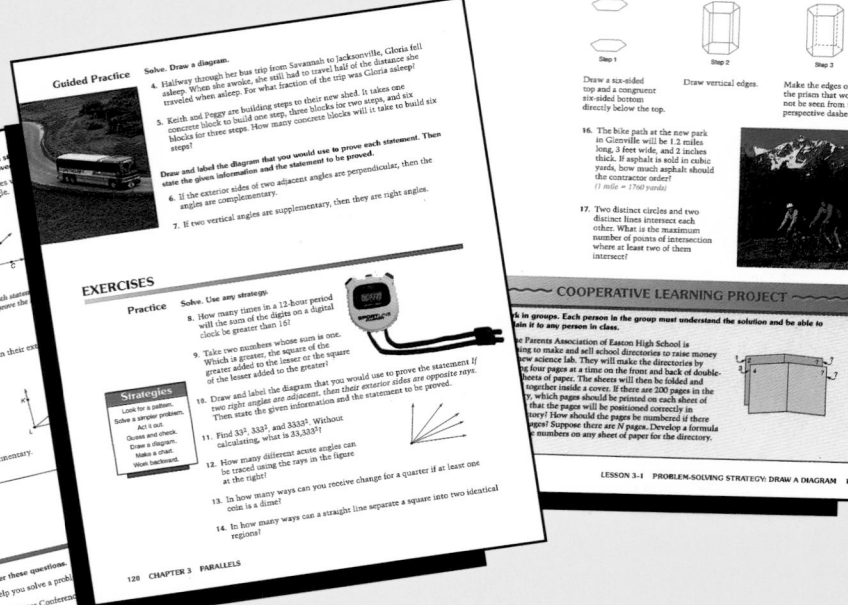

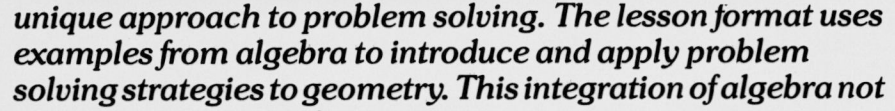

PROBLEM SOLVING
Each chapter contains numerous Problem-solving activities including a **Problem-Solving Strategy** lesson. Students are often shown a concept using a skill or concept from algebra, then they are asked to solve the problem using geometry.

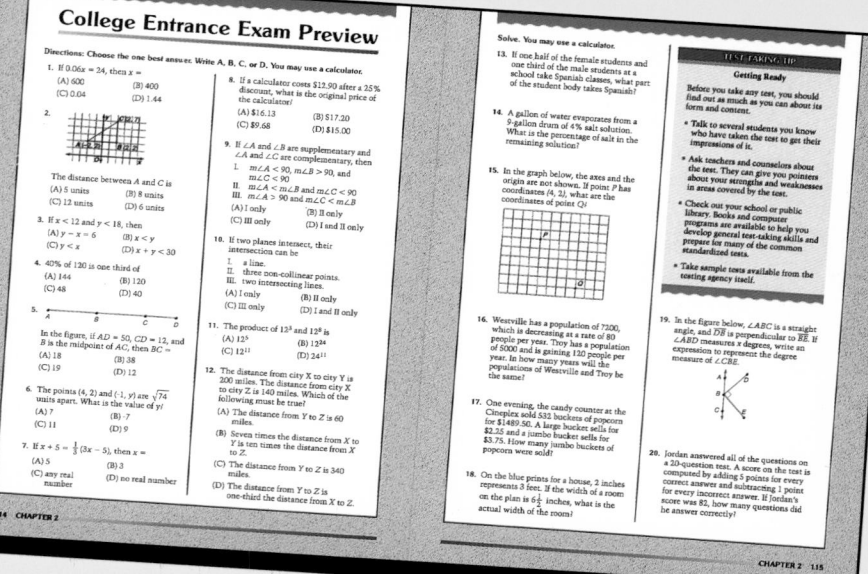

At the end of every even-numbered chapter, you will find a **College Entrance Exam Preview.** This feature provides students the opportunity to practice solving the types of problems that appear on ACT and SAT examinations.

6

CONTINUOUS REVIEW

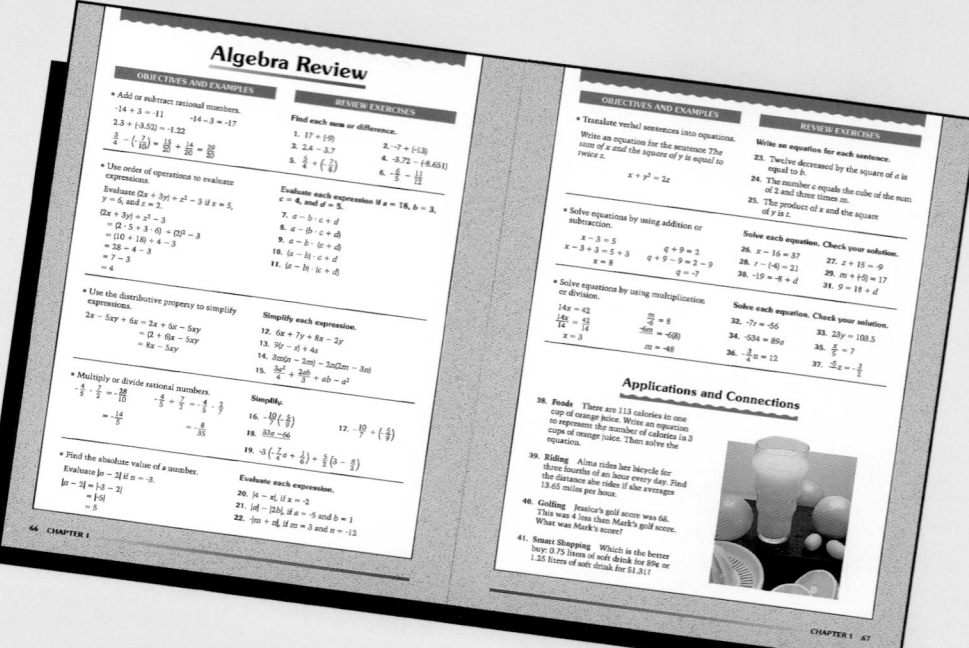

An **Algebra Review** is included at the end of every odd-numbered chapter. This feature gives students the opportunity to hone their understanding of algebraic skills and concepts that are integrated within lessons and to maintain ideas that are needed in later mathematics courses.

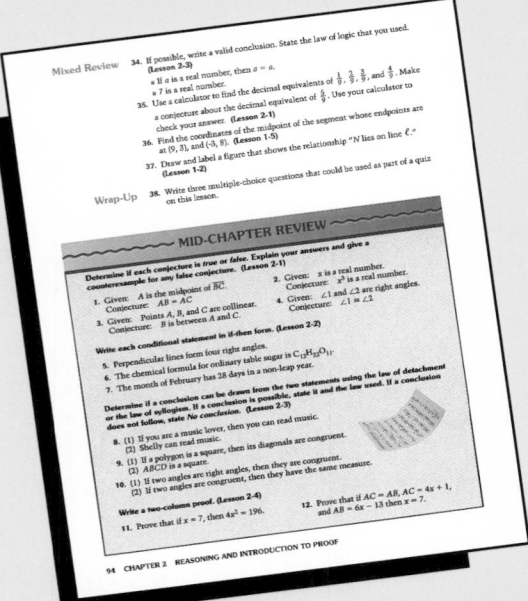

The textbook provides numerous opportunities to review and reinforce the skills needed to succeed in geometry. Each lesson contains a **Mixed Review**—a blend of previously-taught skills and concepts. Each problem is referenced to the related lesson so students can easily go back and restudy important mathematical concepts. The problems that comprise each **Mid-Chapter Review** are also referenced to the related lessons.

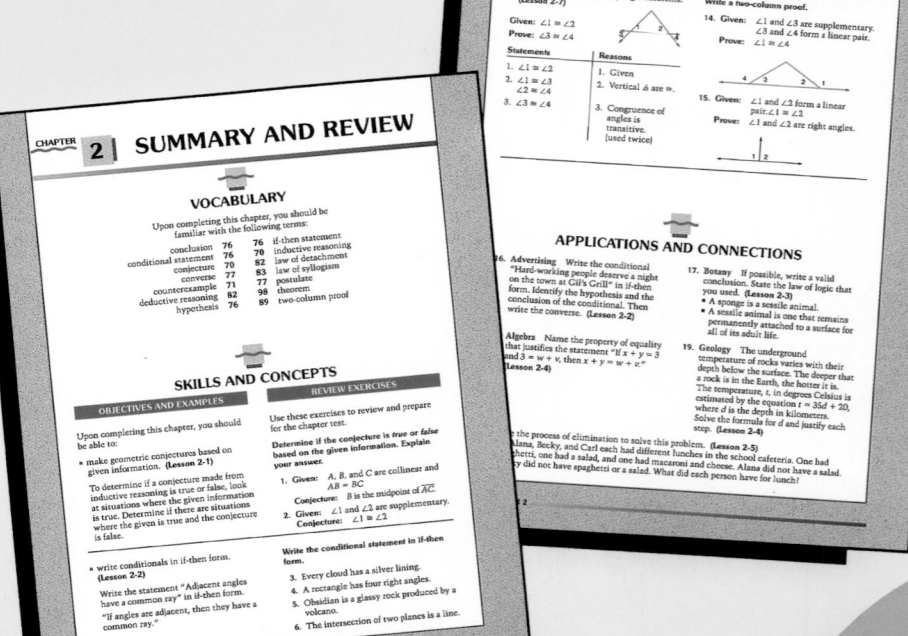

In addition, each chapter has a **Chapter Summary and Review**. This unique combination of objectives, examples, and exercises helps your students better understand and retain what they have learned.

"A mathematics curriculum should include a refinement and extension of methods of mathematical problem solving so that students can apply integrated mathematical problem-solving strategies to solve problems from within and outside mathematics."
—NCTM Standards

Improve Your Students' Ability To Communicate Mathematically

In order for your students to succeed in mathematics, they must be able to reflect upon and clarify their thinking about mathematical ideas and relationships.

GEOMETRY: Application and Connections offers numerous problems, activities, and features that develop and enhance your students' communication skills.

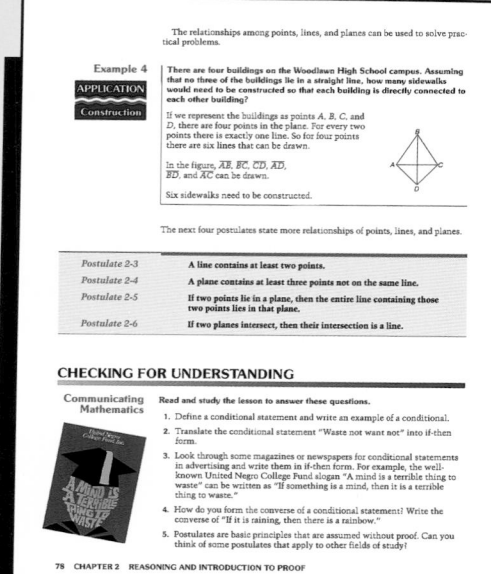

COMMUNICATION

Every exercise set contains several **Communicating Mathematics** problems. These problems provide opportunities for students to express mathematical concepts verbally, in writing, or through the use of pictures, symbols, models, tables, or graphs.

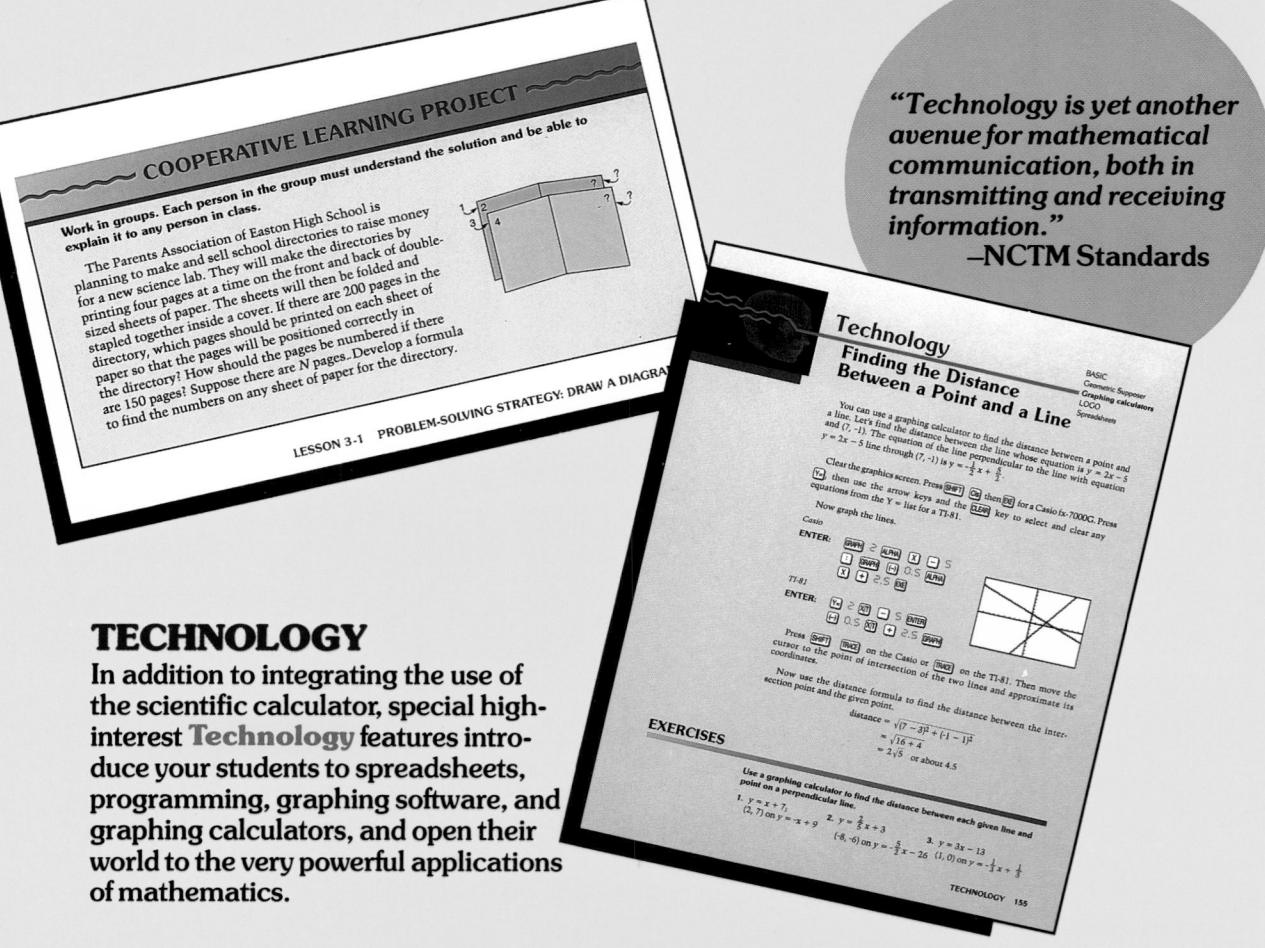

A **Cooperative Learning Project** is contained in every chapter. It provides multiple opportunities for discussion, questioning, listening, and summarizing—all important techniques needed to communicate successfully in mathematics.

"Technology is yet another avenue for mathematical communication, both in transmitting and receiving information."
–NCTM Standards

TECHNOLOGY

In addition to integrating the use of the scientific calculator, special high-interest **Technology** features introduce your students to spreadsheets, programming, graphing software, and graphing calculators, and open their world to the very powerful applications of mathematics.

Geometric Constructions are integrated throughout the program.

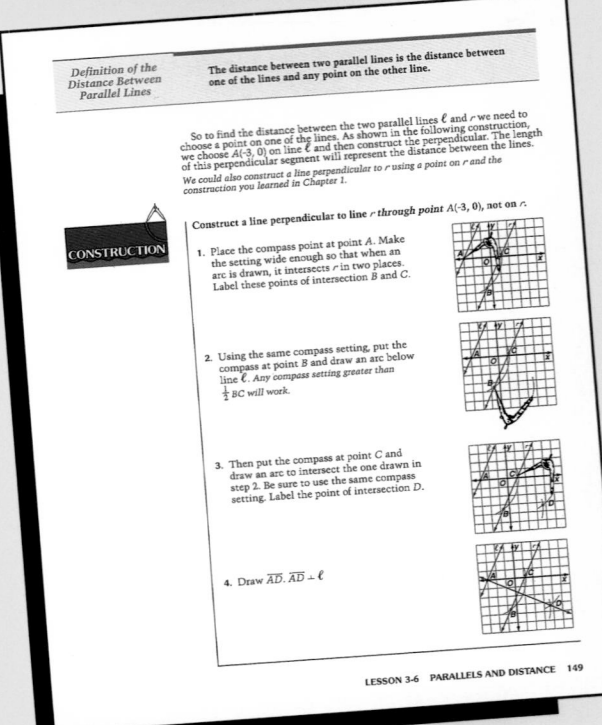

Definition of the Distance Between Parallel Lines	The distance between two parallel lines is the distance between one of the lines and any point on the other line.

So to find the distance between the two parallel lines ℓ and r we need to choose a point on one of the lines. As shown in the following construction, we choose $A(-3, 0)$ on line ℓ and then construct the perpendicular. The length of this perpendicular segment will represent the distance between the lines. We could also construct a line perpendicular to r using a point on r and the construction you learned in Chapter 1.

CONSTRUCTION

Construct a line perpendicular to line r through point $A(-3, 0)$, not on r.

1. Place the compass point at point A. Make the setting wide enough so that when an arc is drawn, it intersects r in two places. Label these points of intersection B and C.

2. Using the same compass setting, put the compass at point B and draw an arc below line ℓ. Any compass setting greater than $\frac{1}{2}BC$ will work.

3. Then put the compass at point C and draw an arc to intersect the arc drawn in step 2. Be sure to use the same compass setting. Label the point of intersection D.

4. Draw $\overline{AD}$. $\overline{AD} \perp \ell$

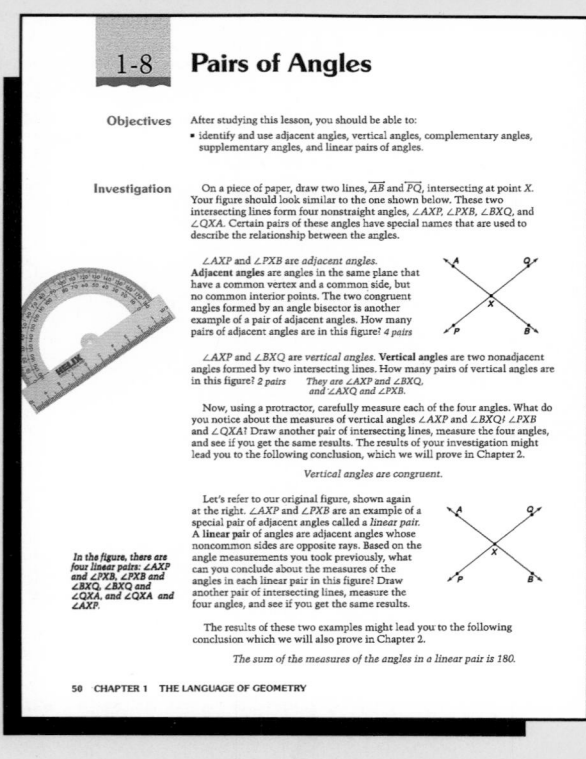

1-8 Pairs of Angles

Objectives
After studying this lesson, you should be able to:
- identify and use adjacent angles, vertical angles, complementary angles, supplementary angles, and linear pairs of angles.

Investigation
On a piece of paper, draw two lines, $\overleftrightarrow{AB}$ and $\overleftrightarrow{PQ}$, intersecting at point X. Your figure should look similar to the one shown below. These two intersecting lines form four nonstraight angles, $\angle AXP$, $\angle PXB$, $\angle BXQ$, and $\angle QXA$. Certain pairs of these angles have special names that are used to describe the relationship between the angles.

$\angle AXP$ and $\angle PXB$ are *adjacent angles*. **Adjacent angles** are angles in the same plane that have a common vertex and a common side, but no common interior points. The two congruent angles formed by an angle bisector is another example of a pair of adjacent angles. How many pairs of adjacent angles are in this figure? *4 pairs*

$\angle AXP$ and $\angle BXQ$ are *vertical angles*. **Vertical angles** are two nonadjacent angles formed by two intersecting lines. How many pairs of vertical angles are in this figure? *2 pairs They are $\angle AXP$ and $\angle BXQ$, and $\angle AXQ$ and $\angle PXB$.*

Now, using a protractor, carefully measure each of the four angles. What do you notice about the measures of vertical angles $\angle AXP$ and $\angle BXQ$? $\angle PXB$ and $\angle QXA$? Draw another pair of intersecting lines, measure the four angles, and see if you get the same results. The results of your investigation might lead you to the following conclusion, which we will prove in Chapter 2.

Vertical angles are congruent.

Let's refer to our original figure, shown again at the right. $\angle AXP$ and $\angle PXB$ are an example of a special pair of adjacent angles called a *linear pair*. A **linear pair** of angles are adjacent angles whose noncommon sides are opposite rays. Based on the angle measurements you took previously, what can you conclude about the measures of the angles in each linear pair in this figure? Draw another pair of intersecting lines, measure the four angles, and see if you get the same results.

In the figure, there are four linear pairs: $\angle AXP$ and $\angle PXB$, $\angle PXB$ and $\angle BXQ$, $\angle BXQ$ and $\angle QXA$, and $\angle QXA$ and $\angle AXP$.

The results of these two examples might lead you to the following conclusion which we will also prove in Chapter 2.

The sum of the measures of the angles in a linear pair is 180.

Investigations provide students the opportunity to discover geometric relationships by using hands-on activities and inductive reasoning.

More Investigations are provided in the back of the student edition.

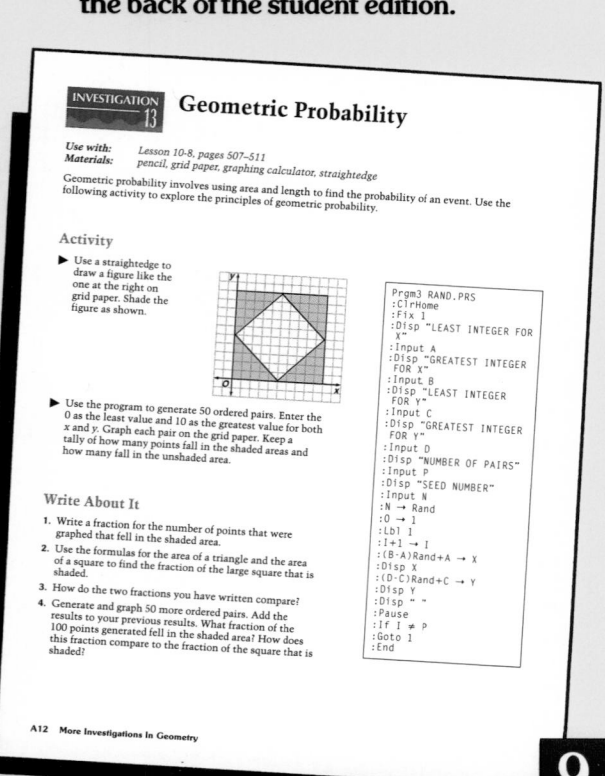

INVESTIGATION 13 Geometric Probability

Use with: Lesson 10-8, pages 507–511
Materials: pencil, grid paper, graphing calculator, straightedge

Geometric probability involves using area and length to find the probability of an event. Use the following activity to explore the principles of geometric probability.

Activity
▶ Use a straightedge to draw a figure like the one at the right on grid paper. Shade the figure as shown.

▶ Use the program to generate 50 ordered pairs. Enter the 0 as the least value and 10 as the greatest value for both x and y. Graph each pair on the grid paper. Keep a tally of how many points fall in the shaded areas and how many fall in the unshaded area.

Write About It
1. Write a fraction for the number of points that were graphed that fell in the shaded area.
2. Use the formulas for the area of a triangle and the area of a square to find the fraction of the large square that is shaded.
3. How do the two fractions you have written compare?
4. Generate and graph 50 more ordered pairs. Add the results to your previous results. What fraction of the 100 points generated fell in the shaded area? How does this fraction compare to the fraction of the square that is shaded?

```
Prgm3 RAND.PRS
:ClrHome
:Fix 1
:Disp "LEAST INTEGER FOR
    X"
:Input A
:Disp "GREATEST INTEGER
    FOR X"
:Input B
:Disp "LEAST INTEGER
    FOR Y"
:Input C
:Disp "GREATEST INTEGER
    FOR Y"
:Input D
:Disp "NUMBER OF PAIRS"
:Input P
:Disp "SEED NUMBER"
:Input N
:N → Rand
:0 → I
:Lbl 1
:I+1 → I
:(B-A)Rand+A → X
:Disp X
:(D-C)Rand+C → Y
:Disp Y
:Disp " "
:Pause
:If I ≠ P
:Goto 1
:End
```

Portfolio

A portfolio is representative samples of your work, collected over a period of time. Begin your portfolio by selecting an item that shows something new you learned in this chapter.

A **Portfolio** suggestion appears in one of the last two lessons of each chapter. Students are asked to select items from their work that represent different aspects of their mathematical knowledge.

Two **Journal** entries appear in each chapter, giving students the opportunity to keep a record of their thoughts and ideas about the mathematics they are studying.

Wrap-Up

36. Journal Entry Occasionally you will be asked to record some of your thoughts about the geometry you are learning in a journal. Start your journal by writing a few sentences about the importance of having a coordinate system and knowing how it works.

Help Students Develop Logical Reasoning Skills

Developing each student's ability to reason logically has always been a goal of geometry. In Chapter 2, the lessons on induction, deduction, and logic focus on reasoning as preparation for the work on two-column proofs.

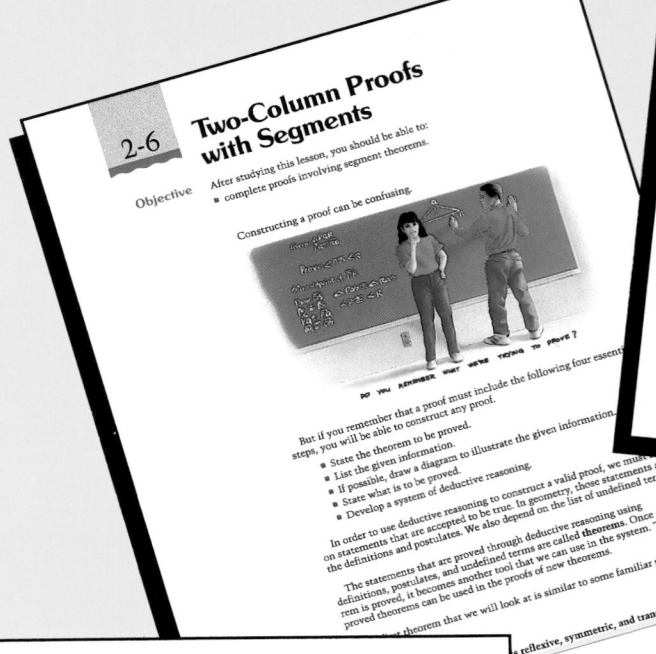

Throughout the text, students are presented a balance between two-column and paragraph proofs."

Exercises page (102)

Practice   Copy and complete each proof.

20. Given: $DA = EL$
Prove: $DE = AL$

Statements	Reasons
a. __?__	
b. $DA = DE + EA$ $EL = EA + AL$	a. Given
c. __?__	b. __?__
d. $DE = AL$	c. Substitution property of equality
	d. __?__

21. Given: $\overline{AB} \cong \overline{CD}$
M is the midpoint of $\overline{AB}$.
N is the midpoint of $\overline{CD}$.
Prove: $\overline{AM} \cong \overline{CN}$

Statements	Reasons
a. $\overline{AB} \cong \overline{CD}$ M is the midpoint of $\overline{AB}$. N is the midpoint of $\overline{CD}$.	a. __?__
b. $AB = CD$	b. __?__
c. __?__ __?__	c. Definition of midpoint
d. $AM + MB = AB$ $CN + ND = CD$	d. __?__
e. $AM + MB = CN + ND$	e. __?__
f. $AM + AM = CN + CN$	f. __?__
g. $2AM = 2CN$	g. Substitution property of equality
h. $AM = CN$	h. __?__
i. $\overline{AM} \cong \overline{CN}$	i. __?__

Write a two-column proof.

22. Given: $RS = ST$
Prove: $RT = 2ST$

23. Given: $MP = NP$
$PO = PL$
Prove: $MO = NL$

Two-Column Proofs lesson page

2-6   Two-Column Proofs with Segments

Objective   After studying this lesson, you should be able to:
■ complete proofs involving segment theorems.

Constructing a proof can be confusing.

But if you remember that a proof must include the following four essential steps, you will be able to construct any proof.
■ State the theorem to be proved.
■ List the given information.
■ If possible, draw a diagram to illustrate the given information.
■ State what is to be proved.
■ Develop a system of deductive reasoning.

In order to use deductive reasoning to construct a valid proof, we must rely on statements that are accepted to be true. In geometry, those statements are the definitions and postulates. We also depend on the list of undefined terms.

The statements that are proved through deductive reasoning are called **theorems**. Once a theorem is proved, it becomes another tool that we can use in the system. That is, proved theorems can be used in the proofs of new theorems.

... reflexive, symmetric, and transitive.

Lesson 3-3 page (129)

Example 1   A road crosses a set of railroad tracks. If the measure of $\angle 6$ is 110, find $m\angle 3$.

Since $\angle 2$ and $\angle 6$ are corresponding angles, $m\angle 2 = m\angle 6$. $m\angle 2 = m\angle 3$ because they are vertical angles. Therefore, $m\angle 6 = m\angle 3$ by the transitive property of equality. So, $m\angle 3 = 110$.

Notice that in Example 1, $\angle 4$ and $\angle 5$ form a pair of alternate interior angles. This is an application of another of the special relationships between the angles formed by two parallel lines and a transversal. These relationships are summarized in Theorems 3-1 through 3-3. You will be asked to prove Theorems 3-1 and 3-2 in Exercises 46 and 47, respectively.

Theorem 3-1 Alternate Interior Angle Theorem	**If two parallel lines are cut by a transversal, then each pair of alternate interior angles is congruent.**
Theorem 3-2 Consecutive Interior Angle Theorem	**If two parallel lines are cut by a transversal, then each pair of consecutive interior angles is supplementary.**
Theorem 3-3 Alternate Exterior Angle Theorem	**If two parallel lines are cut by a transversal, then each pair of alternate exterior angles is congruent.**

The proof of Theorem 3-3 that is given below is called a **paragraph proof**. The statements and reasons are written informally in a paragraph. But the steps in a paragraph proof are the same as those in a two-column proof.

Proof of Theorem 3-3

Given: $p \parallel q$
ℓ is a transversal of p and q.

Prove: $\angle 1 \cong \angle 8; \angle 2 \cong \angle 7$

Paragraph Proof:
We are given that $p \parallel q$. If two parallel lines are cut by a transversal, corresponding angles are congruent. So, $\angle 1 \cong \angle 5$ and $\angle 2 \cong \angle 6$. $\angle 5 \cong \angle 8$ and $\angle 6 \cong \angle 7$ because vertical angles are congruent. Therefore, $\angle 1 \cong \angle 8$ and $\angle 2 \cong \angle 7$ since congruence of angles is transitive.

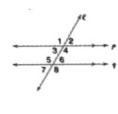

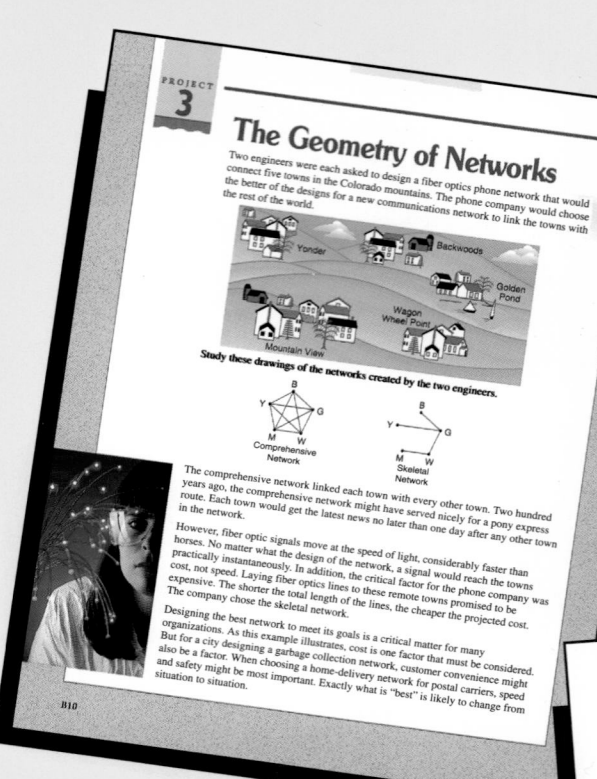

Extended Projects at the back of the Student Edition are open-ended investigations that require several weeks to complete. They are appropriate for individual or group work. Titles are:
• *Geometry of Miniature Golf*
• *Geometry in the Workplace*
• *The Geometry of Networks*
• *String Art Designs*

Each lesson contains **Critical Thinking** problems which challenge your students to develop and apply higher order thinking skills.

Critical Thinking   **44.** Each figure below shows noncollinear rays with a common endpoint.

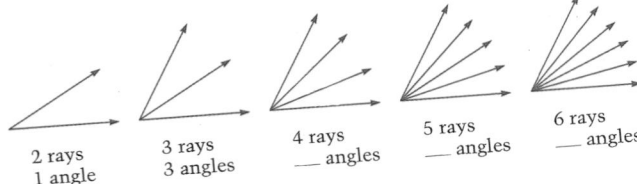

2 rays
1 angle

3 rays
3 angles

4 rays
__ angles

5 rays
__ angles

6 rays
__ angles

a. Count the number of angles in each figure.
b. Do you see a pattern? Try to predict the number of angles that are formed by 7 rays. by 10 rays.
c. Write a formula for the number of angles formed by n noncollinear rays with a common endpoint.

Table of Contents

Making conjectures, gathering evidence, and building an argument to support such notions are fundamental to doing mathematics.
—NCTM Standards

We Make It Easy For You To Organize, Present, Assess, and Enhance The Content In Every Chapter

With **GEOMETRY: Applications and Connections:** *everything you could ever need in teacher support is conveniently located right at your fingertips. Plan your class period from a variety of teaching strategies that make it easy for you to meet your teaching goals while allowing you to create the best, most captivating atmosphere for learning.*

Four **Interleaf Pages** precede each chapter. They provide a quick and easy reference to **Previewing, Organizing,** and **Enhancing the Chapter.**

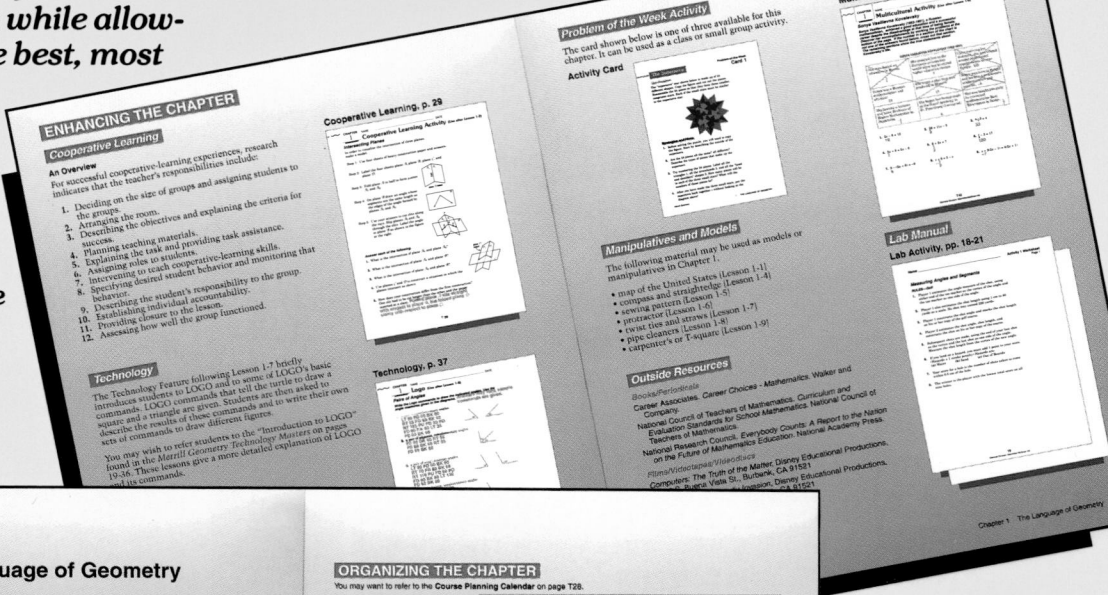

Within the **Interleaf Pages** you will also find a variety of strategies and activities to enhance your students' learning experience. Some of the topics include:

- Cooperative Learning Strategies
- List of Manipulatives used in the chapter
- Technology Highlights and Suggestions
- Critical Thinking Strategies
- Outside Resources

A convenient-to-use **6-Step Teaching Plan** organizes the content in every chapter. The plan provides you with a variety of interesting and time-saving ideas to help you Introduce, Teach, Evaluate, Reteach, Apply, and Extend each lesson.

Closing the Lesson uses activities that involve speaking, writing, and modeling to bring closure to the lesson. Teachers can use these activities to **assess** students' understanding of the lesson concepts.

For every lesson there is at least one **Math Power** question that provides challenging and interesting ways to engage your students in connections, problem solving, communication, or reasoning.

An Abundance Of Resource Materials

No other geometry program can give you as many unique, challenging, and thought-provoking support materials as the new GEOMETRY: Applications and Connections. At your disposal, you can choose from an abundance of resources to help you support and extend the content in every lesson.

Transparencies

Teaching Transparencies contain a full-color transparency for each lesson and chapter opener. The package contains captivating photographs, graphs, completely-worked examples, and overlays as well as a repeat of the 5-Minute Checks found in the Teacher's Wraparound Edition.

A Teacher's Guide is included with pictures of the transparencies, objectives, teaching suggestions, and extension activities for each transparency.

The Real-World Applications: Transparencies and Blackline Masters contain at least two transparencies for each chapter. Each transparency shows real-life photographs and current statistical information that students use to explore situations presented on an accompanying worksheet. Complete teaching suggestions and answers are also provided.

Technology

Technology Masters contain calculator and computer activities to help your students practice using technological tools to develop algebraic skills and applications.

The **Teacher's Guide for Software Resources** describes many popular commercial software titles and how they can be used with *Merrill Geometry*.

Graphing Calculators in the Mathematics Classroom demonstrates how to use Texas Instruments and Casio graphing calculators to explore various topics in mathematics.

Geometric Supposer is innovative, computer software ideal for constructing and studying geometric figures. This component is available through Sunburst Communications (see back cover for details).

Applications

Activities Masters contains four interesting activities for each chapter to help your students get the most out of their lessons. They include:

- Application Activities
- Mixed Problem Solving Activities
- Cooperative Learning Activities

Multicultural Activity Masters offer an activity for each chapter that relates mathematics to cultures or persons from various cultures.

Tech Prep Applications offer students the opportunity to see how algebra skills are applied in the workplace through real-life problem solving.

Hands-On Activities

The **Algebra and Geometry Overhead Manipulative Resources** contain manipulatives, such as a protractor, a compass, spinners, and special transparencies that can be used with an overhead projector.

The **Lab Manual** contains 20 activities, each of which consists of a complete description and teaching instruction, a two-page student recording sheet and worksheet, and an independent activity.

Assessment

The Test and Review Generator, available in Apple, IBM, and Macintosh formats, provides a valuable resource for creating your own quizzes, tests, and worksheets.

Evaluation Masters provide a thorough representation of the chapter content through a variety of multiple-choice and free-response chapter tests, quizzes, a mid-chapter test, and cumulative reviews, as well as semester and final tests.

The **Performance Assessment** booklet contains open-ended assessment items and a scoring rubric for each chapter.

Alternative Assessment in the Mathematics Classroom includes suggestions and ideas for projects, portfolios, questioning, and other assessment strategies.

Cooperative Learning

Cooperative Learning in the Mathematics Classroom describes how to implement cooperative learning groups successfully. Also see **Cooperative Learning Activities** in the **Activities Masters.**

Problem-of-the-Week Cards give you another fun and interesting way to motivate your students to think mathematically.

Meeting Individual Needs

Spanish Resources give a Spanish translation of the English-language glossary in the Student Edition. Key chapter objectives are also provided in Spanish.

Reteaching Masters explore lesson concepts using alternative methods, such as modeling and graphing.

Practice Masters provide additional practice for the concept exercises found in each lesson.

Enrichment Masters contain stimulating activities, including games and puzzles, to help extend and enrich the main ideas in each lesson.

And More

The **Flow Proof and Indirect Proof** booklet provides a way for teachers to add flow proofs to the course. Blackline masters on flow proof and indirect proofs are included.

A **Solutions Manual** provides a complete solution for every problem in the Student Edition.

Lesson Plans, one for each lesson, helps you plan your daily lessons by making it easy for you to make the best of the learning materials for your class.

Involving Parents and the Community in the Mathematics Classroom presents suggestions on how parents and the community can be active participants in supporting mathematics instruction.

Give Your Students The Advantage of Geometry: Applications and Connections Strong Geometry Content...Reinforced By Applications And Connections!

Merrill
Geometry
Applications and Connections

GLENCOE

Macmillan/McGraw-Hill

New York, New York   Columbus, Ohio   Mission Hills, California   Peoria, Illinois

Send all inquiries to:

GLENCOE DIVISION
Macmillan/McGraw-Hill
936 Eastwind Drive
Westerville, OH 43081

ISBN: 0-02-824438-9 (Student's Edition)
ISBN: 0-02-824439-7 (Teacher's Wraparound Edition)

Printed in the United States of America.

1 2 3 4 5 6 7 8 9 10 VH 03 02 01 00 99 98 97 96 95 94

AUTHORS

Gail F. Burrill teaches mathematics at Whitnall High School, Greenfield, Wisconsin. Ms. Burrill obtained her B.S. in Mathematics from Marquette University and her M.S. degree in Mathematics from Loyola University. Ms. Burrill received a Presidential Award for Excellence in Teaching Mathematics and Science in 1985. She is a past president of the Wisconsin Mathematics Council and received a Wisconsin Distinguished Mathematics Educator Award. She was a member of the Board of Directors of the National Council of Teachers of Mathematics and is the Chair of the Adolescence and Young Adulthood Mathematics Standards Committee for the National Board for Professional Teaching Standards and of the Mathematics Committee for Initial Teacher Certification for the Council of Chief State School Officers. Ms. Burrill is a coauthor for *Merrill Algebra Essentials*, a co-editor of *Statistics Across the Curriculum* and *Algebra for the Twenty-First Century Conference Proceedings*, and author of articles on teaching mathematics and statistics.

Timothy D. Kanold is the Mathematics-Science Chairman and mathematics teacher at Adlai Stevenson High School, Lincolnshire, Illinois. Mr. Kanold obtained his B.S. degree in Mathematics Education and his M.S. degree in Mathematics from Illinois State University. He also holds a C.A.S. degree from the University of Illinois. Mr. Kanold is active in numerous professional mathematical organizations for which he frequently speaks, and was a member of the Regional Services Committee of the National Council of Teachers of Mathematics. He also served as one of seventeen members for NCTM's Professional Standards for Teaching Mathematics commission. He is the 1986 National Presidential Awardee for Excellence in Mathematics Teaching for Illinois and is a past-president of the Council for Presidential Awardees of Mathematics. He is the author of a chapter on effective classroom teaching practices in NCTM's 1990 yearbook and coauthor of *Merrill Informal Geometry*.

Jerry J. Cummins is the Mathematics/Science Division Chairman for Lyons Township High School, LaGrange, Illinois. Mr. Cummins obtained his B.S. degree in Mathematics Education and M.S. degree in Educational Administration and Supervision from Southern Illinois University. He also holds an M.S. degree in Mathematics Education from the University of Oregon. Mr. Cummins has spoken at many local, state, and national mathematics conferences, and is a past member of the Regional Services Committee of the National Council of Teachers of Mathematics. He is currently a member of the Board of Directors of the National Council of Supervisors of Mathematics, representing the Central States. Mr. Cummins received an Illinois State Presidential Award for Excellence in Teaching of Mathematics in 1984; and is a coauthor of *Merrill Informal Geometry* and Merrill's *Programming in BASIC*.

Lee E. Yunker is a teacher and chairman of the Mathematics Department at West Chicago Community High School, West Chicago, Illinois. Mr. Yunker obtained his B.S. degree from Elmhurst College and his M.Ed. in Mathematics from the University of Illinois, Urbana, Illinois. Mr. Yunker frequently speaks on a variety of topics and is recognized as a leading proponent of fractal geometry for the secondary curriculum. He participated in the first U.S./Korea Seminar on a Comparative Analysis of Mathematics Education in the United States and Korea at the Seoul National University and codirected international symposia on Fractals, Chaos, and Dynamics at Fermilab and the Plasma Physics Lab at Princeton University. Mr. Yunker is a past member of the Board of Directors of both the NCTM and the NCSM. Mr. Yunker is a State Presidential Award Winner for Excellence in Mathematics Teaching. He is a coauthor of *Merrill Advanced Mathematical Concepts*, and *Fractals for the Classroom: Strategic Activities, Volumes One and Two*, co-published by NCTM and Springer-Verlag.

CONSULTANT

Alan G. Foster
Former Chairperson of Mathematics Department
Addison Trail High School
Addison, Illinois

REVIEWERS

Richard Albright
Mathematics Department Chairperson
Hempfield Area Senior High School
Greensburg, Pennsylvania

Rosemary Aragon
Mathematics Teacher
El Rancho High School
Pico Rivera, California

John Bisbikis
Director: Mathematics & Science
Reavis High School
Burbank, Illinois

Jennifer Carmen
Mathematics Teacher
Spring Valley High School
Columbia, South Carolina

Tina Cindea
Mathematics Teacher
Hoover High School
North Canton, Ohio

Patricia Dandridge
Mathematics Teacher
Armstrong High School
Richmond, Virginia

Charles DiGruttolo
Mathematics Department Chairperson
North Allegheny School District
Wexford, Pennsylvania

Mary J. Dubsky
Mathematics Instructional Specialist
Baltimore City Public Schools
Baltimore, Maryland

Vivian P. Fernandez
Mathematics Teacher
H. B. Plant High School
Tampa, Florida

Dianne Foster
Mathematics Teacher
Fairley High School
Memphis, Tennessee

Carol Green
Mathematics Teacher
Hoover High School
North Canton, Ohio

Dennis W. Hodges
Mathematics Teacher
Poly High School
Riverside, California

Dr. Larry L. Houser
Supervisor of Mathematics
Carroll County Public Schools
Westminster, Maryland

David Howell
Mathematics Supervisor
New Haven Public Schools
New Haven, Connecticut

iv

Table of Contents

1 The Language of Geometry   6

2 Reasoning and Introduction to Proof   68

APPLICATIONS AND CONNECTIONS

Technology

What would your life be like without technology? Imagine not having computer games, scanners at the store, microwaves and televisions with digital inputs, or hand-held calculators. It's hard to imagine! Technology plays a very large role in our lives.

In fact, calculators and computers have become so essential that it would be rare for your life not to be affected by these amazingly versatile machines. They are vital to businesses, education, industry, retail, and research just to name a few. Even law enforcement agencies and the sports industry rely heavily on technology to perform many important tasks.

The Technology pages and some of the Investigations in this text let you use technology to explore patterns, make conjectures, and discover mathematics. You will learn to use programs written in the BASIC computer language as well as computer software and spreadsheets. You will also investigate mathematical concepts using graphing calculators and LOGO.

Technology

More Investigations in Geometry

The Geometric Supposer was developed by Education Development Center, Newton, MA 02160, and published by Sunburst Communications, Inc.

Keystrokes are provided for both Casio and Texas Instruments graphing calculators.

3 Parallels

4 Congruent Triangles

162

APPLICATIONS AND CONNECTIONS

5 Applying Congruent Triangles 214

6 Quadrilaterals 264

APPLICATIONS
AND CONNECTIONS

Special Features

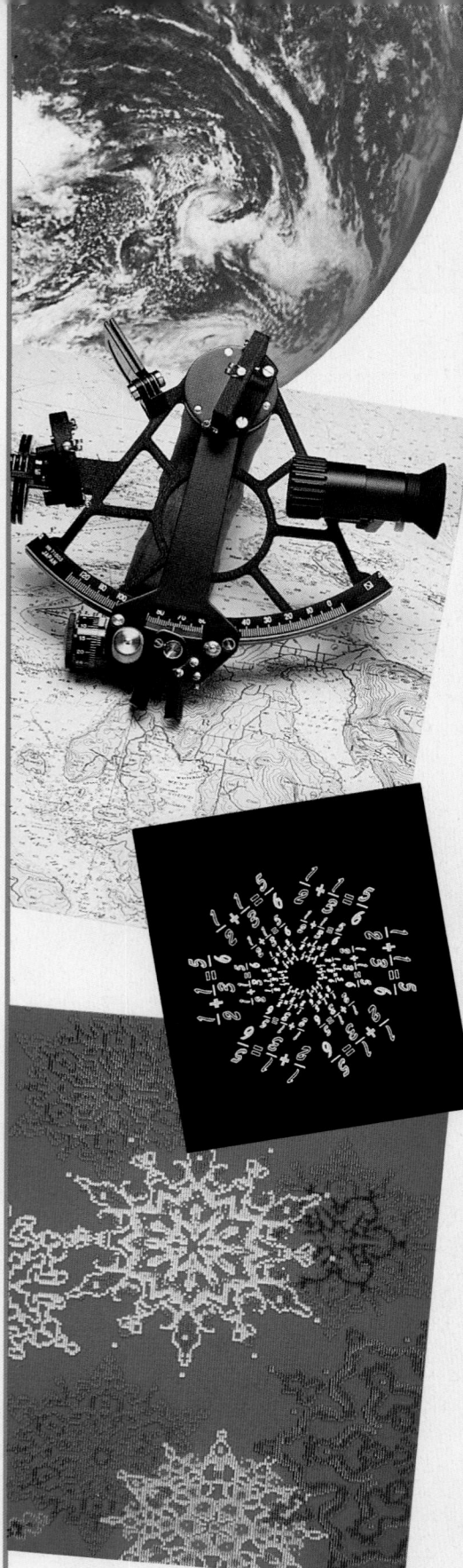

Why did the study of mathematics cost Hypatia, one of the first known women mathematicians, her life? Read the **History Connection** on page 29 to find out. These features contain information about real people from the past and present and from many different cultures who have had a great influence on what you study in geometry today.

When am I ever going to use geometry? It may be sooner than you think. You'll find geometry in many of the subjects you study in school. In the **Fine Arts Connection** on page 141, you'll see how geometry is used to make unusual drawings.

How can working together with my classmates help me solve problems? The fun, but challenging, problems presented in each **Cooperative Learning Project** gives you an opportunity to cooperate, not compete, with other students. The **Developing Reasoning Skills** features also give you a chance to apply your abilities in logic.

History Connections

Connections

7 Similarity 306

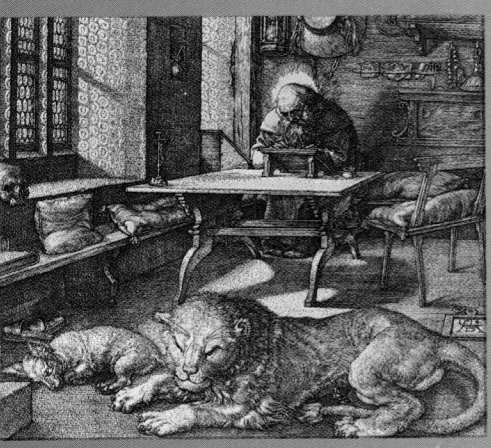

8 Right Triangles and Trigonometry 358

APPLICATIONS AND CONNECTIONS

Algebra Review and College Entrance Exam Preview

Algebra Review

"Why is there algebra review in a geometry book?" "I thought after I took algebra last year, I was finished with it, at least for a while." These are things you may ask when you see the pages in this book entitled Algebra Review.

Geometry and algebra are closely connected. You can't have one without the other! For example, the solutions of a linear equation in algebra correspond to the graph of the equation on a coordinate plane in geometry. You can use algebra to explore what happens to the volume of a rectangular prism if one or two dimensions double.

The Algebra Review pages will not only help you connect algebra and geometry; they will help you maintain your algebraic and problem-solving skills. Algebra Reviews are provided on pages 66–67, 160–161, 262–263, 356–357, 462–463, 570–571, and 678–679.

College Entrance Exam Preview

Have you ever thought about what you want to do after you graduate from high school? There are many things to consider—college, a full-time job, combination of part-time job and college, military service, and so on. The courses you take and the decisions that you make now will help shape your future after high school. If you want to go to college, you need to begin thinking about what you would like to major in and what college or university you will attend.

To get into most colleges and universities, you need to take the SAT (Scholastic Achievement Test) or the ACT (American College Test). Approximately 40% of the questions on the math portions of the SAT and the ACT relate to geometry. To help you practice for geometry questions, as well as other math questions on these tests and other similar tests, you can use the College Entrance Exam Previews. These are provided after every other chapter in this text. They are on pages 114–115, 212–213, 304–305, 406–407, 522–523, and 618–619.

9 Circles

408

10 Polygons and Area

464

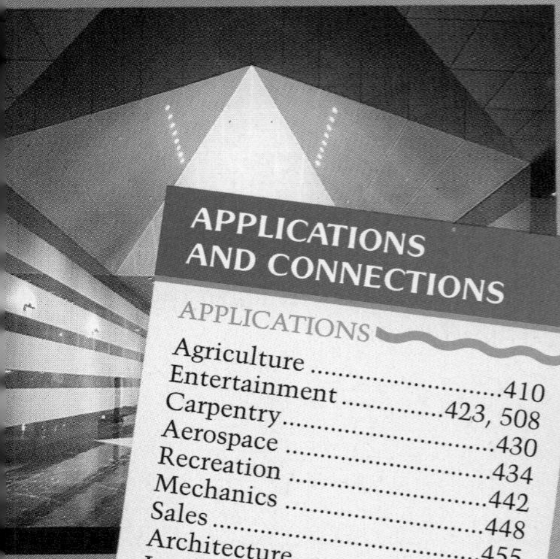

APPLICATIONS AND CONNECTIONS

xiii

Investigations in Geometry and Extended Projects

Did you know you can find the formula for the area of a triangle by folding paper? You can represent many geometric concepts by using manipulatives. A manipulative can be a piece of paper, a protractor, a mira™, or even a graphing calculator. Investigations using manipulatives are included in the lessons throughout this book. Pages A1–A16 contain 17 additional Investigations in Geometry covering various topics.

More Investigations in Geometry

What does miniature golf have in common with geometry? Turn to page B2 and you will find a project to work on with others in your class that explores the ways that geometry works in sports like miniature golf, basketball, and billiards. There are four Extended Projects on pages B1–B16 that use the geometry you will learn over the year to investigate specific topics in sports, careers, transportation, and art.

Extended Projects

11 Surface Area and Volume 524

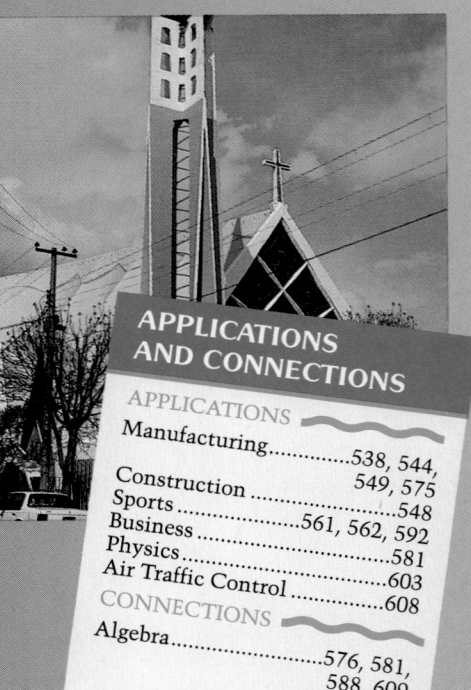

12 More Coordinate Geometry 572

13 Loci and Transformations 620

APPLICATIONS AND CONNECTIONS

To The Teacher

The purpose of this 28-page *Teacher's Guide* is to provide an introduction to the format and philosophy of the *Merrill Geometry Teacher's Wraparound Edition*. It is also intended to relate some background information on several contemporary issues facing mathematics educators in the 1990s, such as the use of technology and alternative assessment strategies. Suggested time schedules for six-week and nine-week grading periods and clearly-defined instructional objectives are included to further make the learning of geometry smooth for both students and teachers.

Teacher's Guide Table of Contents

How to Use the Six-Step Teaching Plan in Merrill Geometry

What do you search for when making a new textbook selection? You may search for a total program that is easy to teach. Your **Merrill Geometry Teacher's Wraparound Edition** delivers the collective teaching experience of its authors, consultants, and reviewers so that you will have the wealth of reliable information you search for. By furnishing you with an effective teaching model, this book saves you preparation time and energy. You, in turn, are free to spend that time and energy on your most important responsibility—your students.

As a professional, you will be pleased to find this program provides you with readily available activities to engage your students throughout the entire class period.

Each chapter begins with **Multicultural Notes** that gives

Connections and Applications provide you with real-world examples and exercises found in the chapter.

additional information about the concepts introduced in the Chapter Opener. A **Class Project** is also provided that is intended to be on-going throughout the chapter. The **Connections and Applications** chart provides you with a list of real-world examples and exercises found in the chapter.

Each lesson includes a comprehensive six-part teaching plan that, when utilized consistently, makes it easy for you to teach and easy for your students to learn.

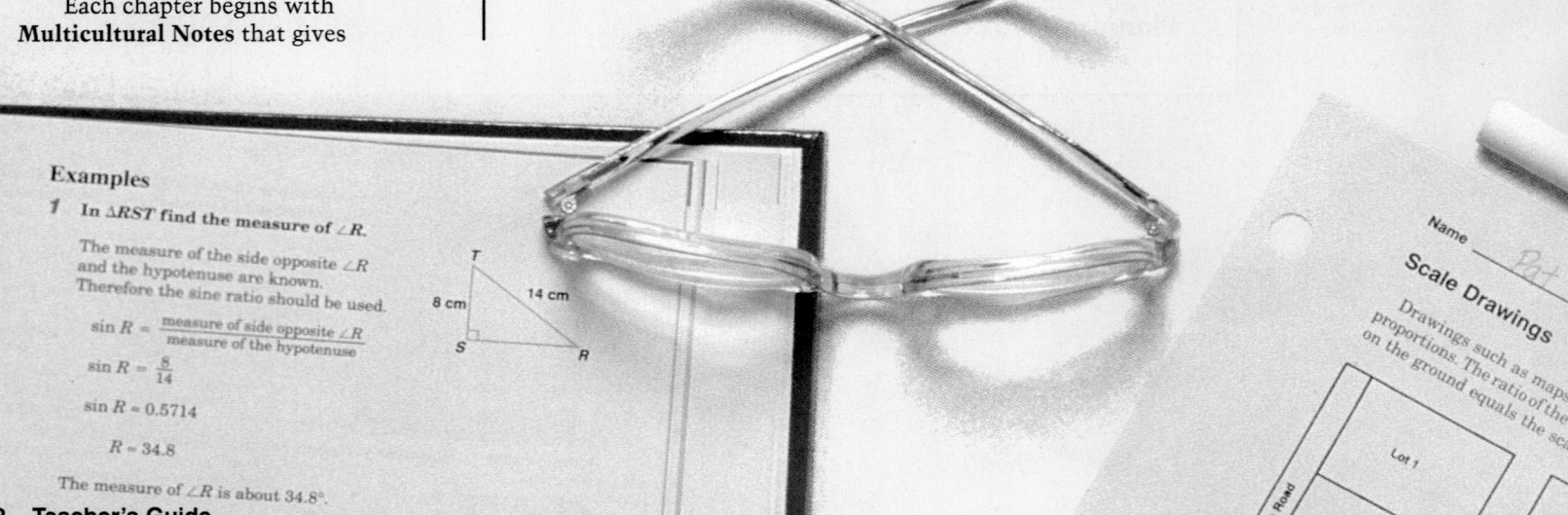

Examples

1 In $\triangle RST$ find the measure of $\angle R$.

The measure of the side opposite $\angle R$ and the hypotenuse are known. Therefore the sine ratio should be used.

$$\sin R = \frac{\text{measure of side opposite } \angle R}{\text{measure of the hypotenuse}}$$

$$\sin R = \frac{8}{14}$$

$$\sin R = 0.5714$$

$$R = 34.8$$

The measure of $\angle R$ is about $34.8°$.

8 cm   14 cm

Scale Drawings

Drawings such as maps of proportions. The ratio of the dis on the ground equals the scale

Name _____

Lot 1

1 INTRODUCING THE LESSON

INTRODUCING THE LESSON, or the anticipatory set as it is sometimes called, is the first step of the **Merrill Geometry** teaching plan.

INTRODUCING THE LESSON begins with two pre-lesson activities to engage your students. The **5-Minute Check** includes one to five questions from the previous lesson. This allows you to check retention of skills and concepts. **Motivating the Lesson** helps prepare students for learning the day's lesson by piquing their interest. It is intended to help focus the attention of the class so the lesson can begin.

The latter activity may also provide time for students to interact with you, thus enabling you to modify the lesson to fit what students already know. This activity usually can be completed within the first five minutes of class and should be a direct lead-in to the concepts that will be presented. By focusing your students, you will provide the structural framework for what is to come.

2 TEACHING THE LESSON

TEACHING THE LESSON, the second step of the teaching plan, is the heart of any lesson. The primary aim of the **Merrill Geometry** teaching plan is to give you the tools to accomplish the admittedly difficult task of enabling your students to learn geometric concepts. Effective **Teaching Tips** as well as **Chalkboard Examples** are provided in this part of the teaching cycle.

ALTERNATE TEACHING STRATEGIES provides you various methods of teaching the content of the lesson. These strategies include Using Cooperative Groups, Using Manipulatives, Using Technology, and Using Critical Thinking, just to name a few.

With the materials presented in the TEACHING THE LESSON step of the six-part teaching plan, your efficiency and productivity as a teacher will increase. The TEACHING THE LESSON step brings together the major elements that form a sound teaching approach.

3 EVALUATING THE LESSON

As a teacher, you work hard at making the transfer of knowledge as efficient and productive as it can be. One finding of educational researchers is that teachers who closely guide their students during a lesson are more effective. This third step provides **Checking for Understanding** and **Error Analysis** to assist you in identifying and correcting common student errors. **Closing the Lesson** provides you with a quick way of determining if students have mastered the objectives of the lesson and gives students an opportunity for direct communication in written, spoken, or modeled form.

4 RETEACHING THE LESSON

No matter how thoroughly a subject is covered in the classroom, there usually will be students who do not understand the lesson the first time it is taught. A **RETEACHING THE LESSON** activity is provided for every lesson as a way to teach the same concepts or facts differently so they will be more amenable to students' individual learning styles.

Research shows that teachers who closely guide their students during a lesson are more effective.

5 APPLYING THE LESSON

A suggested **HOMEWORK ASSIGNMENT GUIDE** for three levels—Basic, Average, and Enriched—is provided for each lesson. In addition, **Exercise Notes** may be provided that give insight and hints into specific exercises.

6 EXTENDING THE LESSON

Every lesson has an **EXTENDING THE LESSON** activity that enriches and extends the concepts taught in the lesson.

As you review the Teacher's Wraparound Edition to **Merrill Geometry**, you will discover that you and your students are considered very important. With the enormous number of teaching tips and strategies provided by the **Teacher's Wraparound Edition**, you should be able to accomplish the goals of your curriculum with a minimum of time and effort. This is true whether you are teaching geometry for the first time, or whether you are a veteran teacher. The materials allow adaptability and flexibility so that student and curricular needs can be met. ∎

How Merrill Geometry Meets the NCTM Standards

Content that relates to specific NCTM standards are found on the following Student Edition pages:

STANDARD 1:

MATHEMATICS AS PROBLEM SOLVING
11, 12, 17-22, 33-35, 41, 47, 48, 52-55, 60-67, 70-75, 80, 81, 92-115, 118-121, 132-134, 139-141, 146-147, 151-161, 169, 175, 176, 180-182, 189-191, 196-201, 206-213, 221, 222, 228-239, 244, 245, 249, 255-263, 270-274, 279, 280, 285-287, 291-293, 297-305, 311-313, 317-320, 324, 325, 333-335, 340, 341, 346-357, 363, 364, 368-370, 374-375, 380-382, 392, 393, 399-407, 414, 415, 419-421, 426, 427, 432, 433, 438, 439, 444-446, 451-453, 455-463, 471, 472, 477-482, 486-488, 493, 494, 499-501, 503, 505, 506, 510-523, 526-528, 530-535, 540, 541, 546, 547, 551-553, 557-559, 563-571, 578, 579, 584, 585, 589-594, 598-600, 605, 606, 611-619, 625-627, 632, 633, 637-639, 642, 643, 649-651, 656-658, 663, 664, 669-679

STANDARD 2:

MATHEMATICS AS COMMUNICATION
7, 10, 12, 15, 21, 26, 32, 39, 46, 52, 59, 61, 67, 78, 81, 84, 87, 90, 94-96, 100, 104, 119, 124, 133, 134, 144, 151, 154, 166, 169, 174, 176, 179, 182, 187, 191, 194, 199, 204, 222, 226, 231, 232, 235, 239, 245, 248, 254, 257, 268, 273, 274, 277, 280, 284, 287, 290, 310, 316, 331, 341, 348, 364, 375, 382, 391, 396, 410-413, 415-418, 420-423, 425-428, 431, 434, 438-442, 444, 445, 447, 450, 452, 453, 455, 457, 461, 465-468, 471-476, 480-483, 486, 488, 489, 492-496, 498, 502, 504, 507, 508, 511-514, 516, 517, 525, 527-529, 531, 534, 536, 539, 541-544, 547-550, 552-554, 556, 560-562, 565, 574, 576, 577, 580, 582, 585, 588, 591-594, 597, 600-607, 610, 612-613, 621, 622, 624-629, 631, 632, 634-636, 638-647, 651, 653, 659, 661, 664, 665, 667, 671-673

STANDARD 3:

MATHEMATICS AS REASONING
11, 19, 41, 54, 69-113, 121, 126, 127, 138-141, 146, 147, 150, 169, 175, 176, 186-191, 200, 233-236, 272, 273, 278, 280, 284-287, 292, 298, 334, 343, 348, 364, 365, 367, 369, 370, 375, 388, 393, 398-400, 412, 421, 422, 426, 427, 429, 432, 433, 438, 444, 445, 448, 452, 453, 471, 472, 480-482, 487, 488, 493, 500, 503, 506, 513, 514, 516, 517, 526-528, 533-535, 537, 541, 545, 547, 552, 556, 558, 559, 564, 566, 568, 575, 584-585, 588-594, 598-600, 605, 606, 611-619, 625-627, 632, 633, 637-638, 642, 643, 649-651, 656, 658, 663, 664, 669-679

STANDARD 4:

MATHEMATICAL CONNECTIONS
18, 28, 33, 36, 48, 49, 64, 73, 74, 93, 95, 96, 109, 122, 123, 127, 140, 141, 147, 148, 153, 154, 176, 221, 225, 229, 235, 239, 241, 245, 247-249, 267, 290-293, 302, 308, 309, 313, 322, 330, 359, 364-366, 393, 394, 396, 398, 404, 405, 413, 415, 417, 420, 426, 427, 430, 433, 435, 438, 439, 442, 445, 448, 452-455, 457, 460, 463, 465, 466, 471, 478, 479, 484, 487, 488, 491, 494, 496, 497, 500, 503, 506, 508, 511, 512, 516, 517, 520, 525, 529, 534, 541, 547-549, 552-554, 559, 561, 564, 565, 568, 570, 571, 574, 578, 579, 584-590, 595, 606-608, 612, 616, 622, 627-630, 632-634, 639-641, 650, 652, 657, 658, 661, 664, 671, 676, 679

STANDARD 5:

ALGEBRA
18, 42, 66, 67, 75, 109, 114, 115, 160, 175, 185, 239, 262, 263, 284, 285, 290, 291, 356,

357, 406, 407, 415, 420, 427, 433, 438, 439, 446, 453, 455-458, 472, 477, 480-482, 488, 494, 500, 511, 522, 523, 527, 528, 534, 547, 555, 568, 570, 571, 579, 585-591, 606, 610-612, 616-618, 627, 643, 670, 672-675, 677-679

STANDARD 6:

FUNCTIONS
20, 95, 146, 155, 158, 212, 222, 257, 262, 284, 285, 305, 356, 463, 522, 559

STANDARD 7:

GEOMETRY FROM A SYNTHETIC PERSPECTIVE
13-17, 26, 31, 35-38, 40-48, 50-61, 76-80, 102, 103, 106, 121-141, 148-154, 164-182, 184, 186, 202, 204-211, 215-229, 252-254, 266-268, 275, 282-284, 288, 289, 338, 342, 354, 355, 410, 416-418, 428-430, 434, 435-438, 440, 441, 447-449, 466-470, 483, 485, 495-497, 520-522, 529, 530, 536, 539, 542, 543, 548, 554-558, 560-562, 613, 615, 621-627, 631, 634-636, 644-647, 653-655, 659-661, 665-667

STANDARD 8:

GEOMETRY FROM AN ALGEBRAIC PERSPECTIVE
8-11, 18, 24, 25, 27-35, 41, 42, 47, 48, 51-55, 57, 60, 72, 73, 79, 88-94, 105, 108, 109, 111, 130-134, 137-139, 142-154, 164-176, 185-189, 203-211, 217-222, 225-227, 234-236, 240-245, 247-249, 256-258, 267-269, 276, 284, 285, 290-291, 295-297, 314, 315, 330, 331, 336-339, 343-345, 360-375, 381-383, 393, 398, 401-403, 406, 407, 411, 412, 438, 441-442, 447-449, 473-475, 484-491, 503-504, 518-523, 534, 537, 544, 554-556, 568, 574-576, 580-582, 586-619, 624, 627-633, 636-643, 645-669, 674-676

STANDARD 9:

TRIGONOMETRY
245, 371-398, 403-405, 412-414, 434-445, 448-451, 454, 498, 601, 603, 613, 639

STANDARD 10:

STATISTICS
20, 22, 35, 64, 73, 95, 96, 161, 170, 198, 212, 213, 245, 308, 310, 315-319, 335, 360-364, 370, 402, 417, 420, 455-457, 460, 472, 494, 511, 523, 528, 559, 580, 586-591, 618, 619, 643, 679

STANDARD 11:

PROBABILITY
207, 232, 317, 350, 351, 354, 381, 507-511, 517, 520, 521, 528, 559, 570, 679

STANDARD 12:

DISCRETE MATHEMATICS
20-22, 29, 49, 65, 73, 74, 81, 119-121, 134, 141, 147, 155, 158, 169, 170, 183, 198, 200, 201, 207, 210, 212, 232, 239, 245, 260, 272, 273, 280, 281, 287, 299, 302, 349-351, 354, 364, 369, 370, 383, 384, 390, 391, 399-401, 404, 415, 421, 427, 453-457, 467-473, 477, 480-482, 488, 494, 501-504, 507-518, 520-522, 526-551, 553-557, 559, 566-569, 585, 591, 594, 606, 607, 611, 613, 627, 633, 652, 671-673

STANDARD 13:

CONCEPTUAL UNDERPINNINGS OF CALCULUS
146, 147, 158, 349, 351, 406, 463, 522, 561, 562, 582

STANDARD 14:

MATHEMATICAL STRUCTURE
7, 66, 76-79, 83, 88-94, 111, 127, 134, 161, 165, 166, 176, 182, 191, 197, 201, 207, 210, 213, 218, 235, 341, 349-351, 359-361, 365-370, 372, 376, 378-399, 412, 415, 427, 433, 446, 463, 465, 477, 478, 482, 487, 494, 500, 501, 509, 511-516, 520, 526-528, 534, 535, 552, 559, 579, 612, 621-677

Cooperative Learning

"The best answer to the question, 'What is the most effective method of teaching?' is that it depends on the goal, the student, the content, and the teacher. But the next best answer is, 'Students teaching other students.' There is a wealth of evidence that peer teaching is extremely effective for a wide range of goals, content, and students of different levels and personalities."

Wilbert McKeachie, et al, 1986

Cooperative learning groups *learn* things together, not just do things together. Studies show that cooperative learning promotes more learning than competitive or individual learning experiences regardless of student age, subject matter, or learning activity. More difficult learning tasks, such as problem solving, critical thinking, and conceptual learning, come out far ahead when cooperative strategies are used. Studies also show that in classroom settings, adolescents learn more from each other about subject matter than from the teacher.

The basic elements of a cooperative learning group are as follows:
(1) Students must perceive that they "sink or swim together."
(2) Students are responsible for everyone else in the group, as well as themselves, in learning the assigned material.
(3) Students must see that they all have the same goal, that they need to divide up the tasks and share the responsibility equally, and that they will be given one evaluation or reward that will apply to all members of the group.

General guidelines and suggestions for implementing cooperative learning in your geometry classroom are provided on this page and the next. In addition, specific guidelines are provided in the teacher material that precedes each chapter. The **Teacher's Classroom**

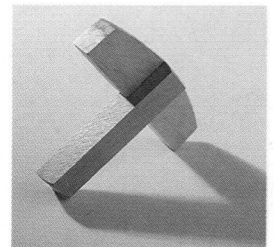

More difficult learning tasks, such as problem solving and critical thinking, come out far ahead when cooperative strategies are used.

Resource also contains a Cooperative Learning Activity in the Activities Booklet that can be used with each chapter.

1. *Arrange your room.* Students in groups should face each other as they work together. It is helpful to number the tables so you can refer to groups by number, or have groups choose a name.

2. *Decide on the size of the group.* Groups work best when teams are composed of two to five students. The materials available might dictate the size of the group.

3. *Assign students to groups.* Each group should be mixed socially, racially, ethnically, sexually, and by learning abilities. Occasionally a student may insist on working alone. This student usually changes his or her mind when seeing that everyone else's grades are better, and the groups are having more fun.

4. *Prepare students for cooperation.* This is a critical step. Tell students about the rationale, procedures, and expected outcomes of this method of instruction. Students need to know that you are not forcing them to be friends, but asking them to work together as they will later on in life with people who come together for a specific purpose.

5. *Plan Teaching Materials.* Distributing materials can help you communicate that the activity is to be a group and not an individual activity. You can provide only one set of materials or one copy of the worksheet to the group. Group members will quickly realize that they need to work together if they are to be successful. You can vary this by providing each member with a worksheet but collect only one of them.

6. *Explain group tasks.* For some activities, each group will need someone to take notes, someone to summarize as the group progresses, and someone to make sure everyone is involved. Classes that have less experience using these methods may need these roles assigned to group members at the beginning of each activity. These jobs should be done by different students each time, so that one student does not feel burdened doing the same job all the time.

7. *Explain the day's lesson.* On the chalkboard or overhead, write the following headings:

■ *Form Groups:* List the number of students in each group.

■ *Topic of the Day:* general academic topic.

■ *Task:* title of activity. At this time, go over instructions and relate the work to previous learning.

■ *Goal:* Indicate whether students will all do individual work of which you will select one person's paper or product to grade, or whether they will produce only one product per group. Student signatures on all the work indicates that they will accept the collected work for their grade.

■ *Cooperative Skills:* List the specific group skills you will be checking. Start with one or two basic skills. The following skills start from basic and move to more advanced.

a. Use quiet voices.
b. Encourage each other to participate.
c. Use each other's names. Use eye contact.
d. Ask your teacher for help only after you have decided as a group that you all need help.
e. Stress that all student contributions are valuable.

After students have some experience working in cooperative groups, you can expect group members to exhibit some or all of the following higher level cooperative skills.

a. Express support and acceptance, both verbal and nonverbal, through eye contact, enthusiasm, and praise.
b. Ask for help or clarification about what is happening.
c. Suggest new ideas.
d. Use appropriate humor that stays on task.
e. Describe feelings using "I messages," such as, "I like the way you praised my idea."
f. Summarize and elaborate on what others have contributed.
g. Develop memory aids and analogies that are clever ways of remembering important points.
h. Criticize ideas, not people.
i. Go beyond the first answer to a question.

Teacher Responsibilities During Cooperative Group Work

1. *Monitor student behavior.* Use a formal observation sheet to count the number of times you observe the behavior expected on that particular assignment for each group. Start with a few behaviors at the beginning and move up to many different behaviors when you feel comfortable doing so. Share your observations with each group.

2. *Provide assistance with the task.* Clarify instructions, review concepts, or answer questions. You will find students who see you nearby will automatically start asking

questions. Your first response should be, "Have you asked everyone in the group?"

Your role will be supportive supervisor rather than direct supervisor; you will help a group that has gotten stuck and is experiencing a high level of frustration. You might do this by asking a few open-ended questions. In a conflict situation, you might ask the group to identify the reason for the difficulty and ask them to come up with some strategies for handling the conflict.

3. *Intervene to teach cooperative skills.* As you observe that some groups have more problems than others with cooperative skills, you may wish to intervene by asking the group to think about why they are not being effective and have them work toward a solution.

4. *Provide closure for the lesson.* Students should be asked to summarize what they have learned and be able to relate it to what they have previously studied. You may want to review the main points and ask students to give examples. You should also answer any final questions.

5. *Evaluate the group process.* In order for groups to be aware of their progress in learning to work together, they must be given time to evaluate or process how they are working together. Allow a few minutes at the end of the lesson for groups to decide if they achieved the criterion you set up. Have them rate themselves on a

scale of one to ten and write down specific ways they could improve.

Keep in mind that cooperative learning does not just "happen." The first few days may seem like bedlam, with some students upset, others mistrustful, and others off task. Both you and your students will make mistakes. Be patient and keep at it. ■

For more information on cooperative learning, see Glencoe's *Cooperative Learning in the Mathematics Classroom*, 1993.

Problem Solving in Geometry

". . . problem solving is much more than applying specific techniques to the solution of classes of word problems. It is a process by which the fabric of mathematics as identified in later standards is both constructed and reinforced."

NCTM Standards (1989, p. 137)

One of the challenges of teaching mathematics is helping students learn to solve problems. Problem solving involves more than coming up with a final answer—it involves the ability to analyze new problems and discover ways to solve them.

Geometric relationships spring directly from spatial relationships in the real world. Consequently, students who perhaps have found algebra uncomfortably abstract may feel very much at home in geometry.

1. EXPLORE *the problem.* Read the problem and identify what is given and what is asked. Jot down important facts from the problem. Sometimes it is helpful to draw a chart or diagram. Think about how the facts are related.

If an equation will be used to solve the problem, choose a variable to represent one of the unspecified numbers in the problem. Read the problem again and use the variable in writing expressions for other unspecified numbers in the problem.

2. PLAN *the solution.* Many different strategies may be used. If an equation will be used to solve the problem, read the problem again. Decide how the unspecified numbers relate to other given information. Write an equation to represent the relationship.

3. SOLVE *the problem.* This involves doing the mathematics and interpreting the answer. If an equation was written, solve the equation and interpret the solution. State the answer to the verbal problem.

4. EXAMINE *the solution.* Check whether the answer makes sense with the conditions of the problem. If not, check your mathematics again. If the mathematics was correct, a mistake was made in "setting up" the problem. In that case, explore the problem again and try a different approach.

Not all real-life problems that involve geometry can be solved by drawing a diagram or making careful measurements. Often one must look for a pattern, consider a variety of possibilities, use logic, or work toward a solution in stages by identifying subgoals.

At every turn, geometric forms emerge in nature and in man-made objects. For this reason, you may find that students naturally accept the idea that geometry is "practical." Once a problem is accepted as practical or interesting, the student will probably be willing to dig in and look for ways to solve it.

Since there is no one strategy that can be relied upon to work for every conceivable situation, students must learn a variety of strategies. This text includes numerous *Problem-Solving Strategy* lessons, such as the list-the-possibilities on pages 19-22 of Chapter 1. Other strategies are introduced in *Problem-Solving Strategy* lessons on pages 95, 118, 198, 230, 272, 349, 399, 455, 480, 526, 592, and 671.

Problem solving involves more than coming up with a final answer.

The four-step problem-solving plan can be used with any strategy that seems appropriate for a given situation.

It is important to create a classroom environment which encourages problem-solving abilities. The following suggestions will prove helpful in building students' confidence in solving complex problems.

■ Encourage students to try a variety of strategies. Praise them for suggesting different ways to approach a problem, even if the suggestions do not always lead to a correct result. Also, spend time "looking back" at problems which were previously solved and discuss alternative ways to solve them.

■ Assume that students will make mistakes when solving problems. An evaluation system which gives partial credit for thoughtful attempts is recommended. For example, you could award 4 points for a correct solution, 3 points for a solution which has the right process but had a small mathematical error, 2 points for a thoughtful attempt with a mistake in "setting up" the solution, and 1 point for other meaningful attempts.

■ Allow sufficient time for the class to explore problems. In some cases it is preferable to spend twice the time on half the problems. Although discussions may seem to move slowly, the extra time will give students more confidence.

■ Some problems may call for a proof. Others may call for discovering and displaying a pattern or deciding whether a conjecture is true or false. Encourage logical thinking, keen observation, and imagination. Some students may find it extremely difficult to put their ideas into a formal, two-column proof or even into the somewhat more natural form of a paragraph proof. However, these students may do a very convincing job of showing by diagrams or manipulatives exactly the key ideas for a solution. When they do so, praise their efforts. It can be the boost they need to keep learning and exploring.

■ Number lines and coordinate planes are used frequently in the text to integrate algebra and geometry. This integration provides students with a number of powerful tools for solving problems and revealing important connections.

■ Throughout the year, emphasize the steps for solving problems. Display a chart listing the steps on the bulletin board, along with a problem for students to solve in their spare time. Problems can be chosen from this text, or from other sources such as *The Mathematics Teacher*.

By following the suggestions on these pages, students will discover that problem-solving is a satisfying, enjoyable experience. ■

Problem 16

Build a model of this figure. Then sketch it.

top view

left view

front view

right view

Using Manipulatives in Your Geometry Classroom

"Physical models and other real-world objects should be used to provide a strong base for the development of students' geometric intuition. . ."

NCTM Standards (1989, p. 157)

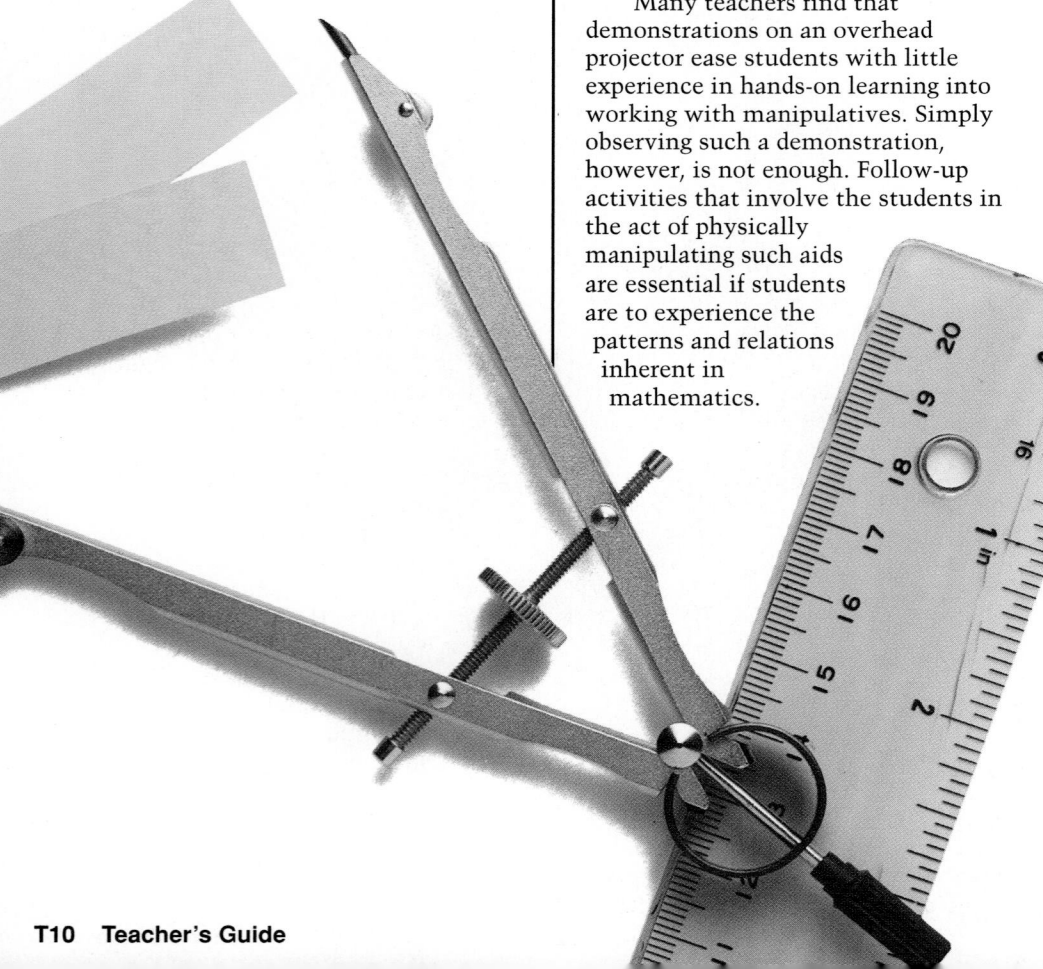

Most teachers agree that the use of manipulative materials helps students build a solid understanding of mathematical concepts and enhances students' achievement in mathematics. The universal anxiety today about achievement in mathematics should prompt educators in this field to heed results from recent studies which indicate that by using manipulative materials at every level, test scores are dramatically improved.

The purpose of using manipulatives is to assist students in bridging the gap from the concrete to the abstract.

Many teachers find that demonstrations on an overhead projector ease students with little experience in hands-on learning into working with manipulatives. Simply observing such a demonstration, however, is not enough. Follow-up activities that involve the students in the act of physically manipulating such aids are essential if students are to experience the patterns and relations inherent in mathematics.

The purpose of using manipulatives is to assist students in bridging the gap from their own concrete environment to the abstract level. Affording students the opportunity for meaningful investigation through modeling with manipulatives not only results in greater understanding of the concepts and skills in question but also provides a fun alternative to everyday, routine problem-solving exercises as well.

Few teachers would deny that the ability to draw geometric figures accurately on paper is a highly desirable skill. However, two-dimensional drawings are not enough. The use of manipulatives plays a crucial role in developing the ability to visualize both two- and three-dimensional figures. Even students who already possess well-developed visualization skills can profit from thoughtfully conceived manipulative activities.

Geometry is concerned with both the unique and the universal properties of geometric forms. For example, if the measurements of the sides or angles of a figure change, certain other features are likely to change as well, while others stay the same.

Many theorems of geometry express the relationships that occur in such situations. Understanding how one

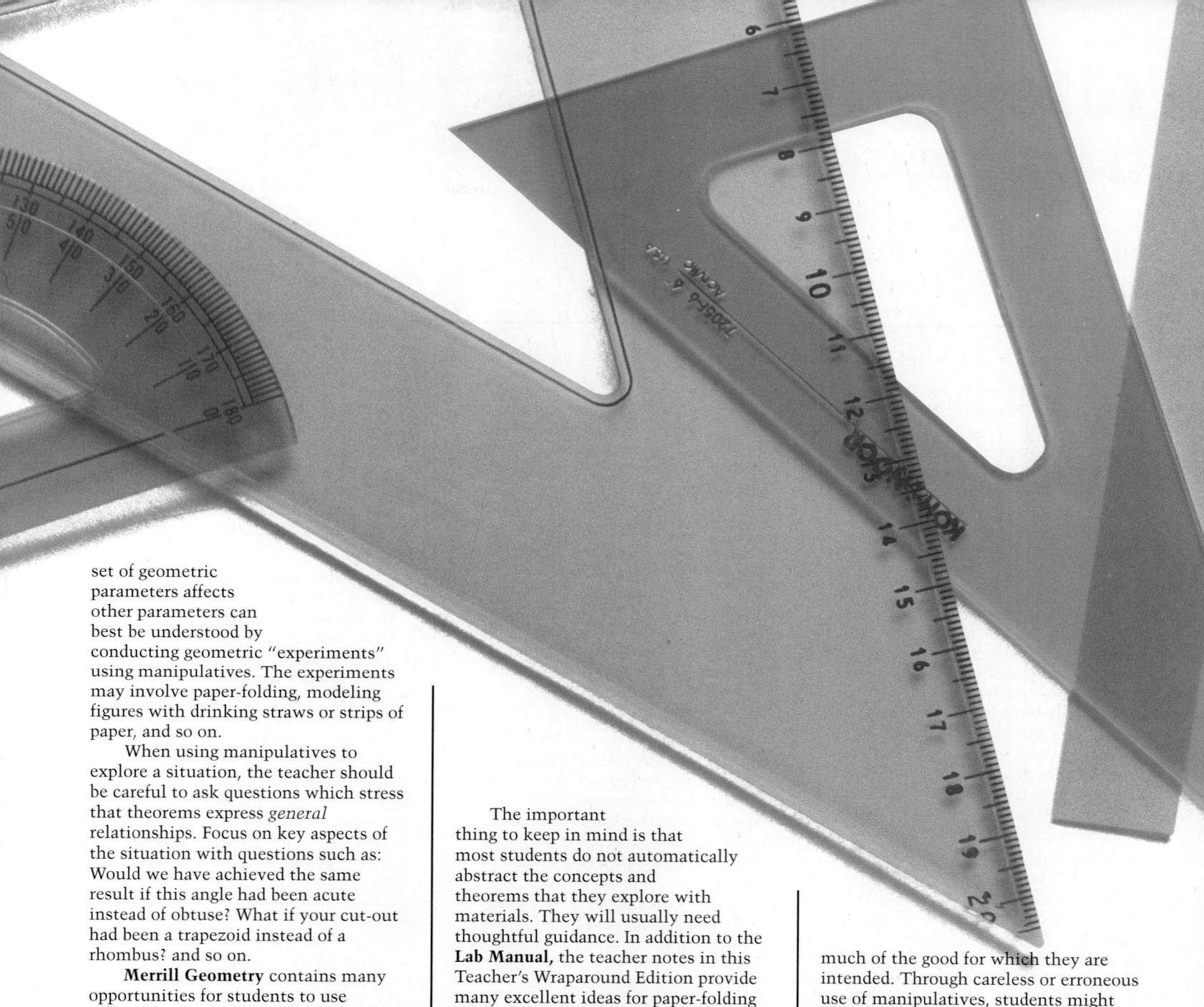

set of geometric parameters affects other parameters can best be understood by conducting geometric "experiments" using manipulatives. The experiments may involve paper-folding, modeling figures with drinking straws or strips of paper, and so on.

When using manipulatives to explore a situation, the teacher should be careful to ask questions which stress that theorems express *general* relationships. Focus on key aspects of the situation with questions such as: Would we have achieved the same result if this angle had been acute instead of obtuse? What if your cut-out had been a trapezoid instead of a rhombus? and so on.

Merrill Geometry contains many opportunities for students to use manipulatives to discover and explore geometric concepts and theorems. Students actually *do* mathematics and are encouraged to make conjectures based on their observations. The **Merrill Geometry Lab Manual** contains many activities that require the use of manipulatives, allowing students to make the connection from the concrete to the abstract.

To make sure that students understand what is expected of them in each activity, the teacher must discuss its goal and model how the manipulative is to be used to achieve it. Encouraging students to suggest ways in which manipulatives can be used helps them to relate concepts and develop mathematical insights.

The important thing to keep in mind is that most students do not automatically abstract the concepts and theorems that they explore with materials. They will usually need thoughtful guidance. In addition to the **Lab Manual,** the teacher notes in this Teacher's Wraparound Edition provide many excellent ideas for paper-folding activities. These ideas are usually provided in the Alternate Teaching Strategies section.

With proper organization and planning, many activities can be used with small groups. Other types of activities will clearly be best used with individuals. In either case, it is helpful to focus on the concepts and relationships involved by asking students to summarize and record their results.

No presentation advocating the use of manipulative materials in the classroom would be totally complete without interjecting a note of caution. Despite the fact that manipulative materials are highly touted, and rightly so, they can, if used incorrectly, undo much of the good for which they are intended. Through careless or erroneous use of manipulatives, students might conclude that there are two distinct mathematical worlds—one of manipulatives and another of symbols—and that each has its own rules.

Summarily if mathematics educators sincerely want to challenge their students in the geometry classroom, they must endorse the proper use of manipulative materials. An endorsement of this sort promises to increase students' understanding of and achievement in mathematics. ■

Alternative Assessment Strategies

Most students would agree that the test is often seen as the bottom line of educational enterprises. Most of them would also agree that the present tests used to determine a student's accomplishment often fall short of the goal of measuring a student's true understanding of the concepts being taught.

Most evaluation materials today include multiple-choice or true/false questions or questions that require objective one-word answers. These types of questions act as a mechanical means of evaluation that focuses on a student's ability to reiterate memorized and practiced definitions and procedures for solving each type of problem. This often does not accurately reflect the student's true capabilities and understanding.

"Mathematics teachers are participating in a major restructuring of the goals and practices of mathematics education. It is essential that assessment strategies be found that can adequately reflect this new conception of the subject."[1]

The purpose of assessment is to identify areas of weakness and strengths for individual students, to assign grades, to gather data for teachers to plan their course of instruction, and to evaluate the current course of instruction. The National Council of Mathematics in their *Curriculum and Evaluation Standards for School Mathematics* (1989) suggests that different types of evaluation materials be used in making assessment. These evaluations are an ongoing process and are used to augment formal assessment, such as the traditional chapter test.

How Do I Begin?

Glencoe has provided many opportunities for you as a teacher to expand the avenues of assessment for your students. These are included in the *Student Edition, Teacher's Wraparound Edition,* and *Teacher's Classroom Resources.*

Some of the following suggestions may help you implement alternative forms of assessment in your classroom.

Open-ended Questions are perhaps the easiest way to employ a new evaluation strategy. In an assessment of this nature, students are forced to think for themselves and to express mathematical ideas in language that corresponds with their mathematical development.

- The **Communicating Mathematics** questions in each lesson ask students to interpret what they have read in the lesson.
- Verbal questions in the **Exercises** often ask students to explain their answers rather than just giving a numerical response.
- **Critical Thinking** questions ask students to develop and apply higher order thinking skills.

Remember that when using open-ended questions, there may not be *one* correct answer, but rather an array of answers and explanations that are acceptable.

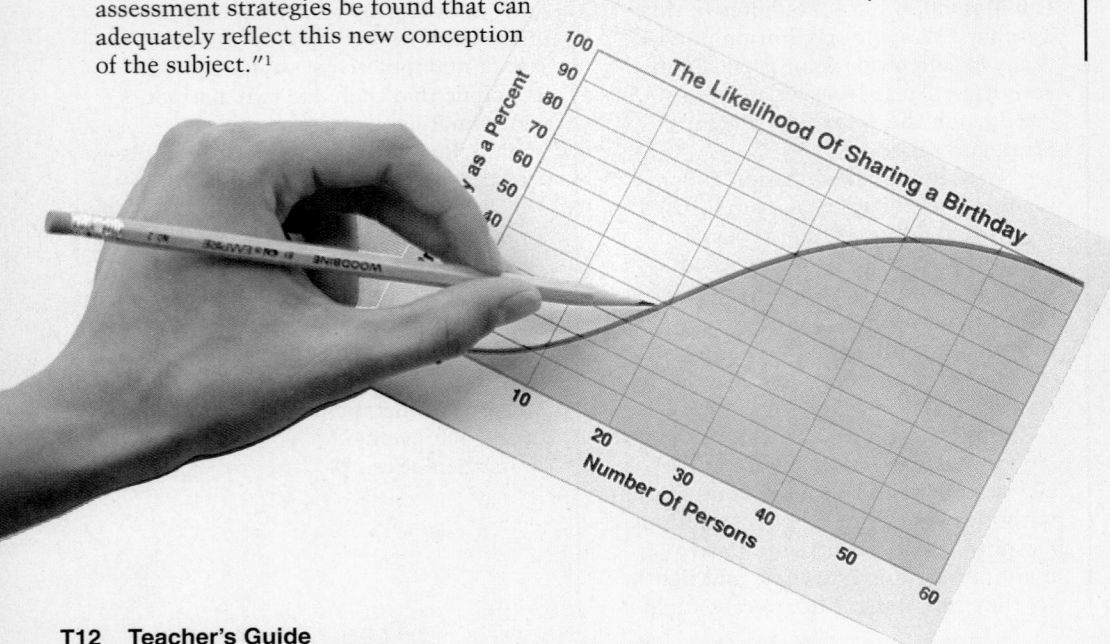

Assessment must be more than testing; it must be a continuous, dynamic, and often informal process.

—NCTM Standards

Classroom Observations are another way of documenting student achievement. While observing your students at work, you often form quite accurate opinions concerning your students' capabilities.

- *Alternate Teaching Strategies* in the *Teacher's Wraparound Edition* suggests activities for use in observing students work.
- The *Cooperative Learning Activities* in the *Activity Masters* in the *Teacher's Classroom Resources* provide another opportunity for watching students work together and for evaluating their understanding of the task at hand.

Performance Assessment is used to determine what students know and what they can do when presented with an authentic problem-solving situation.

- The *Performance Assessment* booklet in the *Teacher's Classroom Resources* contains student assessment items for each chapter, as well as scoring rubrics.

Questioning is an excellent tool for assessing the comprehension of students. Dialogue between you and your students is most beneficial in identifying comprehension errors and the use of process skills.

- *Guided Practice* questions in each lesson allow you to evaluate students' understanding before assigning homework.
- *Wrap-Up* questions in each lesson ask students to verbalize what they have learned in the lesson.
- *Closing the Lesson* in the *Teacher's Wraparound Edition* asks students to summarize the lesson by using speech and writing.

Self-Evaluation permits students to monitor their own progress.

- The *Mid-Chapter Review* in the *Student Edition* gives students an opportunity to check their skills thus far in each chapter.
- The unique *Chapter Summary and Review* in the *Student Edition* allows students to review and practice concepts before a formal evaluation is presented. The use of cooperative group instruction with this review not only provides students the opportunity to reinforce skills, but allows you to observe the strengths and weaknesses of students in an informal setting.

Portfolios are student collections of their work that are representative of their growth as a learner. A *Portfolio Suggestion* appears in one of the last lessons in each chapter.

Journal Entries allow students to express what they are learning. These may involve many different forms of expression such as graphs, drawings, models, and other explanations. Two *Journal Entry* features appear in each chapter.

Other Resources

In addition to the resources provided with the Merrill Geometry program, Glencoe publishes a Mathematics Professional Series. One of the booklets in this series, *Alternative Assessment in the Mathematics Classroom*, contains further information and activities to help you implement other types of evaluation strategies.

1. Clarke, David J., Doug M. Clarke, and Charles J. Lovitt, "Changes in Mathematics Teaching Call for Assessment Alternatives," *Teaching and Learning Mathematics in the 1990s*, (1990 NCTM Yearbook, Reston, VA: NCTM, 1990), p. 118.

Meeting Individual Needs

"We cannot afford to have the majority of our population mathematically illiterate: Equity has become an economic necessity."

NCTM Standards (1989, p. 4)

Multicultural Perspective

Undoubtedly, the United States is a multicultural society. Changing demographics as well as economic and social orders are having a tremendous impact on the schools in this country. However, the term *multicultural* represents more than just *many cultures.* There is a multicultural basis to all knowledge, even mathematics.

From the ancient Egyptians, who used the "Pythagorean" theorem fifteen hundred years *before* Pythagoras, to the ancient Chinese, who calculated the value of π to ten places twelve hundred years *before* the Europeans, mathematics as we know it today has been shaped by many cultures. Even the term *algebra* was contributed by an Arabian mathematician, Al-Khowarizmi.

What is the role of the mathematics educator in all this? Students should have the opportunity to learn about persons from all cultures who have contributed to the development of mathematics. Additionally, students should learn about individuals from all cultures who have been successful in their respective careers.

To this end, each chapter of ***Merrill Geometry*** opens with a Geometry Around the World feature that focuses on contributions past or present by cultures or notable individuals from countries all over parts of the world. The ***Merrill Geometry Activity Masters Booklet*** contains a multicultural worksheet for each chapter to further highlight the fact that mathematics is a universal human endeavor.

As educators, we must also prepare all students for the new jobs of the future that will require mathematical literacy. The mathematics teacher must be in the vanguard of those who demand that *all* students be given the opportunity to study the more advanced forms of mathematics. It is our responsibility as educators to make every effort to prepare the students of today to participate in the complex world of tomorrow.

Students should have the opportunity to learn about persons from all cultures who have contributed to the development of mathematics.

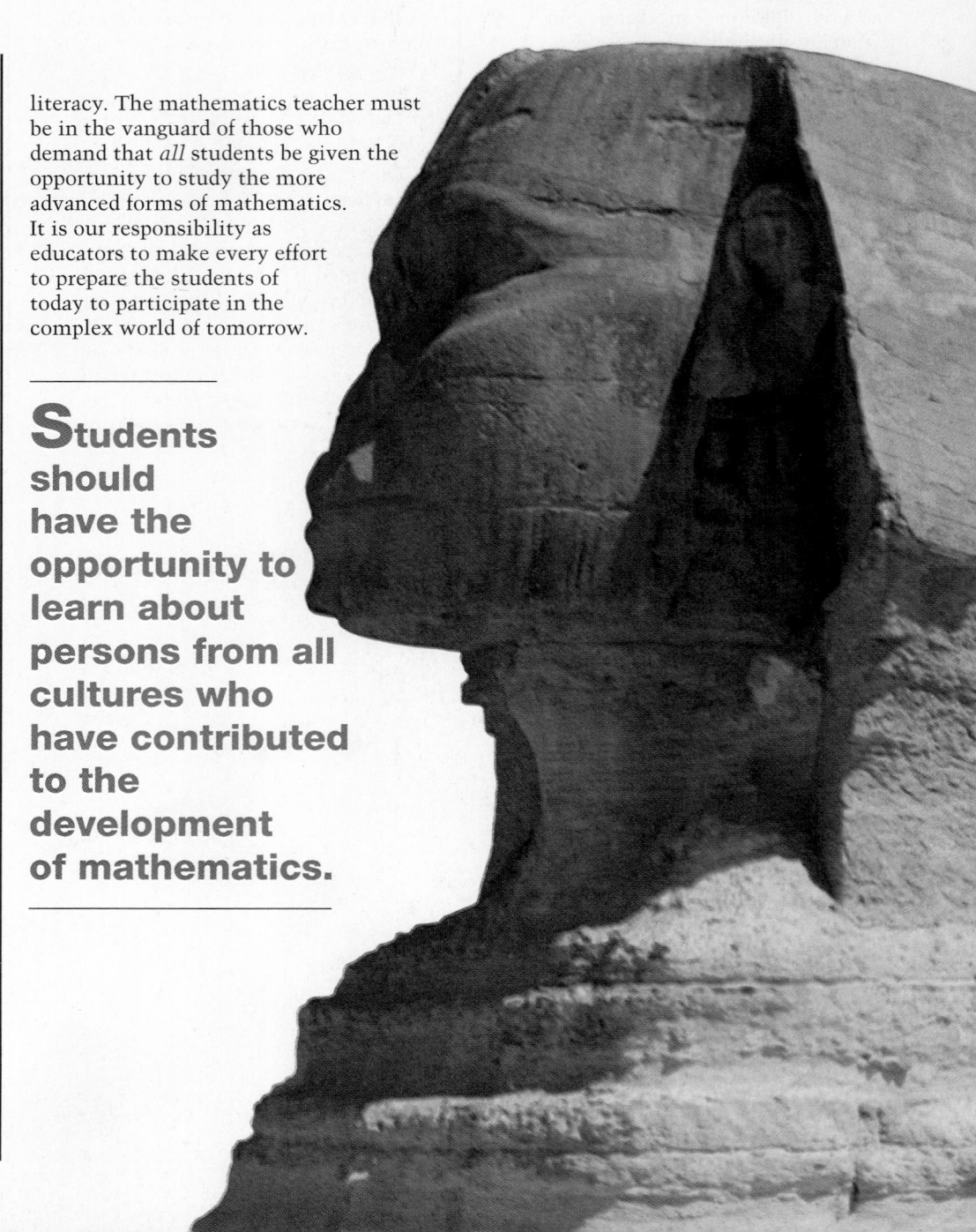

Limited English Proficiency Needs

One of the greatest factors contributing to the under-achievement in mathematics education for the language-minority student is his or her failure to understand the language of instruction. There are, however, strategies which the mathematics teacher can employ to help overcome the obstacles that beset language-minority students.

Ideally, these students will have the opportunity of having new concepts and skills reinforced by discussing them in their native language, whatever that language might be. It may be that a bilingual teacher can meet this need, or perhaps a tutor proficient in the language can be procured to provide this service.

If the student is proficient in his or her native language, perhaps materials written in that language can be provided to supplement classroom instruction.

Teachers in parts of the country with rapidly expanding Hispanic populations have no doubt encountered students who are fully bilingual in English and Spanish and others who definitely feel more secure when additional explanation can be provided in Spanish. The *Merrill Geometry Spanish Resources Booklet* provides chapter objectives and a complete glossary of mathematical terms. It is recommended that teachers make this booklet available to any student who feels a need for it.

If the student is not especially literate in his or her own language, perhaps an oral approach using pictorial materials and/or manipulative devices would be feasible.

When a student does not respond to the prescribed expectations of the school, the teacher needs to substitute developmentally equivalent tasks to shape development. For example, if the student does not participate in classroom discussion, the wise teacher will observe his or her verbal interaction with other students in informal, less structured environments. Because students coming from diverse cultural backgrounds lack common educational experiences, the teacher soon recognizes that the only way to establish a basis for communication is to begin instruction with content that is familiar to everyone.

"The challenge is to find personally interesting and culturally relevant ways of creating new contexts for children, contexts in which the mastery of school skills can be meaningful and rewarding."[1]

By integrating the development of language in such new contexts, we may be able to open the door to the challenging and exciting world of mathematics for the language-minority student.

Using Technology

Students of all cultural backgrounds share a fascination with technology. Teachers should be alert to opportunities to use graphing calculators, the Geometric Supposer, and other technological innovations to motivate students and circumvent language difficulties. Technology is one area in which figures and mathematical symbolism can be used to great advantage, since they tend to be relatively language independent. ■

[1] Bowman, Barbara, T., "Educating Language-Minority Children: Challenges and Opportunities," *Phi Delta Kappan*, October 1989, P. 120.

Integrating Technology Into Your Geometry Classroom

"Students today can't prepare bark to calculate their problems. They depend upon their slates which are more expensive. What will they do when their slate is dropped and it breaks? They will be unable to write!"

Teachers' Conference, 1703

The above quote seems ridiculous today, but in 1703 it was not. Many people may ask, "Couldn't they see enough into the future to know that slates would be required?"; but as the old adage goes, hindsight is twenty-twenty. The difficulty lies in foreseeing the future.

The argument nowadays is in regard to computers and calculators; and while most people agree that technology should be used in the mathematics classroom, few are offering ideas on incorporation, testing, appropriate use, and other areas where teachers have questions. Some use this as an argument against using technology, but that is not the answer to the problem. Instead we must be able to recognize a good idea when we see one and adopt it for our classrooms.

Appropriate Use of Technology

There are many different ideas and definitions of "appropriate use of technology," and rightly so. Every class and every teacher is different. What is appropriate and works for one may not be appropriate or work for another. However, there are some classifications and generalizations that can be made for different grade levels. Keep in mind that many of your students are just learning the technology. You should refrain from getting "high-tech" with them. Give them opportunities for success early so that they can begin to feel comfortable with technology.

Have your students complete an easy calculation for their first encounter. For the students new to technology, this will give them a sense of accomplishment because they can see something they have done; for the more technologically experienced students, this will give them a sense of confidence because they already know what is being done.

At any level of teaching, try to get students to make generalizations about what they see or do with technology.

Using Technology in Your Classroom

Technology opens up many new ideas and opportunities. It is up to you to decide how to present and use technology in your classroom. Many of the standard teaching techniques are appropriate, such as using cooperative groups, or having students work in pairs, but there are also new ways of teaching that are appropriate when using technology in your classroom. For example, you can assign lab partners in each class. Each pair of students would then work together whenever technology is used. This can also be used if you have a limited supply of equipment.

Teaching Aids

There are many technological teaching aids as well as numerous products to assist in the teaching of technology. One of them is a projection panel for the overhead projector. This can be used in conjunction with a demonstration computer and can project the image from the computer onto a screen or wall.

Overhead projector calculators are also available for most models. They can serve the same purpose as a projection panel and demonstration computer.

Another teaching aid is a template of the computer or calculator keyboard that can be used on the overhead or put on the bulletin board

Technology teaches students in a way that piques their interest and leads to questions that show a desire to learn.

for easy reference. (Masters for the TI-34 and TI-81 calculators are provided on pages 6 and 7 in the *Merrill Geometry Lab Manual*.) This can help in conveying the location of keys, especially second-function keys on graphing calculators.

Changes in the Classroom

There will be some changes in your classroom with the onset of technology. One will be your role. It most likely will change from leader to guide. Students will begin to do things on their own and it will be up to you to keep them headed in the right direction. Students will also begin to ask more questions, including more higher-order questions, than before.

You may not have all the answers, but the investigation can be enjoyable and enlightening for both you and your students.

Advantages of Technology

Probably the biggest advantage of technology is the amount of time it can save you. The ease of editing errors, the number of graphs and pictures that can be drawn in a short amount of time, the speed of calculating; all these and other time-saving advantages make technology a major plus for the mathematics classroom.

There are numerous other advantages. One is that students will have a deeper understanding of the concepts being taught. As we move toward a more pictorial society, students are becoming visual learners. Technology teaches them in a way that piques their interest and leads to questions that show a desire to learn.

Another advantage of technology is the cooperative spirit that develops among students. Since students will probably need to work with others when they become members of the work force, it is best for them to learn to work with others while they are in school. With technology, you can teach your students to work cooperatively, which will benefit them in college and in their careers.

Technology Fears

Perhaps the biggest fear, and certainly one that is most often expressed, is that technology will take the place of the teacher. *This will never happen.* There is no way that a computer can do what a teacher does, and in particular, sense what a teacher can. For example, no computer can sense uncertainty of an answer in a student's tone of voice. Few students will be able to turn on a calculator or computer and teach themselves with it. They need teachers to explain the technology and to help them make connections.

You can also see the evidence of needing the teacher when you relate the use of technology in education to its use in the business world. Computers have been in the mainstream of business for quite sometime now, and there has not been a reduction in the number of persons needed. Yet a large number of business executives will tell you they would not want to do their job without the use of a computer. Many teachers who have incorporated technology into their classrooms are saying the same thing.

Computers and calculators are excellent tools for teaching mathematics concepts. Though there are still some who argue their use in the classroom, none can argue their educational advantage. Technology can teach students in ways that were never before possible. In the past, teachers could only dream of being able to do some of the things that they can now do with ease, thanks to technology. While incorporating technology into your mathematics classroom may be difficult at first, in the long run, it will definitely pay off for both you and your students.

Specific guidelines and instructions for using Casio graphing calculators and the TI-81 graphing calculator are provided on pages T18-T24.

Additional information on integrating technology into your geometry classroom can be found in the *Teacher's Guide for Software Resources.*

Using the Graphing Calculator

"Innovative instruction based on a new symbiosis of machine calculation and human thinking can shift the balance of learning toward understanding, insight, and mathematical intuition."

Everybody Counts. (1989, p. 63)

Today's technology offers teachers new and exciting opportunities to teach students in many different ways. It can add different dimensions to mathematics classrooms and can also help students gain a deeper understanding of the concepts being taught. The graphing calculator is one technological tool that can help you teach your students. And while learning to use the graphing calculator and getting started with it may be one of the most difficult problems to tackle, once this is accomplished, the only limits left are the limits of the calculator's capabilities.

In **Merrill Geometry**, there are four Graphing Calculator Technology pages. The chapters in which they occur and their titles are listed below.

Chapter 3: Finding the Distance between a Point and a Line
Chapter 4: Congruent Triangles
Chapter 8: Tangent Ratio
Chapter 12: Perspective Drawing

Instruction is provided for both the Casio fx-7000G graphing calculator and the TI-81 graphing calculator in these pages.

In the Beginning . . .

It may be necessary for you to give your students an introduction to the graphing calculator before you begin one of the graphing calculator technology pages since many may not have used a graphing calculator before. It may also be necessary for you to familiarize yourself with the graphing calculator before teaching these pages. The manuals for the calculators can help you get started. They can also be used as a guide or a reference, and they may clear up questions that you have along the way. The TI-81 manual has a section to help you get started and also has several examples throughout the manual that explain how the calculator can be used to teach certain concepts. You can also talk to other teachers who are using the calculator if you need help getting off the ground with the technology.

Using graphing calculators in your classroom can bring your students together and can help them learn to help each other solve problems.

Getting to Know Your Calculator

Both the Casio fx-7000G and the TI-81 graphing calculators have four "screens" in common; the text screen, the graphics screen, the range screen, and the mode screen. Each screen does something different. The *text screen* is the screen where you complete calculations, input programs, or input commands for the calculator to perform. When you press [AC] on the Casio and [CLEAR] (or in some situations [2nd] [QUIT]) on the TI-81, you are in the text screen.

The *graphics screen* is where the calculator graphs functions. Pressing the [G↔T] key on the Casio lets you alternate between graphics and text screens, while pressing the [GRAPH] key on the TI-81 will get you to the graphics screen.

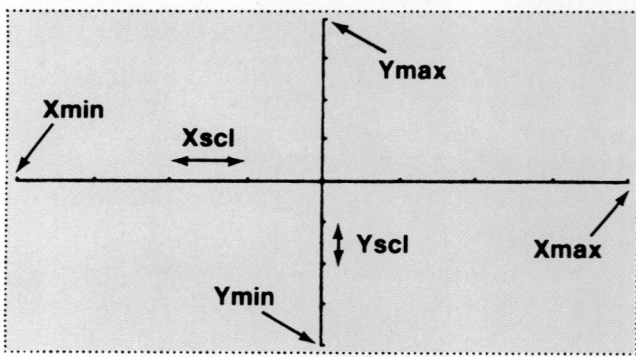

The *range screen* tells you the endpoints of the x- and y-axes and scale of the graphics screen. The TI-81 range screen also tells you the x-resolution, or how clearly your function(s) will be graphed. Pressing [RANGE] on either calculator will get you to the range screen.

And finally, the *mode screen* tells you at what mode settings your calculator is set. On the Casio, the mode screen can be seen when you turn the calculator on. It can also be accessed by pressing the [MDisp] key. To change the mode settings on the Casio, you can press the [MODE] key and the corresponding number for the mode setting you desire. The mode settings are listed under the screen of the calculator. On the TI-81, the mode screen is accessed by pressing the [MODE] key.

Casio

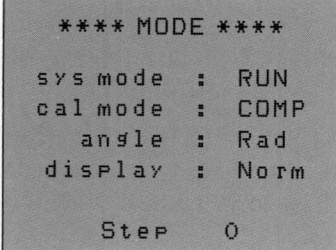

TI-81

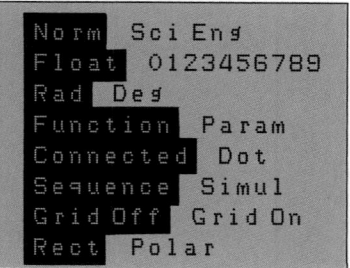

As you may have realized, there is no "=" key on either the Casio fx-7000G graphing calculator or the TI-81 graphing calculator. Instead there is an [ENTER] key on the TI-81 and an [EXE] key on the Casio. This is because each key is more than just a key that completes all of the calculator's arithmetic calculations. It also completes other calculator operations, such as drawing a graph, moving to a new line of a program, selecting equations you want graphed, and so on. Both keys will perform the "=" function, but they will also do much more.

The insert ([INS]), delete ([DEL]), and arrow keys ([⇒], [⇐], [⇑], [⇓] on the Casio and [▶], [◀], [▲], [▼] on the TI-81) can be used for easy editing of inputed commands. On the Casio, the [⇒] and [⇐] arrow keys can be used to go directly to the point of error if you press one of them first when an error message appears. These are called the "replay" keys. The calculator will automatically return to the place where it found the error. You can also use the arrow keys to manually move to the place(s) where you want to insert into or delete from an equation or expression.

Both calculators have second function keys and alphabetical character keys. These are [2nd] and [ALPHA] on the TI-81 and [SHIFT] and [ALPHA] on the Casio. The second function keys ([2nd] or [SHIFT]) allow you to access the characters on the left-hand side above each key. The alphabetical key ([ALPHA]) allows you to access the letters on the right-hand side above each key.

The TI-81 has five graphing keys underneath the screen. These keys all deal with listing, graphing, and exploring functions. The [Y=] key allows you to list up to four functions that you want to graph. The [RANGE] key allows you to set your minimum and maximum values and your scale for the graphics screen. The [ZOOM] key allows you to look at smaller or larger sections of the function(s) you have graphed. The [TRACE] key does just what it says; it allows you to trace along any function on the graphics screen. Finally, the [GRAPH] key graphs the selected functions or returns you to the graphics screen.

Both calculators will let you know if you have done something that it does not understand by giving you an error message. The most common error messages are given when you have a math error or a syntax error. The Casio will list "Ma error" for a math error and "Syn error" for a syntax error and will write the error messages directly underneath the calculation. The TI-81 will write the kind of error on the top line of the error message. Perhaps the easiest way to get a math error on either calculator is to divide a number by zero. There are many other ways to get a math error, however. To see a syntax error, use the [(-)] key instead of the [−] key in an equation and then try to perform the calculation.

Error messages can be extremely frustrating, especially if they keep recurring and you cannot figure out what is wrong. There are some troubleshooting tips to help you find the problem when this situation occurs. First, check to see that your calculator is in the correct mode settings. If it is in write mode and not run mode or if you are in degrees instead of radians, your calculator will not do what you want it to do. Another tip is to use the replay keys on the Casio or the "Goto error" statement on the TI-81 and try to let the calculator do the troubleshooting for you. If you still cannot understand why the calculator gave you an error message, go

through the problem step-by-step and try doing it as the calculator would. Make sure to use parentheses in necessary areas. And if all else fails, try rekeying parts of the problem or the entire problem and then reexecute. This may get rid of an invisible keystroke entry that you did not know was entered.

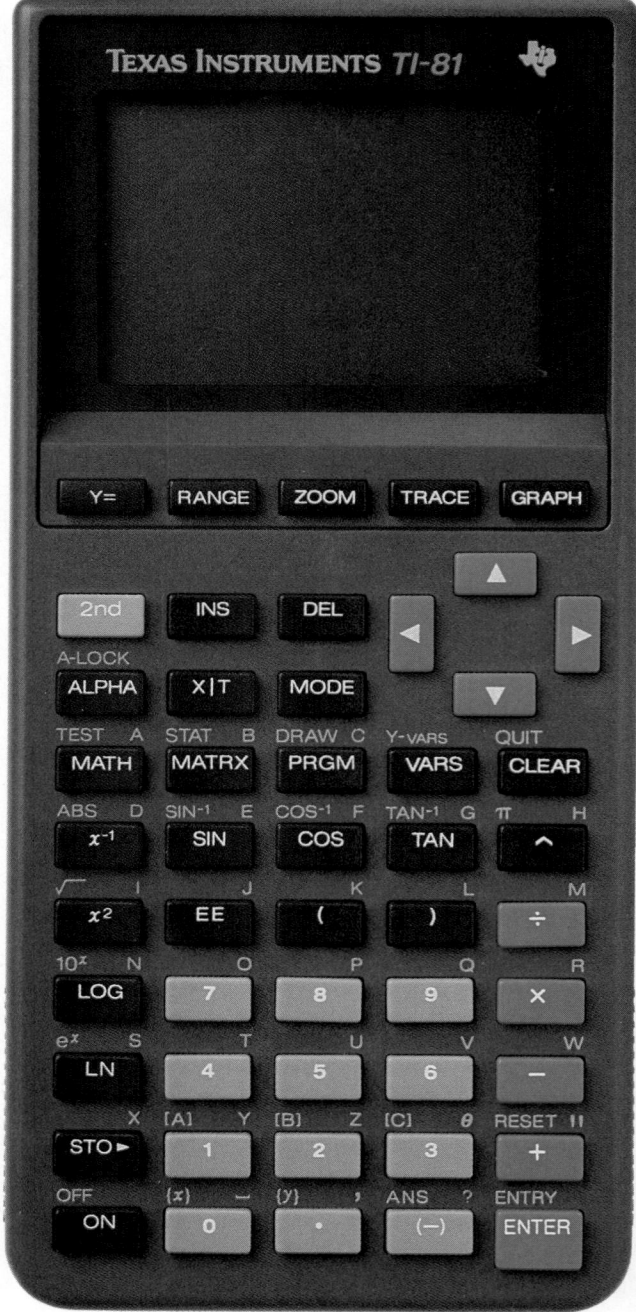

If you are graphing and having problems, check your range. Often an adjustment here will get rid of the problem. A blank screen often happens when you try to zoom or when the graph of the function is not in the range in which your calculator is set. Experimenting with different range values may be the solution here.

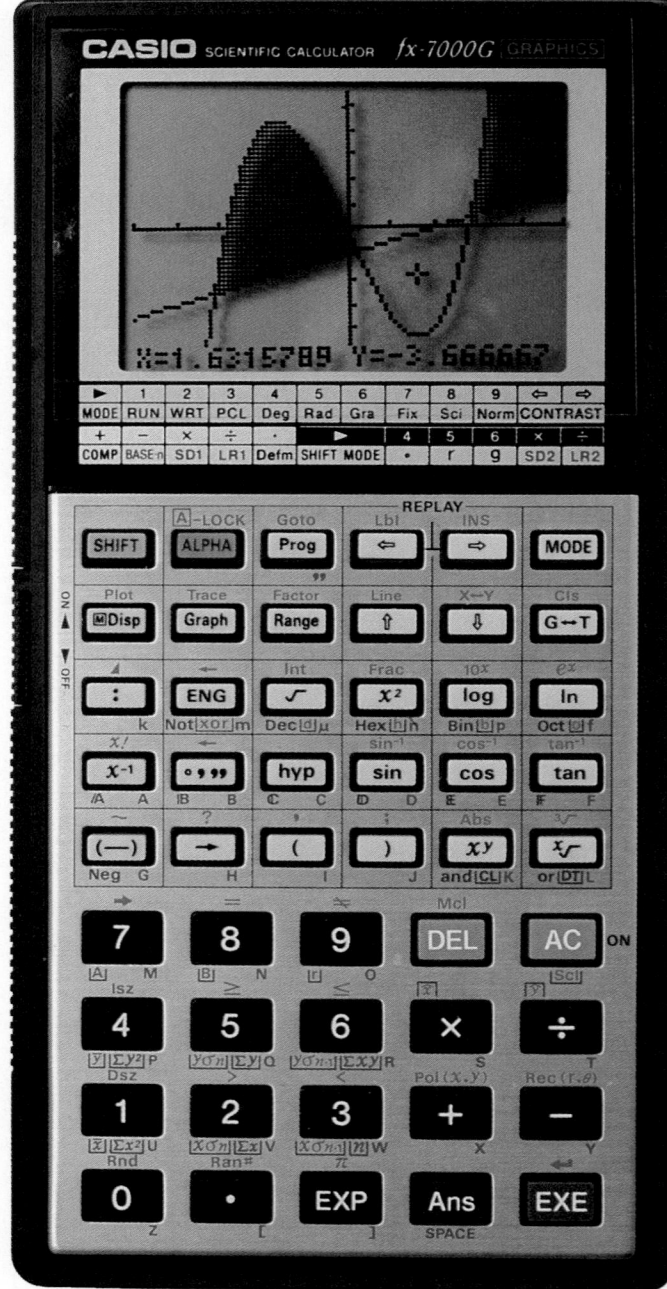

Teaching With the Graphing Calculator

Using the graphing calculator in your classroom will no doubt bring about some changes, if it hasn't done so for you already. There are some things that you can do to make teaching the use of the graphing calculator easier. For example, one of the most helpful teaching aids is an overhead transparency of the graphing calculator keyboard. If you are using the TI-81 graphing calculator, there is a picture of the calculator in front of the TI-81 manual. You may want to make an enlarged copy of it and make a transparency of the keyboard from that. The *Merrill Geometry Lab Manual* (pages 6 and 7) also includes a master of both the TI-34 and the TI-81 calculator layout from which you can make a transparency. If you are using a Casio calculator, there is also a picture of it in the Casio manual.

Enlarging these pictures and making transparencies of them will help you show your students where keys are if they are having trouble finding them or if you are explaining a lesson and need to demonstrate your keystrokes. You can also make a large poster of the calculator's keyboard and hang it in a visible location in the classroom. One of your students may like to do this for extra credit, or someone may just enjoy doing it.

Some of you may have begun teaching with a Casio fx-7000G graphing calculator and are now using TI-81 graphing calculators or a different type of Casio graphing calculator. If this is the case, you will notice that some things are different on each calculator. For example, the exponent key on the Casio is x^y, while on the TI-81 it is the $\wedge$ key.

Graphing calculators can often pique your students' curiosity about mathematics topics. You may begin to hear, "Why did it do that?" or "What's happening?" instead of "What's the answer?" or "I don't understand."

The locations of the arrow keys and trace key on the Casio *fx-7500G* are different from those of the Casio *fx-7000G*. While this may be confusing at first, it will probably not take too long for you to adjust to the new calculator. Finding new key locations or learning all of the new things the calculator can do may be the most difficult things you will have to deal with.

Using new or different calculators can also pose some difficulties if some of your students are still using the other ones. It will help if you know the keystrokes for both calculators so that you can translate one calculator's sequence into the other calculator's sequence. If this is not the case, then you can work with your student(s) to figure out a solution. Try to keep in mind that a solution is not impossible and even though the technology is not the same, the mathematical ideas and concepts that you convey to all your students will be.

The concept of "scale" will probably be one of the most difficult for some of your students to understand and yet is one of the most important when working with graphs. You may want to use pictures and visuals to explain the concept. Ask your students if the range of [–10, 10] by [–10, 10] with a scale of 1 is different from [–20, 20] by [–20, 20] with a scale of 2. Look at each screen on a graphing calculator. Point out that even though the screens may look the same, they are actually extremely different. Try to get your students to get in the habit of checking their range and scale when they are looking at a graph and trying to interpret the information it gives them. Checking range and scale is also an important troubleshooting technique when problems occur.

Along these same lines, zoom in and zoom out are important problem-solving techniques for your students to learn, and there is a technique to

using them. There are a number of ways to zoom in and out. For example, you can manually change your range. In the problem $f(x) = x^3 - 3x^2 + 7$, you can approximate the zero of the function by initially graphing the function in the default viewing window of [–10, 10] by [–10, 10] with a scale of 1 along each axis and then changing this range to [–2, –1] by [–1, 1] with an x-scale of 0.1 and a y-scale of 0.2. You can then repeat this process as often as you like until you reach the desired accuracy, or until you reach the limits of the precision of the calculator.

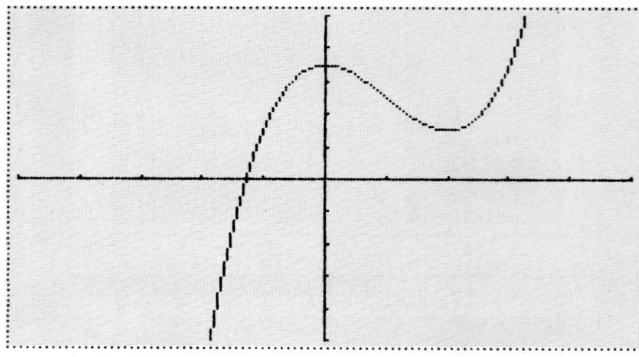

Another way to zoom is to use the ZOOM key on the TI-81. You have the option of zooming in by using a box, zooming in or out by setting factors, or by tracing along the function and zooming in or out at that point. Using the zoom box can be fun for your students because they create the box around the area they want to see. It is also a good way to solve certain problems, like finding the vertex of a parabola. Many times, zooming in at a point will make it difficult to keep the shape of the function you are graphing. The more you zoom in, the more the function will look like a line as shown below.

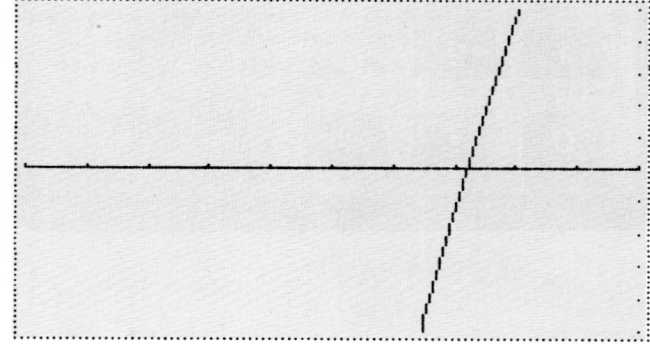

The graphing calculator allows you to look at many new areas of mathematics that until now were restricted at this level because of difficulty.

Teaching your students to know when and how to use a graphing calculator to solve problems will help your students become better problem solvers, and in the end, this is what we really want them to become.

Using the zoom box can help you keep the correct shape, even at very small range values. For finding the vertex of a parabola, you can make square boxes around the vertex and the parabolic shape remains. If you make thin rectangles around the vertex, the function will look like a line very quickly. Your students will need to experiment with this to understand. It may help them if you point out that the box they create will be the next screen of the calculator.

Zooming in or out on a point by factors can be done on both the TI-81 and the Casio. On the TI-81, you use [ZOOM] 4 to set your factors and then zoom in or out. You cannot set your factors for a value less than one. If you try, the calculator will give you an error message. Zooming by a factor of one actually does not zoom at all. It merely redraws the graph in the same viewing window. On the Casio, you can use the [TRACE] key to move to a point on the graph and then press [SHIFT] [×] to zoom in at that point or [SHIFT] [÷] to zoom

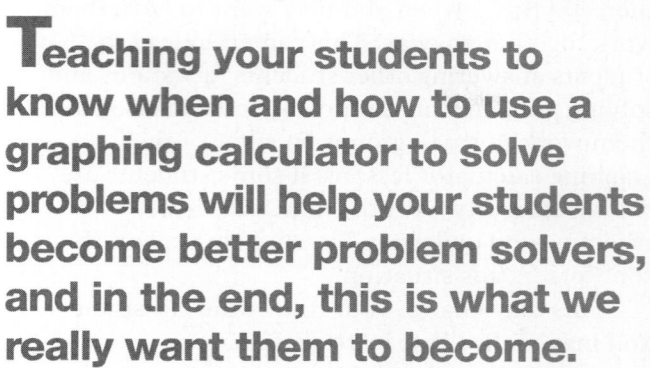

out at that point. The [Factor] key can also be used here. Inserting "[Factor] (a value) [:]" before the command to graph a function will make the calculator zoom in or out. If the value is greater than one, the calculator will zoom in, and if the value is less than one, the calculator will zoom out.

Why Use It?

The graphing calculator offers you much more flexibility than before. Some people may not understand that it is okay to solve problems with a calculator and that most of the time the calculator does not "find the answer" for you but merely helps you to find appropriate solutions to problems. If you do not understand how to interpret the information the calculator provides, it will be of no use to you. For example, if you look at the graph of a line and ask what the slope of the graph is, some students may tell you they do not know how to find it. Still others will look at 2.718281828 . . . and not recognize it as the decimal approximation of e. It is still up to you as the teacher to make connections with the technology and to teach with it. The calculator simply saves time and effort and allows you to go deeper into mathematical concepts with your students than you could in the past.

It may be difficult at times to know when to "say when" with the graphing calculator. For most practical purposes, accuracy of solutions to two or three decimal places is often sufficient, and we can spend too much time finding solutions that are "too technical" if we are not specific with our students as to what we want from them. Your students may find it fun, however, to try to push the machine as far as it can go a few times, and then try to go beyond that point. If necessary, the graphing calculator can find solutions to problems with ten-digit accuracy. Knowing the limits of the machine will help your students understand what they can and cannot expect of it. Trying to get them to understand these limits, to understand what the calculator is doing, and what it is telling them is very important.

It may be difficult for each of your students to have their own graphing calculator. If this is a problem, you can have your students work in pairs like lab partners. Even if each of your students has his or her own graphing calculator,

there are times when you may want to have them work together anyway. This can often lead to students answering other students' questions and solving problems on their own. You can also have them work in small groups on some of the graphing calculator lessons. If some students are having difficulty with the material, those students who understand it can help explain the concepts in this situation.

This may change your role in the classroom. You may realize that instead of being an instructor to your students you become a guide for your students. Graphing calculators can often pique your students' curiosity about mathematics topics, and they will begin to experiment themsleves. You may begin to hear, "Why did it do that?" or "What's happening?" instead of "What's the answer?" or "I don't understand." Your students will actually begin to retain the mathematical content more since they explored and investigated the concepts for themselves.

As was mentioned, some of your students will begin to "take off" with the calculator and try to explore almost everything that it can do. Some may become interested in looking at the programming aspect of the calculator, which you can use to your advantage. For example, you can have some of the students write a program that you could use in one of your classes, like looking at prime factorization. The manual that accompanies the graphing calculator can help get them started, and they may be able to write several useful programs for you to use in your classes.

The graphing calculator allows you to look at many new areas of mathematics that until now were restricted at this level because of difficulty. While it may take time to feel comfortable with using graphing calculators in your classroom, and you may be just beginning to learn how to use them, it is important to keep trying and to keep learning. Teaching your students to know when and how to use a graphing calculator to solve problems will help your students become better problem solvers, and in the end, this is what we really want them to become. ■

For more information on using graphing calculators, see Glencoe's *Graphing Calculators in the Mathematics Classroom*, 1994.

Learning Objectives

1 The Language of Geometry

1-1: Graph ordered pairs on a coordinate plane.
1-2A: Identify and draw models of points, lines, and planes.
1-2B: Identify collinear and coplanar points and intersecting lines and planes.
1-3: Solve problems by making a list of possibilities.
1-4A: Find the distance between two points in a number plane.
1-4B: Find the distance between points in a coordinate plane.
1-5A: Find the midpoint of a segment.
1-5B: Identify and use congruent segments.
1-6A: Identify angles and parts of angles.
1-6B: Use the angle addition postulate to find the measure of angles.
1-7A: Classify angles as acute, obtuse, right, and straight.
1-7B: Identify and use congruent angles and the bisector of an angle.
1-8: Identify and use adjacent angles, vertical angles, complementary angles, supplementary angles, and linear pairs of angles.
1-9A: Identify and use right angles and perpendicular lines.
1-9B: Determine what information can and cannot be assumed from a figure.

2 Reasoning and Introduction to Proof

2-1: Make geometric conjectures based on inductive reasoning.
2-2A: Identify the hypothesis and conclusion of an "if-then" statement.
2-2B: Write the converse of an "if-then" statement.
2-2C: Identify and use basic postulates about points, lines, and planes.
2-3: Use the law of detachment and the law of syllogism in deductive reasoning.
2-4: Use properties of equality in algebraic and geometric proofs.
2-5: Solve problems by eliminating possibilities.
2-6: Complete proofs involving segment theorems.
2-7: Complete proofs involving angle theorems.

3 Parallels

3-1: Solve problems by using a diagram.
3-2A: Describe the relationships between two lines and between two planes.
3-2B: Identify the relationships among pairs of angles formed by pairs of lines and transversals.
3-3: Use the properties of parallel lines to determine angle measures.
3-4A: Recognize angle conditions that produce parallel lines.
3-4B: Prove two lines parallel based on given angle relationships.
3-5A: Find the slope of a line.
3-5B: Use slope to identify parallel and perpendicular lines.
3-6: Recognize and use distance relationships among points, lines, and planes.

4 Congruent Triangles

4-1A: Identify the parts of a triangle.
4-1B: Classify triangles.
4-2A: Apply the angle sum theorem.
4-2B: Apply the exterior angle theorem.
4-3A: Identify congruent triangles.
4-3B: Name and label corresponding parts of congruent triangles.
4-4: Use SAS, SSS, and ASA postulates to test for triangle congruence.
4-5: Use AAS theorem to test for triangle congruence.
4-6: Solve problems by identifying and achieving subgoals.
4-7: Use properties of isosceles and equilateral triangles.

5 Applying Congruent Triangles

5-1: Identify and use medians, altitudes, angle bisectors, and perpendicular bisectors in a triangle.

Planning Your Geometry Course

The charts below give suggested time schedules for three types of courses: I, II, and III, and for two types of grading periods: 9-week and 6-week.

Course I covers Chapters 1-11. It allows for extra time for longer sessions and for reteaching and review. Course II covers Chapters 1-12. Generally, one day is allotted for each lesson, the Chapter Review, and the Chapter Test. Course III covers Chapters 1-13. This course is intended for students who master concepts quickly and retain skills well.

COURSE PLANNING CALENDAR
6-Week Grading Periods

Grading Period	TYPE OF COURSE I Chapter	I Days	II Chapter	II Days	III Chapter	III Days
1	1 2 Lessons 2-1 to 2-6	17 10	1 2	16 13	1 2	15 12
2	2 Lessons 2-7 to end 3 4 Lessons 4-1 to 4-5	4 13 10	3 4	12 13	3 4 5 Lessons 5-1 to 5-3	11 12 5
3	4 Lessons 4-6 to end 5 6 Lessons 6-1 to 6-5	5 14 9	5 6	13 12	5 Lessons 5-4 to end 6 7	7 11 12
4	6 Lessons 6-6 to end 7 8 Lessons 8-1 to 8-5	4 15 10	7 8	14 15	8 9	13 13
5	8 Lessons 8-6 to end 9 10 Lessons 10-1 to 10-3	6 16 5	9 10 Lessons 10-1 to 10-8	15 12	10 11	15 12
6	10 Lessons 10-4 to end 11	13 14	10 Lessons 10-9 to end 11 12	4 13 13	12 13	12 15
Total Days		**165**		**165**		**165**

COURSE PLANNING CALENDAR
9-Week Grading Periods

Grading Period	TYPE OF COURSE I Chapter	I Days	II Chapter	II Days	III Chapter	III Days
1	1 2 3	17 14 13	1 2 3	16 13 12	1 2 3 4 Lessons 4-1 to 4-3	15 12 11 5
2	4 5 6	15 14 13	4 5 6	13 13 12	4 Lessons 4-4 to end 5 6 7	7 12 11 12
3	7 8 9 Lessons 9-1 to 9-4	15 16 7	7 8 9	14 15 15	8 9 10	13 13 15
4	9 Lessons 9-5 to end 10 11	9 18 14	10 11 12	16 13 13	11 12 13	12 12 15
Total Days		**165**		**165**		**165**

Although most school years consist of 180 days, this planning guide is based on 165 days per year. This time frame will allow for special events that might occur during the school day causing classes to be shortened or omitted and also for cancellation of school due to weather conditions.

Symbols

h	altitude*	$\rightarrow$	is mapped onto
$\angle$	angle	$m\angle A$	measure of $\angle A$
a	apothem*	$m\overset{\frown}{AB}$	measure of arc AB
$\approx$	approximately equal to	$\sqrt{}$	nonnegative square root
$\overset{\frown}{AB}$	minor arc with endpoints A and B	(x, y)	ordered pair
$\overset{\frown}{ACB}$	major arc with endpoints A and B	(x, y, z)	ordered triple
		$\parallel$	is parallel to
A	area of a polygon or circle surface area of a sphere*	$\nparallel$	is not parallel to
		$\square$	parallelogram
B	area of base of a prism, cylinder, pryamid, or cone*	P	perimeter*
		$\perp$	is perpendicular to
b	base of a triangle, parallelogram, or trapezoid*	π	pi
		n-gon	polygon with n sides
$\odot P$	circle with center P	r	radius of a circle*
C	circumference*	$\overrightarrow{PQ}$	ray with endpoint P passing through Q
$\cong$	is congruent to		
$\leftrightarrow$	corresponds to	$\overline{RS}$	segment with endpoints R and S
cos	cosine		
$^\circ$	degree	s	side of a regular polygon*
d	diameter of a circle* distance*	$\sim$	is similar to
		sin	sine
AB	distance between points A and B*	ℓ	line ℓ length of a rectangle* slant height*
$=$	equals, is equal to		
$\neq$	is not equal to	m	slope
$>$	is greater than	tan	tangent
A'	the image of preimage A	T	total surface area*
$<$	is less than	Δ	triangle
L	lateral area*	$\overrightarrow{AB}$	vector from A to B
$\overleftrightarrow{DE}$	line containing points D and E	V	volume*

* indicates that this is the symbol for the measure of the item listed.

1

Understanding the Lesson

Each lesson is organized into lessons to make learning manageable. Each lesson begins with an application followed by a well-developed mathematical concept that is explained using several examples. At the end of each lesson, you will complete a variety of exercises.

Objectives tell you exactly what you should be able to do after studying the lesson and completing the exercises.

Interesting math-related trivia and historical facts, presented in **FYI**—"for your information"—enhance the relevance of the mathematics content.

To help you understand each new concept, **example** problems that illustrate the concept are completely worked out. Many are based on real-world applications.

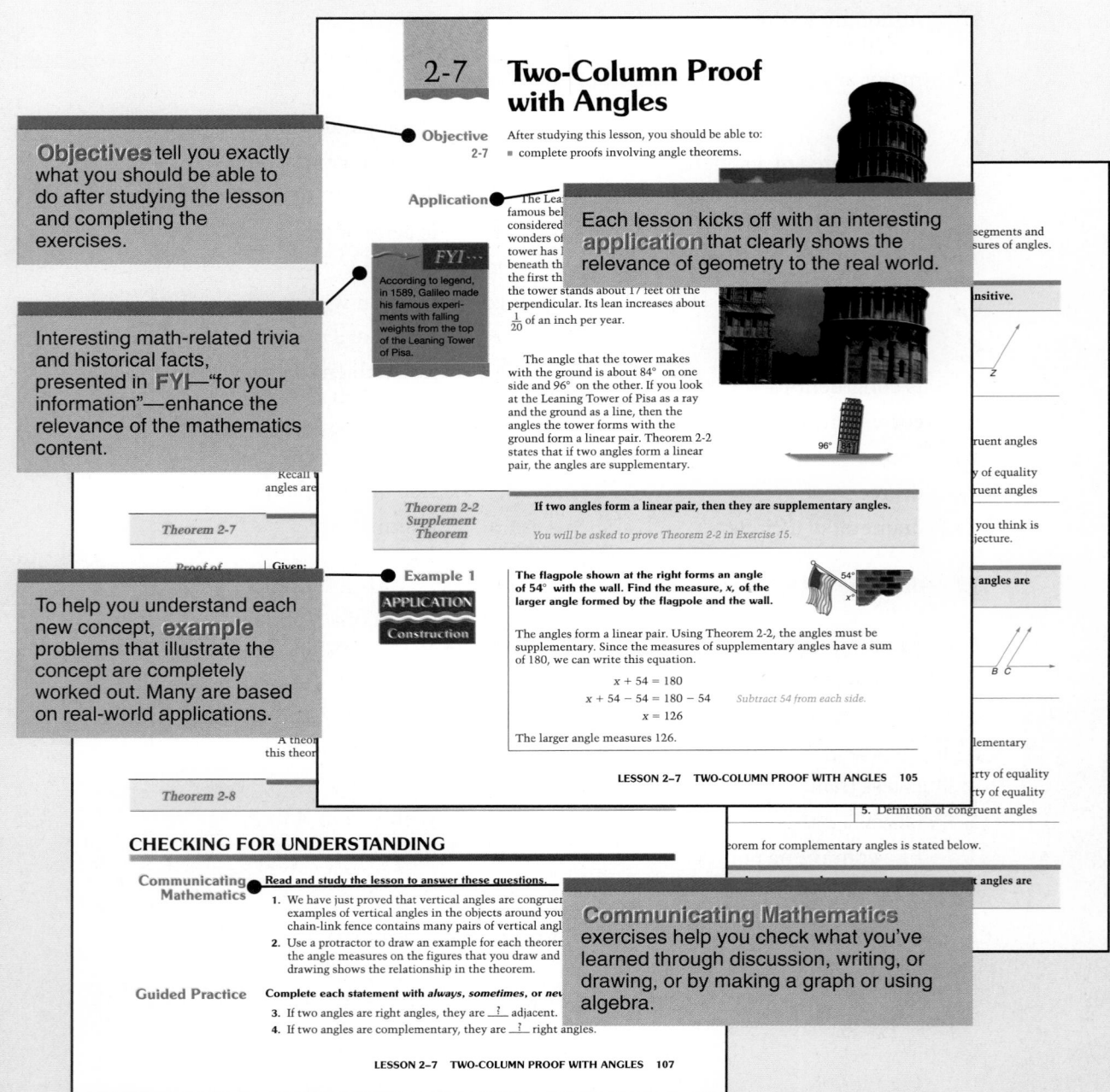

2-7 Two-Column Proof with Angles

Objective 2-7

After studying this lesson, you should be able to:
■ complete proofs involving angle theorems.

Application

The Lea... famous bel... considered... wonders of... tower has... beneath th... the first th... the tower stands about 17 feet off the perpendicular. Its lean increases about $\frac{1}{20}$ of an inch per year.

FYI···
According to legend, in 1589, Galileo made his famous experiments with falling weights from the top of the Leaning Tower of Pisa.

The angle that the tower makes with the ground is about 84° on one side and 96° on the other. If you look at the Leaning Tower of Pisa as a ray and the ground as a line, then the angles the tower forms with the ground form a linear pair. Theorem 2-2 states that if two angles form a linear pair, the angles are supplementary.

Theorem 2-2 Supplement Theorem

If two angles form a linear pair, then they are supplementary angles.

You will be asked to prove Theorem 2-2 in Exercise 15.

Example 1

APPLICATION
Construction

The flagpole shown at the right forms an angle of 54° with the wall. Find the measure, x, of the larger angle formed by the flagpole and the wall.

The angles form a linear pair. Using Theorem 2-2, the angles must be supplementary. Since the measures of supplementary angles have a sum of 180, we can write this equation.

$$x + 54 = 180$$
$$x + 54 - 54 = 180 - 54 \quad \text{Subtract 54 from each side.}$$
$$x = 126$$

The larger angle measures 126.

LESSON 2–7   TWO-COLUMN PROOF WITH ANGLES   105

Each lesson kicks off with an interesting **application** that clearly shows the relevance of geometry to the real world.

CHECKING FOR UNDERSTANDING

Communicating Mathematics
Read and study the lesson to answer these questions.

1. We have just proved that vertical angles are congruent... examples of vertical angles in the objects around you... chain-link fence contains many pairs of vertical angl...

2. Use a protractor to draw an example for each theorem... the angle measures on the figures that you draw and... drawing shows the relationship in the theorem.

Guided Practice
Complete each statement with *always*, *sometimes*, or *nev...*

3. If two angles are right angles, they are __?__ adjacent.
4. If two angles are complementary, they are __?__ right angles.

LESSON 2–7   TWO-COLUMN PROOF WITH ANGLES   107

Communicating Mathematics exercises help you check what you've learned through discussion, writing, or drawing, or by making a graph or using algebra.

2

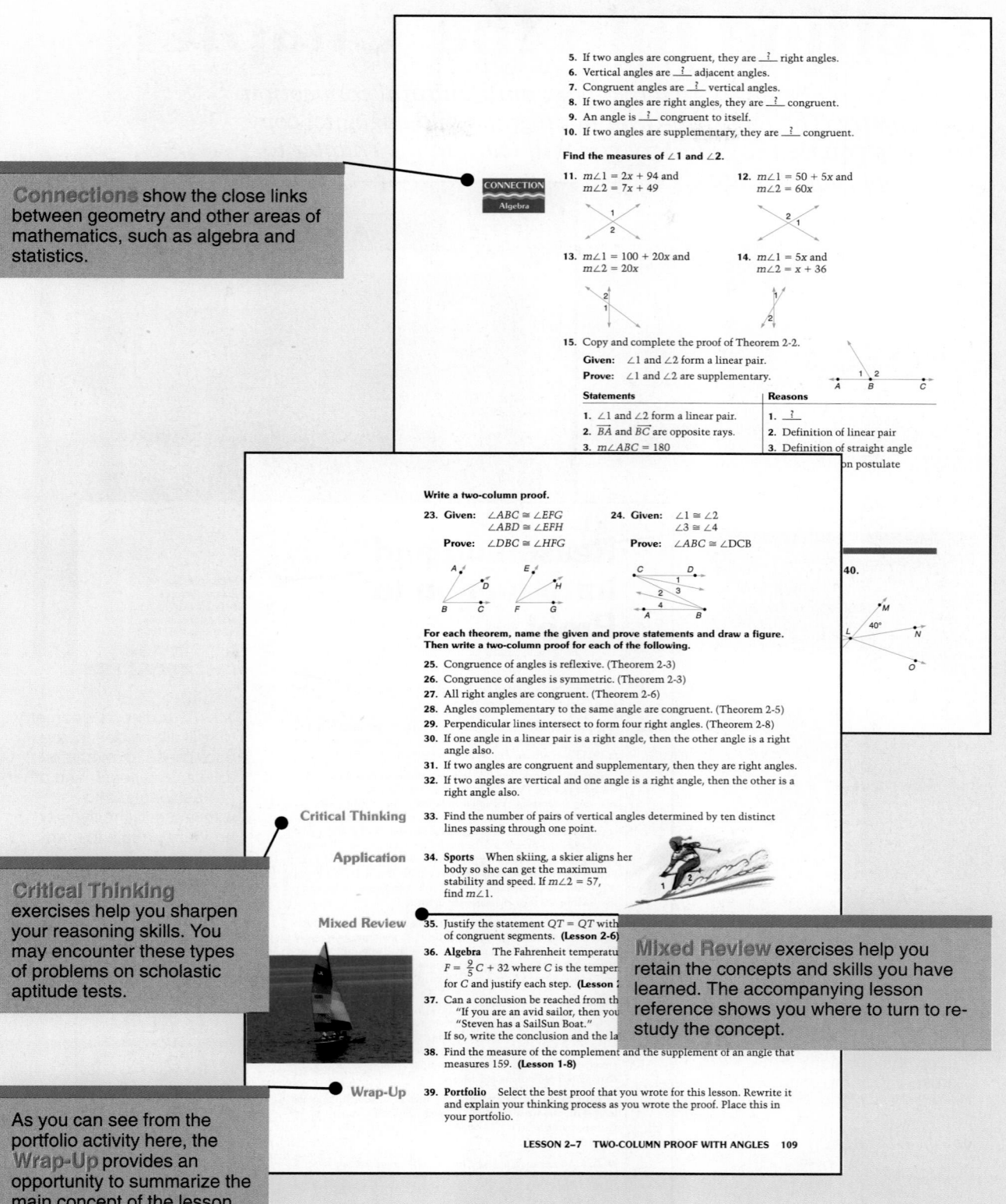

Connections show the close links between geometry and other areas of mathematics, such as algebra and statistics.

5. If two angles are congruent, they are _?_ right angles.
6. Vertical angles are _?_ adjacent angles.
7. Congruent angles are _?_ vertical angles.
8. If two angles are right angles, they are _?_ congruent.
9. An angle is _?_ congruent to itself.
10. If two angles are supplementary, they are _?_ congruent.

Find the measures of ∠1 and ∠2.

CONNECTION
Algebra

11. $m\angle 1 = 2x + 94$ and
$m\angle 2 = 7x + 49$

12. $m\angle 1 = 50 + 5x$ and
$m\angle 2 = 60x$

13. $m\angle 1 = 100 + 20x$ and
$m\angle 2 = 20x$

14. $m\angle 1 = 5x$ and
$m\angle 2 = x + 36$

15. Copy and complete the proof of Theorem 2-2.

Given: ∠1 and ∠2 form a linear pair.
Prove: ∠1 and ∠2 are supplementary.

Statements	Reasons
1. ∠1 and ∠2 form a linear pair.	1. _?_
2. $\overline{BA}$ and $\overline{BC}$ are opposite rays.	2. Definition of linear pair
3. $m\angle ABC = 180$	3. Definition of straight angle
	on postulate

Write a two-column proof.

23. **Given:** ∠ABC ≅ ∠EFG
∠ABD ≅ ∠EFH
Prove: ∠DBC ≅ ∠HFG

24. **Given:** ∠1 ≅ ∠2
∠3 ≅ ∠4
Prove: ∠ABC ≅ ∠DCB

40.

For each theorem, name the given and prove statements and draw a figure. Then write a two-column proof for each of the following.

25. Congruence of angles is reflexive. (Theorem 2-3)
26. Congruence of angles is symmetric. (Theorem 2-3)
27. All right angles are congruent. (Theorem 2-6)
28. Angles complementary to the same angle are congruent. (Theorem 2-5)
29. Perpendicular lines intersect to form four right angles. (Theorem 2-8)
30. If one angle in a linear pair is a right angle, then the other angle is a right angle also.
31. If two angles are congruent and supplementary, then they are right angles.
32. If two angles are vertical and one angle is a right angle, then the other is a right angle also.

Critical Thinking

33. Find the number of pairs of vertical angles determined by ten distinct lines passing through one point.

Application

34. **Sports** When skiing, a skier aligns her body so she can get the maximum stability and speed. If $m\angle 2 = 57$, find $m\angle 1$.

Mixed Review

35. Justify the statement $QT = QT$ with of congruent segments. **(Lesson 2-6)**
36. **Algebra** The Fahrenheit temperatu $F = \frac{9}{5}C + 32$ where C is the temper for C and justify each step. **(Lesson**
37. Can a conclusion be reached from th "If you are an avid sailor, then you "Steven has a SailSun Boat." If so, write the conclusion and the la
38. Find the measure of the complement and the supplement of an angle that measures 159. **(Lesson 1-8)**

Wrap-Up

39. **Portfolio** Select the best proof that you wrote for this lesson. Rewrite it and explain your thinking process as you wrote the proof. Place this in your portfolio.

LESSON 2–7 TWO-COLUMN PROOF WITH ANGLES 109

Critical Thinking exercises help you sharpen your reasoning skills. You may encounter these types of problems on scholastic aptitude tests.

Mixed Review exercises help you retain the concepts and skills you have learned. The accompanying lesson reference shows you where to turn to re-study the concept.

As you can see from the portfolio activity here, the **Wrap-Up** provides an opportunity to summarize the main concept of the lesson.

3

Getting into the Chapter

Every chapter begins with a two-page multicultural connection to geometry. The large full-color photograph and engaging copy will help you tie the geometry you will learn in the chapter to real people and cultures.

C H A P T E R 2

The list of **chapter objectives** lets you know what you can expect to learn in the chapter.

In **Geometry in Action,** you can begin to actually apply the geometry that is presented in the chapter.

Reasoning and Introduction to Proof

CHAPTER OBJECTIVES

In this chapter, you will:
- Make conjectures.
- Use the laws of logic to make conclusions.
- Write proofs involving segment and angle theorems.

GEOMETRY AROUND THE WORLD
United States

What rectangle filled with three circles helps keep you safe every day? Give up? The answer is a traffic light, developed in 1923 by an African-American inventor named Garrett Morgan.

Born in Kentucky in 1877, Morgan moved to Cleveland, Ohio, when he was 18. There, he found work repairing sewing machines and soon invented a belt fastener to make the machines operate more efficiently. Later, he invented a gas mask to protect fire fighters inside smoke-filled buildings. The patented device won a gold medal from the International Exposition for Sanitation and Safety. Morgan and three others wore the masks when they entered a gas-filled tunnel to save workers trapped by an explosion. During World War I, Morgan's invention protected Allied soldiers from breathing the deadly gases their enemies used in battle.

Concern for safety also motivated Morgan, at age 48, to invent a three-way automatic electric traffic light. At the time, he was said to be the only African-American in Cleveland who owned a car. Morgan patented his device and later sold the rights to market it to the General Electric Company. He died in 1963.

GEOMETRY IN ACTION

Garrett Morgan systematically went about developing his inventions. First, he identified the problem to be solved. How can sewing machines be made to operate more efficiently? How can people be protected from breathing deadly fumes? How can traffic be regulated to protect pedestrians and drivers?

What do you suppose Morgan did after he identified the problem? Write the steps you think he might have gone through to invent the traffic light.

◀ *Park Avenue in New York City* Inset: *Garrett Morgan*

Geometry Around the World connects geometry to real life by describing its usefulness to inventors, artists, architects, and other professionals, and its relevance to the lives of ordinary people in many cultures.

This modern traffic light looks different from Garrett Morgan's original invention, but the purpose is the same — saving lives.

69

4

Wrapping Up the Chapter

Review pages at the end of each chapter allow you to complete your mastery of the material. The vocabulary, objectives, examples, and exercises help you make sure you understand the skills and concepts presented in the chapter.

Each Chapter Summary and Review opens with a listing of vocabulary words that were introduced in the chapter. You can use these to check your understanding of the chapter.

VOCABULARY

Upon completing this chapter, you should be familiar with the following terms:

conclusion	76	76	if-then statement
conditional statement	76	70	inductive reasoning
conjecture	70	82	law of detachment
converse	77	83	law of syllogism
counterexample	71	77	postulate
deductive reasoning	82	98	theorem
hypothesis	76	89	two-column proof

The second part of the Chapter Summary and Review helps you review the important skills and concepts you developed in the chapter. You can use the objectives and examples provided in the left column to help you complete the exercises in the right column.

SKILLS AND CONCEPTS

OBJECTIVES AND EXAMPLES

Upon completing this chapter, you should be able to:

■ make geometric conjectures based on given information. **(Lesson 2-1)**

To determine if a conjecture made from inductive reasoning is true or false, look at situations where the given information is true. Determine if there are situations where the given is true and the conjecture is false.

■ write conditionals in if-then form. **(Lesson 2-2)**

Write the statement "Adjacent angles have a common ray" in if-then form.

"If angles are adjacent, then they have a common ray."

REVIEW EXERCISES

Use these exercises to review and prepare for the chapter test.

Determine if the conjecture is *true* or *false* based on the given information. Explain your answer.

1. **Given:** *A*, *B*, and *C* are collinear and $AB = BC$
   Conjecture: *B* is the midpoint of $\overline{AC}$.
2. **Given:** $\angle 1$ and $\angle 2$ are supplementary.
   Conjecture: $\angle 1 \cong \angle 2$

Write the conditional statement in if-then form.

3. Every cloud has a silver lining.
4. A rectangle has four right angles.
5. Obsidian is a glassy rock produced by a volcano.
6. The intersection of two planes is a line.

OBJECTIVES AND EXAMPLES

■ complete proofs involving angle theor... **(Lesson 2-7)**

Given: $\angle 1 \cong \angle 2$
Prove: $\angle 3 \cong \angle 4$

Statements	Reasons
1. $\angle 1 \cong \angle 2$	1. Given
2. $\angle 1 \cong \angle 3$ $\angle 2 \cong \angle 4$	2. Vertical ∡ ar...
3. $\angle 3 \cong \angle 4$	3. Congruence ... angles is transitive. (used twice)

APPLICATIONS AND CONNECTIONS

16. **Advertising** Write the conditional "Hard-working people deserve a night on the town at Gil's Grill" in if-then form. Identify the hypothesis and the conclusion of the conditional. Then write the converse. **(Lesson 2-2)**

18. **Algebra** Name the property of equality that justifies the statement "If $x + y = 3$ and $3 = w + v$, then $x + y = w + v$." **(Lesson 2-4)**

17. **Botany** If possible, write a valid conclusion. State the law of logic th... you used. **(Lesson 2-3)**
   ■ A sponge is a sessile animal.
   ■ A sessile animal is one that rema... permanently attached to a surface... all of its adult life.

19. **Geology** The underground temperature of rocks varies with the depth below the surface. The deeper a rock is in the Earth, the hotter it i... The temperature, *t*, in degrees Celsi... estimated by the equation $t = 35d$ ... where *d* is the depth in kilometers. Solve the formula for *d* and justify e... step. **(Lesson 2-4)**

20. Use the process of elimination to solve this problem. **(Lesson 2-5)**
   Alana, Becky, and Carl each had different lunches in the school cafeteria. One had... spaghetti, one had a salad, and one had macaroni and cheese. Alana did not have a sa... Becky did not have spaghetti or a salad. What did each person have for lunch?

The **Applications and Connections** problems help you connect the material to the world beyond your textbook.

...oof.

theorems. **(Lesson 2-6)**

Theorem 2-1 states that congruence of segments is reflexive, symmetric, and transitive.

13. **Given:** $\overline{AM} \cong \overline{CN}$
    $\overline{MB} \cong \overline{ND}$
    Prove: $\overline{AB} \cong \overline{CD}$

The Language of Geometry

CHAPTER 1

PREVIEWING THE CHAPTER

This chapter introduces some of the geometric terms that are the basis for the study of geometry. By beginning with a review of the coordinate plane, the development uses this plane to make a logical transition from algebra to geometry. The undefined terms *point, line,* and *plane* are then used to define other geometric terms, such as *angles, segments,* and *rays.* The chapter concludes by describing relationships among the defined terms, extending the ideas they convey, and looking into how they relate to each other to extend geometric concepts.

Problem-Solving Strategy Students learn to list possibilities as an effective strategy for solving many non-routine problems.

Lesson Objective Chart

Lesson (Pages)	Lesson Objectives	State/Local Objectives
1-1 (8-12)	**1-1:** Graph ordered pairs on a coordinate plane.	
1-2 (13-18)	**1-2A:** Identify and draw models of points, lines, and planes.	
	1-2B: Identify collinear and coplanar points and intersecting lines and planes.	
1-3 (19-22)	**1-3:** Solve problems by making a list of possibilities.	
1-4 (23-29)	**1-4A:** Find the distance between two points on a number line.	
	1-4B: Find the distance between points in a coordinate plane.	
1-5 (30-35)	**1-5A:** Find the midpoint of a segment.	
	1-5B: Identify and use congruent segments.	
1-6 (36-42)	**1-6A:** Identify angles and parts of angles.	
	1-6B: Use the angle addition postulate to find the measure of angles.	
1-7 (43-48)	**1-7A:** Classify angles as acute, obtuse, right, and straight.	
	1-7B: Identify and use congruent angles and the bisector of an angle.	
1-8 (50-55)	**1-8:** Identify and use adjacent angles, vertical angles, complementary angles, supplementary angles, and linear pairs of angles.	
1-9 (56-61)	**1-9A:** Identify and use right angles and perpendicular lines.	
	1-9B: Determine what information can and cannot be assumed from a figure.	

ORGANIZING THE CHAPTER

You may want to refer to the **Course Planning Calendar** on page T28.

Lesson Planning Guide

Lesson (Pages)	Pacing Chart (days) Course			Reteaching	Practice	Enrichment	Evaluation	Technology	Lab Manual	Activities: Mixed Problem Solving	Applications	Cooperative Learning Activity	Multicultural	Transparencies
	I	**II**	**III**											
1-1 (8-12)	1.5	1.5	1.5	p. 1	p. 1	p. 1		p. 1						1-1
1-2 (13-18)	1.5	1.5	1.5	p. 2	p. 2	p. 2						p. 29		1-2
1-3 (19-22)	1	1	1		p. 3					p. 1				1-3
1-4 (23-29)	2	1.5	1.5	p. 3	p. 4	p. 3	Quiz A, p. 9							1-4
1-5 (30-35)	2	1.5	1.5	p. 4	p. 5	p. 4	Mid Chapter Test, p. 13							1-5
1-6 (36-42)	2	2	1.5	p. 5	p. 6	p. 5	Quiz B, p. 9		pp.18-21				p. 1	1-6
1-7 (43-48)	2	2	1.5	p. 6	p. 7	p. 6	Quiz C, p. 10							1-7
1-8 (50-55)	1.5	1.5	1.5	p. 7	p. 8	p. 7		p.37	pp.22-25					1-8
1-9 (56-61)	1.5	1.5	1.5	p. 8	p. 9	p. 8	Quiz D, p. 10		pp.26-29		p. 15			1-9
Review (62-64)	1	1	1	Multiple Choice Tests, Forms 1A and 2B, pp. 1-4 Free Response Tests, Forms 2A and 2B, pp. 5-8										
Test (65)	1	1	1	Cumulative Review, pp. 11-12 Standardized Tests Practice Questions, p. 14										

Course I: Chapters 1-11; Course II: Chapters 1-12; Course III: Chapters 1-13

Other Chapter Resources

Student Edition

Chapter Opener, pp. 6-7
Architecture Connection, p. 12
Journal Entry, pp. 12, 42
Cooperative Learning Project, p. 22
History Connection, p. 29
Mid-Chapter Review, p. 35
Developing Reasoning Skills, p. 42
Technology, p. 49
Portfolio, p. 55
Algebra Review, pp. 66-67
More Investigations in Geometry, p. A2
Extended Project 1, pp. B2-B5

Teacher's Classroom Resources

Transparency 1-0
Real World Applications Transparencies, 1, 2
Performance Assessment Booklet, pp. 1-2
Problem-of-the-Week Activity Cards, 1, 2, 3
Tech Prep Applications Booklet, pp. 1-2
LOGO Instruction Materials, Technology Masters pp. 19-36

Other Supplements

Algebra and Geometry Overhead Manipulative Resources
Glencoe Mathematics Professional Series

Software

Test and Review Generator (Apple, IBM, and Macintosh)
Teacher's Guide for Software Resources

ENHANCING THE CHAPTER

Cooperative Learning

An Overview

For successful cooperative-learning experiences, research indicates that the teacher's responsibilities include:

1. Deciding on the size of groups and assigning students to the groups.
2. Arranging the room.
3. Describing the objectives and explaining the criteria for success.
4. Planning teaching materials.
5. Explaining the task and providing task assistance.
6. Assigning roles to students.
7. Intervening to teach cooperative-learning skills.
8. Specifying desired student behavior and monitoring that behavior.
9. Describing the student's responsibility to the group.
10. Establishing individual accountability.
11. Providing closure to the lesson.
12. Assessing how well the group functioned.

Technology

The Technology Feature following Lesson 1-7 briefly introduces students to LOGO and to some of LOGO's basic commands. LOGO commands that tell the turtle to draw a square and a triangle are given. Students are then asked to describe the results of these commands and to write their own sets of commands to draw different figures.

You may wish to refer students to the "Introduction to LOGO" found in the *Merrill Geometry Technology Masters* on pages 19-36. These lessons give a more detailed explanation of LOGO and its commands.

Critical Thinking

The development of critical thinking skills is crucial for any real understanding of the concepts presented in this course. Although there are numerous exercises so labeled throughout the text, you should look for additional opportunities to ask questions that encourage students to classify and compare, identify and extend patterns, make and test predictions, make generalizations and draw conclusions, make conjectures and draw inferences, clarify by giving specific examples, look for more than one solution, look for more than one way to arrive at a solution, justify a solution, and relate a situation to other situations.

Cooperative Learning, p. 29

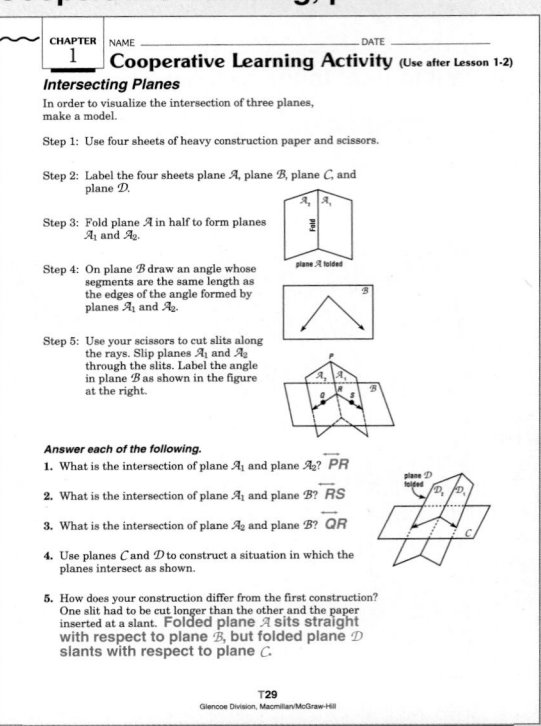

Technology, p. 37

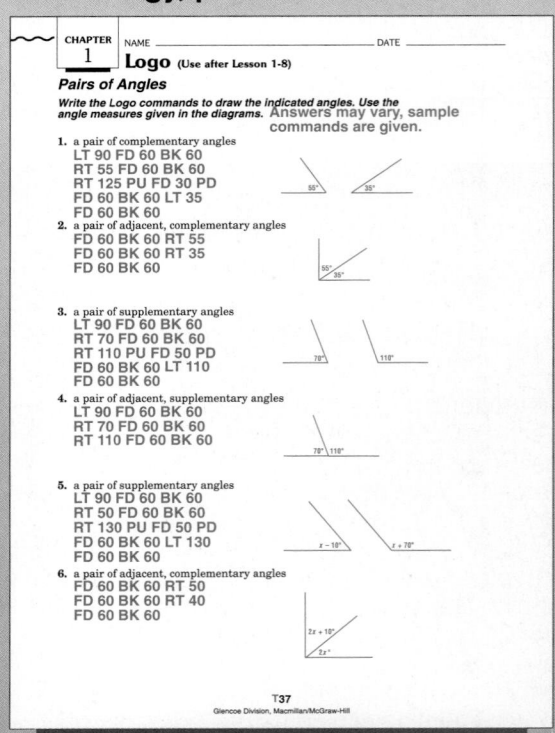

Problem of the Week Activity

The card shown below is one of three available for this chapter. It can be used as a class or small group activity.

Activity Card

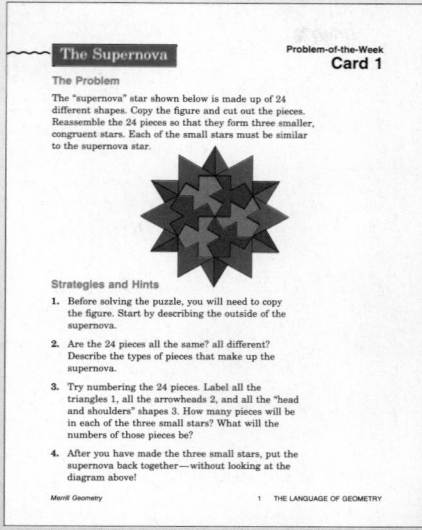

The Supernova

Problem-of-the-Week
Card 1

The Problem

The "supernova" star shown below is made up of 24 different shapes. Copy the figure and cut out the pieces. Reassemble the 24 pieces so that they form three smaller, congruent stars. Each of the small stars must be similar to the supernova star.

Strategies and Hints

1. Before solving the puzzle, you will need to copy the figure. Start by describing the outside of the supernova.

2. Are the 24 pieces all the same? all different? Describe the types of pieces that make up the supernova.

3. Try numbering the 24 pieces. Label all the triangles 1, all the arrowheads 2, and all the "head and shoulders" shapes 3. How many pieces will be in each of the three small stars? What will the numbers of those pieces be?

4. After you have made the three small stars, put the supernova back together—without looking at the diagram above!

Merrill Geometry   1   THE LANGUAGE OF GEOMETRY

Manipulatives and Models

The following material may be used as models or manipulatives in Chapter 1.

- map of the United States (Lesson 1-1)
- compass and straightedge (Lesson 1-4)
- sewing pattern (Lesson 1-5)
- protractor (Lesson 1-6)
- twist ties and straws (Lesson 1-7)
- pipe cleaners (Lesson 1-8)
- carpenter's or T-square (Lesson 1-9)

Outside Resources

Books/Periodicals

Career Associates. *Career Choices - Mathematics.* Walker and Company.

National Council of Teachers of Mathematics. *Curriculum and Evaluation Standards for School Mathematics.* National Council of Teachers of Mathematics.

National Research Council. *Everybody Counts: A Report to the Nation on the Future of Mathematics Education.* National Academy Press.

Films/Videotapes/Videodiscs

Computers: The Truth of the Matter, Disney Educational Productions, 500 S. Buena Vista St., Burbank, CA 91521

Computers: The Friendly Invasion, Disney Educational Productions, 500 S. Buena Vista St., Burbank, CA 91521

Software

BASIC
Logo, Logo Foundation, 250 West 57th St., Suite 2603, New York, NY 10107

Multicultural

Multicultural Activity, p. 1

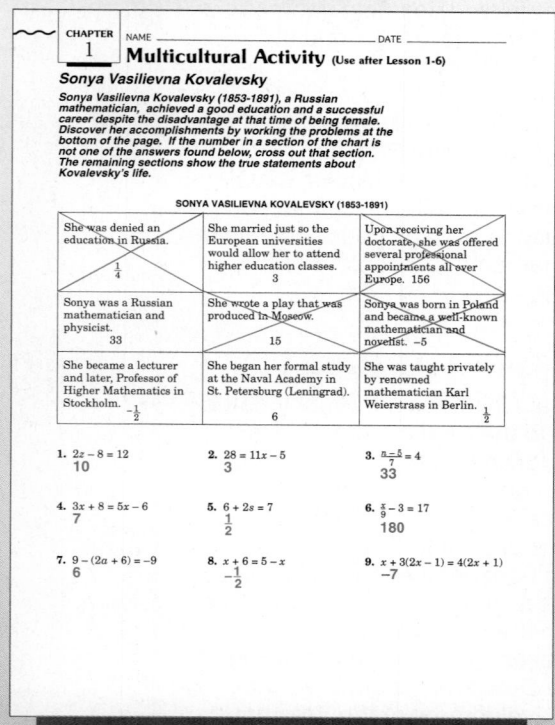

CHAPTER 1   NAME _____ DATE _____
Multicultural Activity (Use after Lesson 1-6)

Sonya Vasilievna Kovalevsky

Sonya Vasilievna Kovalevsky (1853-1891), a Russian mathematician, achieved a good education and a successful career despite the disadvantage at that time of being female. Discover her accomplishments by working the problems at the bottom of the page. If the number in a section of the chart is not one of the answers found below, cross out that section. The remaining sections show the true statements about Kovalevsky's life.

SONYA VASILIEVNA KOVALEVSKY (1853-1891)

She was denied an education in Russia. $\frac{1}{4}$	She married just so the European universities would allow her to attend higher education classes. 3	Upon receiving her doctorate, she was offered several professional appointments all over Europe. 156
Sonya was a Russian mathematician and physicist. 33	She wrote a play that was produced in Moscow. 15	Sonya was born in Poland and became a well-known mathematician and novelist. −5
She became a lecturer and later, Professor of Higher Mathematics in Stockholm. $-\frac{1}{2}$	She began her formal study at the Naval Academy in St. Petersburg (Leningrad). 6	She was taught privately by renowned mathematician Karl Weierstrass in Berlin. $\frac{1}{2}$

1. $2z - 8 = 12$
   10

2. $28 = 11x - 5$
   3

3. $\frac{a-5}{7} = 4$
   33

4. $3x + 8 = 5x - 6$
   7

5. $6 + 2s = 7$
   $\frac{1}{2}$

6. $\frac{x}{9} - 3 = 17$
   180

7. $9 - (2a + 6) = -9$
   6

8. $x + 6 = 5 - x$
   $-\frac{1}{2}$

9. $x + 3(2x - 1) = 4(2x + 1)$
   −7

Lab Manual

Lab Activity, pp. 18-21

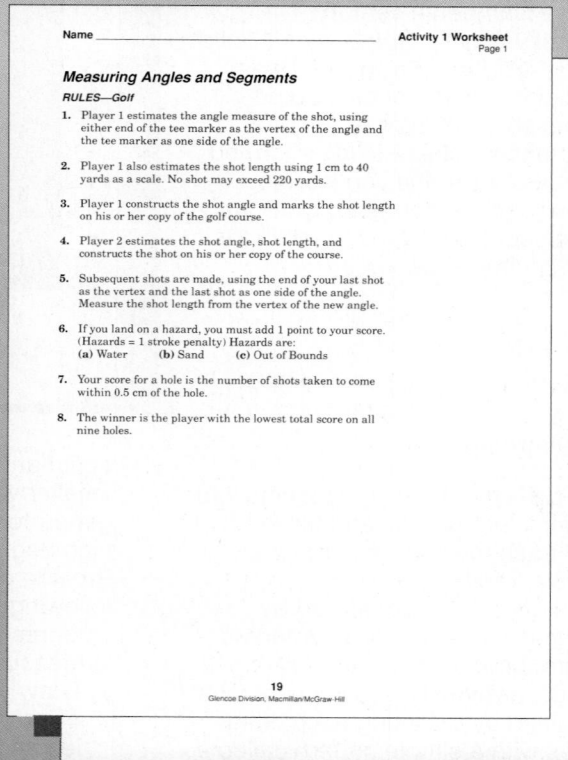

Name _____   Activity 1 Worksheet
Page 1

Measuring Angles and Segments
RULES—Golf

1. Player 1 estimates the angle measure of the shot, using either end of the tee marker as the vertex of the angle and the tee marker as one side of the angle.

2. Player 1 also estimates the shot length using 1 cm to 40 yards as a scale. No shot may exceed 220 yards.

3. Player 1 constructs the shot angle and marks the shot length on his or her copy of the golf course.

4. Player 2 estimates the shot angle, shot length, and constructs the shot on his or her copy of the course.

5. Subsequent shots are made, using the end of your last shot as the vertex and the last shot as one side of the angle. Measure the shot length from the vertex of the new angle.

6. If you land on a hazard, you must add 1 point to your score. (Hazards = 1 stroke penalty) Hazards are:
   (a) Water   (b) Sand   (c) Out of Bounds

7. Your score for a hole is the number of shots taken to come within 0.5 cm of the hole.

8. The winner is the player with the lowest total score on all nine holes.

19
Glencoe Division, Macmillan/McGraw-Hill

Using The Chapter Opener

This two-page introduction to the chapter provides students with an opportunity to see how geometry is used throughout the world in various cultures.

Transparency 1-0, available in the *Merrill Geometry Package*, provides another full-color visual and motivational activity that you can use to engage your students in the mathematical content of the chapter.

Multicultural Notes

China Chinese cartography dates back to the third century and is strikingly beautiful. Chinese maps drawn on silk represent the first application of a coordinate system. Places on a map were located along horizontal and vertical axes created by the woven threads onto which the map was drawn. However, French mathematician René Descartes is credited with the development of the Western coordinate system, in the seventeenth century.

Russia Sonya Kovalevskaya was a brilliant Russian mathematician of the nineteenth century. Kovalevskaya's *Rotation of a Solid Body Around a Fixed Point* was completed in the academic atmosphere of interest in finite sequences. These studies formed the basis of Helge von Koch's snowflake phenomenon in 1904, which contributed to Mandelbrot's work in fractal geometry.

Chapter Project

Materials pencil, pen, unlined 11" x 17" paper, posterboard, ruler, magnifying glass

Procedure Organize students into cooperative groups and tell them that each member is to draw a simple fractal.

A fractal can be generated by starting with a simple geomentric figure, or *initiator*, and modifying it in successive steps. The initiator is modified by replacing each of its sides with a simple pattern called a *generator*. Repeating this process again and again with smaller and smaller versions of the original generator results in a figure with a high degree of self-similarity. Provide each group with the following instructions. Caution students to be extremely accurate in measuring each line.

1. Draw your initiator in the center of an unlined sheet of paper, leaving at least 7.5 cm all around. For your first fractal, select a geometric shape in which all sides are equal in length, or in which unequal sides are even-numbered multiples of the shortest side.
2. Draw a simple generator consisting of straight lines emerging from a single baseline the same length as the shortest side of your initiator. The length of each line segment should be an even-numbered multiple of the shortest line segment.
3. Draw over each side of your initiator with one or more copies of generator.

The Language of Geometry

GEOMETRY AROUND THE WORLD

Have you ever seen a map of Great Britain? If so, then you know its long coastline juts and jags like tricky pieces of a jigsaw puzzle. Like clouds, mountains, and other natural formations, coastlines are irregular in shape. Nature is not usually straight and smooth! Yet, mathematics—particularly geometry—prefers to deal with straight lines and smooth curves. How then can we use mathematics to make accurate models of the irregular shapes found in nature and elsewhere?

This question intrigued mathematician Benoit Mandelbrot. Before Mandelbrot began seeking answers in the mid-1970s, no way existed for creating accurate mathematical representations of nature's irregularities. Because other mathematicians either ignored or minimized the problem, Mandelbrot developed a mathematical method for describing and reconstructing what he named **fractals**—shapes that are irregular or broken. This new field of mathematics is called **fractal geometry.**

GEOMETRY IN ACTION

In geometry, **similar** forms have the same shape, even if they are different sizes. Fractals have **self-similar** shapes. This means that the smaller and smaller details of a form have the same geometrical character as the original, larger form. To verify this, use a magnifying glass to enlarge a small portion of the fractal image shown at the right. This beautiful computer-generated picture was generated using the mathematical formulas of fractal geometry.

◀ *Coastline of Great Britain*   Inset photo: *Benoit Mandelbrot*

7

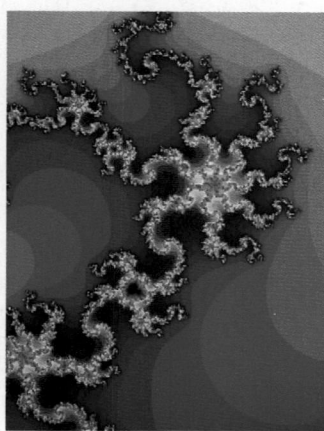

CHAPTER OBJECTIVES

In this chapter, you will:
- Graph ordered pairs on a coordinate plane.
- Find the distance between points.
- Identify and use angle relationships.

Do you see the pattern repeated in this fractal image? What would you see if you enlarged any section?

Connections and Applications

4. Replace every line segment of the figure from 3 with one or more copies of your generator.

5. Repeat 4 as often as is physically possible.

Review all the fractals. Instruct each group to select its most attractive fractal and draw it on posterboard. Have each group present its fractal to the class for discussion.

Resources

Peitgen, Heinz-Otto, and Peter H. Richter, *The Beauty of Fractals,* Springer-Verlag

Friedhoff, Richard Mark, "Fractals," in *Visualization - The Second Computer Revolution,* Harry N. Abrams, Inc.

Peterson, Ivars, *The Mathematical Tourist - Snapshots of Modern Mathematics,* W. H. Freeman

Lesson Resources

Lesson Resources

- Reteaching Master 1-1
- Practice Master 1-1
- Enrichment Master 1-1
- Technology Master, p. 1

 Transparency 1-1 contains the 5-Minute Check and a teaching aid for this lesson.

INTRODUCING THE LESSON

 5-Minute Check

1. If $x = 7$ and $y = 2$, find the value of $4x + 7y$.   **42**
2. If $x = 3$, $y = 6$, and $z = 4$, find the value of $x^2 + 3yz$.   **81**
3. What is a coordinate of a point?   **The number that corresponds to the point on the number line**
4. Solve for y in $y = 6x - 8$ if
   a. $x = 4$ **b.** $x = 1$ **16, −2**
5. Is (2, 3) a solution to $y = 3x - 7$? Is (1, −4) a solution?   **no; yes**

Motivating the Lesson

Draw a coordinate plane on the chalkboard. Blindfold a student and have him or her pick a spot on the coordinate plane (like Pin the Tail on the Donkey). Have the student tell the coordinates of the point selected, to the nearest whole number.

TEACHING THE LESSON

Teaching Tip   Note that the coordinate plane itself is sometimes called a graph.

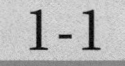 **1-1**

Connections from Algebra: The Coordinate Plane

Objective
1-1

After studying this lesson, you should be able to:
- graph ordered pairs on a coordinate plane.

Application

This past summer, Jaime had the opportunity to attend an Amy Grant concert at Poplar Creek. His ticket was for Seat 27, Row KK. When Jaime arrived at the concert, he used a branch of math called **coordinate geometry** to find his seat.

In this lesson, you will use what you already know about algebra and coordinate geometry to help you make a smooth transition into high school geometry.

FYI...

According to legend, René Descartes got the idea for coordinate geometry while watching a fly walk on a tiled ceiling.

We don't often recognize the everyday uses of mathematics in the world around us, but without math, things would not run as smoothly as they do. In Jaime's case, the number and letters on his ticket actually represent a point in a coordinate system used to identify seats. Without such a system, it would be hard to get people seated in a timely and organized way.

Some of the terms you have used in your study of the coordinate system in algebra are summarized below and shown in the figure at the right.

Origin: point O, ordered pair (0, 0)

Axes: x-axis and y-axis

Quadrants: regions labeled I, II, III, and IV

Coordinate Plane: plane containing the x-axis and y-axis

The notation A(-3, 2) can also be used to indicate that point A is named by the ordered pair (-3, 2).

Point A is located in quadrant II and has **coordinates** (-3, 2). These coordinates, given in an **ordered pair**, locate point A relative to the origin and axes. The first coordinate, -3, called the **x-coordinate**, indicates the number of units to move left or right from the origin. The second coordinate, 2, called the **y-coordinate**, indicates the number of units to move up or down from the origin.

8   CHAPTER 1   THE LANGUAGE OF GEOMETRY

ALTERNATE TEACHING STRATEGIES

Using Graphing Calculators

Explain *collinear* and *noncollinear* both pictorially and algebraically. For example, graph the equation $y = 2x + 3$ and locate three points on that line. Check to make sure these points satisfy the equation. Explain that graphing and algebra can both be used to solve problems correctly.

Using Maps

Have students use an atlas to locate three cities in the United States. Have them list the map sectors in which each city can be found.

Example 1

APPLICATION
Cartography

On the map at the right, letters and numbers are used to form ordered pairs that name sectors on the map. Name all the sectors that Interstate Highway 75 passes through.

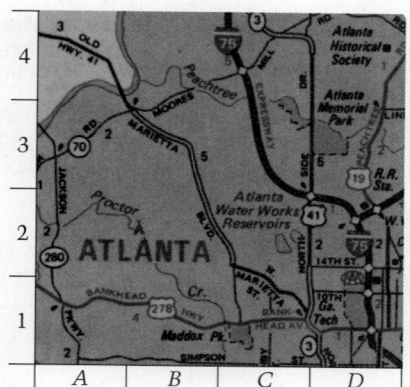

Interstate 75 first appears at the top of the map in sector $(C, 4)$. It then travels down through sectors $(C, 3)$ and $(C, 2)$ and right through sector $(D, 2)$ before traveling down again and exiting the map through sector $(D, 1)$.

Locating cities on a map is very similar to locating points on the coordinate plane.

Example 2

Write the ordered pairs that name points R, S, and T.

Point R: The x-coordinate is -2 and the y-coordinate is -5. Thus, the ordered pair is (-2, -5).

Point S: The x-coordinate is 1 and the y-coordinate is 4. Thus, the ordered pair is (1, 4).

Point T: The ordered pair for point T is (0, 1). Why?

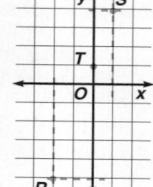

Look at R, S, and T in Example 2. It appears from their graphs that these points all lie on the same line. We call such points **collinear**. To say that points in the coordinate plane are collinear means that the coordinates of those points all satisfy the same linear equation. In this case, points R, S, and T all lie on the graph of $y = 3x + 1$ since the coordinates of each of the points satisfy (are a solution of) that equation.

Point	x	y	$y = 3x + 1$
$R(-2, -5)$	-2	-5	$-5 = 3(-2) + 1$ ✓
$S(1, 4)$	1	4	$4 = 3(1) + 1$ ✓
$T(0, 1)$	0	1	$1 = 3(0) + 1$ ✓

Is the point $U(3, 8)$ collinear with points R, S, and T? Since $8 \neq 3(3) + 1$, the coordinates of U do not satisfy the equation $y = 3x + 1$, which means that point U *does not* lie on the same line as R, S, and T. Since point U is *not* collinear with points R, S, and T, points R, S, T, and U are called **noncollinear** points.

LESSON 1-1 CONNECTIONS FROM ALGEBRA: THE COORDINATE PLANE 9

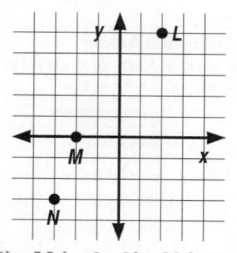

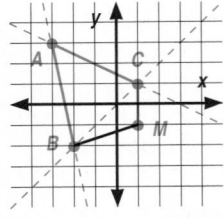

Example 3

How can you locate five points in a coordinate plane so that you are sure that no three of these points will be collinear?

First, plot two points in the plane. Then, draw a line through the points and plot another point not on that line.

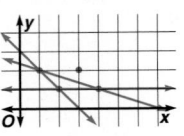

Next, draw all possible lines through pairs of these three points and plot a fourth point not on any of these lines.

Finally, draw all possible lines through pairs of these four points and plot a fifth point not on any of these lines. These five points must be noncollinear.

CHECKING FOR UNDERSTANDING

Communicating Mathematics

Read and study the lesson to answer these question. **See margin.**

1. Explain the difference between the ordered pairs (3, 5) and (5, 3).
2. Refer to the situation at the beginning of the lesson. For the concert, Jaime was seated in Seat 27, Row KK. Why do you think letters were used for the rows and numbers were used for the seats in each row?
3. How would you determine whether or not the graphs of $y = 3x + 2$ and $y = -x - 6$ intersect at the point (-2, 3)?
4. How could you show that the points representing the cities of Chicago, Denver, and Seattle on a map are noncollinear?

Guided Practice

In the figure below, triangle PQR ($\triangle PQR$) is drawn in the coordinate plane. Use the figure to answer each question.

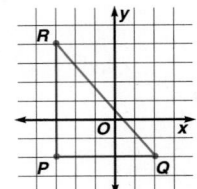

5. In which quadrant is vertex P located? **III**
6. In which quadrant is vertex Q located? **IV**
7. Which axis intersects side $\overline{PQ}$? **y-axis**
8. Which vertex of $\triangle PQR$ has the greatest x-coordinate? What are its coordinates? **Q; (2, -2)**
9. Which vertex of $\triangle PQR$ has the greatest y-coordinate? What are its coordinates? **R; (-3, 4)**
10. Name the type of angle formed by sides $\overline{RP}$ and $\overline{PQ}$. **right angle**
11. Describe how you would find the perimeter of $\triangle PQR$. **See margin.**

RETEACHING THE LESSON

Have students recreate a drawing from a list of coordinates. Draw a picture (such as a house or a television) on a coordinate plane, taking care to make corners that lie on whole number coordinates. List the coordinates of each point of the picture, indicating connections between points. Have students plot the list of points on graph paper and draw lines between points as specified.

Additional Answers

1. (3,5) x-coordinate is 3, y-coordinate is 5
   (5,3) x-coordinate is 5, y-coordinate is 3.
2. To differentiate between "vertical" rows and "horizontal" rows of seats.
3. Check to see if the point (-2,3) satisfies both equations.
4. Draw a line connecting each of the two cities, and see if the other city is on that line.

EXERCISES

Practice

Write the ordered pair for each point shown at the right.

12. P (-4, -1)   13. Q (3, -1)

14. R (3, 4)   15. S (-2, 4)

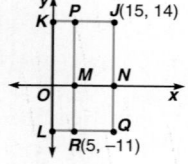

16-21. See margin.
Graph each point on one coordinate plane.

16. $A(5, -2)$ 17. $B(3, 6)$ 18. $C(-6, 0)$

19. $D(-4, 3)$ 20. $E(-3, -3)$ 21. $F(0, 4)$

In the figure at the right, all of the segments shown are parallel to either the x- or the y-axis. Determine the ordered pair that represents each point.

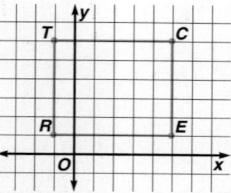

22. K (0, 14)   23. L (0, -11)

24. M (5, 0)   25. N (15, 0)

26. P (5, 14)   27. Q (15, -11)

Points $A(5, 7)$ and $B(-1, 1)$ lie on the graph of $y = x + 2$. Determine whether the following points are collinear with A and B.

28. $C(0, 2)$ yes   29. $D(1, -1)$ no   30. $E(-3, -2)$ no   31. $F(-3, -1)$ yes

32. Refer to the figure at the right to answer each question.

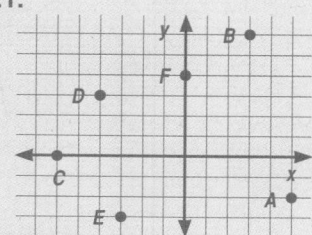

   a. What is the x-coordinate of any point collinear with points R and T? -1

   b. What is the y-coordinate of any point collinear with points C and T? 6

   c. Find the perimeter of figure *RECT*.
      22 units

33. a. and b.
    See Solutions Manual.

33. Make a table of values to determine the coordinates of three points that lie on the graph of $y = 3x + 5$. Use the headings x, $3x + 5$, y, and (x, y).

   a. Use these three points to draw the line in a coordinate plane.

   b. Make a table of values to determine three points on the graph of $y = -2x - 10$. Then draw the line in the same coordinate plane.

   c. Based on your graphs, what is the point of intersection of the lines with equations $y = 3x + 5$ and $y = -2x - 10$? (-3, -4)

Critical Thinking

34. Describe the possible locations, in terms of quadrants or axes, for point $A(x, y)$ if x and y satisfy the following conditions.

   a. $xy < 0$ II or IV   b. $xy > 0$ I or III   c. $xy = 0$ x-axis or y-axis

LESSON 1-1   CONNECTIONS FROM ALGEBRA: THE COORDINATE PLANE   11

Additional Answer

11. Find the lengths of each side using the distance formula and then add the sides together.

Closing the Lesson

Modeling Activity Have each student use a coordinate plane to make the first letter of his or her name. Have them list the coordinates for each point in the order that the points should be connected to draw the letter.

APPLYING THE LESSON

Homework Exercises

Assignment Guide
Basic: 12-27, 34-36
Average: 15-30, 34-36
Enriched: 18-36

Exercise Note

For Exercise 32c, remind students that the perimeter of a rectangle is the sum of the measures of all four sides.

Additional Answer

16.-21.

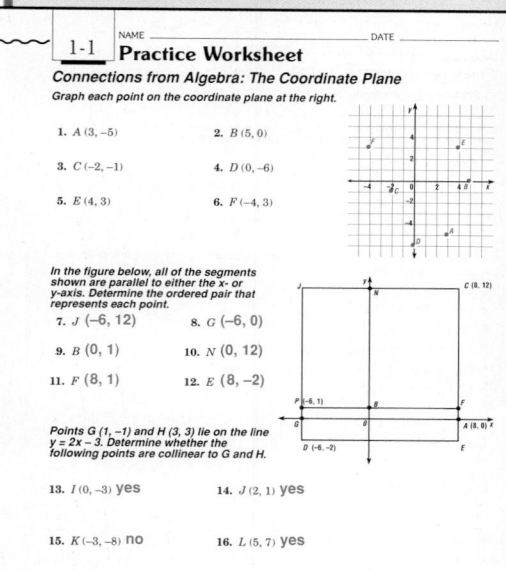

Practice Masters Booklet, p. 1

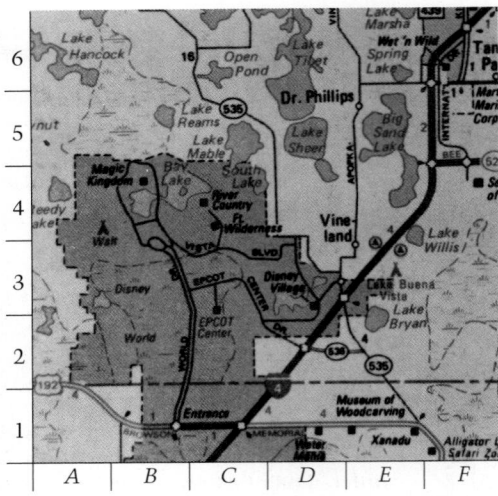

Enrichment Masters Booklet, p. 1

Application

35e. (C, 1), (D, 1),
(D, 2), (E, 3), (E, 4),
(F, 4),(F, 5), (F, 6)

35. **Cartography** Refer to the map above to answer each question.
   a. What part of Walt Disney World is in sector (B, 4)? **Magic Kingdom**
   b. In what sector is the city of Vineland? **(E, 3)**
   c. In what sectors is Lake Tibet? **(D, 5), (D, 6)**
   d. What road goes from sector (B, 3) to sector (D, 2)? **EPCOT Center Dr.**
   e. Name all the sectors that Interstate Highway 4 passes through.

Wrap-Up

36. **Journal Entry** Occasionally you will be asked to record some of your thoughts about the geometry you are learning in a journal. Start your journal by writing a few sentences about the importance of having a coordinate system and knowing how it works. **Answers may vary. A typical answer is to have a way of describing the location of an object in a plane numerically.**

~ ARCHITECTURE CONNECTION ~

Walt Disney's EPCOT Center is designed to be a model of a city of the future. EPCOT, the Experimental Prototype Community of Tomorrow, is home to the world's largest geodesic sphere, Spaceship Earth. The sphere is eighteen stories high with a diameter of 180 feet. The outer skin of the sphere is made up of interlocking aluminum triangles that look like glass.

The geodesic forms that inspired the design for Spaceship Earth were developed by R. Buckminster Fuller. Mr. Fuller spent years tinkering with geometric shapes before discovering the basis for the geodesic structure. He found that buildings of this type are able to contain more space and use less building material than buildings of conventional design.

12   CHAPTER 1   THE LANGUAGE OF GEOMETRY

Enrichment Masters Booklet, p. 1

1-1 NAME _____ DATE _____
Enrichment Worksheet

Coordinate Pictures

By connecting the points for two ordered pairs, you can make a line segment. Line segments can be combined to make pictures.

Graph the two ordered pairs in each exercise, and connect them with a line segment. After you draw each segment, identify the picture.

1. (−2, 5.5) and (5, 5.5)
2. (−3, 4) and (4, 4)
3. (−2, 3) and (3, 3)
4. (−2, −0.5) and (3, −0.5)
5. (1, −1.5) and (3, −1.5)
6. (−3, −2) and (4, −2)
7. (−3, −3) and (4, −3)
8. (−4, −4) and (5.5, −4)
9. (−3, −4.5) and (4, −4.5)
10. (−3.5, −5) and (3.5, −5)
11. (−4, −5.5) and (3, −5.5)
12. (−4.5, −6) and (2.5, −6)
13. (−6.5, −6.5) and (3.5, −6.5)
14. (−6.5, −7) and (3.5, −7)
15. (−3, 4) and (−3, 3)
16. (−2, −0.5) and (−2, 3)
17. (3, −0.5) and (3, 3)
18. (4, −3) and (4, 4)
19. (5, −1.5) and (5, 5.5)
20. (3.5, −6.5) and (3.5, −7)
21. (5.5, −4) and (5.5, −4.5)
22. (−6.5, −6.5) and (−6.5, −7)
23. (4, −2) and (5, −0.5)
24. (4, −3) and (5, −1.5)   25. (−3, 4) and (−2, 5.5)   26. (4, 4) and (5, 5.5)
27. (−6.5, −6.5) and (−4, −4) 28. (5.5, −4) and (3.5, −6.5) 29. (5.5, −4.5) and (3.5, −7)
30. What does the picture show? **A computer**

T1
Glencoe Division, Macmillan/McGraw-Hill

EXTENDING THE LESSON

Math Power: Connections

Make a table of values to determine five points that lie on the graph of $y = x^2 − 2x + 6$. Use the following values of x: 1, 2, 3, 4, and 5. Plot the five points. Do they appear to be collinear? **Points: (1,5), (2,6), (3,9), (4,14), (5,21); no**

Architecture Connection

The Architecture Connection feature introduces students to persons or cultures who were involved in the development of mathematics. You may want students to further research R. Buckminster Fuller or EPCOT Center.

Points, Lines, and Planes

Objectives
1-2A
1-2B

After studying this lesson, you should be able to:
- identify and draw models of points, lines, and planes, and
- identify collinear and coplanar points and intersecting lines and planes.

Application

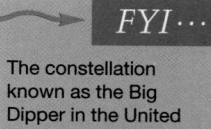

FYI···

The constellation known as the Big Dipper in the United States is called the Plow in Scotland.

Astronomers usually name the different constellations in the night sky by looking at the figure formed when segments are drawn to connect some or all the stars that make up the constellation. Thus, the same constellation might have different names in different parts of the world because of the way that its stars are connected.

Each star in constellations like the Big Dipper suggests the simplest figure studied in geometry—a **point**. In geometry, points do not have any actual size, though they sometimes represent objects, such as stars, that do have size. A point is usually named by a capital letter, and, as you have already seen, in the coordinate plane, a point can also be named by an ordered pair. *All geometric figures are made up of points.*

Suppose a segment connecting two points, *A* and *B*, is extended indefinitely in both directions. This geometric figure is called a **line**.

In plane geometry, a line means a straight line.

A line has no thickness or width, although a picture of a line does. A line is often named by a lowercase script letter. The line at the right is line *k*. If the names of two points on a line are known, such as points *A* and *B* in the figure at the right, then the line can be denoted as follows.

line *AB* $\overleftrightarrow{AB}$ line *BA* $\overleftrightarrow{BA}$

Arrows are drawn on each end of the line to suggest that it goes on forever.

A third basic geometric figure is a **plane**. You are already familiar with the coordinate plane from your study of algebra. Planes are also suggested by flat surfaces such as window panes and walls. Unlike these surfaces, a plane has no thickness and extends indefinitely in all directions.

The four-sided figure used to represent a plane is usually a parallelogram, even though a plane has no edges.

Planes are often represented or modeled using four-sided figures like the one at the right. A plane can be named by a capital script letter or by three *noncollinear points in the plane*. Thus, the plane at the right is plane *R* or plane *PQS*.

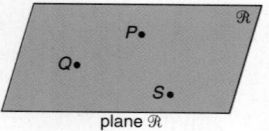

plane *R*

ALTERNATE TEACHING STRATEGIES

Using Discussion

Have students look up the words *point*, *line*, and *plane* in the dictionary. Does the dictionary use examples and descriptions to define these words or does it define them in some other way? Discuss other words, such as *equals*, *number*, or *operation*, that cannot be defined easily.

Using Cooperative Groups

Have each group make a model of a figure with points, lines, and planes. They can use paper, cardboard, toothpicks, pens, pencils, pipe cleaners, and other things that can be used to represent points, lines, or planes. Have each group show its creation and identify the places of intersection.

Lesson Resources

- Reteaching Master 1-2
- Practice Master 1-2
- Enrichment Master 1-2
- Activity Master, p. 29

Transparency 1-2 contains the 5-Minute Check and a teaching aid for this lesson.

INTRODUCING THE LESSON

5-Minute Check

(over Lesson 1-1)

1. Which quadrant is in the lower left-hand part of a coordinate plane? **quadrant III**

2. Which axis is the vertical axis, and which is the horizontal axis? **the *y*-axis is the vertical axis and the *x*-axis is the horizontal axis**

3. Graph three points in a coordinate plane that lie on the same line. **Sample answer:**

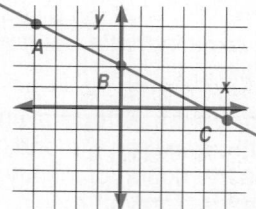

4. Write the ordered pair of the point with an *x*-coordinate of 4 and a *y*-coordinate of −3. **(4, −3)**

5. What are collinear points? **points that lie on the same line**

Bring in pictures of art or design that contain clear examples of points, lines, and planes; for example, a pointillist painting or a floor plan of a house.

TEACHING THE LESSON

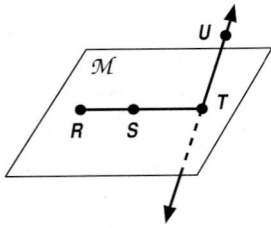

Chalkboard Example

For Example 1
Refer to the figure below.

a. Are the points *S*, *T*, and *U* collinear? **no**
b. Are points *R*, *S*, and *T* coplanar? **yes**
c. Use three points to define a plane other than plane *M*.
   Sample answer: Points *U*, *R*, and *T* would form plane *URT*.

Teaching Tip   When discussing points, explain that a point has no dimension.

Teaching Tip   After drawing a line with arrows on the end, discuss the notion of infinity. What or where is "forever"?

Teaching Tip   When discussing lines, explain that two points determine a line but a line contains an infinite number of points.

All planes, lines, and points are contained in space. **Space** is the set of all points.

In geometry, the terms *point*, *line*, and *plane* are considered *undefined terms* since they have only been explained using examples and descriptions. Even though they are undefined, these terms can still be used to define other geometric terms and properties.

You may recall from the previous lesson that collinear points are points that lie on the same line. Similarly, **coplanar** points are points that lie in the same plane. The points that you plotted in a coordinate plane in the previous lesson were coplanar points. *All points plotted in a coordinate plane are coplanar.*

Example 1 | **Refer to the figure at the right to answer each question.**

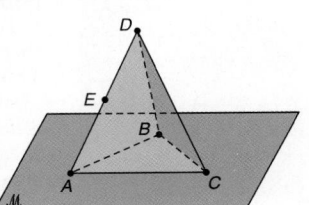

a. Are points *A*, *E*, and *D* collinear?
   Since points *A*, *E*, and *D* lie on $\overleftrightarrow{AD}$, they are collinear.

b. Are points *A*, *B*, *C*, and *D* coplanar?
   Points *A*, *B*, and *C* lie in plane *M*, but point *D* does *not* lie in plane *M*. Thus, the four points are not coplanar.

c. How many planes appear in this figure?
   There are 4 planes: Plane *M* (or plane *ABC*), plane *ACD*, plane *ABD*, and plane *CBD*.

Notice that segments AB, CB, and DB are dashed rather than solid. For figures in space, dashed segments and lines are used to represent parts of the three-dimensional figure that are hidden from view.

Figures play an important role in understanding geometric concepts. The drawing and labeling of figures can help you model and visualize various geometric relationships. For example, the figures and descriptions below can help you visualize some important relationships among points, lines, and planes.

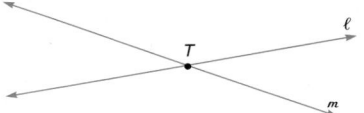

P is on *m*.
P is in *m*.
m contains *P*.
m passes through *P*.

ℓ and *m* intersect at *T*.
ℓ and *m* intersect in *T*.
ℓ and *m* both contain *T*.
T is the intersection of ℓ and *m*.

*The **intersection** of two figures is the set of points that are in both figures.*

14   CHAPTER 1   THE LANGUAGE OF GEOMETRY

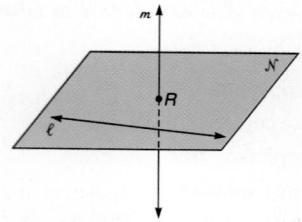

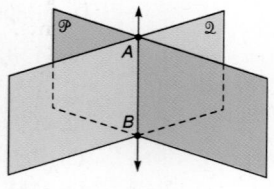

ℓ and R are in $\mathcal{N}$.

$\mathcal{N}$ contains R and ℓ.

m intersects $\mathcal{N}$ at R.

R is the intersection of m with $\mathcal{N}$.

$\overleftrightarrow{AB}$ is in $\mathcal{P}$ and is in $\mathcal{Q}$.

$\mathcal{P}$ and $\mathcal{Q}$ both contain $\overleftrightarrow{AB}$.

$\mathcal{P}$ and $\mathcal{Q}$ intersect in $\overleftrightarrow{AB}$.

$\overleftrightarrow{AB}$ is the intersection of $\mathcal{P}$ and $\mathcal{Q}$.

Example 2

Draw and label a figure in the coordinate plane showing lines $\overleftrightarrow{MN}$ and $\overleftrightarrow{PQ}$ intersecting at X and a point Y not on either $\overleftrightarrow{MN}$ or $\overleftrightarrow{PQ}$. Use $M(1, 1)$, $N(-6, 4)$, $P(0, -3)$, and $Q(5, 2)$ as given points.

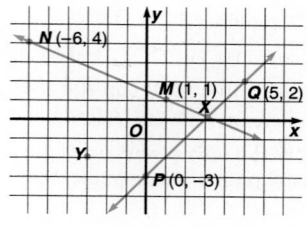

X must be the point of intersection of $\overleftrightarrow{MN}$ and $\overleftrightarrow{PQ}$. Y can be any point that is not on $\overleftrightarrow{MN}$ and is not on $\overleftrightarrow{PQ}$.

CHECKING FOR UNDERSTANDING

Communicating Mathematics

Read and study the lesson to answer these questions.

1. Refer to the application at the beginning of the lesson. What geometric figures do the stars in the night sky represent? **points**

2. **point, line, plane**

2. What are the three undefined terms presented in this lesson?

3. Draw and label line ℓ intersecting plane $\mathcal{P}$ at point D where ℓ is not in plane $\mathcal{P}$. **See margin.**

4. *True* or *false*: Collinear points are also coplanar. **true**

5. *True* or *false*: Coplanar points are also collinear. **false**

Guided Practice

Draw and label a figure for each relationship. **See margin.**

6. Point A lies on line MN.

7. Plane $\mathcal{M}$ contains line n and point R.

8. Lines ℓ and m intersect at point P.

9. Plane $\mathcal{N}$ and line CD intersect at point T.

Chalkboard Example

For Example 2
Draw and label two planes $\mathcal{M}$ and $\mathcal{N}$ that intersect at line AB and draw a line ℓ that intersects planes $\mathcal{M}$ and $\mathcal{N}$ in only one point.

Sample answer:

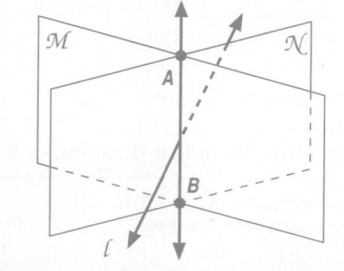

Additional Answers

8.

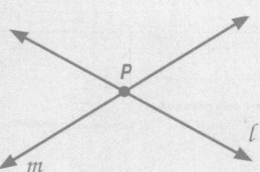

9.

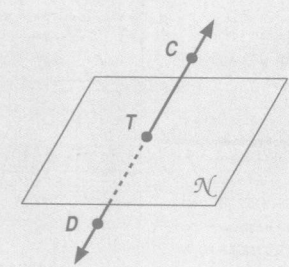

Additional Answers

3. 6.

7.

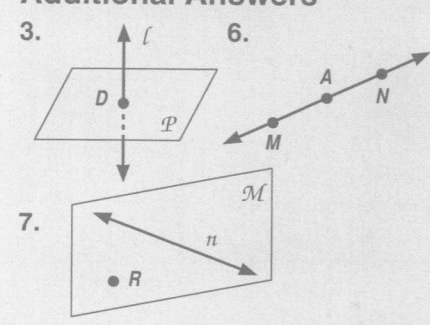

Checking for Understanding

Exercises 1-23 are designed to help you assess students' understanding through reading, writing, speaking, and modeling. You should work through Exercises 1-5 with your students and then monitor their work on Exercises 6-23.

Closing the Lesson

Modeling Activity Describe specific figures that contain points, lines, and planes to your students and have them draw each figure. For example, you may have them draw a plane that contains two intersecting lines, or a plane that contains three points that are not collinear.

APPLYING THE LESSON

Homework Exercises

Assignment Guide

Basic: 24-44, 51-55, 57-68
Average: 27-46, 51-68
Enriched: 31-68

Reteaching Masters Booklet, p. 2

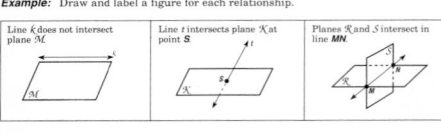

NAME _____ DATE _____
1-2 **Reteaching Worksheet**

Points, Lines, Planes

Points, lines, and planes can be related in many different ways. Figures can be used to show these relationships. When two figures have one or more points in common, the figures are said to **intersect**. When points lie on the same line, the points are said to be **collinear**. When points lie in the same plane, the points are said to be **coplanar**.

Example: Draw and label a figure for each relationship.

Line *k* does not intersect plane *M*.	Line *t* intersects plane *K* at point *S*.	Planes *R* and *S* intersect in line *MN*.

Draw and label a figure for each relationship.

1. Lines *JK* and *EF* are not in plane *M* but intersect plane *M* at *X*.
2. Lines *m* and *n* intersect at point *Q*.

3. Points *R*, *S*, and *T* are in plane *M* but point *W* does not lie in plane *M*.
4. The intersection of planes *A*, *B*, and *C* is line *EF*.

Refer to the figure to answer these questions.
5. Are points *H*, *J*, *K*, and *L* coplanar? yes
6. Name three lines that intersect at *X*. WX, KX, XY
7. What points do plane *WXYZ* and *HW* have in common? W
8. Are points *W*, *X*, and *Y* collinear? no
9. Are points *W*, *X*, *Y*, and *H* coplanar? no

T2
Glencoe Division, Macmillan/McGraw-Hill

Determine whether each statement is *true* or *false*.

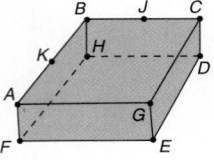

10. *A*, *B*, and *C* are collinear. false
11. *A*, *B*, and *C* are coplanar. true
12. *E*, *F*, *G*, and *H* are coplanar. false
13. *B*, *J*, and *G* are coplanar. true
14. *A*, *K*, *C*, and *G* are coplanar. true

Refer to the figure at the right to answer each question.

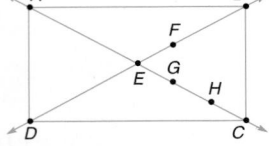

15. What is the intersection of $\overleftrightarrow{DB}$ and $\overleftrightarrow{GH}$? E
16. Are *F*, *B*, and *E* collinear? coplanar? yes; yes
17. Are *F*, *G*, and *H* collinear? coplanar? no; yes
18. What points are collinear with *A* and *E*? C, G, H

Refer to the figure at the right to answer each question.

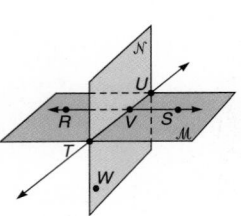

19. What is the intersection of planes *M* and *N*? line TU
20. Are *R*, *S*, *V*, and *T* coplanar? yes
21. What points are coplanar with *S*, *T*, and *V*? R, U
22. Are there more than three points on $\overleftrightarrow{RS}$? If so, how many points are on $\overleftrightarrow{RS}$? yes; infinitely many
23. Are *T*, *U*, *V*, and *W* the only points on plane *N*? If no, how many points are on plane *N*? no; infinitely many

EXERCISES

Practice 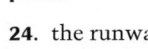 **State whether each of the following is best modeled by a point, line, or plane.**

A 24. the runway landing lights at Byrd International Airport line
25. the floor in your classroom plane
26. the median strip on a two-lane highway line
27. the contrail left by an airplane flying at high altitudes line
28. each colored dot, or pixel, on a television screen point
29. a page from this book plane

Draw and label a figure for each relationship. See Solutions Manual.

30. $\overleftrightarrow{AB}$ contains point *R*.
31. *ℓ* contains point *P* and lies in plane *N*.
32. Lines *AB* and *ℓ* both contain point *X*.
B 33. The intersection of planes *G* and *H* is $\overline{CD}$.
34. Lines *PQ* and *m*, and plane *H* intersect at *T*.

16   CHAPTER 1   THE LANGUAGE OF GEOMETRY

RETEACHING THE LESSON

Use paper, a pen or pencil and glue or tape to demonstrate what happens when a line and a plane intersect, or when a plane and a plane intersect. Poke the pen or pencil through the paper, or tape two pieces of paper together to give students a visual demonstration of the concepts.

35. Planes $\mathcal{A}$, $\mathcal{B}$, and $\mathcal{C}$ intersect at P.

36. $\overleftrightarrow{RS}$ and plane $\mathcal{L}$ do not intersect.

37. Planes $\mathcal{M}$, $\mathcal{N}$, and $\mathcal{R}$ do not intersect.

38. A, B, and C lie on ℓ, but D does not lie on ℓ.

39. n contains Q and R, but does not contain P and S.

Refer to the figure at the right to answer each question. *This figure is a pyramid, which you will study in Chapter 11.* **See margin.**

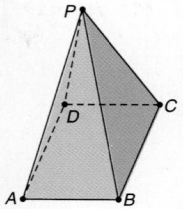

40. The flat surfaces of the pyramid are called **faces**. Name the five planes that contain the faces of the pyramid.

41. Are points A, D, P, and C coplanar?

42. Name three lines that intersect at B.

43. Name two planes that intersect in line PD.

44. Name a line and a plane that intersect in point P.

45. What do the dashed segments in the figure represent?

CONNECTION
Modeling

46. On a separate sheet of paper, repeat the steps shown below to make a drawing of a box. *This figure is also called a rectangular solid.* **See students' work.**

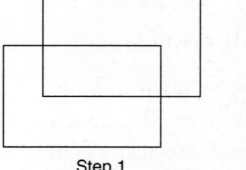
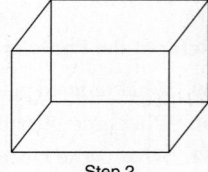
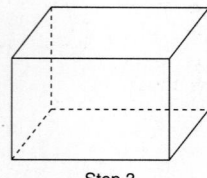

Step 1   Step 2   Step 3

Draw and label a figure for each relationship. **See margin.**

47. Noncollinear points P, Q, and R lie in plane $\mathcal{A}$, point S does not lie in plane $\mathcal{A}$, and P, Q, R, and S lie in plane $\mathcal{B}$.

48. The intersection of planes $\mathcal{C}$, $\mathcal{D}$, $\mathcal{E}$, and $\mathcal{F}$ is point X.

49. Planes $\mathcal{G}$ and $\mathcal{H}$ each intersect plane $\mathcal{J}$ but do not intersect each other.

50. Planes $\mathcal{K}$ and $\mathcal{L}$ intersect each other and they both intersect plane $\mathcal{M}$, but there are *no* points common to all three planes. **See margin.**

Critical Thinking

In your classroom, you can think of the floor and ceiling as models of *horizontal* planes and the walls as models for *vertical* planes. Answer the following questions about horizontal and vertical planes.

51. Can two horizontal planes intersect? no

52. Can two vertical planes intersect? yes

53. Must any line that lies in a vertical plane be a vertical line? no

54. Must any line that lies in a horizontal plane be a horizontal line? yes

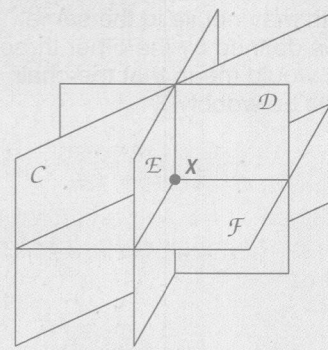
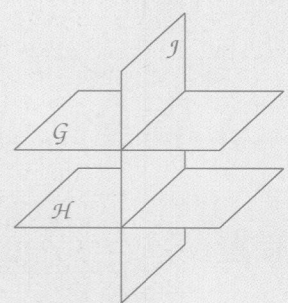
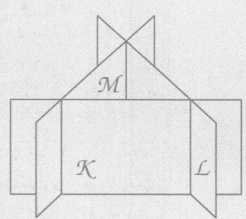
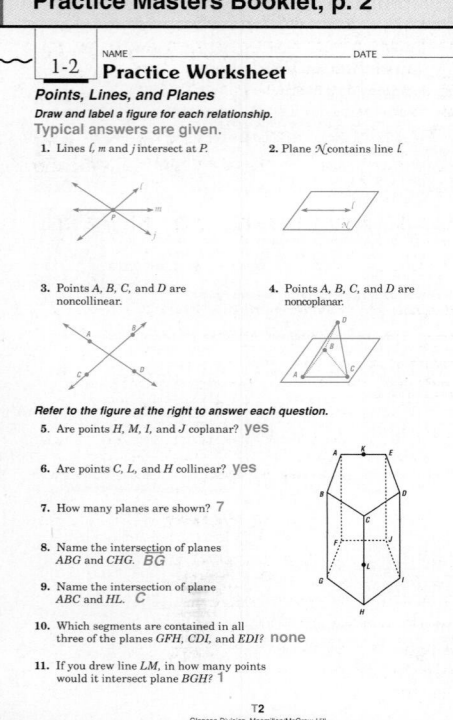

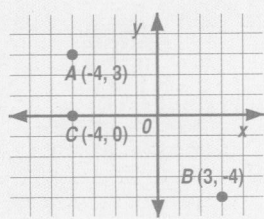
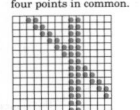
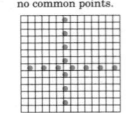
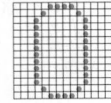
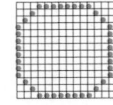
Applications

55. **Carpentry**   Mr. Johnstone is building some new chairs for his dinette table. If he wants to be sure that these chairs will not wobble, should he build chairs with three legs or with four legs? Explain. See margin.

56. **Printing**   In order to print a color photo for this book, dots of four colors are used to break a photo down into its component parts. You can use a magnifying glass to see the dots. Each photo is separated into four primary colors as shown below.

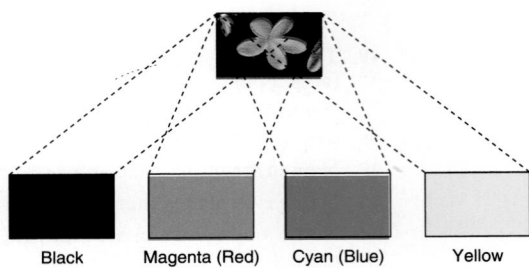

Black   Magenta (Red)   Cyan (Blue)   Yellow

The photos in this book are printed at 1200 dpi (dots per square inch). What is the maximum number of different colored dots that could be used to print a 5-inch by 8-inch rectangular color photo? *Hint: Recall that the formula for the area of a rectangle is area = length × width.*
5 · 8 · 1200 or 48,000

Mixed Review   Graph each point on one coordinate plane. (Lesson 1-1) See margin.

57. $A(-4, 3)$ 58. $B(3, -4)$ 59. $C(-4, 0)$

Refer to the figure at the right to answer each question. (Lesson 1-1)

60. What ordered pair names W? (0, 3)
61. What ordered pair names Z? (-1, -2)
62. What is the x-coordinate of any point that is collinear with X and Y? 5
63. What is the y-coordinate of any point that is collinear with Z and Y? -2

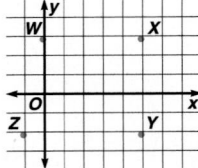

Wrap-Up   64. Name the three important geometric figures described in this lesson. Then give an example of something that is modeled by each of the figures. point, line, plane; See students' work for examples of models.

Looking Ahead
Algebra Review

You will need to find square roots in the next lesson. Find each square root to the nearest hundredth.

Examples:

a. $\sqrt{1296} = \sqrt{9 \cdot 9 \cdot 4 \cdot 4}$
$= \sqrt{36^2}$
$= 36$

b. $\sqrt{530}$

Enter: 530 $\boxed{\sqrt{x}}$ 23.0217289

Therefore, $\sqrt{530}$ to the nearest hundredth is 23.02.

65. $\sqrt{961}$ 31   66. $\sqrt{3025}$ 55   67. $\sqrt{775}$ 27.84   68. $\sqrt{6436}$ 80.22

EXTENDING THE LESSON

Math Power: Reasoning

Have one student name a number. Have the next student name a number that is less (or greater) than the previous number. Repeat this process until every student has had a chance. Ask your students how long they could go on doing this. Explain that this demonstrates the concept of infinity.

1-3 Problem-Solving Strategy: List the Possibilities

Objective 1-3
After studying this lesson, you should be able to:
- solve problems by making a list of possibilities.

Application

Mr. and Mrs. Jeremy are planning to plant a rectangular vegetable garden in their backyard. They want the garden to have an area of at least 15 square yards, but they only have 18 yards of wire mesh fence to use for fencing. What are the possible dimensions for the Jeremys' garden if they plan to use all the fencing and for the sides to have whole number lengths?

The four steps for solving any problem are listed below.

Problem-Solving

1. **Explore the problem.**
2. **Plan the solution.**
3. **Solve the problem.**
4. **Examine the solution.**

Let's use the four-step plan to find the dimensions of the Jeremys' garden.

EXPLORE The garden is to be a rectangle with an area of at least 15 square yards. The Jeremys only have 18 yards of fencing material, so the perimeter of the rectangle will be at most 18 yards.

PLAN You may recall that the formulas for the perimeter and area of a rectangle are as follows.

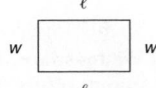

$$\text{perimeter} = 2\ell + 2w \qquad\qquad \text{area} = \ell w$$

ℓ represents the length and w represents the width.

Thus, to solve this problem, we must find all whole numbers ℓ and w such that $18 = 2\ell + 2w$ and $15 \leq \ell w$.

One possible approach we can use to find the solution is to *list the possibilities*. By making an organized list or table of all the rectangles with perimeters of 18 yards and with sides of whole number length, we can determine the ones with areas greater than or equal to 15 square yards.

LESSON 1-3   PROBLEM-SOLVING STRATEGY: LIST THE POSSIBILITIES   19

ALTERNATE TEACHING STRATEGIES

Using Problem Solving

A number of problem-solving techniques, such as making a table or drawing a diagram, can be incorporated into the strategy of making a list. Discuss other problem-solving strategies with the students. Have them list real world problems and figure out a problem- solving strategy together.

Using Discussion

Brainstorm solutions to some of the problems in this lesson with students. This is a good lesson to demonstrate that sometimes bouncing ideas around a group can lead to a solution.

Lesson Resources

- Practice Master 1-3
- Activity Master, p. 1

Transparency 1-3 contains the 5-Minute Check and a teaching aid for this lesson.

INTRODUCING THE LESSON

 5-Minute Check

(over Lesson 1-2)

1. How many points are necessary to define a line? **2** How many points are necessary to define a plane? **3**
2. Write three ways to denote a line that contains points *D* and *E*.
   Sample answer: line *DE*, line *ED*, and $\overleftrightarrow{DE}$
3. State four ways to express the relationships among the points, lines, and planes in the figure below.
   Sample answers: *Q* is in $\mathcal{W}$; $\mathcal{Z}$ and $\mathcal{W}$ intersect in $\overleftrightarrow{AB}$; ℓ and $\overleftrightarrow{AB}$ intersect at *T*; *T* is on ℓ.

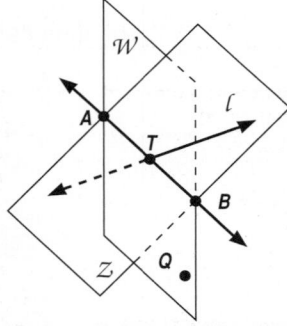

4. How many points, lines, and planes exist in space?
   an infinite number

Motivating the Lesson

Give students a list of three types of physical characteristics. For example, curly or straight hair, blue or brown or green eyes, and tall or short height. Ask how many different combinations of characteristics can result.

Teaching Tip   When working with the opening problem, solve the equation $18 = 2l + 2w$ for w and substitute values for l.

Teaching Tip   After finding the dimensions that satisfy the conditions of the opening problem, ask students what dimensions they think the Jeremys should choose for their garden. Since the original problem indicates the garden should be *at least* 15 square yards, the best possible choice would be 5 yards by 4 yards, since it maximizes area.

Chalkboard Example

For the Example
Jessica needs to buy a can of vegetables, a can of fruit, and some bread from the grocery store, and she wants to spend the least money possible. She finds that one brand of vegetable has beans, corn, and peas all on special for the same low price. A brand of fruit has peaches, pears and pineapple all on special for the same low price. Also, the store is selling French bread, wheat bread, and Italian bread for the same low price. How many different combinations of groceries can she buy?   **27**

SOLVE First, we need to list all whole numbers ℓ and w such that $18 = 2\ell + 2w$ along with the corresponding values for ℓw. Then, we can find all the values in the list where $15 \leq \ell w$.

ℓ	w	$2\ell + 2w$	ℓw	$15 \leq \ell w$
1	8	18	8	
2	7	18	14	
3	6	18	18	✔
4	5	18	20	✔
5	4	18	20	✔
6	3	18	18	✔
7	2	18	14	
8	1	18	8	

Why are the values $\ell = 0$, $w = 9$ and $\ell = 9$, $w = 0$ not listed?

Thus, there are four possibilities for the dimensions of the Jeremys' garden: 3 yards by 6 yards, 4 yards by 5 yards, 5 yards by 4 yards, and 6 yards by 3 yards.

EXAMINE Our answers satisfy the conditions of the problem. A rectangular garden that is 3 yards by 6 yards, 4 yards by 5 yards, 5 yards by 4 yards, or 6 yards by 3 yards has a perimeter less than or equal to 18 yards and an area greater than or equal to 15 square yards.

Whenever you are listing possibilities, it may help you to make a table or a tree diagram to be sure that you do not omit any possibilities.

Example

On Wednesdays, the Cliff House restaurant offers three dinner specials. One is a shrimp dinner with either rice pilaf or a baked potato. The second is a lobster dinner with either rice pilaf or a vegetable medley. The third is a chicken dinner with either the rice pilaf, vegetable medley, or a baked potato. Each special dinner also comes with either soup or salad. How many different dinners specials can you order on Wednesdays?

The tree diagram on page 21 shows the various combinations.

20   CHAPTER 1   THE LANGUAGE OF GEOMETRY

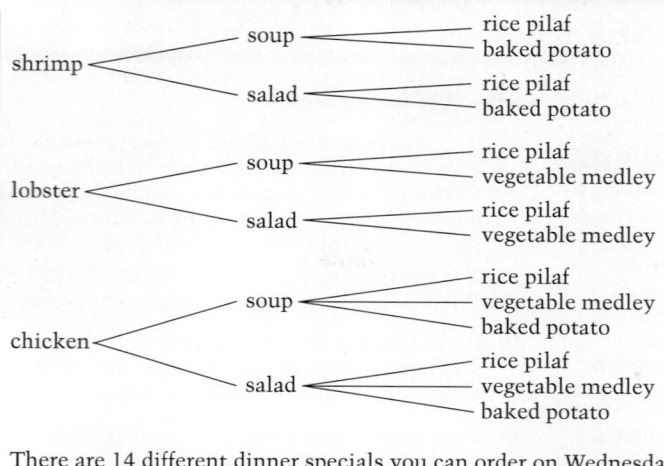

shrimp
— soup — rice pilaf / baked potato
— salad — rice pilaf / baked potato

lobster
— soup — rice pilaf / vegetable medley
— salad — rice pilaf / vegetable medley

chicken
— soup — rice pilaf / vegetable medley / baked potato
— salad — rice pilaf / vegetable medley / baked potato

There are 14 different dinner specials you can order on Wednesdays.

Teaching Tip In a tree diagram, the total number of answers includes all possibilities listed on the right side.

EVALUATING THE LESSON

Checking for Understanding

Exercises 1-7 are designed to help you assess students' understanding through reading, writing, speaking, and modeling. You should work through Exercises 1-3 with your students and then monitor their work on Exercises 4-7.

Error Analysis

When making a table, students may have difficulty deciding on column headings. Explain that the first columns list the data and the other columns list the steps needed to obtain a solution.

Closing the Lesson

Speaking Activity Ask students to name at least three advantages to using a list of possibilities to solve problems.
Sample answer: It can help you organize your thoughts, it can help you organize your data, it can save you time in finding a solution to the problem.

CHECKING FOR UNDERSTANDING

Communicating Mathematics

Read and study the lesson to answer each question.

1. When you use the strategy of listing possibilities, why is it important to make your list organized? **See margin.**

2. organized list, table, tree diagram

2. Name three different ways you can display possibilities.

3. Refer to the application at the beginning of the lesson. What does it mean to say a rectangle has a perimeter of 18 yards? **The sum of the lengths of its sides is 18 yards.**

Guided Practice

Solve each problem by listing possibilities.

4. The president, vice president, secretary, and treasurer of the Debate Team are to be seated in a row of four chairs for a yearbook picture. How many different seating arrangements are possible? **24 arrangements**

5. 10 combinations

5. A vending machine dispenses products that each cost 50¢. The machine will only accept quarters, dimes, and nickels. How many different combinations of coins must the machine be programmed to accept?

6. All of the points A, B, C, D, and E are on a circle. List all of the lines that contain exactly two of these five points. **See margin.**

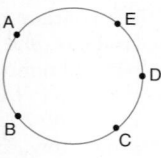

7. Sarah, Victor, Janel, and Kirby checked their coats at the door of the Colonnade Room Restaurant. The coat checker is in quite a hurry when he returns their coats. How many different ways can their coats be returned so that no one receives the right one? **9**

RETEACHING THE LESSON

Some students may have difficulty understanding that the area of a figure can change even though its perimeter does not. Have students calculate the area of different figures (circles, triangles, rectangles, etc.) that have the same perimeter. Have them make a list that compares the areas to find which is greatest.

Additional Answers

1. to be sure that you list all of the possibilities and that you do not omit any important items

6. $\overleftrightarrow{AB}$, $\overleftrightarrow{AC}$, $\overleftrightarrow{AD}$, $\overleftrightarrow{AE}$, $\overleftrightarrow{BC}$, $\overleftrightarrow{BD}$, $\overleftrightarrow{BE}$, $\overleftrightarrow{CD}$, $\overleftrightarrow{CE}$, $\overleftrightarrow{DE}$

APPLYING THE LESSON

Homework Exercises

Assignment Guide

Basic: 8-12
Average: 9-13
Enriched: 10-14

Exercise Note

For Exercise 7, list the six possible arrangements for the three people. Check each arrangement to see if the comments fit.

Additional Answers

10.

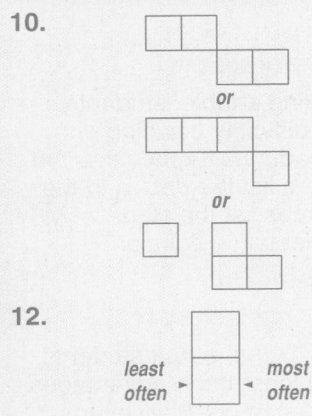

or

or

12.

least often ▶ ◀ most often

Practice Masters Booklet, p. 3

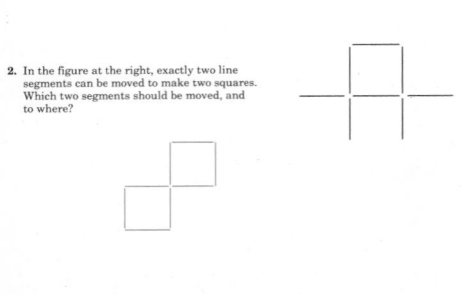

1-3 NAME _____ DATE _____
Practice Worksheet
Problem–Solving Strategy: List the Possibilities
Solve. Use any strategy.

1. On a certain island, Borks always tell the truth, Beeks always lie, and Bicks sometimes tell lies and sometimes tell the truth. From the following statements by Fill, Foll, and Fall, determine who is the Bork, who is the Beek, and who is the Bick.

Fill: Foll is the Bork.
Foll: Fill is the Bick.
Fall: Fill is lying.

Fill is the Bick. Foll is the Bork. Fall is the Beek.

2. In the figure at the right, exactly two line segments can be moved to make two squares. Which two segments should be moved, and to where?

3. Tim can choose form a tan shirt, a blue shirt, and a green shirt. He can choose from black slacks or blue jeans. He can choose from a windbreaker, a sweatshirt, or a jacket. How many different outfits can he wear if he will not wear the sweatshirt with the black slacks? 15

T3
Glencoe Division, Macmillan/McGraw-Hill

Practice

Strategies

Look for a pattern.
Solve a simpler problem.
Act it out.
Guess and check.
Draw a diagram.
Make a chart.
Work backward.

9. 22 pieces
11. Sample answer:
$3 \times (3 + 3 \div 3) - 3 \div 3 = 11$

Solve. Use any strategy.

8. Tim, Renee, and Sandra are walking down the hall single file. Tim always tells the truth, and Sandra *never* tells the truth. The student walking in the front says, "Tim is in the middle." The student in the middle says," I am Renee." The student in the back says, "Sandra is in the middle." Name the students in order from front to back. **Renee, Sandra, Tim**

9. You can cut a pizza into a maximum of 7 pieces with only 3 straight cuts. What is the greatest number of pieces you can make with 6 straight cuts?

10. In the figure at the right, exactly two line segments can be removed to make four squares. Which two segments should be removed? **See margin.**

11. Place operation symbols and any necessary grouping symbols in the sentence below to make it correct.
$$3\ 3\ 3\ 3\ 3\ 3 = 11$$

12. Line segments are used to make up the digits of the numbers in the display of a digital clock.
    a. Which line segment is used least often when forming the digits 0 to 9?
    b. Which segment is used most often? **See margin.**

13. Ted and Mary traded in their old car which averaged 22 miles per gallon. The EPA sticker on the new car stated that it should average 37 miles per gallon. If Ted and Mary drive about 12,000 miles per year and gasoline is about $1.20 per gallon, how much should they expect to save on gasoline in the first year of owning their new car? **about $265**

14. An airline gives each of its flight attendants one red shirt, one white shirt, one blue shirt, a navy blazer, one pair of navy pants, and one pair of navy pin-striped pants. How many different outfits can a flight attendant wear if the blazer is optional? *(Hint: Find the outfits possible without the blazer, then add the blazer to each outfit.)* **12 outfits**

COOPERATIVE LEARNING PROJECT

Work in groups. Each person in the group must understand the solution and be able to explain it to any person in class.

Three students are blindfolded and stand in a single-file line. Karen takes three hats from a box containing three red hats and two yellow hats and places one on each of the blindfolded students. She tells the blindfolded students how many hats of each color there were in the box and removes their blindfolds. The student in the back looks at the hats on the two students in front of him and says "I don't know what color hat I am wearing." The student in the center hears that statement, looks at the hat on the student in front of her, and says the same thing. The student in the front says "I know what color hat I am wearing." What color hat is he wearing? Explain his logic. **See Solutions Manual.**

EXTENDING THE LESSON

Math Power: Connections

The school lunchroom provides a selection of 2 kinds of soup, 3 kinds of sandwiches, 4 different desserts, and 3 beverages. How many different combinations of soup, sandwich, dessert, and beverage can a student make?
72

Cooperative Learning Project

This activity provides students an opportunity to *learn* things together, not just do things together. You may wish to refer to pages T6-T7 and page 6c for the various elements of cooperative groups and specific goals and strategies for using them.

1-4 Finding the Measures of Segments

Objectives
1-4A
1-4B

After studying this lesson, you should be able to:
- find the distance between points on a number line, and
- find the distance between points in a coordinate plane.

Application

In designing their deck, Bill and Teresa Hartford decided it should be unlike any they had ever seen. However, this design created a real challenge for contractors who were asked to provide construction bids. The bids varied widely because of the way each contractor figured the measurements for the lumber needed and the lumber that would be wasted after cutting.

The idea of measurement is an important mathematical concept. Without it, many things would be impossible. For example, the contractors would not know how much lumber is needed to build the Hartfords' deck. Like Sally, you have already had quite a bit of experience measuring with rulers.

In geometry, the distance between two points is used to define the measure of a segment. We discussed segments in the previous lesson when we talked about connecting pairs of stars in a constellation. Segments can be defined by using the idea of *betweenness* of points.

In the figure at the right, point N is **between** M and P while point Q is *not* between M and P. For N to be between M and P, all three points must be collinear. **Segment MP**, written $\overline{MP}$, consists of points M and P and all points between M and P. The **measure** of $\overline{MP}$, written MP (without a bar over the letters), is the distance between M and P. Thus, the measure of a segment is the same as the distance between its two endpoints.

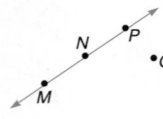

In order to quantify the measure of a segment, you must measure the segment using a device, like a ruler, that has a *unit of measure*, such as inches.

LESSON 1-4   FINDING THE MEASURES OF SEGMENTS   23

ALTERNATE TEACHING STRATEGIES

Using Manipulatives

Bring in a piece of rope and have students mark off a segment to be used as a unit of measure. Have them give it a name. They can use the new unit to measure the distance between objects in the classroom. Explain that inches, feet, centimeters, etc., are all units of measure used to find distance.

Using Questioning

Draw a line segment on the chalkboard and ask students how they would go about drawing another segment that has the same length. Construct the segment with the compass and point out the similarity to their suggestions (e.g., that the compass acts like a ruler and a pencil).

1-4 Lesson Notes

Lesson Resources

- Reteaching Master 1-4
- Practice Master 1-4
- Enrichment Master 1-4
- Evaluation Master, Quiz A, p. 9

 Transparency 1-4 contains the 5-Minute Check and a teaching aid for this lesson.

INTRODUCING THE LESSON

 5-Minute Check

(over Lesson 1-3)

Solve by making a list, a table, or a tree diagram.

1. Angela needs to go to the grocery store, the dry cleaners, and the post office. In how many different orders can she run her three errands?   **6**
2. At the park, Jason and Angelique can ride their bikes, play Frisbee, go on a nature walk, or play on the playground. They can do one, some, or all of these activities. How many possible combinations of activities, in any order, can Jason and Angelique do?   **15**

Motivating the Lesson

Give each student a ruler and tell them simply to measure the length of their index finger. They may soon begin asking where to begin measuring, at the knuckle or at the point where the index finger and middle finger split. Some may also ask how accurate you want the answer. Discuss the different aspects of measurement.

TEACHING THE LESSON

Teaching Tip   When discussing the figure, point out that $\overline{NP}$ is *not* the same as $\overline{MP}$, while the line defined by M and P is the same as the line defined by N and P.

Chapter 1   23

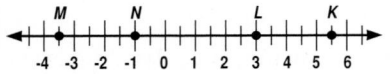
In the comic above, Sally placed her ruler so that one of Snoopy's lips was on 6 and the other was on 9. She could have placed the ruler so that one lip was on 0 and the other was on 3. In fact, two points on any line can always be paired with real numbers so that one point is paired with zero and the other is paired with a positive number. This correspondence allows you to measure the distance between any two points, and thus, the length of any segment. This is called the **ruler postulate**.

Distance can be measured using centimeters, inches, or any other convenient unit of measure.

Postulate 1-1 **Ruler Postulate**	**The points on any line can be paired with the real numbers so that, given any two points *P* and *Q* on the line, *P* corresponds to zero, and *Q* corresponds to a positive number.**

*A **postulate** is a statement that is assumed to be true. You will study postulates more in depth in Chapter 2.*

The distance between points may be measured using a *number line*.

To find the measure of $\overline{AB}$, you first need to identify the coordinates of *A* and *B*. The coordinate of *A* is 1 and the coordinate of *B* is 5. Since measure is always a positive number, you can subtract the lesser coordinate from the greater one, or find the *absolute value* of the difference. When you use absolute value, the order in which you subtract the coordinates does not matter.

Finding the distance from A to B or from B to A results in the same measure.

distance from A to B

$$|5 - 1| = |4|$$
$$= 4$$

distance from B to A

$$|1 - 5| = |\text{-}4|$$
$$= 4$$

The measure of $\overline{AB}$ is 4 or $AB = 4$.

Example 1

Find *AB*, *BC*, and *AC* on the number line shown below.

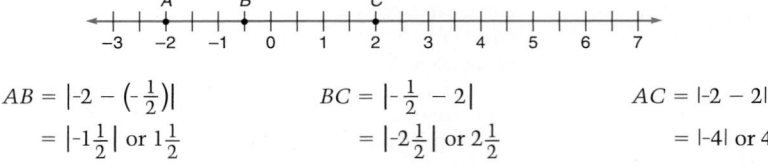

$$AB = |\text{-}2 - (\text{-}\tfrac{1}{2})|$$
$$= |\text{-}1\tfrac{1}{2}| \text{ or } 1\tfrac{1}{2}$$

$$BC = |\text{-}\tfrac{1}{2} - 2|$$
$$= |\text{-}2\tfrac{1}{2}| \text{ or } 2\tfrac{1}{2}$$

$$AC = |\text{-}2 - 2|$$
$$= |\text{-}4| \text{ or } 4$$

In Example 1, *B* is between *A* and *C* and $AB + BC = AC$ since $1\tfrac{1}{2} + 2\tfrac{1}{2} = 4$. This example and others like it lead us to the following postulate.

Postulate 1-2 Segment Addition Postulate	If Q is between P and R, then $PQ + QR = PR$. If $PQ + QR = PR$ then Q is between P and R.

Example 2

Find the measure of $\overline{MN}$ if M is between K and N, $KM = 2x - 4$, $MN = 3x$, and $KN = 26$.

Since M is between K and N, $KM + MN = KN$.

$KM + MN = KN$

$(2x - 4) + 3x = 26$ $KM = 2x - 4$, $MN = 3x$, $KN = 26$

$5x - 4 = 26$ *Add 4 to both sides.*

$5x = 30$

$x = 6$

$MN = 3x$

$= 3(6)$ or 18

The measure of $\overline{MN}$ is 18.

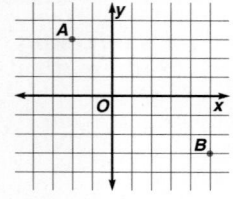

You can find the measure of segments in the coordinate plane by using the distance formula. You will derive this formula in Chapter 8.

The Distance Formula	The distance, d, between any points with coordinates (x_1, y_1) and (x_2, y_2) is given by the following formula. $$d = \sqrt{(x_2 - x_1)^2 + (y_2 - y_1)^2}$$ *The distance between points is the same no matter which point is called (x_1, y_1).*

Example 3

Find the length of the segment with endpoints $A(-2, 3)$ and $B(5, -3)$.

Let $(-2, 3)$ be (x_1, y_1) and $(5, -3)$ be (x_2, y_2).

$d = \sqrt{(x_2 - x_1)^2 + (y_2 - y_1)^2}$ *Distance formula*

$= \sqrt{[5 - (-2)]^2 + (-3 - 3)^2}$

$= \sqrt{7^2 + (-6)^2}$

$= \sqrt{85}$

≈ 9.22

The length of $\overline{AB}$ is about 9.22 units.

A compass and straightedge can be used to construct a segment with the same length as a given segment without knowing the exact length of the segment.

LESSON 1-4   FINDING THE MEASURES OF SEGMENTS   25

Teaching Tip For Example 3, remind students that x is represented by the first number in an ordered pair, and y is represented by the second number.

Chalkboard Examples

For Example 2
Find the measure of $\overline{IJ}$ if J is between I and M, $IJ = 3x + 2$, $JM = 18$, and $IM = 5x$ **32**

For Example 3
Find the distance between points $W(1, 2)$ and $Z(-4, -2)$. $\sqrt{41}$ **or about 6.403**

Chapter 1   25

Checking for Understanding

Exercises 1-18 are designed to help you assess students' understanding through reading, writing, speaking, and modeling. You should work through Exercises 1-4 with your students and then monitor their work on Exercises 5-18.

Error Analysis

Some students may not know what values to assign to x_1, x_2, y_1, and y_2. Try writing the formula with four different variables to illustrate that x_1 and x_2 are different.
When calculating the distance between two points, some students may have difficulty subtracting a negative number. Review how to subract a negative number. Have students put a negative number in parentheses.

Closing the Lesson

Modeling Activity Have students measure the length of a pen cap. Have them draw a segment with that length using a ruler and then construct another segment of the same length using a compass.

Additional Answers

1. No; you can use 18 for x_2 as long as you use 8 for y_2, 5 for x_1, and 7 for y_1.
2. Since one lip was on the 6 and the other lip was on the 9, Sally knew that the length of Snoopy's mouth had to be 9 – 6, or 3 inches.
3. Answers will vary. Sample answers:

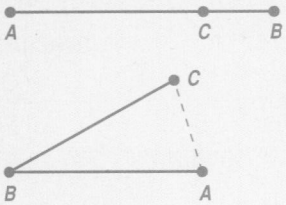

CONSTRUCTION

Construct a segment that has the same length as $\overline{XY}$.

1. Use a straightedge to draw a line on your paper.

2. Choose any point on that line. Label it P.

3. Place the compass at point X and adjust the compass setting so that the pencil is at point Y.

4. Using that setting, place the compass at point P and draw an arc that intersects the line. Label the point of intersection, Q.

5. By construction, $XY = PQ$.

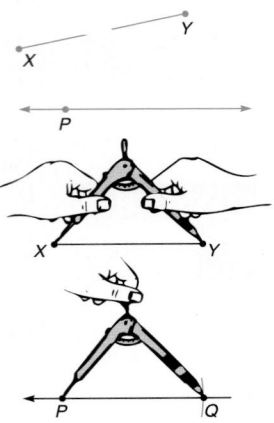

Because the measures of segments are real numbers, they can be compared. To compare the measure of $\overline{AB}$ to the measures of $\overline{CD}$, $\overline{EF}$, and $\overline{GH}$ shown below, you could set your compass width to match the measure of $\overline{AB}$ and then compare this to the measure of each segment.

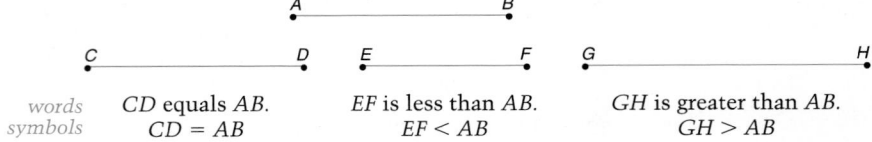

words	CD equals AB.	EF is less than AB.	GH is greater than AB.
symbols	$CD = AB$	$EF < AB$	$GH > AB$

CHECKING FOR UNDERSTANDING

Communicating Mathematics

Read and study the lesson to answer each question. 1-3: See margin.

1. When using the distance formula to find the distance between points $A(18, 8)$ and $B(5, 7)$, do you have to choose 18 for x_1? Explain.

2. Refer to the comic on page 23. Explain how Sally knew that the length of Snoopy's mouth was "lip to lip, three inches."

3. Draw $\overline{AB}$ and $\overline{BC}$ such that $AB + BC \neq AC$.

4. Use a compass to compare the lengths of the following segments. List them in order from shortest to longest. $GH < XY < AB < MN < KL$

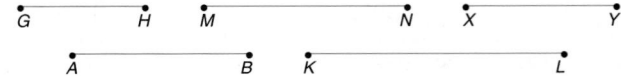

Guided Practice

Refer to the number line at the right to find each measure.

5. *AB* 4
6. *CD* 3
7. *BD* 6
8. *CB* 3
9. *DA* 10
10. *AC* 7

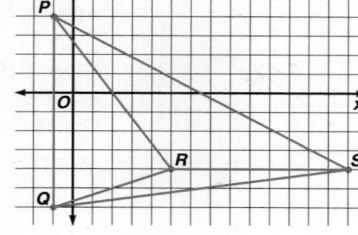

Refer to the coordinate plane at the right to find each measure. If the measure is not a whole number, round the result to the nearest hundredth.

11. *PQ* 10
12. *SR* 9
13. *RP* 10
14. *PS* 17
15. *QR* 6.32
16. *QS* 15.13

17. If *B* is between *A* and *C*, *AB* = *x*, *BC* = 2*x* + 1, and *AC* = 22, find the value of *x* and the measure of $\overline{BC}$. 7; 15

18. Construct a segment that is twice as long as $\overline{MN}$, shown at the right. **See margin.**

EXERCISES

Practice   Refer to the number line below to find each measure.

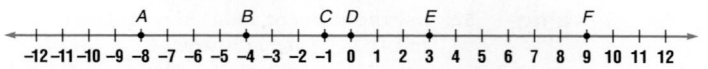

A

19. *CD* 1
20. *BF* 13
21. *CF* 10
22. *EB* 7
23. *BA* 4
24. *FE* 6
25. *FA* 17
26. *AC* 7

Given that *J* is between *H* and *K*, find each missing measure.

27. *HJ* = 17, *JK* = 6, *HK* = __?__ 23
28. *HJ* = 4.8, *JK* = 7, *HK* = __?__ 11.8

B

29. *HJ* = 23.7, *JK* = __?__, *HK* = 35.2 11.5
30. *HJ* = __?__, *JK* = $2\frac{1}{2}$, *HK* = $6\frac{2}{5}$ $3\frac{9}{10}$

Refer to the coordinate plane at the right to find each measure. If the measure is not a whole number, round the result to the nearest hundredth.

31. *AB* 5
32. *CF* 10
33. *DG* 13
34. *HE* 17
35. *JF* 5
36. *AD* 4.12
37. *GE* 1.41
38. *JB* 5.39
39. *CH* 9.49
40. *HG* 17.46

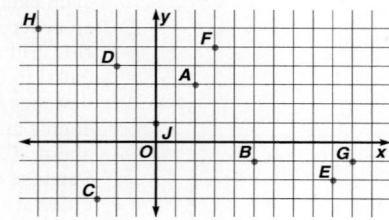

RETEACHING THE LESSON

Have students count the horizontal spaces between two points to find $|x_2 - x_1|$ and the vertical spaces to find $|y_2 - y_1|$. Then demonstrate that performing the subtractions using the coordinates gives the same distances.

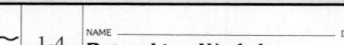
 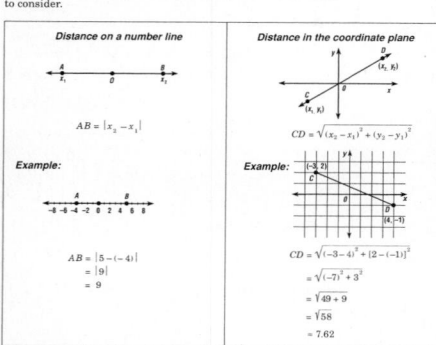
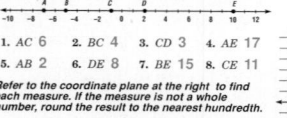
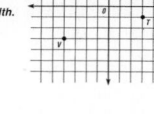

Additional Answers

45.

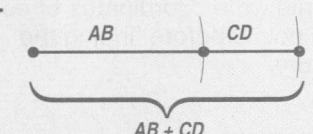

$AB + CD$

46.

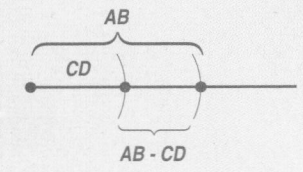

$AB - CD$

47.

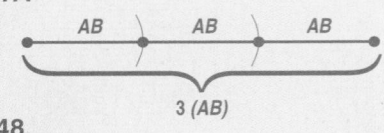

$3 (AB)$

48.

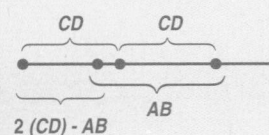

$2 (CD) - AB$

Practice Masters Booklet, p. 4

NAME _____ DATE _____

1-4 Practice Worksheet

Finding the Measure of Segments

Given that B is between A and C, find each missing measure.

1. $AB = 5.3$, $BC = \underline{\ ?\ }$, $AC = 6.7$ **1.4**   2. $AB = 21$, $BC = 4.3$, $AC = \underline{\ ?\ }$ **25.3**

3. $AB = \underline{\ ?\ }$, $BC = 18.9$, $AC = 23$ **4.1**   4. $AB = 6\frac{3}{4}$, $BC = \underline{\ ?\ }$, $AC = 10$ **3$\frac{1}{4}$**

If B is between A and C, find the value of x and the measure of BC.

5. $AB = 3x$, $BC = 5x$, $AC = 8$ **1, 5**

6. $AB = 3(x + 7)$, $BC = 2(x - 3)$, $AC = 50$ **7, 8**

Refer to the coordinate plane at the right to find each measure.
If the measure is not a whole number, round the result to the nearest hundredth.

7. AB **5.83**   8. BD **9.43**

9. AE **7.81**   10. CE **10.44**

11. AD **5**   12. BE **9**

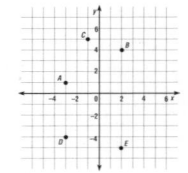

CONNECTION
Algebra

If B is between A and C, find the value of x and the measure of $\overline{BC}$.

41. $AB = 3$, $BC = 4x + 1$, $AC = 8$ **1; 5**

42. $AB = x + 2$, $BC = 2x - 6$, $AC = 20$ **8; 10**

43. $AB = 24$, $BC = 3x$, $AC = 7x - 4$ **7; 21**

44. $AB = 3$, $BC = 2x + 5$, $AC = 11x + 2$ **$\frac{2}{3}$; $\frac{19}{3}$**

Given $\overline{AB}$ and $\overline{CD}$ shown at the right, construct segments with measures equal to the following measures. See margin.

```
A _____ B

C _____ D
```

45. $AB + CD$ **46.** $AB - CD$

47. $3(AB)$ **48.** $2(CD) - AB$

49. Find the perimeter of the triangle with vertices $X(2, -1)$, $Y(5, 3)$, and $Z(-3, 11)$. Round your result to the nearest hundredth. **29.31 units**

50. Find the value of a so that the distance between points $A(4, 7)$ and $B(a, 3)$ is 5 units. **$a = 7$ or $a = 1$**

51. Modeling   Draw a figure that satisfies all of the following conditions. See margin.
(1) Points V, W, X, Y, and Z are all collinear,
(2) V is between Y and Z,
(3) X is next to V, and
(4) $WY = YX$.

Critical Thinking

52. Use the segment addition postulate to show that points $R(1, 1)$, $S(5, 4)$, and $T(-7, -5)$ are collinear. **$TR = 10$, $RS = 5$, $TS = 15$. Since $TR + RS = TS$, R is between T and S, and R, S, and T are collinear.**

53. Points A, B, and C are collinear. If $AB = x$, $BC = 2x + 3$, and $AC = 3x - 6$, which point is between the other two points? **A is between B and C.**

Application

54. Telecommunications   In order to set long distance rates, phone companies will first superimpose an imaginary coordinate grid over the United States. Then the location of each exchange is represented by an ordered pair. The units on this grid are approximately equal to 0.316 mile. So, a distance of 3 units on the grid equals an actual distance of about 3(0.316) or 0.948 mile. Suppose the exchanges in two cities are located at (158, 562) and (387, 213). Find the actual distance between these cities, to the nearest mile. **132 miles**

28   CHAPTER 1   THE LANGUAGE OF GEOMETRY

Additional Answer

51. Sample answer:

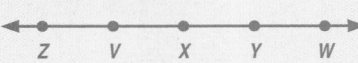

Z   V   X   Y   W

Computer

55. Use the BASIC program at the right to find the distance between each pair of points whose coordinates are given.

55a. distance formula

    a. What is represented by line 30 of the program?
    b. (5, -1), (11, 7) **10**
    c. (0.67, -4), (3, -2) ≈**3.07**
    d. (12, -2), (-3, 5) ≈**16.55**

```
10 INPUT "ENTER COORDINATES OF
   POINT (X1, Y1)."; X1, Y1
20 INPUT "ENTER COORDINATES OF
   POINT (X2, Y2)."; X2, Y2
30 D = SQR((X2 - X1)^2 +
   (Y2 - Y1)^2)
40 PRINT "DISTANCE FROM ("; X1;
   ", "; Y1;") TO (";X2;", "
   Y2;") IS ";D;" UNITS."
50 END
```

Mixed Review

Refer to the figure at the right to answer each question.

56. What ordered pair names D? **(Lesson 1-1)** (-1, 3)

57. Which points are in quadrant IV? **(Lesson 1-1)** E

58. What is the point of intersection of $\overleftrightarrow{BD}$ and $\overleftrightarrow{EC}$? **(Lesson 1-2)** A

59. Which points are *not* on $\overleftrightarrow{BC}$? **(Lesson 1-2)** D, A, E, O

60. Modeling Draw and label a figure to show plane $\mathcal{R}$ contains point A and line ℓ. **(Lesson 1-2)** **See margin.**

61. Solve by listing possibilities. **(Lesson 1-3)**
Telecommunications The telephone area codes in the U.S. and Canada are three-digit numbers where the first digit is 2, 3, 4, 5, 6, 7, 8, or 9, the second digit is 0 or 1, and the third digit is any digit other than 0. How many different area codes start with the digit 6? **18 area codes**

Wrap-Up

62. Write a five-question quiz about this lesson. Be sure to include answers to your questions. **See students' work.**

HISTORY CONNECTION

Hypatia

    Hypatia was the first woman known to have made significant contributions to the field of mathematics. She was the daughter of the Greek mathematician Theon, whose version of Euclid's *Elements* became the traditional geometry text. She taught at the famous Library of Alexandria in Egypt, considered the intellectual center of the ancient world. Hypatia wrote important commentaries on the works of the mathematician Appollonius and the scientist Ptolemy. Her interests also included the study of astronomy and philosophy.

    Because Hypatia was important and respected among scholars of the era, she became the target of criticism from fanatics who equated science to paganism. In March of A.D. 415, she was brutally murdered by an angry mob. Soon after her death, the library was destroyed, and the Dark Ages began, limiting the serious study of mathematics for the next 500 years.

LESSON 1-4 **FINDING THE MEASURES OF SEGMENTS** 29

EXTENDING THE LESSON

Math Power: Connections
On the coordinate plane points $A(-2,-5)$, $B(2,-2)$, $C(7,10)$, and $D(3,7)$ are located. Segments AB, BC, CD, and DA are drawn to form a four-sided figure. What is the perimeter of the figure? **36**

History Connection
The History Connection features introduce students to persons or cultures who were involved in the development of mathematics. You may want students to further research Hypatia.

Additional Answer

60.

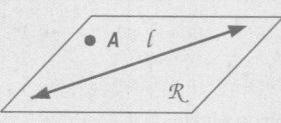

Enrichment Masters Booklet, p.3

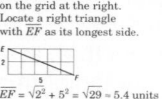

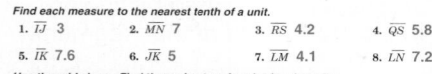

Chapter 1 29

INTRODUCING THE LESSON

 5-Minute Check

(over Lesson 1-4)

1. If $CB + CD = BD$, name two possible arrangements for these three points on the segment.
   B, C, D or **D, C, B**

Find each measure using the figure below.

2. *ST*   **4**

3. *VW*   **9**

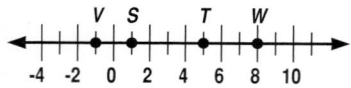

```
     V   S      T    W
  ←-+-+-+-+-+-+-+-+-+-+-+-+→
    -4  -2  0   2   4   6   8   10
```

4. Find *EG* if *F* is between *E* and *G*, $EG = 3x - 1$, $EF = 4$, and $FG = x - 1$.   **5**

5. Find the length of the segment with endpoints $K(-1, -1)$ and $L(4, 6)$.   **8.6**

Motivating the Lesson

Have each student try to find the center of a piece of paper without measuring or marking with a pen or pencil. (Fold the piece of paper in half lengthwise and width-wise; the center is the intersection of the creases.) Explain that, in mathematics, the midpoint of a segment is calculated by finding the halfway point of that segment.

1-5   Segment Relationships

Objectives

After studying this lesson, you should be able to:

1-5A ▪ find the midpoint of a segment, and

1-5B ▪ identify and use congruent segments.

Application

The machine used to drill the holes in compact disks must place the hole in the exact center of each CD. If a CD is $4\frac{11}{16}$ inches in diameter, how far from the edge of the CD should the center of the drill be placed?

In order to find the exact center of a CD, you must locate the *middle point* of a line segment that is a diameter of the CD. This point, called the **midpoint** of the segment, divides the diameter into two segments that have the same length.

Definition of Midpoint	The midpoint, **M**, of $\overline{PQ}$ is the point between **P** and **Q** such that $PM = MQ$.

A diameter of the compact disk is $4\frac{11}{16}$ inches long. So the length of a segment from the edge of the CD to the center is $2\frac{11}{32}$ inches. *Why?*

Thus, the center of the drill should be placed $2\frac{11}{32}$ inches from the edge of the CD.

In algebra, you may have determined the midpoint of a segment on a number line or in the coordinate plane using one of the following formulas.

Midpoint on a Number Line	The coordinate of the midpoint of a line segment whose endpoints have coordinates *a* and *b* is $$\frac{a + b}{2}.$$

Midpoint in the Coordinate Plane	The coordinates of the midpoint of a line segment whose endpoints have coordinates (x_1, y_1) and (x_2, y_2) are $$\left(\frac{x_1 + x_2}{2}, \frac{y_1 + y_2}{2}\right).$$

30   CHAPTER 1   THE LANGUAGE OF GEOMETRY

ALTERNATE TEACHING STRATEGIES

Using Logical Reasoning

It may be helpful to have students look up some of the vocabulary in this section in the dictionary. For example, if your students look at the word *bisector*, the prefix *bi* means "two" and the word *sector* means "cutting." A simple definition for bisector then would be "cutting in two." (Point out that in mathematics, the two parts must be equal.)

Using Models

Bring a sewing pattern to class and show students the places on the pattern that are marked with arrows. Explain that when you sew the pieces together, you match these places to make sure the garment fits correctly. In geometry, hash marks are similar in that they mark segments of figures and objects that have the same measure.

Example 1

If *M*(-1, 7) is the midpoint of $\overline{GH}$ and the coordinates of *G* are (2, 5), what are the coordinates of *H*?

Let (2, 5) be (x_1, y_1) and let (x_2, y_2) be the coordinates of *H*.
Now use the expression for the coordinates of the midpoint to find x_2 and y_2.

$$\left(\frac{x_1 + x_2}{2}, \frac{y_1 + y_2}{2}\right) = (-1, 7)$$

The coordinates of the midpoint, M, are (-1, 7).

$$\frac{x_1 + x_2}{2} = -1 \qquad \frac{y_1 + y_2}{2} = 7$$

The x- and y-coordinates must be equal.

$$\frac{2 + x_2}{2} = -1 \qquad \frac{5 + y_2}{2} = 7$$

$$2 + x_2 = -2 \qquad 5 + y_2 = 14$$

$$x_2 = -4 \qquad y_2 = 9$$

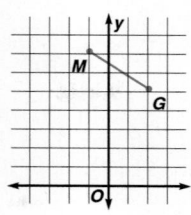

The coordinates of *H*(x_2, y_2) are (-4, 9).

The midpoint can also be considered a segment bisector.

Any segment, line, or plane that intersects a segment at its midpoint is called a **segment bisector.** In the figure at the right, *M* is the midpoint of $\overline{PQ}$. Thus, point *M*, $\overline{TM}$, $\overrightarrow{RM}$, and plane $\mathcal{N}$ are all bisectors of $\overline{PQ}$ and are said to bisect $\overline{PQ}$.

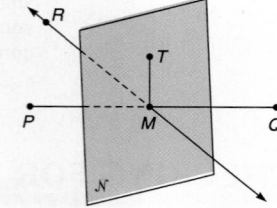

You can use a compass to find the midpoint of any segment, and thus, bisect the segment.

This construction draws a bisector that is perpendicular to the segment.

Using a compass and straightedge, bisect a segment.

1. Use a straightedge to draw the segment you wish to bisect. Name it $\overline{XZ}$.

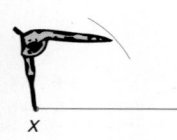

2. Place the compass at point *X*. Adjust the compass so that its width is greater than $\frac{1}{2}XZ$.

3. Draw arcs above and below $\overline{XZ}$.

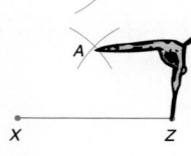

4. Using the same compass setting, place the compass at point *Z*. Draw arcs above and below $\overline{XZ}$ that intersect the two arcs previously drawn. Label the points of intersection *A* and *B*.

5. Use a straightedge to draw $\overleftrightarrow{AB}$ that will intersect $\overline{XZ}$. Label the point of intersection *Y*.

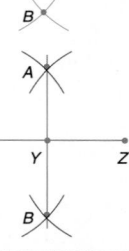

Point *Y* is the midpoint of $\overline{XZ}$, and $\overleftrightarrow{AB}$ is a bisector of $\overline{XZ}$. Also, $XY = YZ = \frac{1}{2}XZ$.

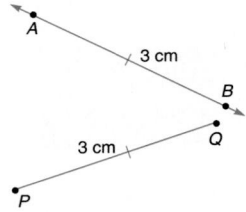

In the figure at the right, $AB = PQ$ since $\overline{AB}$ and $\overline{PQ}$ have the same lengths. Segments that are equal in length are called **congruent segments.** To indicate that $\overline{AB}$ and $\overline{PQ}$ are congruent, we write $\overline{AB} \cong \overline{PQ}$, which is read "segment AB is congruent to segment PQ." In a diagram, small "hash marks," like the ones in red at the right, are used to indicate congruent segments.

The definition of congruent segments tells us that the statements $AB = PQ$ and $\overline{AB} \cong \overline{PQ}$ are equivalent. Therefore, we will use them interchangeably. For example, if you know that M is the midpoint of $\overline{KN}$, then you could write that $\overline{KM} \cong \overline{MN}$ rather than $KM = MN$.

The concept of congruence can be applied to other figures and objects. In geometry, two objects are **congruent** if they have the exact same size *and* shape. For many of the geometric figures we will be discussing in this text, such as angles, triangles, circles, and arcs, more specific definitions for congruence will be provided.

CHECKING FOR UNDERSTANDING

Communicating Mathematics

Read and study the lesson to answer each question. 1, 2, 4: See margin.

1. If $AB = BC$, must B be the midpoint of $\overline{AC}$? Explain.

2. Draw two segments that bisect each other.

3. 1; infinitely many

INVESTIGATION

3. How many midpoints does a segment have? How many bisectors? Prepare a convincing argument to share with your classmates.

4. Suppose two points, X and Y, are drawn on a piece of paper. Show how you could find the midpoint of $\overline{XY}$ by simply folding the paper.

Guided Practice

Refer to the number line below to find the coordinate of the midpoint of each segment.

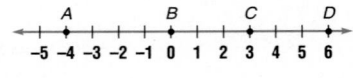

5. $\overline{BD}$ 3

6. $\overline{AB}$ -2

7. $\overline{DA}$ 1

8. $\overline{BC}$ $1\frac{1}{2}$

9. $\overline{CD}$ $4\frac{1}{2}$

10. $\overline{CA}$ $-\frac{1}{2}$

Refer to the coordinate plane at the right to find the coordinates of the midpoint of each segment.

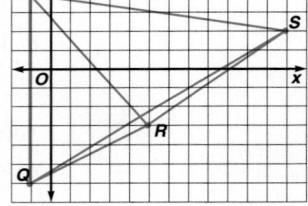

11. $\overline{PQ}$ (-1, -1)

12. $\overline{PR}$ $\left(2, \frac{1}{2}\right)$

13. $\overline{RQ}$ $\left(2, -4\frac{1}{2}\right)$

14. $\overline{SP}$ $\left(5\frac{1}{2}, 3\right)$

15. $\overline{QS}$ $\left(5\frac{1}{2}, -2\right)$

16. $\overline{RS}$ $\left(8\frac{1}{2}, -\frac{1}{2}\right)$

32 CHAPTER 1 THE LANGUAGE OF GEOMETRY

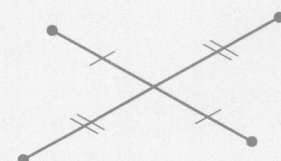

17. If E is the midpoint of $\overline{DF}$, $DE = 5x - 3$, and $EF = 3x + 5$, find the value of x and the measure of $\overline{DF}$. $x = 4$; 34

18. Copy $\overline{AB}$ shown at the right. Then use a compass and straightedge to bisect the segment. **See margin.**

APPLYING THE LESSON

Homework Exercises

Assignment Guide

Basic: 19-39, 46-54
Average: 22-42, 46-54
Enriched: 25-54
All: Mid-Chapter Review, 1-14

EXERCISES

Practice   Refer to the figure below to determine whether each statement is *true* or *false*.

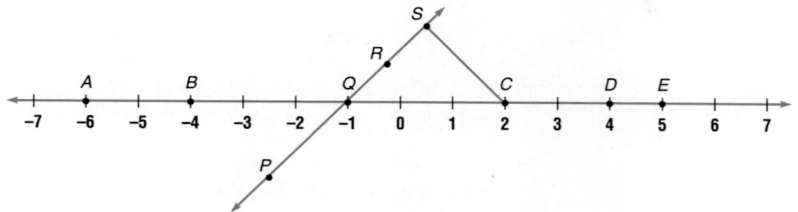

Additional Answer
18.

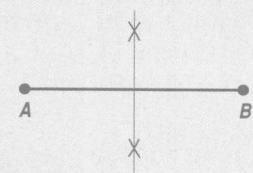

19. Q is the midpoint of $\overline{BC}$. true   **20.** D is the midpoint of $\overline{CE}$. false

21. $\overleftrightarrow{RP}$ bisects $\overline{AD}$. true   **22.** $\overline{CS}$ bisects $\overline{EQ}$. true

23. $\overline{AB} \cong \overline{BQ}$ false   **24.** $\overline{QB} \cong \overline{CE}$ true   **25.** $\overline{BC} \cong \overline{QE}$ true

26. $AQ > QE$ false   **27.** $EC > BQ$ false   **28.** $AC \le DB$ true

Given the coordinates of one endpoint of $\overline{AB}$ and its midpoint, M, find the coordinates of the other endpoint.

29. $A(-1, 5)$, $M(2, 5)$ $B(5, 5)$ **30.** $B(3, -2)$, $M(-3, 1)$ $A(-9, 4)$

31. $M(-2, 2)$, $B(-6, -4)$ $A(2, 8)$ **32.** $A(-1, -3)$, $M(0.5, -6.5)$ $B(2, -10)$

CONNECTION
Algebra

In the figure at the right, $\overleftrightarrow{CX}$ bisects $\overline{AB}$ at X and $\overleftrightarrow{CD}$ bisects $\overline{XB}$ at Y. Given the following conditions, find the value of x and the measure of the indicated segment.

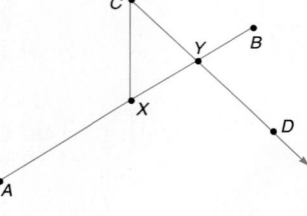

33. $AX = 2x + 11$, $XB = 4x - 5$; $\overline{AB}$ 8; 54

34. $AB = x + 3$, $AX = 3x - 1$; $\overline{XB}$ 1; 2

35. $YB = 23 - 2x$, $XY = 2x + 3$; $\overline{AB}$ 5; 52

36. $AX = 27 - x$, $XB = 13 - 3x$; $\overline{XY}$ -7; 17

37. $AB = 5x - 4$; $XY = x + 1$; $\overline{AX}$ 8; 18

RETEACHING THE LESSON

Have students use one of their shoestrings or a piece of string and fold it in half. They have just divided the string into two segments of equal length. Point out that the "folding" point is actually the midpoint of the segment and that when they are looking for the midpoint of a segment, they are actually looking for the "folding" point.

Reteaching Masters Booklet, p. 4

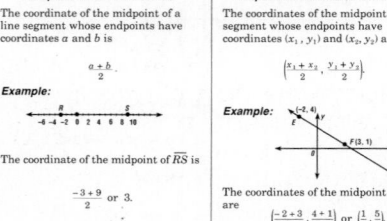

Practice Masters Booklet, p. 5

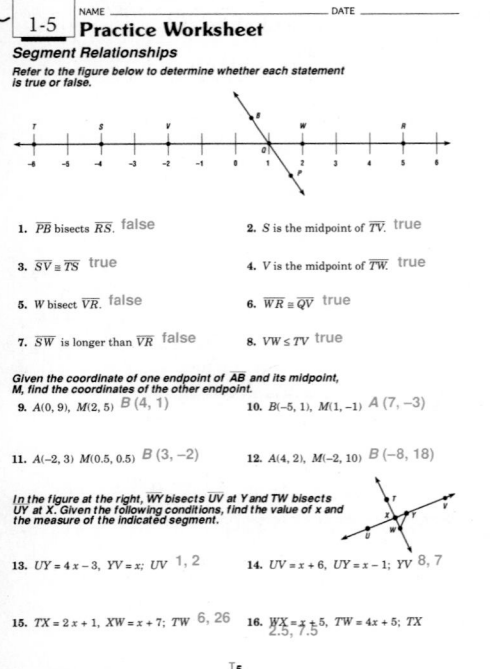

If $XY = 8x - 5$, $YZ = 4x + 7$, and $XZ = 34$, answer each question.

38. For what value of x are $\overline{XY}$ and $\overline{YZ}$ congruent? $x = 3$

39. If $\overline{XY}$ and $\overline{YZ}$ are congruent, is Y the midpoint of $\overline{XZ}$? *(Hint: Investigate the measure of $\overline{XZ}$.)* **See margin.**

Copy each segment shown below. Then use a compass and straightedge to bisect each segment. See students' work.

40. W ——— R
41.  B F P Y
42.

43. Find the coordinates of points P and Q on $\overline{AB}$ which has endpoints $A(2, 3)$ and $B(8, -9)$. P is between A and Q and $\overline{AP} \cong \overline{PQ} \cong \overline{QB}$. $P(4, -1)$, $Q(6, -5)$

44. The coordinates of K and L are $(8, 12)$ and $(-4, 0)$. Find the coordinates of a point N on $\overline{KL}$ such that $KN = \frac{1}{4}KL$. $(5, 9)$

45. If S is between R and T, $RT = 24$, $RS = x^2 + 8$, and $ST = 3x + 6$, find the value of x and determine if S is the midpoint of $\overline{RT}$. $x = 2$, yes

Critical Thinking

CONSTRUCTION

46. Copy $\triangle ABC$ shown at the right.
   a. Construct the lines that bisect and are perpendicular to each side of the triangle using the construction on page 31.
   b. What conjecture could you make about these three lines?
   c. Draw two different triangles and test your conjecture on these triangles.
   b. The three lines intersect at one point.
   c. See students' work.

47. Make another copy of $\triangle ABC$. Use the construction on page 31 to find the midpoints of $\overline{AB}$ and $\overline{AC}$. Label them M and N. Draw $\overline{MN}$. Use a compass to compare the lengths of $\overline{MN}$ and $\overline{BC}$. What conjectures could you make about $\overline{MN}$ and $\overline{BC}$? $2(MN) = BC$ and $\overline{BC} \parallel \overline{MN}$.

Application

48. **Carpentry** Mr. Juarez needs to cut some pieces of lumber into 10-foot lengths, but he left his tape measure at home. He has a 4-foot long board and a 2-foot long board. See margin.
   a. Describe how he could use the boards to cut the lumber to the required length.
   b. What geometric properties is Mr. Juarez using in order to cut the lumber to the required length?

49. Point B lies on the same vertical line as A(-1, 2). If AB = 3 what are the coordinates of B? **(Lesson 1-1)** (-1, 5) or (-1, -1)

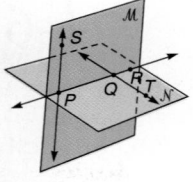

50. Refer to the figure at the right. **(Lesson 1-2)**
    a. What points lie in plane M? P, Q, R, S
    b. Are points S, Q, and T coplanar? Why or why not? Yes, since any three points are coplanar

51. Points W, X, Y, and Z are collinear. How many ways can you use two letters to name the line that contains these four points? **(Lesson 1-3)** 12 ways

52. Find AB, given A(-1, 4) and B(6, -20). **(Lesson 1-4)** 25

53. If D, E, and F are collinear, DE = 12, EF = 9, and DF = 3, which point is between the other two? **(Lesson 1-4)** F is between D and E.

Wrap-Up 54. Write a description for the coordinates of the midpoint of a line segment in the coordinate plane using the word "average." See margin.

Additional Answer

54. The coordinates of the midpoint of a line segment in the coordinate plane are the average of the x-coordinates and y-coordinates of the endpoints of the line segment.

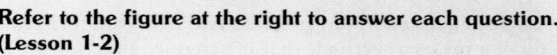

MID-CHAPTER REVIEW

Write the ordered pair for each point. Refer to the coordinate plane shown at the right. (Lesson 1-1)

1. A (1, 3)   2. B (-1, 1)   3. C (4, -2)

4. *True* or *false:* Point E is in Quadrant III. **(Lesson 1-1)** true

5. What is the y-coordinate of any point collinear with C and D? **(Lesson 1-1)** -2

Refer to the figure at the right to answer each question. (Lesson 1-2)

6. Name a point not on plane RST. U, V, W, or X

7. Name three lines that intersect at point S. $\overrightarrow{RS}$, $\overrightarrow{TS}$, $\overrightarrow{VS}$

8. Name the intersection of planes RWX and UTY. $\overleftrightarrow{XY}$

9. *True* or *false:* $\overleftrightarrow{YT}$ and $\overleftrightarrow{WX}$ are noncoplanar lines. true

10. Wheels "R" Us sells bicycles, tricycles, and unicycles. They have one more bicycle than unicycle in stock. If there are 60 pedals and 80 wheels, how many bicycles, tricycles, and unicycles are there in stock? **(Lesson 1-3)** 3 unicycles, 4 bicycles, and 23 tricycles

11. If R, S, and T are collinear, RS = 3x − 6, ST = 2x + 9, and RT = 13, which point is between the other two? **(Lesson 1-4)** T is between R and S.

12. If B is between A and C, AB = 4x − 9, BC = 7 − x, and AC = 2x + 3, find the value of x and the measure of $\overline{AC}$. **(Lesson 1-4)** x = 5; 13

13. Find MN and the coordinates of the midpoint of $\overline{MN}$, given M(7, 7) and N(-1, 1). **(Lesson 1-5)** 10; (3, 4)

14. If DE = 4x − 9, and EF = 7 + 2x, find the value of x so that $\overline{DE} \cong \overline{EF}$. **(Lesson 1-5)** x = 8

LESSON 1-5   SEGMENT RELATIONSHIPS   35

EXTENDING THE LESSON

Math Power: Connection

On the coordinate plane, plot A(−4,−6) and B(8,2). Find the coordinates of D so D is between A and B and DB = 3AD.   (−1,−4)

Mid-Chapter Review

The Mid-Chapter Review provides students with a brief review of the concepts and skills in Lessons 1-1 through 1-5. Lesson numbers are given at the end of problems or instruction lines so students may review concepts not yet mastered.

Enrichment Masters Booklet, p. 4

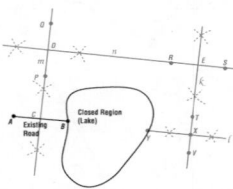

1-5 **Enrichment Worksheet**

Construction Problem

The diagram below shows segment $\overline{AB}$ adjacent to a closed region. The problem requires that you construct another segment $\overline{XY}$ to the right of the closed region such that points A, B, X, and Y are collinear. You are not allowed to touch or cross the closed region with your compass or straightedge.

Follow these instructions to construct a segment $\overline{XY}$ so that it is collinear with segment $\overline{AB}$.

1. Construct the perpendicular bisector of $\overline{AB}$. Label the midpoint as point C, and the line as m.

2. Mark two points P and Q on line m that lie well above the closed region. Construct the perpendicular bisector n of $\overline{PQ}$. Label the intersection of lines m and n as point D.

3. Mark points R and S on line n that lie well to the right of the closed region. Construct the perpendicular bisector k of $\overline{RS}$. Label the intersection of lines n and k as point E.

4. Mark point Y on line k so that Y is below line n and so that $\overline{EY}$ is congruent to $\overline{DC}$.

5. Mark points T and V on line k and on opposite sides of X, so that $\overline{XT}$ and $\overline{XV}$ are congruent. Construct the perpendicular bisector l of $\overline{TV}$. Call the point where the line l hits the boundary of the closed region point Y. $\overline{XY}$ corresponds to the new road.

T4

Lesson Resources

- Reteaching Master 1-6
- Practice Master 1-6
- Enrichment Master 1-6
- Multicultural Master p. 1
- Evaluation Master, Quiz B, p. 9
- Lab Manual, pp. 18-21

 Transparency 1-6 contains the 5-Minute Check and a teaching aid for this lesson.

INTRODUCING THE LESSON

 5-Minute Check

(over Lesson 1-5)

1. Refer to the figure below to find two segments that point *F* bisects. $\overline{EG}$, $\overline{DH}$

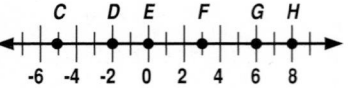

```
      C   D   E   F   G   H
  ←+---+---+---+---+---+---+---+---+→
    -6  -4  -2   0   2   4   6   8
```

2. Given the coordinates of the endpoint *L* (−1, −1) and midpoint *M* (−3, 2), find the coordinates of the endpoint *B* of $\overline{LB}$. *B* (−5, 5)
3. If $\overline{CY}$ bisects $\overline{DX}$ at point *P*, find the value of *x* and the measure of $\overline{PX}$ if *DX* = 7*x* − 5 and *DP* = −5*x* + 6. 1, 1
4. Name all segments that are congruent in the figure below. $\overline{AB} \cong \overline{MN}$, $\overline{BC} \cong \overline{QR}$, $\overline{CD} \cong \overline{XY}$

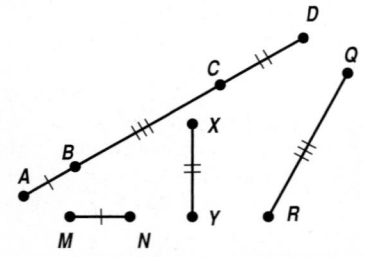

Objectives

1-6A
1-6B

After studying this lesson, you should be able to:
- identify angles and parts of angles, and
- use the angle addition postulate to find the measures of angles.

Application

Compass headings are always measured in a clockwise direction.

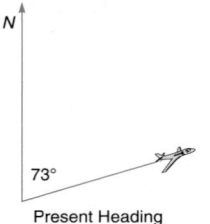

N

73°

Present Heading

A laser beam shooting out into space would be a model for a ray.

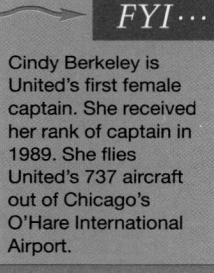

FYI···

Cindy Berkeley is United's first female captain. She received her rank of captain in 1989. She flies United's 737 aircraft out of Chicago's O'Hare International Airport.

Captain Cindy Berkeley, a pilot for United Airlines, is on approach for a landing at Chicago's O'Hare International Airport. Her present compass heading is 73 degrees. This heading refers to the measure of the *angle* formed by the flight path of the plane and an imaginary path in the direction due north. The tower has informed Captain Berkeley to land on runway 9. She knows that multiplying the runway number by 10 gives her the compass heading for a landing on that runway. So the compass heading for her landing must be 90°. How many degrees and in what direction must Captain Berkeley turn in order to land on runway 9?

This problem will be solved in Example 3, but first we need to review and discuss angles and how to find their measures.

In geometry, an **angle** is defined in terms of the two *rays* that form the angle. You can think of a **ray** as a segment that is extended indefinitely in *one* direction. Rays have exactly one endpoint and that point is always named first when naming the ray. Like segments, rays can also be defined using betweenness of points.

Ray *PQ*, written $\overrightarrow{PQ}$, consists of the points on $\overline{PQ}$ and all points *S* on $\overrightarrow{PQ}$ such that *Q* is between *P* and *S*.

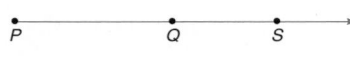

Any given point on a line determines exactly two rays, called **opposite rays.** This point is the common endpoint of the opposite rays. In the figure below, $\overrightarrow{PQ}$ and $\overrightarrow{PR}$ are opposite rays, and *P* is the common endpoint.

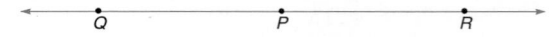

Opposite rays can be defined as a figure formed by two collinear rays with a common endpoint, since the two rays lie on the same line. Similarly, an **angle** can be defined as a figure formed by two *noncollinear* rays with a common endpoint. The two rays are called the **sides** of the angle. The common

36 CHAPTER 1 THE LANGUAGE OF GEOMETRY

ALTERNATE TEACHING STRATEGIES

Using Models

Use one student to demonstrate a ray. Have him or her lift one arm sideways, and use the shoulder as the endpoint and the rest of the arm as the extension of the ray. Extend the ray by letting the student hold a yardstick or pointer in the up-raised hand. Demonstrate angles by using one arm and the side of the student's body as the rays.

Using Computers

Have students use LOGO to draw a representation of a ray, retract the turtle, and draw another representation of a ray. Have students draw angles using turns of different measures and practice turns to the right and left.

endpoint is called the **vertex**. The figure formed by opposite rays is often referred to as a **straight angle** even though it does *not* satisfy our definition for an angle.

In the figure at the right, the sides of the angle are $\overrightarrow{YX}$ and $\overrightarrow{YZ}$, and the vertex is Y. This angle could be named $\angle Y$, $\angle XYZ$, $\angle ZYX$, or $\angle 1$. When letters are used to name an angle, the letter that names the vertex is used either as the only letter or as the middle of three letters.

An angle is named by a single letter only when there is no chance of confusion. For example, it is not obvious which angle shown at the right is $\angle A$ since there are three different angles that have A as a vertex. *Can you name them?*

Whenever two or more angles have a common vertex, you need to use either three letters or a number to name each angle.

Example 1

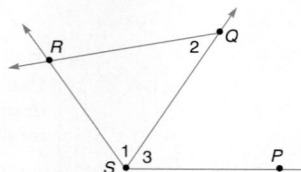

Refer to the figure at the right to answer each question.

a. What number names $\angle QSP$? 3

b. What is the vertex of $\angle 2$? Q

c. What are the sides of $\angle 1$? $\overrightarrow{SQ}$ and $\overrightarrow{SR}$

An angle separates a plane into three distinct parts, the **interior** of the angle, the **exterior** of the angle, and the angle itself.

A point is in the interior of an angle if it does not lie on the angle itself and it lies on a segment whose endpoints are on the sides of the angle. Neither of the endpoints of this segment can be the vertex of the angle.

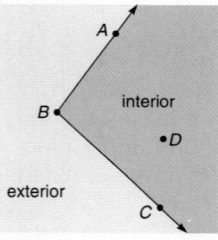

In the figure at the right, point D and all other points in the *blue* region are in the interior of $\angle B$. Any point that is not on the angle or in the interior of the angle is in the exterior of the angle. The *yellow* region is the exterior of $\angle B$.

Just as a ruler can be used to measure the length of a segment, a *protractor* can be used to find the **measure of an angle** in degrees. To find the measure of an angle, place the center point of the protractor over the vertex of the angle.

Motivating the Lesson
Ask students where they have heard the term *ray* and to what it referred. Draw the example and point out that it is called a ray because it has a starting point but no definite ending point.

TEACHING THE LESSON

Chalkboard Example

For Example 1
Refer to the figure below.

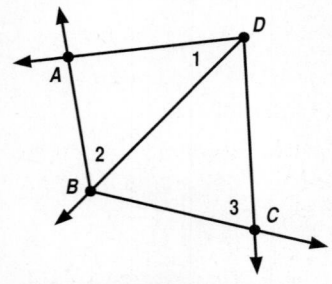

a. What number names $\angle ABD$?   2
b. What is the vertex of $\angle 3$? C
c. What are the sides of $\angle 2$? ray *BA*, ray *BD*

Teaching Tip   When defining *ray*, tell students to pick a point on a number line and cut off one end at that point. What is left is a ray.

Teaching Tip   When discussing the interior and exterior of an angle, point out that, just as the axes of a graph are not in any quadrant, the angle rays are not in the interior or exterior of the angle.

Teaching Tip   When teaching students to use a protractor, use an overhead projector with a clear protractor to demonstrate. You may wish to use the transparency with moveable rays.

Teaching Tip   If the sides of the angle do not reach far enough on the protractor to read them, students can extend them.

Teaching Tip   When teaching students to read a protractor, explain that the top scale is used if the bottom ray is pointing to the left, the bottom scale if the ray is pointing to the right.

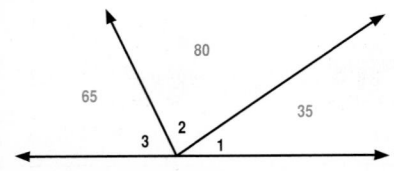
Then align the mark labeled 0 on either side of the scale with one side of the angle. This has been done for ∠XYZ shown below.

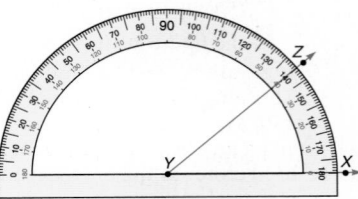

Using the inner scale of the protractor, shown in blue, you can see that ∠Y is a 40-degree (40°) angle. Thus, we say that the degree measure of ∠XYZ is 40. This can also be written as m∠XYZ = 40.

The protractor postulate guarantees that there is only one 40° angle on each side of $\overrightarrow{YX}$.

Postulate 1-3 *Protractor Postulate*	**Given $\overrightarrow{AB}$ and a number *r* between 0 and 180, there is exactly one ray with endpoint *A*, extending on each side of $\overrightarrow{AB}$, such that the measure of the angle formed is *r*.**

Example 2

Use a protractor to find the degree measure of each numbered angle.

m∠1 = 30   m∠2 = 95

m∠3 = 18   m∠4 = 37

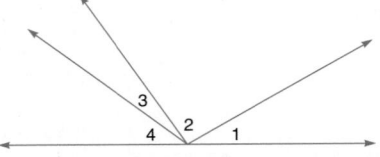

In Lesson 1-4, a measurement relationship between the lengths of segments, called the *segment addition postulate*, was introduced. A similar relationship exists between the measure of angles.

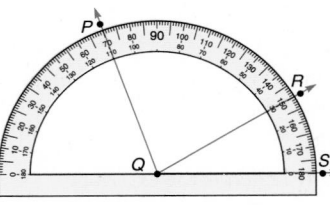

In the figure at the left, you can see that point *R* is in the interior of ∠PQS. m∠PQS = 110 and m∠RQS = 30.

The sides of ∠PQR align with the marks labeled 110 and 30 on the inner scale. So m∠PQR = 110 − 30 or 80.

Since 80 + 30 = 110, m∠PQR + m∠RQS = m∠PQS. This example and others like it, lead us to the following postulate about angle measures.

38   CHAPTER 1   THE LANGUAGE OF GEOMETRY

Example 3

APPLICATION

Aviation

Refer to the problem presented at the beginning of the lesson. Let $\overrightarrow{AP}$ represent the path of Captain Berkeley's plane, and let $\overrightarrow{AR}$ represent the path for a landing on runway 9. Determine the number of degrees that the plane must be turned to land on runway 9 by determining the measure of $\angle PAR$.

The compass heading for the path of Captain Berkeley's plane, $\overrightarrow{AP}$, is 73°. Using the formula given in the problem, we know that the compass heading for a landing on runway 9 is 9(10) or 90°. $\overrightarrow{AP}$ and $\overrightarrow{AR}$ at the right represent the paths corresponding to these compass headings. We can use the angle addition postulate to find $m\angle PAR$.

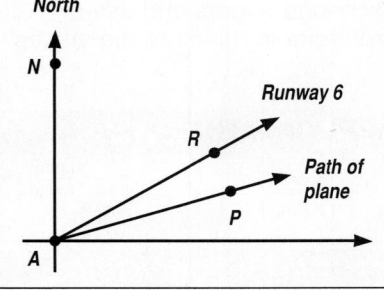

$m\angle NAP + m\angle PAR = m\angle NAR$
$73 + m\angle PAR = 90$
$m\angle PAR = 17$

Thus, Captain Berkeley must turn the plane 17° right to land on runway 9.

CHECKING FOR UNDERSTANDING

Communicating Mathematics

Read and study the lesson to answer each question.

1. Refer to the application at the beginning of the lesson. What would be the compass heading of an airplane for a landing on runway 13? **130°**

2. What is the intersection of two opposite rays? **the common endpoint**

3. Explain in your own words why a straight angle does not fit our definition of angle. **A straight angle is formed by two *collinear*, not noncollinear, rays.**

4. Draw $\overrightarrow{PQ}$ and $\overrightarrow{RS}$ so that the intersection of $\overrightarrow{PQ}$ and $\overrightarrow{RS}$ is $\overrightarrow{PR}$. **See margin.**

Guided Practice

Draw two angles that satisfy the following conditions. 5–7. See margin.

5. The angles intersect in a single point.

6. The angles intersect in two points.

7. The angles intersect in a ray.

CONNECTION
Algebra

8. Suppose $\overrightarrow{AB}$ and $\overrightarrow{AC}$ are opposite rays on a number line. If the coordinate of A is 0 and the coordinate of B is 2, is the coordinate of C a positive or a negative number? **negative number**

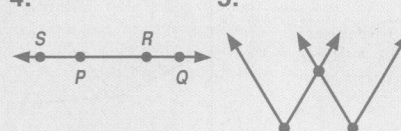
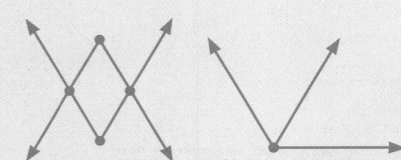

Error Analysis

Some students may have difficulty knowing which angle measure to read on a protractor. Tell them, if the angle looks big (i.e. the sides of the angle are far apart), they should use the larger measure. If it looks small (i.e. the sides of the angle are close together), they should use the smaller measure. If they still cannot decide, compare the angle to a 90° angle.

Closing the Lesson

Writing Activity Have each of your students draw three angles on a piece of paper. Have them exchange papers and use a protractor to measure the angles.

Reteaching Masters Booklet, p. 5

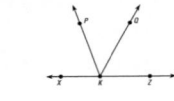

Use the figure below to answer each question.

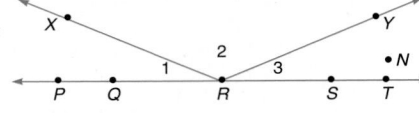

9. What are two other names for $\overrightarrow{QS}$? **QR, QT**

10. What is the endpoint of $\overrightarrow{SP}$? **S**

11. *True or false:* $\overrightarrow{RX}$ and $\overrightarrow{RT}$ are opposite rays. **false**

12. $\overrightarrow{RX}, \overrightarrow{RY}$ 12. What are the sides of ∠2?

13. Name a point that lies on ∠3. **Y, R, S, or T**

14. Name all of the angles that have $\overrightarrow{RY}$ for a side. **∠PRY, ∠XRY, ∠TRY**

15. Name a point in the exterior of ∠PRY. **N, S, or T**

16. Complete: $m\angle XRT = m\angle 2 + \underline{?}$. **m∠3**

Find the measure of the following angles in the figure at the right.

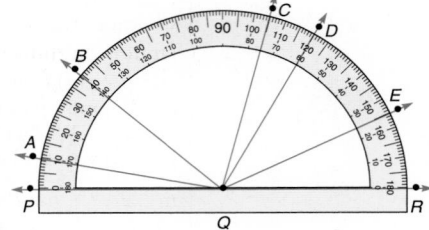

17. ∠PQA **10**

18. ∠RQE **25**

19. ∠PQC **105**

20. ∠AQB **30**

EXERCISES

Practice **Find the measure of the following angles in the figure above.**

A

21. ∠BQD **80**   22. ∠EQC **50** 23. ∠AQC **95** 24. ∠AQE **145**

Use the figure below to answer each question.

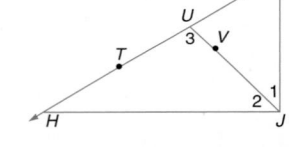

25. What is the vertex of angle 2? **J**

26. Name a straight angle. **∠HUK**

27. Name a point in the interior of ∠4. **V**

B

28. Name all the angles that have J as the vertex. **∠HJK, ∠HJU, ∠UJK**

29. Do ∠3 and ∠4 have a common side? If so, name it. **no**

30. Do ∠2 and ∠J name the same angle? Explain. **No, since ∠J could refer to ∠1, ∠2, or ∠HJK**

Draw two angles that satisfy the following conditions. **See margin.**

31. The angles intersect in three points.

32. The angles intersect in four points.

33. The angles intersect in a segment.

RETEACHING THE LESSON

To help students grasp the angle addition postulate, have them number the angles with which they are working and use the angle numbers to write the addition equation. This way, they will not get lost in all the letters involved in naming the angles.

Additional Answers

31.   32.

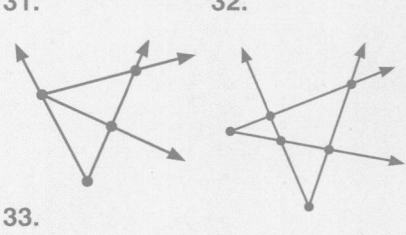

33.

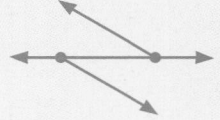

CONNECTION
Algebra

In the figure, $\overrightarrow{XP}$ and $\overrightarrow{XT}$ are opposite rays. Given the following conditions, find the value of x and the measure of the indicated angle.

34. $m\angle SXT = 3x - 4$, $m\angle RXS = 2x + 5$,
   $m\angle RXT = 111$; $m\angle RXS$ **22; 49**

35. $m\angle PXQ = 2x$, $m\angle QXT = 5x - 23$;
   $m\angle QXT$ **29, 122**

36. $m\angle QXR = x + 10$, $m\angle QXS = 4x - 1$,
   $m\angle RXS = 91$; $m\angle QXS$ **34; 135**

37. $m\angle QXR = 3x + 5$, $m\angle QXP = 2x - 3$, $m\angle RXP = x + 50$; $m\angle RXT$ **12; 118**

38. $m\angle TXS = x + 4$, $m\angle SXR = 3x + 4$, $m\angle RXP = 2x + 4$; $m\angle PXS$ **28; 148**

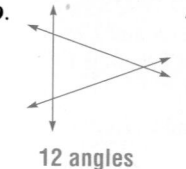 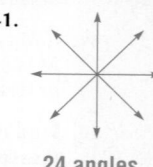 

How many angles, not including straight angles, are shown in each figure?

▷

39.   40.   41.   42.

12 angles   **12 angles**   **24 angles**   **24 angles**

43. How many points on $\overrightarrow{PQ}$ are 2 units from P? 2 units from Q? **1; 2 if $PQ \geq 2$, 1 if $PQ < 2$**

Critical Thinking   44. Each figure below shows noncollinear rays with a common endpoint.

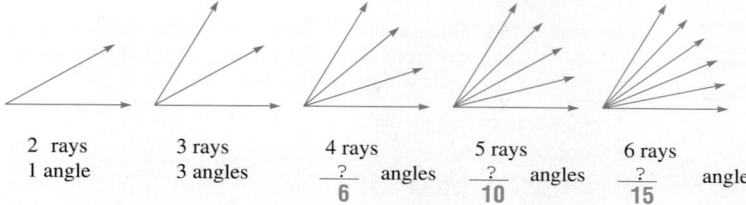

2 rays   3 rays   4 rays   5 rays   6 rays
1 angle   3 angles __?__ angles __?__ angles __?__ angles
                     6   **10**   **15**

a. Count the number of angles in each figure.
b. Do you see a pattern? Try to predict the number of angles that are formed by 7 rays. by 10 rays. **21 angles; 45 angles**
c. Write a formula for the number of angles formed by n noncollinear rays with a common endpoint. $\dfrac{n(n-1)}{2}$

Applications   45. **Golf** The *loft* of a golf club is the measure of the angle that the head of the club would form with a vertical ray. Golf clubs of the same type (irons or woods) are numbered so that greater numbers indicate greater amounts of loft. For example, a 9-iron has more loft than a 3-iron.

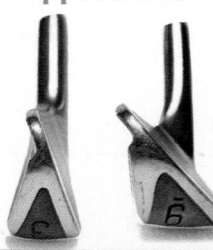

a. Explain how you think the loft of a club affects the path of a shot.
b. Draw a picture to show how the path of a shot hit with a 9-iron might differ from the path of a shot hit with a 3-iron. **See margin.**
   45a. See margin.

LESSON 1-6   RAYS AND ANGLES   41

Exercise Notes

For Exercises 34-38, it may help your students to number the angles and use the numbers in the addition equations.

Additional Answers

45a. As the loft of the club increases, the ball will travel higher in the air and for a shorter distance, as long as the ball is struck with the same amount of force.

45b.

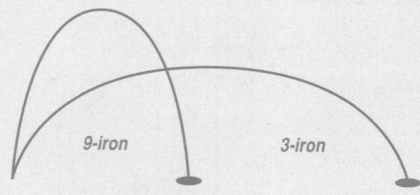

9-iron   3-iron

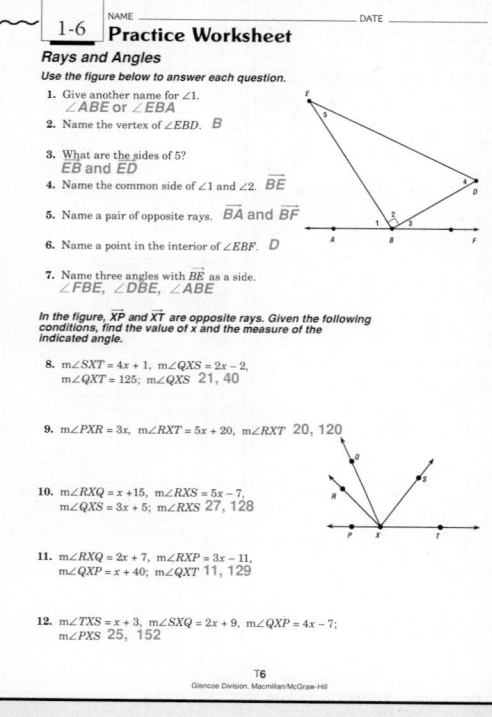

Additional Answer
48.

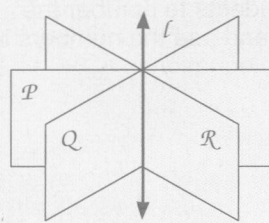

46. Botany Botanists have found that the angle between the main branches of a tree and its trunk remains constant in each species. Measure the angles between several branches and the trunk of the tree in the photograph at the right. Are the angles all about the same? What is the measure of each angle?
Answers may vary.

Mixed Review

47. Find the ordered pair for the point with *x*-coordinate 2 that lies on the line $x + 3y = -1$. **(Lesson 1-1)** (2, -1)

48. Draw and label a figure to show that the intersection of planes $\mathcal{P}$, $\mathcal{Q}$, and $\mathcal{R}$ is line ℓ. **(Lesson 1-2)** **See margin.**

49. If *M* is the midpoint between *K* and *L* on a number line, the coordinate of *M* is 3, and the coordinate of *L* is -2, is the coordinate of *K* greater than 0 or less than 0? **(Lesson 1-4)** **greater than 0**

50. Find *BC* if *B* is between *A* and *C*, $AC = 12$, $AB = 5x - 3$, and $BC = 3x - 1$. **(Lesson 1-4)** **5**

51. Find the midpoint of $\overline{CD}$ if the coordinates of *C* are (-5, -2) and the coordinates of *D* are (3, 6). **(Lesson 1-5)** (-1, 2)

52. If $\overline{XY}$ bisects $\overline{WZ}$ at *X*, $WX = 2x - 3$, and $XZ = 5x - 24$, what is the value of *x*? **(Lesson 1-5)** $x = 7$

Wrap-Up

53. Journal Entry Write an explanation of the angle addition postulate, different from the one presented in this lesson, that you could present to a classmate in your journal. **See students' work.**

DEVELOPING REASONING SKILLS

Copy the figure shown at the right. Then draw line segments through the nine dots that satisfy the following conditions.

1. Use only straight line segments.

2. You may only pass through a dot one time.

3. Once you begin drawing the lines, you may not lift your pencil until you are finished.

4. You may use up to 4 line segments with three changes of direction.

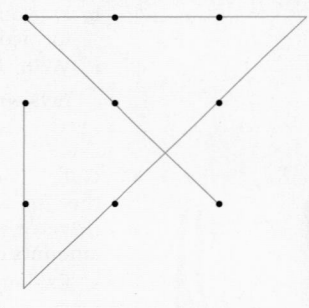

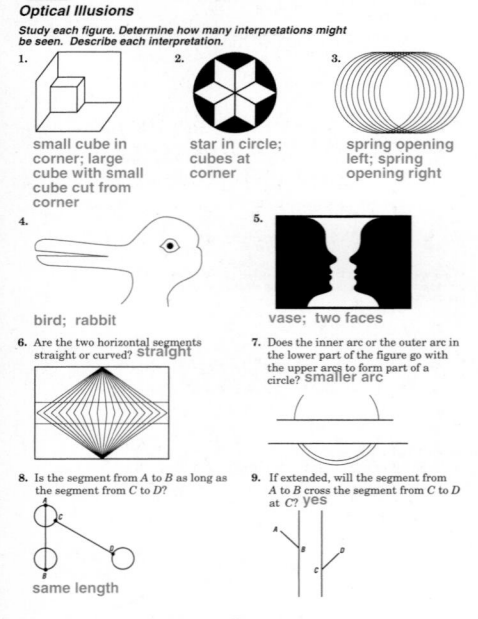

EXTENDING THE LESSON

Math Power: Reasoning

Ask students why they think the protractor postulate needed only a number between 0 and 180. What does it mean when they hear, "Someone did a 180° turn," or "She did a 180 on her skateboard"? It may help them to look at a protractor and see that it forms a semicircle. What happens if they put two protractors together along the straight edge? How many degrees are in a circle?
They form a circle; 360.

Objectives

After studying this lesson, you should be able to:

1-7A ▪ classify angles as acute, obtuse, right, and straight, and

1-7B ▪ identify and use congruent angles and the bisector of an angle.

Application

Have you ever noticed how some diamonds "sparkle" more than others even though there appears to be no difference in their shapes? The amount of brilliance with which a diamond sparkles depends on the angle of its faces and how they catch and reflect light. Early jewelers were unaware that they could cut diamonds in certain ways to give them more brilliance. Today, thanks to the work of the Polish mathematician Tolkowsky, gem cutters know the exact angles to cut the faces of diamonds to produce many different levels of brilliance.

Gem cutters use many different tools to determine exactly where to cut a diamond so that each of its faces will be at a desired angle. They must use these tools since they cannot simply use a protractor to draw the appropriate angles on the diamond. You, however, can use a protractor to draw angles with specific measures.

Example 1

Use a protractor to draw a 65° angle.

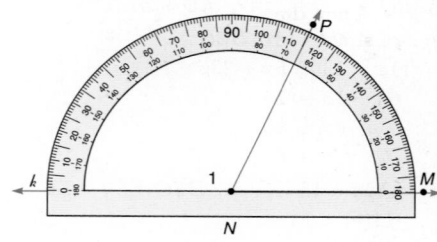

1. Draw line *k* with point *N* on line *k*.
2. Place the center point of the protractor on *N* and align the mark labeled 0 on the inner scale with line *k*. Draw point *M* at the 0 mark.
3. Locate and draw point *P* at the mark labeled 65 on the inner scale.
4. Draw $\overrightarrow{NP}$. Angle *MNP* is a 65° angle.

What is the measure of ∠1 in the figure above? **115**

In geometry, angles are classified according to their measures.

LESSON 1-7   CLASSIFYING ANGLES   43

ALTERNATE TEACHING STRATEGIES

Using Manipulatives

Twist three twist ties together to form one thick tie. Stick the tie into the ends of two straws, to use as a hinge for creating angles with the straws. Have students form an angle, compare the angle to the corner of a piece of paper, and determine if the angle formed is acute, right, or obtuse. Have students measure the angles formed.

Using Applications

Discuss different applications of angles with your students. For example, you could bring in a sextant or a picture of a sextant and discuss how sailors use angle measures to calculate where they are at sea, or you could bring in a transit or a picture of a transit and discuss how surveyors use it in construction.

1-7 Lesson Notes

Lesson Resources

• Reteaching Master 1-7
• Practice Master 1-7
• Enrichment Master 1-7
• Evaluation Master, Quiz C, p. 10

 Transparency 1-7 contains the 5-Minute Check and a teaching aid for this lesson.

INTRODUCING THE LESSON

⏱ **5-Minute Check**

(over Lesson 1-6)

Refer to the figure below.

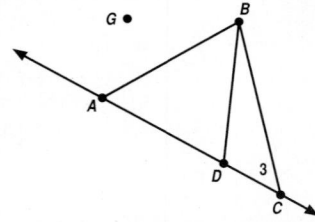

1. Name the angles with point *B* as their vertex.
   ∠ABD, ∠DBC, ∠ABC
2. Give one name for the angle that ∠3 represents.
   Sample answer: ∠BCD
3. Is point *G* in the interior or the exterior of ∠DBA?   exterior
4. Find the value of *x* and m ∠ABD if m ∠ABC = 71, m ∠DBC = 2x − 3, and m ∠ABD = 3x + 4.   14, 46

Motivating the Lesson

Have each student make three or four different-size angles on a piece of paper, using his or her thumb and index finger as sides. Ask them how they might find the measures of the angles.

TEACHING THE LESSON

Teaching Tip   At the end of Example 1, note that m∠1 + m∠MNP = 115 + 65 = 180.

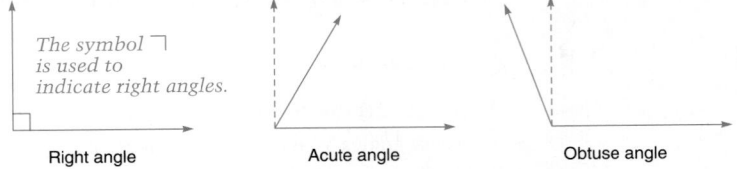

The symbol ⌐ is used to indicate right angles.

Right angle   Acute angle   Obtuse angle

A corner of a sheet of paper forms a right angle. You may use it to help you determine if an angle is right, acute, or obtuse. The edge of the paper can be used to determine straight angles.

Definition of Right Acute, and Obtuse Angles	**A right angle is an angle whose measure is 90. An acute angle is one whose measure is less than 90. An obtuse angle is one whose measure is greater than 90.**

In Lesson 1-5, you learned that congruent segments have the same length. Similarly, **congruent angles** have the same measure.

In the figure at the right, m∠*PQR* = m∠*SQV* since each has a measure of 50. Therefore, the two angles are congruent, which you can indicate by writing ∠*PQR* ≅ ∠*SQV*. In a diagram, small "arcs," like the ones in red shown at the right, are used to indicate congruent angles.

The definition of congruent angles tells us that statements such as m∠*A* = m∠*B* and ∠*A* ≅ ∠*B* are equivalent. Therefore, we will use them interchangeably throughout the remainder of this book.

Example 2

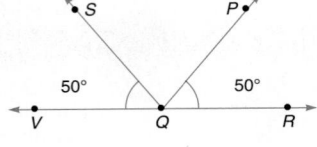

Point *D* is in the interior of ∠*ABC*. Find *m*∠*ABC* if ∠*ABD* ≅ ∠*DBC*, *m*∠*ABD* = 11*x* − 13, and *m*∠*DBC* = 5*x* + 23.

Since ∠*ABD* ≅ ∠*DBC*, m∠*ABD* = m∠*DBC*.

$$m\angle ABD = m\angle DBC$$
$$11x - 13 = 5x + 23$$
$$6x - 13 = 23$$
$$6x = 36$$
$$x = 6$$

m∠*ABD* = 11*x* − 13	m∠*DBC* = 5*x* + 23
= 11(6) − 13	= 5(6) + 23
= 53	= 53

m∠*ABC* = m∠*ABD* + m∠*DBC*   *Angle addition postulate*
        = 53 + 53
        = 106

44   CHAPTER 1   THE LANGUAGE OF GEOMETRY

A compass and straightedge can be used to construct an angle that is congruent to a given angle without knowing the degree measure of the angle.

CONSTRUCTION

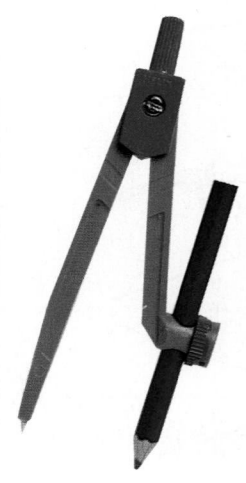

Teaching Tip After constructing an angle congruent to a given angle, have students draw obtuse and right angles and copy them by construction.

Construct an angle congruent to a given angle.

1. Draw an angle like ∠A on your paper.

2. Use a straightedge to draw a ray on your paper. Label its endpoint E.

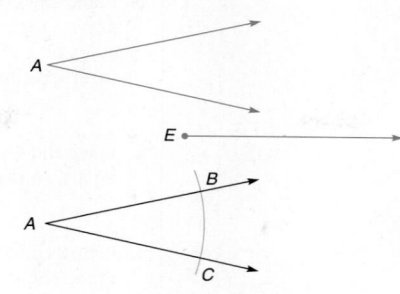

3. Put the compass at point A and draw a large arc that intersects both sides of ∠A. Label the points of intersection B and C.

4. Using the same compass setting, put the compass at point E and draw a large arc that starts above the ray and intersects the ray. Label the point of intersection F.

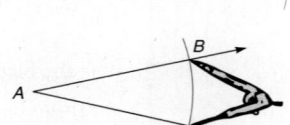

5. Set the point of your compass on C and adjust so that the pencil tip is on B.

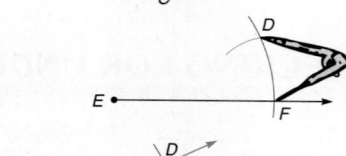

6. Using that setting, place the compass at point F and draw an arc to intersect the larger arc you drew in Step 4. Label the point of intersection D.

7. Use a straightedge to draw $\overrightarrow{ED}$.

Thus, $m\angle BAC = m\angle DEF$, or $\angle BAC \cong \angle DEF$, by construction.

A *segment bisector* separates a segment into two congruent segments since it intersects the midpoint of the segment. Similarly, we can talk about an *angle bisector* separating an angle into two congruent angles.

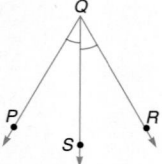

For $\overrightarrow{QS}$ to be the **angle bisector** of ∠PQR, point S must be on the interior of ∠PQR and ∠PQS ≅ ∠SQR, as shown at the right.

The construction on the next page shows how a compass and straightedge can be used to find the angle bisector of a given angle.

LESSON 1-7 CLASSIFYING ANGLES 45

Teaching Tip
After constructing the bisector of a given angle, have students make an obtuse and a right angle, and construct their bisectors.

EVALUATING THE LESSON

Checking for Understanding
Exercises 1-18 are designed to help you assess students' understanding through reading, writing, speaking, and modeling. You should work through Exercises 1-4 with your students and then monitor their work on Exercises 5-18.

Closing the Lesson
Speaking Activity Going around the room, have each student tell you one of the steps in an activity described in this lesson. For example, have students tell you how to draw an angle with specific measure, how to construct a congruent angle, or how to bisect an angle.

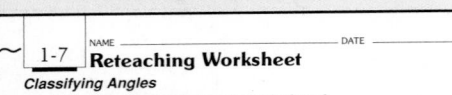

CONSTRUCTION

Construct the bisector of a given angle.

1. Draw an angle like ∠P on your paper.

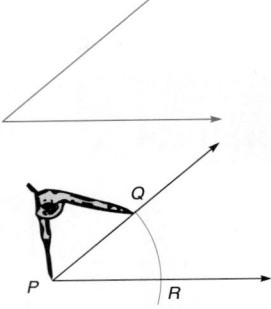

2. Place the compass at point P and draw a large arc that intersects both sides of ∠P. Label the points of intersection Q and R.

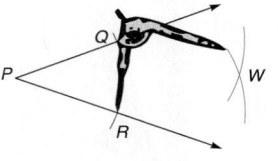

3. Place the compass at point Q and draw an arc in the interior of the angle.

4. Using the same compass setting, place the compass at point R and draw a large arc that intersects the arc drawn in Step 3. Label the point of the intersection W.

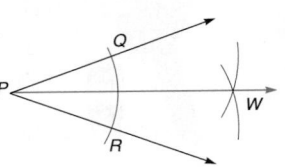

5. Draw $\overrightarrow{PW}$.

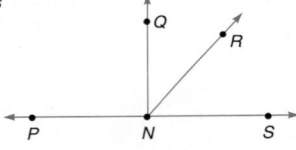

$\overrightarrow{PW}$ is the bisector of ∠QPR.

m∠QPW = m∠WPR, or ∠QPW ≅ ∠WPR

CHECKING FOR UNDERSTANDING

Communicating Mathematics

Read and study the lesson to answer each question. 2-4: See margin.

1. An angle has how many different bisectors? Explain. exactly one; protractor postulate
2. Explain why all right angles are congruent.
3. Explain why not all acute angles are congruent.
4. Draw and label a figure to show ∠AOB ≅ ∠BOC and ∠AOD ≅ ∠DOC. Be sure to indicate each pair of congruent angles.

Guided Practice

Use a protractor to draw angles having each measure. See Solutions Manual.

5. 45   6. 60   7. 125
8. 100   9. 29   10. 144

State whether each angle in the figure *appears* to be acute, obtuse, right, or straight.

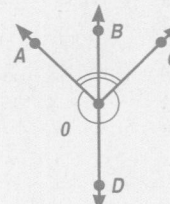

11. ∠SNR acute   12. ∠QNP right
13. ∠SNP straight   14. ∠RNP obtuse
15. ∠SNQ right   16. ∠QNR acute

46   CHAPTER 1   THE LANGUAGE OF GEOMETRY

Additional Answers

2. Right angles all have a measure of 90°. Thus, right angles all have the same measure and are therefore congruent.

3. Acute angles do not always have the same measure. For example, a 30° angle and a 70° angle are both acute. Since they do not have the same measures, they cannot be congruent.

4.

17. If ∠A is an acute angle and m∠A = 3x + 12, write a compound inequality to describe all the possible values for x. 0 < 3x + 12 < 90 or -4 < x < 26

18. If ∠M ≅ ∠N, m∠M = 8n − 17, and m∠N = 7n − 3, is ∠N acute, obtuse, right, or straight? obtuse

APPLYING THE LESSON

Homework Exercises

Assignment Guide
Basic: 19-36, 43-51
Average: 22-39, 43-51
Enriched: 25-51

EXERCISES

Practice

State whether each angle in the figure *appears* to be acute, obtuse, right, or straight.

A

19. ∠MAL acute   20. ∠LBC right

21. ∠ALC obtuse   22. ∠BLN acute

23. ∠ABC straight 24. ∠LMA obtuse

25. ∠ACN acute   26. ∠CNM obtuse

27-28: See margin

Refer to the figure to answer each question.

B

27. Name all pairs of congruent angles.

28. Name all segments that bisect angles and name the angles that they bisect.

CONNECTION
Algebra

29. If m∠AHM = 3x + 5 and m∠TMH = 7x − 27, find m∠AHM.   29

30. If m∠MAH = 2x + 5 and m∠TAH = 7x − 10, find m∠MAT. 22

31. If m∠HTA = 130 − x and m∠HTM = 3x + 2, find m∠MTA. 56

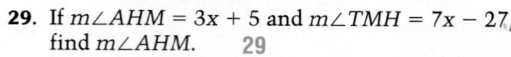
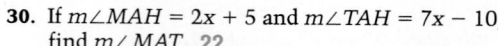

In the figure, $\overrightarrow{AM}$ bisects ∠LAR and $\overrightarrow{AS}$ bisects ∠MAR. Given the following conditions, find the value of x and the measure of the indicated angle.

32. m∠MAR = 2x + 13, m∠MAL = 4x − 3; m∠RAL 8; 58

33. m∠RAL = x + 32, m∠MAR = x − 31; m∠LAM 94; 63

34. m∠RAS = 25 − 2x, m∠SAM = 3x + 5; m∠LAR 4; 68

35. m∠RAM = 31 − x, m∠LAM = 17 − 3x, m∠SAR -7; 19

36. m∠RAL = 5x − 7, m∠MAS = x + 3, m∠MAR 19; 44

37. Suppose ∠PQR is a right angle and T is in the interior of ∠PQR. If m∠PQT is four times m∠TQR, find m∠TQR. 18

38. In the figure, ∠LOJ is an obtuse angle. If m∠LOJ = 5x + 25, write a compound inequality to describe all the possible values for x. 90 < 5x + 25 < 180 or 13 < x < 31

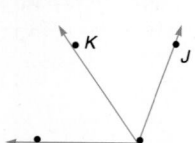

39. If m∠KOJ = 8x − 17, m∠KOL = 3x + 28, and m∠JOL = 110, does $\overrightarrow{OK}$ bisect ∠LOJ? yes

LESSON 1-7   CLASSIFYING ANGLES   47

Exercise Notes

For Exercises 32-36, it may be easier for students if they use numbers for the angles instead of letters. Also, redraw the diagram and mark the congruent angles prior to solving the problems.

For Exercise 42, n ≠ −11 because the value for m ∠SPT would be −33 and angles cannot have negative measures.

Additional Answers

27. ∠MHA and ∠HMT, ∠MAH and ∠TAH, ∠ATM and ∠HTM

28. $\overrightarrow{TM}$ bisects ∠HTA; $\overrightarrow{AH}$ bisects ∠MAT.

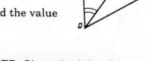
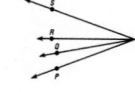
RETEACHING THE LESSON

If students are having difficulty remembering which angles are acute, right, and obtuse, have them develop mnemonic devices to help them remember. For example, things that are cute are usually small (puppies, babies) and an acute angle has a smaller measure; the word *obtuse* has the most letters of the three words, and these angles will have the greatest measures.

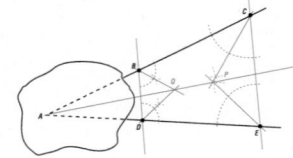

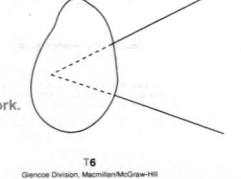
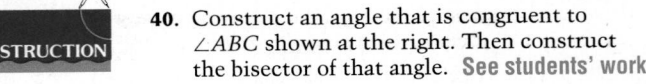

40. Construct an angle that is congruent to ∠*ABC* shown at the right. Then construct the bisector of that angle. **See students' work.**

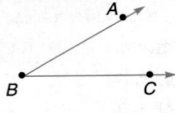

41. Suppose ∠*JKM* and ∠*MKJ* are right angles. If $m\angle JKM = 23x - 6y$ and $m\angle MKJ = 7x + 6y$, find the values of *x* and *y*. **x = 6, y = 8**

42. If *S* is in the interior of ∠*RPT*, $m\angle RPT = 76$, $m\angle RPS = n^2 - 12$, and $m\angle SPT = 4n + 11$, find the value of *n* and determine if $\overrightarrow{PS}$ bisects ∠*RPT*. **n = 7; no**

Critical Thinking

43. As the hands of a clock move from 3:00 A.M. to 3:00 P.M., how many times will they be at right angles with each other? **24 times (twice each hour)**

44. Copy △*ABC* shown at the right. Then draw the rays that bisect each angle of the triangle using the construction on page 46.
    a. What conjecture could you make about these three rays?
    b. Draw two different triangles and test your conjecture on these triangles. **The three rays intersect at one point**

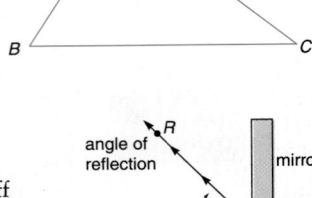

Application

45. **Physics** When a beam of light reflects off a plane mirror, its *angle of incidence* is congruent to its *angle of reflection*. If $m\angle IMR = 80$, find the angle of incidence and $m\angle IMN$. **m∠IMP = 40, m∠IMN = 50**

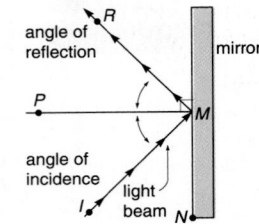

Mixed Review

46. Would the best model for the intersection of two adjacent walls and the ceiling in a room be a point, a line, or a plane? **(Lesson 1-2)** **point**

In the figure below, $\overleftrightarrow{MS}$ and $\overleftrightarrow{TQ}$ intersect at *P*. Refer to this figure to answer each question.

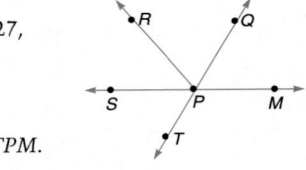

47. If $SP = 3x + 11$, $PM = 2x + 1$, and $MS = 27$, find the value of *x*. **(Lesson 1-4)** **3**

48. If $\overrightarrow{PR}$ bisects $\overline{TQ}$, $PQ = x + 7$, and $TQ = 5x - 1$, find *PT*. **(Lesson 1-5)** **12**

49. false; since R is not in the interior of ∠TPM

49. *True* or *false*: $m\angle TPR + m\angle RPM = m\angle TPM$. Explain. **(Lesson 1-6)**

50. If $m\angle SPR = 3d - 11$, $m\angle RPQ = 3d + 19$, and $m\angle RPM = 7d + 1$, find $m\angle QPM$. **(Lesson 1-6)** **58**

Wrap-Up

51. Look up the words *acute* and *obtuse* in a dictionary. Compare their everyday meanings to their mathematical meanings. **See students' work.**

48   CHAPTER 1   THE LANGUAGE OF GEOMETRY

EXTENDING THE LESSON

Math Power: Problem Solving

Have your students draw an angle whose measure is greater than 180°. It may help them to use the twist ties and straws first to make the angle. Ask them what they notice about the "exterior" of this extra large angle. **It will be acute, right, or obtuse.**

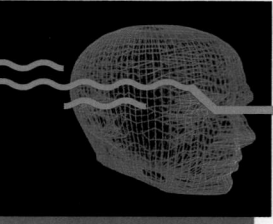

Technology
Using LOGO

Using Technology

Objective This optional page shows how to use LOGO to perform mathematical computations and to enhance and extend mathematical concepts.

Teaching Suggestions

Have students complete this lesson on the computer. They do not need to write out the commands, since they can run the program to see if their work is correct. This can save time and lead to interesting ideas, since students may think of something they would like to draw while they are typing commands. Cooperative groups can also work well on this lesson. Have each group design a figure and use LOGO to draw it. Have students experiment with LOGO to draw a circle with only the commands listed on this page.

LOGO is a very powerful computer programming language. You can use LOGO to examine and manipulate words, numbers, and lists. Its best-known feature is its turtle graphics. This feature allows us to create drawings with simple commands.

To use LOGO, you must first load the language into your computer. Insert the disk into drive 1 and close the door. To boot the LOGO disk, hold down the CONTROL and ⌂ keys with two fingers on your left hand and press the RESET key with a finger on your right hand. Now, release all three keys at once.

Once LOGO is loaded, type DRAW to clear the screen and locate the turtle, the small triangle used to draw, in the center of the screen. The basic LOGO commands are as follows:

FD Forward   LT Left   CS Clear screen
BK Back   RT Right   DRAW
PU Pen Up   PD Pen Down   HOME

The LOGO commands shown below have the turtle draw a rectangle and a triangle.

```
DRAW
FD 50 RT 90
FD 75 RT 90
FD 50 RT 90
FD 75 PU FD 10
PD FD 30 LT 120
FD 30 LT 120
FD 30 HT
```

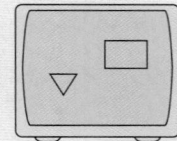

EXERCISES

1. vertical segment 80 units long

1. Describe the results of the commands DRAW FD 80 BK 80.

2. Type the command HT. What happens? Now type ST. **The turtle disappears when you type HT and reappears when you type ST.**
Write the LOGO commands to draw each figure. See margin.

3.   **4.**   **5.**

6. Write the LOGO commands to draw your initials.
   See students' work.

TECHNOLOGY   49

Additional Answers

3. Draw FD50, RT90, FD25, RT90, FD50, BK25, LT90, FD50, RT90, FD25, RT90, FD75

4. Draw FD100, RT90, FD100, RT90, FD100, RT90, FD100, RT90, FD50, RT90, FD100, RT90, FD50, RT90, FD50, RT90, FD100

5. Draw FD100, RT90, FD100, RT90, FD100, RT90, FD100, BK25, RT90, FD25, LT90, FD25, RT90, FD25, RT90, FD50, RT90, FD50, LT90, FD25, LT90, FD75, LT90, FD75

INTRODUCING THE LESSON

 5-Minute Check

(over Lesson 1-7)

Use a protractor to draw an angle having each measure.

1. 30
2. 123
3. 18
4. 130
See students' work.

Determine if each angle appears acute, obtuse, right, or straight.

5.   **6.**

acute   obtuse

7. Ray *SW* bisects ∠*TSR*,
m ∠*TSW* = *x* + 2,
m ∠*WSR* = 2*x* − 3
Find the value of *x* and
m ∠*TSR*.   5, 14

Motivating the Lesson

Have each student use two pipe cleaners or twist ties that are different colors and twist them together at their midpoints. Have them adjust the pipe cleaners or twist ties so that they look like two intersecting lines. Which angles appear to be congruent? **The vertical angles.** If they move one line, do the vertical angles still look congruent? **Yes.** Ask other questions relating to terms in this lesson.

1-8 Pairs of Angles

Objective
1-8

After studying this lesson, you should be able to:
▪ identify and use adjacent angles, vertical angles, complementary angles, supplementary angles, and linear pairs of angles.

Investigation

On a piece of paper, draw two lines, $\overleftrightarrow{AB}$ and $\overleftrightarrow{PQ}$, intersecting at point X. Your figure should look similar to the one shown below. These two intersecting lines form four nonstraight angles, ∠AXP, ∠PXB, ∠BXQ, and ∠QXA. Certain pairs of these angles have special names that are used to describe the relationship between the angles.

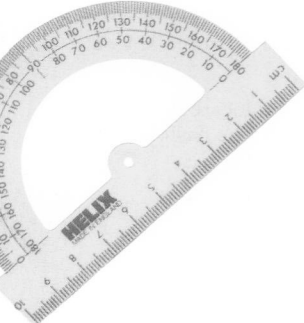

∠AXP and ∠PXB are *adjacent angles*. **Adjacent angles** are angles in the same plane that have a common vertex and a common side, but no common interior points. The two congruent angles formed by an angle bisector is another example of a pair of adjacent angles. How many pairs of adjacent angles are in this figure? *4 pairs*

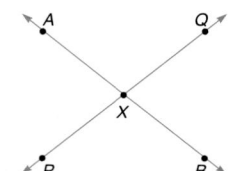

∠AXP and ∠BXQ are *vertical angles*. **Vertical angles** are two nonadjacent angles formed by two intersecting lines. How many pairs of vertical angles are in this figure? *2 pairs*   *They are ∠AXP and ∠BXQ, and ∠AXQ and ∠PXB.*

Now, using a protractor, carefully measure each of the four angles. What do you notice about the measures of vertical angles ∠AXP and ∠BXQ? ∠PXB and ∠QXA? Draw another pair of intersecting lines, measure the four angles, and see if you get the same results. The results of your investigation might lead you to the following conclusion, which we will prove in Chapter 2.

Vertical angles are congruent.

> **INVESTIGATION**
>
> You can learn more about vertical angles in Investigation 1 on page A2.

Let's refer to our original figure, shown again at the right. ∠AXP and ∠PXB are an example of a special pair of adjacent angles called a *linear pair*. A **linear pair** of angles are adjacent angles whose noncommon sides are opposite rays. Based on the angle measurements you took previously, what can you conclude about the measures of the angles in each linear pair in this figure? Draw another pair of intersecting lines, measure the four angles, and see if you get the same results.

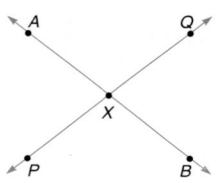

In the figure, there are four linear pairs: ∠AXP and ∠PXB, ∠PXB and ∠BXQ, ∠BXQ and ∠QXA, and ∠QXA and ∠AXP.

The results of these two examples might lead you to the following conclusion which we will also prove in Chapter 2.

The sum of the measures of the angles in a linear pair is 180.

50   CHAPTER 1   THE LANGUAGE OF GEOMETRY

ALTERNATE TEACHING STRATEGIES

Using Critical Thinking

Instruct students to make two paper cones that are the same size, tape the tips of the cones together exactly opposite each other, flatten the cones, and trace along their edges. Use the figure to explore the relationships of the angles.

Using Investigation

You can guide students to discover that vertical angles are congruent. In Investigation 1 on page A2 of **More Investigations in Geometry,** students use paper folding and measurement to explore vertical angles.

Example 1

CONNECTION

Algebra

In the figure, $\overrightarrow{AB}$ and $\overrightarrow{CD}$ intersect at Z. Find the value of x and the measure of $\angle CZB$.

Since $\angle AZC$ and $\angle BZD$ are vertical angles, $m\angle AZC = m\angle BZD$.

$$m\angle AZC = m\angle BZD$$
$$5x - 22 = 3x + 16$$
$$2x = 38$$
$$x = 19$$
$$m\angle AZC = 5x - 22$$
$$= 5(19) - 22$$
$$= 73$$

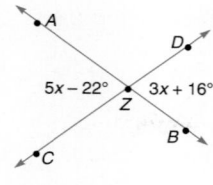

Since $\angle AZC$ and $\angle CZB$ are a linear pair, $m\angle AZC + m\angle CZB = 180$.

$$m\angle AZC + m\angle CZB = 180$$
$$73 + m\angle CZB = 180$$
$$m\angle CZB = 107$$ The measure of $\angle CZB$ is 107.

In Example 1, the sum of the measures of $\angle AZC$ and $\angle CZB$ is 180. If the sum of the measures of two angles is 180, the angles are called **supplementary angles.** When two angles are supplementary, each angle is said to be a *supplement* of the other angle.

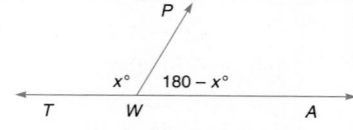

$\angle TWP$ and $\angle PWA$ are supplementary.

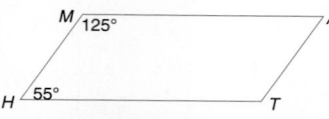

$\angle H$ is a supplement of $\angle M$, or $\angle M$ is a supplement of $\angle H$.

Since the sum of the measures of a linear pair of angles is 180, we can now say that *two angles that form a linear pair must be supplementary.*

Example 2

CONNECTION

Algebra

If $\angle PQS$ and $\angle SQR$ are supplementary, find $m\angle SQT$ and $m\angle TQR$.

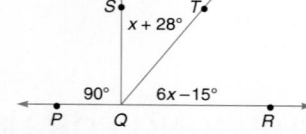

Since $\angle PQS$ and $\angle SQR$ are supplementary, the sum of their measures is 180.

$$m\angle PQS + m\angle SQR = 180$$
$$90 + m\angle SQR = 180$$ *Substitute 90 for $m\angle PQS$.*
$$90 + (m\angle SQT + m\angle TQR) = 180$$ *Angle addition postulate*
$$90 + (x + 28) + (6x - 15) = 180$$ *Substitute $x + 28$ for $m\angle SQT$ and $6x - 15$ for $m\angle TQR$.*
$$7x + 103 = 180$$
$$7x = 77$$
$$x = 11$$

$m\angle SQT = x + 28$ $m\angle TQR = 6x - 15$
$\quad\quad\quad = (11) + 28$ or 39 $\quad\quad = 6(11) - 15$ or 51

LESSON 1-8   PAIRS OF ANGLES   51

Teaching Tip   When discussing adjacent angles, have students look up the word *adjacent*.

Teaching Tip   When defining vertical angles, point out that they have only one point in common – the vertex. Students may use this to help them remember what vertical angles are.

Teaching Tip   When discussing linear pairs of angles, point out that since *linear* means "dealing with lines" and *pair* means "two," another way to define *linear pair* would be "two angles that make a line."

Chalkboard Examples

For Example 1
In the figure, line *MN* and line *OP* intersect at *D*. Find the value of *x* and m $\angle ODN$.
15, 131

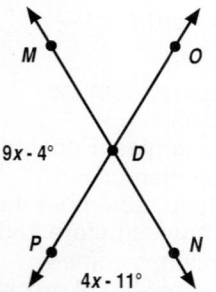

For Example 2
If $\angle BCE$ and $\angle ECD$ are supplementary, find m $\angle ECF$ and m $\angle FCD$.
90, 27

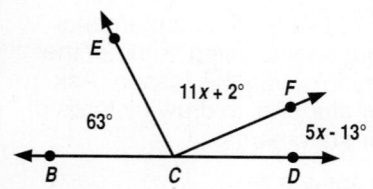

In Example 2, the sum of the measures of $\angle SQT$ and $\angle TQR$ is 90. If the sum of the measures of two angles is 90, the angles are called **complementary angles.** Whenever two angles are complementary, each angle is said to be the *complement* of the other angle.

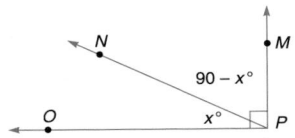

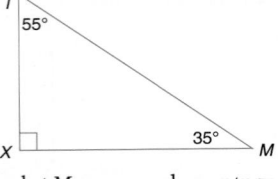

$\angle NPO$ is a complement of $\angle NPM$.
$\angle NPM$ is a complement of $\angle NPO$.

$\angle I$ and $\angle M$ are complementary.

Example 3

CONNECTION
Algebra

The measure of a supplement of an angle is 2.5 times as large as the measure of a complement of the angle. Find the measure of the angle.

EXPLORE Let x = the measure of the angle.
Then $180 - x$ = the measure of its supplement, and
$90 - x$ = the measure of its complement.

PLAN Write an equation that represents the relationship in this problem.

$$\underbrace{\text{The supplement}}_{180 - x} \quad \underset{=}{\text{is}} \quad \underset{2.5\,\times}{\text{2.5 times}} \quad \underbrace{\text{the complement.}}_{(90 - x)}$$

SOLVE
$$180 - x = 2.5(90 - x)$$
$$180 - x = 225 - 2.5x$$
$$1.5x = 45$$
$$x = 30$$

The measure of the angle is 30.

EXAMINE Is the measure of the supplement of a 30° angle 2.5 times as large as the measure of its complement?

Measure of supplement: $180 - 30 = 150$
Measure of complement: $90 - 30 = 60$
Since $2.5(60) = 150$, the solution is correct.

CHECKING FOR UNDERSTANDING

Communicating Mathematics

Read and study the lesson to answer each question.

1. Give an explanation for why you think a linear pair of angles is called "linear." **Two sides of the pair of angles form a line.**

2. false; Any two angles whose measures have a sum of 180 are supplementary.

2. *True* or *false:*   All pairs of supplementary angles are also linear pairs. Explain.

3. Complete: Adjacent angles are angles in the same plane that have a common ? and ? but no common ? . **vertex; side; interior points**

4. Describe in your own words the difference between complementary and supplementary angles. **See margin.**

Guided Practice

Find the measure of the complement and the supplement of an angle having the indicated measure.

8. $(90 - x), (180 - x)$

5. 38 **52, 142**
6. 63 **27, 117**
7. 110 **no complement, 70**
8. x

Refer to the figure at the right to name the following pairs of angles.

9. obtuse vertical angles **∠NML and ∠PMK**

10. ∠JMK and ∠KML
11. ∠JMP and ∠JML
12. Sample answers:
∠NMP and ∠PMK,
∠NMJ and ∠JMK,
∠NML and ∠KML
14. ∠JMK and ∠NMP

10. adjacent complementary angles
11. congruent supplementary angles
12. noncongruent supplementary angles
13. adjacent angles that do *not* form a linear pair **Sample answers: ∠NMP and ∠PMJ, ∠PMJ and ∠JMK, ∠JMK and ∠KML**
14. nonadjacent complementary angles

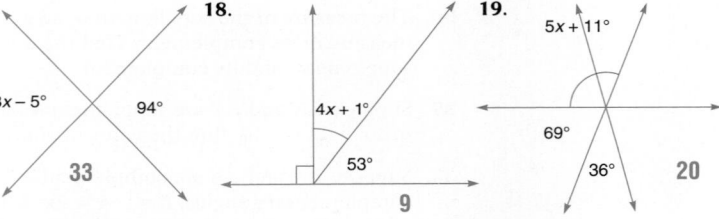

CONNECTION
Algebra

15. Suppose ∠A is a complement of ∠B. Find the value of x, $m\angle A$, and $m\angle B$ if $m\angle A = 7x + 4$ and $m\angle B = 4x + 9$. **7; 53; 37**

16. Suppose ∠P is a supplement of ∠Q. Find the value of x, $m\angle P$, and $m\angle Q$ if $m\angle P = 6x + 4$ and $m\angle Q = 10x$. **11; 70; 110**

EXERCISES

Practice A

Find the value of x.

17.
$3x - 5°$ $94°$
33

18.
$4x + 1°$ $53°$
9

19.
$5x + 11°$ $69°$ $36°$
20

Identify each pair of angles as adjacent, vertical, complementary, supplementary, and/or as a linear pair.

20. ∠CFE and ∠AFC **adjacent**
21. ∠BCF and ∠FCD **adjacent, complementary**
22. ∠AFE and ∠DFB **vertical**
23. adjacent, supplementary, linear pair B
23. ∠CBF and ∠ABF
24. ∠AFB and ∠CFB **adjacent, complementary**
25. ∠CBF and ∠FDE **supplementary**

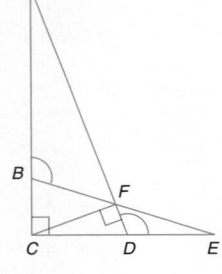

RETEACHING THE LESSON

Divide your class into small groups and have each group solve problems similar to the exercises at the end of this lesson. Have students who understand the material assist those who are having difficulty. Go around the room and have each student explain at least one step in solving the problems.

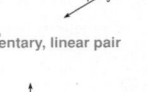
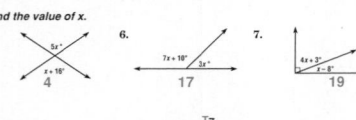

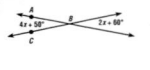
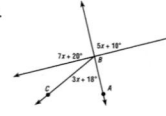
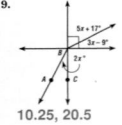
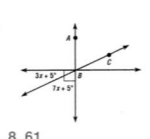
Find the value of *x* and *m∠ABC*.

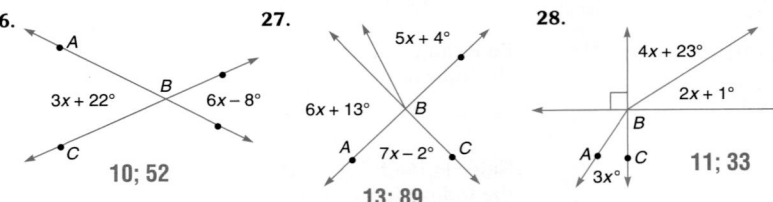

26.   3x + 22°   6x − 8°   10; 52

27.   5x + 4°   6x + 13°   7x − 2°   13; 89

28.   4x + 23°   2x + 1°   3x°   11; 33

CONNECTION

Algebra

Solve.

29. Find the measures of two supplementary angles if the measure of the larger angle is 44 more than the measure of the smaller. **112, 68**

30. Find the measure of two complementary angles if the difference in the measures of the two angles is 12. **51, 39**

31. The measure of an angle is one-third the measure of its supplement. Find the measure of the angle. **45**

32. The measure of an angle is one-fourth the measure of its complement. Find the measure of the angle. **18**

33. The measure of an angle is 6 more than twice the measure of its complement. Find the measures of both angles. **28, 62**

34. The measure of an angle is 5 less than 4 times the measure of its supplement. Find the measure of both angles. **37, 143**

 35. The measure of the supplement of an angle is 6 times the measure of its complement. Find the measures of the angle, its supplement, and its complement. **72, 108, 18**

36. The measure of the supplement of an angle is 60 less than 3 times the measure of its complement. Find the measures of the angle, its supplement, and its complement. **15, 165, 75**

37. Suppose ∠X and ∠Y are supplementary angles. If $m\angle X = x^2 - 9x$ and $m\angle Y = 11x + 12$, find the value of *x*, *m∠X*, and *m∠Y*. **12, 36, 144**

38. Suppose ∠A and ∠B are complementary angles, and ∠C and ∠D are also complementary angles. If $m\angle A = 2x + 3$, $m\angle B = y - 2$, $m\angle C = 2x - y$, and $m\angle D = x - 1$, find the values of *x* and *y*, *m∠A*, *m∠B*, *m∠C*, and *m∠D*. **36, 17, 75, 15, 55, 35**

Critical Thinking

39. Determine whether the following statement is *always, sometimes,* or *never* true: *The measure of an acute angle is equal to the difference of the measure of its supplement and twice the measure of its complement.* Be sure to justify your answer. **See margin.**

40. In the figure at the right, ∠2 and ∠3 are complementary angles. Are ∠1 and ∠4 complementary? Why or why not? **See margin.**

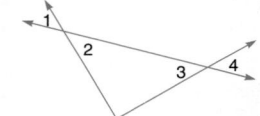

41. Ski Jumping In order for ski jumpers to achieve the maximum distance on a jump, they need to make the angle between their body and the front of their skis as small as possible. This allows them to get the proper extension over the tips of their skis. If a ski jumper's body is aligned so that the angle between the body and the front of the skis is 10°, what will be the angle that the tail of the skis forms with the body? *Hint: Think about the relationship between the ski jumper's body and the skis.* **170°**

Mixed Review

Use the number line at the right to answer each question.

42. If $LN = 10$, find NS. **(Lesson 1-4)** **4**

43. Find the coordinate of N if it is the midpoint of $\overline{LS}$. **(Lesson 1-5)** **1**

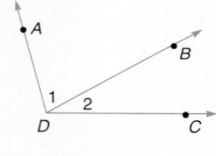

Use the figure at the right to answer each question.

44. Find the value of x if $m\angle 1 = 3x + 2$, $m\angle 2 = 4x - 1$, and $m\angle ADC = 148$. **(Lesson 1-6)** **21**

45. Is $\overrightarrow{DB}$ the bisector of $\angle ADC$ if $m\angle 1 = 2x$, $m\angle 2 = 28$, and $m\angle ADC = 5x - 14$? Justify your answer. **(Lesson 1-7)** **yes;** $m\angle 1 = m\angle 2$

46. Distinct lines $\overrightarrow{AB}$, $\overrightarrow{CD}$, and $\overrightarrow{EF}$ all lie in the same plane and intersect at point X. How many distinct pairs of vertical angles are formed at the point of intersection? **(Lesson 1-8)** **6**

Wrap-Up

47. Name the five different angle pairs discussed in this lesson and draw an example of each of these pairs. **See margin.**

LESSON 1-8   PAIRS OF ANGLES   55

EXTENDING THE LESSON

Math Power: Communication

Using Exercises 24-25, have small groups list the steps in finding the answers. Have someone from each group explain the steps they used to solve the problem. Tell them that they have just given a kind of *proof* of the statements, $\angle AFB$ and $\angle CFB$ are complementary and $\angle CBF$ and $\angle FDE$ are supplementary.

Additional Answer

47. *Adjacent angles* are in the same plane and have a common vertex and a common side but no common interior points. *Vertical angles* are the two nonadjacent angles formed by two intersecting lines. *Linear pairs of angles* are adjacent and have noncommon sides that are opposite rays. *Supplementary angles* have measures that sum to 180. *Complementary angles* have measures that sum to 90. See students' drawings.

Enrichment Masters Booklet, p. 7

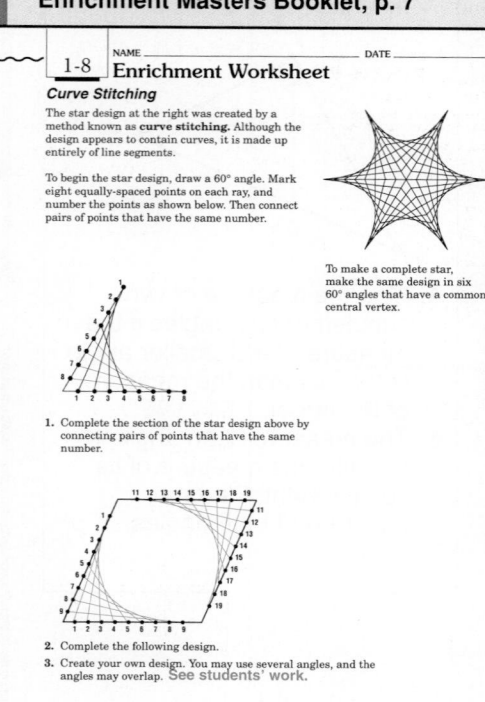

Objectives
1-9A
1-9B

After studying this lesson, you should be able to:
- identify and use right angles and perpendicular lines, and
- determine what information can and cannot be assumed from a figure.

Application

When carpenters put up the studs for the wall in a new home, they must be sure that each stud is at a *right angle* to the floor of the home. To check this, they can use a device called a carpenter's square. When the right angle of the carpenter's square is placed against the angle formed by a stud and the floor, its edges should lie flush against both the stud and the floor.

The figure at the right can be used as a model for the proper positioning of the studs in a wall relative to the floor. In this figure, each of the studs is *perpendicular* to the floor.

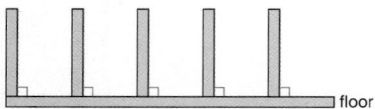

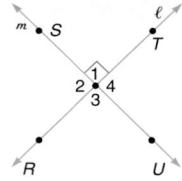

Perpendicular lines are two lines that intersect to form a right angle. In the figure at the left, lines ℓ and m are perpendicular. To indicate this, we write $\ell \perp m$, which is read "ℓ is perpendicular to m." Similarly, line segments and rays can be perpendicular to lines or other line segments and rays if they intersect to form a right angle. For example, in the figure, $\overline{RT} \perp \overline{SU}$, $\overline{US} \perp \overline{RT}$, and $\overline{TR} \perp \overline{US}$.

In the figure, $\angle 1$ is a right angle. Since $\angle 1$ and $\angle 3$ are vertical angles, what can you conclude about $\angle 3$? *It is also a right angle.*

Now, consider $\angle 2$ and $\angle 4$. Since $\angle 1$ forms a linear pair with $\angle 2$ and with $\angle 4$, what can you conclude about $\angle 2$ and $\angle 4$? *They are both right angles.*

If you draw two different lines, n and p, that are perpendicular, do you think the relationships between the four angles formed will be the same? *yes*

Based on this example, we could make the following conclusion, which will be proved in Chapter 2.

Perpendicular lines intersect to form four right angles.

56 CHAPTER 1 THE LANGUAGE OF GEOMETRY

Lesson Resources

- Reteaching Master 1-9
- Practice Master 1-9
- Enrichment Master 1-9
- Evaluation Master, Quiz D, p. 10
- Activity Master, p. 15
- Lab Manual, pp. 26-29

 Transparency 1-9 contains the 5-Minute Check and a teaching aid for this lesson.

INTRODUCING THE LESSON

 5-Minute Check

(over Lesson 1-8)

1. Draw an example of adjacent angles, vertical angles, complementary angles, supplementary angles, and a linear pair of angles. Label all angles that are congruent.

See students' work.

Identify each pair of angles as adjacent, vertical, complementary, supplementary, and/or a linear pair.

2. $\angle FJG$ and $\angle HJG$ **adjacent, complementary**

3. $\angle JGF$ and $\angle HGJ$ **adjacent, linear pair, and supplementary**

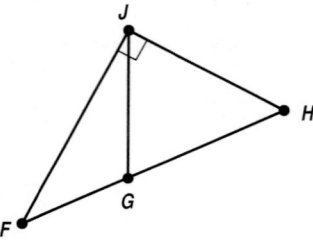

4. Find the measure of two supplementary angles if the measure of the smaller angle is 32 less than the measure of the larger.   **74, 106**

5. The measure of an angle is one-fifth the measure of its complement. Find the measure of both angles. **15, 75**

ALTERNATE TEACHING STRATEGIES

Using Models

Bring in a carpenter's square (or a T-square) or borrow one from an industrial technology teacher. Show students how carpenters use the tool. Have some students use the tool themselves so they can see how easy it is to draw right angles with it.

Using Manipulatives

Before defining perpendicular lines, have students use a piece of paper and tape to make a cube or rectangular box. Ask them to describe the relationship between the sides of the figure and the base or top of the figure. They may have difficulty finding just the right word. Explain that the word they are looking for is *perpendicular*.

Example 1

CONNECTION
Algebra

If $\overrightarrow{EB} \perp \overrightarrow{EC}$ and $\angle AEC$ and $\angle DEC$ form a linear pair, find $m\angle AEB$ and $m\angle DEC$.

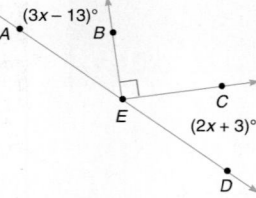

Since $\overrightarrow{EB} \perp \overrightarrow{EC}$, $\angle BEC$ is a right angle. Thus, $m\angle BEC = 90$. Since $\angle AEC$ and $\angle DEC$ form a linear pair, we know from our work in Lesson 1-8 that $m\angle AEC + m\angle DEC = 180$.

We can use the given information and the angle addition postulate to find the value of x.

$$m\angle AEC + m\angle DEC = 180$$
$$(m\angle BEC + m\angle AEB) + m\angle DEC = 180 \quad \text{Angle addition postulate}$$
$$[90 + (3x - 13)] + (2x + 3) = 180 \quad \text{Substitute 90 for } m\angle BEC,$$
$$5x + 80 = 180 \quad \quad 3x - 13 \text{ for } m\angle AEB, \text{ and}$$
$$5x = 100 \quad \quad 2x + 3 \text{ for } m\angle DEC.$$
$$x = 20$$

$$m\angle AEB = 3x - 13 \quad\quad\quad m\angle DEC = 2x + 3$$
$$= 3(20) - 13 \quad\quad\quad\quad = 2(20) + 3$$
$$= 47 \quad\quad\quad\quad\quad\quad = 43$$

CONSTRUCTION

A compass and straightedge can be used to construct a line perpendicular to a given line through a point on the line, *or* through a point not on the line.

Construct a line perpendicular to line ℓ and passing through point T on ℓ.

1. Place the compass at point T. Using the same compass setting, draw arcs to the right and left of T, intersecting line ℓ. Label the points of intersection D and K.

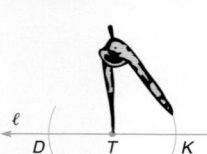

2. Open the compass to a setting greater than DT. Put the compass at point D and draw an arc above line ℓ.

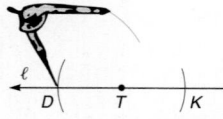

3. Using the same compass setting as in Step 2, place the compass at point K and draw an arc intersecting the arc previously drawn. Label the point of intersection S.

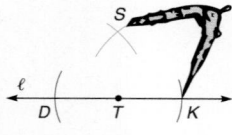

4. Use a straightedge to draw $\overleftrightarrow{ST}$.

$\overleftrightarrow{ST}$ is perpendicular to ℓ at T.

LESSON 1-9 RIGHT ANGLES AND PERPENDICULAR LINES 57

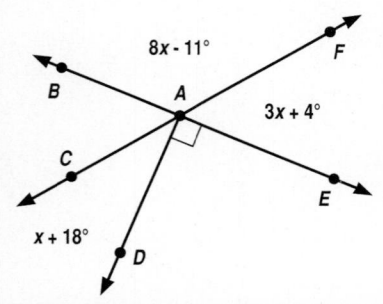

Construct a line perpendicular to line ℓ and passing through point Q *not* on ℓ.

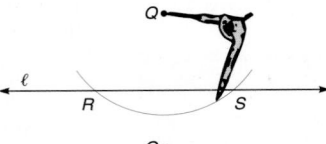

1. Place the compass at point Q. Draw an arc that intersects line ℓ in two different places. Label the points of intersection R and S.

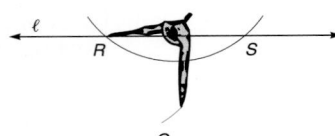

2. Open the compass to a setting greater than $\frac{1}{2}RS$. Put the compass at point R and draw an arc below line ℓ.

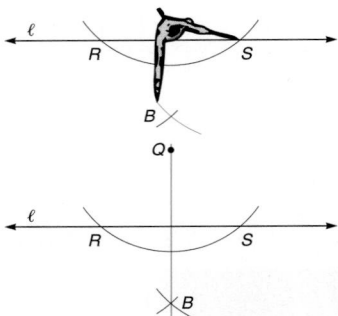

3. Using the same compass setting, place the compass at point S and draw an arc intersecting the arc drawn in Step 2. Label the point of intersection B.

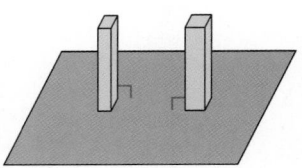

4. Use a straightedge to draw $\overleftrightarrow{QB}$.

$\overleftrightarrow{QB}$ is perpendicular to ℓ.

In the application at the beginning of the lesson, we could have modeled the floor of the home using a plane instead of a line segment, as in the figure at the right. In this case, how could we determine whether the stud is perpendicular to the floor?

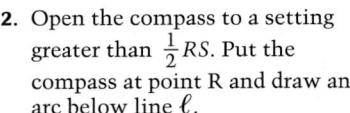

If a stud is perpendicular to the floor, then each side of the stud must be perpendicular to the portion of the floor that it intersects. Similarly, if *a line is perpendicular to a plane*, then the line must be perpendicular to every line in the plane that intersects it. Thus, $\overleftrightarrow{PQ} \perp \mathcal{M}$ and $\overleftrightarrow{PQ}$ must be perpendicular to every line in $\mathcal{M}$ that intersects it.

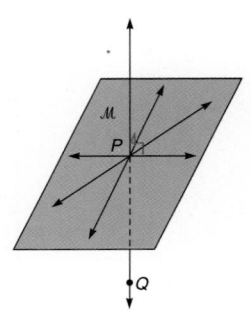

We can also talk about line segments and rays being perpendicular to planes. For example, in the figure, $\overline{PQ} \perp \mathcal{M}$ and $\overrightarrow{PQ} \perp \mathcal{M}$.

In this chapter, figures have been used to help describe or demonstrate different relationships among points, segments, lines, rays, and angles. Whenever you draw a figure, there are certain relationships that can be assumed from the figure and others that cannot be assumed.

Can be Assumed from Figure 1

All points shown are coplanar.

$\overrightarrow{CE}$, $\overrightarrow{DA}$, and $\overrightarrow{DB}$ intersect at D.

C, D, and E are collinear.

D is between C and E.

B is in the interior of $\angle ADE$.

$\angle CDE$ is a straight angle.

$\angle CDA$ and $\angle ADB$ are adjacent angles.

$\angle CDB$ and $\angle BDE$ are a linear pair.

$\angle CDA$ and $\angle ADE$ are supplementary.

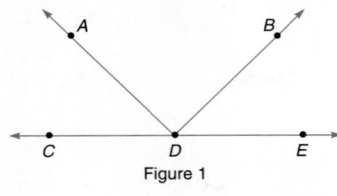

Figure 1

Cannot be Assumed from Figure 1

$\overline{CD} \cong \overline{DE}$

$\angle CDA \cong \angle EDB$

$\overrightarrow{DA} \perp \overrightarrow{DB}$

Figure 2, shown at the right, is marked so that these additional relationships are true.

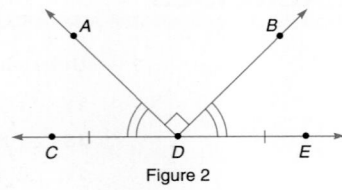

Figure 2

CHECKING FOR UNDERSTANDING

Communicating Mathematics

Read and study the lesson to answer each question.

1. What symbol do we use to indicate that two lines are perpendicular? **1. in words, ⊥; in a diagram ¬**

2. Two lines are perpendicular if they intersect to form a linear pair of angles that are also __?__. **congruent**

3. If line ℓ intersects plane $\mathcal{P}$ at point T and $\ell \perp \mathcal{P}$, what must be true about any line, m, in $\mathcal{P}$ that passes through T? $m \perp \ell$

4. From the figure at the right, can you assume that B is between A and C? that B is the midpoint of $\overline{AC}$? that $AB + BC = AC$? **yes; no; yes**

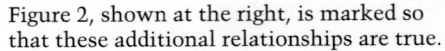

Guided Practice

Refer to the figure at the right to answer each question.

5. Which segment is perpendicular to $\overline{QA}$? $\overline{CQ}$

6. Which angles are complementary to $\angle BQC$? **6. $\angle AQB$ and $\angle CQD$**

7. Is $\angle BQC \cong \angle DQE$? Explain. **yes; See margin.**

8. If $m\angle AQB = 4x - 15$ and $m\angle BQC = 2x + 9$, what is the value of x and $m\angle CQD$? **16; 49**

LESSON 1-9   RIGHT ANGLES AND PERPENDICULAR LINES   59

Additional Answer

7. $\angle BQD$ and $\angle CQE$ are right angles, so m $\angle BQD$ = 90 and m $\angle CQE$ = 90. Therefore m $\angle BQD$ = m $\angle CQE$. m $\angle BQD$ = m $\angle BQC$ + m $\angle CQD$ and m $\angle CQE$ = m $\angle CQD$ + m $\angle DQE$ by the angle addition postulate. By substitution, m $\angle BQC$ + m $\angle CQD$ = m $\angle CQD$ + m $\angle DQE$; m $\angle BQC$ = m $\angle DQE$.

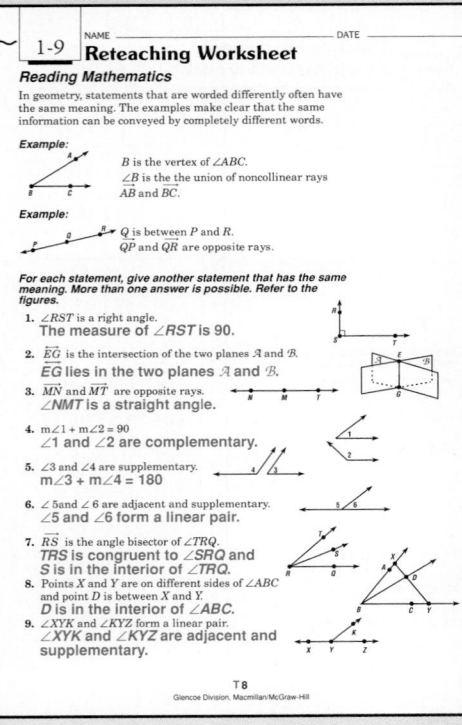

Closing the Lesson

Speaking Activity Have students tell you the steps in constructing a line perpendicular to line *l* that passes through a point on line *l*. Do this by having each student state the next step in the construction. Do the same for the construction of a line perpendicular to line *l* and passing through a point not on *l*.

APPLYING THE LESSON

Homework Exercises

Assignment Guide

Basic: 17-34, 40-47
Average: 20-37, 40-47
Enriched: 23-47

Practice Master Booklet, p. 9

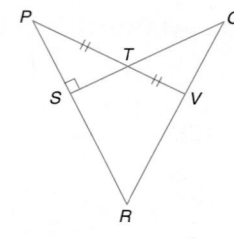

```
        NAME _____ DATE _____
1-9  Practice Worksheet
Right Angles and Perpendicular Lines
For each figure, find the value of x. Then determine if AB ⊥ CD.
1.                          2.

   5, no                      10, yes

3.                          4.

   8, yes                     27, no

Determine whether each relationship can be assumed from
the figure. Write yes or no.
5. ∠BFE is a right angle.  no

6. AD ⊥ AC  yes

7. ED ≅ EC  no

8. F bisects AB.  no

9. ∠AEF and ∠BEF are congruent.  no

10. AC = AE + EC  yes

11. BC ⊥ BD  no

12. ∠AED ≅ ∠BEC  yes

                T9
     Glencoe Division, Macmillan/McGraw-Hill
```

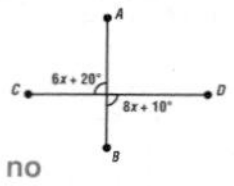

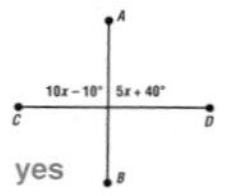

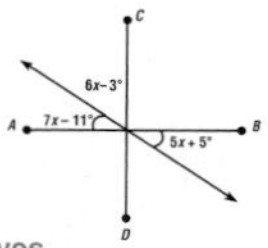

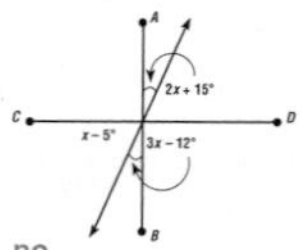

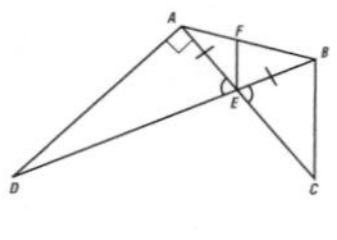

Determine whether each relationship can be assumed from the figure.

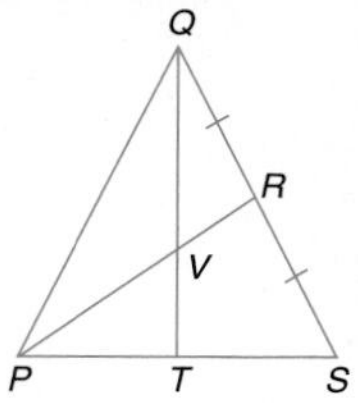

9. *V* is between *Q* and *T*. **yes**
10. $\overrightarrow{PR}$ bisects $\angle QPS$. **no**
11. $PT = TS$ **no**
12. $\overrightarrow{PR}$ bisects $\overline{QS}$. **yes**
13. $\overline{QT} \perp \overline{PS}$ **no**
14. $\angle QRV$ is a right angle. **no**
15. $\angle QVP$ and $\angle QVR$ form a linear pair. **yes**

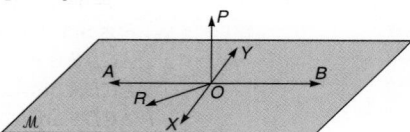

16. In the figure at the right, $\overrightarrow{OP} \perp \mathcal{M}$ and $\overrightarrow{AB} \perp \overrightarrow{XY}$. How many right angles are in this figure? **9**

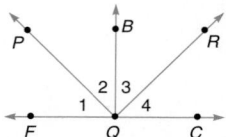

EXERCISES

Practice

A

Determine if the given information is enough to conclude that $\overrightarrow{QP} \perp \overrightarrow{QR}$.

17. $\angle 1$ and $\angle 3$ are complementary. **no**
18. $\angle 1$ and $\angle 4$ are complementary. **yes**
19. $\angle 2 \cong \angle 3$ **no**
20. $\angle 1 \cong \angle 4$ **no**
21. $m\angle 1 + m\angle 4 = m\angle 2 + m\angle 3$ **yes**
22. $m\angle 1 + m\angle 2 = m\angle 3 + m\angle 4$ **no**
23. $\angle 1 \cong \angle 2$ and $\angle 3 \cong \angle 4$ **yes**

B

For each figure, find the value of *x* and determine if $\overline{AB} \perp \overline{CD}$.

24.   25.   26.

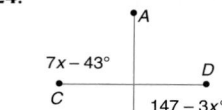 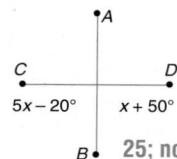 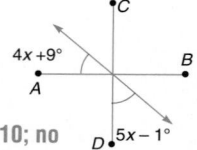

19; yes   **25; no**   **10; no**

Determine whether each relationship can be assumed from the figure.

27. $\angle QVT$ is a right angle. **no**
28. $\overline{QR} \perp \overline{PV}$ **no**
29. *T* is the midpoint of $\overline{PV}$. **yes**
30. $\overline{PV}$ bisects $\overline{QS}$. **no**
31. $\angle SPT$ and $\angle VQT$ are congruent. **no**
32. $PS = QV$ **no**
33. $PV = TV + PT$ **yes**
34. $\angle STP \cong \angle VTQ$ **yes**

60   CHAPTER 1   THE LANGUAGE OF GEOMETRY

35. Draw $\overleftrightarrow{PR}$. Construct line ℓ perpendicular to $\overleftrightarrow{PR}$ through P and line m perpendicular to $\overleftrightarrow{PR}$ through R. Now, locate point S on line m so that $RS = RP$. Finally, construct line k perpendicular to ℓ through S. What figure have you constructed? **a square**

36. $\overleftrightarrow{AB}$ and $\overleftrightarrow{CD}$ intersect at E. F lies in the interior of $\angle CEA$ and G lies in the interior of $\angle AED$. Also, $\angle CEA$ and $\angle FEG$ are right angles. Find $m\angle FEA$ if $m\angle CEF = 3x - 24$ and $m\angle AEG = 2x + 10$. **12**

37. $\overleftrightarrow{AB}$ and $\overleftrightarrow{CD}$ intersect at Q and R is in the interior of $\angle AQC$. If $m\angle DQA = 2x - y$, $m\angle AQR = x$ and $m\angle RQC = y$, find the values of x and y so that $\overleftrightarrow{AB} \perp \overleftrightarrow{CD}$. **$x = 60$, $y = 30$**

38. Find $m\angle BPC$ in the figure if $\overline{AC} \perp \overline{BC}$, $m\angle APC = 7x + 3$, $m\angle BPC = 16y$, $m\angle ACP = 3x + 2y$, and $m\angle BCP = 3x + 4y$. **128**

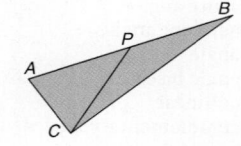

39. Find the values of x and y if $\overleftrightarrow{AB} \perp \overleftrightarrow{MN}$ and $\mathcal{L}$ contains $\overleftrightarrow{MN}$, $m\angle MTB = 2x + 6y$, $m\angle ATN = 4x + 3y$, and $m\angle BTN = \frac{8}{3}x + 5y$. **$x = 15$, $y = 10$**

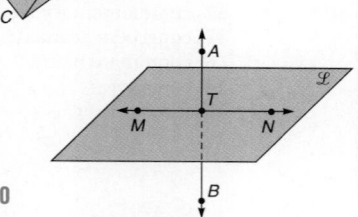

Critical Thinking

40. Given a line in a plane and a point on that line, explain why there is exactly one line in the plane perpendicular to the given line through the given point. **See margin.**

Application

41. **Framing** The corner of a frame for a painting is made by joining two pieces of wood so that they are perpendicular, as shown at the right. If $\angle 1$ is a 45° angle, what must be the measure of $\angle 2$? **45**

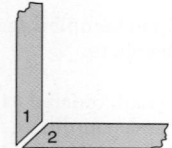

Mixed Review

Refer to the figure to answer each question.

42. If $AB = 2x - 3$, $BC = 3x + 13$, and $AC = 30$, find the value of x. **(Lesson 1-4) 4**

43. Name all the bisectors of $\overline{BE}$. **(Lesson 1-5)**

43. $\overline{CF}$, $\overline{AD}$, $\overline{AF}$, $\overline{FD}$, F

44. What angles have $\overrightarrow{CE}$ as a side? **(Lesson 1-6)**

44. $\angle ACE$, $\angle FCE$, $\angle CEB$

45. If $m\angle BCF = 5x + 11$, $m\angle FCD = 3x + 23$, for what value of x does $\overrightarrow{CF}$ bisect $\angle ACE$? **(Lesson 1-7) $x = 6$**

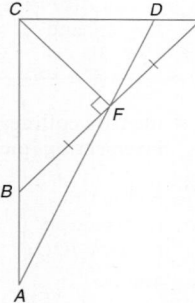

46. If $m\angle AFB = d + 10$ and $m\angle CFD = 6d - 11$, find $m\angle DFE$. **(Lesson 1-8) 23**

Wrap-Up

47. Based on your homework and classroom discussions, what concepts from this lesson do you think should appear on a chapter test? **See students' work.**

LESSON 1-9   RIGHT ANGLES AND PERPENDICULAR LINES   61

EXTENDING THE LESSON

Math Power: Problem Solving

Have students work in cooperative groups to find the sum of the measures of the angles inside a square or rectangle. Have them draw a square or rectangle by constructing perpendicular lines. Then have them find the measures of the angles inside and add them. Will this work for every square or rectangle? **Yes.** Have them explain why.

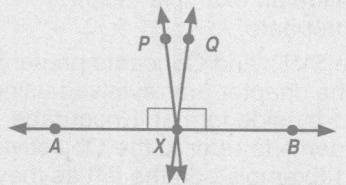
Enrichment Masters Booklet, p. 8

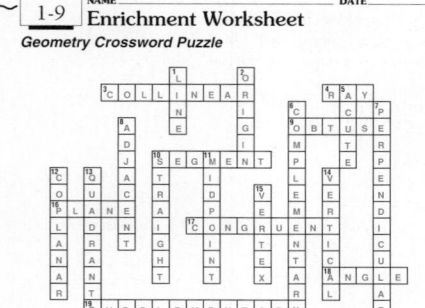

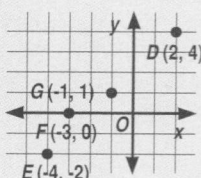

VOCABULARY

Upon completing this chapter, you should be familiar with the following terms:

44	acute angles	13	line	8	quadrants
50	adjacent angles	50	linear pair	36	ray
36	angle	30	midpoint	44	right angle
45	angle bisector	44	obtuse angle	23	segment
9	collinear	36	opposite rays	31	segment bisector
52	complementary angles	9	ordered pair	37	straight angle
32	congruent segments	8	origin	51	supplementary angles
8	coordinate plane	56	perpendicular lines	50	vertical angles
14	coplanar	13	plane	8	x- and y-axes
14	intersection	13	point	8	x- and y-coordinates

SKILLS AND CONCEPTS

OBJECTIVES AND EXAMPLES	REVIEW EXERCISES

Upon completing this chapter, you should be able to:

Use these exercises to review and prepare for the chapter test.

■ graph ordered pairs on a coordinate plane. **(Lesson 1-1)**

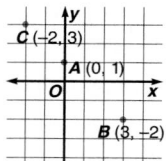

Graph A(0, 1), B(3, -2), and C(-2, 3).

Graph each point. See margin.

1. $D(2, 4)$ 2. $E(-4, -2)$

3. $F(-3, 0)$ 4. $G(-1, 1)$

5. If $x > 0$ and $y < 0$, in which quadrant is the point $P(x, y)$ located? **Quadrant IV**

■ identify collinear and coplanar points and intersecting lines and planes. **(Lesson 1-2)**

Name the intersection of plane JDC and $\overleftrightarrow{FG}$.

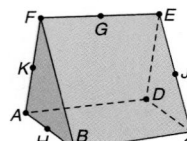

Point E

Refer to the figure at the left to answer each question.

6. Are E, A, K, and G coplanar? **yes**

7. What points do plane BCEF and $\overline{ED}$ have in common? **point E**

8. What three lines intersect at D? $\overleftrightarrow{ED}$, $\overleftrightarrow{AD}$, and $\overleftrightarrow{CD}$

■ find the distance between points on a number line. **(Lesson 1-4)**

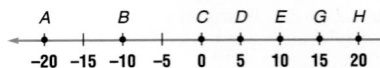

What is the distance between A and E?

$$AE = |-20 - 10|$$
$$= |-30|$$
$$= 30$$

Refer to the number line at the left to answer each question.

9. Find the distance between A and G. 35

10. Find the distance between E and B. 20

11. Which point(s) is 10 units from point E?
    C and H

■ Find the midpoint of a segment. **(Lesson 1-5)**

For the number line above, which segments have D as the midpoint?

Since CD = DE and BD = DH, D is the midpoint of $\overline{CE}$ and of $\overline{BH}$.

12. Refer to the number line above to find the coordinate of the midpoint of $\overline{AG}$. $-\frac{5}{2}$

13. **Algebra**   Find the midpoint of $\overline{XY}$ given points X(-2, 7) and Y(8, 1). (3, 4)

14. **Algebra**   If Q is the midpoint of $\overline{PR}$, PQ = x + 6, and PR = 5x − 3, find QR. 11

■ identify and use congruent segments. **(Lesson 1-5)**

For the number line above, which segments are congruent to $\overline{CG}$?

$CG = |15 - 0|$ or 15

Since $BD = |5 - (-10)|$ or 15, $\overline{BD} \cong \overline{CG}$.
Since $DH = |20 - 5|$ or 15, $\overline{DH} \cong \overline{CG}$.

15. If GH = 17 and the coordinate of J is 3, find the coordinate of K if $\overline{JK} \cong \overline{GH}$.
    −14 or 20

If AB = 8x − 7, BC = 4x + 9, and AC = 13x − 2, answer each question.

16. For what value of x are $\overline{AB}$ and $\overline{BC}$ congruent? x = 4

17. If A, B, and C are collinear and $\overline{AB} \cong \overline{BC}$, is B the midpoint of $\overline{AC}$? yes

---

■ use angle addition to find the measures of angles. **(Lesson 1-6)**

In the figure, if m∠PXR = 125, m∠1 = 40 − x, and m∠2 = 2x + 70, find the value of x.

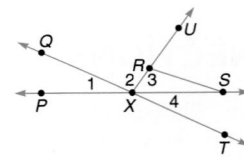

$$m\angle 1 + m\angle 2 = m\angle PXR$$
$$(40 - x) + (2x + 70) = 125$$
$$x = 15$$

Refer to the figure at the left to answer each question.

18. If m∠1 = 37, find m∠QXS. 143

19. If m∠2 = 3x − 20, m∠3 = 3x − 19, and m∠QXS = 147, find the value of x. 31

20. If m∠3 = 77 − x, m∠4 = 2x + 7, and m∠RXT = 3x, find m∠3 and m∠4.
    35; 91

A 2-page Cumulative Review from the *Evaluation Masters* is shown below. It can be used to review skills and concepts presented thus far in the text. Standardized Test Practice Questions are also provided in the *Evaluation Masters*.

Evaluation Masters, pp. 11-12

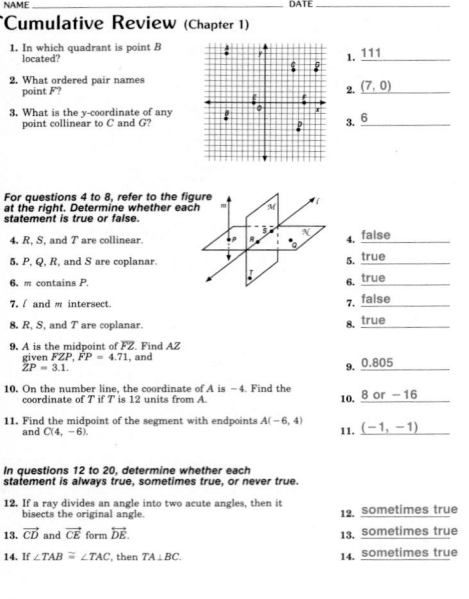

NAME _____ DATE _____

Cumulative Review (Chapter 1)

1. In which quadrant is point B located?   **1.** 111
2. What ordered pair names point F?   **2.** (7, 0)
3. What is the y-coordinate of any point collinear to C and G?   **3.** 6

For questions 4 to 8, refer to the figure at the right. Determine whether each statement is true or false.

4. R, S, and T are collinear.   **4.** false
5. P, Q, R, and S are coplanar.   **5.** true
6. m contains P.   **6.** true
7. ℓ and m intersect.   **7.** false
8. R, S, and T are coplanar.   **8.** true
9. A is the midpoint of FZ. Find AZ given FZP, FP = 4.71, and ZP = 3.1.   **9.** 0.805
10. On the number line, the coordinate of A is −4. Find the coordinate of T if T is 12 units from A.   **10.** 8 or −16
11. Find the midpoint of the segment with endpoints A(−6, 4) and C(4, −6).   **11.** (−1, −1)

In questions 12 to 20, determine whether each statement is always true, sometimes true, or never true.

12. If a ray divides an angle into two acute angles, then it bisects the original angle.   **12.** sometimes true
13. CD and CE form DE.   **13.** sometimes true
14. If ∠TAB ≅ ∠TAC, then TA⊥BC.   **14.** sometimes true

11
Glencoe Division, MacMillan/McGraw-Hill

NAME _____ DATE _____

Cumulative Review (Chapter 1 continued)

15. If two adjacent congruent angles have measures of 2x + 40 and 3x + 15, then each is a right angle.   **15.** always true
16. If two angles form a linear pair, then they are supplementary.   **16.** always true
17. An obtuse angle has a supplement but no complement.   **17.** always true
18. If an angle is acute, then the complement of the supplement is an obtuse angle.   **18.** never true
19. Two acute angles are complementary.   **19.** sometimes true
20. Every angle has a supplement.   **20.** always true

For questions 21 to 26, refer to the figure at the below.

21. Name the sides of ∠1.   **21.** ED and EC
22. Name a point in the interior of ∠DEB.   **22.** C
23. Name an angle adjacent to ∠AEB.   **23.** ∠BEC or ∠BED
24. If m∠AEB = 75 and m∠AEC = 100, find m∠BEC.   **24.** 25
25. If EB bisects ∠AED and m∠DEB = 61, find m∠AED.   **25.** 122
26. If EB bisects ∠AED, EC bisects ∠BED, and m∠BEC = 30, find m∠AEC.   **26.** 90
27. Find the value of y.   **27.** y = 40

For questions 28 and 29, refer to the figure at the right.

28. Find m∠2 if ∠1 and ∠2 are complementary and m∠1 = 40.   **28.** 50
29. Find the value of x if m∠1 = 4x − 3 and m∠2 = x + 8.   **29.** x = 17

12
Glencoe Division, MacMillan/McGraw-Hill

OBJECTIVES AND EXAMPLES	REVIEW EXERCISES

- identify and use congruent angles and the bisector of an angle. **(Lesson 1-7)**

  In the figure for exercises 18-20, if $m\angle 4 = m\angle 1$, $\overrightarrow{XR}$ bisects $\angle QXS$, and $\overrightarrow{XS}$ bisects $\angle TXR$, does $\overrightarrow{XQ}$ bisect $\angle PXR$?

  Since $\overrightarrow{XR}$ bisects $\angle QXS$, $m\angle 2 = m\angle 3$.
  Since $\overrightarrow{XS}$ bisects $\angle TXR$, $m\angle 3 = m\angle 4$.
  Thus, $m\angle 2 = m\angle 1$ and $\overrightarrow{XQ}$ bisects $\angle PXR$.

Refer to the figure for exercises 18-20 to answer each question.

21. If $\angle 2 \cong \angle 3$, is any angle bisected? If so, which one? **yes; ∠QXS**
22. If $\overrightarrow{QX}$ bisects $\angle PXR$, $m\angle 1 = 6x - 7$, and $m\angle 2 = 9x - 31$, find $m\angle PXR$. **82**
23. If $\angle A \cong \angle B$, $m\angle A = 3n + 55$, and $m\angle B = 8n$, is $\angle B$ acute or obtuse? **acute**

- identify and use adjacent angles, vertical angles, complementary angles, supplementary angles, and linear pairs of angles. **(Lesson 1-8)**

  vertical angles:
  $\angle 1$ and $\angle 5$:
  $\angle ANF$ and
  $\angle BNE$
  congruent
  adjacent angles:
  $\angle BND$ and
  $\angle DNF$

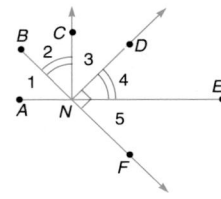

Refer to the figure at the left to name the following pairs of angles. 25, 26. See margin.

24. adjacent complementary angles ∠5, ∠4 or ∠2, ∠3
25. linear pair of angles that includes $\angle 5$
26. supplementary angles that includes $\angle 2$
27. **Algebra** The measure of an angle is 10 less than three times the measure of its complement. Find the measure of both angles. **65, 25**

- identify and use right angles and perpendicular lines. **(Lesson 1-9)**

  In the figure above, is $\overline{AE} \perp \overline{CN}$?

  $\angle 4$ and $\angle 5$ are complementary. Since $\angle 1$ and $\angle 5$ are vertical angles, $\angle 1 \cong \angle 5$. Since $\angle 2 \cong \angle 4$, $\angle 1$ and $\angle 2$ are complementary. Thus, $\overline{AE} \perp \overline{CN}$.

28. In the figure above, if $m\angle 4 = 2x - 1$ and $m\angle 5 = 3x - 4$, find $m\angle 1$. **53**
29. In the figure above, could you conclude that $\overline{AE} \perp \overline{CN}$ if $\angle 1$ was congruent to $\angle 4$ and $\angle 2$ was *not* congruent to $\angle 4$? **no**
30. $\angle J$ and $\angle K$ are vertical angles. Are $\angle J$ and $\angle K$ right angles if $m\angle J = 20x - 11$ and $m\angle K = 13x + 24$? **no**

APPLICATIONS AND CONNECTIONS

31. **Statistics** The weekly geometry quiz in Mrs. Lao's class consists of 5 true-false questions. Is it possible for each of her 33 students to have a different pattern of answers? **(Lesson 1-3)** no, since there are only 32 different patterns
32. **Aviation** The path of an airplane is described as 56° east of north. Draw a diagram that represents this flight path. **(Lesson 1-5)** See margin.

Additional Answers

25. Sample answer: ∠FNA and ∠5
26. ∠CNF and ∠2

32.

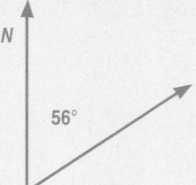

Draw and label a figure for each relationship. See Solutions Manual.

1. Lines ℓ, m, and n all intersect at point X.　　2. Planes $\mathcal{Q}$ and $\mathcal{R}$ do not intersect.

3. Plane $\mathcal{P}$ contains point A but does not contain $\overleftrightarrow{BC}$.

4. Graph $A(4, 3)$, $B(-2, -5)$, $C(-3, 4)$, and $D(0, -1)$ on a coordinate plane. See Solutions Manual.

Refer to the coordinate grid to answer each question.

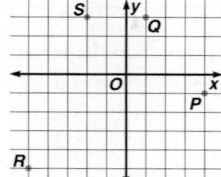

5. What ordered pair names point S? **(-2, 3)**
6. What is the length of $\overline{PQ}$? **5 units**
7. What are the coordinates of the midpoint of $\overline{QR}$? **(-2, -1)**
8. What is the y-coordinate of any point collinear to Q and S? **3**

Refer to the number line to answer each question.

9. What is the measure of $\overline{AC}$? **6**
10. What is the coordinate of the midpoint of $\overline{CF}$? **3**
11. What segment is congruent to $\overline{BF}$? **$\overline{AD}$**
12. What is the coordinate of G if C is between D and G and $DG = 14$? **-10**

Refer to the figure at the right to answer each question. 16. Sample answers: $\angle 3$ and $\angle 4$, $\angle 4$ and $\angle VCE$, $\angle VCE$ and $\angle VCA$, $\angle VCA$ and $\angle 3$

13. Name two points on line ℓ. **A, C, E**
14. Name the sides of $\angle 1$. **$\overrightarrow{VA}$ and $\overrightarrow{VC}$**
15. Which of the numbered angles appears to be obtuse? **$\angle 7$**
16. Name a pair of congruent supplementary angles.
17. Name a pair of adjacent angles that do not form a linear pair. **Sample answers: $\angle 6$ and $\angle 5$, $\angle 5$ and $\angle 2$, $\angle 2$ and $\angle 1$**
18. If $\angle 1 \cong \angle 5$, does $\overrightarrow{VG}$ bisect $\angle BVF$? **yes**
19. *True or false*: $\overline{VB} \perp \overline{VF}$ **False**
20. *True or false*: $\overline{CG}$ bisects $\overline{AE}$. **True**
21. If $AC = 4x + 1$ and $CE = 16 - x$, find AE. **26**
22. If $m\angle BVF = 7x - 1$ and $m\angle FVA = 6x + 12$, is $\overleftrightarrow{AB} \perp \overrightarrow{VF}$? **yes**
23. Which two angles must be complementary if $\angle AVF$ is a right angle? **$\angle 5$ and $\angle 6$ or $\angle 5$ and $\angle 1$**
24. If $m\angle 5 = 3x + 14$, $m\angle 6 = x + 30$, and $m\angle FVB = 9x - 11$, find $m\angle FVB$. **88**

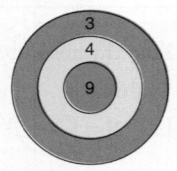

25. **Sports** Three darts are thrown at the target shown at the right. If we assume that each of the darts lands within one of the rings, how many different point totals are possible? **10**

Bonus $P(-8, 11)$ and $Q(16, 1)$ are the endpoints of a diameter of a circle. Find the coordinates of the center of the circle and two other points on the circle. **center: (4, 6); possible points: (9, 18), (-1, -6), (-8, 1), (16, 11)**

Test and Review Generator software is provided in Apple, IBM, and Macintosh versions. You may use this software to create your own tests or worksheets, based on the needs of your students.

The **Performance Assessment Booklet** provides an alternate assessment for evaluating student progress. An assessment for this chapter can be found on pages 1–2.

Using the Chapter Test

This page may be used as a test or as a review. In addition, two multiple-choice tests (Forms 1A and 1B) and two free-response tests (Forms 2A and 2B) are provided in the *Evaluation Masters*. Chapter 1 Test, Form 1A is shown below.

Evaluation Masters, pp. 1-2

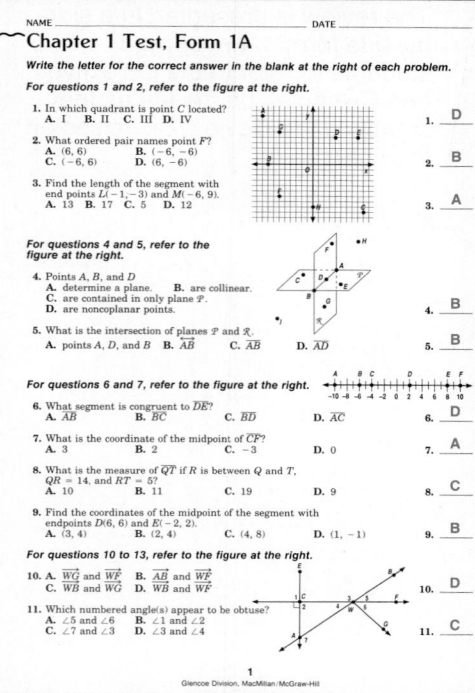

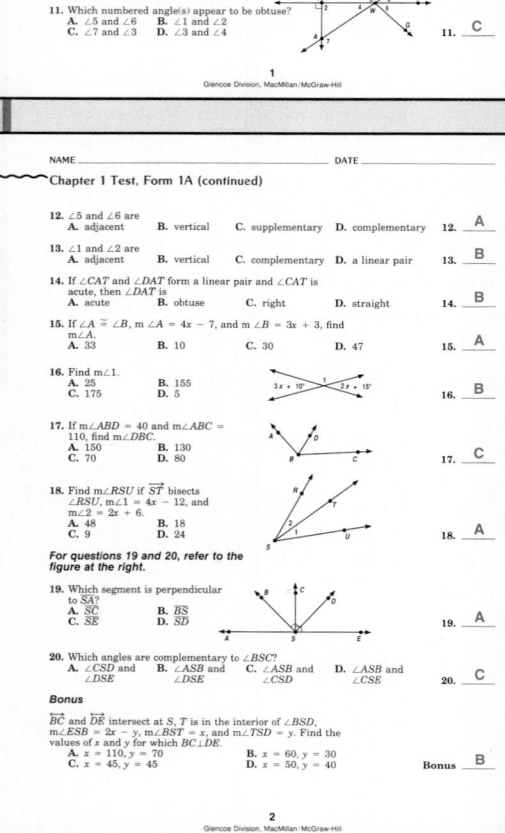

Using the Algebra Review

The goal of this two-page review of algebraic skills, concepts, and applications is as follows:

- It provides students a chance to review important concepts from algebra that will be useful as they study geometry.

- It gives students an opportunity to retain the concepts they learned in previous algebra courses and may need for future mathematics courses.

The review is presented in a side-by-side format. Encourage students to refer to the Objectives and Examples on the left as they complete the Review Exercises on the right.

OBJECTIVES AND EXAMPLES	REVIEW EXERCISES

■ Add or subtract rational numbers.

$-14 + 3 = -11 \qquad -14 - 3 = -17$

$2.3 + (-3.52) = -1.22$

$\frac{3}{4} - \left(-\frac{7}{10}\right) = \frac{15}{20} + \frac{14}{20} = \frac{29}{20}$

Find each sum or difference. 4. 4.931

1. $17 + (-9)$ **8**
2. $-7 + (-13)$ **−20**
3. $2.4 - 3.7$ **−1.3**
4. $-3.72 - (-8.651)$
5. $\frac{5}{4} + \left(-\frac{7}{8}\right)$ **$\frac{3}{8}$**
6. $-\frac{6}{5} - \frac{11}{12}$ **$-\frac{127}{60}$**

■ Use order of operations to evaluate expressions.

Evaluate $(2x + 3y) \div z^2 - 3$ if $x = 5$, $y = 6$, and $z = 2$.

$(2x + 3y) \div z^2 - 3$
$= (2 \cdot 5 + 3 \cdot 6) \div (2)^2 - 3$
$= (10 + 18) \div 4 - 3$
$= 28 \div 4 - 3$
$= 7 - 3$
$= 4$

Evaluate each expression if $a = 18$, $b = 3$, $c = 4$, and $d = 5$.

7. $a - b \cdot c + d$ **11**
8. $a - (b \cdot c + d)$ **1**
9. $a - b \cdot (c + d)$ **−9**
10. $(a - b) \cdot c + d$ **65**
11. $(a - b) \cdot (c + d)$ **135**

■ Use the distributive property to simplify expressions.

$2x - 5xy + 6x = 2x + 6x - 5xy$
$\qquad = (2 + 6)x - 5xy$
$\qquad = 8x - 5xy$

14. $-mn - 6m^2 + 6n^2$

Simplify each expression.

12. $6x + 7y + 8x - 2y$ **$14x + 5y$**
13. $9(r - s) + 4s$ **$9r - 5s$**
14. $3m(n - 2m) - 2n(2m - 3n)$
15. $\frac{3a^2}{4} + \frac{2ab}{3} + ab - a^2$ **$\frac{5ab}{3} - \frac{a^2}{4}$**

■ Multiply or divide rational numbers.

$-\frac{4}{5} \cdot \frac{7}{2} = -\frac{28}{10} \qquad -\frac{4}{5} \div \frac{7}{2} = -\frac{4}{5} \cdot \frac{2}{7}$

$\qquad = -\frac{14}{5} \qquad\qquad\qquad = -\frac{8}{35}$

Simplify.

16. $-\frac{10}{7}\left(-\frac{5}{9}\right)$ **$\frac{50}{63}$**
17. $-\frac{10}{7} \div \left(-\frac{5}{9}\right)$ **$\frac{18}{7}$**
18. $\frac{33a - 66}{-11}$ **$-3a + 6$**
19. $-3\left(-\frac{7}{4}a + \frac{1}{6}\right) + \frac{5}{2}\left(3 - \frac{a}{2}\right)$ **$4a + 7$**

■ Find the absolute value of a number.

Evaluate $|n - 2|$ if $n = -3$.

$|n - 2| = |-3 - 2|$
$\qquad = |-5|$
$\qquad = 5$

Evaluate each expression.

20. $|4 - x|$, if $x = -2$ **6**
21. $|a| - |2b|$, if $a = -5$ and $b = 1$ **3**
22. $-|m + n|$, if $m = 3$ and $n = -12$ **−9**

OBJECTIVES AND EXAMPLES	REVIEW EXERCISES

■ Translate verbal sentences into equations.

Write an equation for the sentence *The sum of x and the square of y is equal to twice z.*

$$x + y^2 = 2z$$

Write an equation for each sentence.

23. Twelve decreased by the square of a is equal to b. $12 - a^2 = b$

24. The number c equals the cube of the sum of 2 and three times m. $c = (2 + 3m)^3$

25. The product of x and the square of y is t. $xy^2 = t$

■ Solve equations by using addition or subtraction.

$$x - 3 = 5 \qquad q + 9 = 2$$
$$x - 3 + 3 = 5 + 3 \qquad q + 9 - 9 = 2 - 9$$
$$x = 8 \qquad q = -7$$

Solve each equation. Check your solution.

26. $x - 16 = 37$ **53**   27. $z + 15 = -9$ **-24**

28. $r - (-4) = 21$ **17**   29. $m + (-5) = 17$ **22**

30. $-19 = -8 + d$ **-11**   31. $9 = 18 + d$ **-9**

■ Solve equations by using multiplication or division.

$$14x = 42 \qquad \frac{m}{-6} = 8$$
$$\frac{14x}{14} = \frac{42}{14} \qquad \frac{-6m}{-6} = -6(8)$$
$$x = 3 \qquad m = -48$$

Solve each equation. Check your solution.

32. $-7r = -56$ **8**   33. $23y = 103.5$ **4.5**

34. $-534 = 89a$ **-6**   35. $\frac{x}{5} = 7$ **35**

36. $-\frac{3}{4}n = 12$ **-16**   37. $\frac{-5}{3}z = -\frac{3}{2}$ **$\frac{9}{10}$**

Applications and Connections

38. **Foods** There are 113 calories in one cup of orange juice. Write an equation to represent the number of calories in 3 cups of orange juice. Then solve the equation. $c = 3(113);$ **339**

39. **Riding** Alma rides her bicycle for three fourths of an hour every day. Find the distance she rides if she averages 13.65 miles per hour. **10.2375 miles**

40. **Golfing** Jessica's golf score was 68. This was 4 less than Mark's golf score. What was Mark's score? **72**

41. **Smart Shopping** Which is the better buy: 0.75 liters of soft drink for 89¢ or 1.25 liters of soft drink for $1.31? **1.25 liters**

2 Reasoning and Introduction to Proof

PREVIEWING THE CHAPTER

This chapter leads the students from the concepts of inductive and deductive reasoning to the presentation of formal, two-column proofs. Students begin by using inductive reasoning to make conjectures, determining whether conjectures are true or false, and finding counterexamples. Next, they identify if-then statements, converses, and postulates about lines, points, and planes. Then, students use two laws of deductive reasoning, detachment and syllogism. The properties of equality are presented and students use them to justify certain statements in algebraic proofs. Finally, students justify steps in and construct their own two-column proofs and are introduced to theorems. The geometric concepts explored involve congruence of segments and angles, as well as supplementary, complementary, and vertical angles.

Problem-Solving Strategy Students learn to solve problems that involve several clues by using a systematic process of elimination.

Lesson Objective Chart

Lesson (Pages)	Lesson Objectives	State/Local Objectives
2-1 (70-74)	**2-1**: Make geometric conjectures based on inductive reasoning.	
2-2 (76-81)	**2-2A**: Identify the hypothesis and conclusion of an "if-then" statement.	
	2-2B: Write the converse of an "if-then" statement.	
	2-2C: Identify and use basic postulates about points, lines, and planes.	
2-3 (82-87)	**2-3**: Use the law of detachment and the law of syllogism in deductive reasoning.	
2-4 (88-94)	**2-4**: Use properties of equality in algebraic and geometric proofs.	
2-5 (95-97)	**2-5**: Solve problems by eliminating possibilities.	
2-6 (98-104)	**2-6**: Complete proofs involving segment theorems.	
2-7 (105-109)	**2-7**: Complete proofs involving angle theorems.	

ORGANIZING THE CHAPTER

You may want to refer to the **Course Planning Calendar** on page T28.

Lesson Planning Guide

Blackline Masters Booklets

Lesson (Pages)	Pacing Chart (days) Course I	II	III	Reteaching	Practice	Enrichment	Evaluation	Technology	Lab Manual	Activities Mixed Problem Solving	Applications	Cooperative Learning Activity	Multicultural	Transparencies
2-1 (70-74)	1.5	1.5	1.5	p. 9	p. 10	p. 9		p. 2						2-1
2-2 (76-81)	1.5	1.5	1.5	p. 10	p. 11	p. 10	Quiz A, p. 23	p. 38	pp.30-33		p. 16			2-2
2-3 (82-87)	2	2	1.5	p. 11	p. 12	p. 11								2-3
2-4 (88-94)	2	2	1.5	p. 12	p. 13	p. 12	Quiz B, p. 23 Mid-Chapter Test, p. 27					p. 30		2-4
2-5 (95-97)	1	1	1		p. 14					p. 2				2-5
2-6 (98-104)	2	2	2	p. 13	p. 15	p. 13	Quiz C, p. 24							2-6
2-7 (105-109)	2	1	1	p. 14	p. 16	p. 14	Quiz D, p. 24						p. 2	2-7
Review (110-112)	1	1	1	Multiple Choice Tests, Forms 1A and 1B, pp. 15-18 Free Response Tests, Forms 2A and 2B, pp. 19-22										
Test (113)	1	1	1	Cumulative Review. pp. 25-26 Standardized Tests Practice Questions, p. 28										

Course I: Chapters 1-11; Course II: Chapters 1-12; Course III: Chapters 1-13

Other Chapter Resources

Student Edition

Chapter Opener, pp. 68-69
History Connection, p. 74
Journal Entry, pp. 74, 109
Technology, p. 75
Mid-Chapter Review, p. 94
Cooperative Learning Project, p. 97
Portfolio, p. 103
College Entrance Exam Preview, pp. 114-115
Extended Project 1, pp. B2-B5

Teacher's Classroom Resources

Transparency 2-0
Real World Applications Transparencies, 3, 4
Performance Assessment Booklet, pp. 3-4
Problem-of-the-Week Activity Cards, 4, 5, 6
Tech Prep Applications Booklet, pp. 3-4

Other Supplements

Flow Proof and Indirect Proof
Glencoe Mathematics Professional Series

Software

Test and Review Generator (Apple, IBM, and Macintosh)
Teacher's Guide for Software Resources

ENHANCING THE CHAPTER

Cooperative Learning

Deciding on the Size of Groups and Assigning Students to the Groups

Considerable research indicates that, for most schools, six is the maximum number of students to assign to a cooperative-learning group. A large group of this size provides more opportunities to have members with different cooperative-learning skills to be helpful to the whole group. It can also decrease the time required to do the assigned task since there are more members with more talents to do the work. However, because group skills must be learned by students, few may have the skills required for a group of this size. Therefore, if your students lack these skills, it is advisable to begin with groups of no more than two or three students each.

Research indicates that a heterogeneous group will allow for a more effective cooperative-learning situation than will a homogeneous group. Therefore, it is inadvisable to allow students to choose their own groups. A more desirable method would be to randomly assign students by having them count off. A better method is to form groups so that each group has members of varying levels of ability.

Technology

The Technology Feature following Lesson 2-1 employs the *Geometric Supposer* software from Sunburst. This software package provides an environment in which your students can explore geometric concepts. The feature focuses on using the *Supposer* to draw and investigate many different quadrilaterals. Students use a chart to record their findings about the quadrilaterals they draw and are then asked to analyze the data.

A *Geometric Supposer Correlation* that correlates the worksheets found in the *Geometric Supposer* package with the student lessons in Merrill Geometry can be found on pages 14-18 in the *Merrill Geometry Technology Masters.* You may wish to use this correlation to assign further work with the *Supposer.*

Critical Thinking

Identifying and extending patterns is not only a useful strategy for solving problems but also a strategy that is valuable for discovering and mastering new mathematical content. Students should be encouraged to examine patterns, make conjectures about general properties based on their observations, and verify their conjectures. Have students suggest possible pairs, such as arm length and shoe size or height and hand span, where data can be collected and plotted, a prediction equation proposed and drawn, and the results confirmed or rejected by collecting additional data.

Cooperative Learning, p. 30

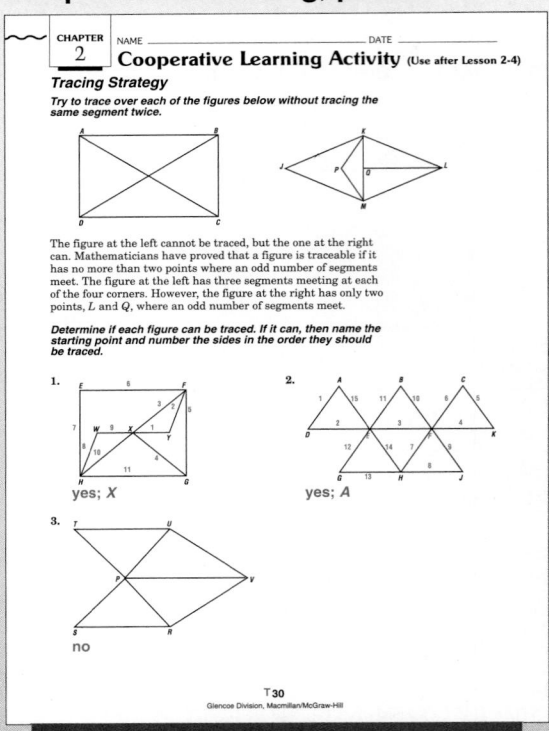

Technology, p. 2

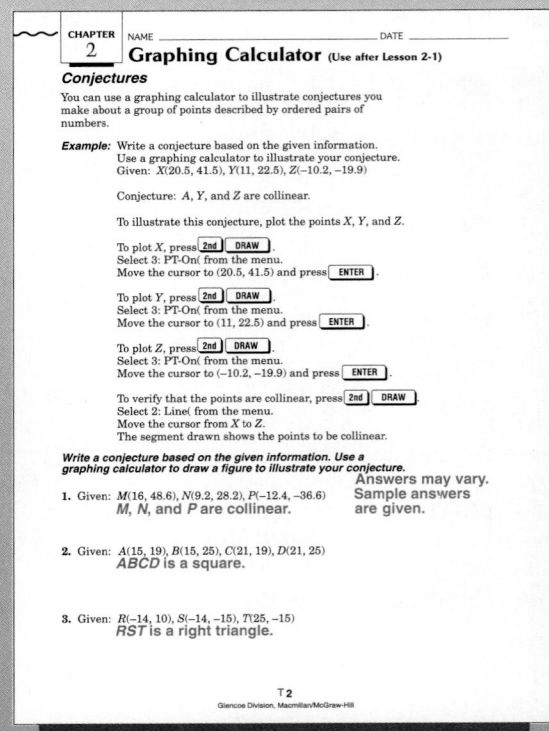

Problem of the Week Activity

The card shown below is one of three available for this chapter. It can be used as a class or small group activity.

Activity Card

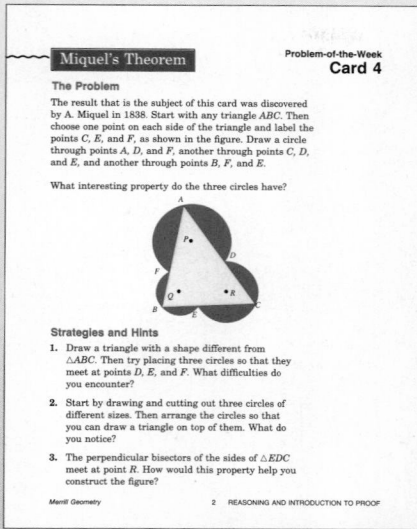

Miquel's Theorem

Problem-of-the-Week
Card 4

The Problem

The result that is the subject of this card was discovered by A. Miquel in 1838. Start with any triangle *ABC*. Then choose one point on each side of the triangle and label the points *C*, *E*, and *F*, as shown in the figure. Draw a circle through points *A*, *D*, and *F*, another through points *C*, *D*, and *E*, and another through points *B*, *F*, and *E*.

What interesting property do the three circles have?

Strategies and Hints

1. Draw a triangle with a shape different from △*ABC*. Then try placing three circles so that they meet at points *D*, *E*, and *F*. What difficulties do you encounter?

2. Start by drawing and cutting out three circles of different sizes. Then arrange the circles so that you can draw a triangle on top of them. What do you notice?

3. The perpendicular bisectors of the sides of △*EDC* meet at point *R*. How would this property help you construct the figure?

Merrill Geometry   2   REASONING AND INTRODUCTION TO PROOF

Manipulatives and Models

The following materials may be used as models or manipulatives in Chapter 2.

- scientific calculator (Lesson 2-1)
- newspaper or magazine advertisements (Lesson 2-1)
- properties of equality flash cards (Lesson 2-4)
- colored yarn (Lesson 2-6)
- large cardboard angle (Lesson 2-7)

Outside Resources

Books/Periodicals

Cupillari, Antonella. *The Nuts and Bolts of Proofs.* Wadsworth Publishing Company

National Council of Teachers of Mathematics. Thirteenth Yearbook, *Nature of Proof.* National Council of Teachers of Mathematics.

Films/Videotapes/Videodiscs

The Birth of Modern Geometry, The Media Guild, 11722 Sorrento Valley Rd., Suite E, San Diego, CA 92121

Geometric Forms in Nature, Simon and Schuster, 108 Wilmot Dr., Deerfield, IL 60015

Software

Geometric Supposer: Quadrilaterals, WINGS for Learning/Sunburst, 101 Castleton St., Pleasantville, NY 10570

Multicultural

Multicultural Activity, p. 2

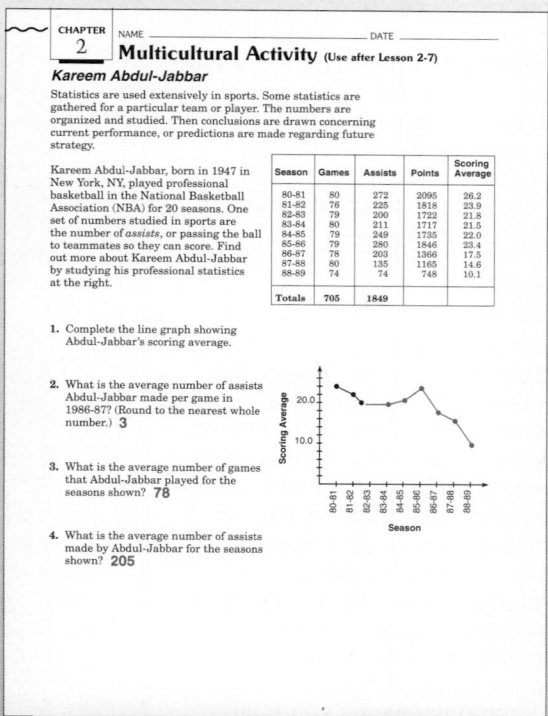

CHAPTER 2   NAME _____ DATE _____

Multicultural Activity (Use after Lesson 2-7)

Kareem Abdul-Jabbar

Statistics are used extensively in sports. Some statistics are gathered for a particular team or player. The numbers are organized and studied. Then conclusions are drawn concerning current performance, or predictions are made regarding future strategy.

Kareem Abdul-Jabbar, born in 1947 in New York, NY, played professional basketball in the National Basketball Association (NBA) for 20 seasons. One set of numbers studied in sports are the number of *assists*, or passing the ball to teammates so they can score. Find out more about Kareem Abdul-Jabbar by studying his professional statistics at the right.

Season	Games	Assists	Points	Scoring Average
80-81	80	272	2095	26.2
81-82	76	225	1818	23.9
82-83	79	200	1722	21.8
83-84	80	211	1717	21.5
84-85	79	249	1735	22.0
85-86	79	280	1846	23.4
86-87	78	203	1366	17.5
87-88	80	135	1165	14.6
88-89	74	74	748	10.1
Totals	**705**	**1849**		

1. Complete the line graph showing Abdul-Jabbar's scoring average.

2. What is the average number of assists Abdul-Jabbar made per game in 1986-87? (Round to the nearest whole number.) **3**

3. What is the average number of games that Abdul-Jabbar played for the seasons shown? **78**

4. What is the average number of assists made by Abdul-Jabbar for the seasons shown? **205**

Lab Manual

Lab Activity, pp. 30-33

Name _____   Activity 4 Worksheet
                                              Page 1

If-Then Statements

Cut out the triangles given to you by your teacher.
Tear the angles from each triangle as shown at the right.

1. What is the sum of the angles of the triangle? _____ Draw a picture of the model which leads to your conclusion.

2. Write your answer to question 1 as a conditional statement in the if-then form.

3. Each of your cut-out triangles has two acute angles. Use the models to draw a conclusion about the relationship of the angles. Illustrate your models below.

   a.   b.   c.

4. Write conditional statements for the models you discovered in question 3.

   a. _____
   b. _____
   c. _____

5. For each statement in question 4, write the converse and state whether it is true or false.

   a. _____   True   False
   b. _____   True   False
   c. _____   True   False

31

Glencoe Division, Macmillan/McGraw-Hill

Using the Chapter Opener

This two-page introduction to the chapter provides students with an opportunity to see how geometry is used throughout the world in various cultures. **Transparency 2-0**, available in the *Merrill Geometry Package*, provides another full-color visual and motivational activity that you can use to engage your students in the mathematical content of the chapter.

Multicultural Notes

Japan Akio Morita is chairman of the Sony Corporation, one of the most registered trademarks in the world. Morita, whose name means "prosperous rice field," comes from a family of wealthy sake (rice wine) brewers. He was born in 1921 in Kasugaya, Japan, and majored in physics at Osaka Imperial University. In 1946 he and Masaru Ibuka formed an electronics equipment manufacturing company called Tokyo Telecommunications Company. Twelve years later the name was changed to Sony.

Spain Antonio de Torres was born in 1817 near Almeria, Spain, and began his study of guitar construction as a young man. By the 1850s he was building guitars in his own shop. Torres believed that the guitar's soundboard–the top, or "table"–was the most crucial part of the instrument. In 1862, he set out to prove his belief by designing and building a new classical guitar. The back and sides of Torres' guitar were cardboard, reinforced by wooden strips. He made the soundboard of top-quality spruce with a new system of fan struts.

Chapter Project

Material pencil, paper, ruler, posterboard, alphabet and geometric stencils.

Procedure Organize students into cooperative groups of artists. Tell them each student is to select a form of Op Art (or optical art) to try. Point out that Op Art is a form of abstract art that uses straight lines or geometric patterns to create a special visual effect.

Provide each group with the following instructions for creating Op Art.

Begin your Op Art by using stencils to draw your name, a word, or a series of geometric shapes. Measure and draw equally-spaced vertical lines through your stencil drawing. Alternately color either a vertical column or part of each letter or geometric shape. Where the column is shaded, leave letter parts unshaded, and vice versa.

Begin your second Op Art form by drawing a name, a word, or a series of geometric shapes. Measure and draw equally-spaced horizontal lines through your stencil drawing. Finally color alternate rows.

Reasoning and Introduction to Proof

CHAPTER OBJECTIVES

In this chapter, you will:
- Make conjectures.
- Use the laws of logic to make conclusions.
- Write proofs involving segment and angle theorems.

Connections and Applications

Lesson	Connections (C) and Applications (A)	Examples	Exercises
2-1	A: Botany	2	33
	C: Algebra		9-10 17-20 24-26 29
	A: Statistics		32
2-2	A: Construction	4	
	A: Biology		55
	A: Advertising		56
2-3	A: Advertising	2	41
	A: Chemistry	3	
	A: Geology		39
	A: Biology		40
2-4	C: Algebra	1, 2	
	A: Banking		31
	A: Physics		32
	A: Language Arts		33
2-5	A: Geology	1	
2-6	A: Law		31
	A: Advertising		32
2-7	A: Construction	1	
	C: Algebra		11-14
	A: Sports		34

GEOMETRY AROUND THE WORLD
United States

What rectangle filled with three circles helps keep you safe every day? Give up? The answer is a traffic light, developed in 1923 by an African-American inventor named Garrett Morgan.

Born in Kentucky in 1877, Morgan moved to Cleveland, Ohio, when he was 18. There, he found work repairing sewing machines and soon invented a belt fastener to make the machines operate more efficiently. Later, he invented a gas mask to protect fire fighters inside smoke-filled buildings. The patented device won a gold medal from the International Exposition for Sanitation and Safety. Morgan and three others wore the masks when they entered a gas-filled tunnel to save workers trapped by an explosion. During World War I, Morgan's invention protected Allied soldiers from breathing the deadly gases their enemies used in battle.

Concern for safety also motivated Morgan, at age 48, to invent a three-way automatic electric traffic light. At the time, he was said to be the only African-American in Cleveland who owned a car. Morgan patented his device and later sold the rights to market it to the General Electric Company. He died in 1963.

GEOMETRY IN ACTION

Garrett Morgan systematically went about developing his inventions. First, he identified the problem to be solved. How can sewing machines be made to operate more efficiently? How can people be protected from breathing deadly fumes? How can traffic be regulated to protect pedestrians and drivers?

What do you suppose Morgan did after he identified the problem? Write the steps you think he might have gone through to invent the traffic light.

◀ *Park Avenue in New York City*   Inset: *Garrett Morgan*

This modern traffic light looks different from Garrett Morgan's original invention, but the purpose is the same — saving lives.

69

Begin your third Op Art form by drawing a letter, a short word, or a geometric shape. Draw vertical and horizontal parallel lines across your stencils, varying the spacing of the lines to create visual hills and valleys. Color alternate spaces.

Review each group's Op Art. Instruct each group to select its most attractive drawing and redraw it on posterboard.

Resources

Vare, Ethlie, and Greg Ptacek. *Mothers of Invention*. William Morrow and Company

Flein, Aaron E. *The Hidden Contributors: Black Scientists and Inventors in America*. Doubleday & Company

Carwell, Hattie. *Blacks in Science*. Expositions Press

- Reteaching Master 2-1
- Practice Master 2-1
- Enrichment Master 2-1
- Technology Master, p. 2

 Transparency 2-1 contains the 5-Minute Check and a teaching aid for this lesson

INTRODUCING THE LESSON

 5-Minute Check

(over Chapter 1)

Graph each point on one coordinate plane.

1. $A(4,-1)$ 2. $B(0,3)$
3. $C(-1,-2)$ 4. $D(-2,0)$

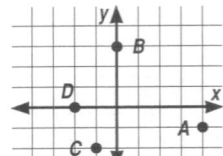

5. Find the length of a segment with endpoints $A(2, 5)$ and $B(-1,1)$.   **5**
6. If $\angle A$ is supplementary to $\angle B$ and the measure of $\angle A$ is twice the measure of $\angle B$, find the measure of both angles. **60, 120**

Motivating the Lesson

Tell students, "I have been to Pottersville three times in my life. Every time I went, it was raining. I think it must always rain in Pottersville." Ask students to discuss this type of reasoning.

TEACHING THE LESSON

Chalkboard Example

For Example 1
$\angle A$ is complementary to $\angle B$. Write a conjecture about the relationship of their measures.
$m\angle A + m\angle B = 90$

2-1 Inductive Reasoning and Conjecturing

Objective
2-1
After studying this lesson, you should be able to:
- make geometric conjectures based on inductive reasoning.

Application

After making a few observations, the caveman in the comic has made a **conjecture.** A conjecture is an educated guess. Looking at several specific situations to arrive at a conjecture is called **inductive reasoning.** For centuries, mathematicians have used inductive reasoning to develop the geometry that we study and use today.

"Water boils down to nothing... snow boils down to nothing... ice boils down to nothing... everything boils down to nothing."

Drawing by Ed Fisher, © 1966 Saturday Review, Inc.

You have had some experiences with geometry, so you can make conjectures about geometry from given information. However, not all conjectures are true. For example, the caveman conjectured that everything boils down to nothing. But, if he boiled something like a potato, he would find that his conjecture was false.

Example 1

Points A, B, and C lie on a segment. Write a conjecture about the relationship of points A, B, and C. Draw a figure to illustrate your conjecture.

Given: Points A, B, and C lie on a segment.
Conjecture: A, B, and C are collinear.

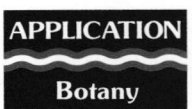

A conjecture that is based on several observations may be true, but not necessarily.

Example 2

APPLICATION
Botany

Shana has been studying the growth of several different species of plants that she has planted in her backyard. The weather has been unusually dry for this time of the year. Plant A is thriving and plant B is shriveled and dying. Both plants receive several hours of strong sunlight each day. Make a list of conjectures that Shana can make and investigate as to why the plants are performing differently.

70   CHAPTER 2   REASONING AND INTRODUCTION TO PROOF

ALTERNATE TEACHING STRATEGIES

Using Calculators

Have students find the decimal equivalent of fractions less than 1 that have a denominator of 99. After a few trials, ask them to make a conjecture about how to find such decimals without using a calculator, based on the pattern they have observed.   **The pattern is that a two-digit form of the numerator repeats infinitely; for example, 76/99 = 0.767676...; 4/99 = 0.040404....**

Using Critical Thinking

If there are three points in the <u>same</u> plane, A, B, and C, such that $\overline{AB}$, $\overline{BC}$, and $\overline{AC}$ do not form a triangle, what can be said about A, B, and C?   **They must be collinear.**

Some conjectures are

- Plant *A* requires less water than plant *B*;
- Plant *A* requires strong sunlight and plant *B* prefers shade;
- Plant *B* requires different soil than is available in Shana's area.

Can you name some more conjectures about Shana's plants?

Sometimes we, like the caveman, use inductive reasoning to make a conjecture and later determine that the conjecture is false. It takes only one false example to show that a conjecture is not true. The false example is called a **counterexample**.

Example 3

Given that points *A*, *B*, and *C* lie on a line segment, Jerry conjectured that *B* is between *A* and *C*. Determine if his conjecture is true or false. Explain your answer.

Given: Points *A*, *B*, and *C* lie on a segment.

Conjecture: *B* is between *A* and *C*.

In the figure above, *A*, *B*, and *C* lie on the segment, but *A* is between *B* and *C*. Since we can find a counterexample for the conjecture, the conjecture is false.

Example 4

Write a conjecture that is based on the given information. Draw a figure to illustrate your conjecture. Explain why you think your conjecture is true.

Given: ∠*B* is supplementary to ∠*A*.
∠*B* is supplementary to ∠*C*.

Conjecture: ∠*A* ≅ ∠*C*

For example, suppose *m*∠*B* is 143. Then *m*∠*A* would be 37 since $180 - 143 = 37$. *m*∠*C* would also be $180 - 143$ or 37. Therefore, ∠*A* ≅ ∠*C* since they have the same measure. *This example supports the conjecture.*

Later on in this chapter, you will learn how to establish the truth of a conjecture. But for now, remember that one example or even one hundred examples do not establish the truth of a conjecture.

CHECKING FOR UNDERSTANDING

Communicating Mathematics

Read and study the lesson to answer these questions.

1. In your own words, explain the meaning of *conjecture*. **See margin.**
2. How can you prove that a conjecture is false? **Give a counterexample.**
3. Explain how the caveman's inductive reasoning led him to a false conjecture. What could he have done differently that would lead him to a different conjecture? **See margin.**

LESSON 2-1 INDUCTIVE REASONING AND CONJECTURING **71**

Additional Answers

1. A conjecture is a guess about what will *always* be true, though based on limited evidence.
3. He only tested water, snow, and ice. If he had tested other substances, he could have made different observations.

Chalkboard Examples

For Example 2
The tulips planted under the maple tree come up beautifully every year. The tulips planted under the evergreens are not doing well. What are some conjectures you could make to explain this? **Sample answer: the soil under the maple tree is better.**

For Example 3
Given that the points *A*, *B*, and *C* lie on a line segment and *B* is between *A* and *C*, Susan conjectured that *B* is the midpoint of $\overline{AC}$.

Determine if her conjecture is true or false. Explain your answer. **False; although *A*, *B*, and *C* lie on the same segment, and *B* is between *A* and *C*, *B* could be closer to *A* than to *C* and, therefore, not be the midpoint.**

For Example 4
Write a conjecture that is based on the given information. Draw a figure to illustrate your conjecture. Explain why you think your conjecture is true.
Given: *m*∠*A* < *m*∠*B*, *m*∠*B* < *m*∠*C* **See students' work. Sample conjecture: *m*∠*A* < *m*∠*B*.**

Teaching Tip After Example 3, ask students if one counterexample is enough to determine that a conjecture is false. Have them explain their answers.

EVALUATING THE LESSON

Checking for Understanding
Exercises 1–10 are designed to help you assess students' understanding through reading, writing, speaking, and modeling. You should work through Exercises 1–4 with your students and then monitor their work on Exercises 5–10.

Left sidebar

Closing the Lesson

Speaking Activity Ask volunteers to give you an example of a conjecture drawn from a given set of facts. The volunteers should decide to give a true conjecture or a false conjecture. The other students should respond by stating whether the conjectures are true or false and give reasons for their answers.

APPLYING THE LESSON

Homework Exercises

Assignment Guide
Basic: 11-25, 31-38
Average: 13-27, 31-38
Enriched: 16-38

Exercise Notes

For Exercises 11-13, encourage students to try to draw more than one diagram of the given data.

Additional Answer

4. Answers may vary. Sample answer: Earth is the center of the universe.

Reteaching Masters Booklet, p. 9

2-1 NAME _____ DATE _____
Reteaching Worksheet
Inductive Reasoning and Conjecturing

In daily life, you frequently look at several specific situations and reach a general conclusion based on these specific cases. For example, you might receive excellent service in a restaurant several times and conclude that the service is always good. Of course, you are not guaranteed that the service will be good when you return.

This type of reasoning in which you look at several facts and then make an educated guess based on these facts is called **inductive reasoning**. The educated guess is called a **conjecture**. Not all conjectures are true. When you find an example which shows the conjecture is false, this example is called a **counterexample**.

Example: Determine if the conjecture is true or false based on the given information. Explain your answer and give a counterexample if false.

Given: $\overline{AB} \cong \overline{BC}$
Conjecture: B is the midpoint of AC.

In the figure, $\overline{AB} \cong \overline{BC}$, but B is not the midpoint of $\overline{AC}$. So the conjecture is false.

Determine if the conjecture is true or false based on the given information. Explain your answer and give a counterexample for any false conjecture.

1. Given: Collinear points D, E, and F
   Conjecture: $DE + EF = DF$ false; If F is between D and E (or if D is between E and F), then $DE + EF \neq DF$. See figures below.

2. Given: $\angle A$ and $\angle B$ are supplementary.
   Conjecture: $\angle A$ and $\angle B$ are adjacent angles. false; If $\angle A$ and $\angle B$ do not have the same vertex, they cannot be adjacent. See figure below.

3. Given: $\angle D$ and $\angle F$ are supplementary.
   $\angle E$ and $\angle F$ are supplementary.
   Conjecture: $\angle D \cong \angle E$ true; If m$\angle F = 25$, them m$\angle D = 180 - 25$ or 155 and m$\angle E = 180 - 25$ or 155. Since m$\angle D = $ m$\angle E$, then $\angle D \cong \angle E$.

4. Given: AB is perpendicular to BC.
   Conjecture: $\angle ABC$ is a right angle. true, If the sides of an angle are perpendicular, the angle is a right angle.

T9
Glencoe Division, Macmillan/McGraw-Hill

72   Chapter 2

Main column

Guided Practice

Determine if the conjecture is *true* or *false* based on the given information. Explain your answer. See margin.

5. **Given:** points A, B, and C
   Conjecture: A, B, and C are collinear.

6. **Given:** $\angle A$ and $\angle C$ are complementary angles.
   $\angle B$ and $\angle C$ are complementary angles.
   Conjecture: $\angle A \cong \angle B$

Write a conjecture based on the given information. Draw a figure to illustrate your conjecture. See margin.

7. **Given:** $\angle A$ and $\angle B$ are right angles.

8. **Given:** $\overline{AB}$, $\overline{BC}$, $\overline{CD}$

9. **Given:** $P(0, -3)$, $R(0, 3)$, $Q(0, 0)$

10. **Given:** $A(-1, -3)$, $B(3, 0)$, $C(3, -3)$

CONNECTION
Algebra

EXERCISES

Practice

A

Determine if the conjecture is *true* or *false* based on the given information. Explain your answer and give a counterexample for any false conjecture.

11–12. See margin.

11. **Given:** noncollinear points A, B, and C
    Conjecture: $\overline{AB}$, $\overline{BC}$, and $\overline{AC}$ form a triangle.

12. **Given:** collinear points A, B, and C
    Conjecture: $\overline{AB}$, $\overline{BC}$, and $\overline{AC}$ form a triangle.

13. **Given:** $\overline{AB}$, $\overline{BC}$, and $\overline{CD}$
    Conjecture: A, B, C, and D are collinear. See Solutions Manual.

B

Write a conjecture based on the given information. If appropriate, draw a figure to illustrate your conjecture. See Solutions Manual.

14. $\overline{AB}$ and $\overline{CD}$ intersect at E.

15. Point Q is between R and S.

16. $\angle ABC$ and $\angle DBE$ are vertical angles.

CONNECTION
Algebra

17. $Q(5, 2)$, $P(-2, 2)$, $R(-5, 2)$

18. $A(1, 5)$, $B(1, 1)$, $C(-2, 4)$, $D(-2, 0)$

Write the equation you think should come next in each sequence. Check your answers with a calculator.

CONNECTION
Algebra

19. $1^2 = 1$
    $11^2 = 121$
    $111^2 = 12,321$
    $1111^2 = 1,234,321$

20. $1^3 = 1^2 - 0^2$
    $2^3 = 3^2 - 1^2$
    $3^3 = 6^2 - 3^2$
    $4^3 = 10^2 - 6^2$

RETEACHING THE LESSON

Have students write the letter of the true conjecture that can be made from the given information.

1. Given: $\angle A$ is complementary to $\angle B$.
   a. m$\angle A <$ m$\angle B$
   b. m$\angle A +$ m$\angle B = 180$
   c. m$\angle A +$ m$\angle B = 90$ c

2. Given: $\overline{AB}$ is perpendicular to $\overline{BC}$ at B.
   a. A, B, and C are collinear.
   b. m$\angle ABC = 90$
   c. $AB < BC$ b

Write a conjecture based on the given information. See Solutions Manual.

21. D is the midpoint of $\overline{AB}$, and E is the midpoint of $\overline{AC}$.

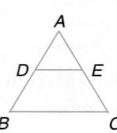

22. $WXYZ$ is a rectangle.

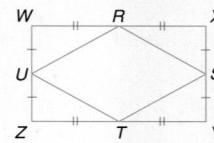

Determine if each conjecture is *true* or *false*. Explain your answers and give a counterexample for any false conjecture. See Solutions Manual.

23. **Given:** $\overline{ST} \cong \overline{TU}$
    Conjecture: T is the midpoint of $\overline{SU}$.

24. **Given:** x is a real number.
    Conjecture: x^2 is a nonnegative number.

25. **Given:** $ABCD$ is a rectangle.
    Conjecture: $\overline{AC}$ and $\overline{BD}$ are congruent.

26. **Given:** $W(-2, 3)$, $X(1, 7)$, $Y(5, 4)$, and $Z(2, 0)$
    Conjecture: $WXYZ$ is a square.

Write a conjecture based on the given information. Draw a figure to illustrate your conjecture. Write a sentence or two to explain why you think your conjecture is true. See Solutions Manual.

27. Points A, B, C, D, E with no three collinear

28. $\overline{AB}$, $\overline{BC}$, $\overline{CD}$, $\overline{DE}$, $\overline{EA}$ with only A, B, and C collinear

29. $A(-3, 0)$, $B(0, 3)$, $C(4, 1)$, $D(-1, -4)$

30. Draw several quadrilaterals with each pair of opposite sides parallel. Use a protractor to measure the pairs of opposite angles in each figure. Make a conjecture. **Sample answer: Quadrilaterals whose opposite sides are parallel have opposite angles that are congruent.**

Critical Thinking

31. **Number Theory** The expression $n^2 - n + 41$ has a prime value for $n = 1$, $n = 2$, and $n = 3$. You might conjecture that this expression always generates a prime number for any positive integral value of n. Try different values of n to test the conjecture. Answer true if you think it is always true. Answer false and give a counterexample if you think it is false.
    false; $n = 41$

Applications

32. **Statistics** Work in pairs. Use a tape measure to measure your partner's height and the distance around your partner's head. **32a. See students' work.**

    a. Make a conjecture about the relationship of the two measurements.

    b. Compare your conjecture to other students' measurements. **Answers may vary. A person's height is approximately three times the distance around his or her head.**

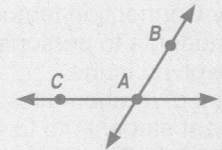

LESSON 2-1   INDUCTIVE REASONING AND CONJECTURING   **73**

Additional Answers

5. False. A, B, and C could be as shown. They are not collinear.

6. True. If $m\angle C = 25$, then $m\angle A = 90 - 25$, or 65, and $m\angle B = 90 - 25$, or 65. Since $m\angle A = m\angle B$, $\angle A \cong \angle B$.

Answers for Exercises 7-10 may vary. Sample answers are given. Given conjectures are not necessarily true.

7. $\angle A \cong \angle B$

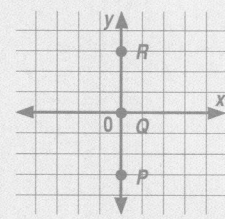
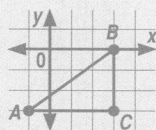

a. **Answers may vary.**   b. **Yes, the fungus is killing the plants.**

33. Botany In the 1920s, some Japanese farmers observed that some rice plants were growing taller and thinner than normal rice plants and then drooping over, making them impossible to harvest.

   a. Make some conjectures about why the plants were drooping.

   b. The scientists who researched the problem discovered that fungus was growing on the drooping rice plants, while the healthy plants had no fungus. Does this observation prompt a new conjecture?

   c. How might the scientists have tested the conjecture they made? **Introduce the fungus to some healthy plants and see if they droop.**

Mixed Review

34. Determine whether you can assume that ∠*ACD* and ∠*BCD* are adjacent from the figure at the right. **(Lesson 1-8) yes**

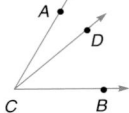

35. Use a protractor to draw a 65° angle. **(Lesson 1-7) See students' work.**

36. Kim and Ryan are making pizzas for the band's fall fund-raiser. A pizza can have thin or thick crust and either pepperoni, mushrooms, or green peppers. How many different pizzas can be made? **(Lesson 1-3) 6**

37. Is the top of your desk best modeled by a point, line, or a plane? **(Lesson 1-1) plane**

Wrap-Up

Journal Entry

38. Journal Entry Select a problem you did from this exercise set that illustrates some of the main ideas of this section. Rewrite the problem in your journal. Thoroughly explain how the problem was done and how it relates to conjectures. **See students' work.**

~ HISTORY CONNECTION ~

Most of the geometry that you are familiar with is *Euclidean Geometry,* named after the Greek mathematician Euclid. In about 300 B.C., Euclid unified the works of many schools and mathematicians into his *Elements*. It was so comprehensive a book that it made every other book on geometry obsolete. *Elements* begins by establishing fundamental concepts from which all of the remaining concepts are proven using deductive reasoning.

For centuries, mathematicians believed that Euclid's geometry was the only geometry. However, it is now known that other geometries exist that are equally valid. These *non-euclidean geometries* begin with a different foundation of concepts from which other concepts are deduced and proven.

Enrichment Masters Booklet, p. 9

NAME _____ DATE _____

2-1 Enrichment Worksheet

Counterexamples

When you make a conclusion after examining several specific cases, you have used **inductive reasoning**. However, you must be cautious when using this form of reasoning. By finding only one **counterexample**, you disprove the conclusion.

Example: Is the statement $\frac{1}{x} \le 1$ true when you replace x with 1, 2, and 3? Is the statement true for all integers? If possible, find a counterexample. $\frac{1}{1} = 1$, $\frac{1}{2} < 1$, and $\frac{1}{3} < 1$. But when $x = \frac{1}{2}$, then $\frac{1}{x} = 2$. This counterexample shows that the statement is not always true.

Answer each question.

1. The coldest day of the year in Chicago occured in January for five straight years. Is it safe to conclude that the coldest day in Chicago is always in January? **No**

2. Suppose John misses the school bus four Tuesdays in a row. Can you safely conclude that John misses the school bus every Tuesday? **No**

3. Is the equation $\sqrt{k^2} = k$ true when you replace k with 1, 2, and 3? Is the equation true for all integers? If possible, find a counterexample. **It is true for 1, 2, and 3. It is not true for negative integers? Sample: –2**

4. Is the statement $2x = x + x$ true when you replace x with $\frac{1}{2}$, 4 and 0.7? Is the statement true for all real numbers? If possible, find a counterexample. **It is true for all real numbers.**

5. Suppose you draw four points A, B, C, and D and then draw $\overline{AB}$, $\overline{BC}$, $\overline{CD}$, and $\overline{DA}$. Does this procedure give a quadrilateral always or only sometimes? Explain your answers with figures. **only sometimes Example: Counterexample:**

6. Suppose you draw a circle, mark three points on it, and connect them. Will the angles of the triangle be acute? Explain your answer with figures. **no, only sometimes Example: Counterexample:**

T9
Glencoe Division, Macmillan/McGraw-Hill

EXTENDING THE LESSON

Math Power: Communication

Have students collect examples of true and false conjectures made in everyday life to present to the class as an oral report. Possible sources are advertising, newspaper or magazine articles, and detective stories.

History Connection

The History Connection features introduce students to persons or cultures involved in the development of mathematics. You may want students to further research Euclid's *Elements*.

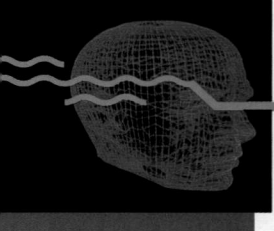

Technology
Conjectures

BASIC
▶ **Geometric Supposer**
Graphing calculators
LOGO
Spreadsheets

As you know, a conjecture is an educated guess based on observations of a particular situation. Let's use the Geometric Supposer to make some conjectures about the diagonals of quadrilaterals.

The Geometric Supposer: Quadrilaterals will allow you to draw and investigate many different quadrilaterals. A quadrilateral is a four-sided plane figure. We will begin by drawing a parallelogram, which is a special quadrilateral in which both pairs of opposite sides are parallel. To draw a parallelogram, press *N* to begin. Then choose *(1) Parallelogram* from the menu. A menu of different types of parallelograms will appear. Choose *(1) Random*. A parallelogram will appear on the screen.

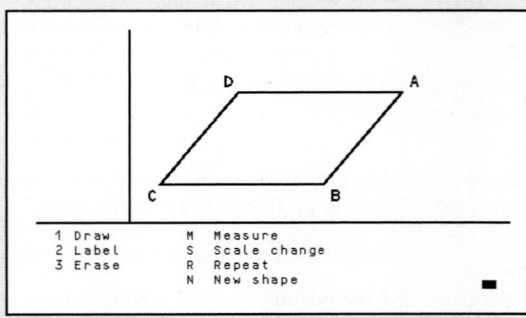

A diagonal of a quadrilateral is a segment that connects a pair of opposite vertices. So the diagonals of your parallelogram *ABCD* are $\overline{AC}$ and $\overline{BD}$. To find the lengths of the diagonals, press *(M) Measure*. Then choose *(1) Length* from the menu. Enter *AC* and *RETURN*. Record the length of $\overline{AC}$ and repeat for $\overline{BD}$.

EXERCISES

Use the Geometric Supposer to draw three examples of each different type of parallelogram, trapezoid, and kite.

1. Use a chart to record the lengths of the diagonals for each type of quadrilateral that you draw. See students' work.

2. Is there a pattern in the measures of the diagonals of a certain type of quadrilateral? Explain. The diagonals of each rectangle and of each square are congruent.

TECHNOLOGY   75

Using Technology
Objective This optional page shows how the Geometric Supposer can be used to create parallelograms, trapezoids, and kites and then investigate their diagonals.

Teaching Suggestions
Have students work in small groups at the computer. Let them familiarize themselves with the program by drawing different types of *quadrilaterals* and measuring their sides and angles.

Then have them concentrate on parallelograms, including rectangles, squares, and kites. Let them measure sides, angles, and diagonals in order to discover properties of these geometric shapes.

Finally, have them use the computer to answer Exercises 1-2.

If time permits, have groups share their conjectures about the properties of these geometric shapes.

Lesson Resources

- Reteaching Master 2-2
- Practice Master 2-2
- Enrichment Master 2-2
- Evaluation Master, Quiz A, p. 23
- Activity Master, p. 16
- Technology Master, p. 38
- Lab Manual, pp. 30-33

 Transparency 2-2 contains the 5-Minute Check and a teaching aid for this lesson.

INTRODUCING THE LESSON

 5-Minute Check

(over Lesson 2-1)

Determine if the conjecture is true or false based on the given information. Explain your answer and give a counterexample for any false conjecture.

1. Given: ∠A and ∠B are supplementary.
   Conjecture: ∠A and ∠B are not congruent.   **False. Each could measure 90°.**
2. Given: m∠A > m∠B; m∠B > m∠C
   Conjecture: m∠A > m∠C   **true**
3. Given: $\overline{AB}$, $\overline{BC}$, $\overline{AC}$
   Conjecture: A, B, and C are collinear.   **False. The three segments may form a triangle.**
4. Given: ∠A and ∠B are vertical angles.
   Conjecture: ∠A and ∠B are congruent.   **true**

Motivating the Lesson

The coach has said, "If you miss three practices, you will be off the team," and you have just missed your third practice. What do you think will happen?

TEACHING THE LESSON

Teaching Tip   After reading the first paragraph, ask the students to recall another word related to *hypothesis*.   **hypothetical**

2-2   If-Then Statements, Converses, and Postulates

Objectives   After studying this lesson, you should be able to:
- 2-2A   ■ identify the hypothesis and conclusion of an "if-then" statement,
- 2-2B   ■ write the converse of an "if-then" statement, and
- 2-2C   ■ identify and use basic postulates about points, lines, and planes.

Application

President Clinton's statement about education is an **if-then** or **conditional statement.** The portion of the sentence immediately following *if* is called the **hypothesis,** and the part immediately following *then* is called the **conclusion.**

Conditional statements are the basis of logic. In logic, the hypothesis is often represented by p and the conclusion by q. The conditional "If p then q" is written in symbols as $p \rightarrow q$ and is read "p implies q."

If we are going to compete and win again, we are all going to have to work harder and smarter and become lifelong learners.

Example 1

Identify the hypothesis and conclusion of the conditional "If a hot dog is a foot long, then it is 12 inches long."

Hypothesis: a hot dog is a foot long

Conclusion: it is 12 inches long

Note that "if" is not used when you write the hypothesis and "then" is not used when you write the conclusion.

Sometimes a conditional statement is written without using "if" and "then." For example, Ben Franklin's saying, "A stitch in time saves nine," can be written as the conditional "If you make a stitch in time, then you will save nine."

Example 2

Write the statement "Adjacent angles have a common vertex" in if-then form.

The hypothesis is that two angles are adjacent and the conclusion is that the angles have a common vertex. So, the conditional can be written as follows:

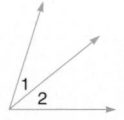

If two angles are adjacent, then they have a common vertex.

ALTERNATE TEACHING STRATEGIES

Using Questioning

True or false? If false, give a counterexample.
1. If a conditional statement is true, its converse is true.   **false**
2. If a conditional statement is false, its converse is false.   **false**
3. If a conditional statement is true, its converse may or may not be true.   **true**

Using Logical Reasoning

Give an example of a false conditional statement whose converse is true.
Sample answer: If a pet has four legs, it is a dog. This is a false statement. Its converse is "If a pet is a dog, it has four legs," which is a true statement.

Sometimes you must add information to a statement when you write it in if-then form. For example, in Example 2 it was necessary to know adjacent angles came in pairs in order for the if-then statement to be clear.

You can form another if-then statement by interchanging the hypothesis and conclusion of a conditional. This new statement is called the **converse** of the original conditional. The converse of "If two angles are adjacent, then they have a common vertex" is "If two angles have a common vertex, then they are adjacent angles."

If a conditional is not in if-then form, it may be easier to write it in that form before writing the converse. The converse of a true conditional is not necessarily true. *The converse of p → q is q → p.*

Example 3

> **Write the converse of the true conditional "Vertical angles are congruent." Determine if the converse is true or false. If it is false, give a counterexample.**
>
> First write the conditional in if-then form.
>
> The hypothesis is that two angles are vertical and the conclusion is that the angles are congruent. So, the if-then form of the conditional is as follows.
>
> **If-Then Form:** If two angles are vertical, then they are congruent.
>
> Now exchange the hypothesis and the conclusion to form the converse of the conditional.
>
> **Converse:** If two angles are congruent, then they are vertical.
>
> The converse of the conditional is false since two congruent angles are not necessarily vertical. A counterexample is shown below.
>
>

See pages 695-704 for a complete list of the postulates in this book.

Geometry is built on conditional statements called **postulates.** Postulates are principles that are accepted to be true without proof. The first two postulates describe the ways that points, lines, and planes are related.

Postulate 2-1	**Through any two points there is exactly one line.** *If there are two points, then there is exactly one line that contains them.*
Postulate 2-2	**Through any three points not on the same line there is exactly one plane.** *If there are three points not on the same line, then there is exactly one plane that contains them.*

The relationships between points, lines, and planes can be used to solve practical problems.

Example 4

APPLICATION
Construction

There are four buildings on the Woodlawn High School campus. Assuming that no three of the buildings lie in a straight line, how many sidewalks would need to be constructed so that each building is directly connected to each other building?

If we represent the buildings as points A, B, C, and D, there are four points in the plane. For every two points there is exactly one line. So for four points there are six lines that can be drawn.

In the figure, $\overline{AB}$, $\overline{BC}$, $\overline{CD}$, $\overline{AD}$, $\overline{BD}$, and $\overline{AC}$ can be drawn.

Six sidewalks need to be constructed.

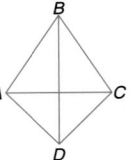

The next four postulates state more relationships of points, lines, and planes.

Postulate 2-3	**A line contains at least two points.**
Postulate 2-4	**A plane contains at least three points not on the same line.**
Postulate 2-5	**If two points lie in a plane, then the entire line containing those two points lies in that plane.**
Postulate 2-6	**If two planes intersect, then their intersection is a line.**

CHECKING FOR UNDERSTANDING

Communicating Mathematics

Read and study the lesson to answer these questions.   1. See Solutions Manual.

1. Define a conditional statement and write an example of a conditional.

2. Translate the conditional statement "Waste not want not" into if-then form. If you waste not, then you will want not.

3. Look through some magazines or newspapers for conditional statements in advertising and write them in if-then form. For example, the well-known United Negro College Fund slogan "A mind is a terrible thing to waste" can be written as "If something is a mind, then it is a terrible thing to waste." Answers may vary.

4. How do you form the converse of a conditional statement? Write the converse of "If it is raining, then there is a rainbow." See Solutions Manual.

5. Postulates are basic principles that are assumed without proof. Can you think of some postulates that apply to other fields of study? Answers may vary. A sample answer is that in science the existence of atoms is assumed.

78   CHAPTER 2   REASONING AND INTRODUCTION TO PROOF

Additional Answers

6. Hypothesis: you work for 8 hours
   Conclusion: you work for one-third of a day

7. Hypothesis: two lines are perpendicular
   Conclusion: they intersect

8. Hypothesis: you are sixteen years old
   Conclusion: you may get a drivers license

9. Hypothesis: $x = 4$
   Conclusion: $x^2 = 16$

10. If there are clouds, then it is raining.   False; it may be cloudy and not raining.

11. If an angle is acute, then it is 37°.   False; an angle that measures 58° is acute.

12. If three points lie on a straight line, then they are collinear.   true

13. If he or she may serve as President, then he or she is a native-born United States citizen who is at least thirty-five years old.   true

Guided Practice

Identify the hypothesis and conclusion of each conditional statement.
See margin.

6. If you work for 8 hours, then you work for one third of a day.
7. If two lines are perpendicular, then they intersect.
8. If you are sixteen years old, then you may get a driver's license.
9. If $x = 4$, then $x^2 = 16$.

Write the converse of each conditional. Determine if the converse is *true* or *false*. If it is false, give a counterexample. See margin.

10. If it is raining, then there are clouds.
11. If an angle measures 37°, then it is acute.
12. If three points are collinear, then they lie on a straight line.
13. If a native-born United States citizen is at least thirty-five years old, then he or she may serve as President.

Write each conditional statement in if-then form. See margin.

14. Congruent angles have the same measure.
15. Two planes intersect in a line.
16. What goes up must come down.
17. A recycled aluminum can is remelted and back in the store within six weeks.

In the figure, *R*, *P*, and *S* are collinear. Points *R*, *P*, *S*, and *T* lie in plane $\mathcal{M}$. Use the postulates you have learned to determine whether each statement is *true* or *false*.

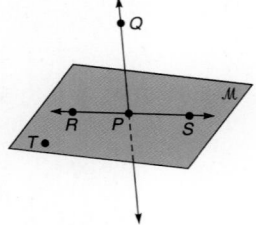

18. P, Q, and R lie in plane $\mathcal{M}$. false
19. $\overline{PS}$ does not lie in plane $\mathcal{M}$. false
20. P, Q, R, and S are coplanar. true
21. Q, R, and T are collinear. false

EXERCISES

Practice
A

Identify the hypothesis and conclusion of each conditional statement.
See margin.

22. If it is Memorial Day, then it is a holiday.
23. If a candy bar is a Milky Way®, then it contains caramel.
24. If a container holds 32 ounces, then it holds a quart.

In the figure, *P*, *Q*, and *R* are collinear. Points *P* and *S* lie in plane $\mathcal{M}$. Points *Q* and *T* lie in plane $\mathcal{N}$. Determine whether each statement is *true* or *false*.

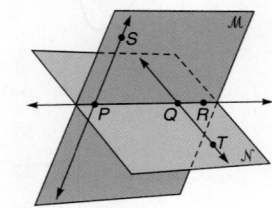

25. Q lies in plane $\mathcal{M}$. true
26. P, Q, and R lie in plane $\mathcal{M}$. true
27. Q does not lie in plane $\mathcal{N}$. false
28. P, Q, S, and T are coplanar. false
29. $\overline{QT}$ lies in plane $\mathcal{N}$. true

LESSON 2-2   IF-THEN STATEMENTS, CONVERSES, AND POSTULATES   79

APPLYING THE LESSON

Homework Exercises

Assignment Guide
Basic: 22-38, 54, 55, 57-66
Average: 25-41, 54, 56-66
Enriched: 38-66

Additional Answers

14. If two angles are congruent, then they have the same measure.
15. If two planes intersect, then the intersection is a line.
16. If something goes up, then it will come down.
17. If an aluminum can is recycled, then it is remelted and back in the store within six weeks.
22. Hypothesis: it is Memorial Day
    Conclusion: it is a holiday
23. Hypothesis: a candy bar is a Milky Way™
    Conclusion: it contains caramel
24. Hypothesis: a container holds 32 ounces
    Conclusion: it holds a quart

Reteaching Masters Booklet, p. 10

2-2 | NAME _____ DATE _____
Reteaching Worksheet

If-Then Statements, Converses, and Postulates

If-then statements are commonly used in everyday life. For example, an advertisement might say, "If you buy our product, then you will be happy." Notice that an if-then statement has two parts, a *hypothesis* (the part following "if") and a *conclusion* (the part following "then").

Sometimes statements that are not in if-then form can be reworded so they are in if-then form. However, it may be necessary to add or change words in order to do this.

When you interchange the hypothesis and conclusion of a conditional statement, a new if-then statement called the **converse** is formed.

Example: Rewrite the following statement in if-then form. Then identify the hypothesis and conclusion. Finally write the converse.

All elephants are mammals.

If an animal is an elephant, then it is a mammal.
Hypothesis: an animal is an elephant.
Conclusion: it is a mammal.
Converse: If an animal is a mammal, then it is an elephant.

Identify the hypothesis and conclusion of each conditional statement.

1. If today is Monday, then tomorrow is Tuesday.
   H: today is Monday; C: tomorrow is Tuesday
2. If a truck weighs 2 tons, then it weighs 4000 pounds.
   H: a truck weighs 2 tons; C: it weighs 4000 pounds

Write each conditional statement in if-then form.

3. All chimpanzees love bananas.
   If an animal is a chimpanzee, then it loves bananas.
4. Collinear points lie on the same line.
   If points are collinear, then they lie on the same line.

Write the converse of each conditional. Determine if the converse is true or false. If it is false, give a counterexample.

5. If an animal is a fish, then it can swim. If an animal can swim, then it is a fish. false; Dogs can swim but they are not fish.
6. All right angles are congruent. If angles are congruent, then they are right angles. false; Two 60° angles are congruent but are not right angles.

T10
Glencoe Division, Macmillan/McGraw-Hill

RETEACHING THE LESSON

Ask students to match the hypotheses on the left with a conclusion at the right that makes a true conditional statement.

1. If two angles form a linear pair,
   c
2. If two angles are vertical angles,
   a
3. If two adjacent angles form a right angle,   b

a. then the angles are congruent.
b. then the angles are complementary.
c. then the angles are supplementary.

B Write each conditional statement in if-then form. **See margin.**

30. Right angles are congruent.
31. A car has 4 wheels.
32. A square has 4 sides.
33. Acute angles are less than 90°.
34. A triangle contains exactly 3 angles.
35. Parallel lines do not intersect.

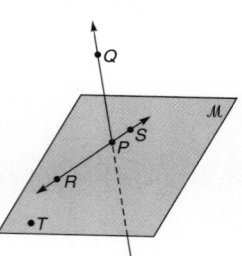

Write the converse of each conditional. Determine if the converse is *true* or *false*. If it is false, give a counterexample. **See margin.**

36. If the month is January, then it has 31 days.
37. If the distance of a race is 10 kilometers, then it is about 6.2 miles.
38. Springer spaniels are dogs.

State the postulate that explains each relationship.

39. Exactly one line contains Q and P. 2-1
40. There are at least two points on line QP. 2-3
41. The entire line containing R and S lies in plane $\mathcal{M}$. 2-5
42. There are at least three points in plane $\mathcal{M}$. 2-4
43. The intersection of plane $\mathcal{M}$ and the plane determined by Q, P, and R is line RP. 2-6

C **State the number of lines that can be drawn that contain the given set of points taken two at a time.**

44. two points one
45. three collinear points one
46. three noncollinear points three
47. four points, no three of which are collinear six
48. five points, no three of which are collinear ten
49. six points, no three of which are collinear fifteen
50. *Look for a pattern* in your answers to Exercises 44 through 49. What conjecture can you make about the number of lines through seven points, no three of which are collinear? 21

State the number of planes that can be drawn that contain the given set of points taken three at a time.

51. three noncollinear points one
52. three collinear points infinitely many
53. five points, no four of which are coplanar ten

Critical Thinking

54. Give examples of each of the following. **Answers may vary. See Solutions Manual.**

   a. a conditional and its converse that are both true

   b. a conditional and its converse that are both false

   c. a true conditional whose converse is false

   d. a false statement whose converse is true

   55. See margin.

Applications

55. Biology Use a diagram to illustrate the following conditional about the animal kingdom. "If an animal is a butterfly, then it is an arthropod."

56. Advertising A billboard reads "If you want a fabulous vacation, try Georgia."

   a. Write the converse of the conditional. **See margin.**

   b. What do you think the advertiser wants you to conclude about vacations in Georgia? **They are fabulous.**

   c. Does the advertisement say that vacations in Georgia are fabulous? **no**

Computer

In BASIC, an IF-THEN statement is used to compare two numbers. It tells the computer what to do based on the results of the comparison. The program below uses an IF-THEN statement to find the greatest number in a list.

57. Change the DATA statement to find the greatest number in each list. **57b. 1023**

   a. 84, 70, 22, 90, 31, 68, 92, 19, 36, 75 **92**

   b. 112, 524, 923, 987, 473, 811, 476, 216, 892, 1023

```
10  FOR I = 1 TO 10
20  READ A(I)
30  NEXT I
40  LET L = 1
50  FOR K = 2 TO 10
60  IF A(K) > A(L) THEN GOTO 80
70  GOTO 90
80  LET L = K
90  NEXT K
100 PRINT A(L)
110 END
120 DATA 43, 65, 78, 95, 21,
    56, 1, 42, 101, 97
```

58. How could you change the program to find the least number in the list? **Change the > to a < in line 60.**

Mixed Review

59. false; A, B, and P are not necessarily collinear.

59. Given that $AP = PB$, David made the conjecture that P is the midpoint of $\overline{AB}$. Do you think his conjecture is true or false? Explain. **(Lesson 2-1)**

60. Find the measures of two supplementary angles if the measure of the one angle is 36 more than the measure of the other. **(Lesson 1-8) 72, 108**

61. Suppose $\angle MON$ is a right angle and L is in the interior of $\angle MON$. If $m\angle MOL$ is five times $m\angle LON$, find $m\angle LON$. **(Lesson 1-7) 15**

62. $M(-3, 5)$ is the midpoint of $\overline{AB}$. If the coordinates of A are $(-7, 6)$, find the coordinates of B. **(Lesson 1-5) (1, 4)**

63. B is between A and C, $AB = 6x - 1$, $BC = 2x + 4$, and $AC = 9x - 3$. Find AC. **(Lesson 1-4) 51**

                                                     64. See margin.

64. Draw and label a figure that shows lines m and ℓ intersecting at point P. **(Lesson 1-2)**

65. Points $A(4, -3)$ and $B(-2, 9)$ lie on the line whose equation is $y = -2x + 5$. Determine whether $N(7, -2)$ is collinear to A and B. **(Lesson 1-1) no**

Wrap-Up

66. Write a five-question quiz about this lesson. Be sure to include answers to your questions. **See students' work.**

LESSON 2-2   IF-THEN STATEMENTS, CONVERSES, AND POSTULATES   81

EXTENDING THE LESSON

Math Power: Reasoning

Name two hypotheses that would let you conclude that two angles are congruent. **Sample answers: If two angles are vertical angles; if two angles are formed by perpendicular lines; if two angles each measure 30°**

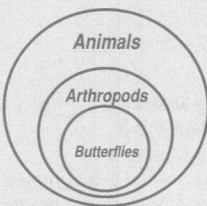
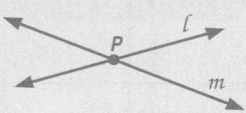

INTRODUCING THE LESSON

 5-Minute Check

(over Lesson 2-2)

Write each conditional statement in if-then form.

1. All triangles have three angles.   **If a figure is a triangle, then it has three angles.**
2. Every Thursday, Julia goes swimming.   **If it is Thursday, then Julia goes swimming.**

Write the converse of each conditional. Determine if the converse is true or false. If it is false, give a counterexample.

3. If a figure is a rectangle, then it has four sides.   **If a figure has four sides, then it is a rectangle. False; a trapezoid has four sides and is not a rectangle.**
4. If a number is divisible by 6, then it is divisible by 2.   **If a number is divisible by 2, then it is divisible by 6. False; 4 is divisible by 2 but not by 6.**

Motivating the Lesson

Present this example to the class: If Joe goes to the ball game, he will not go to the movies. Joe went to the ball game. What conclusion can you draw?   **Joe did not go to the movies.**

Compare the above example with this: If Kay goes to the ball game, she will not go to the movies. Kay did not go to the movies. Can you conclude that Kay went to the ball game?   **No**

2-3 Deductive Reasoning

Objective 2-3

After studying this lesson, you should be able to:
- use the law of detachment or the law of syllogism in deductive reasoning.

Application

If you like walking,
you'll love AirSports.

Jeanine enjoys walking the nature trail at the park each day. Assuming that the conditional statement in the advertisement is true, she will love AirSports.

This is an example of the use of the **law of detachment.** The law of detachment offers us a way to draw conclusions from if-then statements. It says that whenever a conditional is true and its hypothesis is true, we can conclude that its conclusion is true.

Law of Detachment	If $p \rightarrow q$ is a true conditional and p is true, then q is true.

Deductive reasoning uses a rule to make a specific conclusion. Inductive reasoning uses several examples to make a conjecture or rule.

The law of detachment and the other laws of logic can be used to provide a system for reaching logical conclusions. This system is called **deductive reasoning.** Deductive reasoning is one of the cornerstones of the study of geometry. The following example illustrates how the law of detachment can be used to draw a valid conclusion.

Example 1

"If two numbers are negative, then their product is positive" is a true conditional, and -3 and -4 are negative numbers. Use the law of detachment to state a valid conclusion.

The hypothesis is that two numbers are negative. -3 and -4 are indeed two negative numbers. Since the conditional is true and the given statement satisfies the hypothesis, the conclusion is true. So, the product of -3 and -4 is positive.

ALTERNATE TEACHING STRATEGIES

Using Cooperative Groups

Form groups of four students. Ask each group to create six if-then statements. Have each group write two examples of the law of detachment and two examples of the law of syllogism, using the conditional statements they created.

Using Problem Solving

Write a true conditional that will let you conclude that $\angle A$ is a right angle, using the law of detachment.   **Sample answer: If $\angle A$ measures 90, then $\angle A$ is a right angle.**

Knowing that the conditional is true and that the conclusion is satisfied will not allow us to say the hypothesis follows. Consider this counterexample. The product of 5 and 9 is 45, a positive number, but 5 and 9 are not two negative numbers.

Valid reasoning includes a true conditional paired with given information that satisfies the hypothesis. Invalid reasoning results when a true conditional is paired with information that satisfies the conclusion.

Example 2

APPLICATION

Advertising

Determine if a true conclusion can be reached from the two statements "If you want a steak that's grilled to perfection, then go to Morton's" and "Gail went to Morton's" using the law of detachment. If a valid conclusion is possible, state it.

Hypothesis: you want a steak that's grilled to perfection

Conclusion: go to Morton's

Given: Gail went to Morton's.

Morton's Restaurant wants you to conclude that Gail went there because she wanted a steak grilled to perfection. However, she may have gone there because they have good service. Since the given information satisfied the conclusion instead of the hypothesis, we cannot make a valid conclusion.

A second law in logic is the **law of syllogism.** It looks very much like the transitive property of equality that you should remember from your studies in algebra.

Law of Syllogism	If $p \rightarrow q$ and $q \rightarrow r$ are true conditionals, then $p \rightarrow r$ is also true.

Example 3

APPLICATION

Chemistry

FYI···

Mercury is the only metal that is liquid at room temperature. It is used in thermometers and barometers.

Determine if a valid conclusion can be reached from the two statements "If a metal is liquid at room temperature, then it is mercury" and "If a metal is mercury, then its chemical symbol is Hg" using the law of syllogism.

Let *p, q,* and *r* represent each part of the statements.

p: a metal is liquid at room temperature

q: it is mercury

r: its chemical symbol is Hg

The given statements can be represented as $p \rightarrow q$ and $q \rightarrow r$. So, according to the law of syllogism we can conclude that $p \rightarrow r$. That is "If a metal is liquid at room temperature, then its chemical symbol is Hg."

LESSON 2-3   DEDUCTIVE REASONING   83

Checking for Understanding

Exercises 1-15 are designed to help you assess students' understanding through reading, writing, speaking, and modeling. You should work through Exercises 1-4 with your students and then monitor their work on Exercises 5-15.

Error Analysis

Determining whether a valid conclusion follows can be difficult if students get caught up in the content of the statements. Encourage students to analyze each exercise by using letters to represent parts of statements. This should make the structure of the argument clearer.

Closing the Lesson

Writing Activity Ask students to compare and contrast the two laws of deductive reasoning that were presented in this lesson.

Additional Answer

1. Sample answer: If Joan goes to the movies, she will spend half her allowance. Joan goes to the movies.
Conclusion: Joan spends half her allowance.

Communicating Mathematics

Read and study the lesson to answer these questions.

1. Give an example of a correct use of the law of detachment. **See margin.**

2. What is required to use the law of detachment to reach a valid conclusion? **a true conditional and given information that satisfies the hypothesis**

3. "Those who choose Tint and Trim Hair Salon have impeccable taste; and you have impeccable taste" is an example of how an advertiser can misuse the law of detachment to make you come to an invalid conclusion. **3a. I should choose Tint and Trim Hair Salon.**

   a. What conclusion do they want you to make?

   b. Write another example of this type of incorrect use of logic. **See Solutions Manual.**

4. Use the law of syllogism to derive a valid conclusion from these two conditionals. "If two angles are a linear pair, then they are supplementary" and "If two angles are supplementary, then their measures total 180." **If two angles are a linear pair, then their measures total 180.**

Guided Practice

Determine if statement (3) follows from statements (1) and (2) by the law of detachment or the law of syllogism. If it does, state which law you used.

5. (1) If a student is enrolled at Lyons High, then the student has an ID number.
   (2) Joel Nathan is enrolled at Lyons High.
   (3) Joel Nathan has an ID number. **yes; detachment**

6. (1) If an angle measures 123, then it is obtuse.
   (2) $m\angle C = 123$.
   (3) $\angle C$ is obtuse. **yes; detachment**

7. (1) If your car needs more power, use Powerpack Motor Oil.
   (2) Marcus uses Powerpack Motor Oil.
   (3) Marcus needed more power in his car. **no**

8. (1) If you like pizza with everything, then you'll like Jimmy's Pizza.
   (2) If you like Jimmy's Pizza, then you are a pizza connoisseur.
   (3) If you like pizza with everything, then you are a pizza connoisseur. **yes; syllogism**

9. (1) If a rectangle has four congruent sides, then it is a square.
   (2) A square has diagonals that are perpendicular.
   (3) A rectangle has diagonals that are perpendicular. **no**

Determine if a conclusion can be reached from the two given statements using the law of detachment or the law of syllogism. If a conclusion is possible, state it and the law that is used. If a conclusion does not follow, state "No conclusion."

10. (1) If you want the best hamburger in town, then buy a Biggie Burger.
    (2) Pat Gorman bought a Biggie Burger. **no conclusion**

11. (1) If $\overline{AB}$ is a segment, then $\overline{AB} \cong \overline{AB}$.
    (2) $\overline{CD}$ is a segment. $\overline{CD} \cong \overline{CD}$; **detachment**

12. If two angles form a linear pair, then they are adjacent; syllogism

13. Planes $\mathcal{M}$ and $\mathcal{N}$ intersect in a line; detachment

12. (1) If two angles form a linear pair, then they share a common ray.
    (2) If two angles share a common ray then they are adjacent.

13. (1) Two planes intersect in a line.
    (2) Planes $\mathcal{M}$ and $\mathcal{N}$ intersect.

14. (1) Sponges belong to the phylum porifera.
    (2) Sponges are animals. **no conclusion**

15. (1) Bobby Rahal has raced in the Indianapolis 500.
    (2) Only professional race car drivers have raced in the Indianapolis 500.
    Bobby Rahal is a professional race car driver; detachment

EXERCISES

Practice

Determine if statement (3) follows from statements (1) and (2) by the law of detachment or the law of syllogism. If it does, state which law was used.

16. (1) If you are not satisfied with a tape, then you can return it within a week for a full refund.
    (2) Joe is not satisfied with a tape. **yes; detachment**
    (3) Joe can return the tape within a week for a full refund.

17. (1) If fossil fuels are burned, then acid rain is produced.
    (2) If acid rain falls, wildlife suffers.
    (3) If fossil fuels are burned, then wildlife suffers. **yes; syllogism**

CONNECTION
Algebra

18. (1) If x is a real number, then x^2 is nonnegative.
    (2) x^2 is nonnegative.
    (3) x is a real number. **no**

19. (1) If an angle measures less than 90, then it is acute.
    (2) $m\angle A$ is less than 90.
    (3) $\angle A$ is acute. **yes; detachment**

LESSON 2-3   DEDUCTIVE REASONING   85

RETEACHING THE LESSON

Develop diagrams of the law of detachment and the law of syllogism.

Write these on the chalkboard.
Law of detachment
If _____ , then _____ .
_____ is true.
Conclusion: _____ .
Have students fill in the blanks with several different true conditionals.

Law of syllogism
If _____ , then _____ .
If _____ , then _____ .
Conclusion: If _____ ,then
_____ .

Again, have students fill in the blanks with different statements to get a sense of the structure of this type of argument.

For Exercise 26, no valid conclusion is possible based on the laws of deductive reasoning. However, the statement "∠*A* is a right angle" is a valid conclusion of the converse of this conditional statement, which happens to be true also. Point this out, since students may be confused because a true statement about ∠*A* is obvious from the given statements. A similar situation arises in Exercise 28.

For Exercise 38, elicit that valid conclusions can be drawn only from true conditionals and true statements.

Additional Answer

27. **If an ordered pair for a point has 0 as its *x*-coordinate, then it is not contained in any of the four quadrants; syllogism.**

Practice Masters Booklet, p. 12

2-3 Practice Worksheet

Deductive Reasoning

Determine if a conclusion can be reached from the two given statements using the law of detachment or the law of syllogism. If a conclusion is possible, state it and the law that is used. If a conclusion does not follow, state "no conclusion".

1. If Jim is a Texan, then he is an American.
   Jim is a Texan. Jim is an American.; detachment
2. If spot is a dog, then he has four legs.
   Spot has four legs. no conclusion
3. If Rachel lives in Tampa, then Rachel lives in Florida.
   If Rachel lives in Florida, then Rachel lives in the U.S.A. If Rachel lives in Tampa, then Rachel lives in the U.S.A.; syllogism
4. If October 12 is a Monday, then October 13 is a Tuesday.
   October 12 is a Monday. October 13 is a Tuesday.; detachment
5. If Henry studies his algebra, then he passes the test.
   If Henry passes the test, then he will get a good grade. If Henry studies his algebra, then he will get a good grade.; syllogism

Determine if statement (3) follows from statements (1) and (2) by the law of detachment or the law of syllogism. If it does, state which law was used.

6. (1) If the measure of an angle is greater than 90, then it is obtuse.
   (2) m∠T is greater than 90.
   (3) ∠T is obtuse. yes; detachment
7. (1) If Pedro is taking history, then he will study about World War II.
   (2) Pedro will study about World War II.
   (3) Pedro is taking history. no
8. (1) If Julie works after school, then she works in a department store.
   (2) Julie works after school.
   (3) Julie works in a department store. yes; detachment
9. (1) If William is reading, then he is reading a magazine.
   (2) If William is reading a magazine, then he is reading a magazine about computers.
   (3) If William is reading, then he is reading a magazine about computers. yes; syllogism
10. (1) A vocalist can read music.
    (2) Ann Marie can read music.
    (3) Ann Marie is a vocalist. no

T12
Glencoe Division, Macmillan/McGraw-Hill

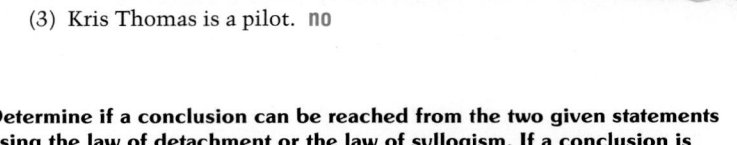

20. (1) Careful bicycle riders wear helmets.
    (2) Riders who wear helmets have fewer injuries.
    (3) Careful bicycle riders have fewer injuries. **yes; syllogism**

21. (1) All pilots must pass a physical examination.
    (2) Kris Thomas must pass a physical examination.
    (3) Kris Thomas is a pilot. **no**

Determine if a conclusion can be reached from the two given statements using the law of detachment or the law of syllogism. If a conclusion is possible, state it and the law that is used. If a conclusion does not follow, state "No conclusion."

22. (1) If you are looking for the excitement of a new car, then you should make tracks to your Pontiac® dealer.
    (2) Ann made tracks to the Pontiac® dealer. **no conclusion**

23. (1) If *A* is between *B* and *C*, then *A*, *B*, and *C* are collinear.
    (2) *A* is between *B* and *C*. **A, B, and C are collinear; detachment**

24. (1) If a quadrilateral is a rectangle, then it has four right angles.
    (2) A rectangle has diagonals that are congruent. **no conclusion**

25. (1) If two lines intersect, then they have a point in common.
    (2) Lines *p* and *q* intersect. **p and q have a point in common; detachment**

26. (1) If an angle is right, then it measures 90°.
    (2) m∠A = 90 **no conclusion**

27. (1) If an ordered pair for a point has 0 as its *x*-coordinate, then the point lies on the *y*-axis.
    (2) If a point lies on the *y*-axis, then it is not contained in any of the four quadrants. **See margin.**

28. (1) In an ordered pair, if the *x*-coordinate is negative and the *y*-coordinate is positive, then the point lies in Quadrant II.
    (2) Point *Q* lies in Quadrant II. **no conclusion**

29. (1) If ∠*A* ≅ ∠*B* and ∠*B* ≅ ∠*C*, then ∠*A* ≅ ∠*C*.
    (2) ∠*A* ≅ ∠*C*. **no conclusion**

30. (1) Parallel lines do not intersect.
    (2) If lines do not intersect, then they have no points in common. **Parallel lines have no points in common; syllogism**

31. (1) If *M* is the midpoint of $\overline{AB}$, then *AM* = *MB*.
    (2) *FG* = *GH*. **no conclusion**

32. (1) Right angles are congruent.
    (2) ∠*A* ≅ ∠*B* **no conclusion**

33. (1) Basalt is an igneous rock.
    (2) Igneous rocks were formed by volcanos. **Basalt was formed by volcanos; syllogism**

Additional Answers

Answers for Exercises 34-37 may vary. Sample answers are given.

34a. (2) I'm looking for a fun car to drive.
     (3) I need a Tigercub.
34b. (2) Someone who needs a Tigercub must have a good driving record.
     (3) If you are looking for a fun car to drive, then you must have a good driving record.

35a. (2) Angles *X* and *Y* are adjacent and supplementary.
     (3) Angles *X* and *Y* are right angles.
35b. (2) Right angles measure 90°.
     (3) Angles that are adjacent and supplementary measure 90°.

Using the given statement, create a second statement and a valid conclusion that illustrates the correct use of the law of detachment. Then write a statement and a conclusion that illustrate the correct use of the law of syllogism. **See margin.**

34. If you're looking for a fun car to drive, then you need a Tigercub.

35. Angles that are adjacent and supplementary are right angles.

36. If the coordinates of a point satisfy the equation of a line, then the point lies on the line.

37. All physicians have graduated from medical school.

Critical Thinking

38. An advertisement states that "If you like skiing, then you'll love SnowLinks." You like to ski, but when you went to SnowLinks, you didn't like it there. Where did the logic break down? **See margin.**

Applications

If possible, write a valid conclusion. State the law of logic that you used.

39. **Geology**
   ▪ If a mineral sample is a sample of quartz, then the sample has a hardness factor of 7.
   ▪ If a mineral sample has a hardness factor greater than 5, then it can scratch glass. **See margin.**

40. **Biology**
   ▪ All species in the plant family Maalvaceae have five petals.
   ▪ A wild rose has five petals. **no valid conclusion**

41. **Advertising** Conditionals and logic are often used in advertising. Look through some newspapers and magazines for advertisements that use logic and evaluate the arguments. **See students' work.**

Mixed Review
42. If a geometry test score is 89, then it is above average.

42. Write the statement "An 89 is an above average score on the geometry test" in if-then form. **(Lesson 2-2)**

43. Is an angle that measures 67° acute, obtuse, right, or straight? **(Lesson 1-7)** acute

44. Find the ordered pair for the midpoint of $\overline{GH}$ with endpoints $G(4, 8)$ and $H(-3, 0)$. **(Lesson 1-5)** $\left(\frac{1}{2}, 4\right)$

45. Use the distance formula to find the measure of $\overline{XY}$ with endpoints $X(5, -3)$ and $Y(0, -5)$. **(Lesson 1-4)** $\sqrt{29}$

46. Draw and label a figure that shows perpendicular lines ℓ and m. **(Lesson 1-2)** **See Solutions Manual.**

Wrap-Up
47. Write and design an advertisement for one of your favorite products that uses the law of detachment to convince a person your argument is true. **See students' work.**

LESSON 2-3   DEDUCTIVE REASONING   87

EXTENDING THE LESSON

Math Power: Problem Solving

Arrange these statements so that, by the law of syllogism, you can conclude that Dexter has four legs.
A. All cats have four legs.
B. Dexter is in the basket.
C. If Alice has a pet, it is a cat.
D. If there is anything in the basket, it is Alice's pet.   D and B let you conclude that Dexter is Alice's pet. Then C and A let you conclude that Dexter has four legs.

Lesson Resources

• Reteaching Master 2-4
• Practice Master 2-4
• Enrichment Master 2-4
• Evaluation Master, Quiz B, p. 23
• Evaluation Master, Mid-Chaper Test, p. 27
• Activity Master, p. 30

 Transparency 2-4 contains the 5-Minute Check and a teaching aid for this lesson.

INTRODUCING THE LESSON

 5-Minute Check

(over lesson 2-3)

Draw a conclusion if possible.

1. All rectangles have congruent diagonals. *ABCD* is a rectangle. **ABCD has congruent diagonals.**

2. All squares have four congruent sides. *GHIJ* has four congruent sides. **no conclusion**

3. If *ℓ* is perpendicular to *m*, then ∠*ABC* is a right angle. If ∠*ABC* is a right angle, then ∠*CBD* is complementary to ∠*DBA*. *ℓ* is perpendicular to *m*. **∠CBD is complementary to ∠DBA.**

4. If *x* is divisible by 4, it is an even number. If *x* is divisible by 3, it may be an even or odd number. *x* is an even number. **no conclusion**

Motivating the Lesson

What can you conclude if you know that ∠*A* measures 40° and ∠*B* measures 40°? ∠*A* ≅ ∠*B*

TEACHING THE LESSON

Teaching Tip After reading the properties of equality table, remind students that *a*, *b*, and *c* can be fractions or decimals for any of these properties.

Objective
2-4

After studying this lesson, you should be able to:
■ use properties of equality in algebraic and geometric proofs.

Certain rules apply to every field of study. Gravity is one of the rules of science.

You are familiar with many of the rules of algebra. These rules, along with various defined operations and sets of numbers form a mathematical system. Working within the rules of the system allows you to perform algebraic operations.

Geometry is another example of a mathematical system. Since it also deals with variables, numbers, and operations, many of the rules of algebra are also used in geometry. Some of the important ones are listed in the table below.

Properties of Equality for Real Numbers	
Reflexive Property	For every number a, $a = a$.
Symmetric Property	For all numbers a and b, if $a = b$, then $b = a$.
Transitive Property	For all numbers a, b, and c, if $a = b$ and $b = c$, then $a = c$.
Addition and Subtraction Properties	For all numbers a, b, and c, if $a = b$, then $a + c = b + c$ and $a - c = b - c$.
Multiplication and Division Properties	For all numbers a, b, and c, if $a = b$, then $a \cdot c = b \cdot c$, and if $c \neq 0$, $\frac{a}{c} = \frac{b}{c}$.
Substitution Property	For all numbers a and b, if $a = b$, then a may be replaced by b in any equation or expression.
Distributive Property	For all numbers a, b, and c, $a(b + c) = ab + ac$.

You will need to recognize and use these properties in problems.

ALTERNATE TEACHING STRATEGIES

Using Critical Thinking

Have students name several ways to conclude that two angles are congruent. Some possibilities are proving that they are both right angles, showing that they have equal parts, and showing that they are each equal to a third angle.

Using Discussion

Ask students to discuss how formal proofs relate to the law of detachment and the law of syllogism presented in lesson 2-4. The proofs use both of these laws in drawing conclusions.

Since segment measures and angle measures are real numbers, these properties from algebra can be used to discuss their relationships. Some examples of these applications are shown below.

Property	Segments	Angles
Reflexive	$AB = AB$	$m\angle C = m\angle C$
Symmetric	If $XY = YZ$, then $YZ = XY$.	If $m\angle 1 = m\angle 2$, then $m\angle 2 = m\angle 1$.
Transitive	If $MN = NO$ and $NO = OP$, then $MN = OP$.	If $m\angle K = m\angle L$ and $m\angle L = m\angle M$, then $m\angle K = m\angle M$.

Example 1

CONNECTION
Algebra

Name the property of equality that justifies each statement.

Statements	Properties
a. If $5 = x$, then $x = 5$.	**a.** Symmetric property
b. If $\frac{1}{2}x = 9$, then $x = 18$.	**b.** Multiplication property
c. If $AB = 2x$ and $AB = CD$, then $CD = 2x$.	**c.** Substitution and symmetric properties
d. If $2AB = 2CD$, then $AB = CD$.	**d.** Division property

You can use these properties as reasons for the step-by-step solution of an equation.

Example 2

CONNECTION
Algebra

Justify each step in solving $2x - 3 = \frac{2}{3}$.

Statements	Reasons
1. $2x - 3 = \frac{2}{3}$	**1.** Given
2. $3(2x - 3) = 2$	**2.** Multiplication property
3. $6x - 9 = 2$	**3.** Distributive property
4. $6x = 11$	**4.** Addition property
5. $x = \frac{11}{6}$	**5.** Division property

Example 2 is a proof of the conditional "If $2x - 3 = \frac{2}{3}$, then $x = \frac{11}{6}$." The given information relates to the hypothesis of the conditional. It is the starting point of the proof. The conclusion, $x = \frac{11}{6}$, is the end of the proof. The fact that reasons (properties) are listed with the steps leading to the conclusion makes this sequence a proof.

Proofs in geometry can be organized in the same manner. The algebra properties and definitions, postulates, and other true statements can be used as reasons. Most of the time we will write proofs in geometry in **two-column** form. These are considered to be formal proofs.

LESSON 2-4 PROPERTIES FROM ALGEBRA AND PROOF 89

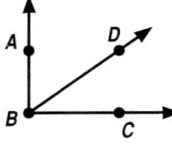
Example 3

Justify the steps for the proof of the conditional "If *AB = CD*, then *AC = BD*." *Remember that AB, CD, AC, and BD represent real numbers.*

Given: $AB = CD$
Prove: $AC = BD$

Statements	Reasons
1. $AB = CD$	1. ?
2. $BC = BC$	2. ?
3. $AB + BC = CD + BC$	3. ?
4. $AC = AB + BC$ $BD = BC + CD$	4. ?
5. $AC = BD$	5. ?

Reason 1: "Given" since it follows from the hypothesis
Reason 2: Reflexive property of equality
Reason 3: Addition property of equality
Reason 4: Segment addition postulate
Reason 5: Substitution property of equality   *Applied twice to Step 3.*

CHECKING FOR UNDERSTANDING

Communicating Mathematics

Read and study the lesson to answer these questions.

1. Make a flash card for each of the properties of equality in this lesson. On the front of the card put the name of the property. On the back of the card, put the explanation that goes with the property. Practice your flash cards.

2. Describe the differences between the reflexive, symmetric, and transitive properties. **See students' work.**

3. In your own words, explain the meaning of *proof*. **See students' work.**

4. What part of a conditional is related to the *Given* statement of a proof? What part is related to the *Prove* statement? **hypothesis; conclusion**

Guided Practice

Answers may vary. Sample answers are given.

Name the property of equality that justifies each statement.

5. If $3x + 7 = 12$, then $3x = 5$. **Subtraction**
6. If $2(x + 5) = 13$, then $2x + 10 = 13$. **Distributive**
7. If $5x = 7$, then $x = \frac{7}{5}$. **Division**
8. If $AB = CD$, then $AB + EF = CD + EF$. **Addition**
9. If $m\angle A + m\angle B = 180$ and $m\angle B = 30$, then $m\angle A + 30 = 180$. **Substitution**

Copy each proof, then name the property that justifies each statement.

10. Prove that if $2x + 3 = 7$, then $x = 2$.

Given: $2x + 3 = 7$
Prove: $x = 2$

Statements	Reasons
a. $2x + 3 = 7$	**a.** _?_ Given
b. $2x = 4$	**b.** _?_ Subtraction property of equality
c. $x = 2$	**c.** _?_ Division property of equality

11. Prove that if $m\angle 1 = m\angle 3$, then $m\angle ABD = m\angle CBE$.

Given: $m\angle 1 = m\angle 3$
Prove: $m\angle ABD = m\angle CBE$

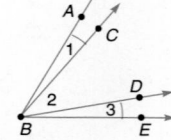

Statements	Reasons
a. $m\angle 1 = m\angle 3$	**a.** _?_ Given
b. $m\angle 2 = m\angle 2$	**b.** _?_ Reflexive prop. of equality
c. $m\angle 1 + m\angle 2 = m\angle 3 + m\angle 2$	**c.** _?_ Addition property of equality
d. $m\angle ABD = m\angle 1 + m\angle 2$ $m\angle CBE = m\angle 3 + m\angle 2$	**d.** _?_ Angle addition postulate
e. $m\angle ABD = m\angle CBE$	**e.** _?_ Substitution prop. of equality

EXERCISES

 Practice

A ▶

Answers may vary. Sample answers are given.

Name the property of equality that justifies each statement.

12. If $x + 4 = -3$, then $x = -7$. **Subtraction**

13. If $y = 2x + 3$ and $x = 2$, then $y = 7$. **Substitution**

14. If $\frac{1}{2}m\angle F = \frac{1}{2}m\angle G$, then $m\angle F = m\angle G$. **Multiplication**

15. If $AB + BC = AC$ and $AC = EF + GH$, then $AB + BC = EF + GH$. **Transitive**

16. If $m\angle A = 90$ and $m\angle B = 90$, then $m\angle A = m\angle B$. **Substitution**

17. $m\angle A = m\angle A$. **Reflexive**

18. If $m\angle 1 = m\angle 2$, then $m\angle 2 = m\angle 1$. **Symmetric**

19. If $AB + BC = 12$, then $BC = 12 - AB$. **Subtraction**

20. If $x + y = 9$ and $x - y = 12$, then $2x = 21$. **Addition**

21. If $AB - CD = EF - CD$, then $AB = EF$. **Addition**

LESSON 2-4   PROPERTIES FROM ALGEBRA AND PROOF   91

Closing the Lesson
Speaking Activity Give students the statements "$\angle 1 \cong \angle 2$" and "$\angle 1$ and $\angle 2$ are a linear pair." Ask them to discuss what conclusion(s) they can draw and to describe how they would write a formal proof.

APPLYING THE LESSON

Homework Exercises

Assignment Guide

Basic: 12-24 30-31, 34-38
Average: 16-27, 30-32, 34-38
Enriched: 19-38
All: Mid-Chapter Review, 1-12

Additional Answers

26. Given: $4 - x = 10$
Prove: $x = -6$
Statements (Reasons)
a. $4 - x = 10$ (Given)
b. $-x = 6$ (Subtraction prop. of equality)
c. $x = -6$ (Multiplication prop. of equality)

27. Given: $m\angle M = m\angle P$, $m\angle N = m\angle P$
Prove: $m\angle M = m\angle N$
Statements (Reasons)
a. $m\angle M = m\angle P$, $m\angle N = m\angle P$ (Given)
b. $m\angle M = m\angle N$ (Transitive prop. of equality)

28. Given: $x - 1 = \dfrac{x - 10}{-2}$
Prove: $x = 4$
Statements (Reasons)
a. $x - 1 = \dfrac{x - 10}{-2}$ (Given)
b. $-2(x - 1) = x - 10$ (Multiplication prop. of equality)
c. $-2x + 2 = x - 10$ (Distributive prop.)
d. $12 = 3x$ (Addition prop. of equality)
e. $4 = x$ (Division prop. of equality)
f. $x = 4$ (Symmetric prop. of equality)

Reteaching Masters Booklet, p. 12

Copy each proof, then name the property that justifies each statement.

22. Prove that if $\frac{2}{3}x = -8$, then $x = -12$.

Given: $\frac{2}{3}x = -8$
Prove: $x = -12$

Statements	Reasons
a. $\frac{2}{3}x = -8$	a. __?__ Given
b. $2x = -24$	b. __?__ Multiplication prop. of equality
c. $x = -12$	c. __?__ Division prop. of equality

23. Prove that if $5 = 2 - \frac{1}{2}x$, then $x = -6$.

Given: $5 = 2 - \frac{1}{2}x$
Prove: $x = -6$

Statements	Reasons
a. $5 = 2 - \frac{1}{2}x$	a. __?__ Given
b. $2 - \frac{1}{2}x = 5$	b. __?__ Symmetric prop. of equality
c. $2(2 - \frac{1}{2}x) = 10$	c. __?__ Multiplication prop. of equality
d. $4 - x = 10$	d. __?__ Distributive prop.
e. $-x = 6$	e. __?__ Subtraction prop. of equality
f. $x = -6$	f. __?__ Multiplication prop. of equality

24. Prove that if $2x - 7 = \frac{1}{3}x - 2$, then $x = 3$.

Given: $2x - 7 = \frac{1}{3}x - 2$
Prove: $x = 3$

Statements	Reasons
a. $2x - 7 = \frac{1}{3}x - 2$	a. __?__ Given
b. $3(2x - 7) = 3(\frac{1}{3}x - 2)$	b. __?__ Multiplication prop. of equality
c. $6x - 21 = x - 6$	c. __?__ Distributive prop.
d. $5x - 21 = -6$	d. __?__ Subtraction property of equality
e. $5x = 15$	e. __?__ Addition property of equality
f. $x = 3$	f. __?__ Division property of equality

RETEACHING THE LESSON

Name the property that justifies each statement.

1. If $x = 4$ and $2x + y = 4$, then $2(4) + y = 4$. substitution prop. of equality

2. If $2x - 5 = 3$, then $2x - 5 + 5 = 3 + 5$. addition prop. of equality

3. If $\angle 1 \cong \angle 2$ and $\angle 2 \cong \angle 3$, then $\angle 1 \cong \angle 3$. transitive prop. of equality

4. $AB = AB$ reflexive prop. of equality

25. Prove that if $m\angle ABD = m\angle EFH$ and $m\angle 2 = m\angle 4$, then $m\angle 1 = m\angle 3$.

Given: $m\angle ABD = m\angle EFH$
$m\angle 2 = m\angle 4$

Prove: $m\angle 1 = m\angle 3$

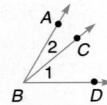
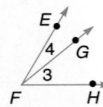

Statements	Reasons
a. $m\angle ABD = m\angle EFH$ $m\angle 2 = m\angle 4$	**a.** __?__ Given
b. $m\angle ABD = m\angle 1 + m\angle 2$ $m\angle EFH = m\angle 3 + m\angle 4$	**b.** __?__ Angle addition postulate
c. $m\angle 1 + m\angle 2 = m\angle 3 + m\angle 4$	**c.** __?__ Substitution prop. of equality
d. $m\angle 1 + m\angle 4 = m\angle 3 + m\angle 4$	**d.** __?__ Substitution prop. of equality
e. $m\angle 1 = m\angle 3$	**e.** __?__ Subtraction prop. of equality

Write a complete proof for each of the following. See margin.

26. If $4 - x = 10$, then $x = -6$.

27. If $m\angle M = m\angle P$ and $m\angle N = m\angle P$, then $m\angle M = m\angle N$.

28. If $x - 1 = \dfrac{x - 10}{-2}$, then $x = 4$.

29. If $m\angle ABC = 90$, $m\angle EDC = 90$, and $m\angle 1 = m\angle 3$, then $m\angle 2 = m\angle 4$.

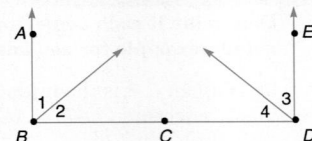

Critical Thinking

30. Choose a basic rule from a field of study or a sport and negate it. Investigate the results. For example, what would change about the game of golf if the player with the highest score wins? **See students' work.**

Applications

31. Banking The formula for finding the amount in a bank account after adding the amount earned from simple interest is $A = p + prt$, where p is the principal, r is the annual interest rate, and t is the time in years. Solve the formula for p and justify each step. **See margin.**

32. Physics The distance, s, that an object travels is found by $s = \frac{1}{2}at^2 + v_o t$, where a is the acceleration, t is the time, and v_o is the initial velocity. Solve the formula for a and justify each step. **See margin.**

33. Language Arts Find relationships other than equality that are reflexive, symmetric, or transitive. For example, "is a relative of" is symmetric and "is taller than" is transitive. **See students' work.**

Additional Answers

31. Given: $A = p + prt$

Prove: $p = \dfrac{A}{1 + rt}$

Statements   (Reasons)

a. $A = p + prt$ (Given)

b. $A = p(1 + rt)$ (Distributive prop.)

c. $\dfrac{A}{1 + rt} = p$ (Division prop. of equality)

d. $p = \dfrac{A}{1 + rt}$ (Symmetric prop. of equality)

32. Given $s = \frac{1}{2}at^2 + v_o t$

Prove: $a = \dfrac{2s - 2vt}{t^2}$

Statements   (Reasons)

a. $s = \frac{1}{2}at^2 + v_o t$ (Given)

b. $s - v_o t = \frac{1}{2}at^2$ (Subtraction prop. of equality)

c. $2(s - v_o t) = at^2$ (Multiplication prop. of equality)

d. $2s - 2v_o t = at^2$ (Distributive prop.)

e. $\dfrac{2s - 2v_o t}{t^2} = a$ (Division prop. of equality)

f. $a = \dfrac{2s - 2v_o t}{t^2}$ (Symmetric prop. of equality)

Practice Masters Booklet, p. 13

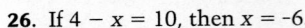

Additional Answers

29. Given: $m\angle ABC = 90$, $m\angle EDC = 90$, $m\angle 1 = m\angle 3$

Prove: $m\angle 2 = m\angle 4$

Statements   (Reasons)

a. $m\angle ABC = 90$, $m\angle EDC = 90$, $m\angle 1 = m\angle 3$ (Given)

b. $m\angle ABC = m\angle EDC$ (Substitution prop. of equality)

c. $m\angle ABC = m\angle 1 + m\angle 2$, $m\angle EDC = m\angle 3 + m\angle 4$ (Angle addition postulate)

d. $m\angle 1 + m\angle 2 = m\angle 3 + m\angle 4$ (Substitution prop. of equality)

e. $m\angle 1 + m\angle 2 = m\angle 1 + m\angle 4$ (Substitution prop. of equality)

f. $m\angle 2 = m\angle 4$ (Subtraction prop. of equality)

Mixed Review

34. If possible, write a valid conclusion. State the law of logic that you used. **(Lesson 2-3)**
   - If a is a real number, then $a = a$.
   - 7 is a real number. 7 = 7; detachment

35. Use a calculator to find the decimal equivalents of $\frac{1}{9}$, $\frac{2}{9}$, $\frac{3}{9}$, and $\frac{4}{9}$. Make a conjecture about the decimal equivalent of $\frac{5}{9}$. Use your calculator to check your answer. **(Lesson 2-1)** $\frac{5}{9} = 0.\overline{5}$

36. Find the coordinates of the midpoint of the segment whose endpoints are at (9, 3), and (-3, 8). **(Lesson 1-5)** $\left(3, \frac{11}{2}\right)$

37. Draw and label a figure that shows the relationship "N lies on line ℓ." **(Lesson 1-2)** See margin.

Wrap-Up

38. Write three multiple-choice questions that could be used as part of a quiz on this lesson. See students' work.

MID-CHAPTER REVIEW

Determine if each conjecture is *true* or *false*. Explain your answers and give a counterexample for any false conjecture. (Lesson 2-1) See margin.

1. Given: A is the midpoint of $\overline{BC}$.
   Conjecture: $AB = AC$
2. Given: x is a real number.
   Conjecture: x^3 is a real number.
3. Given: Points A, B, and C are collinear.
   Conjecture: B is between A and C.
4. Given: $\angle 1$ and $\angle 2$ are right angles.
   Conjecture: $\angle 1 \cong \angle 2$

Write each conditional statement in if-then form. (Lesson 2-2) See margin.

5. Perpendicular lines form four right angles.
6. The chemical formula for ordinary table sugar is $C_{12}H_{22}O_{11}$.
7. The month of February has 28 days in a non-leap year.

Determine if a conclusion can be drawn from the two statements using the law of detachment or the law of syllogism. If a conclusion is possible, state it and the law used. If a conclusion does not follow, state *No conclusion*. (Lesson 2-3)

8. (1) If you are a music lover, then you can read music.
   (2) Shelly can read music. no conclusion
9. (1) If a polygon is a square, then its diagonals are congruent.
   (2) $ABCD$ is a square.
10. (1) If two angles are right angles, then they are congruent.
    (2) If two angles are congruent, then they have the same measure.

9. The diagonals of *ABCD* are congruent; detachment   10. See margin.

Write a two-column proof. (Lesson 2-4) See Solutions Manual.

11. Prove that if $x = 7$, then $4x^2 = 196$.
12. Prove that if $AC = AB$, $AC = 4x + 1$, and $AB = 6x - 13$ then $x = 7$.

EXTENDING THE LESSON

Math Power: Applications

In pipeline design the average velocity, u, is given by the equation

$$u = \frac{4q}{\pi D^2}$$

where D is the pipe diameter (ft) and q is the volumetric flow rate (ft³/s). Solve the formula for q.

$$q = \frac{\pi D^2 u}{4}$$

Mid-Chapter Review

The Mid-Chapter Review provides strudents with a brief review of the concepts and skills in Lessons 2-1 through 2-4. Lesson numbers are given at the end of problems or instructional lines so students may review concepts not yet mastered.

Problem-Solving Strategy: Process of Elimination

Objective
2-5
After studying this lesson, you should be able to:
- solve problems by eliminating possibilities.

Many everyday problems have several possible solutions. Deductive reasoning can be used to eliminate some of those possibilities and choose the correct solution.

Example

CONNECTION
Geology

On a recent geology test, Rena was given five different mineral samples to identify using the portion of a mineral characteristics chart shown at the right. Rena made the following observations about the samples.

1. **Sample C is softer than glass.**
2. **Samples D and E are red and Sample C is brown.**
3. **Samples B and E are harder than glass.**

Mineral	Color	Hardness
Biotite	brown or black	softer than glass
Halite	white	softer than glass
Hematite	red	softer than glass
Feldspar	white, pink, or green	harder than glass
Jasper	red	harder than glass

Make a chart showing the sample names and the minerals. Use the observations to mark Xs where possibilities are eliminated and ✔s where matches are found.

Observation 1 indicates that Sample C is softer than glass. So, the minerals that are harder than glass, feldspar and jasper, can be eliminated as possible choices for Sample C.

Sample	A	B	C	D	E
Biotite					
Halite					
Hematite					
Feldspar			X		
Jasper			X		

Observation 2 tells us that Samples D and E must be the minerals that are red, namely hematite and jasper. Sample C must be biotite.

Sample	A	B	C	D	E
Biotite			✔	X	X
Halite				X	X
Hematite					
Feldspar			X	X	X
Jasper			X		

Lesson Resources
- Practice Master 2-5
- Activity Master, p. 2
 Transparency 2-5 contains the 5-Minute Check and a teaching aid for this lesson.

INTRODUCING THE LESSON

 5-Minute Check

(over Lesson 2-4)

Name the property that justifies each statement.

1. If $3x = 15$ and $5y = 15$, then $3x = 5y$.   **Substitution prop. of equality**
2. If $4z = -12$, then $z = -3$.   **Division prop. of equality**
3. If $AB = CD$ and $CD = EF$, then $AB = EF$.   **Transitive prop. of equality**
4. If $45 = m\angle A$, then $m\angle A = 45$.   **Symmetric prop. of equality**

Motivating the Lesson
If your book is either in your bag or in your desk, and it is not in your bag, what can you conclude?   **It is in your desk.**

TEACHING THE LESSON

Chalkboard Example

For the Example
Sarah and Candace are friends. One is wearing a yellow shirt. The other is wearing a green shirt. One plays basketball. One plays soccer. The girl in the yellow shirt is older than the girl in the green shirt, who plays basketball. Candace is younger than Sarah. Who is wearing which color? Who plays what sport?   **Sarah, yellow, soccer; Candace, green, basketball**

ALTERNATE TEACHING STRATEGIES

Using Problem Solving
Three brothers, Joe, Dan, and Zack, participate in three different sports: swimming, baseball, and soccer. Neither the oldest brother nor Joe swims. Zack and Joe use a ball in their games. Dan is the middle child. The youngest plays baseball. Who plays what sport, and what is their birth order?   **Zack, oldest, soccer; Dan, middle, swimming; Joe, youngest, baseball**

Using Connections
Explain how a doctor eliminates possibilities when examining a patient. The doctor's questions and/or lab tests are designed to rule out possibilities as part of the diagnostic process.

Checking for Understanding

Exercises 1-4 are designed to help you assess students' understanding through reading, writing, speaking, and modeling. You should work through Exercises 1-2 with your students and then monitor their work on Exercises 3-4.

Closing the Lesson

Speaking Activity Have students explain how the process of elimination can be used to solve problems. Have them give an example of a problem that can be solved this way.

Observation 3 indicates that Sample B and Sample E must be either feldspar or jasper.

Sample	A	B	C	D	E
Biotite		X	✔	X	X
Halite		X		X	X
Hematite		X			X
Feldspar			X	X	X
Jasper		X			

Each row and column must have only one ✔, so we can now complete the chart and draw our conclusions.

Sample	A	B	C	D	E
Biotite	X	X	✔	X	X
Halite	✔	X	X	X	X
Hematite	X	X	X	✔	X
Feldspar	X	✔	X	X	X
Jasper	X	X	X	X	✔

Sample A - halite, Sample B - feldspar, Sample C - biotite, Sample D - hematite, Sample E - jasper

CHECKING FOR UNDERSTANDING

Communicating Mathematics

Read and study the lesson to answer these questions.

1. Describe an effective way of keeping track of the possible solutions you have eliminated. **Make a table and mark eliminations with an X.**

2. Would the chart used to solve the example work if there were two samples of the same mineral? Why or why not? **No, you could not eliminate enough possibilities to make a conclusion.**

Guided Practice

Use the process of elimination to solve each problem.

3. 9th - Anthony, 10th - Erin, 11th - Brad, 12th -Lisa

3. Anthony, Erin, Lisa, and Brad each represent a different grade in the Briggs High School Student Council. Erin is older than Anthony, but younger than Brad. Lisa is older than Brad. Who represents each grade?

4. In Chemistry lab, Al was given four different metal samples to identify. They were gallium, a metal that melts when held in the hand; mercury, which is liquid at room temperature; lithium, which will float in water; and calcium, which bubbles slowly when placed in water. When Al was holding Sample 1, it was a liquid. Sample 2 is a solid and sank to the bottom when dropped in a beaker of water. Bubbling action occurred when Al dropped Sample 4 in the water. Identify each sample.

4. 1 - mercury;
2 - gallium;
3 - lithium; 4 - calcium

Solve by eliminating possibilities.

1. Juanita, Beverly, and Alicia each won a trophy. The trophies were for the spelling bee, the archery contest, and the science fair. Alicia is not a good speller. Beverly did not enter the science fair and is not a good speller either. Who won what?
Alicia, science; Beverly, archery; Juanita, spelling

2. There are three prize boxes at Star's Department Store: a red, a yellow, and a blue. One box contains two tickets to a ball game; one contains a coupon for a free TV; the third contains $1000 in $100 bills. The yellow box contains only one item. The blue box does not contain money. Which box has the tickets to the game? blue

EXERCISES

Practice

7. Umeko - Drama Club, delivery person; Jim - Spanish Club, tutor; Gwen - marching band, lifeguard

9. The jeans box contained T-shirts and jeans, the T-shirts box contained jeans, and the jeans and T-shirts box contained T-shirts.

Solve. Use any strategy.

5. As I stood in the cafeteria line, I observed that there were nine more people behind me than there were ahead of me. There were three times as many people in line as there were people ahead of me. How many people were behind me? **19**

6. If you cut one corner off of a square, how many corners would you have left? **5**

7. Umeko, Jim, and Gwen each participate in an extra-curricular activity and have an after-school job. They are in the Spanish Club, the Drama Club, and the marching band. One of them is a pizza delivery person, one is a math tutor, and one is a lifeguard at the community pool. Jim is tutoring the Drama Club member's brother in Algebra. The Spanish Club member cannot swim or drive a car. The lifeguard is teaching Umeko to read music. Who does what?

8. At how many different times during a 24-hour period are all of the digits on a digital clock the same? **12**

9. Three cartons of clothes were delivered to Dunbar's. One contained jeans, one T-shirts, and one had both jeans and T-shirts. All of the boxes were mislabeled. Jack pulled a T-shirt from the box marked "jeans and T-shirts." Which box contains what?

10. The Boston Tea Party was a notable event of the eighteenth century. The sum of the digits of the year it occurred is 18. The ones digit of the year is $\sqrt[4]{81}$. The Boston Tea Party took place on December 16, _?_ . **1773**

COOPERATIVE LEARNING PROJECT

Work in groups. Each person in the group must understand the solution and be able to explain it to any person in class.

During the first five days of Michelle's summer vacation, she spent each day with a different person: Zach, Luisa, Marcus, Kelly, and her mother. During that week, Michelle spent her mornings swimming, playing chess, shopping, biking, and picnicking. Her afternoons were spent playing tennis, walking, listening to the radio, skateboarding, and painting her room. Use the strategy of eliminating possibilities to determine which day she spent with each person and what they did together in the morning and afternoon of each day.

1. Michelle and Zach spent the afternoon skateboarding.
2. It rained all day on Friday, so Michelle spent the day in the house.
3. Luisa, who cannot swim, spent Thursday with Michelle. They didn't go shopping.
4. Michelle went biking with Marcus two days before helping her mother paint her room.
5. Michelle didn't play tennis on Tuesday or on the day she went bicycling. She didn't go swimming on the day she painted her room.
6. Michelle's mother doesn't play chess. **See margin.**

LESSON 2-5   PROBLEM-SOLVING STRATEGY: PROCESS OF ELIMINATION   97

EXTENDING THE LESSON

Math Power: Reasoning

Use the clues. Which clue was not necessary?

Find a three-digit number that
1. has no digit repeated
2. is divisible by 3
3. is even
4. has no digit less than 1 or greater than 3
5. has a ones' digit that is greater than its hundreds' digit   **132, clue 2**

Cooperative Learning Project

This activity provides students an opportunity to *learn* things together, not just do things. You may wish to refer to pages T6-T7 and page 68c for the various elements of cooperative groups and specific goals and strategies for using them.

Practice Masters Booklet, p. 14

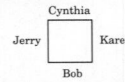

Lesson Resources

- Reteaching Master 2-6
- Practice Master 2-6
- Enrichment Master 2-6
- Evaluation Master, Quiz C, p. 24

 Transparency 2-6 contains the 5-Minute Check and a teaching aid for this lesson

INTRODUCING THE LESSON

 5-Minute Check

(over Lesson 2-5)

Solve by the process of elimination.

1. Find a number greater than 45 but less than 63 that is divisible by 4 but not divisible by 8 or 10. **52**
2. Joan, Tyler, Ana, and Fred ran a race. Neither Joan nor Fred was last. Ana finished just before Tyler and just after Fred. In what order did they finish? **Joan, Fred, Ana, Tyler**

Motivating the Lesson

What do you think proof means to a scientist? Give an example of how a scientist might prove a theory.

TEACHING THE LESSON

Teaching Tip When reading Theorem 2-1, ask students to tell you what *congruent segments* means.

2-6 Two-Column Proofs with Segments

Objective
2-6

After studying this lesson, you should be able to:
- complete proofs involving segment theorems.

Constructing a proof can be confusing.

DO YOU REMEMBER WHAT WE'RE TRYING TO PROVE?

But if you remember that a proof must include the following five essential steps, you will be able to construct any proof.

- State the theorem to be proved.
- List the given information.
- If possible, draw a diagram to illustrate the given information.
- State what is to be proved.
- Develop a system of deductive reasoning.

In order to use deductive reasoning to construct a valid proof, we must rely on statements that are accepted to be true. In geometry, those statements are the definitions and postulates. We also depend on the list of undefined terms.

The statements that are proved through deductive reasoning using definitions, postulates, and undefined terms are called **theorems**. Once a theorem is proved, it becomes another tool that we can use in the system. That is, proved theorems can be used in the proofs of new theorems.

The first theorem that we will look at is similar to some familiar properties from algebra.

Theorem 2-1	**Congruence of segments is reflexive, symmetric, and transitive.**

ALTERNATE TEACHING STRATEGIES

Using Communication
Write a paragraph explaining why, if $\overline{AC} \cong \overline{BD}$, you can conclude that $\overline{AB} \cong \overline{CD}$.

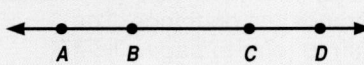

Using Modeling
Congruent figures have the same size and shape. Look around the classroom and identify any objects that you think are congruent. Especially look for items that could be represented by congruent segments. **Sample answer: the place where the wall and ceiling meet and the place where the same wall and floor meet**

Theorem 2-1 can be written in symbols as follows.

Reflexive Property
$$\overline{AB} \cong \overline{AB}$$

Symmetric Property
If $\overline{AB} \cong \overline{CD}$, then $\overline{CD} \cong \overline{AB}$.

Transitive Property
If $\overline{AB} \cong \overline{CD}$ and $\overline{CD} \cong \overline{EF}$, then $\overline{AB} \cong \overline{EF}$.

The symmetric part of Theorem 2-1 is proved below. You will be asked to prove the reflexive and transitive parts in Exercises 4 and 3 respectively.

You can use the properties of algebra in geometric proofs. Notice that the symmetric property of equality is used in the proof of Theorem 2-1.

Proof of
Symmetric Part of
Theorem 2-1

Given: $\overline{AB} \cong \overline{CD}$
Prove: $\overline{CD} \cong \overline{AB}$

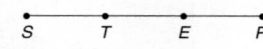

Statements	Reasons
1. $\overline{AB} \cong \overline{CD}$	1. Given
2. $AB = CD$	2. Definition of congruent segments
3. $CD = AB$	3. Symmetric property of equality
4. $\overline{CD} \cong \overline{AB}$	4. Definition of congruent segments

Recall that since the measures of segments are real numbers, the properties of algebra can be used to prove relationships with segment measures.

Since AB and CD represent real numbers, the Symmetric property of equality can be used in Step 3.

Example 1

$\overline{STEP}$ *represents the segment containing points S, T, E, and P. T is between S and E and E is between T and P.*

Justify each step in the proof.

Given: $\overline{STEP}$
Prove: $SP = ST + TE + EP$

Statements	Reasons
1. $\overline{STEP}$	1. $\underline{\ \ ?\ \ }$
2. $SP = ST + TP$	2. $\underline{\ \ ?\ \ }$
3. $TP = TE + EP$	3. $\underline{\ \ ?\ \ }$
4. $SP = ST + TE + EP$	4. $\underline{\ \ ?\ \ }$

Reason 1: Given
Reason 2: Segment addition postulate
Reason 3: Segment addition postulate
Reason 4: Substitution property of equality

Chalkboard Examples

For Example 1
Justify each step in the proof.

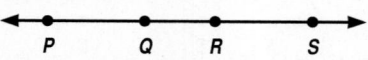

Given: Points P, Q, R, and S are collinear.
Prove: $PQ = PS - QS$
Statements (Reasons)
1. Points P, Q, R, and S are collinear. (Given)
2. $PS = PQ + QS$ (Segment addition postulate)
3. $PS - QS = PQ$ (Subtraction prop. of equality)
4. $PQ = PS - QS$ (Symmetric prop. of equality)

Chalkboard Examples

For Example 2
Write a two column proof.

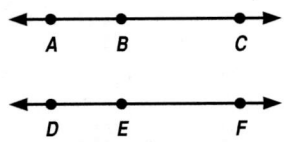

Given $\overline{AC} \cong \overline{DF}$, $\overline{AB} \cong \overline{DE}$
Prove: $\overline{BC} \cong \overline{EF}$
Statements <u>(Reasons)</u>
a. $\overline{AC} \cong \overline{DF}$, $\overline{AB} \cong \overline{DE}$ (Given)
b. $AC = DF$, $AB = DE$
   (Definition of congruent segments)
c. $AC - AB = DF - DE$
   (Subtraction prop. of equality)
d. $AC = AB + BC$, $DF = DE + EF$ (Segment addition postulate)
e. $AC - AB = BC$, $DF - DE = EF$
   (Subtraction prop. of equality)
f. $DF - DE = BC$
   (Substitution prop. of equality)
g. $BC = EF$ (Substitution prop. of equality)
h. $\overline{BC} \cong \overline{EF}$ (Definition of congruent segments)

Teaching Tip In Example 2, students may not recognize that, in statement 3, equal quantities are added to each side.

EVALUATING THE LESSON

Checking for Understanding

Exercises 1-19 are designed to help you assess students' understanding through reading, writing, speaking, and modeling. You should work through Exercises 1-4 with your students and then monitor their work on Exercises 5-19.

Example 2 **Write a two-column proof.**

Given: $\overline{RS} \cong \overline{UV}$
$\overline{ST} \cong \overline{VW}$

Prove: $\overline{RT} \cong \overline{UW}$

Statements	Reasons
1. $\overline{RS} \cong \overline{UV}$ $\overline{ST} \cong \overline{VW}$	1. Given
2. $RS = UV$ $ST = VW$	2. Definition of congruent segments
3. $RS + ST = UV + VW$	3. Addition property of equality
4. $RS + ST = RT$ $UV + VW = UW$	4. Segment addition postulate
5. $RT = UW$	5. Substitution property of equality *Twice*
6. $\overline{RT} \cong \overline{UW}$	6. Definition of congruent segments

CHECKING FOR UNDERSTANDING

Communicating Mathematics

1. Answers may vary. A sample answer is a statement of the theorem, of what is to be proved, of what is given, and a logical argument.

Read and study the lesson to answer these questions.

1. In your own words, describe what must be included in a valid proof.

2. Why can the properties of algebra be used to establish relationships between the measures of segments? **The measures of segments are real numbers.**

3. Copy and complete the proof of the transitive part of Theorem 2-1.

Given: $\overline{AB} \cong \overline{CD}$
$\overline{CD} \cong \overline{EF}$

Prove: $\overline{AB} \cong \overline{EF}$

Statements	Reasons
a. $\overline{AB} \cong \overline{CD}$ $\overline{CD} \cong \overline{EF}$	a. _?_ Given
b. $AB = CD$ $CD = EF$	b. _?_ Definition of congruent segments
c. $AB = EF$	c. _?_ Transitive property of equality
d. $\overline{AB} \cong \overline{EF}$	d. _?_ Definition of congruent segments

4. Write a two-column proof of the reflexive part of Theorem 2-1.

See margin.

Additional Answer

4. Given: $\overline{AB}$
   Prove: $\overline{AB} \cong \overline{AB}$

Statements (Reasons)
a. $\overline{AB}$ is a line segment.
   (Given)
b. $AB = AB$ (Reflexive prop. of equality)
c. $\overline{AB} \cong \overline{AB}$ (Definition of congruent segments)

Guided Practice

Justify each statement with a property from algebra or a property of congruent segments. See margin.

5. $\overline{PS} \cong \overline{PS}$

6. If $AB + BC = BC + CD$, then $AB = CD$.

7. If $\overline{XY} \cong \overline{OP}$, then $\overline{OP} \cong \overline{XY}$.

8. If $2MN = TS$, then $MN = \frac{1}{2}TS$.

9. If $GH = 12$ and $GH + HI = GI$, then $12 + HI = GI$.

10. If $\overline{PQ} \cong \overline{QR}$ and $\overline{QR} \cong \overline{RT}$, then $\overline{PQ} \cong \overline{RT}$.

11. If $AN - 8 = IN - 8$, then $AN = IN$.

12. If $EF = GH$ and $GH = JK$, then $EF = JK$.

Write the given and the prove statements that you would use to prove each theorem. Draw a figure if applicable. See margin.

13. If an angle is a right angle, then its measure is 90.

14. All rational numbers are real.

15. If two angles are vertical, then they are congruent.

16. If two lines are perpendicular, then they form four right angles.

17. The sum of the degree measures of the angles of a triangle is 180.

18. The diagonals of a rectangle are congruent.

19. Copy and complete the proof.

Given: $\overline{LE} \cong \overline{MR}$
$\overline{EG} \cong \overline{RA}$

Prove: $\overline{LG} \cong \overline{MA}$

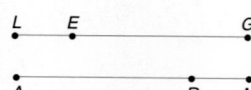

Statements	Reasons
a. $\underline{\ ?\ }$ $\overline{LE} \cong \overline{MR}$ $\underline{\ ?\ }$ $\overline{EG} \cong \overline{RA}$	a. Given
b. $LE = MR$ $EG = RA$	b. $\underline{\ ?\ }$ Definition of congruent segments
c. $LE + EG = LG$ $MR + RA = MA$	c. $\underline{\ ?\ }$ Segment addition postulate
d. $LE + EG = MR + RA$	d. Addition property of equality
e. $\underline{\ ?\ }$ $LG = MA$	e. Substitution property of equality
f. $\overline{LG} \cong \overline{MA}$	f. $\underline{\ ?\ }$ Definition of congruent segments

LESSON 2-6 TWO-COLUMN PROOFS WITH SEGMENTS 101

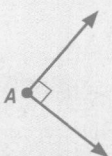
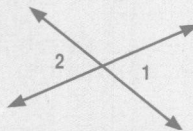
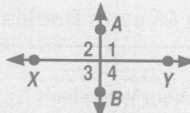
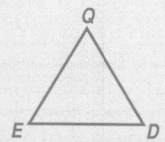

Homework Exercises

Assignment Guide

Basic: 20-25, 30, 31, 33-39
Average: 22-27, 30, 32-39
Enriched: 25-39

Additional Answers

22. Statements (Reasons)
   a. $RS = ST$ (Given)
   b. $RT = RS + ST$ (Segment addition postulate)
   c. $RT = ST + ST$ (Substitution prop. of equality)
   d. $RT = 2ST$ (Substitution prop of equality)

23. Statements (Reasons)
   a. $MP = NP$, $PO = PL$ (Given)
   b. $MP + PO = NP + PL$ (Addition prop. of equality)
   c. $MO = MP + PO$, $NL = NP + PL$ (Segment addition postulate)
   d. $MO = NL$ (Substitution prop. of equality)

Reteaching Masters Booklet, p. 13

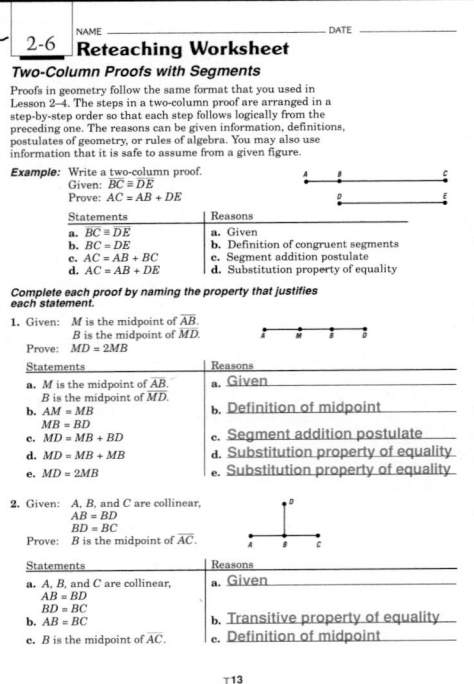

Practice   Copy and complete each proof.

20. **Given:** $DA = EL$
    Prove: $DE = AL$

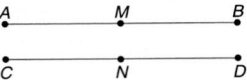

Statements	Reasons
a. __?__ $DA = EL$	a. Given
b. $DA = DE + EA$ $EL = EA + AL$	b. __?__ Segment addition postulate
c. __?__ $DE + EA = EA + AL$	c. Substitution property of equality
d. $DE = AL$	d. __?__ Subtraction property of equality

21. **Given:** $\overline{AB} \cong \overline{CD}$
       M is the midpoint of $\overline{AB}$.
       N is the midpoint of $\overline{CD}$.
    Prove: $\overline{AM} \cong \overline{CN}$

Statements	Reasons
a. $\overline{AB} \cong \overline{CD}$ M is the midpoint of $\overline{AB}$. N is the midpoint of $\overline{CD}$.	a. __?__ Given
b. $AB = CD$	b. __?__ Definition of congruent segments
c. __?__ $AM = MB$ __?__ $CN = ND$	c. Definition of midpoint
d. $AM + MB = AB$ $CN + ND = CD$	d. __?__ Segment addition postulate
e. $AM + MB = CN + ND$	e. __?__ Substitution property of equality
f. $AM + AM = CN + CN$	f. __?__ Substitution property of equality
g. $2AM = 2CN$	g. Substitution property of equality
h. $AM = CN$	h. __?__ Division property of equality
i. $\overline{AM} \cong \overline{CN}$	i. __?__ Definition of congruent segments

Write a two-column proof. See margin.

22. **Given:** $RS = ST$
    Prove: $RT = 2ST$

23. **Given:** $MP = NP$
       $PO = PL$
    Prove: $MO = NL$

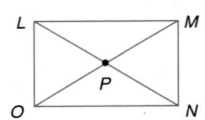

RETEACHING THE LESSON

Have students work in small groups. Give each group three pieces of string or yarn, all the same length but different colors. Ask the groups to use the strings to demonstrate the reflexive, symmetric, and transitive properties of congruence of line segments.

24. Given: $AC = AD$
$AB = AE$
Prove: $BC = ED$

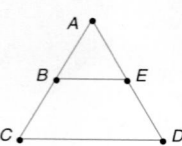

25. Given: $\overline{SA} \cong \overline{ND}$
Prove: $\overline{SN} \cong \overline{AD}$

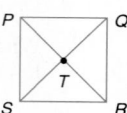

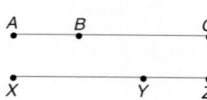
Portfolio

Select an item from this chapter that shows your creativity and place it in your portfolio.

26. Given: $\overline{BC} \cong \overline{YX}$
$\overline{AC} \cong \overline{ZX}$
Prove: $\overline{AB} \cong \overline{ZY}$

27. Given: $\overline{QT} \cong \overline{RT}$
$\overline{TS} \cong \overline{TP}$
Prove: $\overline{QS} \cong \overline{RP}$

C ▶ For each statement, name the given and prove statements, and draw a figure. Then write a two-column proof. See Solutions Manual.

28. If two points separate a segment AB into three congruent segments, then the measure of $\overline{AB}$ is three times the measure of one of the three shorter segments.

29. The midpoints of two segments of equal measure separate the segments into segments with equal measures.

Critical Thinking

30. If you were given that $\overline{EG} \cong \overline{KM}$, $\overline{KM} \cong \overline{JH}$, $\overline{EJ} \cong \overline{GH}$, $\overline{FI} \cong \overline{GH}$, F is the midpoint of EG, L is the midpoint of $\overline{KM}$, and I is the midpoint of $\overline{JH}$, list three statements that you could prove using the postulates, theorems, and definitions that you have learned. Answers may vary. Sample answers are $\overline{EG} \cong \overline{JH}$, and $\overline{EF} \cong \overline{FG} \cong \overline{KL} \cong \overline{LM} \cong \overline{JI} \cong \overline{IH}$.

Applications

31. Law Translate the following lawyer's argument into a two-column proof. "The law states that if a driver proceeds through a red traffic light that is in proper working order, that driver is subject to a $50 fine. The defendant was seen driving through a red traffic light at the corner of Washington and Elm. The traffic computer shows no indication that the signal was down. Therefore, the defendant is guilty and subject to a $50 fine." See Solutions Manual.

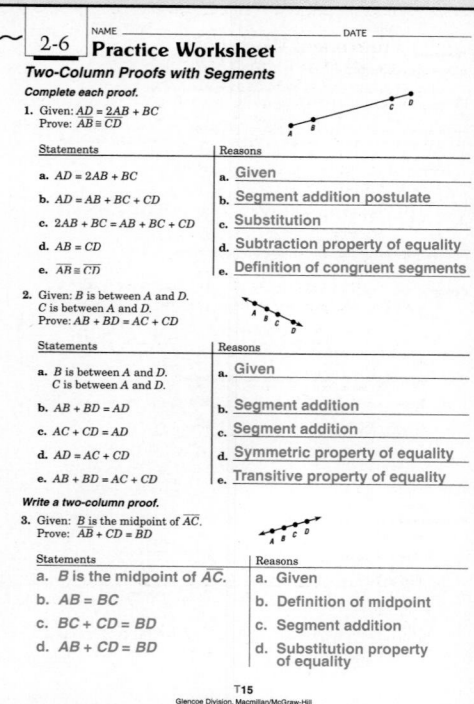

Practice Masters Booklet, p. 15

---

32. Advertising A television ad states "The Runaround is the best small truck on the market. It is priced well below any comparable truck. The Runaround is fun to drive, with room for four and plenty of cargo space. We think you'll find that it's all you need in a truck!"

32a. It is priced well below any comparable truck. It's fun to drive. It has room for four and plenty of cargo space.

a. What reasons do the advertisers give for claiming that "The Runaround is the best small truck on the market"?

b. Do you think they present a convincing argument? **Answers may vary**

c. What other concerns might a car buyer have that the advertisers have not mentioned? **Answers may vary. A sample answer is fuel economy.**

Mixed Review

33. Four friends have birthdays in January, February, August, and September. Amy was not born in the winter. Emma celebrates her birthday during summer vacation. Timothy's birthday is the month after Pablo's. When is each one's birthday? **(Lesson 2-5)** Jan. - Pablo, Feb. - Timothy, Aug. - Emma, Sept. - Amy

34. Name the algebraic property that justifies the statement "If $3x = 12$, then $x = 4$." **(Lesson 2-4)** Division or multiplication property of equality

35. Translate the statement "A student must maintain a C average to be eligible to play a varsity sport" into if-then form. **(Lesson 2-2)**

36. Give a counterexample to show that "What goes up must come down" is a false conditional. **(Lesson 2-1)** a satellite

37. Angles AND and NOR are complementary. If $m\angle AND = 4m\angle NOR$, find the measures of the angles. **(Lesson 1-8)** $m\angle AND = 72$, $m\angle NOR = 18$

38. Refer to the number line to find each length. **(Lesson 1-4)**

a. MN **5 units**

b. NO **2 units**

c. MO **7 units**

d. PM **8 units**

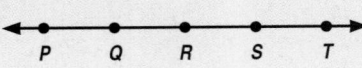

35. If a student maintains a C average, then he or she is eligible to play a varsity spo▮

Wrap-Up

39. Write an example to illustrate what you think is the most important concept in this lesson. **See students' work.**

104   CHAPTER 2   REASONING AND INTRODUCTION TO PROOF

EXTENDING THE LESSON

Math Power: Using Reasoning

Given points P, Q, R, S and T are collinear, and $\overline{PQ} \cong \overline{ST}$, can you prove that $\overline{PR} \cong \overline{TR}$? Explain your answer.

No. To prove $\overline{PR}$ and $\overline{TR}$ are congruent, we must know that $\overline{QR}$ and $\overline{RS}$ are congruent.

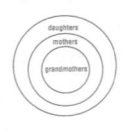

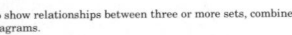
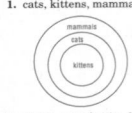 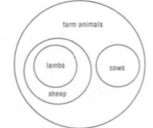

2-7

Two-Column Proof with Angles

Objective
2-7
After studying this lesson, you should be able to:
- complete proofs involving angle theorems.

Application

The Leaning Tower of Pisa, the famous bell tower in Pisa, Italy, is considered to be one of the seven wonders of the modern world. The tower has leaned ever since the ground beneath the tower began to shift after the first three stories were built. Today, the tower stands about 17 feet off the perpendicular. Its lean increases about $\frac{1}{20}$ of an inch per year.

The angle that the tower makes with the ground is about 84° on one side and 96° on the other. If you look at the Leaning Tower of Pisa as a ray and the ground as a line, then the angles the tower forms with the ground form a linear pair. Theorem 2-2 states that if two angles form a linear pair, the angles are supplementary.

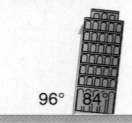

Theorem 2-2 **Supplement** **Theorem**	**If two angles form a linear pair, then they are supplementary angles.** *You will be asked to prove Theorem 2-2 in Exercise 15.*

Example 1

APPLICATION
Construction

The flagpole shown at the right forms an angle of 54° with the wall. Find the measure, x, of the larger angle formed by the flagpole and the wall.

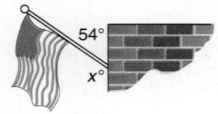

The angles form a linear pair. Using Theorem 2-2, the angles must be supplementary. Since the measures of supplementary angles have a sum of 180, we can write this equation.

$$x + 54 = 180$$
$$x + 54 - 54 = 180 - 54 \qquad \textit{Subtract 54 from each side.}$$
$$x = 126$$

The larger angle measures 126.

INTRODUCING THE LESSON

5-Minute Check
(over Lesson 2-6)

Write a reason for each statement.

1. If $\overline{AB} \cong \overline{CD}$, then $AB = CD$. **Definition of congruent segments**
2. If $GH = JK$, then $GH + LM = JK + LM$. **Addition prop. of equality**
3. R, D, and S are collinear. $RS = RD + DS$ **Segment addition postulate**
4. If $WX = YZ$, then $WX - UV = YZ - UV$ **Subtraction prop. of equality**

Motivating the Lesson

Suppose you had to draw an angle that had the same measure as a given angle, $\angle ABC$. How would you do it without a protractor? **Sample answer: Use tracing paper.**

TEACHING THE LESSON

ALTERNATE TEACHING STRATEGIES

Using Models

Cut out a large cardboard angle. Use it at the chalkboard to demonstrate the theorems of this lesson.

Using Problem Solving

$\angle A$ is supplementary to $\angle B$ and complementary to $\angle C$. If m$\angle C$ is 26, find m$\angle A$ and m$\angle B$. **m$\angle A$ = 64, m$\angle B$ = 116.**

Chalkboard Example

For the Example
The angle formed by a ladder and the ground is 30°. Find the measure, x, of the larger angle formed by the ladder and the ground. **150°**

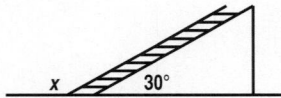

The relationships from algebra that we found to be true for segments and the measures of segments are also true for angles and the measures of angles. The congruence relationships are stated in Theorem 2-3.

Theorem 2-3	**Congruence of angles is reflexive, symmetric, and transitive.**

Proof of Transitive Part of Theorem 2-3	**Given:** ∠*X* ≅ ∠*Y* ∠*Y* ≅ ∠*Z* **Prove:** ∠*X* ≅ ∠*Z*	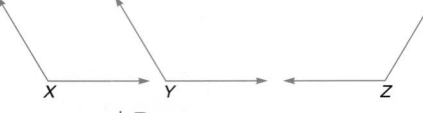

The proof of the transitive portion of Theorem 2-3 is given. You will be asked to prove the reflexive and symmetric portions in Exercises 25 and 26 respectively.

Statements	Reasons
1. ∠*X* ≅ ∠*Y* ∠*Y* ≅ ∠*Z*	1. Given
2. m∠*X* = m∠*Y* m∠*Y* = m∠*Z*	2. Definition of congruent angles
3. m∠*X* = m∠*Z*	3. Transitive property of equality
4. ∠*X* ≅ ∠*Z*	4. Definition of congruent angles

If two angles are supplementary to the same angle, what do you think is true about the angles? Draw several examples and make a conjecture.

Theorem 2-4	**Angles supplementary to the same angle or to congruent angles are congruent.**

Proof of Theorem 2-4	**Given:** ∠*A* and ∠*B* are supplementary. ∠*C* and ∠*B* are supplementary. **Prove:** ∠*A* ≅ ∠*C*	

Statements	Reasons
1. ∠*A* and ∠*B* are supplementary. ∠*C* and ∠*B* are supplementary.	1. Given
2. m∠*A* + m∠*B* = 180 m∠*C* + m∠*B* = 180	2. Definition of supplementary
3. m∠*A* + m∠*B* = m∠*C* + m∠*B*	3. Substitution property of equality
4. m∠*A* = m∠*C*	4. Subtraction property of equality
5. ∠*A* ≅ ∠*C*	5. Definition of congruent angles

You will be asked to prove this theorem in Exercise 28.

A similar theorem for complementary angles is stated below.

Theorem 2-5	**Angles complementary to the same angle or to congruent angles are congruent.**

Draw two right angles. What do you think is true about these angles? They are congruent. Since right angles are defined as having a measure of 90, they are all congruent by the definition of congruent angles. You will be asked to prove this in Exercise 27.

Theorem 2-6	**All right angles are congruent.**

Recall that in your investigations in Chapter 1, you discovered that vertical angles are congruent. We will prove this as a theorem now.

Theorem 2-7	**Vertical angles are congruent.**

Proof of Theorem 2-7

Given: $\angle 1$ and $\angle 2$ are vertical angles.
Prove: $\angle 1 \cong \angle 2$

Statements	Reasons
1. $\angle 1$ and $\angle 2$ are vertical angles.	1. Given
2. $\angle 2$ and $\angle 4$ form a linear pair. $\angle 1$ and $\angle 4$ form a linear pair.	2. Definition of linear pair
3. $\angle 2$ and $\angle 4$ are supplementary. $\angle 1$ and $\angle 4$ are supplementary.	3. If 2 ∕s form a linear pair, then they are supp.
4. $\angle 1 \cong \angle 2$	4. ∕s supp. to the same $\angle$ are $\cong$.

A theorem that follows from Theorem 2-7 is stated below. You will prove this theorem in Exercise 29.

Theorem 2-8	**Perpendicular lines intersect to form four right angles.**

CHECKING FOR UNDERSTANDING

Communicating Mathematics

1. Answers may vary. A sample answer is angles formed by the legs on a directors chair.

Read and study the lesson to answer these questions.

1. We have just proved that vertical angles are congruent. Find some examples of vertical angles in the objects around you. For example, a chain-link fence contains many pairs of vertical angles.

2. Use a protractor to draw an example for each theorem in the lesson. Write the angle measures on the figures that you draw and explain why your drawing shows the relationship in the theorem. **See Solutions Manual.**

Guided Practice

Complete each statement with *always*, *sometimes*, or *never*.

3. If two angles are right angles, they are __?__ adjacent. **sometimes**

4. If two angles are complementary, they are __?__ right angles. **never**

EVALUATING THE LESSON

Checking for Understanding

Exercises 1-15 are designed to help you assess students' understanding through reading, writing, speaking, and modeling. You should work through Exercises 1-2 with your students and then monitor their work on Exercises 3-15.

Closing the Lesson

Writing Activity Have students summarize in their own words the different ways to prove that one angle is congruent to another.

APPLYING THE LESSON

Homework Exercises

Assignment Guide
Basic: 16-26, 33-39
Average: 19-29, 33-39
Enriched: 22-39

Reteaching Masters Booklet, p. 14

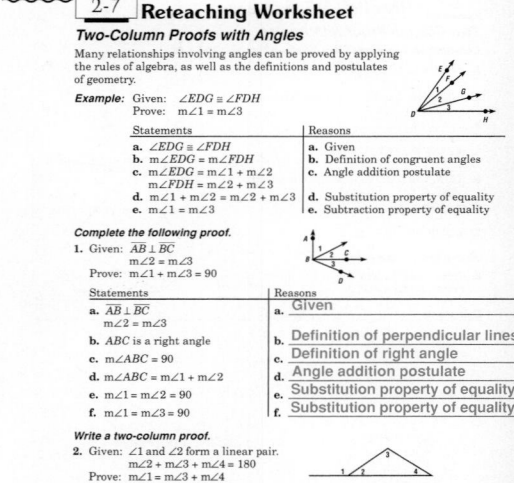

RETEACHING THE LESSON

Display the diagram below. Have students name as many pairs of congruent angles as they can.

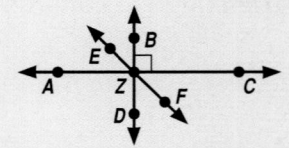

$\angle AZB \cong \angle BZC \cong \angle CZD \cong \angle DZA;$
$\angle AZE \cong \angle FZC; \angle EZB \cong \angle FZD;$
$\angle AZF \cong \angle CZE$

Additional Answer

23. Statements (Reasons)
 a. ∠ABC ≅ ∠EFG, ∠ABD ≅ ∠EFH (Given)
 b. m∠ABC = m∠EFG, m∠ABD = m∠EFH (Definition of congruent angles)
 c. m∠ABC = m∠ABD + m∠DBC, m∠EFG = m∠EFH + m∠HFG (Angle addition postulate)
 d. m∠ABD + m∠DBC = m∠EFH + m∠HFG (Substitution prop. of equality)
 e. m∠DBC = m∠HFG (Subtraction prop. of equality)
 f. ∠DBC ≅ ∠HFG (Definition of congruent angles)

---

5. If two angles are congruent, they are __?__ right angles. **sometimes**
6. Vertical angles are __?__ adjacent angles. **never**
7. Congruent angles are __?__ vertical angles. **sometimes**
8. If two angles are right angles, they are __?__ congruent. **always**
9. An angle is __?__ congruent to itself. **always**
10. If two angles are supplementary, they are __?__ congruent. **sometimes**

Find the measures of ∠1 and ∠2.

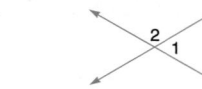
CONNECTION
Algebra

m∠1 = 112, m∠2 = 112
11. m∠1 = 2x + 94 and m∠2 = 7x + 49

m∠1 = 60, m∠2 = 120
12. m∠1 = 50 + 5x and m∠2 = 60x

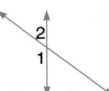

13. m∠1 = 100 + 20x and m∠2 = 20x   m∠1 = 140 m∠2 = 40

14. m∠1 = 5x and   m∠1 = 45 m∠2 = x + 36   m∠2 = 45

15. Copy and complete the proof of Theorem 2-2.

 Given: ∠1 and ∠2 form a linear pair.

 Prove: ∠1 and ∠2 are supplementary.

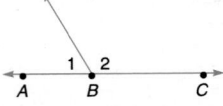

Statements	Reasons
1. ∠1 and ∠2 form a linear pair.	1. __?__ Given
2. $\overrightarrow{BA}$ and $\overrightarrow{BC}$ are opposite rays.	2. Definition of linear pair
3. m∠ABC = 180	3. Definition of straight angle
4. __?__ m∠ABC = m∠1 + m∠2	4. Angle addition postulate
5. 180 = m∠1 + m∠2	5. __?__ Substitution prop. of equality
6. ∠1 and ∠2 are supplementary.	6. __?__ Def. of supplementary

EXERCISES

Practice
A

17. ∠MLN or ∠PLQ

20. ∠PLQ or ∠MLN

Complete each statement if m∠RLQ = 30 and m∠MLN = 40.

16. ∠MLR ≅ __?__ ∠PLO or ∠MLR
17. ∠QLM and __?__ are supplementary.
18. m∠MLR = __?__ 110
19. m∠OLP = __?__ 110
20. ∠NLP and __?__ are supplementary.
21. m∠NLO = __?__ 30
22. m∠RLP = __?__ 70

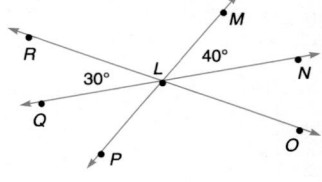

Additional Answer

24. Statements (Reasons)
 a. ∠1 ≅ ∠2, ∠3 ≅ ∠4 (Given)
 b. m∠1 = m∠2, m∠3 = m∠4 (Definition of congruent angles)
 c. m∠ABC = m∠2 + m∠4, m∠DCB = m∠1 + m∠3 (Angle addition postulate)
 d. m∠1 + m∠3 = m∠2 + m∠4 (Addition prop. of equality)
 e. m∠ABC = m∠DCB (Substitution prop. of equality)
 f. ∠ABC ≅ ∠DCB (Definition of congruent angles)

Write a two-column proof. See margin.

23. Given: $\angle ABC \cong \angle EFG$
$\angle ABD \cong \angle EFH$

Prove: $\angle DBC \cong \angle HFG$

24. Given: $\angle 1 \cong \angle 2$
$\angle 3 \cong \angle 4$

Prove: $\angle ABC \cong \angle DCB$

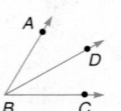 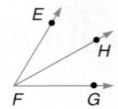 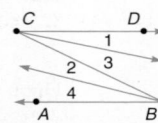

For each theorem, name the given and prove statements and draw a figure. Then write a two-column proof for each of the following. 25.–26. See margin.

25. Congruence of angles is reflexive. (Theorem 2-3)
26. Congruence of angles is symmetric. (Theorem 2-3)
27. All right angles are congruent. (Theorem 2-6)
28. Angles complementary to the same angle are congruent. (Theorem 2-5)
29. Perpendicular lines intersect to form four right angles. (Theorem 2-8)
30. If one angle in a linear pair is a right angle, then the other angle is a right angle also. **For answers to Exercises 27–32, see Solutions Manual.**
31. If two angles are congruent and supplementary, then they are right angles.
32. If two angles are vertical and one angle is a right angle, then the other is a right angle also.

Critical Thinking
33. 90 pairs of angles

33. Find the number of pairs of vertical angles determined by ten distinct lines passing through one point.

Application

34. **Sports** When skiing, a skier aligns her body so she can get the maximum stability and speed. If $m\angle 2 = 57$, find $m\angle 1$. **123**

Mixed Review

35. Justify the statement $QT = QT$ with a property from algebra or a property of congruent segments. **(Lesson 2-6)** Reflexive prop. of equality

36. **Algebra** The Fahrenheit temperature, F, is found by the formula $F = \frac{9}{5}C + 32$ where C is the temperature in Celsius. Solve the formula for C and justify each step. **(Lesson 2-4)** See Solutions Manual.

37. Can a conclusion be reached from the following two statements?
"If you are an avid sailor, then you need a SailSun Boat."
"Steven has a SailSun Boat." no conclusion
If so, write the conclusion and the law of logic used. **(Lesson 2-3)**

38. Find the measure of the complement and the supplement of an angle that measures 159. **(Lesson 1-8)** no complement, 21

Wrap-Up

39. **Journal Entry** Write a paragraph in your journal about what you think is the most important thing you learned in this lesson. How do you think this knowlege will help you in your further studies? See students' work.

EXTENDING THE LESSON

Math Power: Connections
Find $m\angle C$ if $\angle C$ is congruent to $\angle A$, $m\angle A = 3x$, $m\angle B = x + 20$ and $\angle A$ and $\angle B$ are supplementary angles. **120**

Additional Answers

25. **Given:** $\angle A$ is an angle.
Prove: $\angle A \cong \angle A$

Statements   (Reasons)
a. $\angle A$ is an angle   (Given)
b. $m\angle A = m\angle A$ (Reflexive prop. of equality)
c. $\angle A \cong \angle A$ (Definition of congruent angles)

26. **Given:** $\angle A \cong \angle B$
Prove: $\angle B \cong \angle A$

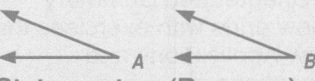

Statements   (Reasons)
a. $\angle A \cong \angle B$ (Given)
b. $m\angle A = m\angle B$ (Definition of congruent angles)
c. $m\angle B = m\angle A$ (Symmetric prop. of equality)
d. $\angle B \cong \angle A$ (Definition of congruent angles)

Enrichment Masters Booklet, p. 14

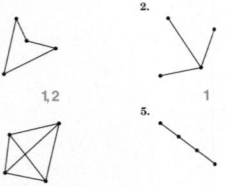

Additional Answers

3. If something is a cloud, then it has a silver lining.
4. If a polygon is a rectangle, then it has four right angles.
5. If a rock is obsidian, then it is a glassy rock produced by a volcano.
6. If two planes intersect, then their intersection is a line.
7. $\angle A$ and $\angle B$ have measures with a sum of 90; law of detachment
8. no conclusion
9. The sun is in constant motion; syllogism.
10. Given: $12x + 24 = 0$
    Prove: $x = -2$
    Statements   (Reasons)
    a. $12x + 24 = 0$ (Given)
    b. $12x = -24$ (Subtraction prop. of equality)
    c. $x = -2$ (Division prop. of equality)

VOCABULARY

Upon completing this chapter, you should be familiar with the following terms:

conclusion	**76**	**76**	if-then statement
conditional statement	**76**	**70**	inductive reasoning
conjecture	**70**	**82**	law of detachment
converse	**77**	**83**	law of syllogism
counterexample	**71**	**77**	postulate
deductive reasoning	**82**	**98**	theorem
hypothesis	**76**	**89**	two-column proof

SKILLS AND CONCEPTS

OBJECTIVES AND EXAMPLES	REVIEW EXERCISES

Upon completing this chapter, you should be able to:

Use these exercises to review and prepare for the chapter test.

■ make geometric conjectures based on given information. **(Lesson 2-1)**

To determine if a conjecture made from inductive reasoning is true or false, look at situations where the given information is true. Determine if there are situations where the given is true and the conjecture is false.

Determine if the conjecture is *true* or *false* based on the given information. Explain your answer.

1. **Given:** A, B, and C are collinear and
   $AB = BC$ <u>true</u>
   Conjecture: B is the midpoint of $\overline{AC}$.

2. **Given:** $\angle 1$ and $\angle 2$ are supplementary.
   Conjecture: $\angle 1 \cong \angle 2$ **false**

■ write conditionals in if-then form. **(Lesson 2-2)**

Write the statement "Adjacent angles have a common ray" in if-then form.

"If angles are adjacent, then they have a common ray."

Write the conditional statement in if-then form. See margin.

3. Every cloud has a silver lining.
4. A rectangle has four right angles.
5. Obsidian is a glassy rock produced by a volcano.
6. The intersection of two planes is a line.

Additional Answer

11. Given: $MN = PN$, $NL = NO$
    Prove: $ML = PO$

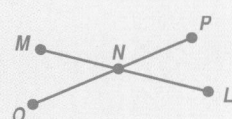

Statements   (Reasons)
a. $MN = PN$, $NL = NO$ (Given)
b. $MN + NL = PN + NO$ (Addition prop. of equality)
c. $ML = MN + NL$, $PO = PN + NO$ (Segment addition postulate)
d. $ML = PO$ (Substitution prop. of equality)

- use the laws of logic to draw a conclusion. **(Lesson 2-3)**

  The law of detachment states that if $p \rightarrow q$ is a true conditional and p is true, then q is true.

  The law of syllogism states that if $p \rightarrow q$ the $q \rightarrow r$ are true conditionals, then $p \rightarrow r$ is also true.

If possible, write a conclusion. State the law of logic that you used. See margin.

7. (1) Angles that are complementary have measures with a sum of 90.
   (2) $\angle A$ and $\angle B$ are complementary.

8. (1) Well-known athletes appear on Wheaties™ boxes.
   (2) Michael Jordan appeared on Wheaties™ boxes.

9. (1) The sun is a star.
   (2) Stars are in constant motion.

- use properties of equality in algebraic and geometric proofs. **(Lesson 2-4)**

  Prove that if $ST = UV$ then $SU = TV$.

  Given: $ST = UV$
  Prove: $SU = TV$

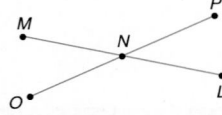

Statements	Reasons
1. $ST = UV$	1. Given
2. $ST + TU$ $= TU + UV$	2. Addition property of equality
3. $SU = ST + TU$ $TV = TU + UV$	3. Segment addition postulate
4. $SU = TV$	4. Substitution property

Write a complete proof for each of the following. See margin.

10. If $12x + 24 = 0$, then $x = -2$.

11. If $MN = PN$ and $NL = NO$, then $ML = PO$.

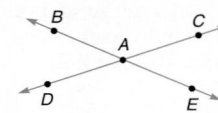

12. If $m\angle BAC + m\angle BAD = 180$, $m\angle DAE + m\angle CAE = 180$, and $m\angle BAD = m\angle CAE$, then $m\angle DAE = m\angle BAC$.

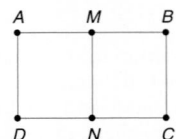

- complete proofs involving segment theorems. **(Lesson 2-6)**

  Theorem 2-1 states that congruence of segments is reflexive, symmetric, and transitive.

Write a two-column proof. See Solutions Manual.

13. **Given:** $\overline{AM} \cong \overline{CN}$
    $\overline{MB} \cong \overline{ND}$
    Prove: $\overline{AB} \cong \overline{CD}$

To provide a brief in-class review, you may wish to read the following questions to the class and require a verbal response.

1. Determine if the conjecture is true or false based on the given information. Explain your answer.
   Given: $\angle ABC$ and $\angle CBD$ form a linear pair.
   Conjecture: $AB + BD = AD$
   true

2. Write the conditional statement in if-then form. Vertical angles are congruent.   **If two angles are vertical angles, then they are congruent.**

If possible, write a conclusion. State the law of logic you used.

3. (1) If Mary goes to the library, she will not finish her math homework.
   (2) Mary goes to the library.
   Conclusion: Mary will not finish her math homework; detachment.

4. (1) If $x = 2$, then $6x = 12$.
   (2) If $6x = 12$, then $3x = 6$.
   Conclusion: If $x = 2$, then $3x = 6$; syllogism

Which property of equality can be used to justify the statement?

5. If $x + 2 = 8$, then $x = 6$.
   Subtraction prop. of equality

6. If $AB = BC$ and $BC = CD$, then $AB = CD$.   **Transitive prop. of equality**

Write a two-column proof.

7. Given: $\angle 2 \cong \angle 3$
   Prove: $\angle 1 \cong \angle 4$

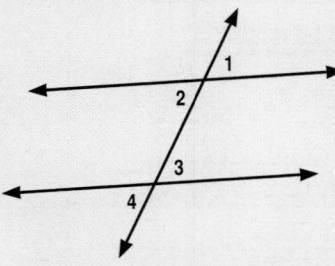

Statements   (Reasons)
a. $\angle 2 \cong \angle 3$ (Given)
b. $\angle 1 \cong \angle 2, \angle 3 \cong \angle 4$ (Vertical angles are congruent.)
c. $m\angle 2 = m\angle 3, m\angle 1 = m\angle 2, m\angle 3 = m\angle 4$ (Definition of congruent angles)
d. $m\angle 1 = m\angle 4$ (Substitution)
e. $\angle 1 \cong \angle 4$ (Definition of congruent angles)

Additional Answer

12. Given: $m\angle BAC + m\angle BAD = 180, m\angle DAE + m\angle CAE = 180, m\angle BAD = m\angle CAE$
    Prove: $m\angle DAE = m\angle BAC$
    Statements   (Reasons)
    a. $m\angle BAC + m\angle BAD = 180, m\angle DAE + m\angle CAE = 180, m\angle BAD = m\angle CAE$ (Given)
    b. $m\angle BAC + m\angle BAD = m\angle DAE + m\angle CAE$ (Substitution prop. of equality)

c. $m\angle BAC + m\angle CAE = m\angle DAE + m\angle CAE$ (Substitution prop. of equality)
d. $m\angle BAC = m\angle DAE$ (Subtraction prop. of equality)
e. $m\angle DAE = m\angle BAC$ (Symmetric prop. of equality)

The Cumulative Review shown below can be used to review skills and concepts presented thus far in the text. Standardized Test Practice Questions are also provided in the *Evaluation Masters Booklet*.

Evaluation Masters Booklet, pp. 25-26

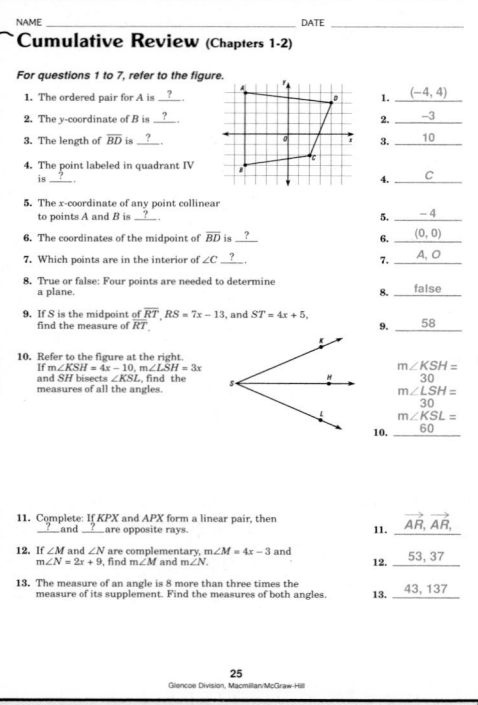

- complete proofs involving angle theorems. **(Lesson 2-7)**

Given: ∠1 ≅ ∠2
Prove: ∠3 ≅ ∠4

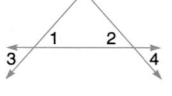

Statements	Reasons
1. ∠1 ≅ ∠2	1. Given
2. ∠1 ≅ ∠3 ∠2 ≅ ∠4	2. Vertical ⩘ are ≅.
3. ∠3 ≅ ∠4	3. Congruence of angles is transitive. (used twice)

Write a two-column proof. See margin.

14. **Given:** ∠1 and ∠3 are supplementary.
    ∠3 and ∠4 form a linear pair.
    Prove: ∠1 ≅ ∠4

15. **Given:** ∠1 and ∠2 form a linear pair
    ∠1 ≅ ∠2
    Prove: ∠1 and ∠2 are right angles.
    See Solutions Manual.

17. A sponge remains permanently attached to a surface for all of its adult life. syllogism

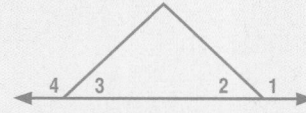

APPLICATIONS AND CONNECTIONS

16. **Advertising**   Write the conditional "Hard-working people deserve a night on the town at Gil's Grill" in if-then form. Identify the hypothesis and the conclusion of the conditional. Then write the converse. **(Lesson 2-2)** See Solutions Manual.

18. **Algebra**   Name the property of equality that justifies the statement "If $x + y = 3$ and $3 = w + v$, then $x + y = w + v$." **(Lesson 2-4)** Substitution or transitive property of equality

17. **Botany**   If possible, write a valid conclusion. State the law of logic that you used. **(Lesson 2-3)**
    - A sponge is a sessile animal.
    - A sessile animal is one that remains permanently attached to a surface for all of its adult life.

19. **Geology**   The underground temperature of rocks varies with their depth below the surface. The deeper that a rock is in the Earth, the hotter it is. The temperature, t, in degrees Celsius is estimated by the equation $t = 35d + 20$, where d is the depth in kilometers. Solve the formula for d and justify each step. **(Lesson 2-4)** See Solutions Manual.

20. Use the process of elimination to solve this problem. **(Lesson 2-5)**
    Alana, Becky, and Carl each had different lunches in the school cafeteria. One had spaghetti, one had a salad, and one had macaroni and cheese. Alana did not have a salad. Becky did not have spaghetti or a salad. What did each person have for lunch? Alana - spaghetti; Becky - macaroni and cheese; Carl - salad

---

Additional Answers

14. Given ∠1 and ∠3 are supplementary. ∠3 and ∠4 form a linear pair.
    Prove: ∠1 ≅ ∠4

Statements   (Reasons)
a. ∠1 and ∠3 are supplementary. ∠3 and ∠4 form a linear pair. (Given)

b. ∠3 and ∠4 are supplementary (If 2 ∠s form a linear pair, they are supp.)

c. $m∠1 + m∠3 = 180$, $m∠3 + m∠4 = 180$ (Definition of supplementary)

d. $m∠1 + m∠3 = m∠3 + m∠4$ (Substitution prop. of equality)

e. $m∠1 = m∠4$ (Subtraction prop. of equality)

f. ∠1 ≅ ∠4 (Definition of congruent angles)

Determine if each conjecture is *true* or *false*. Explain your answers and give a counterexample for any false conjecture. See Solutions Manual.

1. **Given:** x is a real number.
   Conjecture: $-x < 0$

2. **Given:** $\angle 1 \cong \angle 2$
   Conjecture: $\angle 2 \cong \angle 1$

3. **Given:** $\angle 1$ and $\angle 2$ form a linear pair.
   Conjecture: $m\angle 1 + m\angle 2 = 180$

4. **Given:** $3x^2 = 48$
   Conjecture: $x = 4$

Write the conditional statement in if-then form. Identify the hypothesis and the conclusion of the conditional. Then write the converse. See Solutions Manual.

5. Through any two points there is exactly one line.

6. A rolling stone gathers no moss.

7. Wise investments with Petty-Bates pay off.

8. Two parallel planes do not intersect.

If possible, write a conclusion. State the law of logic that you used. See Solutions Manual.

9. (1) Wise investments with Petty-Bates pay off.
   (2) Investments that pay off build for the future.

10. (1) Perpendicular lines intersect.
    (2) Lines ℓ and m are perpendicular.

11. (1) Vertical angles are congruent.
    (2) $\angle 1$ is congruent to $\angle 2$.

12. (1) All integers are real numbers.
    (2) 7 is an integer.

Name the property of equality that justifies each statement. Sample answers are given.
13. **Symmetric** 16. **Substitution**

13. If $m\angle A = m\angle B$, then $m\angle B = m\angle A$.

14. If $x + 9 = 12$, then $x = 3$. **Subtraction**

15. If $2ST = 4UV$, then $ST = 2UV$. **Division**

16. If $AB = 7$ and $CD = 7$, then $AB = CD$.

17. Anthony, Eric, and Karen each bought a car. One bought a Honda, one bought a Ford, and one bought a Volkswagen. Anthony did not buy a foreign car. Karen did not buy a Honda. Who bought which car? **Anthony - Ford; Eric - Honda; Karen - Volkswagen**

Write a two-column proof. See Solutions Manual.

18. **Given:** $\overline{AC} \cong \overline{BD}$
    Prove: $\overline{AB} \cong \overline{CD}$

19. **Given:** $m\angle 1 = m\angle 3 + m\angle 4$
    Prove: $m\angle 3 + m\angle 4 + m\angle 2 = 180$

20. Prove that if two angles are supplementary and one angle is a right angle, then the other one is a right angle also.

Bonus The *inverse* of a conditional $p \rightarrow q$ is not $p \rightarrow$ not q. Write the inverse of "All dogs are mammals." **If an animal is not a dog, then it is not a mammal.**

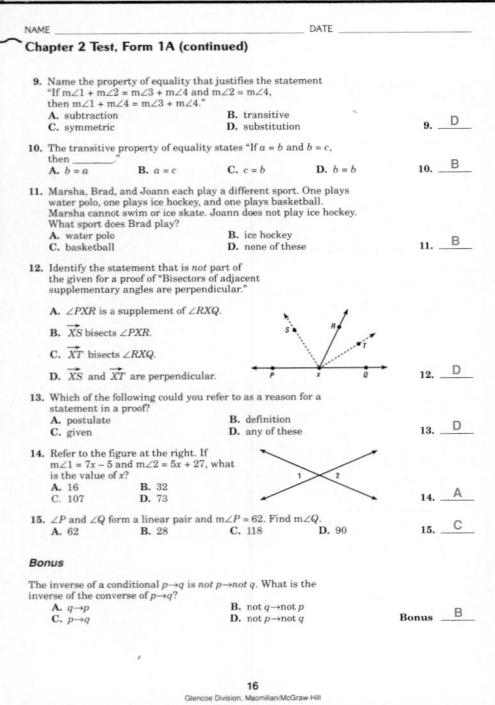

Using the College Entrance Exam Preview

The questions on these pages may be used to help students prepare for college entrance exams such as the SAT test. These questions require careful analysis and a thorough understanding of the concepts.

These pages can be used as an overnight assignment.

After students have completed the pages, discuss how each problem can be solved, or provide copies of the solution from the *Merrill Geometry Solutions Manual*.

Directions: Choose the one best answer. Write A, B, C, or D. You may use a calculator.

1. If $0.06x = 24$, then $x =$
B
  (A) 600   (B) 400
  (C) 0.04   (D) 1.44

2.
A
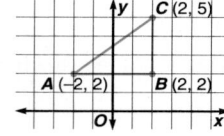

The distance between A and C is
  (A) 5 units   (B) 8 units
  (C) 12 units   (D) 6 units

3. If $x < 12$ and $y < 18$, then
D
  (A) $y - x = 6$ (B) $x < y$
  (C) $y < x$ (D) $x + y < 30$

4. 40% of 120 is one third of
A
  (A) 144   (B) 120
  (C) 48   (D) 40

5.
C
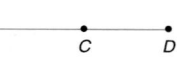

In the figure, if $AD = 50$, $CD = 12$, and B is the midpoint of $\overline{AC}$, then $BC =$
  (A) 18   (B) 38
  (C) 19   (D) 12

6. The points $(4, 2)$ and $(-1, y)$ are $\sqrt{74}$
D units apart. What is the value of y?
  (A) 7   (B) -7
  (C) 11   (D) 9

7. If $x + 5 = \frac{1}{3}(3x - 5)$, then $x =$
D
  (A) 5   (B) 3
  (C) any real number   (D) no real number

8. If a calculator costs $12.90 after a 25%
B discount, what is the original price of the calculator?
  (A) $16.13   (B) $17.20
  (C) $9.68   (D) $15.00

9. If $\angle A$ and $\angle B$ are supplementary and
D $\angle A$ and $\angle C$ are complementary, then
  I. $m\angle A < 90$, $m\angle B > 90$, and $m\angle C < 90$
  II. $m\angle A < m\angle B$ and $m\angle C < 90$
  III. $m\angle A > 90$ and $m\angle C < m\angle B$
  (A) I only   (B) II only
  (C) III only   (D) I and II only

10. If two planes intersect, their
A intersection can be
  I.   a line.
  II.   three non-collinear points.
  III. two intersecting lines.
  (A) I only   (B) II only
  (C) III only   (D) I and II only

11. The product of 12^3 and 12^8 is
C
  (A) 12^5 (B) 12^{24}
  (C) 12^{11} (D) 24^{11}

12. The distance from city X to city Y is
B 200 miles. The distance from city X to city Z is 140 miles. Which of the following must be true?
  (A) The distance from Y to Z is 60 miles.
  (B) Seven times the distance from X to Y is ten times the distance from X to Z.
  (C) The distance from Y to Z is 340 miles.
  (D) The distance from Y to Z is one-third the distance from X to Z.

Solve. You may use a calculator.

13. If one half of the female students and one third of the male students at a school take Spanish classes, what part of the student body takes Spanish? **cannot be determined from the information given**

14. A gallon of water evaporates from a 9-gallon drum of 4% salt solution. What is the percentage of salt in the remaining solution? **4.5%**

15. In the graph below, the axes and the origin are not shown. If point P has coordinates $(4, 2)$, what are the coordinates of point Q?

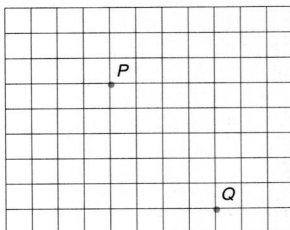

(8, –3)

16. Westville has a population of 7200, which is decreasing at a rate of 80 people per year. Troy has a population of 5000 and is gaining 120 people per year. In how many years will the populations of Westville and Troy be the same? **11 years**

17. One evening, the candy counter at the Cineplex sold 532 buckets of popcorn for $1489.50. A large bucket sells for $2.25 and a jumbo bucket sells for $3.75. How many jumbo buckets of popcorn were sold? **195 jumbo buckets**

18. On the blue prints for a house, 2 inches represents 3 feet. If the width of a room on the plan is $6\frac{1}{2}$ inches, what is the actual width of the room? **9 feet 9 inches**

19. In the figure below, $\angle ABC$ is a straight angle, and $\overline{DB}$ is perpendicular to $\overline{BE}$. If $\angle ABD$ measures x degrees, write an expression to represent the degree measure of $\angle CBE$. **90 – x**

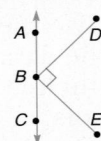

20. Jordan answered all of the questions on a 20-question test. A score on the test is computed by adding 5 points for every correct answer and subtracting 1 point for every incorrect answer. If Jordan's score was 82, how many questions did he answer correctly? **17**

3

Parallels

PREVIEWING THE CHAPTER

This chapter introduces students to parallel lines and segments while demonstrating their use in geometry and their applications to the real world. Students look at the meaning of parallel and how to prove lines parallel by using the angles formed with parallel lines and a transversal. In the beginning of the chapter, angles are named and classified by their location in relation to the parallel lines and the transversal. These relationships are then applied to congruence of angles and perpendicular lines, and are used in proofs. At this point in the development, paragraph proofs are introduced. Finally, students learn how to construct parallel lines using a straightedge and compass. The chapter concludes with a connection to algebra where students find slopes of lines and use the distance formula to solve problems involving parallel lines.

Problem-Solving Strategy Students use the strategy *draw a diagram* to help them organize and visualize the data presented in problems and to translate words into pictures, which is a necessary skill in understanding and interpreting proofs.

Lesson Objective Chart

Lesson (Pages)	Lesson Objectives	State/Local Objectives
3-1 (118-121)	**3-1**: Solve problems by using a diagram.	
3-2 (122-127)	**3-2A**: Describe the relationships between two lines and between two planes.	
	3-2B: Identify the relationships among pairs of angles formed by pairs of lines and transversals.	
3-3 (128-134)	**3-3**: Use the properties of parallel lines to determine angle measures.	
3-4 (135-141)	**3-4A**: Recognize angle conditions that produce parallel lines.	
	3-4B: Prove two lines parallel based on given angle relationships.	
3-5 (142-147)	**3-5A**: Find the slope of a line.	
	3-5B: Use slope to identify parallel and perpendicular lines.	
3-6 (148-154)	**3-6**: Recognize and use distance relationships among points, lines, and planes.	

ORGANIZING THE CHAPTER

You may want to refer to the **Course Planning Calendar** on page T28.

Lesson Planning Guide

Lesson (Pages)	Pacing Chart (days) Course I	II	III	Blackline Masters Booklets: Reteaching	Practice	Enrichment	Evaluation	Technology	Lab Manual	Activities: Mixed Problem Solving	Applications	Cooperative Learning Activity	Multicultural	Transparencies
3-1 (118-121)	1	1	1		p. 17								p. 3	3-1
3-2 (122-127)	2	2	1.5	p. 15	p. 18	p. 15	Quiz A, p. 37		pp.34-37					3-2
3-3 (128-134)	2	2	1.5	p. 16	p. 19	p. 16	Quiz B, p. 37 Mid-Chapter Test, p. 41	p. 39						3-3
3-4 (135-141)	2	1.5	1.5	p. 17	p. 20	p. 17	Quiz C, p. 38			p. 3				3-4
3-5 (142-147)	2	1.5	1.5	p. 18	p. 21	p. 18		p. 3				p. 31		3-5
3-6 (148-154)	2	2	2	p. 19	p. 22	p. 19	Quiz D, p. 38				p. 17			3-6
Review (156-158)	1	1	1	Multiple Choice Tests, Forms 1A and 1B, pp. 29-32 Free Response Tests, Forms 2A and 2B, pp. 33-36 Cumulative Review. pp. 39-40 Standardized Tests Practice Questions, p. 42										
Test (159)	1	1	1											

Course I: Chapters 1-11; Course II: Chapters 1-12; Course III: Chapters 1-13

Other Chapter Resources

Student Edition

Chapter Opener, pp. 116-117
Cooperative Learning Project, p. 121
History Connection, p. 127
Mid-Chapter Review, p. 134
Journal Entry, pp. 134, 141
Fine Arts Connection, p. 141
Portfolio, p. 147
Technology, p. 155
Algebra Review, pp.160-161
More Investigations in Geometry, pp. A2-A4
Extended Project 1, pp. B2-B5

Teacher's Classroom Resources

Transparency 3-0
Real World Applications Transparencies, 5, 6
Performance Assessment Booklet, pp. 5-6
Problem-of-the-Week Activity Cards, 7, 8, 9
Tech Prep Applications Booklet, pp. 5-6
LOGO Instruction Materials Technology Masters pp.19-36

Other Supplements

Flow Proof and Indirect Proof
Algebra and Geometry Overhead Manipulative Resources
Glencoe Mathematics Professional Series

Software

Test and Review Generator (Apple, IBM, and Macintosh)
Teacher's Guide for Software Resources

ENHANCING THE CHAPTER

Cooperative Learning

Arranging the Room

Providing a physical environment conducive to cooperative-learning activities is important if success is to be achieved when using this learning technique. How the room is arranged should indicate to students what is expected of them as well as make it easy for both you and the groups to accomplish the defined goals. Since you will want to monitor the groups, they should be arranged in a way that permits you to pass among them, unobtrusively if possible, and also placed apart far enough so that the groups do not interfere with each other's learning. The students in each group must be able to see all of the pertinent materials, to see and converse with one another without disturbing students in other groups, and to exchange ideas and materials with other members of the group in a convenient manner. Among the best arrangements is one where the group members sit in a circle, although any arrangement that permits each group member to have eye contact with and easy access to all other members of the group also would be satisfactory.

Technology

The Technology Feature following Lesson 3-6 shows how a graphing calculator can be used to find the distance between a point and a line. The key sequence to graph two lines on the same screen is given for both the Casio fx-7000G and the TI-81. The TRACE function is used to approximate the coordinates of the intersection of the two lines. The distance formula is then used to find the distance between the intersection point and the given point. Be sure students understand that this distance is the same as the distance between the given point and the given line. You may wish to have students explain why the procedure used in this feature gives the desired distance.

Critical Thinking

One technique that you may find useful to stimulate critical thinking and productive discussion is to challenge students with problems that have multiple methods of solution. Many of the problems that involve real-life applications of the content in this chapter can be used to demonstrate this technique. When students work independently or in small groups to solve these problems, assign the additional task of finding at least two different ways to solve the problem. Have the methods discussed in class, focusing on the unique features of each method and the similarities and differences among them.

Cooperative Learning, p. 31

Technology, p. 39

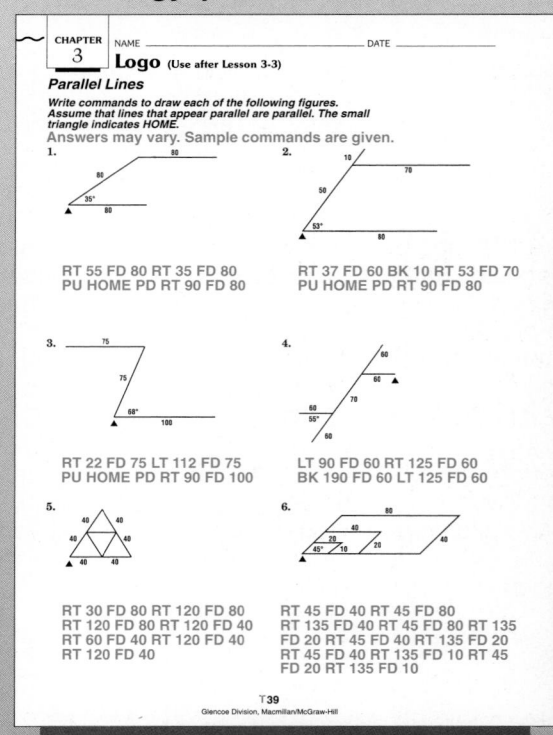

Problem of the Week Activity

The card shown below is one of three available for this chapter. It can be used as a class or small group activity.

Activity Card

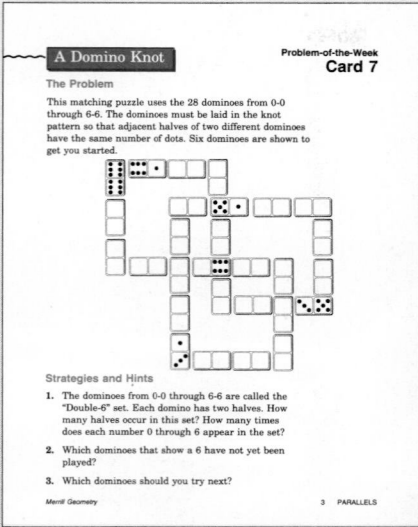

A Domino Knot

Problem-of-the-Week
Card 7

The Problem

This matching puzzle uses the 28 dominoes from 0-0 through 6-6. The dominoes must be laid in the knot pattern so that adjacent halves of two different dominoes have the same number of dots. Six dominoes are shown to get you started.

Strategies and Hints

1. The dominoes from 0-0 through 6-6 are called the "Double-6" set. Each domino has two halves. How many halves occur in this set? How many times does each number 0 through 6 appear in the set?

2. Which dominoes that show a 6 have not yet been played?

3. Which dominoes should you try next?

Merrill Geometry   3   PARALLELS

Manipulatives and Models

The following materials may be used as models or manipulatives in Chapter 3.

• blueprints (Lesson 3-1)
• hexagonal prism (Lesson 3-1)
• pipe cleaners (Lesson 3-2)
• examples of M.C. Escher's works (Lesson 3-4)
• string (Lesson 3-6)
• pyramid (Lesson 3-6)
• graphing calculator (Page 155)

Outside Resources

Books/Periodicals

Bakst, Aaron. *Mathematical Puzzles and Pastimes.* Van Nostrand Reinhold Company.

Bell, E.T. *Men of Mathematics.* Simon and Schuster.

Fox, Linda, L. Brody, and Diane Tobin. *Women and the Mathematical Mystique.* John Hopkins University Press.

Films/Videotapes/Videodiscs

Angles, The Media Guild, 11722 Sorrento Valley Rd., Suite E, San Diego, CA 92121

Geometry in Our World, National Council of Teachers of Mathematics, 1906 Association Dr., Reston, VA 22091

Software

IBM Geodraw, EduQuest, 4111 Northside Pkwy NW, P.O. Box 2150, Atlanta, GA 30055

The Geometer's Sketchpad, Key Curriculum Press, 2512 Martin Luther King Jr. Way, P.O. Box 2304, Berkeley, CA 94702

Multicultural

Multicultural Activity, p. 3

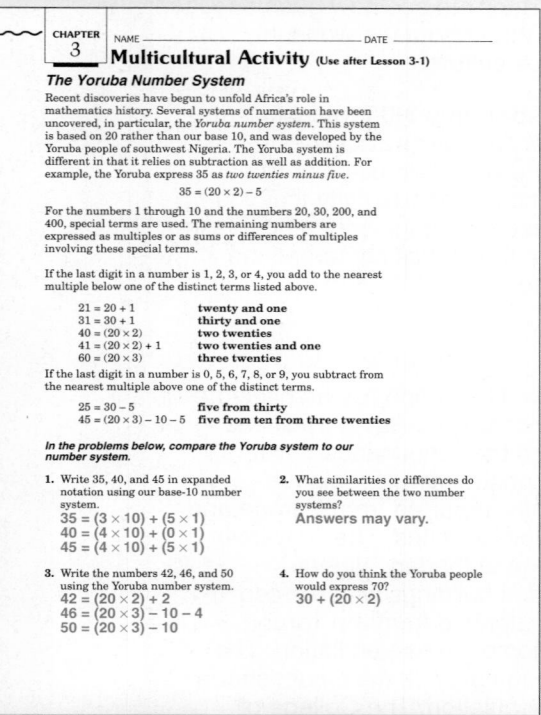

CHAPTER 3   NAME _____   DATE _____

Multicultural Activity (Use after Lesson 3-1)

The Yoruba Number System

Recent discoveries have begun to unfold Africa's role in mathematics history. Several systems of numeration have been uncovered, in particular, the *Yoruba number system*. This system is based on 20 rather than our base 10, and was developed by the Yoruba people of southwest Nigeria. The Yoruba system is different in that it relies on subtraction as well as addition. For example, the Yoruba express 35 as *two twenties minus five.*

$$35 = (20 \times 2) - 5$$

For the numbers 1 through 10 and the numbers 20, 30, 200, and 400, special terms are used. The remaining numbers are expressed as multiples or as sums or differences of multiples involving these special terms.

If the last digit in a number is 1, 2, 3, or 4, you add to the nearest multiple below one of the distinct terms listed above.

$21 = 20 + 1$	**twenty and one**
$31 = 30 + 1$	**thirty and one**
$40 = (20 \times 2)$	**two twenties**
$41 = (20 \times 2) + 1$	**two twenties and one**
$60 = (20 \times 3)$	**three twenties**

If the last digit in a number is 0, 5, 6, 7, 8, or 9, you subtract from the nearest multiple above one of the distinct terms.

$25 = 30 - 5$	**five from thirty**
$45 = (20 \times 3) - 10 - 5$	**five from ten from three twenties**

In the problems below, compare the Yoruba system to our number system.

1. Write 35, 40, and 45 in expanded notation using our base-10 number system.
   $35 = (3 \times 10) + (5 \times 1)$
   $40 = (4 \times 10) + (0 \times 1)$
   $45 = (4 \times 10) + (5 \times 1)$

2. What similarities or differences do you see between the two number systems?
   Answers may vary.

3. Write the numbers 42, 46, and 50 using the Yoruba number system.
   $42 = (20 \times 2) + 2$
   $46 = (20 \times 3) - 10 - 4$
   $50 = (20 \times 3) - 10$

4. How do you think the Yoruba people would express 70?
   $30 + (20 \times 2)$

Lab Manual

Lab Activity, pp. 34-37

Name _____   Activity 5 Worksheet
Page 1

Parallel Lines

1. Place a piece of tape in the space below. Using the edges of the tape to represent parallel lines, draw a transversal, and mark the congruent angles.

2. Label the angles in problem 1 and identify the following:
   alternate interior angles _____
   alternate exterior angles _____
   corresponding angles _____
   consecutive interior angles _____

3. Using two pieces of tape, model and define the following:

Example: parallelogram

definition: Quadrilateral with opposite sides parallel

a. rectangle   definition: _____

b. square   definition: _____

35
Glencoe Division, Macmillan/McGraw-Hill

Using The Chapter Opener

This two-page introduction to the chapter provides students with an opportunity to see how geometry is used throughout the world in various cultures.

Transparency 3-0, available in the *Merrill Geometry Package*, provides another full-color visual and motivational activity that you can use to engage your students in the mathematical content of the chapter.

Multicultural Notes

Africa Contemporary architecture in Africa uses building traditions that go back thousands of years and construction techniques recently imported from Europe and the United States. The University College at Ibadan, Nigeria, includes buildings with pierced walls, derived from the Yoruba tradition of cross-ventilation. The buildings provide maximum shade and ventilation. The College of Engineering in Ibadan was designed by Oluwole Olumuyiwa, and S. I. Kola-Bankole built the new Botany Laboratory.

Brazil Oscar Niemeyer Suares Filho is the best-known and most influential South American architect of the twentieth century. He was the chief architect of the new capital city of Brasilia, begun in 1960. His designs offer the most complete expressions of modern architecture and planning anywhere. His striking use of concrete in the designs for buildings of the Secretariat, Congress, Supreme Court, Presidential Palace, Cathedral, and National Theater demonstrate Niemeyer's outstanding achievement as both architect and engineer.

Chapter Project

Materials plain paper, tape, pencil, duplicating machine

Procedure Organize students into cooperative groups of historical architectural researchers. Assign each group a culture (Native American, Babylonian, Japanese, Egyptian, Ancient Greek, Chinese, Aztec, or any other culture that might be of interest). Have each group collect pictures of typical traditional architecture of the given culture. Have them prepare an eight-page booklet of the architectural examples.

When all of the groups have prepared their booklets, have groups exchange their materials. Have group members examine the materials and research modern architecture in the same cultures to obtain examples of structures present today that may or may not

Parallels

GEOMETRY AROUND THE WORLD
Japan

What do you get when you take the angles and planes of geometry off the printed page and combine them in innovative ways with traditional forms? The answer: buildings by Japanese architect Kenzo Tange that will knock your socks off!

Tange, who received a gold medal from the American Institute of Architects, is one of the greatest architects of the twentieth century. He was trained at the University of Tokyo and also studied architecture in Paris. There, he learned about the geometric building designs favored by some western architects. As a result, his buildings reflect both traditional Japanese design and the more angular forms used in the United States and other countries in the western hemisphere.

For the City Hall building in Kurashiki, Japan, Tange used a geometric design called a **parallelpiped.** A parallelpiped has six faces, each of which is a **parallelogram.** A parallelogram has four sides; its opposite sides are parallel and congruent. The Kurashiki City Hall also has wooden panels and other features used in traditional Japanese buildings. For contrast, Tange used dramatic geometric forms for its roof.

GEOMETRY IN ACTION

As you can see from the photograph, Kurashiki's City Hall is a remarkable-looking building. If you measured the slopes of the left and right inclines of the roof, you would find that the right slope is -0.36 and the left is 0.21. What method do you think was used to compute these slopes?

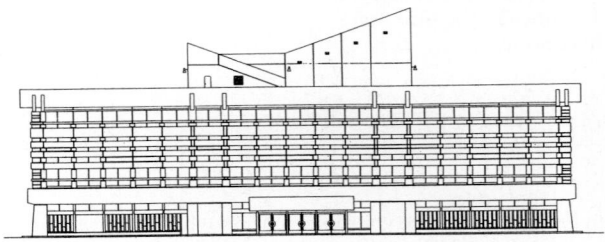

◀ *Kurashiki City Hall*　Inset photo: *Kenzo Tange*

CHAPTER OBJECTIVES

In this chapter you will:
- Use the properties of parallel lines.
- Prove lines parallel.
- Find and use the slope of lines.
- Recognize and use distance relationships between points, lines, and planes.

What geometric forms can you find in this photo of a building designed by Japanese architect Kenzo Tange?

Connections and Applications

Lesson	Connections (C) and Applications (A)	Examples	Exercises
3-1	A: Sports	1	
3-2	A: Air-Traffic Control		51
3-3	C: Algebra	2	16-18 25-27 34-38
	A: Interior Design		52
3-4	C: Algebra	1	6-11 31-32 38 46 48
	A: Construction		43
3-5	C: Algebra	1, 2, 3	21-34 37-42
	A: Demographics		47
	A: Aviation		48
	A: Travel		49
3-6	A: Planning	1	
	A: Transportation		37 39
	A: Interior Design		38
	A: Aviation		46

reflect influences from the ancient civilization. Have them prepare an eight-page booklet to supplement the booklet on the ancient culture. Have each group share both volumes with the entire class.

Resources

Riani, Paolo, *Kenzo Tange*, Crown Publishers, Inc.

Wilson, Richard Guy, *The AIA Gold Medal*, McGraw-Hill Book Company

Abercrombie, Stanley, *Architecture as Art*, Van Nostrand Reinhold Company

Norwich, John Julias, ed., *Great Architecture of the World*, Random House, Inc.

INTRODUCING THE LESSON

 5-Minute Check

(over Chapter 2)

Refer to the figure below.

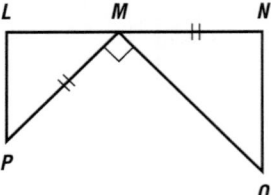

1. Are points *L*, *M*, and *Q* collinear? **no**
2. Find the measure of $\overline{MN}$ if $LM = 5x - 4$, $MN = 6x + 1$, and $LN = 30$. **MN = 19**
3. Can you determine if *M* is the midpoint of $\overline{LN}$? **no**
4. Name an acute angle, an obtuse angle, and a right angle in the figure. **Sample answer: $\angle QMN$ is acute, $\angle PMN$ is obtuse, and $\angle PMQ$ is right.**
5. Are $\angle LMP$ and $\angle NMQ$ complementary? **yes**

Motivating the Lesson

Bring in some blueprints for a building or house. Ask students what blueprints are used for and explain how they can be used to solve problems in construction before you start to build.

3-1 Problem-Solving Strategy: Draw a Diagram

Objective After studying this lesson, you should be able to:
3-1 ■ solve problems by using a diagram.

Sometimes drawing a diagram of the situation described in a problem can help you find the solution. A diagram can help you choose a strategy, organize your information, or may even show you the answer to the problem.

Example 1

APPLICATION
Sports

FYI…

Basketball is the only popular sport that is truly American in origin. It was invented in 1891 by James Naismith.

The varsity basketball teams of the seven high schools in the Mid-State Conference each play every other team twice this season. How many games will there be in the conference this year?

Since there are seven teams and each team plays every other team twice, it seems like there should be a total of $7 \times 6 \times 2$ or 84 games. Let's draw a diagram and see if this conjecture is true.

Draw a diagram of seven noncollinear points to represent the seven teams and label the points *A* through *G*. Use a line segment between two points to represent a game between the two teams. How many line segments are needed to join all seven dots?

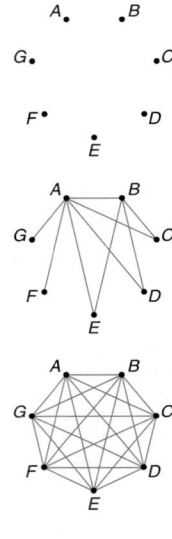

First, draw all of the segments from point *A*. There are six. Next, draw all of the segments from *B*. This adds five more.

Continue to draw line segments until all of the pairs of points are connected. There are $6 + 5 + 4 + 3 + 2 + 1$ or 21 segments. Since all the teams play each other twice, there will be 2×21 or 42 games in the Mid-State Conference this season.

Our conjecture was incorrect. There will be 42, not 84, games.

Diagrams can help you organize your information when you are writing proofs of geometric theorems. You will need to be able to draw a diagram that shows the given information for a theorem.

ALTERNATE TEACHING STRATEGIES

Using Problem Solving

Ask students how they would solve the problem in Example 1. Do they agree with the conjecture given at the beginning of the problem (it says there are 84 games)?

Using Charts

It may help some students to make a chart as well as diagram in this lesson. For Example 1, make a chart with the points in one column and the number of segments drawn in the other. Explain that often a variety of problem-solving techniques can be used and that students should use any strategy to help them solve the problem.

Example 2

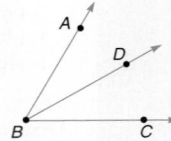

Draw and label the diagram that you would use to prove each statement. Then state the given information and the statement to be proved.

a. The bisector of an angle separates the angle into two angles whose measures are each half of the measure of the original angle.

We are given that an angle has a bisector. Draw an angle $\angle ABC$ with a bisector $\overrightarrow{BD}$.

Given: $\overrightarrow{BD}$ bisects $\angle ABC$.

Prove: $m\angle ABD = \frac{1}{2}m\angle ABC$

$m\angle DBC = \frac{1}{2}m\angle ABC$

Notice that both statements must be proved to prove the statement.

b. If two adjacent angles are complementary, then their exterior sides are perpendicular.

There are two adjacent angles that are complementary. Draw adjacent angles $\angle KLM$ and $\angle MLN$.

We should not mark $\overrightarrow{LK}$ and $\overrightarrow{LN}$ as perpendicular, since that is what is to be proved.

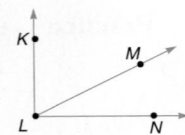

Given: $\angle KLM$ and $\angle MLN$ are complementary.

Prove: $\overrightarrow{LK} \perp \overrightarrow{LN}$

CHECKING FOR UNDERSTANDING

Communicating Mathematics

Read and study the lesson to answer these questions.

1. How can drawing a diagram help you solve a problem? **help choose a strategy, organize your information, or provide the solution**

2. If two new teams joined the Mid-State Conference, how many games would be played? Explain your solution. **7 2 games;**
   $(8 + 7 + 6 + 5 + 4 + 3 + 2 + 1) \times 2$

3. What information should be shown in a diagram that accompanies a proof? **the given information**

Chalkboard Examples

For Example 1
In the freshman football league, there are five teams. No two teams play each other more than once during the season. What is the maximum number of league games played during a season? **10 games**

For Example 2
Draw and label the diagram that you would use to prove each statement. Then state the given information and the statement to be proved.

a. The common side of two adjacent, congruent acute angles is the bisector of the larger angle formed by the two smaller angles.
   Given: $\angle DEF$ and $\angle FEH$ are congruent.
   Prove: Ray EF bisects $\angle DEH$.

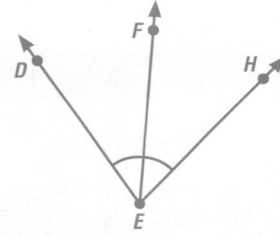

b. If two adjacent angles are supplementary, then they form a linear pair.
   Given: $\angle TUV$ and $\angle VUX$ are supplementary.
   Prove: $\angle TUV$ and $\angle VUX$ form a linear pair.

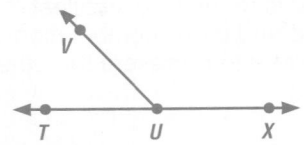

Checking for Understanding

Exercises 1-7 are designed to help you assess students' understanding through reading, writing, speaking, and modeling. You should work through Exercises 1-3 with your students and then monitor their work on Exercises 4-7.

Error Analysis

Students may have difficulty understanding what information is given and what is to be proved. It may help them to put the statements in if-then format like the theorem in Example 2b.

Closing the Lesson

Writing Activity Have each student write a problem in which drawing a diagram would help in finding the solution. The diagram can be a map, a figure, or any other kind of diagram. Have students draw the diagram and list possible ways to find a solution to the problem.

Homework Exercises

Assignment Guide
Basic: 8-14
Average: 10-16
Enriched: 11-17

Exercise Notes

For exercise 12, label the rays and the vertex in the figure, or assign numbers to the four smallest angles and use a combination of those four to represent the other angles.

Guided Practice

Solve. Draw a diagram. See Solutions Manual for diagrams.

4. Halfway through her bus trip from Savannah to Jacksonville, Gloria fell asleep. When she awoke, she still had to travel half of the distance she traveled when asleep. For what fraction of the trip was Gloria asleep? $\frac{1}{3}$

5. Keith and Peggy are building steps to their new shed. It takes one concrete block to build one step, three blocks for two steps, and six blocks for three steps. How many concrete blocks will it take to build six steps? **21**

Draw and label the diagram that you would use to prove each statement. Then state the given information and the statement to be proved. See margin.

6. If the exterior sides of two adjacent angles are perpendicular, then the angles are complementary.

7. If two vertical angles are supplementary, then they are right angles. **See Solutions Manual.**

EXERCISES

Practice   **Solve. Use any strategy.**

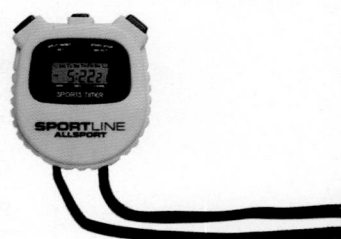

8. How many times in a 12-hour period will the sum of the digits on a digital clock be greater than 16? **84 times**

9. Take two numbers whose sum is one. Which is greater, the square of the greater added to the lesser or the square of the lesser added to the greater? **They are the same.**

Strategies
Look for a pattern.
Solve a simpler problem.
Act it out.
Guess and check.
Draw a diagram.
Make a chart.
Work backward.

10. Draw and label the diagram that you would use to prove the statement *If two right angles are adjacent, then their exterior sides are opposite rays.* Then state the given information and the statement to be proved. **See margin.**

11. Find 33^2, 333^2, and 3333^2. Without calculating, what is $33,333^2$? **1,111,088,889**

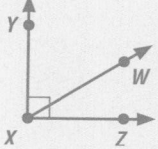

12. How many different acute angles can be traced using the rays in the figure at the right? **10**

13. In how many ways can you receive change for a quarter if at least one coin is a dime? **6**

14. In how many ways can a straight line separate a square into two identical regions? **infinitely many**

Write out directions to a location with which both you and your students are familiar. Have one student draw a map while you read the directions aloud to him or her. Explain that this is an example of drawing a diagram to find a solution to a problem. Discuss other examples.

Additional Answer

6. **Given:** $\overleftrightarrow{XY} \perp \overleftrightarrow{XZ}$
   Prove: $\angle YXW$ and $\angle WXZ$ are complementary.

15. Follow the steps to draw a diagram of a *hexagonal prism*. This is a solid that looks like a six-sided box.

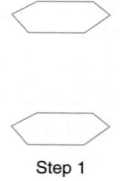

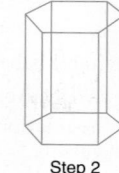

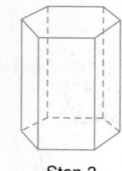

Step 1

Step 2

Step 3

Draw a six-sided top and a congruent six-sided bottom directly below the top.

Draw vertical edges.

Make the edges of the prism that would not be seen from this perspective dashed.

16. The bike path at the new park in Glenville will be 1.2 miles long, 3 feet wide, and 2 inches thick. If asphalt is sold in cubic yards, how much asphalt should the contractor order?
(1 mile = 1760 yards) ≈**117.3 yd³**

17. Two distinct circles and two distinct lines intersect each other. What is the maximum number of points of intersection where at least two of them intersect? **11**

COOPERATIVE LEARNING PROJECT

Work in groups. Each person in the group must understand the solution and be able to explain it to any person in class.

The Parents Association of Easton High School is planning to make and sell school directories to raise money for a new science lab. They will make the directories by printing four pages at a time on the front and back of double-sized sheets of paper. The sheets will then be folded and stapled together inside a cover. If there are 200 pages in the directory, which pages should be printed on each sheet of paper so that the pages will be positioned correctly in the directory? How should the pages be numbered if there are 150 pages? Suppose there are N pages. Develop a formula to find the numbers on any sheet of paper for the directory.
See margin.

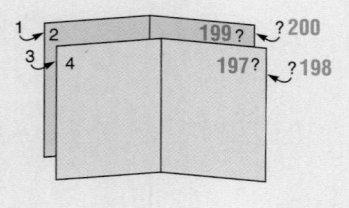

EXTENDING THE LESSON

Math Power: Communication

Ask students to make a general statement about the number of games played in Example 1. Ask how many games would be played if there were 10,000 teams. Then ask how many games would be played if there were *n* teams in the conference.   99,990,000; *n(n −1)*

Cooperative Learning Project

This activity provides students an opportunity to *learn* things together, not just do things together. You may wish to refer to pages T6-T7 and page 116c for the various elements of cooperative groups and specific goals and strategies for using them.

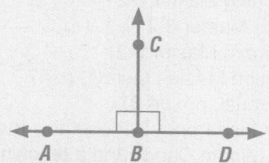

Lesson Resources

- Reteaching Master 3-2
- Practice Master 3-2
- Enrichment Master 3-2
- Evaluation Master, Quiz A, p. 37
- Lab Manual, pp. 34-37

Transparency 3-2 contains the 5-Minute Check and a teaching aid for this lesson.

INTRODUCING THE LESSON

5-Minute Check

(over Lesson 3-1)

1. There are twenty chess teams in the Sun Valley High School Chess Tournament. How many games will be played if each team is eliminated with one loss?
   19

2. Draw and label the diagram that you would use to prove the following theorem: *The bisector of a segment divides the segment into two segments of equal length.*

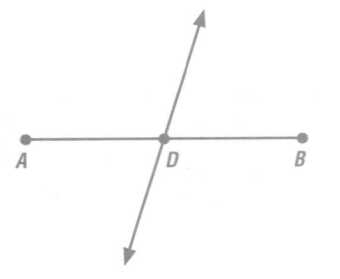

Motivating the Lesson

Bring in a rectangular box (a shoebox or a cereal box) and have students label all corners. Then have them list all planes and segments formed by the box.

Objectives

3-2A
3-2B

After studying this lesson, you should be able to:
- describe the relationships between two lines and between two planes, and
- identify the relationships between pairs of angles formed by pairs of lines and transversals.

Application

Bill Randell is an air-traffic controller. One of his responsibilities is to assign airplanes their cruising altitudes as they head toward their destinations. For safety, airplanes heading eastbound are assigned an altitude level that is an odd number of thousands of feet above the ground and airplanes headed westbound are assigned an altitude level that is an even number of thousands of feet above the ground. The altitude levels can be thought of as **parallel planes**.

While the airplanes are cruising, the paths of two airplanes flying at the same altitude are in the same plane, or **coplanar**. Suppose they are flying some distance apart but going in the same direction. They can be represented by two lines in a plane that never meet. Two lines in a plane that never meet are called **parallel lines**.

In geometry, the symbol $\parallel$ means *is parallel to*. In the figure below, the two lines are parallel.

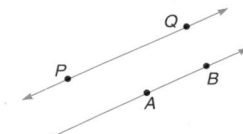

symbols: $\overleftrightarrow{AB} \parallel \overleftrightarrow{PQ}$

words: line AB is parallel to line PQ.

The term parallel and the notation $\parallel$ are also used for segments, rays, and planes. The symbol $\nparallel$ means "is not parallel to."

Parts of lines are parallel if the lines that contain them are parallel. For example in the figure above, $\overline{AB} \parallel \overrightarrow{QP}$.

ALTERNATE TEACHING STRATEGIES

Using Models

Divide the class into small groups and have them use paper, cardboard, pencils, pipe cleaners, glue, tape and anything else they can think of that can be used to represent planes or lines. Have them construct a figure that contains at least four of the geometric representations described in this lesson.

Using Manipulatives

Give each student three pipe cleaners. Place three pipe cleaners on an acetate sheet on the overhead to represent two parallel lines cut by a transversal. Have students place their pipe cleaners on a piece of paper at their desks. Describe the angle relationships formed and ask which angles *appear* to be congruent.

Arrows are used in diagrams to indicate that lines are parallel. In the figure at the right, the arrows on the segments indicate that $\overline{MN} \parallel \overline{OP}$.

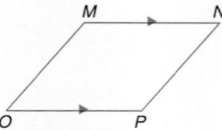

Two planes can intersect or be parallel just like two lines. Recall that the altitude levels of the airplanes are parallel planes. You learned in Chapter 1 that if two planes intersect, they intersect in a line. The figure below is a rectangular prism. Its faces are contained in parallel and intersecting planes.

Remember that plane ABC refers to the plane containing points A, B, and C.

parallel planes:

plane *ADR* ∥ plane *BCS*

plane *RSC* ∥ plane *ABT*

plane *RST* ∥ plane *ADC*

planes intersecting plane *ABC*:

plane *ABT*, in $\overleftrightarrow{AB}$

plane *ADR*, in $\overleftrightarrow{AD}$

plane *RSC*, in $\overleftrightarrow{CD}$

plane *BCS*, in $\overleftrightarrow{BC}$

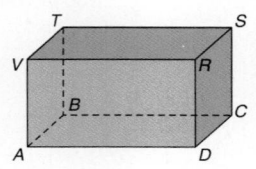

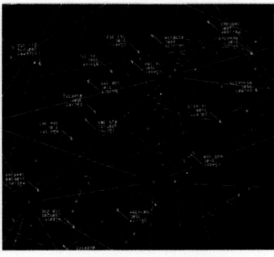

Using Mr. Randell's system, eastbound and westbound airplanes will never be in danger of colliding. The closest that an eastbound airplane can come to a westbound airplane is 1000 feet. Suppose you are in an airplane that is flying northeast at an altitude of 27,000 feet and you see a second airplane flying due west at an altitude of 24,000. The paths of your airplane and the second airplane will never meet, but they are not in the same plane. Lines like those represented by these paths are called **skew lines**.

Skew Lines	**Two lines are skew if they do not intersect and are not in the same plane.**

Example 1

Identify each pair as intersecting, parallel, or skew.

a. $\overline{BA}$ and $\overline{GH}$ parallel

b. $\overline{EH}$ and $\overline{CD}$ skew

c. plane *EAB* and plane *GCB*   intersecting

d. $\overline{HG}$ and plane *EAB*   parallel

e. plane *HGC* and $\overline{BC}$ intersecting

LESSON 3-2 PARALLELS AND TRANSVERSALS 123

Teaching Tip
When defining *transversal*, note that the two lines that are intersected by the transversal do not need to be parallel.

Chalkboard Example

For Example 2
Identify each pair of angles as alternate interior, consecutive interior, alternate exterior, or corresponding angles.

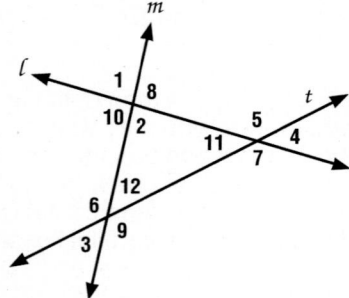

a. ∠6 and ∠10   consecutive interior
b. ∠9 and ∠11   alternate interior
c. ∠1 and ∠5   corresponding
d. ∠3 and ∠8   alternate exterior
e. ∠7 and ∠12   alternate interior
f. ∠4 and ∠8   corresponding

EVALUATING THE LESSON

Checking for Understanding

Exercises 1-21 are designed to help you assess students' understanding through reading, writing, speaking, and modeling. You should work through Exercises 1-3 with your students and then monitor their work on Exercises 4-21.

The runways at Mitchell Field are shown at the right. Notice that runway *t* intersects runways *ℓ* and *m*. A line that intersects two or more lines in a plane at different points is called a **transversal**.

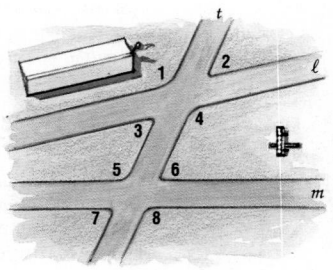

When the transversal *t* intersects lines *ℓ* and *m*, it forms eight angles with these lines. Several of the angles and pairs of angles are given special names.

Interior Angles	∠3, ∠4, ∠5, ∠6
Alternate Interior Angles	∠3 and ∠6, ∠4 and ∠5
Consecutive Interior Angles	∠3 and ∠5, ∠4 and ∠6
Exterior Angles	∠1, ∠2, ∠7, ∠8
Alternate Exterior Angles	∠1 and ∠8, ∠2 and ∠7
Corresponding Angles	∠1 and ∠5, ∠2 and ∠6, ∠3 and ∠7, ∠4 and ∠8

Example 2   Identify each pair of angles as *alternate interior, consecutive interior, alternate exterior,* or *corresponding angles.*

a. ∠7 and ∠11   corresponding

b. ∠2 and ∠9   consecutive interior

c. ∠7 and ∠12   corresponding

d. ∠8 and ∠10   alternate interior

e. ∠4 and ∠8   consecutive interior

f. ∠2 and ∠12   alternate exterior

CHECKING FOR UNDERSTANDING

Communicating Mathematics

1. See margin.
2. See students' work.

Read and study the lesson to answer these questions.

1. What symbol is used to indicate that two lines are parallel? Draw and label two parallel lines and indicate they are parallel using the symbols.

2. Give a real-world example or model of two skew lines.

3. Draw two lines. Label them *q* and *p*. Then draw a transversal *t* that intersects the two lines. Label a pair of corresponding angles, ∠1 and ∠2. Discuss your strategy for identifying corresponding angles. **See margin**

Additional Answers
1. Sample answer: arrows

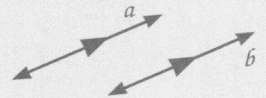

3. Sample answer:

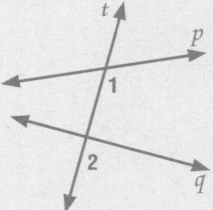

Guided Practice

4. parallel, intersecting, skew

7. parallel, intersecting, skew

4. parallel, intersecting, skew
6. parallel and/or intersecting

Classify each situation as a model of intersecting, parallel, or skew lines.

4. airplane flight paths
5. train tracks parallel
6. lines on writing paper
7. skis on skier
8. plaid fabric
intersecting and parallel
9. airport runway intersecting or parallel

Determine whether each statement is *true* or *false*. If false, explain why.

10. A line that intersects two skew lines is a transversal. F
11. Two lines are parallel if they do not intersect. false; could be skew
12. Skew lines are parallel. false; not in same plane
13. If a line intersects two parallel lines, then it is a transversal. true

10. False; a transversal and the lines it intersects are in the same plane.

Determine whether each statement is *true* or *false.*

14. true

16. true

17. false

18. true

20. true

14. ∠6 and ∠11 are alternate interior angles.
15. ∠4 and ∠6 are vertical angles. false
16. ∠5 and ∠8 are consecutive interior angles.
17. ∠4 and ∠9 are alternate exterior angles.
18. ∠10 and ∠11 are alternate interior angles.
19. ∠7 and ∠11 are corresponding angles. true
20. ∠14 and ∠7 are alternate exterior angles.
21. ∠3 and ∠8 are corresponding angles. true

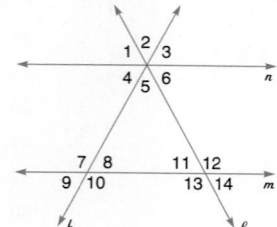

EXERCISES

Practice

State the transversal that forms each pair of angles. Then identify the special angle pair name for the angles. See margin.

A

22. ∠2 and ∠4
23. ∠1 and ∠3
24. ∠TVR and ∠VTS
25. ∠SRV and ∠RVT

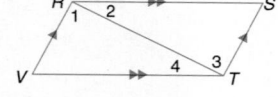

26. ∠11 and ∠8
27. ∠1 and ∠2
28. ∠7 and ∠4
29. ∠7 and ∠12
30. ∠3 and ∠5
31. ∠11 and ∠4

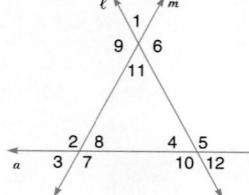

RETEACHING THE LESSON

Draw two parallel lines or two lines cut by a transversal on the chalkboard or overhead. Have students name different parts of the lines that are parallel, or relationships among the angles formed by the lines and the transversal.

Additional Answers

22. $\overleftrightarrow{RT}$; alternate interior angles
23. $\overleftrightarrow{RT}$; alternate interior angles
24. $\overleftrightarrow{TV}$; consecutive interior angles
25. $\overleftrightarrow{RV}$; consecutive interior angles
26. m; consecutive interior angles
27. m; corresponding angles
28. a; alternate interior angles
29. a; corresponding angles
30. a; alternate exterior angles
31. ℓ; consecutive interior angles

Closing the Lesson

Speaking Activity Draw a picture of two lines cut by a transversal on the chalkboard or overhead and label the angles formed. Go around the room and have students name two angles and any relationships they have in the figure.

APPLYING THE LESSON

Homework Exercises

Assignment Guide
Basic: 22-42, 50-58
Average: 25-46, 50-58
Enriched: 29-58

Exercise Notes

For Exercises 14-21, ask students if line n is a transversal for line k and line ℓ. no, since a transversal must intersect two lines at different points

Reteaching Masters Booklet, p. 15

38.

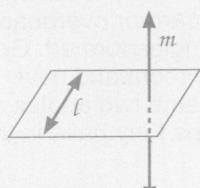

39.

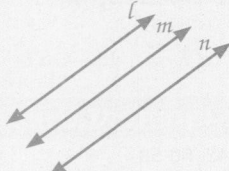

40.

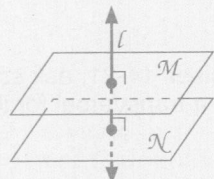

41.

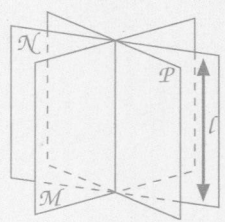

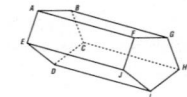

Identify each as a model of intersecting or parallel planes.

32. the pieces of glass in a double-paned window parallel
33. the sides of a box parallel and intersecting
34. a floor and a ceiling parallel
35. the sides of a pup tent intersecting
36. the floor and the top of a table parallel
37. the sides of a roof intersecting

B Draw a figure to illustrate each situation. See margin.

38. two skew lines
39. two lines parallel to a third line
40. two parallel planes with a line perpendicular to both planes
41. two intersecting planes with a line parallel to both planes
42. two lines perpendicular to a plane
43. two parallel planes with a line parallel to both planes

The three-dimensional figure shown at the right is called a right hexagonal prism.   44. $\overline{RU}, \overline{ST}, \overline{CV}, \overline{BW}, \overline{AR}, \overline{RS}, \overline{CB}, \overline{BZ}$

44. Identify all segments that appear to be skew to $\overline{XY}$.
45. Which segments seem parallel to $\overline{ST}$?
46. Which segments seem parallel to $\overline{VW}$?
47. Identify all planes that appear parallel to the plane STU. plane BWX

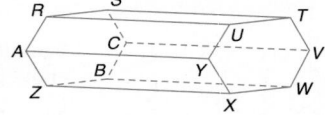

45. $\overline{CV}, \overline{BW}, \overline{ZX}, \overline{AY}, \overline{RU}$ 46. $\overline{UY}, \overline{CB}, \overline{RA}$

C 48. If line ℓ is parallel to line m and line m is parallel to plane $\mathcal{N}$, is $\ell \parallel \mathcal{N}$? If yes, describe a real-life model that demonstrates this concept. If no, draw a counterexample. See margin.

49. If plane A is parallel to plane B and plane B is parallel to plane C, then plane A is parallel to plane C. Explain what this means and state a model in your school that demonstrates this property. See margin.

Critical Thinking

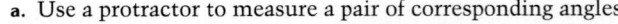

50. Choose two parallel lines on a piece of lined notebook paper and draw a transversal through them.

a. Use a protractor to measure a pair of corresponding angles.

INVESTIGATION

b. Make a conjecture about the relationship between the measures of the corresponding angles you measured. They are congruent.

42.

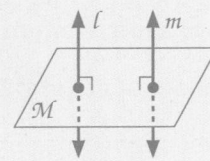

43.

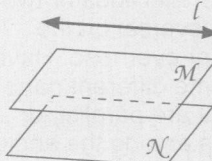

Application

51. Air-Traffic Control Above 30,000 feet, eastbound airplanes are assigned cruising altitudes of 33,000 feet, 37,000 feet, 41,000 feet, and so on. The westbound airplanes cruise altitudes of 31,000 feet, 35,000 feet, 39,000 feet, and so on.

a. What will now be the closest vertical distance two airplanes passing over each other will encounter? **2000 feet**

b. What are some of the advantages of this system of assigning cruising altitudes? **easy to keep track of which airplanes are eastbound and which are westbound; less worry about collisions**

Mixed Review

52. Draw the diagram that you would use to prove the theorem *If the exterior sides of two adjacent angles are opposite rays, then the angles are supplementary.* Then state the given and the statement to be proved. **(Lesson 3-1) See margin.**

53. Write a two-column proof. **(Lesson 2-7)**
Given: $\angle 1 \cong \angle 2$
Prove: $\angle 1 \cong \angle 3$ **See margin.**

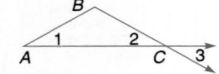

54. Name the property of equality that justifies the statement *If $m\angle A = m\angle B$, then $m\angle B = m\angle A$.* **(Lesson 2-4) Symmetric property of equality**

55. If two lines lie in the same plane and do not intersect, then they are parallel.

55. Write the converse of the conditional *If two lines are parallel, then they lie in the same plane and do not intersect.* **(Lesson 2-2)**

56. Find the coordinates of the midpoint of the segment whose endpoints are $A(10, -4)$ and $B(-6, 0)$. **(Lesson 1-5)** $(2, -2)$

57. T is between R and S. If $TS = 7$ and $RS = 20$, find RT. **(Lesson 1-4)** 13

Wrap-Up

58. Draw two lines and a transversal and label the angles formed. Name the interior angles, the exterior angles, a pair of alternate interior angles, a pair of alternate exterior angles, a pair of corresponding angles, and a pair of consecutive interior angles. **See Solutions Manual.**

HISTORY CONNECTION

The Maori people of South America and New Zealand and the Polynesians of the Pacific Islands were navigating the Pacific Ocean long before the invention of the compass and the sextant. They knew how to navigate by the stars and amazingly they had discovered the geometry and physics behind the wave patterns in the waters around islands.

The Maoris and the Polynesians understood that parallel waves are reflected around islands in patterns. They taught their children to read the patterns of the waves with a *mattang*. Once they learned the patterns, a navigator could feel the motion of the water around his boat to locate nearby islands.

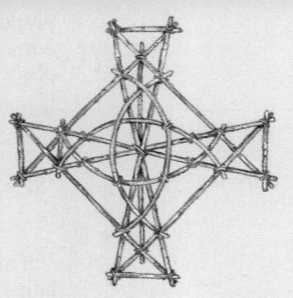

EXTENDING THE LESSON

Math Power: Reasoning

Ask students if two lines can intersect two points. Can they intersect in three points? Discuss the intersection of lines and point out that lines will intersect in either none, one, or an infinite number of points. Have students draw an example of each case.

History Connection

The History Connection features introduce students to persons or cultures involved in the development of mathematics. You may want to further research the Maoris or the Polynesians.

Additional Answers

48. no, because l could be in plane N

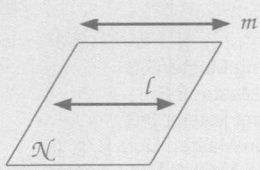

49. If a plane A is parallel to a plane B and plane B is parallel to plane C, then plane A is parallel to plane C. The basement floor is parallel to the ground-level floor and the ground-level floor is parallel to the upstairs floor, so the basement floor is parallel to the upstairs floor.

52. Given: $\overrightarrow{BA}$ and $\overrightarrow{BD}$ are opposite rays.
Prove: $\angle ABC$ and $\angle CBD$ are supplementary.

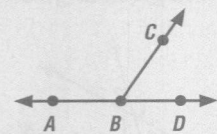

53. Statements   (Reasons)
a. $\angle 1 \cong \angle 2$ (Given)
b. $\angle 2 \cong \angle 3$ (Vertical $\angle$s are $\cong$.)
c. $\angle 1 \cong \angle 3$ (Congruence of angles is transitive.)

Enrichment Masters Booklet, p.15

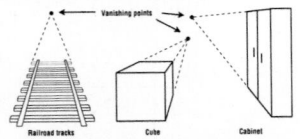
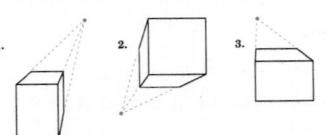
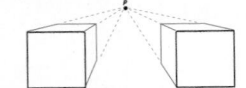

- Reteaching Master 3-3
- Practice Master 3-3
- Enrichment Master 3-3
- Evaluation Master, Quiz B, p. 37
- Evaluation Master, Mid-Chapter Test, p. 41
- Technology Master, p. 39

 Transparency 3-3 contains the 5-Minute Check and a teaching aid for this lesson.

INTRODUCING THE LESSON

 5-Minute Check

(over Lesson 3-2)

Refer to the figure below to identify the special angle pair name for the given angles.

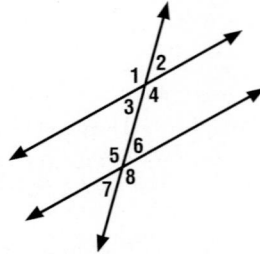

1. ∠1 and ∠8   **alternate exterior**

2. ∠4 and ∠5   **alternate interior**

Draw a figure to illustrate each situation.

3. two perpendicular planes

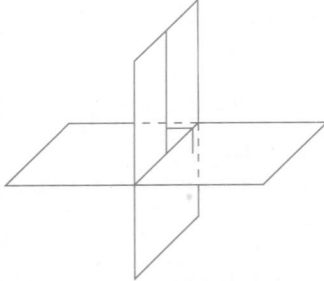

4. two parallel lines and a skew line

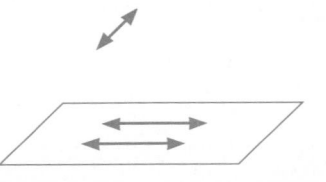

3-3 Using Parallel Lines

Objective
3-3

After studying this lesson, you should be able to:
- use the properties of parallel lines to determine angle measures.

In 300 B.C. parallel lines were defined as lines that "ran along beside each other." The B.C. cartoon is an illustration of an artist's use of a perspective drawing; that is, a drawing that looks like things look to our eyes.

To Peter, the parallel lines appear to meet at a vanishing point in the distance. However parallel lines do not meet in Euclidean geometry. For centuries mathematicians tried to prove that there is exactly one line parallel to a given line through a given point not on the line. When they determined that the proposition could not be proved, other geometries in which parallel lines do meet were explored. These geometries are called *non-Euclidean geometries*. In this text, we concentrate on Euclidean geometry.

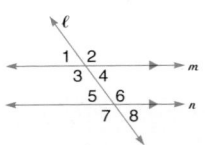

There are several postulates and theorems that help you gain insight into properties of parallel lines. If you investigate the relationships between the corresponding angles formed by two parallel lines cut by a transversal, you will observe that the angles are congruent. This property is accepted as a postulate.

Postulate 3-1 *Corresponding Angles Postulate*	**If two parallel lines are cut by a transversal, then each pair of corresponding angles is congruent.**

This postulate, combined with linear pair and vertical angle properties, helps to establish several angle relationships.

ALTERNATE TEACHING STRATEGIES

Using Charts and Drawings

Have each student draw two parallel lines with a transversal. Have them label the angles from 1 to 8, using the same order as in the picture on page 128. Have them use a protractor to measure all eight angles. Record each student's measures on one big chart. Ask students to form conjectures about the angle relationships.

Using Constructions

Have students construct a perpendicular line through two parallel lines. What can they say about the angles formed? **They all measure 90° and are congruent.** Ask them what would happen if you drew a line through the parallel lines that was not perpendicular. Have them make conjectures about the relationships among the angles.

Example 1

A road crosses a set of railroad tracks. If the measure of ∠6 is 110, find m∠3.

Since ∠2 and ∠6 are corresponding angles, m∠2 = m∠6. m∠2 = m∠3 because they are vertical angles. Therefore, m∠6 = m∠3 by the transitive property of equality. So, m∠3 = 110.

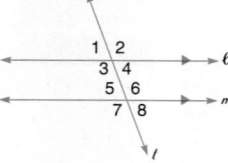

Notice that in Example 1, ∠4 and ∠5 form a pair of alternate interior angles. This is an application of another of the special relationships between the angles formed by two parallel lines and a transversal. These relationships are summarized in Theorems 3-1 through 3-3. You will be asked to prove Theorems 3-1 and 3-2 in Exercises 46 and 47, respectively.

Theorem 3-1 *Alternate Interior Angle Theorem*	**If two parallel lines are cut by a transversal, then each pair of alternate interior angles is congruent.**
Theorem 3-2 *Consecutive Interior Angle Theorem*	**If two parallel lines are cut by a transversal, then each pair of consecutive interior angles is supplementary.**
Theorem 3-3 *Alternate Exterior Angle Theorem*	**If two parallel lines are cut by a transversal, then each pair of alternate exterior angles is congruent.**

The proof of Theorem 3-3 that is given below is called a **paragraph proof**. The statements and reasons are written informally in a paragraph. But the steps in a paragraph proof are the same as those in a two-column proof.

Proof of Theorem 3-3

Given: $p \parallel q$
  ℓ is a transversal of p and q.

Prove: ∠1 ≅ ∠8; ∠2 ≅ ∠7

Paragraph Proof:

We are given that $p \parallel q$. If two parallel lines are cut by a transversal, corresponding angles are congruent. So, ∠1 ≅ ∠5 and ∠2 ≅ ∠6. ∠5 ≅ ∠8 and ∠6 ≅ ∠7 because vertical angles are congruent. Therefore, ∠1 ≅ ∠8 and ∠2 ≅ ∠7 since congruence of angles is transitive.

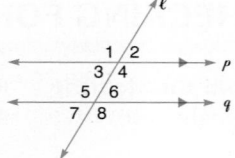

LESSON 3-3   USING PARALLEL LINES   129

Chalkboard Example

For Example 2
Find the values of *x*, *y*, and *z*.

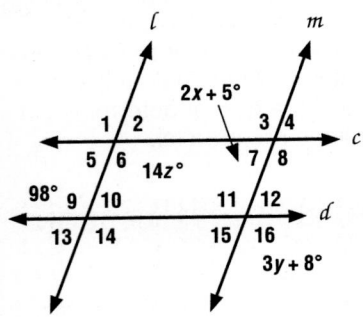

$\ell \parallel m$ and $c \parallel d$

Since $\ell \parallel m$, $\angle 16 \cong \angle 9$ by the alternate exterior angle theorem.

$$m\angle 16 = \angle 9$$
$$3y + 8 = 98$$
$$y = 30$$

Since $c \parallel d$, $\angle 6 \cong \angle 9$ by the alternate interior angle theorem.

$$m\angle 6 = m\angle 9$$
$$14z = 98$$
$$z = 7$$

Since $\ell \parallel m$, $\angle 6$ and $\angle 7$ are supplementary by the consecutive interior angle theorem.

$$m\angle 6 + m\angle 7 = 180$$
$$14z + 2x + 5 = 180$$
$$2x = 77$$
$$x = 38.5$$

Therefore, $x = 38.5$, $y = 30$, and $z = 7$.

EVALUATING THE LESSON

Checking for Understanding

Exercises 1-18 are designed to help you assess students' understanding through reading, writing, speaking, and modeling. You should work through Exercises 1-5 with your students and then monitor their work on Exercises 6-18.

Example 2

Find the values of *x*, *y*, and *z*.

Since $\overrightarrow{AG} \parallel \overrightarrow{BH}$, $\angle CEF \cong \angle EFH$ by the alternate interior angle theorem.

$$m\angle CEF = m\angle EFH$$
$$2x = 82 \qquad \text{\footnotesize $m\angle CEF = 2x, m\angle EFH = 82$.}$$
$$x = 41$$

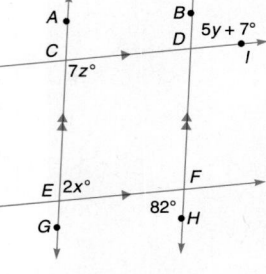

Since $\overrightarrow{CD} \parallel \overrightarrow{EF}$, $\angle DCE$ and $\angle CEF$ are supplementary by the consecutive interior angle theorem.

$$m\angle DCE + m\angle CEF = 180$$
$$7z + 2x = 180 \qquad \text{\footnotesize $m\angle DCE = 7z, m\angle CEF = 2x$.}$$
$$7z + 2(41) = 180 \qquad \text{\footnotesize Substitute 41 for x.}$$
$$7z = 98$$
$$z = 14$$

Since $\overrightarrow{CD} \parallel \overrightarrow{EF}$, $\angle BDI \cong \angle EFH$ by the alternate exterior angle theorem.

$$m\angle BDI = m\angle EFH$$
$$5y + 7 = 82$$
$$5y = 75$$
$$y = 15$$

Therefore, $x = 41$, $y = 15$, and $z = 14$.

There is a special relationship that occurs when one of two parallel lines is cut by a perpendicular line. You will prove this theorem in Exercise 45.

Theorem 3-4 Perpendicular Transversal Theorem	In a plane, if a line is perpendicular to one of two parallel lines, then it is perpendicular to the other.

CHECKING FOR UNDERSTANDING

1. If 2 $\parallel$ lines are cut by a transversal, consec. int. $\angle\!\!\!\angle$ are supp.

Communicating Mathematics

Read and study the lesson to answer these questions.

1. Explain why $\angle 4$ and $\angle 6$ must be supplementary.

2. See margin.

2. If you know that $m\angle 1 = 70$, explain two different strategies you could use to find $m\angle 5$.

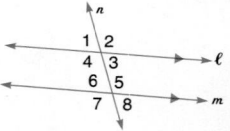

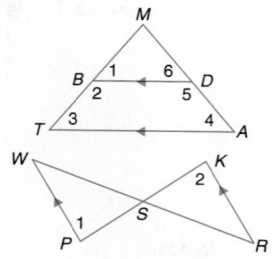

3. Explain what the arrowheads on the lines in both diagrams at the right indicate. **Lines are parallel.**

4. If 2 ∥ lines are cut by a transversal, corresponding ∠s are congruent.

4. If $\overleftrightarrow{BD} \parallel \overleftrightarrow{AT}$ then $\angle 1 \cong \angle 3$ and $\angle 6 \cong \angle 4$. Explain why this is true.

5. If $\overleftrightarrow{WP} \parallel \overleftrightarrow{KR}$, then $\angle 1 \cong \angle 2$. Explain why this is true. **If 2 ∥ lines are cut by a transversal, alt. int. ∠s are ≅.**

Guided Practice

List the conclusions that can be drawn from each figure. **See margin.**

6.

7.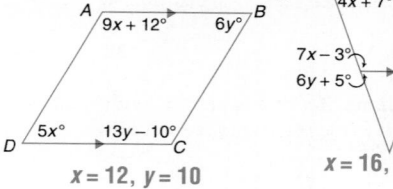

8.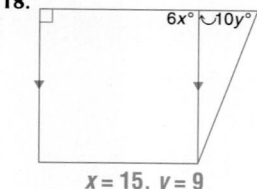

Given $\ell \parallel m$, $m\angle 1 = 98$, and $m\angle 2 = 40$, find the measure of each angle.

9. $m\angle 3$ **82**   10. $m\angle 4$ **98**

11. $m\angle 5$ **82**   12. $m\angle 6$ **140**

13. $m\angle 7$ **40**   14. $m\angle 8$ **40**

15. $m\angle 9$ **140**

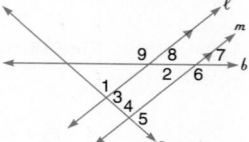

Find the values of x and y.

16.
$x = 12$, $y = 10$

17.
$x = 16$, $y = 11$

18.
$x = 15$, $y = 9$

EXERCISES

Practice

In the figure, $n \parallel p$, $q \perp p$, $\overline{CD} \parallel \overline{AB}$, and $m\angle 1 = 125$. Find the measure of each angle.

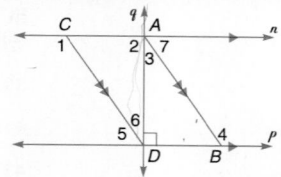

A

19. $\angle 2$ **90**   20. $\angle 3$ **35**

21. $\angle 4$ **125**   22. $\angle 5$ **55**

23. $\angle 6$ **35**   24. $\angle 7$ **55**

LESSON 3-3   USING PARALLEL LINES   131

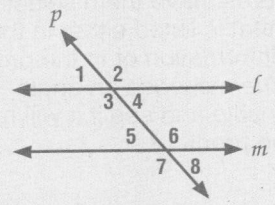
Reteaching Masters Booklet, p.16

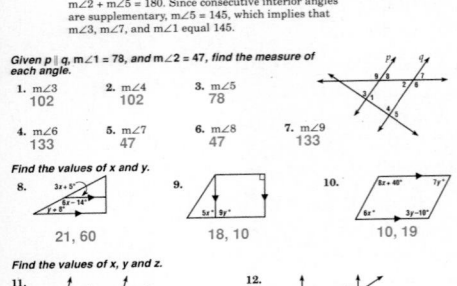
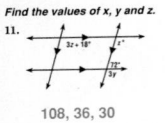
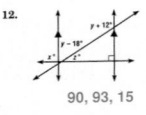

Find the values of x and y.

25.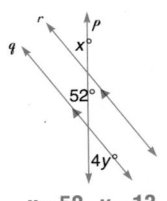

$x = 52$, $y = 13$

26.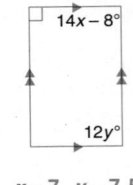

$x = 7$, $y = 7.5$

27.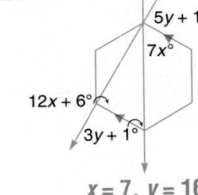

$x = 7$, $y = 16$

B In the figure, $m\angle 2 = 62$, $m\angle 1 = 41$, $\overline{XS} \parallel \overline{YT}$, and $\overline{SY} \parallel \overline{TZ}$. Find the measure of each angle.

28. $\angle 4$ 62
29. $\angle 3$ 77
30. $\angle 5$ 41
31. $\angle 6$ 62
32. $\angle 7$ 77
33. $\angle 8$ 103

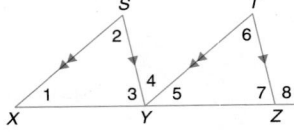

Find the values of x, y, and z.

34.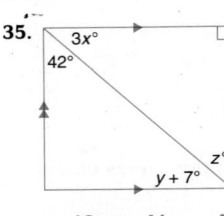

$x = 112$, $y = 28$, $z = 22$

35.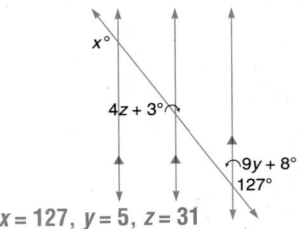

$x = 16$, $y = 41$, $z = 42$

36.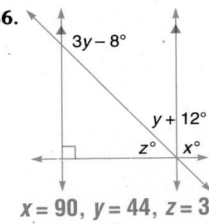

$x = 90$, $y = 44$, $z = 34$

37.

$x = 127$, $y = 5$, $z = 31$

38.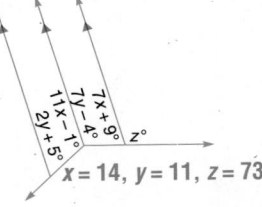

$x = 14$, $y = 11$, $z = 73$

In the figure, $\overline{AC} \parallel \overline{BD}$, $\overline{CB} \parallel \overline{DE}$, $m\angle 1 = 35$, $m\angle 4 = 20$, and $\overline{DE}$ bisects $\angle BDF$. Find the measure of each angle.

39. $\angle 2$ 35
40. $\angle 3$ 35
41. $\angle 5$ 125
42. $\angle 6$ 35
43. $\angle 7$ 35
44. $\angle 8$ 110

RETEACHING THE LESSON

Draw two parallel lines cut by a transversal and number all of the angles formed. List all the corresponding angles that are congruent according to Postulate 3-1, the alternate interior angles that are congruent according to Theorem 3-1, the consecutive interior angles that are supplementary according to Theorem 3-2, and the alternate exterior angles that are congruent according to Theorem 3-3.

45. Copy and complete the proof of Theorem 3-4.

Given: $m \perp \ell$
$\ell \parallel p$

Prove: $m \perp p$

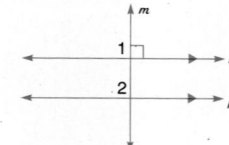

Statements	Reasons
a. $m \perp \ell$ $\ell \parallel p$	a. __?__ Given
b. $\angle 1$ is a right angle.	b. __?__ $\perp$ lines form 4 rt. $\angle$s.
c. __?__ $m\angle 1 = 90$	c. Definition of right angle
d. $\angle 1 \cong \angle 2$	d. __?__
e. __?__ $m\angle 2 = 90$	e. Substitution property of equality
f. $\angle 2$ is a right angle.	f. __?__ Definition of right angle
g. __?__ $m \perp p$	g. Definition of perpendicular lines

d. If 2 ∥ lines are cut by a transversal, corr. $\angle$s are $\cong$.

46. Write a two-column proof of Theorem 3-1. **See margin.**

47. Write a paragraph proof of Theorem 3-2. **See Solutions Manual.**

48. Find measures x and y in the figure at the right, if $\overline{AF} \parallel \overline{BC}$ and $\overline{AE} \parallel \overline{CD}$.
$x = 49$, $y = 76$

49. Given: $\overline{MQ} \parallel \overline{NP}$
$\angle 1 \cong \angle 5$

Prove: $\angle 4 \cong \angle 3$. **See margin.**

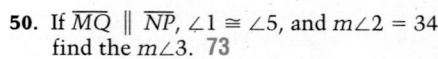
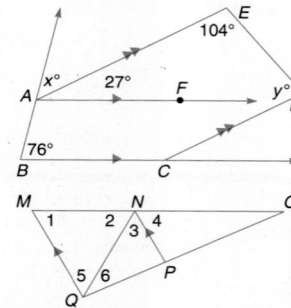

50. If $\overline{MQ} \parallel \overline{NP}$, $\angle 1 \cong \angle 5$, and $m\angle 2 = 34$, find the $m\angle 3$. **73**

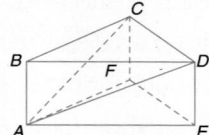

Critical Thinking

51. Planes BCD and AEF are parallel. Name an angle congruent to each given angle.

a. $\angle EAD$ $\angle BDA$

b. $\angle CAF$ $\angle BCA$

c. $\angle ACF$ $\angle BAC$

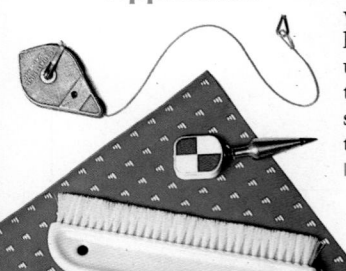

Application

52. Interior Decorating The walls in houses are not perfectly vertical, but wallpaper should be hung vertically to make the pattern look nice. So to hang wallpaper, a true vertical line must be established. The paperhanger uses a plumb bob, which is a piece of string with a weight at the bottom to make the vertical line for the first piece of wallpaper. How can she be sure that all of the other pieces of wallpaper are vertical if she doesn't use the plumb bob again? **The sides of the wallpaper are parallel, so if each new piece is parallel to the last one, they will all be vertical.**

LESSON 3-3   USING PARALLEL LINES   133

Practice Masters Booklet, p. 19

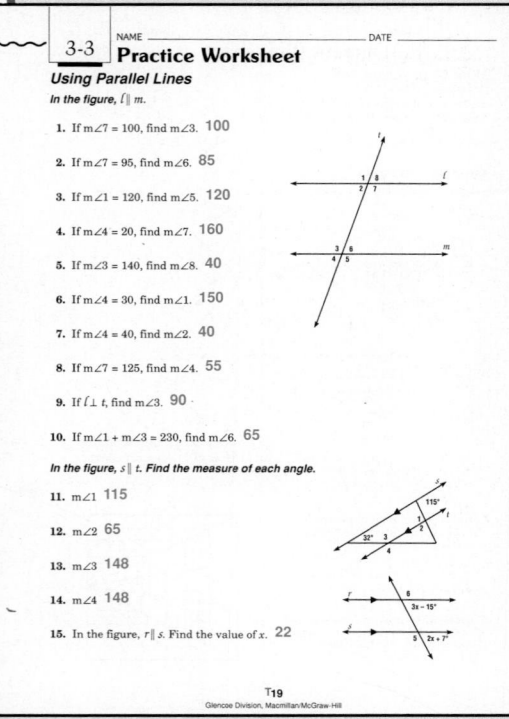

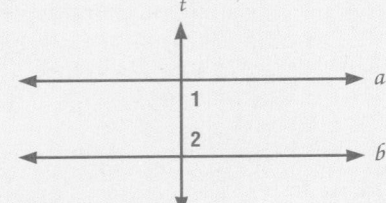
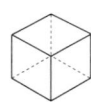
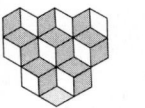
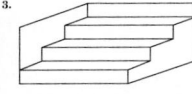 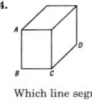
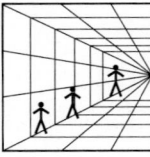
Mixed Review

53. Are the ceiling and the floor of your classroom a model of parallel or intersecting planes? **(Lesson 3-2)** parallel

54. Write a two-column proof. **(Lesson 2-6)**

Given: $\overline{AB} \cong \overline{FE}$
$\overline{BC} \cong \overline{ED}$
Prove: $\overline{AC} \cong \overline{FD}$ See margin.

55. Lines p and m never meet; detachment

55. If possible, write a conclusion from the two statements *If two lines are parallel, then they never meet* and *Lines p and m are parallel.* State the law of logic that you used. **(Lesson 2-3)**

56. The measure of an angle is $9x + 14$ and the measure of its supplement is $12x + 19$. Find the value of x. **(Lesson 1-8)** 7

57. -3 or 9

57. Point T is 6 units from point S on a number line. If the coordinate of point S is 3, what are the possible coordinates for point T? **(Lesson 1-4)**

58. If $x < 0$ and $y < 0$, in which quadrant is the point $Q(x, y)$ located? **(Lesson 1-1)** III

Wrap-Up

59. Journal Entry This lesson presented four major conclusions you can make if you know that two parallel lines are cut by a transversal. List those conclusions and draw a diagram that describes these results. **See Solutions Manual.**

~~~~~~~~~~ **MID-CHAPTER REVIEW** ~~~~~~~~~~

1. Draw and label the diagram that you would use to prove the theorem *If two parallel lines are cut by a transversal so that consecutive interior angles are congruent, then the transversal is perpendicular to the parallels.* Then state the given information and the statement to be proved. **(Lesson 3-1)** See margin.

The three-dimensional figure shown at the right is called a right-triangular prism. (Lesson 3-2)

2. Which segment appears parallel to $\overline{AC}$? $\overline{EF}$

3. Which segments appear to be skew to $\overline{BD}$? $\overline{AC}$, $\overline{EF}$

4. Name the plane that appears parallel to plane ABC. **plane DEF**

5. Which plane appears parallel to plane BCF? **none**

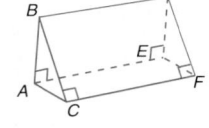

In the figure, $\ell \parallel m$, and $m\angle 2 = 115$. Find the measure of each angle. (Lesson 3-3)

6. $\angle 1$ **65**   7. $\angle 3$ **65**

8. $\angle 4$ **115**   9. $\angle 5$ **65**

10. $\angle 6$ **115**   11. $\angle 7$ **115**

12. $\angle 8$ **65**

134   CHAPTER 3   PARALLELS

EXTENDING THE LESSON

Math Power: Connections

Begin a discussion about non-Euclidean geometry and point out that the parallel postulate does not exist in these geometries. You could demonstrate two non-Euclidean parallel lines by drawing a circle that contains two nonintersecting chords, or by stretching two rubber bands around a ball, making sure they do not cross or touch.

Mid-Chapter Review

The Mid-Chapter Review provides students with a brief review of the concepts and skills in Lesson 3-1 through 3-3. Lesson numbers are given at the end of problems or instruction lines so students may review concepts not yet mastered.

3-4 Proving Lines Parallel

Objectives
3-4A
3-4B

After studying this lesson, you should be able to:
- recognize angle conditions that produce parallel lines, and
- prove two lines are parallel based on given angle relationships.

Application

Have you ever noticed that the yardage markers on a football field are parallel? How would the game be affected if they weren't? The grounds crew must be very careful to position the lines correctly so that the game can run smoothly. They use the properties of parallel lines to ensure a fair game.

INVESTIGATION

Construct a line parallel to a given line through a point *not* on the line.

1. Use a straightedge to draw line ℓ and locate point P not on line ℓ.

2. Now draw a line through P that intersects ℓ. Label the point of intersection X and label angle 1 as shown.

3. Construct an angle congruent to angle 1 using P as a vertex and one side on $\overrightarrow{PX}$. Draw a line through P to form an angle congruent to $\angle 1$. Label the line n and the angle 2.

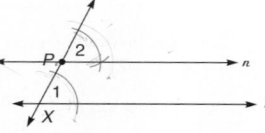

Use a ruler to measure the perpendicular distance between ℓ and n in several different places. Make a conjecture about ℓ and n. *They are parallel.*

What kind of angles are $\angle 1$ and $\angle 2$? *corresponding*

The investigation illustrates a postulate that helps us to prove that two lines are parallel. Notice that this postulate is the converse of Postulate 3-1.

Postulate 3-2	If two lines in a plane are cut by a transversal so that corresponding angles are congruent, then the lines are parallel.

LESSON 3-4   PROVING LINES PARALLEL   **135**

ALTERNATE TEACHING STRATEGIES

Using Writing

Have students write the converses of Postulate 3-1 and each of the theorems listed in Lesson 3-3. Have them compare these to Postulate 3-2 and the theorems in this lesson. They should be the same.

Using Cooperative Groups

Divide the class into small groups and have each group attempt to construct a line parallel to a given line through a point *not* on the line. Have each group explain the steps it took to draw the line and why the two lines are parallel.

3-4 Lesson Notes

Lesson Resources

- Reteaching Master 3-4
- Practice Master 3-4
- Enrichment Master 3-4
- Evaluation Master, Quiz C, p. 38
- Activity Master, p. 3

  Transparency 3-4 contains the 5-Minute Check and a teaching aid for this lesson.

INTRODUCING THE LESSON

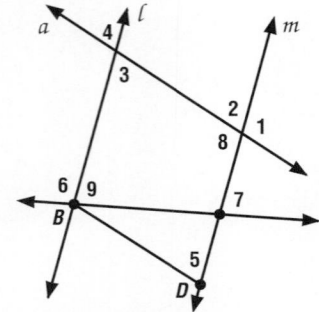

5-Minute Check
(over Lesson 3-3)

Refer to the figure below, $\ell \parallel m$ and $a \parallel \overline{BD}$.

Find the measure of each angle if m$\angle$2 = 63.

1. $\angle 3$ **63**
2. $\angle 4$ **63**
3. $\angle 8$ **117**
4. $\angle 9$ **can't be found with the information given**

Motivating the Lesson

Draw two parallel lines on the chalkboard or overhead and ask your students how they might prove the lines are parallel. Ask them how it might be done using angle relationships.

TEACHING THE LESSON

Teaching Tip For step 3 in the construction, you may want to review how to construct an angle congruent to a given angle (Lesson 1-7).

Chapter 3   135

Teaching Tip When discussing Postulate 3-3, point out that the word *exactly* means two things: there is not more than one line through the point, and there is *always* a line through the point.

The investigation also shows us that there is at least one line through P parallel to ℓ. The following postulate states that there is *exactly* one line parallel to a line through a given point not on the line.

Postulate 3-3 Parallel Postulate	**If there is a line and a point not on the line, then there exists exactly one line through the point that is parallel to the given line.**

There are sets of conditions other than Postulate 3-2 that prove that two lines are parallel. One of them is stated in Theorem 3-5.

Theorem 3-5	**If two lines in a plane are cut by a transversal so that a pair of alternate interior angles is congruent, then the two lines are parallel.**

Proof of Theorem 3-5

Given: $\angle 1 \cong \angle 2$

Prove: $p \parallel q$

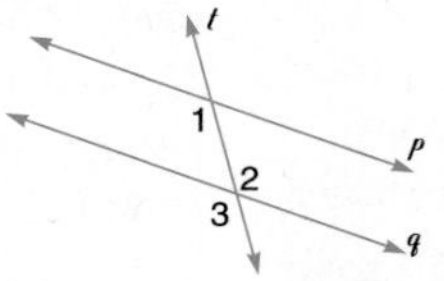

Statements	Reasons
1. $\angle 1 \cong \angle 2$	**1.** Given
2. $\angle 2 \cong \angle 3$	**2.** Vertical angles are congruent.
3. $\angle 1 \cong \angle 3$	**3.** Congruence of angles is transitive.
4. $p \parallel q$	**4.** If 2 lines in a plane are cut by a transversal and corr. ⦞ are $\cong$, the lines are $\parallel$.

Theorems 3-6, 3-7, and 3-8 state three more ways to prove that two lines are parallel. You will be asked to prove these theorems in Exercises 37, 30, and 38 respectively.

Theorem 3-6	**If two lines in a plane are cut by a transversal so that a pair of consecutive interior angles is supplementary, then the lines are parallel.**
Theorem 3-7	**If two lines in a plane are cut by a transversal so that a pair of alternate exterior angles is congruent, then the lines are parallel.**
Theorem 3-8	**In a plane, if two lines are perpendicular to the same line, then they are parallel.**

Notice that Theorems 3-5 through 3-8 are the converses of Theorems 3-1 through 3-4.

Example 1

Find the value of *x* so that $\ell \parallel m$.

If two lines in a plane are cut by a transversal so that a pair of consecutive interior angles is supplementary, then the lines are parallel. So if $m\angle ABC + m\angle BCD = 180$, then $\ell \parallel m$.

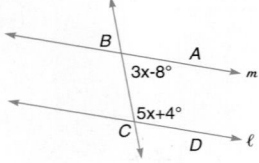

$$(3x - 8) + (5x + 4) = 180$$
$$8x - 4 = 180$$
$$8x = 184$$
$$x = 23$$

You can use the relationships between angles to determine if lines are parallel.

Example 2

If $\angle 1 \cong \angle 2$ and $\angle 3 \cong \angle 4$, which lines are parallel? Explain.

$\overleftrightarrow{NQ}$ is a transversal for $\overleftrightarrow{MN}$ and $\overleftrightarrow{QP}$. $\angle 1$ and $\angle 2$ are congruent alternate interior angles. So since the alternate interior angles are congruent, $\overleftrightarrow{MN} \parallel \overleftrightarrow{QP}$.

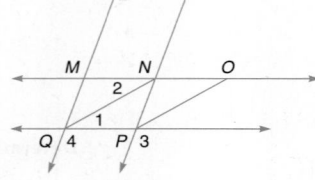

$\overleftrightarrow{QP}$ is a transversal for $\overleftrightarrow{NP}$ and $\overleftrightarrow{MQ}$, and $\angle 3$ and $\angle 4$ are corresponding angles, so $\overleftrightarrow{NP} \parallel \overleftrightarrow{MQ}$.

CHECKING FOR UNDERSTANDING

Communicating Mathematics

Read and study the lesson to answer these questions.

1. How do you think the grounds crew positions the yardage lines on a football field so that all of the lines are parallel? Explain. **See margin.**

2. Name some places besides football fields where it is important that lines be parallel. **Answers may vary. A sample answer is parking lot spaces.**

3. For the figure at the right, justify the statement $\overline{AM} \parallel \overline{HT}$. **See margin.**

4. Your friend claims that $\overline{AT} \parallel \overline{MH}$. Explain why that can't be true. **See margin.**

5. Copy the figure at the right and draw $\overleftrightarrow{AH}$. Is $\angle MAH \cong \angle AHT$? Explain. **Yes, because $\overline{AM} \parallel \overline{HT}$ and if 2 $\parallel$ lines are cut by a transversal alt. int. $\angle$s are $\cong$.**

LESSON 3-4   PROVING LINES PARALLEL   137

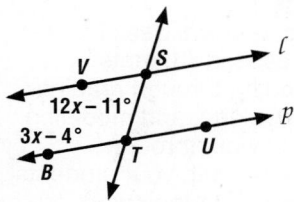
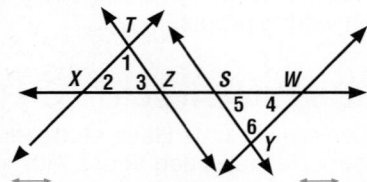

Checking for Understanding

Exercises 1-18 are designed to help you assess students' understanding through reading, writing, speaking, and modeling. You should work through Exercises 1-5 with your students and then monitor their work on Exercises 6-18.

Error Analysis

Your students may get confused as more and more postulates and theorems are introduced and explained. It may help to have them keep an ongoing list of all the postulates and theorems given in the text, for an easy reference when writing proofs.

Closing the Lesson

Modeling Activity Have students construct a four-sided figure with each pair of opposite sides parallel. Tell them that the figure is called a parallelogram and that they will learn more about parallelograms in Chapter 6.

APPLYING THE LESSON

Homework Exercise

Assignment Guide

Basic: 19-35, 42-50
Average: 22-38, 42-50
Enriched: 25-50

Exercise Notes

For Exercise 17, another explanation is that consecutive interior angles are supplementary. For Exercises 19-23, it may help to copy the drawing and mark the information given directly on the diagram.

Guided Practice   Find the value of x so that $\ell \parallel m$.

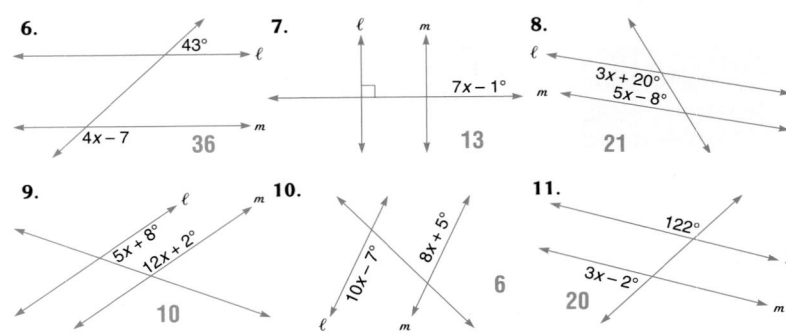

6. 36   7. 13   8. 21

9. 10   10. 6   11. 20

State which segments, if any, are parallel. State the postulate or theorem that justifies your answer.

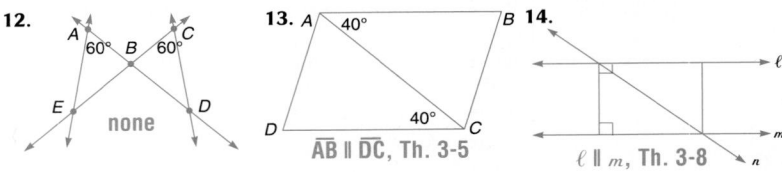

12. none   13. $\overline{AB} \parallel \overline{DC}$, Th. 3-5   14. $\ell \parallel m$, Th. 3-8

Determine if each statement is *true* or *false*. If false, explain why.

15. false; They must all be in the same plane.

15. Two lines that are perpendicular to a third line must be parallel.
16. In a plane, two lines that are parallel to a third line must be parallel. true
17. Two lines are parallel if the alternate interior angles formed by a transversal are supplementary. false; The alternate interior angles would be congruent.
18. Through a point not on a line, there exists exactly one line parallel to the given line. true

EXERCISES

Practice   Given the following information, determine which lines, if any, are parallel. Justify your answer. See margin.

A
19. $\angle HLK \cong \angle GKJ$ 20. $\angle IHL \cong \angle HLK$
21. $\angle FGJ \cong \angle KJG$
22. $m\angle GJK + m\angle HLK = 180$
23. $\overline{HL} \perp \overline{GH}, \overline{GK} \perp \overline{JM}$

24. $\angle 14 \cong \angle 11$ 25. $\angle 1 \cong \angle 9$
26. $\angle 10 \cong \angle 15$
27. $m\angle 16 + m\angle 15 = 180$
28. $m\angle 6 + m\angle 10 = 180$
29. $m\angle 7 + m\angle 10 = 180$

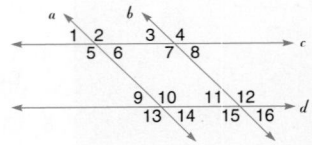

138   CHAPTER 3   PARALLELS

Additional Answers

19. $\overleftrightarrow{GK} \parallel \overleftrightarrow{HL}$, corresponding angles congruent (Postulate 3-2)
20. $\overleftrightarrow{HI} \parallel \overleftrightarrow{KL}$, alternate interior angles congruent (Theorem 3-5)
21. $\overleftrightarrow{FG} \parallel \overleftrightarrow{JK}$, alternate interior angles congruent (Theorem 3-5)
22. $\overleftrightarrow{GJ} \parallel \overleftrightarrow{HL}$, consecutive interior angles supplementary (Theorem 3-6)

23. none
24. $a \parallel b$, alternate interior angles congruent (Theorem 3-5)
25. $c \parallel d$, corresponding angles congruent (Postulate 3-2)
26. $a \parallel b$, alternate interior angles congruent (Theorem 3-5)
27. none
28. $c \parallel d$, consecutive interior angles supplementary (Theorem 3-6)
29. none

30. Copy and complete the proof of Theorem 3-7.

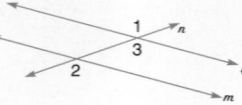

Given: $\angle 2 \cong \angle 1$

Prove: $\ell \parallel m$

Statements	Reasons
a. _?_ $\angle 2 \cong \angle 1$	a. Given
b. $\angle 1 \cong \angle 3$	b. _?_ Vertical $\angle s$ are $\cong$.
c. _?_ $\angle 2 \cong \angle 3$	c. Congruence of angles is transitive.
d. $\ell \parallel m$	d. _?_ If 2 lines in a plane are cut by a transversal and corr. $\angle s$ are $\cong$ the lines are $\parallel$.

 Find the values of x and y that make the blue lines parallel and the red lines parallel.

31.

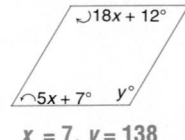

$x = 7$, $y = 138$

32.

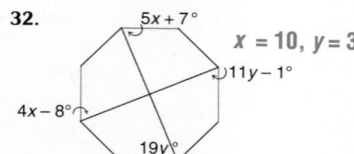

$x = 10$, $y = 3$

33. You are given that two of the numbered angles are supplementary. Using this information, you can prove that $p \parallel q$. List the pairs of angles that you could be given as supplementary. $\angle 2$ and $\angle 3$; $\angle 6$ and $\angle 7$; $\angle 2$ and $\angle 8$; $\angle 6$ and $\angle 4$; $\angle 3$ and $\angle 5$; $\angle 7$ and $\angle 1$; $\angle 5$ and $\angle 8$; $\angle 1$ and $\angle 4$

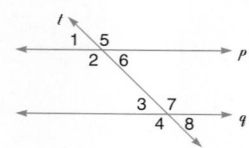

34. If $\ell \not\parallel m$, can $x = 12$? Justify your answer. **No, if $x = 12$, then the angles are supplementary, and by Theorem 3-6, $\ell \parallel m$.**

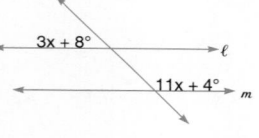

35. Use the information in the figure to determine which lines are parallel. State the theorems that justify your conclusions. **See margin.**

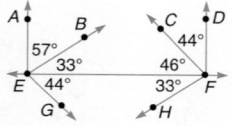

36. Find $m\angle 1$ for the figure at the right. (Hint: Draw a line through X parallel to ℓ and m.) **60**

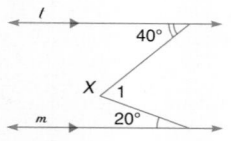

Additional Answers

35. $\overrightarrow{AE} \parallel \overrightarrow{DF}$ since in a plane, if 2 lines are $\perp$ to the same line, they are $\parallel$ $\overrightarrow{EB} \parallel \overrightarrow{FH}$ since if 2 lines in a plane are cut by a transversal and alt. int. $\angle s$ are $\cong$, then the lines are $\parallel$.

RETEACHING THE LESSON

Have a student name an angle relationship, such as alternate interior angles or corresponding angles. Have students state the theorem from this lesson that contains that angle relationship and write it on the chalkboard or overhead. Diagram the theorem, labeling the relevant pair of angles and the parallel lines. You may also want to write the given information and what is to be proved. Do this for all the theorems in this lesson.

Reteaching Masters Booklet, p. 17

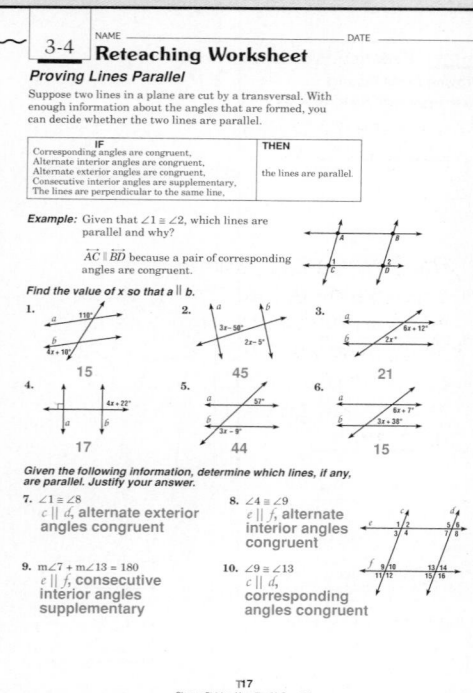

Additional Answers

38. Given: $\ell \perp t$, $m \perp t$
   Prove: $\ell \parallel m$

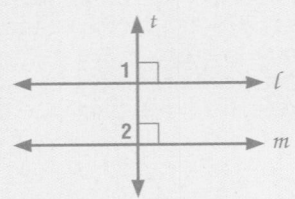

Statements (Reasons)

a. $\ell \perp t$, $m \perp t$ (Given)
b. $\angle 1$ is a right angle.
   $\angle 2$ is a right angle.
   ($\perp$ lines form four rt. $\angle$s.)
c. $\angle 1 \cong \angle 2$ (All rt. $\angle$s are $\cong$.)
d. $\ell \parallel m$ (If 2 lines are cut by
   a transversal and corr.
   $\angle$s are $\cong$, then the lines
   are $\parallel$.)

37. Copy and complete the proof of Theorem 3-6.

   Given: $\angle 2$ and $\angle 3$ are supplementary.
   Prove: $\ell \parallel m$

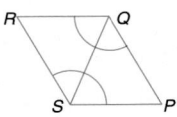

Statements	Reasons
a. $\angle 2$ and $\angle 3$ are supplementary.	a. __?__ Given
b. __?__ $\angle 1$ and $\angle 2$ form a linear pair.	b. Definition of linear pair
c. $\angle 1$ and $\angle 2$ are supplementary.	c. __?__
d. __?__ $\angle 1 \cong \angle 3$	d. If 2 $\angle$s are supp. to the same $\angle$ they are $\cong$.
e. $\ell \parallel m$.	e. __?__

37c. If 2 $\angle$s form a linear pair they are supp.

37e. If 2 lines in a plane are cut by a transversal and corr. $\angle$s are $\cong$, the lines are $\parallel$.

38. Write a two-column proof of Theorem 3-8. **See margin.**

C **Write a two-column proof.** **See margin.**

39. Given: $\angle RQP \cong \angle PSR$
   $\angle SRQ$ and $\angle PSR$ are supplementary.

   Prove: $\overline{QP} \parallel \overline{RS}$

40. Given: $\overline{JK} \perp \overline{KM}$
   $\angle 1 \cong \angle 2$

   Prove: $\overline{LM} \perp \overline{KM}$

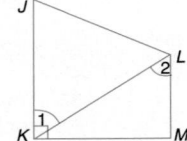

41. Draw and label the diagram that you would use in a proof of the theorem *If two lines are cut by a transversal so a pair of corresponding angles are congruent, then the lines that bisect those angles are parallel.* **See Solutions Manual.**
   a. State the given information and the statement to be proved.
   b. Write the proof.

Critical Thinking **42.** Explain why $\triangle ABC$ as it is shown below cannot exist. **See margin.**

Application **43. Construction** A carpenter uses a special instrument to draw parallel line segments. Darlene wants to make two parallel cuts at an angle of 40° through points D and P. Explain why these lines will be parallel. **Postulate 3-2**

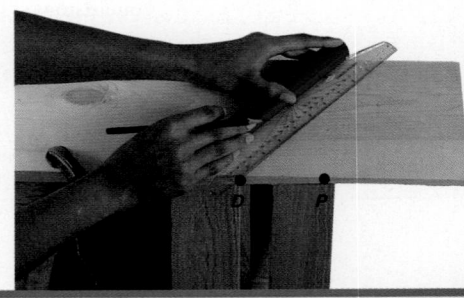

Additional Answers

39.   **Statements** **(Reasons)**
   a. $\angle RQP \cong \angle PSR$, $\angle SRQ$ and $\angle PSR$ are supplementary. (Given)
   b. $m\angle RQP = m\angle PSR$ (Definition of congruent angles)
   c. $m\angle SRQ + m\angle PSR = 180$ (Definition of supplementary)
   d. $m\angle SRQ + m\angle RQP = 180$ (Substitution prop. of equality)
   e. $\angle SRQ$ and $\angle RQP$ are supplementary. (Definition of supplementary)
   f. $\overline{QP} \parallel \overline{RS}$ (If 2 lines are cut by a transversal and consec. int. $\angle$s are supp., then the lines are $\parallel$.)

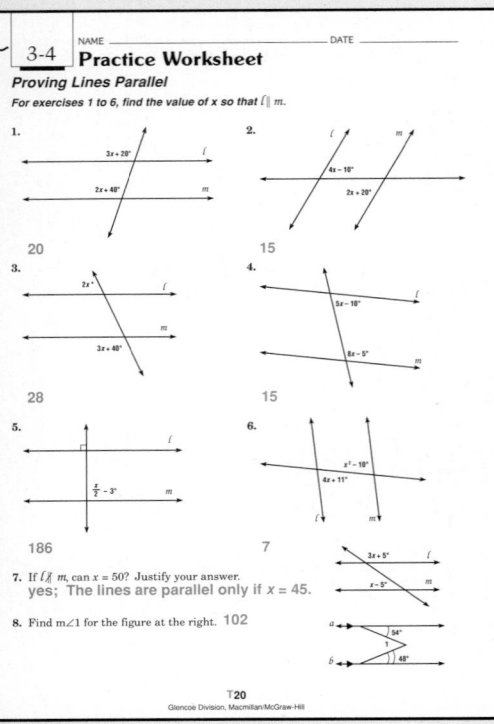

44. Classify the statement *If a line intersects two parallel lines, then it is a transversal* as *true* or *false.* **(Lesson 3-3)** true

45. Are the spokes on a wheel a model of parallel, intersecting, or skew lines? **(Lesson 3-2)** intersecting or skew

46. The formula for finding the total surface area of a cylinder is $A = 2\pi r^2 + 2\pi rh$, where r is the radius of the base and h is the height. Solve the formula for h and justify each step. **(Lesson 2-4)** See margin.

47. Write *A cloud is composed of millions of water droplets* in if-then form. **(Lesson 2-2)** See margin.

48. $\angle M$ and $\angle N$ are vertical angles. Are $\angle M$ and $\angle N$ right angles if $m\angle M = 4x + 14$ and $m\angle N = 6x - 24$? **(Lesson 1-9)** yes

49. Jenny forgot the combination to her gym locker. She remembers that the numbers are 18, 37, and 12, but doesn't remember the order. How many different combinations are possible? **(Lesson 1-3)** 6

Wrap-Up

50. Journal Entry Summarize the five ways that you can prove two lines parallel. See students' work.

FINE ARTS CONNECTION

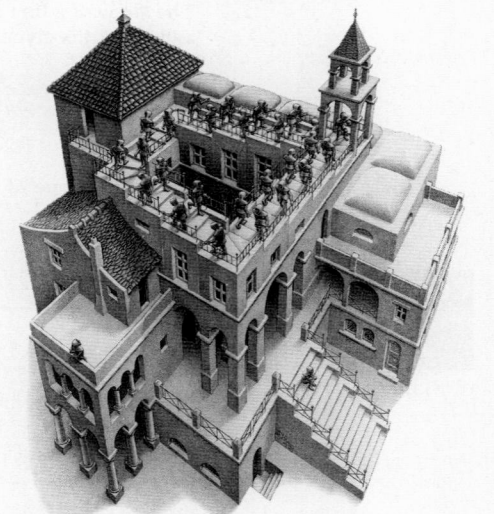

Dutch graphic artist M.C. Escher created some of the most interesting drawings of all time. Born in the Netherlands, he spent a number of years studying art and traveling in Europe. Mr. Escher is famous for his ability to use realistic detail to create bizarre optical effects. Two of his major themes are pattern and visual paradox.

Escher's *Ascending and Descending* first appears to be a picture of a building. But look closely at the stairs! They are impossible in the real world, a visual paradox. But then again, if the stairs are impossible, how did Escher draw them?

©1960 M.C. Escher/Cordon Art-Baarn, Holland

LESSON 3-4   PROVING LINES PARALLEL   141

EXTENDING THE LESSON

Math Power: Communication

Introduce students to the use of "if and only if," using the theorems in Lessons 3-3 and 3-4. Point out that, in order to prove these statements, you must assume the first part and prove the second, and then assume the second part and prove the first.

Fine Arts Connection

The Fine Arts Connection feature introduces students to applications of mathematics in the area of fine arts. You may want to show students other examples of M.C. Escher's work or have them research other artistic examples involving mathematical ideas.

Enrichment Masters Booklet, p. 17

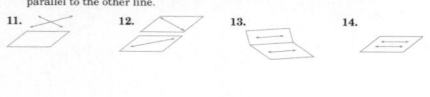

Lesson Resources

• Reteaching Master 3-5
• Practice Master 3-5
• Enrichment Master 3-5
• Activity Master, p. 31
• Technology Master, p. 3

 Transparency 3-5 contains the 5-Minute Check and a teaching aid for this lesson.

INTRODUCING THE LESSON

 5-Minute Check

(over Lesson 3-4)

Refer to the figure below to determine which segments, if any, are parallel and why.

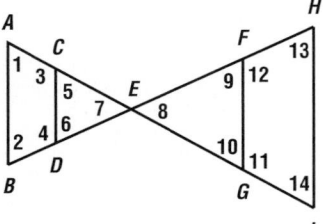

1. $\angle 1 \cong \angle 5$ $\overline{AB} \parallel \overline{CD}$; corresponding angles $\cong$ (Postulate 3-2)
2. $\angle 1 \cong \angle 6$ none
3. $m\angle 11 + m\angle 14 = 180$ $\overline{FG} \parallel \overline{HI}$; consecutive interior angles supp. (Theorem 3-6)
4. Find the values of x and y that make $\overline{AB} \parallel \overline{CD}$ in the figure above if $m\angle 1 = 2x + 5$, $m\angle 5 = 7x - 10$, and $m\angle 3 = 2y + 3x$. $x = 3, y = 80$

Motivating the Lesson

Ask students how they would solve this problem.

A store needs to install a ramp so that people in wheelchairs can shop there. The ramp cannot have a slope of greater than $\frac{1}{10}$. Design a ramp that fits the specified condition.

Objectives

After studying this lesson, you should be able to:

3-5A   ▪ find the slope of a line, and
3-5B   ▪ use slope to identify parallel and perpendicular lines.

Connection

So far in this chapter we have investigated the properties of parallel and perpendicular lines based on geometric relationships. In the seventeenth century philosopher and mathematician Rene Descartes introduced coordinates to the study of geometry. This allowed discussions about lines and shapes to become discussions about numbers and equations. Thus, Descartes literally began the connection of geometry to algebra.

Descartes identified parallel and perpendicular lines in the coordinate plane by investigating the numerical values of the slopes of these lines. As you recall from algebra, one way to find the slope of a line is to examine the vertical and horizontal change between two points on a line. The slope is the ratio of these two changes.

Definition of Slope	The slope of a line containing two points with coordinates (x_1, y_1) and (x_2, y_2) is given by the formula $$m = \frac{y_2 - y_1}{x_2 - x_1}, \text{ where } x_1 \neq x_2.$$ *The slope of a vertical line, where $x_1 = x_2$, is undefined.*

Example 1

Determine the slope of each line.

CONNECTION

Algebra

a.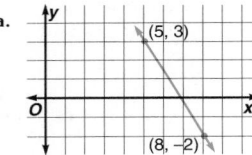

$$m = \frac{y_2 - y_1}{x_2 - x_1}$$

$$= \frac{3 - (-2)}{5 - 8} \text{ or } -\frac{5}{3}$$

Lines with negative slope fall as you go along them from left to right.

b.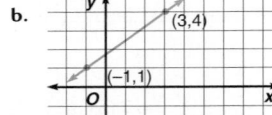

$$m = \frac{y_2 - y_1}{x_2 - x_1}$$

$$= \frac{4 - 1}{3 - (-1)} \text{ or } \frac{3}{4}$$

Lines with positive slope rise as you go along them from left to right.

142   **CHAPTER 3   PARALLELS**

ALTERNATE TEACHING STRATEGIES

Using Models

Extend Motivating the Lesson and ask students what they think slope is. Draw a two-dimesional diagram of the ramp so that it looks like a right triangle. Use those lines to explain the different types of slope that are possible. Which of the lines have slope? Which line must have a slope less than $\frac{1}{10}$? Explain the concepts in this lesson using the ramp.

Using Investigation

You can guide students to discover a method for determining if three points are collinear. In Investigation 2 on pages A2 and A3 of **More Investigations in Geometry**, students use graphing calculators to explore collinear points.

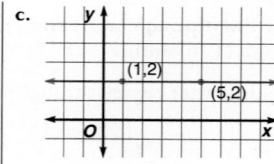

c.

$$m = \frac{y_2 - y_1}{x_2 - x_1}$$
$$= \frac{2 - 2}{5 - 1} \text{ or } 0$$

Lines with a slope of 0 are horizontal.

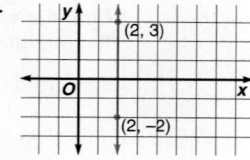

d.

$$m = \frac{y_2 - y_1}{x_2 - x_1}$$
$$= \frac{3 - (-2)}{2 - 2} \text{ undefined}$$

Lines with an undefined slope are vertical.

The graphs of lines *p*, *q*, and *l* are shown at the right. Notice that lines *p* and *q* are parallel and *l* is perpendicular to *p* and *q*. Let's investigate the slopes of these lines.

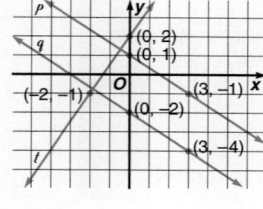

slope of *p*   slope of *q*   slope of *l*

$$m = \frac{1 - (-1)}{0 - 3}$$ $$m = \frac{-2 - (-4)}{0 - 3}$$ $$m = \frac{2 - (-1)}{0 - (-2)}$$

$$= -\frac{2}{3}$$ $$= -\frac{2}{3}$$ $$= \frac{3}{2}$$

Postulate 3-4 could be written "If two lines have the same slope they are parallel and nonvertical and if two lines are parallel and nonvertical, then they have the same slope."

Lines *p* and *q* are parallel, and their slopes are the same. Line *l* is perpendicular to lines *p* and *q*, and its slope is the negative reciprocal of the slopes of *p* and *q*. These results suggest two important algebraic properties of parallel and perpendicular lines.

Postulate 3-4	**Two nonvertical lines have the same slope if and only if they are parallel.**
Postulate 3-5	**Two nonvertical lines are perpendicular if and only if the product of their slopes is -1.**

Note that Postulates 3-4 and 3-5 are written in "if and only if" form. If a conditional and its converse are true, it can be written in "if and only if" form.

Example 2

Draw a line passing through A(3, 2) that is parallel to line ℓ.

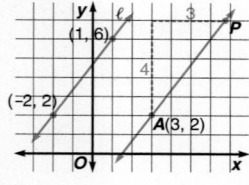

First, find the slope of ℓ. $\quad m = \frac{6 - 2}{1 - (-2)} \text{ or } \frac{4}{3}$

Next, find a point *P* so that the slope of $\overline{AP}$ is $\frac{4}{3}$. Since slope is $\frac{rise}{run}$, start at point *A*. "Rise" 4 units then "run" 3 units. Locate point *P*. Draw $\overrightarrow{PA}$.

CONNECTION

Algebra

LESSON 3-5   SLOPES OF LINES   143

Chalkboard Example

For Example 1
Determine the slope of each line.

a. $-\frac{3}{4}$

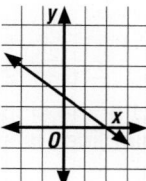

b.

undefined

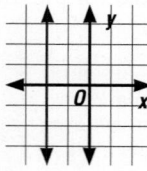

c. 0

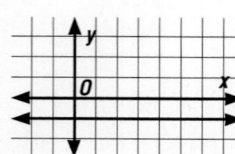

d. $\frac{5}{2}$

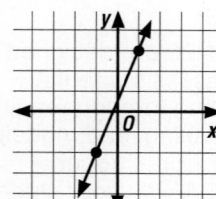

For Example 2
Draw a line passing through A(2,0) that is parallel to the given line.

$$m = \frac{5 - 3}{1 - 0} = \frac{2}{1} = 2$$

Find a point *P* whose rate of change from A(2,0) is $\frac{2}{1}$. Draw $\overrightarrow{PA}$.

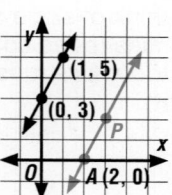

Example 3

Chalkboard Example

For Example 3

Find the value of y so the line through $(8,-2)$ and $(-8,6)$ is perpendicular to the line that passes through $(3, y)$ and $(-3,-8)$.

First find the slope of the line that passes through $(8,-2)$ and $(-8,6)$.

$m = \dfrac{6-(-2)}{-8-(8)} = \dfrac{8}{-16} = -\dfrac{1}{2}$

The product of the slopes of two perpendicular lines is -1; $-\dfrac{1}{2} \cdot \dfrac{2}{1} = -1$.

Now find the value of y by using the formula for the slope of a line.

$2 = \dfrac{-8-y}{-3-3}$

$2 = \dfrac{-8-y}{-6}$

$-8-y = -12$

$-y = -4$

$y = 4$

Example 3

Find the value of x so the line through $(x, 6)$ and $(4, -3)$ is perpendicular to the line that passes through $(1, 6)$ and $(7, -2)$.

First, find the slope of the line that passes through $(1, 6)$ and $(7, -2)$.

$m = \dfrac{y_2 - y_1}{x_2 - x_1}$ *Definition of slope*

$ = \dfrac{6 - (-2)}{1 - 7}$ *Let $(x_1, y_1) = (7, -2)$ and $(x_2, y_2) = (1, 6)$.*

$ = -\dfrac{4}{3}$

The product of the slopes of the two perpendicular lines is -1. Since $-\dfrac{4}{3} \cdot \dfrac{3}{4} = -1$, the slope of the line through $(x, 6)$ and $(4, -3)$ is $\dfrac{3}{4}$.

Now use the formula for the slope of a line to find the value of x.

$m = \dfrac{y_2 - y_1}{x_2 - x_1}$

$\dfrac{3}{4} = \dfrac{6 - (-3)}{x - 4}$ *Slope $= \dfrac{3}{4}$; $(x_1, y_1) = (4, -3)$; $(x_2, y_2) = (x, 6)$*

$\dfrac{3}{4} = \dfrac{9}{x - 4}$

$3(x - 4) = 36$ *Cross multiply.*

$3x - 12 = 36$

$3x = 48$

$x = 16$

The line through $(16, 6)$ and $(4, -3)$ is perpendicular to the line that passes through $(1, 6)$ and $(7, -2)$.

INVESTIGATION

You can learn more about slope and collinear points in Investigation 2 on pages A2–A3.

EVALUATING THE LESSON

Checking for Understanding

Exercises 1-20 are designed to help you assess students' understanding through reading, writing, speaking, and modeling. You should work through Exercises 1-5 with your students and then monitor their work on Exercises 6-20.

Error Analysis

Students may have difficulty remembering that, when you are finding the slope of a line, the y-coordinates are in the numerator and the x-coordinates are in the denominator. If this is a problem have them think of slope as $\frac{rise}{run}$. The y-axis rises (goes up and down) and the x-axis runs (goes left and right).

CHECKING FOR UNDERSTANDING

Communicating Mathematics

1. 0 – horizontal; 5 – rises to the right

2. The slope of a vertical line is undefined; yes

Read and study the lesson to answer these questions.

1. Describe a line whose slope is 0 and a line whose slope is 5.

2. Why does the algebraic definition of parallel lines exclude vertical lines? Are vertical lines parallel to each other? Explain.

3. What type of line is perpendicular to a vertical line? **horizontal**

4. Find the slope for the line containing $A(0, -3)$ and $B(16, 5)$. State the slope of any line perpendicular to $\overleftrightarrow{AB}$. $\dfrac{1}{2}$; -2

5. On the same coordinate system, draw a line that fits each description.
   a. line *a* with positive slope
   b. line *b* with zero slope
   c. line *c* with negative slope
   d. line *d* with an undefined slope
   See students' work.

Guided Practice

Find the slope of the line passing through the given points. Then describe each line as you move from left to right as *rising, falling, horizontal,* or *vertical.*   6. 0, horizontal   7. $-\frac{1}{2}$, falling   8. $-\frac{4}{5}$, falling

6. (1, 1), (3, 1)   7. (-1, 0), (3, -2)   8. (5, 0), (0, 4)

9. (3, 4), (1, 2)   10. (-2, 4), (-1, 3)   11. (8, 2), (8, -5)
   1, rising   -1, falling   undefined, vertical

Use slope to identify each pair of lines as *parallel, perpendicular,* or *neither.*

12. 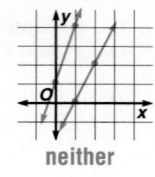   13. 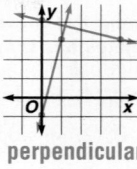   14.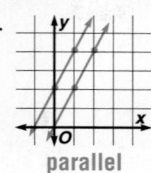

     neither   perpendicular   parallel

State the slope of a line parallel to a line passing through each pair of points. Then state the slope of a line perpendicular to the line passing through each pair of points.

15. (-1, -1), (3, 2)   16. (4, 2), (3, -1)   17. (1, 5), (3, 2)

18. (-7, 5), (1, 1)   19. (-2, -3), (1, 8)   20. (-2, -2), (1, 6)

15. $\frac{3}{4}, -\frac{4}{3}$ 16. $3, -\frac{1}{3}$ 17. $-\frac{3}{2}, \frac{2}{3}$

18. $-\frac{1}{2}, 2$ 19. $\frac{11}{3}, -\frac{3}{11}$ 20. $\frac{8}{3}, -\frac{3}{8}$

EXERCISES

Practice

 A

Determine the slope of each line named below.

21. a 2

22. b 0

23. c $\frac{3}{2}$

24. d -1

25. any line perpendicular to b undefined

26. any line parallel to a 2

27. any line perpendicular to c $-\frac{2}{3}$

28. any line parallel to d -1

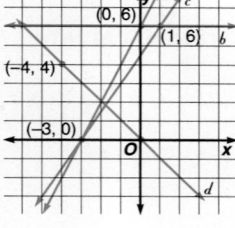

Graph the line that satisfies each description.   See Solutions Manual.

29. slope = 0, passes through $P(2, 6)$

30. slope = -4, passes through $P(-2, 1)$

31. undefined slope, passes through $P(2, 0)$

32. slope = $\frac{2}{5}$, passing through $P(0, -2)$

33. passes through $P(2, 1)$ and is parallel to $\overleftrightarrow{AB}$ with $A(-2, 5)$ and $B(1, 8)$

34. passes through $P(4, 1)$ and is perpendicular to $\overleftrightarrow{CD}$ with $C(0, 3)$ and $D(-3, 0)$

RETEACHING THE LESSON

List the coordinates of two points on the chalkboard. Divide the class in half and have one half use the first point as (x_1, y_1) and the second point as (x_2, y_2). The other half of the class should use the first point as (x_2, y_2) and the second point as (x_1, y_1). Instruct all students to find the slope of the line. Emphasize that it does not matter which point is selected as (x_1, y_1) or (x_2, y_2), but that both coordinates of each point must be in the correct place in the formula for the slope.

Closing the Lesson

Modeling Activity   Have each student state an example of a real object that has either a positive slope, a negative slope, a slope of 0, or an undefined slope. For example, a handrail on an up-staircase has a positive slope.

APPLYING THE LESSON

Homework Exercises

Assignment Guide

Basic: 21-39, 46-47, 50-57
Average: 21-42, 46-48, 50-57
Enriched: 27-57

Reteaching Masters Booklet, p. 18

3-5   NAME _____   DATE _____
Reteaching Worksheet
Slopes of Lines

To find the slope of a line containing two points with coordinates (x_1, y_1) and (x_2, y_2), use the following formula.

$m = \frac{y_2 - y_1}{x_2 - x_1}$, where $x_1 \neq x_2$.

The slope of a vertical line, where $x_1 = x_2$, is undefined.

Two lines have the same slope if and only if they are parallel and nonvertical.

Two nonvertical lines are perpendicular if and only if the product of their slopes is -1.

Example: Find the slope of the line ℓ through (2, -5) and (-1, 3). State the slope of a line parallel to ℓ. Then state the slope of a line perpendicular to ℓ.

Let $(x_1, y_1) = (2, -5)$ and $(x_2, y_2) = (-1, 3)$.
Then $m = \frac{3-(-5)}{-1-2} = -\frac{8}{3}$.
Any line in the coordinate plane parallel to ℓ has slope $-\frac{8}{3}$.
Since $-\frac{8}{3} \cdot \frac{3}{8} = -1$, the slope of a line perpendicular to the line ℓ is $\frac{3}{8}$.

Find the slope of the line through the given points.

1. (-2, -4), (8, 12)   2. (-4, 6), (3, -10)   3. (0, 12), (12, 0)
   $\frac{8}{5}$ $-\frac{16}{7}$ -1

4. (15, -15), (-15, 0)   5. (21, 12), (-6, -4)   6. (7, 0), (-17, 10)
   $-\frac{1}{2}$ $\frac{16}{27}$ $-\frac{5}{12}$

State the slope of a line parallel to the line passing through each pair of points. Then state the slope of a line perpendicular to the line passing through each pair of points.

7. (9, -3), (6, -10)   8. (-8, -12), (4, -1)   9. (5, -2), (9, -6)
   $\frac{7}{3}, -\frac{3}{7}$ $\frac{11}{12}, -\frac{12}{11}$ -1, 1

T18
Glencoe Division, Macmillan/McGraw-Hill

Additional Answers

35. slope of $\overleftrightarrow{AB} = -\frac{1}{3}$; slope of $\overleftrightarrow{BC} = -\frac{1}{3}$. Either $\overleftrightarrow{AB} \parallel \overleftrightarrow{BC}$ or $\overleftrightarrow{AB}$ and $\overleftrightarrow{BC}$ are the same line. Since B is a common point, $\overleftrightarrow{AB}$ is not parallel to $\overleftrightarrow{BC}$. Thus $\overleftrightarrow{AB}$ and $\overleftrightarrow{BC}$ are the same line and A, B, and C are collinear.

36. slope of $\overleftrightarrow{MN} = 2$; slope of $\overleftrightarrow{MO} = 2$. Either $\overleftrightarrow{MN} \parallel \overleftrightarrow{MO}$ or $\overleftrightarrow{MN}$ and $\overleftrightarrow{MO}$ are the same line. Since M is a common point, $\overleftrightarrow{MN}$ is not parallel to $\overleftrightarrow{MO}$. Thus $\overleftrightarrow{MN}$ and $\overleftrightarrow{MO}$ are the same line and M, N, and O are collinear.

37. No; slope of $\overleftrightarrow{AB} = 3$; slope of $\overleftrightarrow{CD} = 3$. $\overleftrightarrow{AB}$ and $\overleftrightarrow{CD}$ are the same line since A, B, C, and D, are collinear.

38. No; slope of $\overleftrightarrow{AB} = 1$; slope of $\overleftrightarrow{CD} = -\frac{1}{3}$. $\overleftrightarrow{AB} \nparallel \overleftrightarrow{CD}$ because they have different slopes.

Practice Masters Booklet, p. 21

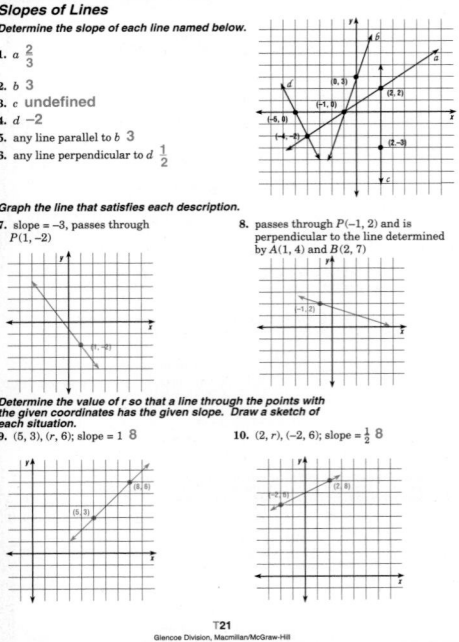

B Use slope to write an argument to show that each group of points is collinear. See margin.

35. $A(6, 2)$, $B(-6, 6)$, $C(3, 3)$ 36. $M(4, 1)$, $N(-2, -11)$, $O(1, -5)$

Determine if $\overleftrightarrow{AB} \parallel \overleftrightarrow{CD}$. Justify your answer. See margin.

37. $A(-2, -7)$, $B(1, 2)$, $C(0, -1)$, $D(3, 8)$

38. $A(2, 1)$, $B(3, 2)$, $C(4, 3)$, $D(1, 4)$

Determine the value of r so that a line through the points with the given coordinates has the given slope. Draw a sketch of each situation.
See Solutions Manual for sketches.

39. $(r, 2)$, $(4, -6)$; slope $= -\frac{8}{3}$ 1

40. $(5, r)$, $(2, 3)$; slope $= 2$ 9

41. $(r, 6)$, $(8, 4)$; slope $= \frac{1}{2}$ 12

42. $(6, r)$, $(9, 2)$; slope $= -\frac{1}{3}$ 3

C

43. A parallelogram is a four-sided polygon whose opposite sides are parallel. Given $A(1, 1)$, $B(6, 2)$, and $C(2, 4)$, find the coordinates of a point D so that A, B, C, and D form a parallelogram. (7, 5), (5, -1), or (-3, 3)

44. The vertices of a figure $ABCD$ are $A(-5, -3)$, $B(5, 3)$, $C(7, 9)$, and $D(-3, 3)$.
   a. Show that the opposite sides of $ABCD$ are parallel. See margin.
   b. Show that the opposite sides of $ABCD$ are congruent. (Hint: Use the distance formula.) See margin.
   c. What type of figure is $ABCD$? parallelogram

45. A line contains the points $(9, 1)$ and $(5, 5)$. Write a convincing argument that the line intersects the y-axis at $(0, 10)$. See Solutions Manual.

Critical Thinking   46. The graph at the right shows the speed of a car at different points in a trip. Describe the movement of the car for each line segment, $\overline{AB}$, $\overline{BC}$, $\overline{CD}$, $\overline{DE}$, $\overline{EF}$, $\overline{FG}$, and $\overline{GH}$. Make a conjecture as to what would cause each type of movement. See Solutions Manual.

Additional Answers

44a. slope of $\overleftrightarrow{AB} = \frac{3}{5}$; slope of $\overleftrightarrow{BC} = 3$; slope of $\overleftrightarrow{CD} = \frac{3}{5}$; slope of $\overleftrightarrow{DA} = 3$. Since the opposite sides have the same slope, they are parallel.

44b. $AB = \sqrt{(-5-5)^2 + (-3-3)^2}$
     $= \sqrt{136}$

$BC = \sqrt{(5-7)^2 + (3-9)^2}$
     $= \sqrt{40}$

$CD = \sqrt{(7-(-3))^2 + (9-3)^2}$
     $= \sqrt{136}$

$DA = \sqrt{(-3-(-5))^2 + (3-(-3))^2}$
     $= \sqrt{40}$

Opposite sides have the same length, so they are congruent.

47.b. The rate of change is the slope of the line that relates population and time.

Applications

47. Demographics The population of Troy was 150,000 in 1980 and 225,000 in 1990. **47c. 300,000**
  a. What is the rate of change for the population of Troy? That is, how much does the population change in one year? **7500**
  b. How does the rate of change relate to the slope of a line?
  c. What do you think the population of Troy will be in the year 2000?

48. Aviation An airplane passing over Richmond at an elevation of 33,000 feet begins its descent to land at Washington, D.C., 107 miles away. How many feet should the airplane descend per mile to land in Washington?

49. Travel The western entrance to the Eisenhower Tunnel in Colorado is at an elevation of 11,160 feet. The tunnel has a downward slope of 0.00895 toward the east and its horizontal distance is 8941 feet long.
  a. Draw and label a diagram of the tunnel. **See margin.**
  b. Find the elevation of the eastern end of the tunnel. **11,080 feet**
48. about 308 feet/mile

Computer

50. The BASIC program at the right finds the slope between two points.
  a. What does line 50 in the program do? **finds the slope**
  b. Use the BASIC program to check your answers to Exercises 6-11.

```
10 PRINT "ENTER THE
   COORDINATES OF POINT A."
20 INPUT X1, Y1
30 PRINT "ENTER THE
   COORDINATES OF POINT B."
40 INPUT X2, Y2
50 M = (Y2-Y1)/(X2-X1)
60 PRINT "THE SLOPE BETWEEN
   POINTS A AND B IS "; M;"."
```

Mixed Review

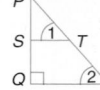

51. Write a two-column proof. **(Lesson 3-3)** See margin.

  Given: $\angle 1 \cong \angle 2$
  $\overline{PQ} \perp \overline{QR}$

  Prove: $\overline{ST} \perp \overline{PQ}$

Portfolio

Select an item from this chapter that you feel shows your best work and place it in your portfolio. Explain why you selected it.

52. List three of the conclusions that can be drawn from the figure. **(Lesson 3-2)** See margin.

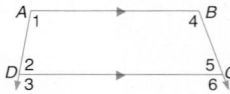

53. See margin.

53. Write a complete proof of *If 5x − 7 = x + 1, then x = 2.* **(Lesson 2-4)**

54. $(\frac{1}{2})^2 = \frac{1}{4}$, and $\frac{1}{2} \nless \frac{1}{4}$

54. Erin observed that 2^2 is greater than 2 and 5^2 is greater than 5, and made a conjecture that *The square of any real number is greater than the number.* Give a counterexample to this conjecture. **(Lesson 2-1)**

55. Find the midpoint of the segment whose endpoints have coordinates (8, 11) and (-4, 7). **(Lesson 1-5)** **(2, 9)**

56. Graph point A(-4, 7) on a coordinate plane. **(Lesson 1-1)** See margin.

Wrap-Up

57. Explain three different methods you can use to prove that two lines are parallel. At least one method should be algebraic. **same slopes; corresponding angles congruent; alternate interior angles congruent**

LESSON 3-5 SLOPES OF LINES 147

EXTENDING THE LESSON

Math Power: Reasoning

Using the example in Motivating the Lesson, have your students figure how long the ramp must be if it replaces steps that are 3 feet high. (The ramp cannot have a slope of greater than $\frac{1}{10}$.) **about 30.15 feet**

Additional Answer

49a.

Alt: 11,160 ft

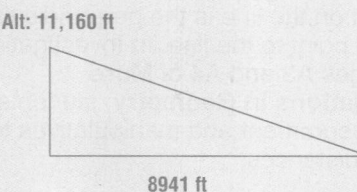

8941 ft

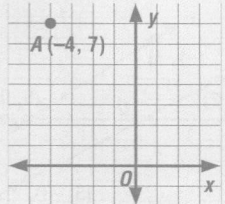

Additional Answers

51. Statements (Reasons)
  a. $\angle 1 \cong \angle 2$, $\overline{PQ} \perp \overline{QR}$ (Given)
  b. $\overline{ST} \parallel \overline{QR}$ (If 2 lines in a plane are cut by a transversal and corr. $\angle$s are $\cong$, the lines are $\parallel$.)
  c. $\overline{ST} \perp \overline{PQ}$ (In a plane, if a line is $\perp$ to one of 2 $\parallel$ lines, it is $\perp$ to the other.)

52. Answers may vary. Sample answers: $\angle 1$ and $\angle 2$ are supplementary; $\angle 1 \cong \angle 3$; $\angle 2$ and $\angle 3$ are supplementary; $\angle 4$ and $\angle 5$ are supplementary; $\angle 4 \cong \angle 6$; $\angle 5$ and $\angle 6$ are supplementary.

53. Statements (Reasons)
  a. $5x - 7 = x + 1$ (Given)
  b. $4x - 7 = 1$ (Subtraction prop. of equality)
  c. $4x = 8$ (Addition prop. of equality)
  d. $x = 2$ (Division prop. of equality)

56.

Enrichment Masters Booklet, p. 18

NAME _____ DATE _____

3-5 Enrichment Worksheet

The Möbius Strip

A Möbius strip is a special surface with only one side. It was discovered by August Ferdinand Möbius, a German astronomer and mathematician.

1. To make a Möbius strip, cut a strip of paper about 16 inches long and 1 inch wide. Mark the ends with the letters *A, B, C,* and *D* as shown below.

Twist the paper once, connecting *A* to *D* and *B* to *C*. Tape the ends together on both sides.
See students' work.

2. Use a crayon or pencil to shade one side of the paper. Shade around the strip until you get back to where you started. What happens?
The entire strip is shaded on both sides.

3. What do you think will happen if you cut the Möbius strip down the middle? Try it.
Instead of two loops, you get one loop that is twice as long as the original one.

4. Make another Möbius strip. Starting a third of the way in from one edge, cut around the strip, staying always the same distance in from the edge. What happens?
Two interlocking loops are formed.

5. Start with another long strip of paper. Twist the paper twice and connect the ends. What happens when you cut down the center of this strip?
Two interlocking loops are formed.

6. Start with another long strip of paper. Twist the paper three times and connect the ends. What happens when you cut down the center of this strip?
One two-sided loop with a knot is formed.

T18
Glencoe Division, Macmillan/McGraw-Hill

- Reteaching Master 3-6
- Practice Master 3-6
- Enrichment Master 3-6
- Evaluation Master, Quiz D, p.38
- Activity Master, p. 17

 Transparency 3-6 contains the 5-Minute Check and a teaching aid for this lesson.

INTRODUCING THE LESSON

 5-Minute Check

(over Lesson 3-5)

Refer to the figure below to determine the slope of each line.

1. any line perpendicular to *a*
$\frac{9}{5}$

2. any line parallel to *b* $-\frac{2}{3}$

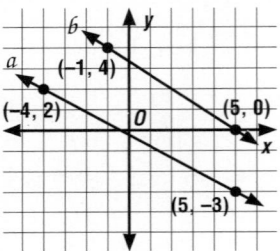

Graph the line that satisfies each description.

3. slope = 4, passes through (1, 2)

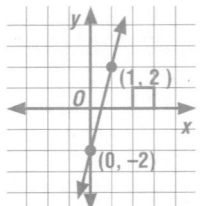

4. slope = 0, passes through (−3, −4)

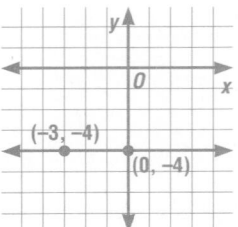

3-6 Parallels and Distance

Objective
3-6

After studying this lesson, you should be able to:
- recognize and use distance relationships between points, lines, and planes.

Application

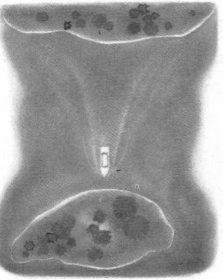

A team of botanists are traveling to begin a research project at the wildlife preserve on Cumberland Island, Georgia. They are loading their supplies into a boat and wish to take the shortest route possible to the island. What is the shortest route?

The shortest segment from a point to a line is the perpendicular segment from the point to the line. This fact is used to define the **distance from a point to a line** and can help the team of botanists choose the shortest route to the island.

Definition of the Distance Between a Point and a Line	**The distance from a line to a point not on the line is the length of the segment perpendicular to the line from the point.** *The measure of the distance between a line and a point on the line is zero.*

INVESTIGATION

You can learn more about the distance from a point to a line in Investigation 3 on pages A3–A4.

So, for the shortest route to the island, the botanists should use a path that is perpendicular to the shoreline.

You can also find the distance between two parallel lines. Consider the lines with equations $y = 2x + 6$ and $y = 2x - 2$. These lines are parallel since their slopes are the same.

According to the definition, two parallel lines do not intersect. An alternate definition says that two lines in a plane are parallel if and only if they are everywhere equidistant. Equidistant means that the distance between the two lines measured along a line perpendicular to the lines is always the same.

Remember that the distance is measured on a perpendicular segment.

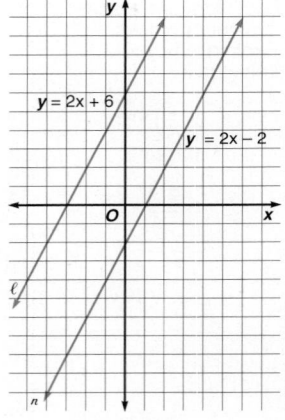

ALTERNATE TEACHING STRATEGIES

Using Investigation

You can guide students to discover that the shortest segment from a line to a point not on the line is the perpendicular from the point to the line. In Investigation 3 on pages A3 and A4 of **More Investigations in Geometry**, students use measurement and manipulatives to explore distances.

Using Vocabulary

Have students think of words that begin with *equ* and look them up in dictionary. Most of the definitions will contain words like "equal," "same," "balanced," etc. Have your students conjecture what *equidistant* means and look it up. Explain how it relates to parallel lines.

The distance between two parallel lines is the distance between one of the lines and any point on the other line.

So to find the distance between the two parallel lines ℓ and r we need to choose a point on one of the lines. As shown in the following construction, we choose $A(-3, 0)$ on line ℓ and then construct the perpendicular. The length of this perpendicular segment will represent the distance between the lines.

We could also construct a line perpendicular to r using a point on r and the construction you learned in Chapter 1.

CONSTRUCTION

Construct a line perpendicular to line r through point A(-3, 0), not on r.

1. Place the compass point at point A. Make the setting wide enough so that when an arc is drawn, it intersects r in two places. Label these points of intersection B and C.

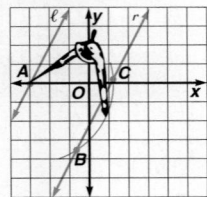

2. Using the same compass setting, put the compass at point B and draw an arc below line ℓ. *Any compass setting greater than $\frac{1}{2} BC$ will work.*

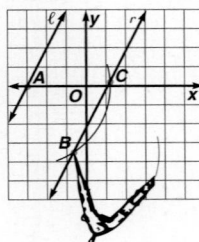

3. Then put the compass at point C and draw an arc to intersect the one drawn in step 2. Be sure to use the same compass setting. Label the point of intersection D.

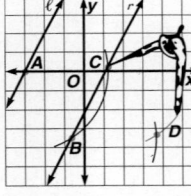

4. Draw $\overleftrightarrow{AD}$. $\overleftrightarrow{AD} \perp \ell$

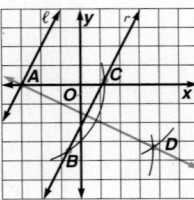

Have each student draw a triangle and label the three vertices. Ask them how far each vertex is from the opposite side. Have them draw the segments they measure and describe how they determined which segments were the best ones to measure.

TEACHING THE LESSON

Teaching Tip   For steps 2 and 3 of the construction of a perpendicular line, you may want to review the construction in Lesson 1-5.

Teaching Tip   When finding the distance between two parallel lines, remind students that distance is always positive.

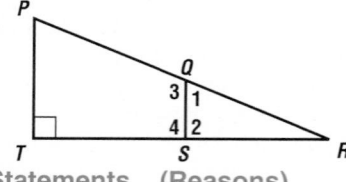
Notice that the construction of the line segment from point A perpendicular to line r intersects line r at approximately $(0, -2)$. To find the distance between the two parallel lines, we can use the distance formula we learned in Lesson 1-4.

$$\text{distance} = \sqrt{(x_2 - x_1)^2 + (y_2 - y_1)^2}$$
$$= \sqrt{(-3 - 0)^2 + (0 - (-2))^2}$$
$$= \sqrt{13}$$

The coordinates of point A are (-3, 0) and the coordinates of point E are (0, -2).

The distance between ℓ and r is $\sqrt{13}$ or about 3.6 units.

Example 1

APPLICATION

Planning

The plan for the new Westerville city park is shown below. Which line segment would you use to find each distance if $\overline{AB} \perp \overline{BC}$ and $\overline{BE} \perp \overline{AC}$?

a. the distance between the gazebo and the path between the footbridge and the shelterhouse

$\overline{AB}$, because $\overline{AB} \perp \overline{BC}$.

b. the distance from the entrance to the path between the gazebo and the shelterhouse

$\overline{DE}$, since $\overline{DE} \perp \overline{AC}$.

c. the distance from the shelterhouse to the path between the footbridge and the gazebo

$\overline{BC}$, since $\overline{BC} \perp \overline{AB}$.

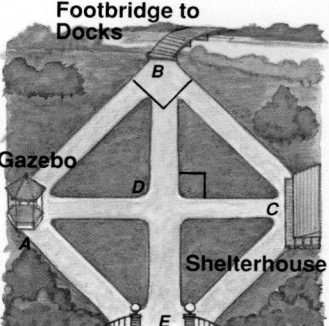

You can use the properties of parallel lines to discover properties of other geometric figures.

Example 2

Write a two-column proof.

Given: Quadrilateral $WXYZ$,
$\overline{XW} \parallel \overline{YZ}$, $\overline{XW} \perp \overline{WZ}$, $\overline{XY} \perp \overline{YZ}$

Prove: $\overline{XY} \parallel \overline{WZ}$

Statements	Reasons
1. $\overline{XW} \parallel \overline{YZ}$ $\overline{XW} \perp \overline{WZ}$ $\overline{XY} \perp \overline{YZ}$	1. Given
2. $\overline{WZ} \perp \overline{YZ}$	2. In a plane, if a line is $\perp$ to one of 2 $\parallel$ lines, then it is $\perp$ to the other.
3. $\overline{XY} \parallel \overline{WZ}$	3. In a plane, if 2 lines are $\perp$ to the same line, then the lines are $\parallel$.

CHECKING FOR UNDERSTANDING

Communicating Mathematics

Read and study the lesson to answer these questions.

1. If two lines are parallel, explain how you can construct a segment that represents the distance between the two lines. **See margin.**

2. no; the distance between them is not constant.

2. Can you find the distance between two coplanar lines that are not parallel? Explain why or why not.

3. $\sqrt{10}$ or about 3.2 units

3. Use graph paper and work with a partner to find the approximate distance between the lines whose equations are $y = 3x - 1$ and $y = 3x + 9$.

4. Think of everyday situations when you might need to find the distance from one point to another point, the distance from a point to a line, and the distance from a line to a line. For example, finding the shortest route from your campsite to the river is an example of the distance from a point to a line. **Answers may vary.**

Guided Practice

Copy each diagram and construct the segment that represents the distance indicated.

5. A to $\overline{XY}$

6. ℓ to P

7. a to b

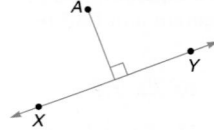
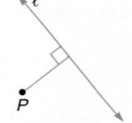
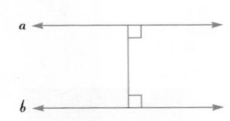

Determine if each statement is *true* or *false*. If the statement is false, explain why.

8. If two lines are everywhere equidistant, then the lines are parallel. **true**

9. The distance between a line on a plane and the plane is 0. **true**

10. The distance between two parallel lines is the length of any segment that connects points on the two lines. **false; must be a $\perp$ segment**

11. If AB is the distance between two lines and A is on one line and B is on the other, then $\overline{AB}$ is perpendicular to both lines. **true**

LESSON 3-6   PARALLELS AND DISTANCE   151

APPLYING THE LESSON

Homework Exercises

Assignment Guide
Basic: 14-30, 36-37, 40-47
Average: 17-32, 36-38, 40-47
Enriched: 20-47

Additional Answers

19. $d = 2\sqrt{10}$

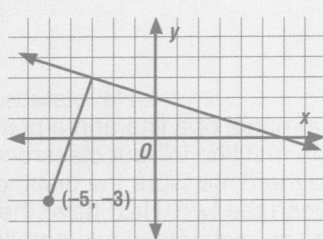

(-5, -3)

20. $d = \sqrt{5}$

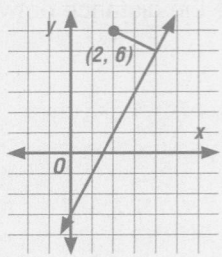

(2, 6)

Reteaching Master Booklet, p. 19

Use a ruler and the definition of parallel lines to determine whether the lines shown in color are parallel. Write *yes* or *no*. Explain your answer.

12.

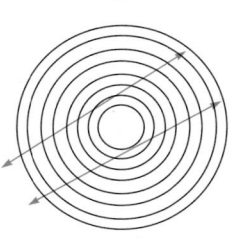

no; not equidistant at all points

13.

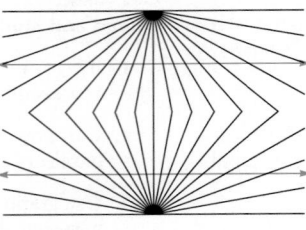

yes; equidistant at all points

EXERCISES

Practice Copy each figure and draw the segment that represents the distance indicated.

14. C to $\overline{FE}$

15. C to $\overrightarrow{DE}$

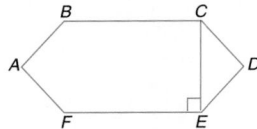

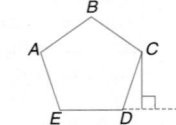

16. C to $\overline{AB}$

17. N to $\overline{MP}$

18. R to $\overleftrightarrow{TS}$

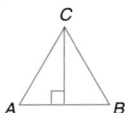

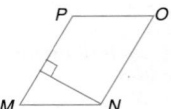

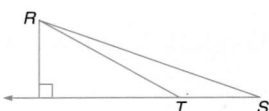

Using graph paper, graph each equation and plot the given point. Then construct a perpendicular segment and find the distance from the point to the line. **See margin.**

CONSTRUCTION

19. $x + 3y = 6$, (-5, -3)

20. $2x - y = 3$, (2, 6)

21. $y = -4x$, (-2, 8)

22. $y = 5$, (-2, 4)

23. $3x + 4y = 1$, (2, 5)

24. $x = 1$, (4, 5)

Draw a figure to illustrate each of the following. Then write any possible conclusions that can be made from the given information. **26–28. See Solutions Manual.**

25. $\overline{AB}$ is perpendicular to $\overrightarrow{CD}$ at B. **See margin.**

26. $\overline{MN}$ is perpendicular to $\overline{NO}$.

27. ℓ is perpendicular to m and n is perpendicular to m.

28. quadrilateral $QUAD$ with $\overline{QU}$ parallel to $\overline{AD}$

RETEACHING THE LESSON

Tape a piece of string to the chalkboard. Draw a line and have a student find the shortest length of string needed to reach the line. Have him or her trace over the string to draw a segment from the point to the line. What do the students notice about the line and the segment? Have other students do the same with different points and lines to test the conjecture. Also, have a student measure the distance between two parallel lines at several different locations. What does he or she notice? Have several students repeat the activity to test the conjecture.

In the figure below, $\overline{PS} \perp \overline{SQ}$, $\overline{PQ} \perp \overline{QR}$, and $\overline{QR} \perp \overline{SR}$. Name the segment whose length represents the distance between the following points and lines.

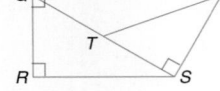

29. P to $\overline{SQ}$ $\overline{PS}$ **30.** R to $\overline{PQ}$ $\overline{RQ}$

31. Q to $\overline{SR}$ $\overline{QR}$ **32.** S to $\overline{QR}$ $\overline{SR}$

33-34. See Solutions Manual.
33. If two lines lie in parallel planes, are the lines parallel? Explain.

34. Explain how you could find the distance between two parallel planes.

35. If a line is perpendicular to one of two parallel planes, is it perpendicular to the other? Explain. **yes**

Critical Thinking

36. An advanced algebra book states that the distance from a point $P(x_1, y_1)$ to a line ℓ with equation $Ax + By + C = 0$ can be found by the formula $d = \dfrac{|Ax_1 + By_1 + C|}{\sqrt{A^2 + B^2}}$. Use the formula to find the distance between the points and lines given in Exercises 19-24. Do you think the formula is valid? Explain. **Yes, it is valid. See students' work.**

Applications

37. Transportation An accident has occurred on Central Avenue and an ambulance has been dispatched from Polyclinic Hospital.

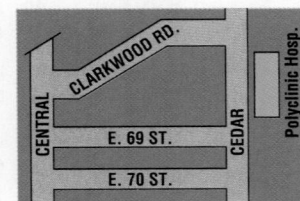

a. E. 69th St.; it is the perpendicular from the point to the line.

  a. What is the shortest route the ambulance could take to the accident? Justify your answer.

  b. What other factors might make the ambulance driver choose a route other than the shortest one? **Answers may vary. Sample answers are heavy traffic and one-way streets.**

38. Interior Design Rosa is putting a chair railing on her dining room walls. In order to ensure that the rail is parallel to the baseboards, she measures and marks 36 inches up from the baseboard in several places along the walls. If she installs the rail at these markings, how does Rosa know that the rail will be parallel to the baseboards? **Parallel lines are everywhere equidistant.**

Additional Answers
21. $d = 0$ **22.** $d = 1$

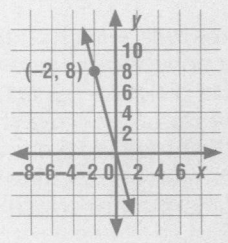

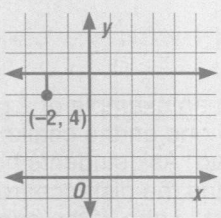

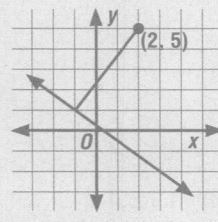
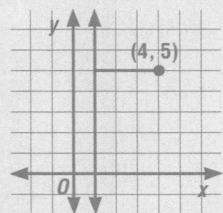

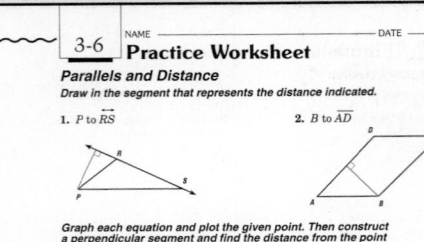
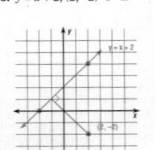
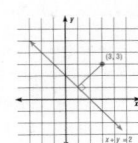
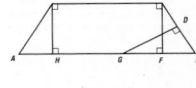

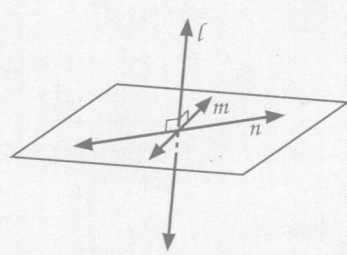
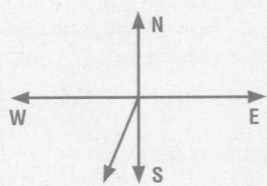

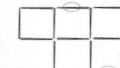
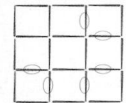

39. Transportation The map below shows a part of downtown Minneapolis-St. Paul. On it, 1 centimeter represents 0.6 kilometers.

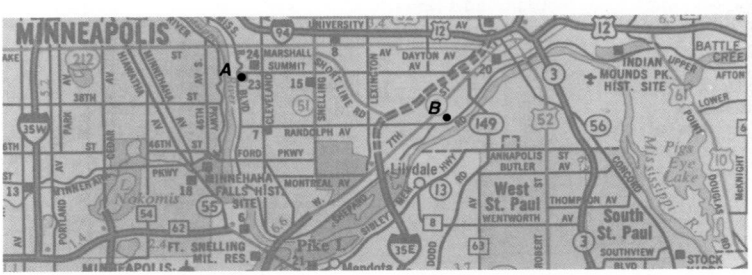

a. Estimate the distance that a bird would fly to get from Saint Thomas College at point *A* to point *B*. **2.1 kilometers**

b. Estimate the distance a new college student would travel in his car to get from Saint Thomas College to point *B*. Assume that he takes the shortest possible route. **2.7 kilometers**

c. About how far would the captain of a riverboat travel to get from point *A* to point *B*? **4.1 kilometers**

d. Compare the distances each one traveled. Who traveled the farthest? Who traveled the shortest? Explain. **riverboat; bird; bird is not restricted to traveling on the roads or in the rivers.**

Mixed Review

40. Find the slope of the line that passes through the points (3, 0) and (8, -2). **(Lesson 3-5)** $-\frac{2}{5}$

41. Draw a figure to illustrate two lines that are perpendicular to a third line, but are not parallel to each other. **(Lesson 3-1) See margin.**

42. Determine if the statement *Parallelism is transitive* is *true* or *false*. **(Lesson 3-1) true**

43. Find the value of *x*. **(Lesson 2-7) 43**

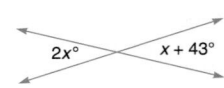

$2x°$ $x + 43°$

44. The sign in front of the Screaming Eagle Rollercoaster says *If you are over 48 inches tall, then you may ride the Screaming Eagle.* Jamal is 54 inches tall. Can he ride the Screaming Eagle? Which law of logic leads you to this conclusion? **(Lesson 2-3) yes; detachment**

45. State the hypothesis and the conclusion of the statement *If two lines are parallel then they are everywhere equidistant.* **(Lesson 2-2) See margin.**

46. Aviation The path of an airplane is described as 22° west of south. Draw a diagram that represents this flight path. **(Lesson 1-5) See margin.**

Wrap-Up

47. Describe how to find the distance between two points, the distance between a point and a line, and the distance between two lines. **See students' work.**

EXTENDING THE LESSON

Math Power: Problem Solving

Bring in an example of a pyramid or draw one on the chalkboard or overhead. Ask students how they would find the distance from the top point to one of the edges of the base, and how they would find the distance from the top point to the base itself. Are the distances the same? **To find the distance** from the top point to an edge, draw a perpendicular segment from the point to the edge. To find the distance from the top point to the base itself, draw a segment perpendicular to the base. The distances will not be the same.

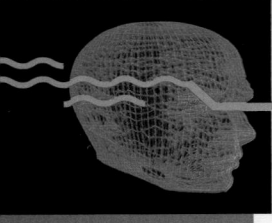

Technology

BASIC
Geometric Supposer
▶ **Graphing calculators**
LOGO
Spreadsheets

Finding the Distance Between a Point and a Line

You can use a graphing calculator to find the distance between a point and a line. Let's find the distance between the line whose equation is $y = 2x - 5$ and $(7, -1)$. The equation of the line perpendicular to the line with equation $y = 2x - 5$ line through $(7, -1)$ is $y = -\frac{1}{2}x + \frac{5}{2}$.

Clear the graphics screen. Press SHIFT Cls then EXE for a Casio fx-7000G. Press Y=, then use the arrow keys and the CLEAR key to select and clear any equations from the Y = list for a TI-81.

Now graph the lines.

Casio

ENTER: GRAPH 2 ALPHA X – 5
: GRAPH (–) 0.5 ALPHA
X + 2.5 EXE

TI-81

ENTER: Y= 2 X|T – 5 ENTER
(–) 0.5 X|T + 2.5 GRAPH

Press SHIFT TRACE on the Casio or TRACE on the TI-81. Then move the cursor to the point of intersection of the two lines and approximate its coordinates.

Now use the distance formula to find the distance between the intersection point and the given point.

$$\text{distance} = \sqrt{(7-3)^2 + (-1-1)^2}$$
$$= \sqrt{16 + 4}$$
$$= 2\sqrt{5} \quad \text{or about 4.5}$$

EXERCISES

1. $\sqrt{2} \approx 1.4$

2. $\sqrt{29} \approx 5.4$

3. $\sqrt{10} \approx 3.2$

Use a graphing calculator to find the distance between each given line and point on a perpendicular line.

1. $y = x + 7$;
   $(2, 7)$ on $y = -x + 9$

2. $y = \frac{2}{5}x + 3$
   $(-8, -6)$ on $y = -\frac{5}{2}x - 26$

3. $y = 3x - 13$
   $(1, 0)$ on $y = -\frac{1}{3}x + \frac{1}{3}$

TECHNOLOGY 155

Using Technology

Objective This optional page shows how graphing calculators can be used to perform mathematical computations and to enhance and extend mathematical concepts.

Teaching Suggestions

Work through the steps in finding the equation of the line perpendicular to the line $y = 2x - 5$ through the point $(7, -1)$. Before clearing the graphics screen on your calculator, check your range by pressing the RANGE key. Set it for the range of $[-10, 10]$ on the x-axis with a scale of 1 and $[-10, 10]$ on the y-axis with a scale of 1.

Point out that the two lines on the graphing calculator do not look perpendicular even though they actually are, because you are looking at something in a rectangular box that is supposed to be in a square box. Have students look at the tick marks on the x-axis and y-axis. Even though they are both the same scale, the tick marks are not the same distance apart on each axis. On the TI-81, you can demonstrate this by graphing the two lines and then pressing ZOOM 5 to make the viewing window a square. The lines will now appear perpendicular.

CHAPTER 3 | SUMMARY AND REVIEW

VOCABULARY

Upon completing this chapter, you should be familiar with the following terms:

coplanar	**122**	**142**	slope
parallel	**122**	**123**	skew lines
parallel planes	**122**	**124**	transversal

SKILLS AND CONCEPTS

OBJECTIVES AND EXAMPLES	REVIEW EXERCISES

OBJECTIVES AND EXAMPLES

Upon completing this chapter, you should be able to:

- describe the relationships between two lines and two planes. **(Lesson 3-2)**

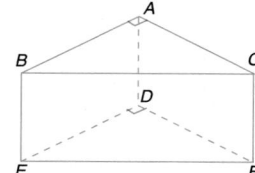

Plane *ABC* and plane *DEF* are parallel.

Segments $\overline{BC}$ and $\overline{EF}$ are parallel.

Segments $\overline{AB}$ and $\overline{DF}$ are skew.

REVIEW EXERCISES

Use these exercises to review and prepare for the chapter test.

Use the figure below to find an example of each of the following.

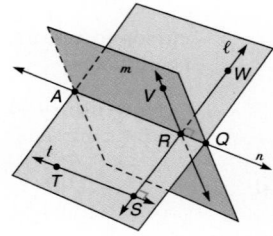

1. two parallel lines *l, n*

2. two skew lines *l, m*

3. two parallel lines and a transversal *l, n, ℓ*

4. two intersecting planes **plane WRA, plane VRA**

5. two noncoplanar lines *l, m*

■ use the properties of parallel lines to determine angle measures. **(Lesson 3-3)**

List the conclusions that can be drawn if $\ell \parallel m$.

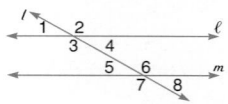

Use the figure below to answer each question.
See margin.

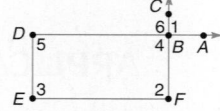

Corresponding angles: $\angle1 \cong \angle5$, $\angle2 \cong \angle6$, $\angle3 \cong \angle7$, and $\angle4 \cong \angle8$

Alternate interior angles: $\angle3 \cong \angle6$, and $\angle4 \cong \angle5$

Consecutive interior angles: $\angle3$ and $\angle5$, and $\angle4$ and $\angle6$ are supplementary.

Alternate exterior angles: $\angle1 \cong \angle8$, and $\angle2 \cong \angle7$

6. If $\overline{AF} \parallel \overline{EB}$, which angles are congruent?

7. If $\overline{AF} \parallel \overline{DC}$, which angles are congruent?

8. If $\overline{AF} \parallel \overline{DC}$, which angle is supplementary to $\angle CAG$? $\angle DCB$, $\angle FAB$

9. If $\overline{EB} \parallel \overline{DC}$, which angle is supplementary to $\angle BCD$? $\angle EBC$, $\angle ABH$

■ prove that two lines are parallel. **(Lesson 3-4)**

Ways to show two lines parallel:

1. Alternate interior angles are congruent.
2. Corresponding angles are congruent.
3. Alternate exterior angles are congruent.
4. Consecutive interior angles are supplementary.
5. Two lines are perpendicular to a third line.

Use the figure below to answer each question.
See margin.

10. Given $\angle1$ and $\angle2$ are supplementary, which lines are parallel and why?

11. Given $\angle5 \cong \angle6$, which lines are parallel and why?

12. Given $\angle6 \cong \angle2$, which lines are parallel and why?

■ find and use the slopes of lines. **(Lesson 3-5)**

Find the slope of the lines parallel to and perpendicular to a line through (4, -2) and (5, 3).

Find the slope of line through (4, -2) and (5, 3).

$$m = \frac{-2-3}{4-5} \text{ or } 5$$

A line parallel has slope 5, and a line perpendicular has slope $-\frac{1}{5}$.

Find the slope of the line through the given points.

13. (0, 4), (-1, -2) **6** 14. (2, 0), (0, -6) **3**

15. (11, 2), (5, 4) $-\frac{1}{3}$ 16. (-1, -5), (3, -7) $-\frac{1}{2}$

Find the slope of the lines parallel and perpendicular to the line through each pair of points. See margin.

17. (-3, 7), (4, -2)   18. (0, 6), (3, 6)
19. (7, -2), (1, -3)   20. (9, -2), (-1, 4)

Additional Answers

6. $\angle FAB$, $\angle ABE$; $\angle FAB$, $\angle HBC$; $\angle GAE$, $\angle AEB$; $\angle FAE$, $\angle DEB$; $\angle GAB$, $\angle EBC$; $\angle GAB$, $\angle ABH$

7. $\angle FAC$, $\angle ACD$; $\angle GAD$, $\angle ADC$

10. $\overline{AD} \parallel \overline{EF}$, $\angle1 \cong \angle4$ since vertical angles are congruent, so $\angle4$ and $\angle2$ are supplementary. So the lines are parallel since consecutive interior angles are supplementary.

11. $\overline{DE} \parallel \overline{CF}$; alternate interior angles are congruent.

12. $\overline{DA} \parallel \overline{EF}$, since corresponding angles are congruent.

17. $-\frac{9}{7}$, $\frac{7}{9}$
18. 0, no slope
19. $\frac{1}{6}$, -6
20. $-\frac{3}{5}$, $\frac{5}{3}$

Alternate Review Strategies

To provide a brief in-class review, you may wish to read the following questions to the class and have them answer verbally.

1. Use the figure below to find an example of each of the following.   **Sample answers given.**

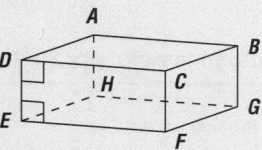

   a. two parallel lines $\overleftrightarrow{DC}$ and $\overleftrightarrow{EF}$
   b. two skew lines $\overleftrightarrow{DC}$ and $\overleftrightarrow{EH}$
   c. two parallel lines and a transversal $\overleftrightarrow{DC}$ and $\overleftrightarrow{EF}$ with transversal $\overleftrightarrow{DE}$
   d. two intersecting lines $\overleftrightarrow{AB}$ and $\overleftrightarrow{BG}$
   e. two coplanar lines $\overleftrightarrow{AB}$ and $\overleftrightarrow{BC}$

2. If $a \parallel b$ and they are intersected by a transversal t, what kinds of pairs of angles would be congruent? supplementary?   **corresponding angles, alternate interior angles, and alternate exterior angles would be congruent; consecutive interior angles would be supplementary.**

3. If two lines are perpendicular to the same line, why can you not be sure that the two lines are parallel?   **They may be in different planes.**

4. How can you find the slope of a line given two points (x_1, y_1) and (x_2, y_2) on the line?   **Divide the value of $(y_2 - y_1)$ by the value of $(x_2 - x_1)$.**

5. How do you find the slope of a line parallel or perpendicular to a line through two given points?   **Find the slope of the line between the two given points. The slope of the parallel line will be the same. The slope of a perpendicular line will be the negative reciprocal of the slope of the given line.**

6. How do you measure the distance between a point and a line?   **Find the length of a segment perpendicular to the line from the point.**

A 2-page Cumulative Review from the *Evaluation Masters* is below. It can be used to review skills and concepts presented thus far in the text. Standardized Test Practice Questions are also provided in the *Evaluation Masters*.

Evaluation Masters, pp. 39-40

NAME _____ DATE _____

~**Cumulative Review** (Chapters 1 – 3)

Refer to the number line below to answer each question.

A B CD E F
-10 -8 -6 -4 -2 0 2 4 6 8 10

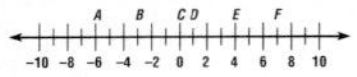

1. What is the coordinate of point *D*? **1.** ___1___
2. What is the measure of $\overline{BE}$? **2.** ___7___
3. What is the coordinate of the midpoint of $\overline{AE}$? **3.** ___-1___
4. *True or false:* $\overline{AD} \cong \overline{CF}$. **4.** ___true___
5. *True or false:* $BD > EF$. **5.** ___true___

Refer to the figure, which shows a rectangular box. Determine whether each statement is true or false.

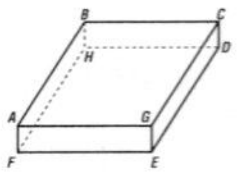

6. $\overline{AB} \parallel \overline{ED}$ **6.** ___true___
7. *D*, *E*, and *F* are collinear. **7.** ___false___
8. $\overline{GE} \perp \overline{EF}$. **8.** ___true___
9. $\overline{AG}$ and $\overline{FH}$ are skew lines. **9.** ___true___

Refer to the figure to answer each question.

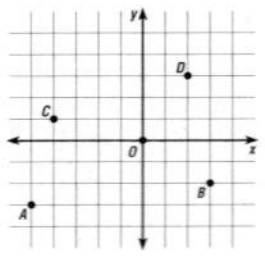

10. What ordered pair names point *A*? **10.** ___(-5, -3)___
11. What is the measure of $\overline{BD}$? **11.** ___$\sqrt{26}$___
12. What are the coordinates of the midpoint of $\overline{CD}$? **12.** ___(-1, 2)___
13. What is the slope of $\overline{AC}$? **13.** ___4___
14. What is the slope of any line parallel to $\overline{BD}$? **14.** ___-5___
15. What is the slope of any line perpendicular to $\overline{AB}$? **15.** ___-8___

39
Glencoe Division, Macmillan/McGraw-Hill

NAME _____ DATE _____

~**Cumulative Review** (Chapters 1 – 3)—continued

Use the figure below to answer each question.

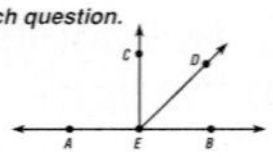

16. True or false: $\overrightarrow{AE}$ and $\overrightarrow{EB}$ are opposite rays. **16.** ___false___
17. Identify the sides of $\angle CED$. **17.** ___$\overrightarrow{EC}$, $\overrightarrow{ED}$___
18. $\overrightarrow{ED}$ bisects $\angle CEB$ and m$\angle DEB$ = 35. Find m$\angle CEB$ **18.** ___70___
19. $\overrightarrow{EC}$ bisects $\angle AED$, m$\angle AEC$ = 2x + 10, and m$\angle AED$ = 6x. Find m$\angle AED$. **19.** ___60___
20. Tell one way you can prove that a conjecture is false. **20.** ___use a counterexample___

Determine if the conjecture is true or false based on the given information. Explain your answer and give a counterexample for any false conjecture.

21. Given: $AC = \frac{1}{2}AB$
    Conjecture: *B* is the midpoint of $\overline{AC}$. **21.** ___false; A, B, and C may not be collinear.___
22. Given: $\overrightarrow{AC}$ and $\overrightarrow{DE}$ intersect at *B*.
    Conjecture: $\angle ABD \cong \angle CBE$ **22.** ___false;___ 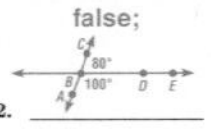
23. Suppose you write, "All adults were once babies" and "All babies were once cute" in if-then form. What law of logic will let you conclude that if a person is an adult, then that person was once cute? **23.** ___law of syllogism___

Solve. Use any strategy.

24. Aaron's license plate has three letters followed by a 4-digit number. The product of the digits is 210, their sum is 17, and the digits are in ascending order. What is the number part of the plate? **24.** ___2 3 5 7___
25. How many whole numbers between 0 and 100 are divisible by both 2 and 3? **25.** ___16___

40
Glencoe Division, Macmillan/McGraw-Hill

OBJECTIVES AND EXAMPLES

▪ use distance relationships between points, lines, and planes. (**Lesson 3-6**)

The distance between a point and a line is the length of the segment perpendicular to the line from the point.

The distance between parallel lines is the distance between one of the lines and any point on the other line.

REVIEW EXERCISES

In the figure below, $\overline{PS} \perp \overline{SQ}$, $\overline{PQ} \perp \overline{QR}$, $\overline{PM} \perp \overline{RM}$, and $\overline{QR} \perp \overline{SR}$. Name the segment whose length represents the distance between the following points and lines.

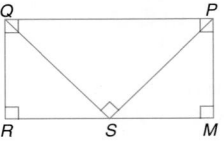

21. from *P* to $\overline{SQ}$ $\overline{PS}$
22. from *R* to $\overline{PQ}$ $\overline{RQ}$
23. from $\overline{RM}$ to $\overline{QP}$ $\overline{RQ}$ or $\overline{MP}$
24. from $\overline{RQ}$ to $\overline{MP}$ $\overline{QP}$ or $\overline{RM}$

APPLICATIONS AND CONNECTIONS

25. **Education** The students in a gym class are standing in a circle. When they count off, the students with numbers 5 and 23 are standing exactly opposite one another. Assuming the students are evenly spaced around the circle, how many students are in the class? (**Lesson 3-1**) **36**

26. **Nature Studies** A park ranger estimates that there are 6000 deer in the Blendon Woods Park. He also estimates that one year ago there were 6100 deer in the park. (**Lesson 3-5**)

    a. What is the rate of change for the number of deer in Blendon Woods Park? **-100 per year**

    b. At the same rate, how many deer will there be in the park in 10 years? **5000**

27. **Travel** At 10:00 A.M., Liz had completed 195 miles of her cross-country trip. By 2:00 P.M., she had traveled a total of 455 miles. Use slope to determine Liz's rate of travel. (**Lesson 3-5**) **65 mph**

    28a. See margin.

28. **Construction** A ramp was installed to give handicapped people access to the new public library. The top of the ramp is three feet higher than the bottom. The lower end of the ramp is 36 feet from the door of the library. (**Lesson 3-5**)

    a. Draw a diagram of the ramp.

    b. Find the slope of the ramp. $\frac{1}{12}$

Additional Answer

28a.

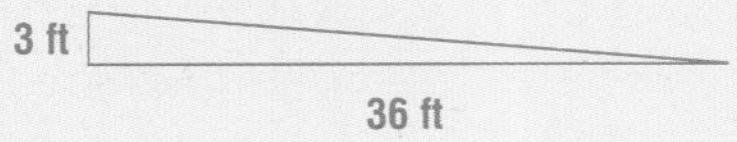

3 ft

36 ft

In the figure, $\ell \parallel m$. Determine whether each statement is *true* or *false*. Justify your answer.

See Solutions Manual.

1. $\angle 1$ and $\angle 14$ are alternate exterior angles.
2. $\angle 5$ and $\angle 11$ are consecutive interior angles.
3. $\angle 2$ and $\angle 6$ are vertical angles.
4. $\angle 6$ and $\angle 12$ are supplementary angles.
5. $\angle 3 \cong \angle 8$
6. $\angle 12 \cong \angle 13$
7. $m\angle 7 + m\angle 10 = 180$
8. $m\angle 4 + m\angle 5 + m\angle 11 = 180$

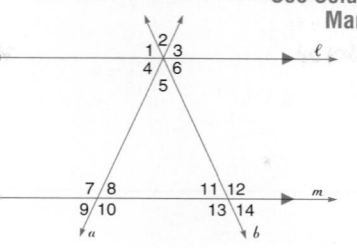

Use the figure at the right to answer each question.

9. Given $\angle 5 \cong \angle 4$, which lines are parallel and why? **9.** $a \parallel b$, **Postulate 3-2**
10. Given $\angle 3 \cong \angle 9$, which lines are parallel and why? **10.** $m \parallel n$, **Theorem 3-5**
11. Given $m\angle 4 + m\angle 9 + m\angle 6 = 180$, which lines are parallel and why? $a \parallel b$; **Theorem 3-6**

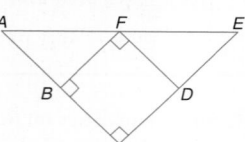

Find the slope of the lines parallel to and perpendicular to a line through the given points.

12. (4, 5), (-2, 5) **0, undefined**
13. (11, 8), (5, -3) $\frac{11}{6}, -\frac{6}{11}$
14. (-3, 1), (7, -1) $-\frac{1}{5}, 5$

Name the segment that represents the distance between the following points and lines.

15. from F to $\overline{CE}$ **$\overline{FD}$**
16. from F to $\overline{AC}$ **$\overline{FB}$**
17. from A to $\overline{CE}$ **$\overline{AC}$**
18. from D to $\overline{BC}$ **$\overline{DC}$**

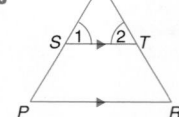

19. Write a two-column proof. **See Solutions Manual.**
    Given: $\angle 1 \cong \angle 2$
    $\overline{ST} \parallel \overline{PR}$
    Prove: $\angle P \cong \angle R$

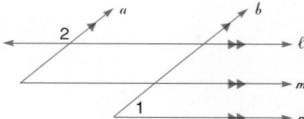

20. **Business** The Carpet Experts cleaning team can clean carpet in a room that is 10 feet by 10 feet in 20 minutes. Draw a diagram and find how long it would take them to do a walk-in closet that is 5 feet by 5 feet. **5 minutes**

Bonus In the figure at the right, $a \parallel b$, $\ell \parallel m$, $m \parallel n$, and $m\angle 1 = 40$. Find $m\angle 2$. **140**

Test and Review Generator software is provided in Apple, IBM, and Macintosh versions. You may use this software to create your own tests or worksheets, based on the needs of your students.

The **Performance Assessment Booklet** provides an alternate assessment for evaluating student progress. An assessment for this chapter can be found on pages 5-6.

Using the Chapter Test
This page may be used as a test or as a review. In addition, two multiple-choice tests (Forms 1A and 1B) and two free-response tests (Forms 2A and 2B) are provided in the *Evaluation Masters*. Chapter 3 Test, Form 1A is shown below.

Evaluation Masters, pp. 29-30

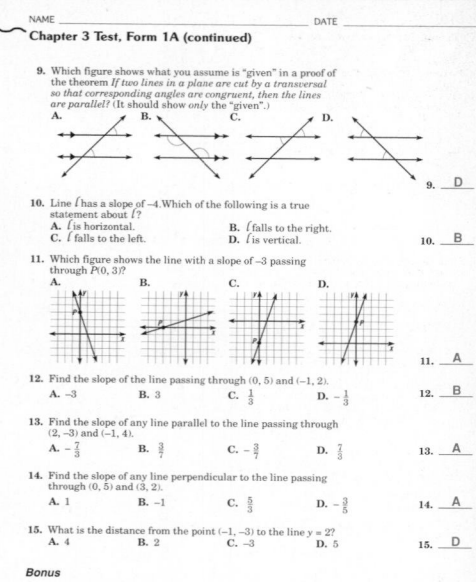

Algebra Review

Using the Algebra Review

The goal of this two-page review of algebraic skills, concepts, and applications is as follows:

- It provides students a chance to review important concepts from algebra that will be useful as they study geometry.

- It gives students an opportunity to retain the concepts they learned in previous courses and may need for future mathematics courses.

The review is presented in a side-by-side format. Encourage students to refer to the Objectives and Examples on the left as they complete the Review Exercises on the right.

Additional Answers

19. $\{n \mid n < 13\}$
20. $\{r \mid r \le -11\}$
21. $\{a \mid a \ge -5.5\}$
22. $\{z \mid z > 6\}$
23. $\{x \mid x \le 7\}$
24. $\{y \mid y > -\frac{1}{3}\}$

OBJECTIVES AND EXAMPLES	REVIEW EXERCISES

■ Solve equations involving more than one operation.

$$2x + 15 = 19$$
$$2x + 15 - 15 = 19 - 15$$
$$\frac{2x}{2} = \frac{4}{2}$$
$$x = 2$$

Solve each equation. Check the solution.

1. $3x - 8 = 22$ **10**
2. $-4y + 5 = 35$ $\frac{-15}{2}$
3. $0.5n + 2 = -7$ **-18**
4. $-6 = 3.1t + 6.4$ **-4**
5. $\frac{x}{-3} + 2 = -21$ **69**
6. $\frac{8 - 5r}{6} = 3$ **-2**

■ Solve proportions.

$$\frac{x}{3} = \frac{x - 5}{2}$$
$$x \cdot 2 = 3 \cdot (x - 5) \qquad \textit{Cross multiply.}$$
$$2x = 3x - 15$$
$$-x = -15$$
$$x = 15$$

Solve each proportion. 12. **-67**

7. $\frac{n}{45} = \frac{6}{15}$ **18**
8. $\frac{35}{55} = \frac{x}{11}$ **7**
9. $\frac{4}{8} = \frac{11}{t}$ **22**
10. $\frac{5}{6} = \frac{a - 2}{4}$ $\frac{16}{3}$
11. $\frac{y + 4}{y - 1} = \frac{4}{3}$ **16**
12. $\frac{z + 7}{6} = \frac{z - 3}{7}$

■ Solve percent problems.

What percent of 75 is 9?
$$\frac{9}{75} = \frac{r}{100}$$
$$100 \left(\frac{9}{75}\right) = r$$
$$12 = r \quad \text{9 is 12\% of 75.}$$

Solve.

13. What number is 60% of 80? **48**
14. Twenty-one is 35% of what number? **60**
15. Eighty-four is what percent of 96? **87.5%**
16. What number is 0.3% of 62.7? **0.1881**

■ Graph inequalities on number lines.

Graph the solution set of $x \ge -3$.

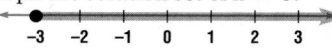

Graph the solution set of each inequality on a number line.

17. $x < -2$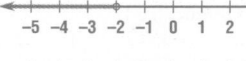
18. $x \ne -4$

■ Solve inequalities by using addition or subtraction.

$$3x - 2 < 4x$$
$$3x - 3x - 2 < 4x - 3x$$
$$-2 < x$$

The solution set is $\{x \mid x > -2\}$.

Solve each inequality. Check the solution.

19. $n - 4 < 9$
20. $r + 8 \le -3$
21. $a - 2.6 \ge -8.1$
22. $5z - 6 > 4z$
23. $3x \le 2x + 7$
24. $y + \frac{7}{8} > \frac{13}{24}$

See margin.

- Multiply and divide monomials.

$$(2ab^2)(3a^2b^3) = (2 \cdot 3)(a \cdot a^2)(b^2 \cdot b^3)$$
$$= 6a^3b^5$$

$$\frac{2x^6y}{8x^2y^2} = \frac{2}{8} \cdot \frac{x^6}{x^2} \cdot \frac{y}{y^2}$$
$$= \frac{x^4}{4y}$$

Simplify. Assume that no denominator is equal to zero. 26. $-12m^3n^4$ 27. $20a^5x^5$

25. $y^3 \cdot y^4 \cdot y$ y^8 26. $(3mn)(-4m^2n^3)$

27. $(-4a^2x)(-5a^3x^4)$ 28. $\frac{42b^7}{14b^4}$ $3b^3$

29. $\frac{y^3xw}{-yxw^2}$ $\frac{-y^2}{w}$ 30. $\frac{-16a^3b^2x^4y}{-48a^4bxy^3}$ $\frac{bx^3}{3ay^2}$

- Find the degree of a polynomial.

Find the degree of $2xy^3 + x^2y$.

degree of $2xy^3$: $1 + 3$ or 4

degree of x^2y: $2 + 1$ or 3

Thus, the degree of $2xy^3 + x^2y$ is 4.

Find the degree of each polynomial.

31. $2^3n^2 + 17n^2t^2$ **4**

32. $4xy + 7rs^4 + 9x^2z^2$ **5**

33. $-6y - 2y^3 + 4 - 8y^2$ **3**

- Find the greatest common factor (GCF) for a set of monomials.

Find the GCF of $15x^2y$ and $45xy^2$.

$15x^2y = ③ \cdot ⑤ \cdot x \cdot Ⓧ \cdot Ⓨ$
$45xy^2 = ③ \cdot 3 \cdot ⑤ \cdot Ⓧ \cdot Ⓨ \cdot y$

The GCF is $3 \cdot 5 \cdot x \cdot y$ or $15xy$.

Find the GCF of the given monomials.

34. $15ab, -5a^2b^2$ **5ab**

35. $16mrt, 30m^2r$ **2mr**

36. $20n^3q, 24n^2p^2$ **4n²**

37. $2x^2y^3z^4, 8xy^2z^3, 5x^2yz^3$ **xyz³**

Applications and Connections

38. **Number Theory** Find two consecutive integers such that twice the greater integer increased by the lesser integer is 50. **16, 17**

39. **Travel** Susan drove 3.35 hours at a rate of 50 miles per hour. To the nearest tenth, how long would it take her to drive the same distance at a rate of 45 miles per hour? **3.7 hours**

40. **Entertainment** The television program with the largest audience to date was the final episode of "M*A*S*H." Of the 162 million people watching television that evening, 77% saw the program. How many people were watching? **124,740,000 people**

41. **Savings** Each week, Mei deposits $68.25 of her paycheck into a savings account for college. She began the summer with $420.75 and now has $898.50 in the account. For how many weeks has Mei made deposits if she received no money in interest during this time? **7 weeks**

42. **Statistics** Namid had an average of 74 on four history tests. What score does he have to get on the 100-point final exam if it counts double and he wants to have an average of 80 or better? **92 or more**

CHAPTER 4

Congruent Triangles

This chapter explores properties of triangles and the ways that triangles can be proven congruent. Students begin by identifying parts of triangles and classifying triangles. They learn to apply the angle sum and exterior angle theorems. Next, students identify congruent triangles and their corresponding parts. They use the SAS, SSS, and ASA postulates, then the AAS theorem, to test for congruence and to write two-column and paragraph proofs about congruent triangles. Then, students explore and use properties of isosceles and equilateral triangles.

Problem-Solving Strategy Students learn to solve problems by identifying and achieving steps or subgoals. The students are shown how this strategy can be used to write a proof.

Lesson Objective Chart

Lesson (Pages)	Lesson Objectives	State/Local Objectives
4-1 (164-169)	**4-1A**: Identify the parts of a triangle.	
	4-1B: Classify triangles.	
4-2 (170-176)	**4-2A**: Apply the angle sum theorem.	
	4-2B: Apply the exterior angle theorem.	
4-3 (177-182)	**4-3A**: Identify congruent triangles.	
	4-3B: Name and label corresponding parts of congruent triangles.	
4-4 (184-191)	**4-4**: Use SAS, SSS, and ASA postulates to test for triangle congruence.	
4-5 (192-197)	**4-5**: Use AAS theorem to test for triangle congruence.	
4-6 (198-201)	**4-6**: Solve problems by identifying and achieving subgoals.	
4-7 (202-207)	**4-7**: Use properties of isosceles and equilateral triangles.	

ORGANIZING THE CHAPTER

You may want to refer to the **Course Planning Calendar** on page T28.

Lesson Planning Guide

Blackline Masters Booklets

Lesson (Pages)	Pacing Chart (days) Course			Reteaching	Practice	Enrichment	Evaluation	Technology	Lab Manual	Activities Mixed Problem Solving	Applications	Cooperative Learning Activity	Multicultural	Transparencies
	I	II	III											
4-1 (164-169)	2	1.5	1.5	p. 20	p. 23	p. 20		p. 40						4-1
4-2 (170-176)	2	1.5	1.5	p. 21	p. 24	p. 21	Quiz A, p. 51							4-2
4-3 (177-182)	2	2	2	p. 22	p. 25	p. 22		p. 4	pp.38-41		p. 18			4-3
4-4 (184-191)	2	2	2	p. 23	p. 26	p. 23	Quiz B, p. 51 Mid-Chapter Test, p. 55						p. 4	4-4
4-5 (192-197)	2	2	1	p. 24	p. 27	p. 24						p. 32		4-5
4-6 (198-201)	1	1	1		p. 28		Quiz C, p. 52			p. 4				4-6
4-7 (202-207)	2	1	1	p. 25	p. 29	p. 25	Quiz D, p. 52							4-7
Review (208-210)	1	1	1	Multiple Choice Tests, Forms 1A and 1B, pp. 43-46 Free Response Tests, Forms 2A and 2B, pp. 47-50										
Test (211)	1	1	1	Cumulative Review. pp. 53-54 Standardized Tests Practice Questions, p. 56										

Course I: Chapters 1-11; Course II: Chapters 1-12; Course III: Chapters 1-13

Other Chapter Resources

Student Edition
Chapter Opener, pp. 163-163
Journal Entry, p. 169, 197
Technology, p. 183
Mid-Chapter Review, p. 191
Cooperative Learning Project,
   p. 201
Portfolio, p. 207
College Entrance Exam Preview,
   pp. 212-213
More Investigations in Geometry,
   pp. A4-A6
Extended Project 2, pp. B6-B9

Teacher's Classroom Resources
Transparency 4-0
Real World Applications
   Transparencies, 7, 8
Performance Assessment Booklet,
   pp. 7-8
Problem-of-the-Week Activity
   Cards, 10, 11
Tech Prep Applications Booklet,
   pp. 7-8

Other Supplements
Flow Proof and Indirect Proof
Algebra and Geometry Overhead
   Manipulative Resources
Glencoe Mathematics Professional
   Series

Software
Test and Review Generator
   (Apple, IBM, and Macintosh)
Teacher's Guide for Software
   Resources

ENHANCING THE CHAPTER

Cooperative Learning

Describing the Objectives and Explaining the Criteria for Success

Before students engage in any cooperative-learning activity, it is important that you specify two types of objectives and make sure that both are clearly understood by all members of the groups. The first objective is the geometric or content objective. For this you clearly describe the mathematical task or experiment that is to be completed. The second objective describes the cooperative-learning skills that will be emphasized during the activity. Examples of these skills include: stay with the group; use quiet voices; communicate support; encourage every-member participation; expand on the other member's answers of explanations; criticize ideas, not people; and so on. Usually no more than one or two of these skills should be stressed per session. In addition to clearly explaining the specific tasks to be performed before the group begins its work, you should also clearly explain the criteria by which the final work will be evaluated. These criteria should be judiciously structured so that students may achieve them without penalizing or being penalized by other students in the group. The criteria also should be fashioned so that they are not only challenging but also realistic.

Technology

The Technology Feature following Lesson 4-3 shows how a graphing calculator can be used to draw triangles. Methods that can be used to draw triangles are given for both Casio fx-7000G and the TI-81. Additional material on these calculators can be found on pages T18-T24. First, one triangle is drawn and then the steps are repeated to draw the second triangle. Students are asked to determine whether the two triangles appear to be congruent. If the triangles do not appear to be congruent, you may wish to have students explain why this is so.

Critical Thinking

When pondering Bloom's taxonomy of thinking processes — knowledge, comprehension, application, analysis, synthesis, and evaluation — people may assume that critical-thinking skills are utilized only at the levels of analysis, synthesis, and evaluation. This not necessarily so. For example, when a student gives an answer to an exercise that calls only for knowledge or comprehension of content, before you say whether the answer is correct, ask the student to explain how the answer was found and to justify it. Then ask others whether they agree with the explanation and justification. Using this procedure on a regular basis will signal students that it is they, not you, who are responsible for doing the thinking.

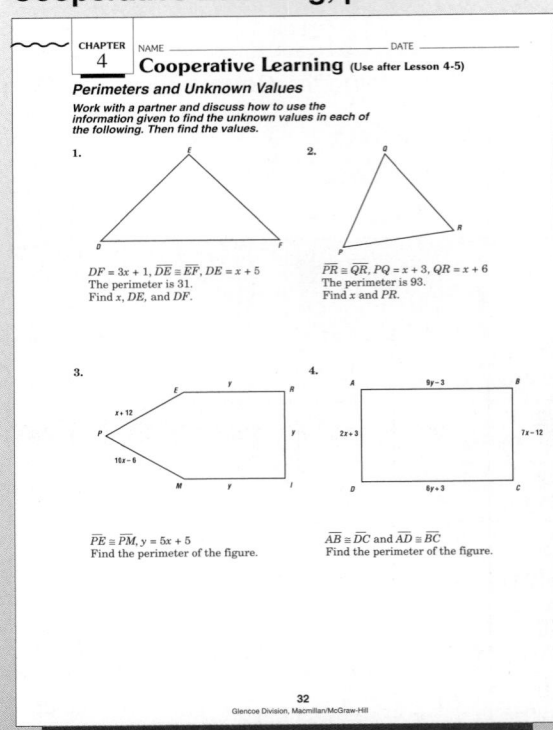

Cooperative Learning, p. 32

Technology, p. 4

Problem of the Week Activity

The card shown below is one of two available for this chapter. It can be used as a class or small group activity.

Activity Card

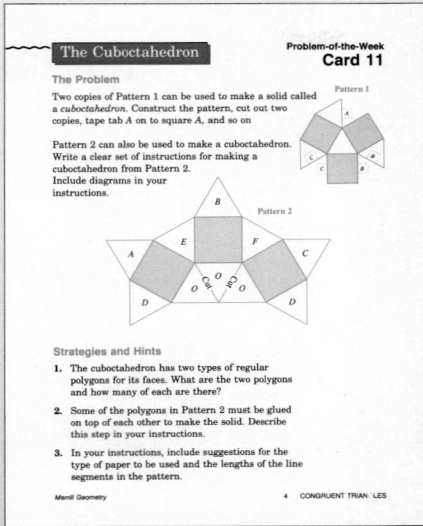

Manipulatives and Models

The following materials may be used as models or manipulatives in Chapter 4.

- straws (Lesson 4-1)
- ruler and protractor (Lesson 4-3)
- graphing calculator (Page 183)
- cardboard, brads, paper fasteners (Lesson 4-5)
- BASIC program (Lesson 4-7)

Outside Resources

Books/Periodicals

Dantzig, T. *The Bequest of the Greeks.* Charles Scribner's Sons.

Dudeney, Henry Ernest. *536 Puzzles & Curious Problems.* Charles Scribner's Sons.

Kadesch, Robert, R. *Math Menagerie.* Harper & Row, Publishers.

Films/Videotapes/Videodiscs

The Birth of Modern Geometry, The Media Guild, 11722 Sorrento Valley Rd., Suite E, San Diego, CA 92121

Software

Geometric Supposer: Triangles, WINGS for Learning/Sunburst, 101 Castleton St., Pleasantville, NY 10570

Multicultural

Multicultural Activity, p. 4

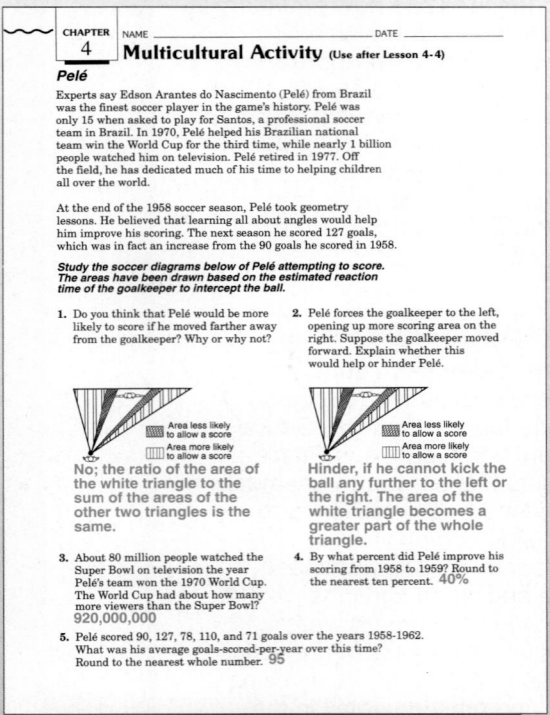

Lab Manual

Lab Activity, pp. 38-41

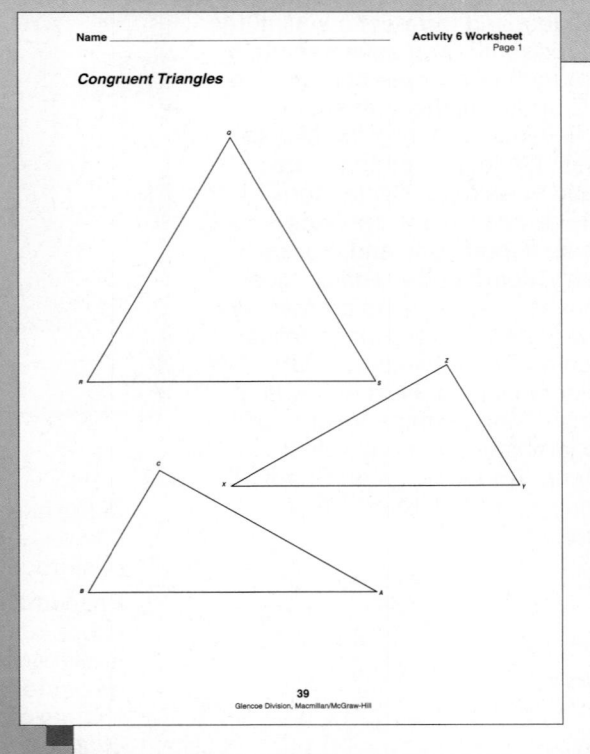

Using the Chapter Opener

This two-page introduction to the chapter provides students with an opportunity to see how geometry is used throughout the world in various cultures. **Transparency 4-0**, available in the *Merrill Geometry Transparency Package*, provides another full-color visual and motivational activity that you can use to engage your students in the mathematical content of the chapter.

Multicultural Notes

Japan Several Western impressionist artists, such as Claude Monet, Georges Seurat, Vincent van Gogh, and Pierre-Auguste Renoir, were very much influenced by the realism and geometric composition of eighteenth-century Japanese prints and wood carvings. Works by Kitagawa Utamaro were especially influential in projecting an open, real world, freely using color and omitting detail in the interest of the picture as a whole.

Africa Countless varieties of European and American art have sprung form African cultures. For example, ivory carvings, bronze plaques, and terra-cotta sculptures of fourteenth- and seventeenth-century Algeria were comparable to Europe's highest artistic achievements during the Middle Ages. Geometric patterns are found in Bakuba, Benin, and Yoruba cloth, wood carvings, house decorations and masks. Today, some of the world's most innovative art is being created by a new generation of African artists, such as Ben Enwonu and Ulli Beier of Nigeria, Hezbon Owiti of Kenya, Malangatana Valente of Mozambique, Vincent Kofi of Ghana, Abdeh Rahman Sherif of Ethiopia, and Eli Kyeyune of Uganda.

Chapter Project

Materials pencil, unlined paper, compass, scissors, glue, posterboard

Procedure Organize students into cooperative groups of geometric artists. Instruct each group to draw on posterboard and cut out several shapes of varying sizes, for a total of fifty or more pieces. The shapes may be geometric, organic, or letters of the alphabet. Instruct students to use the shapes to create the following works of art. In each work, symmetry or balance must be maintained and the direction of action is to be along the edges of the shapes. Have each group present its geometric arrangements to the class for discussion and evaluation.

- *Grid*, a crisscross pattern of shapes arranged along horizontal and vertical lines
- *Circle*, shapes orientated toward a central point
- *Triangle*, arranged along the triangle's edges and outward from a central point.

Congruent Triangles

GEOMETRY AROUND THE WORLD
France

If you have ever watched an artist at work, you know the canvas is gradually filled with geometric shapes that, together, compose the finishing painting. It's the way an artist combines and balances these shapes that determines his or her style and gives paintings a different look and "feel."

Although you may not realize it, your eyes respond in different ways to the shapes within a painting. Diagonal lines provide a painting with energy. A circular shape within a painting will pull your eyes toward its center. Often, the arrangement of objects within a painting creates a pleasing geometric shape for your eyes to travel around.

One of the masters of geometry-based still-life paintings was a French 18th-century artist named Jean Baptiste Simeon Chardin. Chardin sometimes spent days arranging objects he planned to paint so their lines and form pleased him. Only then did he set to work with his palette and brushes.

GEOMETRY IN ACTION

Look closely at Chardin's painting "Laid Out Table" shown at the left. Can you see any triangles in the arrangement of objects in the painting?

◄ *"Laid Out Table"*   Inset photo: *Jean Baptiste Simeon Chardin*

CHAPTER OBJECTIVES

In this chapter, you will:
- Classify triangles and apply theorems involving triangles.
- Prove triangles congruent.
- Solve problems by identifying and achieving subgoals.
- Use properties of isosceles and equilateral triangles.

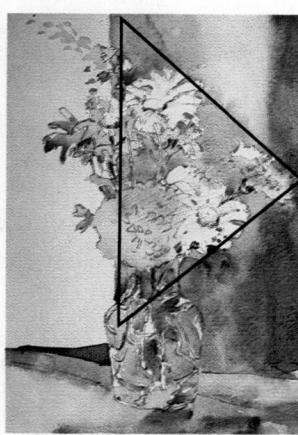

With your finger, trace the shape of the triangle formed by these flowers. What type of triangle is it?

acute, scalene

163

Connections and Applications

Lesson	Connections (C) and Applications (A)	Examples	Exercises
4-1	C: Algebra	2,3	44-45 48-50
	A: Public Works		54
	C: Number Theory		55
	C: Algebra		57 60-61
4-2	A: Construction	1	
	A: Surveying		52
	C: Algebra		54
4-3	A: Automotive	1	
	A: Crafts		40a
	A: Arts		40b
	A: Entertainment		40c
	A: Finance		40d
	A: Art		41
	C: Algebra		43
4-4	C: Algebra	1	
	A: Construction		33
4-5	A: History		32
	A: Home Economics		33
	C: Algebra		37
4-6	C: Number Theory	1	
4-7	A: Construction	1	
	C: Algebra	2	15-17 20-25
	A: Hang Gliding		41
	A: Carpentry		42
	C. Algebra		46

- *Diamond*, pattern with horizontal and vertical lines that divide it into quarters
- *Arc*, shapes arranged along an arc of a circle
- *Two centers*, pattern including any two of the above in which a center is evident
- *Bridge*, two centers joined by a bridge of shapes
- *Radial burst*, shapes spreading out from a central point

Resources

Goldstein, Nathan. *Design and Composition*. Prentice Hall, Inc.

Triado, Juan-Ramon. *The Key to Painting*. Lerner Publications Company.

Hamm, Jack. *First Lessons in Drawing and Painting*. Perigee Books.

Suftudy, Mary, (ed.). *Still Life Painting Techniques*. Watson-Guptill Publications.

Lesson Resources

- Reteaching Master 4-1
- Practice Master 4-1
- Enrichment Master 4-1
- Technology Master, p. 40

Transparency 4-1 contains the 5-Minute Check and a teaching aid for this lesson.

INTRODUCING THE LESSON

 5-Minute Check

(over Chapter 3)

Refer to the figure below.

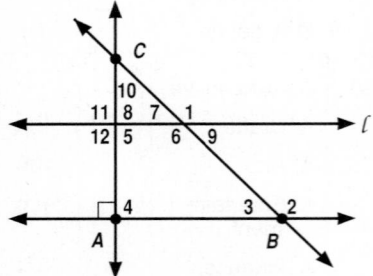

1. Name a pair of consecutive interior angles. **Sample answer: ∠6 and ∠3**
2. If $\ell \parallel \overrightarrow{AB}$, name a pair of congruent angles and state why they are congruent.
   Sample answer: ∠7 and ∠3 because they are corresponding angles
3. If $\ell \parallel \overrightarrow{AB}$, name a pair of supplementary angles.
   Sample answer: ∠3 and ∠6
4. If $\overrightarrow{AB}$ represents the *x*-axis and $\overrightarrow{AC}$ represents the *y*-axis, is the slope of $\overrightarrow{CB}$ positive, negative, zero, or undefined?
   negative
5. If $\ell \parallel \overrightarrow{AB}$, is $\overrightarrow{AC} \perp \ell$? **Yes; $\overrightarrow{AC} \perp \overrightarrow{AB}$, and in a plane, if a line is ⊥ to one of 2 ∥ lines, then it is ⊥ to the other.**

Motivating the Lesson

Ask students to draw a triangle on a sheet of paper and then display what they have drawn. Ask if all types of triangles have been included. After some discussion, have students draw a sketch of any type of triangle that was not included.

4-1 Classifying Triangles

Objectives

After studying this lesson, you should be able to:
4-1A   ▪ identify the parts of a triangle, and
4-1B   ▪ classify triangles.

Application

A side of the cab, the boom, and the support cable of a crane form a triangle. A triangle is a three-sided polygon. A polygon is a closed figure in a plane that is made up of segments called **sides** that intersect *only* at their endpoints, called **vertices**. When the crane reaches out to allow the vertical cable to pick up a boulder, the angle between the side of the cab and the boom is obtuse. The triangle formed is called an **obtuse triangle**.

FYI···

The 893-ton Rosenkranz crane has a height of 663 feet and can lift 33 tons to a height of 525 feet.

Triangle *ABC*, written △*ABC*, has the following parts.

sides: $\overline{AB}, \overline{BC}, \overline{CA}$

vertices: *A, B, C*

angles: ∠*BAC* or ∠*A*, ∠*ABC* or ∠*B*, ∠*BCA* or ∠*C*

The vertices of the triangle can be named in any order.

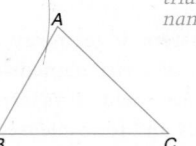

The side opposite ∠*A* is $\overline{BC}$. The angle opposite $\overline{AB}$ is ∠*C*. A similar statement can be made about the remaining side and angle.

One way of classifying triangles is by their angles. All triangles have at least two acute angles, but the third angle can be acute, right, or obtuse. A triangle can be classified using the third angle. We called the triangle formed by the parts of the crane an obtuse triangle because the third angle was obtuse.

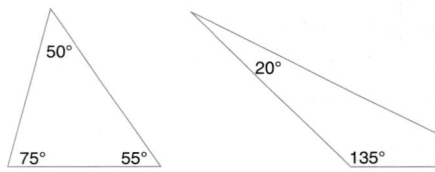

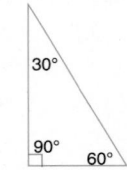

In an **acute triangle,** all the angles are acute.

In an **obtuse triangle,** one angle is obtuse.

In a **right triangle,** one angle is a right angle.

When all of the angles of a triangle are congruent, the triangle is **equiangular**.

ALTERNATE TEACHING STRATEGIES

Using Manipulatives

Provide students with strips of heavy paper and paper fasteners. Ask them to use these to investigate the following:
1. Can a triangle include a right angle and an obtuse angle? **no**
2. Can a triangle include two obtuse angles? **no**
3. If a triangle includes a right angle, what must be true of the other angles? **both acute**

Using Problem Solving

Given *A*(−1, 2) and *B*(3, −2), find *C* such that △*ABC* is a right triangle with the right angle at *A* or *B*. **Sample answer: Any point *C*, other than *A* or *B*, such that *y* = *x* − 5 or *y* = *x* + 3 will form a right triangle.**

Some parts of a right triangle have special names. In right triangle RST, $\overline{RT}$, the side opposite the right angle, is called the **hypotenuse**. The other two sides, $\overline{RS}$ and $\overline{ST}$, are called the **legs**.

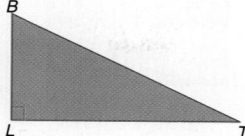

Example 1

The quilt piece shown at the right is a right triangle. If the vertices B, L, and T are labeled as shown, name the angles, the right angle, the hypotenuse, the legs, the side opposite $\angle B$, and the angle opposite $\overline{BL}$.

The angles are $\angle B$, $\angle T$, and $\angle L$. The right angle is $\angle L$. The hypotenuse is the side opposite the right angle, $\overline{BT}$. The legs are $\overline{LB}$ and $\overline{LT}$. The side opposite $\angle B$ is $\overline{LT}$. The angle opposite $\overline{BL}$ is $\angle T$.

Triangles can also be classified according to the number of congruent sides. The slashes on the sides of a triangle mean those sides are congruent.

 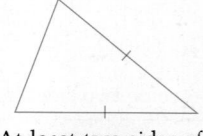 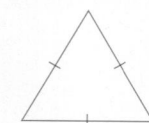

No two sides of a **scalene triangle** are congruent.

At least two sides of an **isosceles triangle** are congruent.

All the sides of an **equilateral triangle** are congruent.

Like the right triangle, the parts of an isosceles triangle have special names. The congruent sides are called **legs**. The angle formed by the legs is the **vertex angle**, and the other two angles are **base angles**. The **base** is the side opposite the vertex angle.

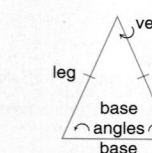

Example 2

Triangle ABC is an isosceles triangle. $\angle A$ is the vertex angle, $AB = 4x - 14$ and $AC = x + 10$. Find the length of the legs.

If $\angle A$ is the vertex angle, then $\overline{BC}$ is the base and $\overline{AB}$ and $\overline{AC}$ are the legs. So, $AB = AC$.

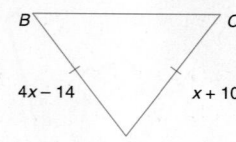

Solve the following equation.

$AB = AC$	
$4x - 14 = x + 10$	*Substitution property of equality*
$3x = 24$	*Addition property of equality*
$x = 8$	*Division property of equality*

If $x = 8$, then $AB = 4(8) - 14$ or 18, and $AC = (8) + 10$ or 18. The legs of isosceles $\triangle ABC$ are 18 units long.

LESSON 4-1   CLASSIFYING TRIANGLES   165

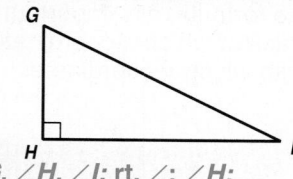

Example 3

Given $\triangle MNP$ with vertices $M(2, -4)$, $N(-3, 1)$, and $P(1, 6)$, use the distance formula to prove $\triangle MNP$ is scalene.

According to the distance formula, the distance between (x_1, y_1) and (x_2, y_2) is $\sqrt{(x_2 - x_1)^2 + (y_2 - y_1)^2}$ units. *The distance formula is given on page 25.*

$$MN = \sqrt{(2 - (-3))^2 + (-4 - 1)^2}$$
$$= \sqrt{25 + 25}$$
$$= \sqrt{50} \text{ or } 5\sqrt{2}$$

$$NP = \sqrt{(-3 - 1)^2 + (1 - 6)^2}$$
$$= \sqrt{16 + 25}$$
$$= \sqrt{41}$$

$$MP = \sqrt{(2 - 1)^2 + (-4 - 6)^2}$$
$$= \sqrt{1 + 100}$$
$$= \sqrt{101}$$

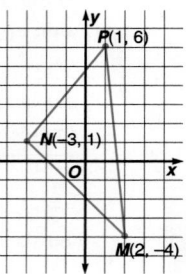

Since no two sides have the same length, the triangle is scalene.

CHECKING FOR UNDERSTANDING

Communicating Mathematics

Read and study the lesson to answer these questions. 2. See students' work.

1. Name some everyday items that are shaped like triangles. Classify each triangle by angles and by sides. **Answers may vary. A sample answer is a boy's bicycle frame. It is scalene and acute.**

2. Draw an isosceles right triangle and label the hypotenuse and legs.

3. Can a triangle be both isosceles and scalene? Explain why or why not.

4. Draw and label a scalene obtuse triangle. Identify the side opposite the obtuse angle. **See students' work.**

5. Draw an equilateral triangle and describe the lengths of the sides. **See students' work.**

3. No, because a scalene triangle has no two sides congruent and an isosceles triangle has at least two sides congruent.

Look around your classroom, your house, or your neighborhood to find an example of each. **Answers may vary.**

6. scalene triangle
7. right scalene triangle
8. isosceles triangle
9. obtuse isosceles triangle
10. equilateral triangle
11. acute scalene triangle

In figure *ACDE*, ∠*E* and ∠*ADC* are right angles and the congruent parts are indicated. **See margin.**

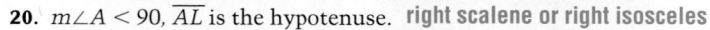

12. Name the right triangle(s).
13. Name the isosceles triangle(s).
14. Which triangle(s) is obtuse?
15. Which triangle(s) is equilateral?
16. Which segment(s) can be called the hypotenuse?
17. Which segment(s) is opposite ∠*C*?

18. Can an isosceles triangle be equilateral? Explain your answer. **See margin.**
19. Find the perimeter of equilateral triangle *JLK* if *JL* = x + 3, and *KJ* = 2x − 5. **33 units**

EXERCISES

Practice

A

Draw and label △*ALT* using the given conditions. If possible, classify each triangle by its angles and by its sides. **See Solutions Manual for drawings.**

20. m∠*A* < 90, $\overline{AL}$ is the hypotenuse. **right scalene or right isosceles**
21. *AL* = *LT*; m∠*L* = 90 **right isosceles**
22. m∠*A* > 90; *AL* < *LT* **obtuse scalene or obtuse isosceles**
23. *AL* < *LT* < *AT* **scalene**
24. *AL* = *LT* = *AT* **equilateral and equiangular**
25. ∠*A* is obtuse; △*ALT* is isosceles **obtuse isosceles**

Triangle *ROM* is isosceles with the congruent sides as marked. Name each of the following.

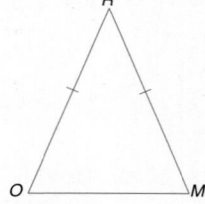

26. sides $\overline{RO}, \overline{OM}, \overline{RM}$
27. angles ∠*R*, ∠*O*, ∠*M*
28. vertex angle ∠*R*
29. base angles ∠*O*, ∠*M*
30. side opposite ∠*R* $\overline{OM}$
31. congruent sides $\overline{RO}$ and $\overline{RM}$
32. angle opposite $\overline{OR}$ ∠*M*

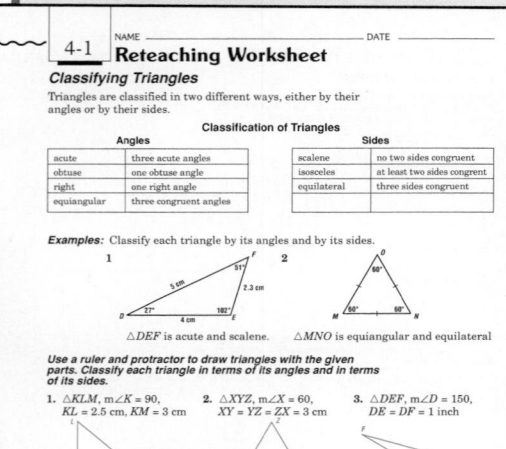

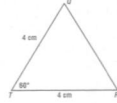

B ▸ Determine whether each statement is *true* or *false*. If it is false, draw a counterexample. See Solutions Manual for drawings.

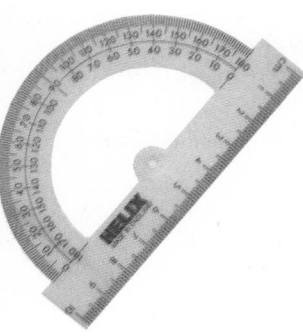

33. All equilateral triangles are isosceles. true
34. A scalene triangle can be obtuse. true
35. A scalene triangle can be acute. true
36. A right triangle is never isosceles. false
37. All obtuse triangles are scalene. false

Use a ruler and protractor to draw triangles with the given parts. Classify each triangle in terms of its angles and in terms of its sides.

38. $\triangle OAT$, $OA = 8$ cm, $m\angle A = 60$, $AT = 4$ cm right, scalene
39. $\triangle WHT$, $m\angle H = 60$, $WH = HT = 4$ cm equiangular, equilateral
40. $\triangle RYE$, $m\angle Y = 90$, $RY = 4$ cm, $m\angle YRE = 60$ right, scalene
41. $\triangle CAR$, $CA = CR = RA = 6$ cm equiangular, equilateral
42. $\triangle COR$, $m\angle O = 120$, $CO = 4$ cm, $RO = 4$ cm obtuse, isosceles

43. $\triangle OAT$ and $\triangle RYE$, and $\triangle WHT$ and $\triangle CAR$; $\triangle OAT$ and $\triangle RYE$
44. The legs are 27 cm long.

43. Which of the triangles described in Exercises 38-42 seem to have the same shape? Which seem to have the same shape and size?

44. Find the measures of the legs of the isosceles triangle RLP if $RL = 4x - 5$, $RP = 2x + 11$, and $LP = x$. The perimeter of $\triangle RLP$ is 62 cm.

45. Given vertices $A(6, 4)$, $L(-2, 4)$, and $F(2, 7)$, describe $\triangle ALF$ in terms of its angles and sides. Explain your reasoning. obtuse, isosceles

C ▸

46. Given $\overline{BC} \parallel \overline{DE}$ and $\overline{AD} \perp \overline{DE}$, prove that $\triangle ABC$ is a right triangle. See margin.

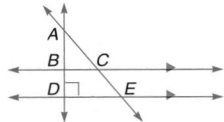

47. Given $m\angle NMO = 20$, prove that $\triangle LMN$ is an obtuse triangle. See Solutions Manual.

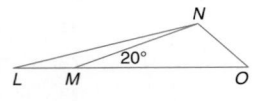

48. $\triangle RST$ is isosceles. Find the perimeter. 14

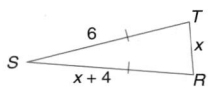

49. $\triangle DEF$ is isosceles with a perimeter between 23 and 32 units. Which angle is the vertex angle? Explain your answer. See margin.

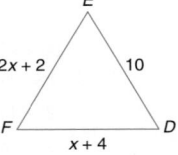

50. Describe the figure formed by connecting the points $R(7, -1)$, $S(9, 4)$, and $T(13, 14)$. a line segment

51. Pyramid *ABCDE* is a solid with square base *BCDE* and faces that are all triangles. If vertex *A* is directly over the center of the square, describe the shape of the four faces. Explain your reasoning. **isosceles triangles; the segments from the vertex *A* to *B*, *C*, *D*, and *E* will be congruent.**

Critical Thinking

52. Using four coplanar points as vertices, no three of which are collinear, what is the maximum number of right triangles that can be drawn? **4**

53. Using four coplanar points as vertices, no three of which are collinear, what is the maximum number of equilateral triangles that can be drawn? **2**

Applications

54. Public Works A fire hydrant is to be located on the highway in such a way that it is as close as possible to two buildings each 1 block from the highway and 1 block apart.

   a. What kind of triangle will be formed using the buildings and the hydrant as vertices? **isosceles**

   b. Why will this triangle satisfy the conditions necessary to locate the fire hydrant? **It is the same distance to each building.**

55. Consider the pattern formed by the dots.

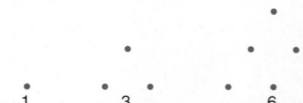

The numbers used to describe each array of dots are called **triangular numbers**. The third triangular number is 6.

   a. Draw the array for the fourth triangular number. **See margin.**

   b. How many dots will be in the array for the eighth triangular number? **36**

Mixed Review

56. **yes; the definition of parallel is that they are everywhere equidistant**

56. Are two parallel planes everywhere equidistant? Explain. **(Lesson 3-6)**

57. Algebra State the slope of the line passing through the points (3, 9), and (-7, 8). **(Lesson 3-6)** **0.1 or $\frac{1}{10}$**

58. Determine if $\overleftrightarrow{RS} \parallel \overleftrightarrow{LM}$ given that $m\angle 1 = 42$ and $m\angle 5 = 48$. Justify your answer. **(Lesson 3-4)** **no; if they were parallel, $m\angle 1 = m\angle 5$.**

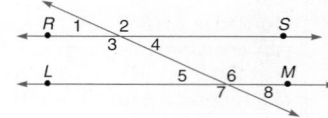

59. Draw a figure to illustrate two intersecting lines with a plane parallel to both lines. **(Lesson 3-2)** **See margin.**

60. **Substitution property of equality**

60. Algebra Name the algebraic property that justifies the statement "If $a = x$ and $a = y$, then $x = y$." **(Lesson 2-4)**

61. Algebra If $\angle 1 \cong \angle 2$, $m\angle 1 = 4x - 7$, and $m\angle 2 = 2x + 5$, find $m\angle 1$. **(Lesson 1-7)** **17**

Wrap-Up

62. Journal Entry In your own words, write three definitions that were presented in this lesson and illustrate each with a labeled diagram. **See students' work.**

LESSON 4-1   CLASSIFYING TRIANGLES   169

EXTENDING THE LESSON

Math Power: Reasoning

Triangles can be classified by their angle measures or by the measures of their sides. Therefore, any triangle has two labels. Which combinations of labels are possible and which are impossible?

Possible: right scalene, right isosceles, acute scalene, acute isosceles, acute equilateral, obtuse scalene, obtuse isosceles. Impossible: right equilateral, obtuse equilateral.

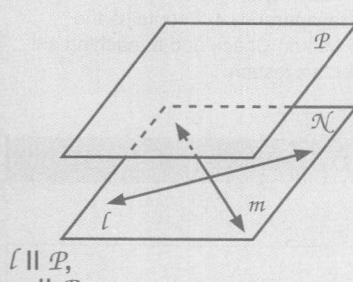
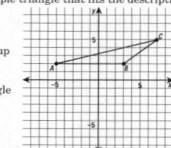

Angle Measures in Triangles

Lesson Resources

- Reteaching Master 4-2
- Practice Master 4-2
- Enrichment Master 4-2
- Evaluation Master, Quiz A, p. 51

 Transparency 4-2 contains the 5-Minute Check and a teaching aid for this lesson.

INTRODUCING THE LESSON

5-Minute Check

(over Lesson 4-1)

Determine whether each statement is true or false. If false, explain why.

1. A right triangle has one angle that measures 90 or greater. **True; it has one angle that measures exactly 90.**

2. A scalene triangle has no two sides with the same measure. **true**

3. An obtuse triangle has three angles measuring less than 90. **False; one angle must measure more than 90.**

4. In an isosceles triangle, all three sides have the same measure. **False; at least two sides have the same measure.**

Solve.

5. The legs of an isosceles triangle measure $2x + 5$ and $3x - 1$. Find the value of x. **6**

6. An equilateral triangle has a perimeter of 54 cm. One side measures $5x - 2$. Find the value of x. **4**

Motivating the Lesson

Have students draw a triangle on a sheet of paper, label the angles, and cut out the triangle. Have students cut off the three angles and fit them together, ray to ray. The angles should form a straight line. Elicit that everyone had the same result, regardless of the shape or his or her triangle.

Objectives
4-2A
4-2B

After studying this lesson, you should be able to:
- apply the angle sum theorem, and
- apply the exterior angle theorem.

Is there any relationship among the angles in a triangle? The students in Ms. Braun's geometry class each drew a triangle and measured the angles. When the results were recorded on the chalkboard, they calculated the sum of the angles to see if there was a pattern. The results looked like those displayed in the stem-and-leaf plot below.

Stem	Leaf
17	6 6 7
	8 8 8 9 9 9
18	0 0 0 0 0 1 1 1
	2 2 2 3 4

18|4 = 184

18|4 means that one student found the sum of the angles in his or her triangle to be 184. Make a conjecture about the sum of the measures of the angles in a triangle.

INVESTIGATION

Test your conjecture by drawing any triangle *ABC* and cutting it out. Fold it along a line parallel to $\overline{AC}$ so vertex *B* is on $\overline{AC}$. Then fold the triangle so that *A* and *C* are on point *B'* as shown.

 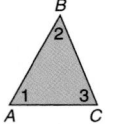 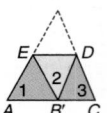 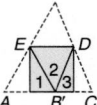

Note that $\angle AB'D$ and $\angle 3$ form a linear pair. Since the angles of a linear pair are supplementary, $m\angle AB'D + m\angle 3 = 180$. By the angle addition postulate, $m\angle 1 + m\angle 2 = m\angle AB'D$. Therefore, by substitution, $m\angle 1 + m\angle 2 + m\angle 3 = 180$.

This leads to the following theorem.

Theorem 4-1 Angle Sum Theorem	**The sum of the measures of the angles of a triangle is 180.**

In order to prove the angle sum theorem, we will need to draw an **auxiliary line**. An auxiliary line is a line or line segment added to a diagram to help in a proof. These are shown as dashed lines in the diagram. Be sure that it is possible to draw any auxiliary lines that you use.

ALTERNATE TEACHING STRATEGIES

Using Models

Ask students to draw any triangle with a straightedge and extend one side of the triangle to form an exterior angle. Have them label the exterior angle 1 and the two remote interior angles 2 and 3. Have them carefully cut out $\angle 2$ and $\angle 3$ and place them on $\angle 1$. The cutout angles should show that $m\angle 1 = m\angle 2 + m\angle 3$.

Using Investigation

You can guide students to discover that the acute angles in a right triangle are complementary. In Investigation 4 on pages A4 and A5 of **More Investigations in Geometry,** students use paper folding to explore the angles of a right triangle.

Proof of the Angle Sum Theorem

Given: $\triangle PQR$

Prove: $m\angle 1 + m\angle 2 + m\angle 3 = 180$

Proof:

Statements	Reasons
1. $\triangle PQR$	1. Given
2. Draw $\overleftrightarrow{AB}$ through R parallel to $\overleftrightarrow{PQ}$.	2. Parallel postulate
3. $\angle 4$ and $\angle PRB$ form a linear pair.	3. Definition of linear pair
4. $\angle 4$ and $\angle PRB$ are supplementary.	4. If 2 $\angle$s form a linear pair, they are supp.
5. $m\angle 4 + m\angle PRB = 180$	5. Definition of supplementary
6. $m\angle 5 + m\angle 3 = m\angle PRB$	6. Angle addition postulate
7. $m\angle 4 + m\angle 5 + m\angle 3 = 180$	7. Substitution property of equality
8. $m\angle 1 = m\angle 4$ $\qquad$ $m\angle 2 = m\angle 5$	8. If 2 $\parallel$ lines are cut by a transversal, alt. int. $\angle$s are $\cong$.
9. $m\angle 1 + m\angle 2 + m\angle 3 = 180$	9. Substitution property of equality

If you know the measures of two angles of a triangle, you can find the measure of the third.

Example 1

The roof support at the right is shaped like a triangle. Two angles each have a measure of 25. Find the measure of the third angle.

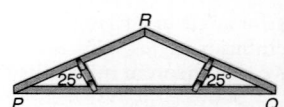

If we label the vertices of the triangle P, Q, and R, then $m\angle P = 25$ and $m\angle Q = 25$. Since the sum of the angles measures is 180, we can write the equation below.

$$m\angle P + m\angle Q + m\angle R = 180 \qquad \textit{Angle sum theorem}$$
$$25 + 25 + m\angle R = 180 \qquad \textit{Substitution property of equality}$$
$$m\angle R = 130 \qquad \textit{Subtraction property of equality}$$

The measure of the third angle is 130.

The Angle Sum Theorem leads to a useful theorem about the angles in two triangles. You will prove this theorem in Exercise 42.

LESSON 4-2   ANGLE MEASURES IN TRIANGLES   171

TEACHING THE LESSON

Teaching Tip   Some students may not understand the stem-and-leaf plot at the beginning of the lesson. Explain that it is a way of recording data; twenty-two different responses are recorded in this stem-and-leaf plot.

Chalkboard Example

For Example 1
A surveyor has drawn a triangle on a map. One angle measures 42 and the other measures 53. Find the measure of the third angle.   **85**

Chalkboard Example

For Example 2

Find the measure of each numbered angle in the figure if $\overrightarrow{AB} \parallel \overrightarrow{CD}$.

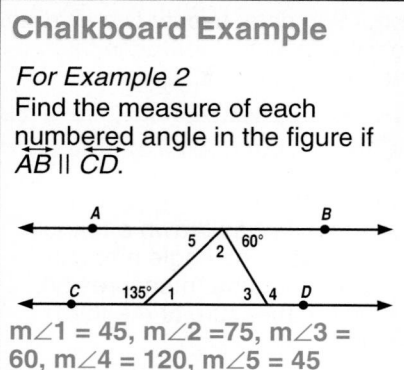

m∠1 = 45, m∠2 =75, m∠3 = 60, m∠4 = 120, m∠5 = 45

Theorem 4-2 Third Angle Theorem	If two angles of one triangle are congruent to two angles of a second triangle, then the third angles of the triangles are congruent.

Suppose you were picking strawberries and started walking from a certain point on a north-south path. You walked at an angle of 60° northeast for 800 feet, turned directly south and walked 400 feet, and then turned 90° clockwise and walked back to the same place where you started.

A diagram of your path is shown at the right. The north/south lines are parallel, forming congruent alternate interior angles. By the supplement theorem, the angle formed when you turned measures 120°.

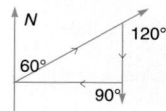

The 120° and 90° angles formed when you turned are called **exterior angles** of the triangle. An exterior angle is formed by one side of a triangle and another side extended. The interior angles of the triangle not adjacent to a given exterior angle are called **remote interior angles** of the triangle. In the figure at the left, ∠BCD is an exterior angle with ∠A and ∠B as its remote interior angles.

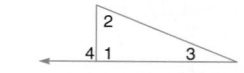

remote interior angles

exterior angle

The measure of an exterior angle and its remote interior angles are related. Look at your path again. Do you have a conjecture about the relationship? Let's investigate.

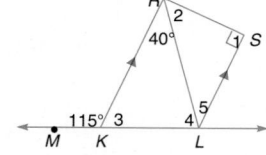

$m\angle 1 + m\angle 2 + m\angle 3 = 180$	*Angle sum theorem*
$m\angle 1 + m\angle 4 = 180$	*Supplement theorem*
$m\angle 1 + m\angle 2 + m\angle 3 = m\angle 1 + m\angle 4$	*Substitution property of equality*
$m\angle 2 + m\angle 3 = m\angle 4$	*Subtraction property of equality*

The measure of an exterior angle of a triangle is equal to the sum of the measures of its remote interior angles. This is called the Exterior Angle Theorem. You will prove this theorem in Exercise 43.

Theorem 4-3 Exterior Angle Theorem	The measure of an exterior angle of a triangle is equal to the sum of the measures of the two remote interior angles.

Example 2

Find the measure of each numbered angle in the figure if $\overline{RK} \parallel \overline{SL}$ and $\overline{RS} \perp \overline{SL}$.

By the exterior angle theorem,
$m\angle KRL + m\angle 4 = m\angle MKR$.

$$m\angle KRL + m\angle 4 = m\angle MKR$$
$$40 + m\angle 4 = 115$$
$$m\angle 4 = 75$$

172   CHAPTER 4   CONGRUENT TRIANGLES

By the angle sum theorem, $m\angle KRL + m\angle 3 + m\angle 4 = 180$.

$$m\angle KRL + m\angle 3 + m\angle 4 = 180$$
$$40 + m\angle 3 + 75 = 180$$
$$m\angle 3 = 65$$

Since $\overline{RK} \parallel \overline{SL}$, and $\angle 5$ and $\angle KRL$ are alternate interior angles, $m\angle 5 = m\angle KRL$.

$$m\angle 5 = 40$$

$\overline{RS} \perp \overline{SL}$ and perpendicular lines form right angles. Therefore, $m\angle 1 = 90$.

$$m\angle 1 + m\angle 5 + m\angle 2 = 180 \qquad \textit{Angle sum theorem}$$
$$90 + 40 + m\angle 2 = 180$$
$$m\angle 2 = 50$$

Therefore, $m\angle 1 = 90$, $m\angle 2 = 50$, $m\angle 3 = 65$, $m\angle 4 = 75$, and $m\angle 5 = 40$.

INVESTIGATION

You can learn more about the acute angles of a right triangle in Investigation 4 on pages A4–A5.

A statement that can easily be proven using a theorem is often called a **corollary** of that theorem. A corollary, just like a theorem, can be used as a reason in a proof. You will be asked to prove Corollary 4-2 in Exercise 44.

Corollary 4-1	**The acute angles of a right triangle are complementary.**
Corollary 4-2	**There can be at most one right or obtuse angle in a triangle.**

Proof of Corollary 4-1

Given: $\triangle RST$, $\angle R$ is a right angle.

Prove: $\angle S$ and $\angle T$ are complementary.

Proof:

Statements	Reasons
1. $\angle R$ is a right angle.	**1.** Given
2. $m\angle R + m\angle S + m\angle T = 180$	**2.** Angle sum theorem
3. $m\angle R = 90$	**3.** Definition of right angle
4. $90 + m\angle S + m\angle T = 180$	**4.** Substitution property of equality
5. $m\angle S + m\angle T = 90$	**5.** Subtraction property of equality
6. $\angle S$ and $\angle T$ are complementary.	**6.** Definition of complementary angles

Teaching Tip After reading Corollary 4-1 and before reading through the proof, ask a volunteer to outline a strategy for proving the statement.

EVALUATING THE LESSON

Checking for Understanding

Exercises 1-17 are designed to help you assess students' understanding through reading, writing, speaking, and modeling. You should work through Exercises 1-4 with your students and then monitor their work on Exercises 5-17.

Closing the Lesson

Writing Activity Have students write a summary, including diagrams, of the relationships among angle measures in triangles that were presented in this lesson.

Additional Answers

4.

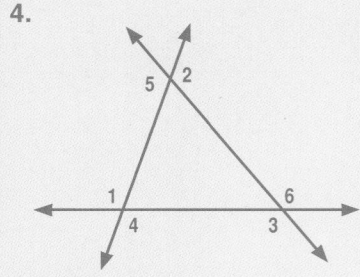

13. ∠1: ∠3, ∠4; ∠5: ∠3, ∠4;
    ∠6: ∠2, ∠4; ∠7: ∠2, ∠4;
    ∠8: ∠2, ∠3; ∠9: ∠2, ∠3

Reteaching Masters Booklet, p. 21

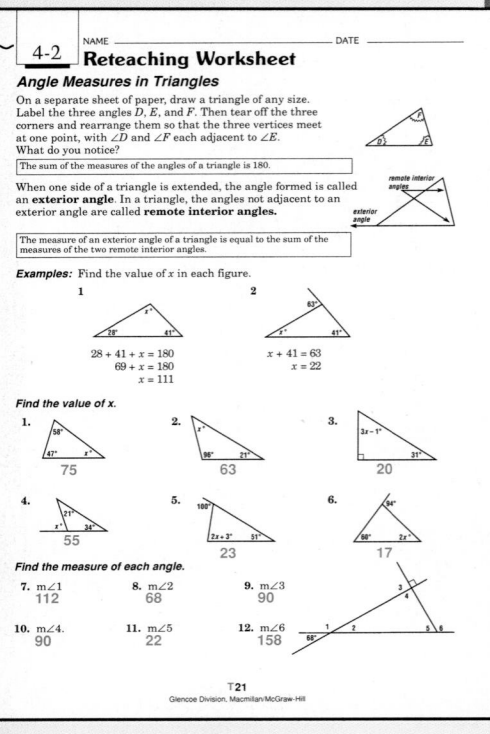

Communicating Mathematics

Read and study the lesson to answer these questions.

1. What is the sum of the measures of the angles in $\triangle GHI$? Compare the sums of the angle measures for the three triangles. **180; all 180**

2. complementary; $m\angle G + m\angle H + m\angle I = 180$ and $m\angle I = 90$.

2. If $m\angle I = 90$, what must be true about $\angle G$ and $\angle H$? Explain.

3. If the measures of $\angle A$, $\angle B$, and $\angle C$ are equal, what is the measure of each angle? Justify your answer. **60; 180 ÷ 3 = 60**

4. Draw a triangle and label an exterior angle at each vertex. **See margin.**

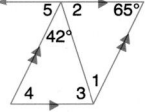

Guided Practice

Find the measure of each angle in the figure at the right.

5. $m\angle 1$ **42**   6. $m\angle 2$ **73**

7. $m\angle 3$ **73**   8. $m\angle 4$ **65**

9. $m\angle 5$ **65**

Find the value of *x*.

10. 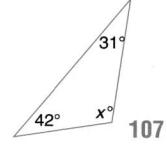 **107**

11. 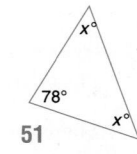 **51**

12. 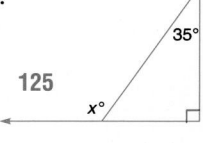

13. Name the exterior angles and their corresponding remote interior angles in the figure at the right. **See margin.**

14. Write an argument to explain why a triangle can or cannot have two right angles. **See Solutions Manual.**

15. Draw a triangle that has exactly two congruent angles. Can you draw another triangle that has two congruent angles, but is a different shape? **See students' drawings; yes**

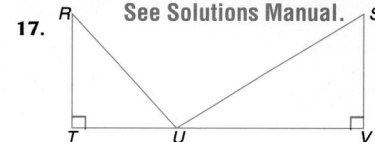

List two conclusions that you can make about the angles in each drawing.

See Solutions Manual.

16. 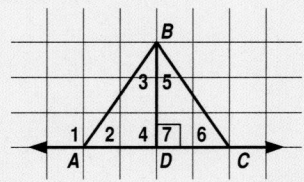   17.

RETEACHING THE LESSON

Have students answer the following questions about this diagram.

1. Which angle is an exterior angle? **∠1**

2. Name a pair of complementary angles. **∠2 and ∠3 or ∠5 and ∠6**

3. $m\angle 1$ is equal to the sum of the measures of which two angles? **∠3 and ∠4**

4. If $m\angle 3 = m\angle 5$, does $m\angle 2 = m\angle 6$? Why or why not? **Yes, each triangle has a right ∠, and since two ∠s of one triangle are congruent to two ∠s of another, the third ∠s are ≅.**

EXERCISES

A Find the value of *x*.

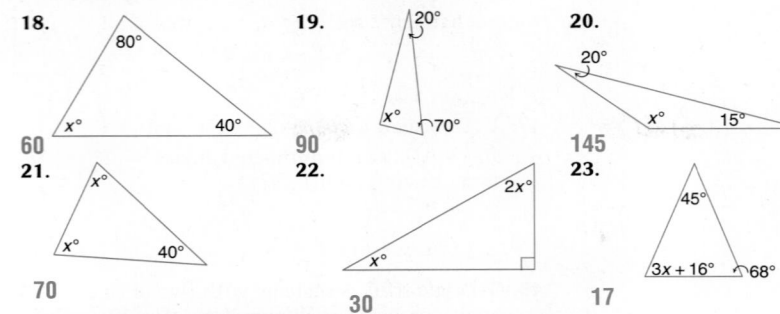

18.
80°
x° 40°
60

19.
20°
x° 70°
90

20.
20°
x° 15°
145

21.
x°
x° 40°
70

22.
2*x*°
x°
30

23.
45°
3*x* + 16° 68°
17

B Find the measure of each angle.

24. m∠1 110   **25.** m∠2 55

26. m∠3 75   **27.** m∠4 55

28. m∠5 50   **29.** m∠6 55

30. m∠7 55   **31.** m∠8 90

32. m∠9 35

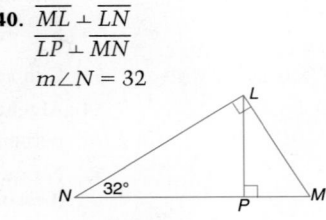

In the figure, $\overline{AB} \perp \overline{BC}$, $\overline{CD} \perp \overline{BC}$, m∠BEC = 150, and ∠ABE ≅ ∠DCE. Find the measure of each angle.

33. ∠AEB 30   **34.** ∠EBC 15

35. ∠CED 30   **36.** ∠ECD 75

37. ∠ECB 15   **38.** ∠ABE 75

List three conclusions that you can make about the measures of the angles in each drawing. **See margin.**

39. $\overline{AB} \parallel \overline{DC}$
m∠ATC = 140
m∠C = 20

C
20° 140°
T
D B
A

40. $\overline{ML} \perp \overline{LN}$
$\overline{LP} \perp \overline{MN}$
m∠N = 32

L
N 32° P M

41. Prove that if a triangle is equiangular, the measure of each angle is 60. **See Solutions Manual.**

42. Prove the third angle theorem (Theorem 4-2). **See Solutions Manual.**

43. Prove the exterior angle theorem (Theorem 4-3). **See Solutions Manual.**

44. Prove that there can be at most one right or obtuse angle in a triangle. (Corollary 4-2) **See Solutions Manual.**

Homework Exercises

Assignment Guide

Basic: 18-41, 50-58
Average: 22-45, 50-58
Enriched: 26-58

Additional Answers

39. m∠*BTD* = 140,
m∠*CTD* = 40,
m∠*ATB* = 40,
m∠*B* = 20,
m∠*A* = 120,
m∠*D* = 120

40. m∠*MLN* = 90,
m∠*N* + m∠*M* = 90,
m∠*M* = 58,
m∠*MPL* = 90,
m∠*NPL* = 90,
m∠*M* + m∠*MLP* = 90,
m∠*N* + m∠*NLP* = 90,
m∠*MLP* = 32,
m∠*NLP* = 58

Practice Masters Booklet, p. 24

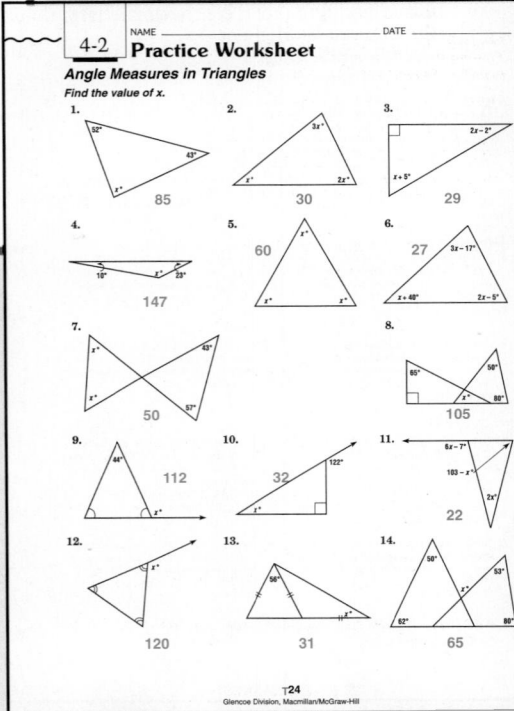

45. **Given:** $\overline{LT} \perp \overline{TS}$
    $\overline{ST} \perp \overline{SR}$
    Prove: $\angle TLR \cong \angle LRS$
    See margin.

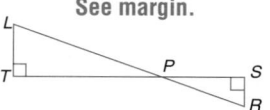

46. **Given:** $\angle RUW \cong \angle VSR$
    Prove: $\angle V \cong \angle W$
    See margin.

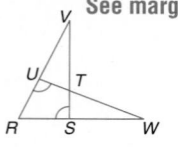

 47. If $\overline{AB}$ bisects $\angle CAD$, $\overline{CD} \perp \overline{AC}$ and
    $\overline{BD} \perp \overline{AD}$, which numbered angles
    must be congruent? $\angle 2 \cong \angle 3$

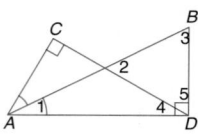

48. Triangle ABC is scalene, with two of its
    angles trisected as shown. If $m\angle A = 30$,
    find $m\angle M$ and $m\angle T$. **80, 130**

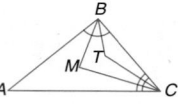

49. What is the sum of the interior angles
    of the quadrilateral in the figure?
    (Hint: Think in terms of triangles.) **360**

Critical Thinking
50. sum of angle
measures > 180; no

50. If you draw a triangle on a globe of Earth, what conjectures could you
    make about the angles in the triangle? Does the Angle Sum Theorem
    work? _(Hint: Look at the latitude and longitude lines on a globe.)_

51. If you could draw a triangle on the inside of a large balloon, what would
    the triangle look like? What conjectures could you make about the angles
    of this triangle? **curved in; sum of angle measures < 180**

Application
52. **Surveying**   Surveyors use a method
    called _triangulation_ to map a region.
    This method locates points by means of
    a network of triangles. Find the
    remaining angle measures in the survey
    shown at the right.

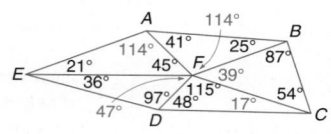

Mixed Review
53. Can a scalene triangle be a right triangle also? **(Lesson 4-1)** yes

54. **Algebra**   The slope of line m is 9. What is the slope of any line
    perpendicular to m? **(Lesson 3-5)** $-\frac{1}{9}$

55. Name the congruence property that justifies the statement "$\angle A \cong \angle A$."
    (Lesson 2-7) Congruence of angles is reflexive.

56. The measure of an angle is one-third the measure of its supplement. Find
    the measure of the angle. **(Lesson 1-8) 45**

57. Find the value of a so that the distance between $(5, 6)$ and $(a, 10)$ is 5
    units. **(Lesson 1-4) 2 or 8**

Wrap-Up
58. State the main theorems in this lesson. Give examples of how they apply
    to an obtuse triangle, an acute triangle, or a right triangle. **See students'
    work.**

EXTENDING THE LESSON

Math Power: Reasoning

1. If the sum of the measures of
   the two remote interior angles of
   a triangle is less than 90, how
   would you classify the triangle?
   obtuse

2. If the sum of the measures of
   the two remote interior angles of
   a triangle is more than 90, is the
   triangle acute?   **not
   necessarily**

Congruent Triangles

Objectives

4-3A
4-3B

After studying this lesson, you should be able to:
- identify congruent triangles, and
- name and label corresponding parts of congruent triangles.

Application

In 1913, Henry Ford began producing automobiles using an assembly line. When products are mass produced, each piece must be interchangeable, so they must have the same size and shape. Each piece is an exact copy of the others, and any piece can be made to coincide with all of the others. Remember from Chapter 1 that figures with the same size and same shape are *congruent*.

Because the triangle is the simplest of the polygons, it seems reasonable to begin a study of congruent polygons by investigating congruent triangles.

INVESTIGATION

Draw a triangle and cut it out. Use it as a pattern to draw a second triangle and cut that triangle out. If one triangle is placed on top of the other, the two coincide or match exactly. This means that each part of the first triangle matches exactly the corresponding part of the second triangle. You have made a pair of congruent triangles.

Note that the order of the letters in the congruence statement indicates the correspondence of the vertices.

If $\triangle ABC$ is congruent to $\triangle RST$ ($\triangle ABC \cong \triangle RST$), the vertex labeled A corresponds to the vertex labeled R, vertex B corresponds to S, and vertex C corresponds to T. This correspondence can be described in terms of angles and sides as follows.

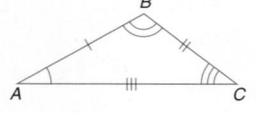

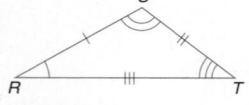

$\angle A$ corresponds to $\angle R$.	$\overline{AB}$ corresponds to $\overline{RS}$.
$\angle B$ corresponds to $\angle S$.	$\overline{BC}$ corresponds to $\overline{ST}$.
$\angle C$ corresponds to $\angle T$.	$\overline{AC}$ corresponds to $\overline{RT}$.

Since the two triangles match exactly, the corresponding parts are congruent.

Definition of Congruent Triangles (CPCTC)

Two triangles are congruent if and only if their corresponding parts are congruent.
The abbreviation CPCTC means Corresponding Parts of Congruent Triangles are Congruent.

ALTERNATE TEACHING STRATEGIES

Using Models

Have the students make paper cutouts of three congruent triangles. Have them label the triangles using nine different letters for the vertices. Then have them use the cutouts to demonstrate the three parts of Theorem 4-4.

Using Logical Reasoning

Two triangles are congruent. The vertices of one are labeled *X*, *Y*, and *Z*. The vertices of the other are labeled *P*, *Q*, and *R*. If $\angle X \cong \angle Q$ and $RP = ZY$, make a true congruence statement about these triangles. **Sample answer:** $\triangle XYZ \cong \triangle QPR$

Lesson Resources

- Reteaching Master 4-3
- Practice Master 4-3
- Enrichment Master 4-3
- Activity Master, p. 18
- Technology Master, p. 4
- Lab Manual, pp. 38-41

Transparency 4-3 contains the 5-Minute Check and a teaching aid for this lesson.

INTRODUCING THE LESSON

5-Minute Check
(over Lesson 4-2)

Refer to the figure below.

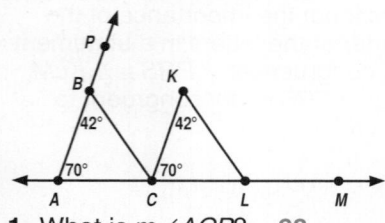

1. What is m$\angle ACB$? **68**
2. What is m$\angle CLK$? **68**
3. What is m$\angle CBP$? **138**
4. Which two angles are the remote interior angles for $\angle MLK$? **$\angle LCK$ and $\angle LKC$**
5. What is m$\angle BCK$? **42**
6. What is m$\angle MLK$? **112**

Motivating the Lesson

Ask students to think of as many different ways as they can of producing two triangles that are the same size and shape.
Sample answers: Use tracing paper, use ruler and protractor, use dot paper.

TEACHING THE LESSON

Teaching Tip In the figures for triangles *ABC* and *RST*, point out how tick marks and arcs are used to indicate congruent segments and angles.

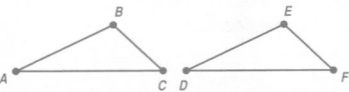
Example 1

APPLICATION
Automotive

A triangular wedge is used to anchor the seat belts of a car.

a. **Draw two identical wedges and label the vertices *P, R,* and *S* on one part and *K, L,* and *M* on the other so that △*PRS* ≅ △*KLM*. Then mark the congruent parts.**

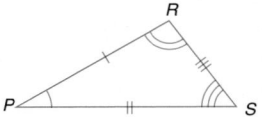 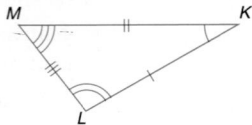

b. **What angle in △*PRS* is congruent to ∠*K* in △*KLM*?**

∠*P* is congruent to ∠*K*.

c. **Which side of △*KLM* is congruent to $\overline{PS}$ in △*PRS*?**

$\overline{KM}$ is congruent to $\overline{PS}$.

Congruence of triangles, like congruence of segments and angles, is reflexive, symmetric, and transitive. This is stated in Theorem 4-4. The proof of the transitive part of this theorem is shown below. You will be asked to prove the reflexive and symmetric parts of the theorem in Exercises 35 and 24, respectively.

Theorem 4-4	**Congruence of triangles is reflexive, symmetric, and transitive.**

Proof of Theorem 4-4 (Transitive Part)

Given: △*ABC* ≅ △*DEF*
△*DEF* ≅ △*GHI*

Prove: △*ABC* ≅ △*GHI*

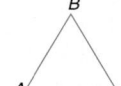 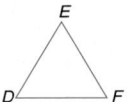 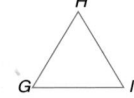

Paragraph Proof:

We are given that △*ABC* ≅ △*DEF*. By the definition of congruent triangles, the corresponding parts of the triangles are congruent. So, ∠*A* ≅ ∠*D*, ∠*B* ≅ ∠*E*, ∠*C* ≅ ∠*F*, $\overline{AB}$ ≅ $\overline{DE}$, $\overline{BC}$ ≅ $\overline{EF}$, and $\overline{AC}$ ≅ $\overline{DF}$. It is also given that △*DEF* ≅ △*GHI*, so by the definition of congruent triangles, ∠*D* ≅ ∠*G*, ∠*E* ≅ ∠*H*, ∠*F* ≅ ∠*I*, $\overline{DE}$ ≅ $\overline{GH}$, $\overline{EF}$ ≅ $\overline{HI}$, and $\overline{DF}$ ≅ $\overline{GI}$. Since congruence of angles is transitive, ∠*A* ≅ ∠*G*, ∠*B* ≅ ∠*H*, and ∠*C* ≅ ∠*I*. Congruence of segments is transitive, so $\overline{AB}$ ≅ $\overline{GH}$, $\overline{BC}$ ≅ $\overline{HI}$, and $\overline{AC}$ ≅ $\overline{GI}$. Therefore, △*ABC* ≅ △*GHI* by the definition of congruent triangles.

178   CHAPTER 4   CONGRUENT TRIANGLES

CHECKING FOR UNDERSTANDING

Communicating Mathematics

Read and study the lesson to answer these questions. See margin.

1. Draw triangles *TLA* and *RSB*. Mark the corresponding parts for $\triangle TLA \cong \triangle RSB$.

2. Describe how you would tell if two triangles were congruent.

3. If two triangles are congruent, what conclusions can you make? Give an example to illustrate your answer.

Guided Practice

Complete each congruence statement.

4. $\triangle ARM \cong \underline{\ ?\ } \triangle LEG$

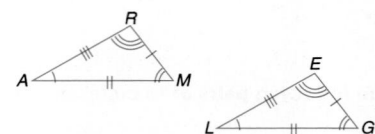

5. $\triangle SPT \cong \underline{\ ?\ } \triangle PSK$

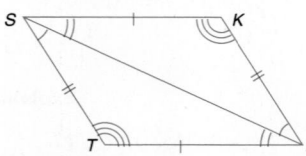

Copy the figures and use the given information to determine which parts are congruent. Determine if the given triangles listed in the *Prove* statement are congruent. **See Solutions Manual.**

6. **Given:** *N* is the midpoint of $\overline{AB}$ and $\overline{CD}$.
   $\overline{AD} \parallel \overline{BC}$
   $\overline{AD} \cong \overline{BC}$

   Prove: $\triangle AND \cong \triangle BNC$

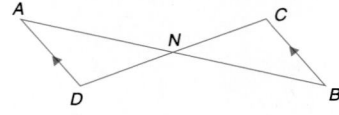

7. **Given:** *W* is the midpoint of $\overline{XZ}$.
   $\triangle XYZ$ is isosceles and right.
   $\overline{YW} \perp \overline{XZ}$
   $\angle X \cong \angle Z$

   Prove: $\triangle WXY \cong \triangle WZY$

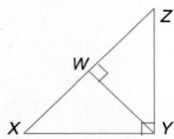

8. Draw two triangles with the same perimeter that are not congruent. **See Solutions Manual.**

EXERCISES

Practice

9. The corresponding parts of the two triangles are congruent as marked in the figure. This can be written as $\triangle ABC \cong \underline{\ ?\ }$. $\triangle EFD$

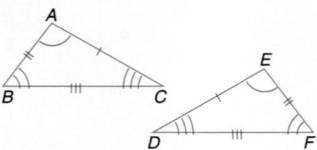

Additional Answers

1.

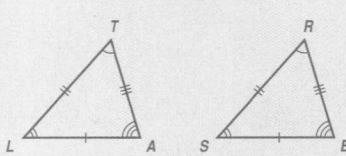

2. See if the six pairs of corresponding parts are congruent.

3. The six pairs of corresponding parts are congruent. For example, if $\triangle ABC \cong \triangle RTS$, then $\angle A \cong \angle R$, $\angle B \cong \angle T$, $\angle C \cong \angle S$, $\overline{AB} \cong \overline{RT}$, $\overline{BC} \cong \overline{TS}$, and $\overline{AC} \cong \overline{RS}$.

EVALUATING THE LESSON

Checking for Understanding

Exercises 1-8 are designed to help you assess students' understanding through reading, writing, speaking, and modeling. You should work through Exercises 1-3 with your students and then monitor their work on Exercises 4-8.

Error Analysis

Students may confuse the corresponding parts of congruent triangles when the triangles are not drawn in the same position. These students may benefit from resketching the triangles on paper so that they have the same orientation.

Closing the Lesson

Modeling Activity Ask students to work in pairs; each student should have a ruler and protractor. One partner draws a triangle without the other seeing it. The other partner, using a ruler and protractor, draws a congruent triangle by following the verbal directions of the first partner. When the second triangle is complete, students compare the triangles.

APPLYING THE LESSON

Homework Exercises

Assignment Guide

Basic: 9-30, 39-47
Average: 12-33, 39-47
Enriched: 17-47

See Solutions Manual for drawings.

Draw triangles *KAT* and *BRO*. Label the corresponding parts for △*KAT* ≅ △*BRO*. Use the figures to complete each statement.

10. ∠*A* ≅ __?__ ∠*R*

11. ∠*B* ≅ __?__ ∠*K*

12. $\overline{OR}$ ≅ __?__ $\overline{TA}$

13. $\overline{KA}$ ≅ __?__ $\overline{BR}$

Write a congruence statement for the congruent triangles in each diagram.

14.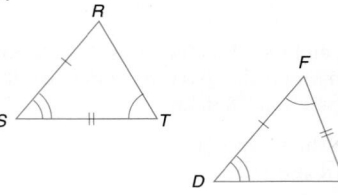

△*OAB* ≅ △*AOD*

15.

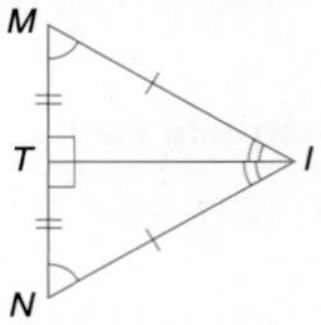

△*MIT* ≅ △*NIT*

16.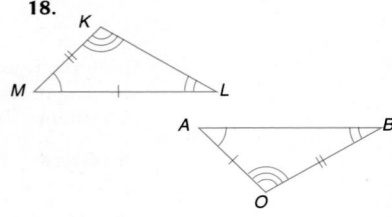

△*TAP* ≅ △*TOL*

Explain why the following pairs of triangles are not congruent. See margin.

17.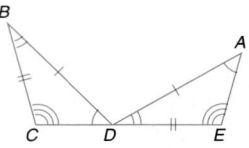

18.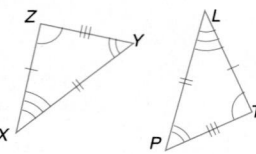

B **Complete each congruence statement.**

19. △*CDB* ≅ __?__ △*EAD*

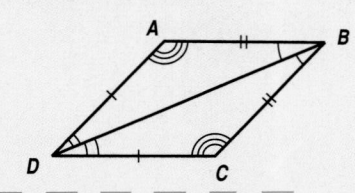

20. △*PTL* ≅ __?__ △*YZX*

21. Given the following, identify the congruent triangles in the figure.

$\overline{AR} \perp \overline{RB}$ △*ABR* ≅ △*ABS*,

$\overline{AS} \perp \overline{SB}$ △*ARO* ≅ △*ASO*, △*BRO* ≅ △*BSO*,

$\overline{AS} \cong \overline{SB}$ △*ASR* ≅ △*BSR*

$\overline{AR} \cong \overline{AS}$

$\overline{RB} \cong \overline{SB}$

∠*RAB* ≅ ∠*SAB*

∠*RBA* ≅ ∠*SBA*

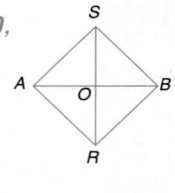

$\overline{AB}$ is the perpendicular bisector of $\overline{RS}$.

Reteaching Masters Booklet, p. 22

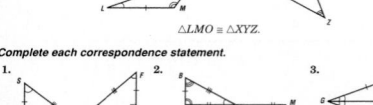

NAME _____ DATE _____

4-3 **Reteaching Worksheet**

Congruent Triangles

When two figures have exactly the same shape and size, they are said to be congruent. For two congruent triangles there are three pairs of corresponding (matching) sides and three pairs of corresponding angles. To write a correspondence statement about congruent triangles, you should name corresponding angles in the same order. Remember that congruent parts are marked by identical markings.

Example: Write a correspondence statement for the triangles in the diagram.

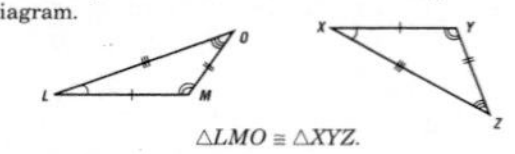

△*LMO* ≅ △*XYZ*.

Complete each correspondence statement.

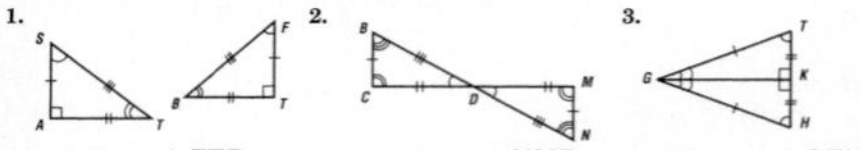

1. △*SAT* ≅ △*FTB*
2. △*BCD* ≅ △*NMD*
3. △*GHK* ≅ △*GTK*

Write a correspondence statement for the congruent triangles in each diagram.

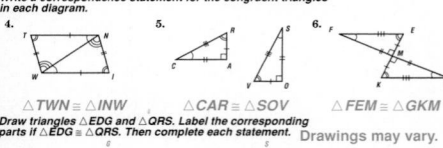

4. △*TWN* ≅ △*INW*
5. △*CAR* ≅ △*SOV*
6. △*FEM* ≅ △*GKM*

Draw triangles △*EDG* and △*QRS*. Label the corresponding parts if △*EDG* ≅ △*QRS*. Then complete each statement. Drawings may vary.

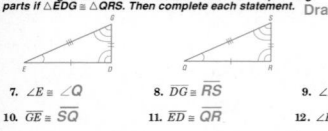

7. ∠*E* ≅ ∠*Q*
8. $\overline{DG}$ ≅ $\overline{RS}$
9. ∠*EDG* ≅ ∠*QRS*
10. $\overline{GE}$ ≅ $\overline{SQ}$
11. $\overline{ED}$ ≅ $\overline{QR}$
12. ∠*EGD* ≅ ∠*QSR*

'22
Glencoe Division, Macmillan/McGraw-Hill

RETEACHING THE LESSON

Have students name the corresponding sides and angles in the figures below.

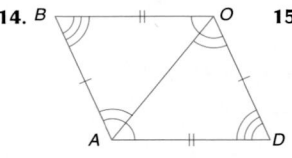
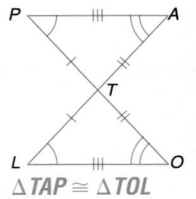

$\overline{AB}$, $\overline{CB}$; $\overline{BD}$, $\overline{BD}$; $\overline{DA}$, $\overline{DC}$
∠*ABD*, ∠*CBD*; ∠*BDA*, ∠*BDC*;
∠*DAB*, ∠*DCB*

22. Given $\triangle CAT \cong \triangle DOG$, $CA = 14$, $AT = 18$, $TC = 21$, and $DG = 2x + 7$, find the value of x. **7**

23. Given $\triangle BLU \cong \triangle RED$, $m\angle L = 57$, $m\angle R = 64$, and $m\angle U = 5x + 4$, find the value of x. **11**

24. Justify each step in the proof of the symmetric part of Theorem 4-4.

Given: $\triangle LMN \cong \triangle OPQ$

Prove: $\triangle OPQ \cong \triangle LMN$

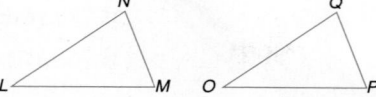

Statements	Reasons
a. $\triangle LMN \cong \triangle OPQ$	**a.** __?__ Given
b. $\angle L \cong \angle O$ $\angle M \cong \angle P$ $\angle N \cong \angle Q$ $\overline{LM} \cong \overline{OP}$ $\overline{MN} \cong \overline{PQ}$ $\overline{LN} \cong \overline{OQ}$	**b.** __?__ CPCTC
c. $\angle O \cong \angle L$ $\angle P \cong \angle M$ $\angle Q \cong \angle N$	**c.** __?__ Congruence of angles is symmetric.
d. $\overline{OP} \cong \overline{LM}$ $\overline{PQ} \cong \overline{MN}$ $\overline{OQ} \cong \overline{LN}$	**d.** __?__ Congruence of segments is symmetric.
e. $\triangle OPQ \cong \triangle LMN$	**e.** __?__ Definition of congruent triangles

If $\triangle BCD \cong \triangle ECA$, determine if each of the statements is *true* or *not necessarily true*. **Explain your answers. See margin.**

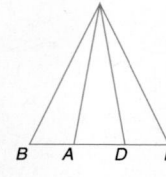

25. $\overline{BD} \cong \overline{AE}$

26. $\overline{AB} \cong \overline{DE}$

27. $\overline{BC} \cong \overline{AC}$

28. $\overline{AC} \cong \overline{DC}$

29. $\angle CBA \cong \angle CED$

30. $\angle BCA \cong \angle ACE$

See Solutions Manual for 31-33.

31. Draw two triangles that have equal areas and are congruent.

32. Draw two triangles that have equal perimeters and are congruent.

33. Draw two triangles that have equal areas but are not congruent.

LESSON 4-3   CONGRUENT TRIANGLES   181

Additional Answer

34. Statements   (Reasons)

a. $\overline{AB} \parallel \overline{RT}$, $\overline{AR} \perp \overline{AB}$, $\overline{BT} \perp \overline{RT}$, $\overline{AB} \cong \overline{RT}$, $\overline{AR} \cong \overline{TB}$ (Given)

b. $\angle BAR$ and $\angle RTB$ are right. ($\perp$ lines form four rt $\angle$s.)

c. $\angle BAR \cong \angle RTB$ (All rt. $\angle$s are $\cong$.)

d. $\angle ABR \cong \angle TRB$ (If 2 $\parallel$ lines are cut by a transversal, alt. int. $\angle$s are $\cong$.)

e. $\angle ARB \cong \angle TBR$ (If 2 $\angle$s in a $\triangle$ are $\cong$ to 2 $\angle$s in another $\triangle$, the third $\angle$s are also $\cong$.)

f. $\overline{BR} \cong \overline{RB}$ (Congruence of segments is reflexive.)

g. $\triangle ABR \cong \triangle TRB$ (Definition of congruent triangles)

Additional Answers

25. $\overline{BD} \cong \overline{AE}$ is true because the segments are corresponding parts of congruent triangles.

26. $\overline{AB} \cong \overline{DE}$ is true. $\overline{DB} \cong \overline{AE}$ because they are corresponding parts of congruent triangles. So, $DB = AE$. By segment addition postulate, $DB = DA + AB$ and $AE = AD + DE$, so $AB = DE$, by substitution and subtraction.

27. $\overline{BC} \cong \overline{AC}$ is not necessarily true. They are not corresponding parts of the triangles.

28. $\overline{AC} \cong \overline{DC}$ is true. $\triangle BCA \cong \triangle ECD$ and the segments are corresponding parts of these congruent triangles.

29. $\angle CBA \cong \angle CED$ is true. The angles are corresponding parts of these congruent triangles.

30. $\angle BCA \cong \angle ACE$ is not necessarily true. $\angle BCA \not\cong \angle ACE$ since $m\angle BCA < m\angle BCD$ and $m\angle BCD = m\angle ACE$.

Practice Masters Booklet, p. 25

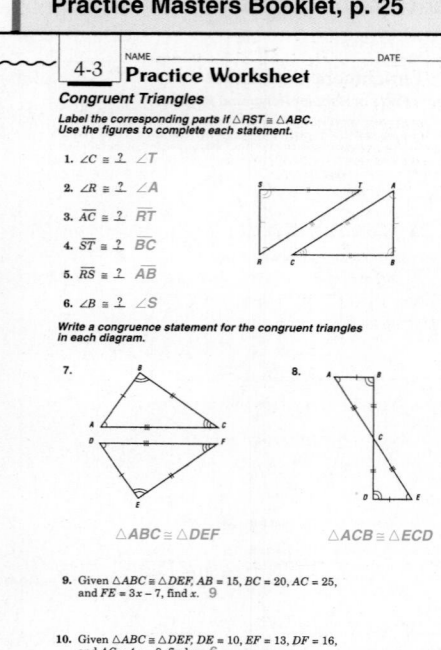

Chapter 4   181

Exercise Notes

For Exercises 36-38, the first step should be to draw a sketch of the given information.

Additional Answers

35. Given: △XYZ
    Prove: △XYZ ≅ △XYZ
    Statements   (Reasons)
    a. △XYZ   (given)
    b. ∠X ≅ ∠X, ∠Y ≅ ∠Y, ∠Z ≅ ∠Z (Congruence of angles is reflexive.)
    c. XY ≅ XY, YZ ≅ YZ, XZ ≅ XZ (Congruence of segments is reflexive.)
    d. △XYZ ≅ △XYZ (Definition of congruent triangles)

36. They are not necessarily congruent. The angles are all the same measure, but the sides may have different lengths. They are the same shape, but may not be the same size.

Enrichment Masters Booklet, p. 22

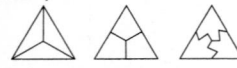

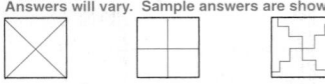

1. Divide each square into four congruent parts. Use three different ways.
   Answers will vary. Sample answers are shown.

2. Divide each pentagon into five congruent parts. Use three different ways.
   Answers will vary. Sample answers are shown.

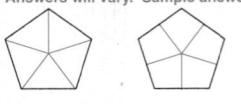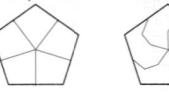

3. Divide each hexagon into six congruent parts. Use three different ways.
   Answers will vary. Sample answers are shown.

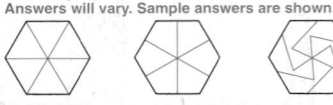

4. What hints might you give another student who is trying to divide figures like those into congruent parts?
   Answers will vary.

T22
Glencoe Division, Macmillan/McGraw-Hill

---

34. **Given:** $\overline{AB} \parallel \overline{RT}$
    $\overline{AR} \perp \overline{AB}$
    $\overline{BT} \perp \overline{RT}$
    $\overline{AB} \cong \overline{RT}$
    $\overline{AR} \cong \overline{TB}$

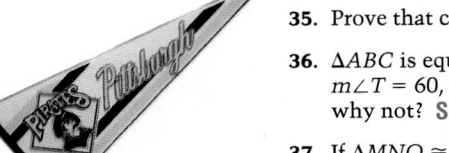

   Prove: △ABR ≅ △TRB **See margin.**

35. Prove that congruence of triangles is reflexive. (Theorem 4-4) **See margin.**

36. △ABC is equilateral and equiangular. △TUV has three congruent sides, $m\angle T = 60$, and $m\angle U = 60$. Are the two triangles congruent? Why or why not? **See margin.**

37. If △MNO ≅ △ONM, prove △MNO is isosceles. **See Solutions Manual.**

38. If △RST ≅ △TSR and △RST ≅ △RTS, prove that △RST is equilateral and equiangular. **See Solutions Manual.**

Critical Thinking

39. Draw two triangles that have five pairs of congruent parts, but are not congruent. **See margin.**

Applications

40. Describe the congruence involved in each of the following situations. **See margin.**
    a. **Crafts**   a pottery maker making a set of dishes
    b. **Arts**   a quilt maker cutting pieces for a quilt
    c. **Entertainment**   a Pittsburgh Pirates pennant
    d. **Finance**   a five-dollar bill and a one-dollar bill

FYI···

Robert Mangold's interest in geometric art began while he was working as a guard at the Museum of Modern Art in New York City.

41. **Art**   Draw a sketch of the painting by Robert Mangold shown at the right. Then label the intersections of lines and name the triangles that appear to be congruent. **Answers may vary. See students' work.**

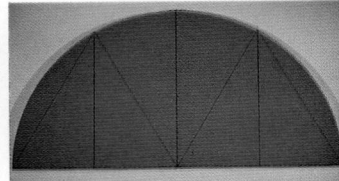

Mixed Review

42. The measures of two interior angles of a triangle are 54 and 79. What is the measure of the exterior angle opposite these angles? **(Lesson 4-2)** 133

43. **Algebra**   The measures of the angles of a triangle are $8x + 1$, $3x - 6$, and $4x - 10$. What are the measures of the angles? **(Lesson 4-2)** 105, 33, 42

44. Is the statement "A right triangle can be scalene." *true* or *false?* Explain. **(Lesson 4-1)** true; Explanations may vary.

45. Find the slope of the line passing through the points with coordinates (7, -3) and (6, -1). **(Lesson 3-5)** –2

46. Angles L and S are vertical. If $m\angle L = 3x + 7$ and $m\angle S = 43$, find the value of x. **(Lesson 1-9)** 12

Wrap-Up

47. Make up a five-question quiz about this section. Be sure to give the answers to your questions. **See students' work.**

EXTENDING THE LESSON

Math Power: Problem Solving

Given: △ABC ≅ △DEF, AB = 2x, AC = y, DE = y, and DF = 6 − x. Find the values of x and y.
x = 2, y = 4

Additional Answers

39. any pair of triangles with three congruent angles and two congruent, but not corresponding, sides

40. All the items described are the same size and shape.

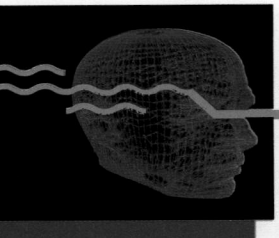

Technology
Congruent Triangles

BASIC
Geometric Supposer
▶ **Graphing calculators**
LOGO
Spreadsheets

A graphing calculator can be used to plot points and draw the line segments that connect them. We will use this feature to graph triangles.

Example

Graph △*ABC* whose vertices are *A*(0, 2), *B*(6, 2) and *C*(5, 4) and △*A'B'C'* whose vertices are *A'*(7, 5), *B'*(13, 5), and *C'*(12, 7). Do the two triangles appear to be congruent?

To draw a triangle on the Casio fx-7000G, plot each point and the line segment between each pair of points.

Enter: [SHIFT] [PLOT] 0 [SHIFT] , 2 [EXE] [SHIFT] [PLOT] 6
[SHIFT] , 2 [EXE] [SHIFT] [LINE] [EXE] [SHIFT] [PLOT] 5
[SHIFT] , 4 [EXE] [SHIFT] [LINE] [EXE] [SHIFT] [PLOT] 0
[SHIFT] , 2 [EXE] [SHIFT] [LINE] [EXE]

To draw a triangle on the TI-81, we will begin by using the line feature in the draw menu. Given two points, a line will be drawn between them.

Enter: [2nd] [DRAW] 2 0 [ALPHA] , 2 [ALPHA] , 6 [ALPHA] ,
2 [ENTER]

Now complete the triangle. Press [2nd] [DRAW] 2 and use the arrow keys to move the cursor to one endpoint of the segment. Press [ENTER]. Then move the cursor to the third vertex. Watch the coordinates given at the bottom of the screen to approximate the position of the point. Press [ENTER] twice. Finally, move the cursor to the other endpoint of the segment and press [ENTER] to complete the triangle.

Repeat the steps to draw the second triangle. It appears that △*ABC* ≅ △*A'B'C'*.

EXERCISES

Graph △*ABC* and △*A'B'C'*. Do the two triangles appear to be congruent?

1. *A*(-8, 1), *B*(-8, -6), *C*(-5, -6); *A'*(3, 5), *B'*(3, -2), *C'*(6, 5) yes
2. *A*(-3, 8), *B*(-3, 0), *C*(-5, 4); *A'*(4, -3), *B'*(4, -10), *C'*(2, -6) no

INTRODUCING THE LESSON

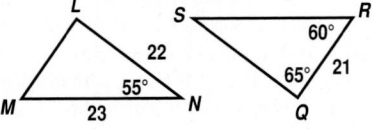

5–Minute Check

(over Lesson 4-3)

Refer to the figure below.

$\triangle LMN \cong \triangle QRS$. Find each of the following:

1. $m\angle L$ **65**   2. $m\angle S$ **55**
3. LM **21**   4. QS **22**
5. RS **23**   6. $m\angle M$ **60**

Motivating the Lesson

Give each student three straws measuring 4 cm, 5 cm, and 6 cm. Ask the students to form as many different triangles from the three straws as they can. Have students compare their triangles with one another's. Ask them what conjecture they can make based on this activity.   **If three sides of one triangle are congruent to three sides of another triangle, the triangles are congruent.**

Objective
4-4

After studying this lesson, you should be able to:
- use SAS, SSS and ASA postulates to test for triangle congruence.

Application

Is it always necessary to show that all of the corresponding parts of two triangles are congruent to be sure that the two triangles are congruent? For example, if you are designing supports for the beams in a roof, must you measure all three sides and all three angles to ensure that the supports are all identical?

Suppose you are given that the lengths of the sides of a triangular support are 3 meters, 5 meters, and 6 meters. How many different braces could you make?

One way to think about this is to construct a model of the triangle with the given dimensions. How many different triangles could you construct? Let's construct a triangle with sides of lengths 3 centimeters, 5 centimeters, and 6 centimeters by following the steps below.

1. On any line ℓ, select a point A.
2. Construct $\overline{AB}$ on ℓ such that $AB = 6$ cm.
3. Using A as the center, draw an arc with radius 5 cm.
4. Using B as the center, draw an arc with radius 3 cm.
5. Let C be the point of intersection of the two arcs.
6. Draw $\overline{AC}$ and $\overline{BC}$.

The figures shown below are not actual size.

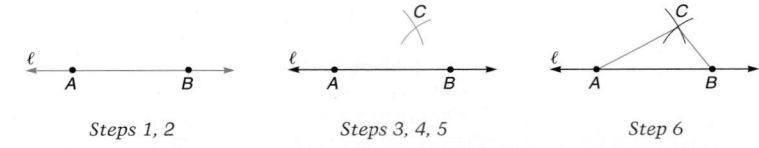

| Steps 1, 2 | Steps 3, 4, 5 | Step 6 |

Try using the same procedure with $AB = 5$ and then with $AB = 3$, and compare all of the triangles. How many different triangles is it possible to construct with sides of the given measures? It seems as if knowing that three sides are congruent is sufficient to guarantee the triangles are congruent. The side-side-side, or SSS, postulate states this fact.

SSS Postulate
Side-Side-Side
If the sides of one triangle are congruent to the sides of a second triangle, then the triangles are congruent.

184   CHAPTER 4   CONGRUENT TRIANGLES

ALTERNATIVE TEACHING STRATEGIES

Using Discussion

Ask students to describe the difference between proving two triangles congruent by SAS and proving them congruent by ASA.   **SAS requires 2 ≅ sides and a ≅ included angle. ASA requires 2 ≅ ∠s and a ≅ included side.**

Using Cooperative Groups

Divide the class into groups of four or five. With ruler and protractor, have each person in the group produce a triangle based on SAS using 5 cm, 30°, and 6 cm. Have the group compare triangles. Repeat this activity for ASA using 35°, 4 cm, 65°; SSA using 5 cm, 6 cm, 45°. Ask which resulted in congruent triangles.   **SAS and ASA**

The SSS postulate can be used to prove triangles congruent.

Example 1

CONNECTION
Algebra

Given △ABC with vertices A(0, 5), B(2, 0), and C(0, 0) and △RST with vertices R(5, 8), S(5, 3), and T(3, 3), show that △ACB ≅ △RST.

Use the distance formula to show that the corresponding sides are congruent.

$$AC = \sqrt{(0-0)^2 + (5-0)^2}$$
$$= \sqrt{25} \text{ or } 5$$

$$RS = \sqrt{(5-5)^2 + (8-3)^2}$$
$$= \sqrt{25} \text{ or } 5$$

$$AB = \sqrt{(0-2)^2 + (5-0)^2}$$
$$= \sqrt{29}$$

$$RT = \sqrt{(5-3)^2 + (8-3)^2}$$
$$= \sqrt{29}$$

$$CB = \sqrt{(0-2)^2 + (0-0)^2}$$
$$= \sqrt{4} \text{ or } 2$$

$$ST = \sqrt{(5-3)^2 + (3-3)^2}$$
$$= \sqrt{4} \text{ or } 2$$

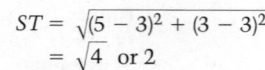

All the pairs of corresponding sides are congruent, so △ACB ≅ △RST by SSS.

Will any other combinations of corresponding and congruent sides and angles determine a unique triangle? Suppose you were given the measures of two sides and the angle that they form, which is called the **included angle**. How many different triangles would you be able to make?

INVESTIGATION

The figures shown are not actual size.

Again, we can investigate by constructing a triangle, given an angle A and sides of lengths $\overline{AB}$ and $\overline{AC}$. Let's use $m\angle A = 60$, $AB = 4$ cm, and $AC = 6$ cm.

1. Use a protractor to draw a 60° angle so that one side of the angle is on line ℓ. Label the vertex A.
2. Using A as the center, draw an arc with radius 4 cm. Label the point of intersection with the ray B.
3. Using A as the center, draw an arc with radius 6 cm. Label the point of intersection with ℓ C.
4. Draw segment BC.

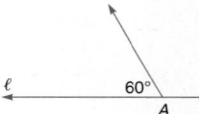 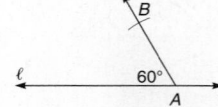 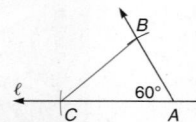

Now try to construct different triangles with the given dimensions. Are they congruent to △ABC?

Chalkboard Example

For Example 1
Given △PQR with vertices P(3, 4), Q(2, 2), and R(7, 2) and △STU with vertices S(6, −3), T(4, −2), and U(4, −7), show that △PQR ≅ △STU. **The distance formula shows that $PQ = \sqrt{5}$, $ST = \sqrt{5}$; $PR = 2\sqrt{5}$, $SU = 2\sqrt{5}$; $QR = 5$, $TU = 5$. So △PQR ≅ △STU by SSS.**

Teaching Tip   Before students read through Example 1, you may want to put the general form of the distance formula on the chalkboard.

Chalkboard Example

For Example 2

Write a two-column proof.

Given: ∠1 and ∠2 are right angles, $\overline{ST} \cong \overline{TP}$.

Prove: ∠3 ≅ ∠4

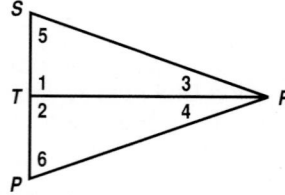

Statements   (Reasons)

1. ∠1 and ∠2 are right angles, $\overline{ST} \cong \overline{TP}$ (Given)
2. ∠1 ≅ ∠2   (All rt ∠s are ≅.)
3. $\overline{TR} \cong \overline{TR}$ (Congruence of segments is reflexive.)
4. △STR ≅ △PTR   (SAS)
5. ∠3 ≅ ∠4   (CPCTC)

SAS Postulate *Side-Angle-Side*	**If two sides and the included angle of one triangle are congruent to two sides and an included angle of another triangle, then the triangles are congruent.**

The following proof uses the SAS postulate.

Example 2

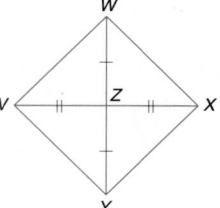

Write a two-column proof.

Given: $\overline{WZ} \cong \overline{YZ}$
$\overline{VZ} \cong \overline{ZX}$

Prove: △VZW ≅ △XZY

Proof:

Statements	Reasons
1. $\overline{WZ} \cong \overline{YZ}$ $\overline{VZ} \cong \overline{ZX}$	1. Given *(side)* *(side)*
2. ∠WZV ≅ ∠YZX	2. Vertical ∡ are ≅. *(included angle)*
3. △VZW ≅ △XZY	3. SAS

If a triangle is constructed using two given angles and the included side, the triangle will be unique. This suggests a third postulate to determine congruent triangles.

ASA Postulate *Angle-Side-Angle*	**If two angles and the included side of one triangle are congruent to two angles and the included side of another triangle, the triangles are congruent.**

Some proofs ask you to show that a pair of corresponding parts of two triangles are congruent. Often you can do this by first proving that the two triangles are congruent. Then use the definition of congruent triangles to show that the corresponding parts are congruent.

Example 3

Write a two-column proof.

Given: $\angle Q$ and $\angle S$ are right angles.
$\overline{QR} \cong \overline{SR}$

Prove: $\angle P \cong \angle T$

Proof:

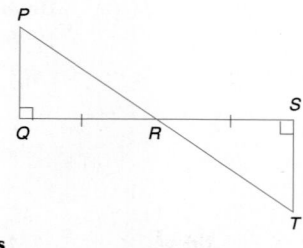

Statements	Reasons
1. $\overline{QR} \cong \overline{SR}$	1. Given *(included side)*
2. $\angle PRQ \cong \angle TRS$	2. Vertical $\angle$s are $\cong$. *(angle)*
3. $\angle Q$ and $\angle S$ are right angles.	3. Given
4. $\angle Q \cong \angle S$	4. All rt. $\angle$s are $\cong$. *(angle)*
5. $\triangle PRQ \cong \triangle TRS$	5. ASA
6. $\angle P \cong \angle T$	6. CPCTC

CHECKING FOR UNDERSTANDING

Communicating Mathematics

Read and study the lesson to answer these questions.

1. Refer to $\triangle ALM$ and $\triangle PRT$ at the right.

   a. Name one additional pair of corresponding parts that need to be congruent in order to prove that $\triangle ALM \cong \triangle PTR$. $\overline{AM} \cong \overline{PR}$

   b. What postulate would you use to prove the triangles are congruent? **ASA**

2. Refer to $\triangle TUW$ and $\triangle QOS$ at the right.

   a. Name one additional pair of corresponding parts that need to be congruent in order to prove that $\triangle TUW \cong \triangle QOS$ by SAS. $\overline{TU} \cong \overline{QO}$

   b. Name one additional pair of corresponding parts that need to be congruent in order to prove that $\triangle TUW \cong \triangle QOS$ by ASA. $\angle W \cong \angle S$

3. Will two triangles be congruent if only two pairs of corresponding parts are congruent? Explain your reasoning. **See margin.**

LESSON 4-4   TESTS FOR CONGRUENT TRIANGLES   187

Chalkboard Example

For Example 3
Write a two-column proof.
Prove the statement.
Given: $\overline{BE}$ bisects $\overline{AD}$,
$\angle A \cong \angle D$.
Prove: $\overline{AB} \cong \overline{DC}$

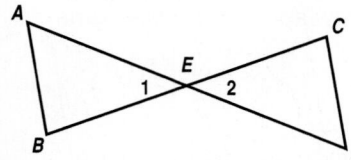

Statements   (Reasons)
1. $\overline{BE}$ bisects $\overline{AD}$, $\angle A \cong \angle D$ (Given)
2. $\angle 1 \cong \angle 2$ (Vertical $\angle$s are $\cong$.)
3. $\overline{AE} \cong \overline{ED}$ (Def. of bisector)
4. $\triangle AEB \cong \triangle DEC$ (ASA)
5. $\overline{AB} \cong \overline{DC}$ (CPCTC)

Closing Lesson

Speaking Activity Write SSS, SAS, and ASA on three index cards. Have volunteers come to the front of the room one at a time, choose a card, and give an example of the postulate to the class. The speaker may use the chalkboard or overhead projector to draw appropriate diagrams.

Guided Practice

Determine whether each pair of triangles are congruent. If they are congruent, indicate the postulate that can be used to prove their congruence.

4.

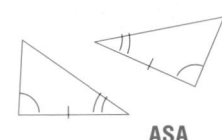

ASA

5.

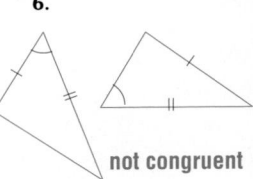

SSS

6.

not congruent

7. Justify each step in the proof.

Given: $\overline{AM} \parallel \overline{CR}$
B is the midpoint of $\overline{AR}$.

Prove: $\triangle ABM \cong \triangle RBC$

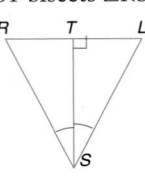

Proof:

Statements	Reasons
a. B is the midpoint of $\overline{AR}$.	**a.** __?__ Given
b. $\overline{AB} \cong \overline{BR}$	**b.** __?__ Definition of a midpoint
c. $\overline{AM} \parallel \overline{CR}$	**c.** __?__ Given
d. $\angle A \cong \angle R$	**d.** __?__ If 2 ∥ lines are cut by a transversal, alt. int. ⚟ are ≅.
e. $\angle ABM \cong \angle RBC$	**e.** __?__ Vertical ⚟ are ≅.
f. $\triangle ABM \cong \triangle RBC$	**f.** __?__ ASA

Copy each figure and mark all congruent parts. Indicate the postulate that can be used to prove their congruence.

8. $\overline{RL} \perp \overline{ST}$ **ASA**
$\overline{ST}$ bisects $\angle RSL$

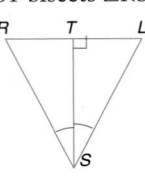

9. $\overline{AD} \parallel \overline{GR}$
$\overline{AD} \cong \overline{GR}$ **SAS**

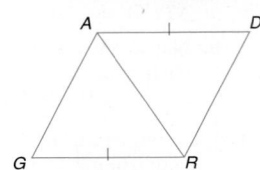

10. $\overline{AB} \cong \overline{BC}$
$\overline{AD} \cong \overline{CD}$ **SSS**

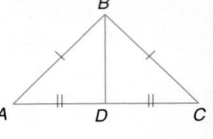

EXERCISES

A

Given figure *ABCD* with $\overline{DB} \perp \overline{DC}$ and $\overline{DB} \perp \overline{AB}$, indicate whether each statement is *true*, *could be true*, or appears to be *false*.

11. $\overline{DC} \parallel \overline{AB}$ **true**

12. $\angle 4$ and $\angle 5$ are a linear pair. **false**

13. $\overline{AD} \cong \overline{BC}$ **could be true**

14. $\overline{AD} \cong \overline{AD}$ **true**

15. $\triangle ABD \cong \triangle CDB$ **could be true**

16. Triangle *DCB* is isosceles. **could be true**

17. $\angle 1 \cong \angle 2$ **could be true**

18. $\angle 2 \cong \angle 3$ **false**

Determine which postulate can be used to prove the triangles congruent. If it is not possible to prove them congruent, write *not possible*.

19.

SAS

20.

not possible

21.

SSS

B Copy each figure and mark all congruent parts. Then complete the prove statement and identify the postulate that can be used to prove the triangles congruent.

22.
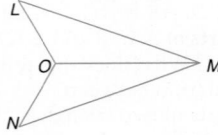

Given: $\angle LMO \cong \angle NMO$
$\angle LOM \cong \angle NOM$

Prove: $\triangle MOL \cong$ ___?___
$\triangle MON$; **ASA**

23.
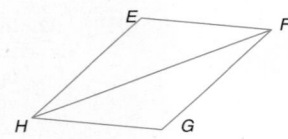

Given: $\overline{EF} \cong \overline{GH}$
$\overline{EH} \cong \overline{GF}$

Prove: $\triangle EFH \cong$ ___?___
$\triangle GHF$; **SSS**

24. *ABCD* is a quadrilateral, $\overline{BD}$ is a diagonal, $\overline{AD} \cong \overline{BC}$ and $\overline{AB} \cong \overline{DC}$.

24a. $\triangle ABD \cong \triangle CDB$ by **SSS**

a. What conclusions can be drawn about $\triangle ABD$ and $\triangle CDB$? Explain.

b. What conclusions can be drawn about $\angle A$ and $\angle C$? Explain.
$\angle A \cong \angle C$ by **CPCTC**

LESSON 4-4   TESTS FOR CONGRUENT TRIANGLES   189

APPLYING THE LESSON

Homework Exercises

Assignment Guide

Basic: 11-26, 32-38
Average: 14-29, 32-38
Enriched: 16-38
All: Mid–Chapter Review, 1-12

Exercise Notes

For Exercise 24, encourage students to make a diagram of the given information first.

Reteaching Masters Booklet, p. 23

NAME _____   DATE _____

4-4   Reteaching Worksheet

Tests for Congruent Triangles

You can show two triangles are congruent with the following:

SSS Postulate (Side–Side–Side)	Three sides of one triangle are congruent to the sides of a second triangle
SAS Postulate (Side–Angle–Side)	Two sides and the included angle of one triangle are congruent to two sides and an included angle of another triangle.
ASA Postulate (Angle–Side–Angle)	Two angles and the included side of one triangle are congruent to two angles and the included side of another triangle.

Examples: Determine whether each pair of triangles are congruent. If they are congruent, indicate the postulate that can be used to prove their congruence.

1.   SAS Postulate   2.   ASA Postulate   3.   not congruent

Which postulate can be used to prove the triangles congruent? If it is not possible to prove them congruent, say so.

1.   SAS   2.   ASA   3.   not possible

Mark all congruent parts in each figure, complete the prove statement, and identify the postulate that proves their congruence.

4.   5.

Given: $\angle BCA \cong \angle DCE$ Given: $\overline{XY} \cong \overline{YZ}$
$\angle B$ and $\angle D$ are right angles. $\overline{PY} \cong \overline{QY}$
$\overline{BC} \cong \overline{CD}$ $\overline{XP} \cong \overline{ZQ}$
Prove: $\triangle CAB \cong \dfrac{\triangle CED}{\text{ASA}}$ Prove: $\triangle XYP \cong \dfrac{\triangle ZYQ}{\text{SSS}}$

T 23
Glencoe Division, Macmillan/McGraw-Hill

RETEACHING THE LESSON

Have students make up three examples, proving two triangles congruent by SSS, SAS, and ASA. Have them use a different sheet of paper for each example. Encourage them to make careful drawings for each. Ask them to keep these sheets for future reference.

Additional Answers

25. Statements (Reasons)
a. $\angle A \cong \angle D$, $\overline{AO} \cong \overline{OD}$ (Given)
b. $\angle AOB \cong \angle DOC$ (Vertical $\angle$s are $\cong$.)
c. $\triangle AOB \cong \triangle DOC$ (ASA)

26. Statements (Reasons)
a. $\overline{AD}$ bisects $\overline{BC}$, $\overline{BC}$ bisects $\overline{AD}$ (Given)
b. $\overline{BO} \cong \overline{OC}$, $\overline{AO} \cong \overline{OD}$ (Definition of bisector)
c. $\angle AOB \cong \angle DOC$ (Vertical $\angle$s are $\cong$.)
d. $\triangle AOB \cong \triangle DOC$ (SAS)

27. Statements (Reasons)
a. $\overline{MO} \cong \overline{PO}$, $\overline{NO}$ bisects $\overline{MP}$. (Given)
b. $\overline{MN} \cong \overline{PN}$ (Definition of bisector)
c. $\overline{NO} \cong \overline{NO}$ (Congruence of segments is reflexive.)
d. $\triangle MNO \cong \triangle PNO$ (SSS)

28. Statements (Reasons)
a. $\overline{NO}$ bisects $\angle POM$, $\overline{NO} \perp \overline{MP}$ (Given)
b. $\angle MON \cong \angle PON$ (Definition of angle bisector)
c. $\angle MNO$ and $\angle PNO$ are right $\angle$s. ($\perp$ lines form 4 rt. $\angle$s.)
d. $\angle MNO \cong \angle PNO$ (All rt. $\angle$s are $\cong$.)
e. $\overline{NO} \cong \overline{NO}$ (Congruence of segments is reflexive.)
f. $\triangle MNO \cong \triangle PNO$ (ASA)

Practice Masters Booklet, p. 26

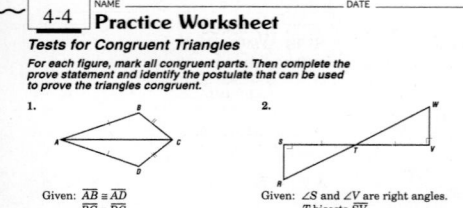

Write a two-column proof. See margin.

25. Given: $\angle A \cong \angle D$
$\overline{AO} \cong \overline{OD}$
Prove: $\triangle AOB \cong \triangle DOC$

26. Given: $\overline{AD}$ bisects $\overline{BC}$.
$\overline{BC}$ bisects $\overline{AD}$.
Prove: $\triangle AOB \cong \triangle DOC$

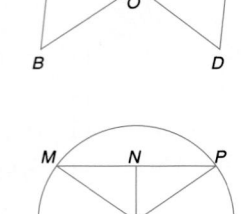

27. Given: $\overline{MO} \cong \overline{PO}$
$\overline{NO}$ bisects $\overline{MP}$.
Prove: $\triangle MNO \cong \triangle PNO$

28. Given: $\overline{NO}$ bisects $\angle POM$.
$\overline{NO} \perp \overline{MP}$
Prove: $\triangle MNO \cong \triangle PNO$

29. Graph $\triangle ABC$ with vertices $A(-3, 1)$, $B(-8, 5)$, $C(-1, 8)$ and $\triangle DEF$ with vertices $D(0, 1)$, $E(4, 6)$ and $F(7, -1)$. Use the distance formula to show that $\triangle ABC \cong \triangle DEF$. **See Solutions Manual.**

See Solutions Manual.

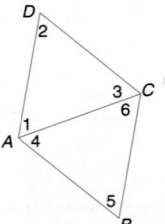

30. Given: $\angle 1 \cong \angle 6$
$\angle 3 \cong \angle 4$
Prove: $\overline{AD} \cong \overline{CB}$

31. Given: $\angle 3 \cong \angle 4$
$\overline{DC} \cong \overline{BA}$
Prove: $\angle 1 \cong \angle 6$

Critical Thinking

32. In the figure $\triangle ACD$, $\overline{DB} \cong \overline{DC}$. List all of the congruent parts of $\triangle ADB$ and $\triangle ADC$. Is $\triangle ADB \cong \triangle ADC$? What does this tell you about SSA relation between corresponding parts of two triangles? **See Solutions Manual.**

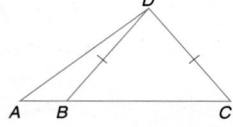

Applications

33. Construction A truss is a triangular-based supportive frame used in construction. One pattern for a roof truss is shown at the right. The vertices of the triangles have been labeled. Name the triangle that appears to be congruent to each of the following triangles.

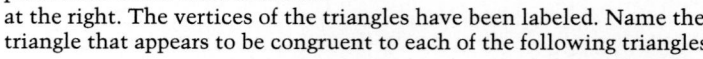

a. $\triangle BCG$ $\triangle DCF$
b. $\triangle AGC$ $\triangle EFC$
c. $\triangle ABG$ $\triangle EDF$
d. $\triangle GCF$ $\triangle FCG$
e. $\triangle ACF$ $\triangle ECG$
f. $\triangle CFE$ $\triangle CGA$

Mixed Review

34. Suppose $\triangle BIG \cong \triangle TOP$. List all the pairs of corresponding parts that are congruent because corresponding parts of congruent triangles are congruent. **(Lesson 4-3)** See margin.

35. The legs of an isosceles triangle are $6x - 6$ units and $x + 9$ units long. Find the length of the legs. **(Lesson 4-1)** 12 units

36. State the hypothesis and the conclusion of the statement "If you want a great pizza go to Katie's." **(Lesson 2-2)** See margin.

37. $\overrightarrow{QT}$ and $\overrightarrow{QS}$ are opposite rays. Describe $\angle TQS$. **(Lesson 1-6)** a straight angle

Wrap-Up

38. Write a summary of the ways to prove triangles congruent that you learned in this lesson. See students' work.

MID-CHAPTER REVIEW

Determine whether each following statement is *true* or *false*. If it is false, draw a counterexample. (Lesson 4-1)

1. A right triangle is equilateral. See margin.

2. A scalene triangle can be a right triangle. true

3. An obtuse triangle can be isosceles. true

4. An isosceles triangle can be equilateral. true

Decide whether it is possible to have a triangle with the following characteristics. (Lesson 4-2)

5. two acute angles and one right angle yes

6. no acute angles no

7. two congruent angles yes

8. three noncongruent angles yes

Draw triangles $\triangle HAT$ and $\triangle TOP$. Label the corresponding parts if $\triangle HAT \cong \triangle TOP$. Use the figures to complete each statement. (Lesson 4-3)

9. $\angle A \cong \underline{\ ?\ } \ \angle O$

10. $\overline{HT} \cong \underline{\ ?\ } \ \overline{TP}$

11. $\angle P \cong \underline{\ ?\ } \ \angle T$

Write a two-column proof. (Lesson 4-4) See margin.

12. **Given:** $\overline{QP} \cong \overline{ST}$
  $\angle P$ and $\angle T$ are right angles.
  R is the midpoint of $\overline{PT}$.

  Prove: $\overline{QR} \cong \overline{SR}$

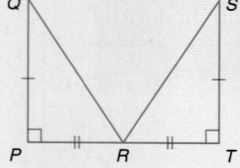

EXTENDING THE LESSON

Math Power: Problem Solving

Can two triangles be proven congruent by SSA (two sides and an angle not included between those sides)? Give reasons or a counterexample for your answer. No; students should draw two triangles that are not congruent even though they each satisfy the SSA condition.

Mid-Chapter Review

The Mid-Chapter Review provides students with a brief review of the concepts and skills in Lessons 4-1 through 4-4. Lesson numbers are given at the end of problems or instruction lines so students may review concepts not yet mastered.

Additional Answers

34. $\angle B \cong \angle T$; $\angle I \cong \angle O$; $\angle G \cong \angle P$; $\overline{BI} \cong \overline{TO}$; $\overline{IG} \cong \overline{OP}$; $\overline{BG} \cong \overline{TP}$

36. Hypothesis: You want a great pizza, Conclusion: go to Katie's.

Mid-Chapter Review

1. False, the hypotenuse must be longer than the legs.

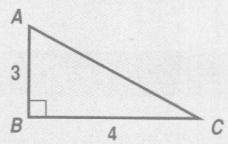

12. Statements (Reasons)
  a. $\overline{QP} \cong \overline{ST}$, $\angle P$ and $\angle T$ are right angles, R is the midpoint of $\overline{PT}$. (Given)
  b. $\angle P \cong \angle T$ (All rt. $\angle$s are $\cong$.)
  c. $\overline{PR} \cong \overline{TR}$ (Definition of midpoint.)
  d. $\triangle QPR \cong \triangle STR$ (SAS)
  e. $\overline{QR} \cong \overline{SR}$ (CPCTC)

Enrichment Masters Booklet, p.23

4-4 NAME _____ DATE _____
Enrichment Worksheet

Congruent Triangles in the Coordinate Plane

If you know the coordinates of the vertices of two triangles in the coordinate plane, you can often decide whether the two triangles are congruent. There may be more than one way to do this.

1. Consider $\triangle ABD$ and $\triangle CDB$ whose vertices have coordinates $A(0, 0)$, $B(2, 5)$, and $D(7, 0)$. Briefly describe how you can use what you know about congruent triangles and the coordinate plane to show that $\triangle ABD \cong \triangle CDB$. You may wish to make a sketch to help you get started.
Answers may vary. Sample answer: Show that the slopes of AB and CD are equal and that the slopes of AD and BC are equal. Conclude that AB ∥ CD and BD ∥ AD. Use the angle relationships for parallel lines and a transversal and the fact that BD is a common side for the triangles to conclude that △ABD ≅ △CDB by ASA.

2. Consider $\triangle PQR$ and $\triangle KLM$ whose vertices are the following points.

$P(1, 2)$	$Q(3, 6)$	$R(6, 5)$
$K(-2, 1)$	$L(-6, 3)$	$M(-5, 6)$

Briefly describe how you can show that $\triangle PQR \cong \triangle KLM$.
Use the distance formula to find the lengths of the sides of both triangles. Conclude that △PQR ≅ △KLM by SSS.

3. If you know the coordinates of all the vertices of two triangles, is it *always* possible to tell whether the triangles are congruent? Explain.
yes; You can use the distance formula and SSS.

T23
Glencoe Division, Macmillan/McGraw-Hill

Lesson Resources

- Reteaching Master 4-5
- Practice Master 4-5
- Enrichment Master 4-5
- Activity Master, p. 32

 Transparency 4-5 contains the 5-Minute Check and a teaching aid for this lesson.

INTRODUCING THE LESSON

5-Minute Check

(over Lesson 4-4)

Give reasons for each step in this proof.

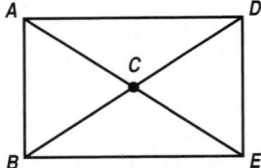

Given: *C* is the midpoint of $\overline{AE}$.
C is the midpoint of $\overline{DB}$.
Prove: $\overline{AB} \cong \overline{DE}$
Statements **(Reasons)**
1. *C* is the midpoint of $\overline{AE}$. *C* is the midpoint of $\overline{DB}$. **(Given)**
2. $\overline{AC} \cong \overline{CE}$ **(Definition of midpoint)**
3. $\overline{DC} \cong \overline{CB}$ **(Definition of midpoint)**
4. $\angle ACB \cong \angle DCE$ **(Vertical ∠s are ≅.)**
5. $\triangle ACB \cong \triangle ECD$ **(SAS)**
6. $\overline{AB} \cong \overline{DE}$ **(CPCTC)**

Motivating the Lesson

Ask students to name as many real-life examples of uses of triangles as they can. **Sample answers: bridges, roofs, signs, clothing design**

TEACHING THE LESSON

Teaching Tip Point out that AAS is a theorem since it can be proven. SSS, ASA, and SAS are all postulates.

4-5 Another Test for Congruent Triangles

Objective
4-5

After studying this lesson, you should be able to:
- use AAS theorem to test for triangle congruence.

Application

> **FYI...**
>
> Quilting became popular in the United States in colonial days because cloth was scarce. In the 1800s when cloth became readily available, quilting grew to be an art form that is still popular today.

Karen is making a quilt that is to be constructed from congruent triangles. How few pairs of corresponding parts of two triangular pieces could she check and still be sure that the pieces are congruent? From the previous lesson, we know that three given sides determine a unique triangle, as well as two sides and an included angle, or two angles and the included side. Karen could also be assured that all of her triangles were congruent if one side and any two pairs of corresponding angles were congruent. This can be proved as a theorem.

Theorem 4-5 AAS Angle-Angle-Side	If two angles and a nonincluded side of one triangle are congruent to the corresponding two angles and side of a second triangle, the two triangles are congruent.

Proof of Theorem 4-5

> **INVESTIGATION**
>
> You can learn more about testing for congruent triangles in Investigation 5 on page A5.

Given: $\angle P \cong \angle A$
$\angle Q \cong \angle B$
$\overline{QR} \cong \overline{BC}$

Prove: $\triangle PQR \cong \triangle ABC$

Proof:

Statements	Reasons
1. $\angle P \cong \angle A$ $\angle Q \cong \angle B$ $\overline{QR} \cong \overline{BC}$	1. Given *angle* *side*
2. $\angle R \cong \angle C$	2. If 2 ∠s in a Δ are ≅ to 2 ∠s in another Δ the third ∠s are ≅ also. *angle*
3. $\triangle PQR \cong \triangle ABC$	3. ASA

192 CHAPTER 4 CONGRUENT TRIANGLES

ALTERNATE TEACHING STRATEGIES

Using Connections

Stella found a triangular piece of scrap wood that she thinks would make a good bookend. She wants to cut another just like it. What other measurement does she need in order to produce a congruent bookend? **either *AC*, ∠*B*, or ∠*C*.**

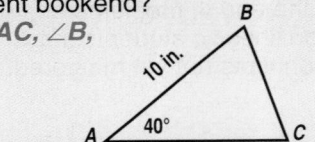

Using Investigation

You can guide students to discover that side-side-angle, or SSA, is not a valid test for triangle congruence. In Investigation 5 on page A5 of **More Investigations in Geometry,** students use measurement and manipulatives to explore two sides and a non-included angle of two triangles to test for triangle congruence.

Could Karen be assured that two of her triangular quilt pieces were congruent if she determined that two pairs of corresponding sides and a pair of corresponding nonincluded angles were congruent (SSA)? Remember that a *counterexample* is enough to show that a statement is not true. The figures at the right show two triangles that meet the conditions for SSA, but clearly are not congruent. Therefore, SSA is not a test for congruence.

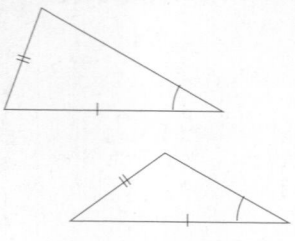

Example 1

Write a paragraph proof.

Given: ∠Q and ∠S are right angles.
∠1 ≅ ∠3

Prove: $\overline{QP} \cong \overline{SR}$

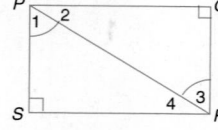

Plan:

$\overline{QP}$ and $\overline{SR}$ are in △PQR and △RSP, respectively. If those two triangles are congruent, the two sides will be congruent by CPCTC.

Paragraph Proof:
We are given that ∠1 ≅ ∠3.   *angle*   It is also given that ∠Q and ∠S are right angles. Since all right angles are congruent, ∠Q ≅ ∠S.   *angle* $\overline{PR} \cong \overline{PR}$ since congruence of segments is reflexive.   *side*   Therefore, △PQR ≅ △RSP by AAS. So, $\overline{QP} \cong \overline{SR}$ by the definition of congruent triangles (CPCTC).

Sometimes the triangles we would like to prove congruent are overlapping. Then it is helpful to draw the two figures separately or to use different colors to distinguish the parts of each triangle.

Example 2

Write a two-column proof to verify the statement *Segments from the vertices of the base angles of an isosceles triangle to the midpoints of the opposite sides are congruent.*

Given: $\overline{AC} \cong \overline{AB}$
D is the midpoint of $\overline{AC}$.
E is the midpoint of $\overline{AB}$.

Prove: $\overline{DB} \cong \overline{EC}$

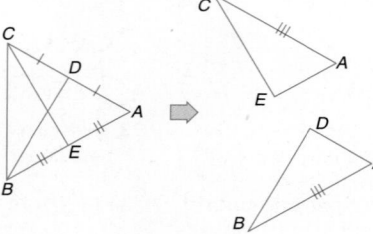

Plan:

$\overline{DB}$ is a side of △DBA, and $\overline{EC}$ is a side of △ECA. Prove these two triangles congruent and then use CPCTC to prove that $\overline{DB}$ is congruent to $\overline{EC}$.

LESSON 4-5   ANOTHER TEST FOR CONGRUENT TRIANGLES   193

Chalkboard Examples

For Example 1
Write a paragraph proof.
Given: J is the midpoint of $\overline{GK}$.
∠H and ∠L are right angles.
Prove: $\overline{HG} \cong \overline{LK}$

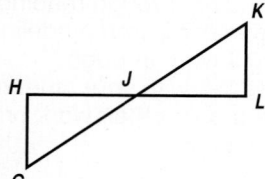

We are given that J is the midpoint of $\overline{GK}$. Therefore, $\overline{GJ} \cong \overline{JK}$. It is also given that ∠H and ∠L are right angles. Since all right angles are congruent, ∠H ≅ ∠L. Since ∠HJG and ∠LJK are vertical angles, ∠HJG ≅ ∠LJK. Therefore, △GHJ ≅ △KLJ by AAS. So, $\overline{HG} \cong \overline{LK}$ by the definition of congruent triangles. (CPCTC)

For Example 2
Write a two-column proof.
Given: $\overline{AD} \cong \overline{AE}$, ∠ACD ≅ ∠ABE
Prove: △ABC is isosceles.

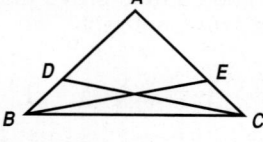

1. $\overline{AD} \cong \overline{AE}$, ∠ACD ≅ ∠ABE (Given)
2. ∠A ≅ ∠A   (Congruence of angles is reflexive.)
3. △ACD ≅ △ABE   (AAS)
4. $\overline{AC} \cong \overline{AB}$ (CPCTC)
5. △ABC is isosceles (Definition of isosceles triangle)

Teaching Tip   For Example 2, draw the figure on the chalkboard and use colored chalk to outline the two triangles being considered.

Checking for Understanding

Exercises 1-16 are designed to help you assess students' understanding through reading, writing, speaking, and modeling. You should work through Exercises 1-5 with your students and then monitor their work on Exercises 6-16.

Error Analysis

When students are trying to write proofs that involve overlapping triangles to be proved congruent, have them redraw the two triangles separately and mark the congruent parts on the separated triangles. This will enable them to see the corresponding parts more clearly, to determine the reason for congruency, and to determine which parts are congruent.

Closing the Lesson

Writing Activity Have students write a paragraph describing how AAS can be used to prove that two triangles are congruent.

Additional Answer

1. Sample answers: Same: all have three parts of the triangle congruent; different: all have different combinations of parts.

Proof:

Statements	Reasons
1. $\overline{AC} \cong \overline{AB}$	1. Given *side*
2. $AC = AB$	2. Definition of congruence
3. $AC = AD + DC$ $AB = AE + EB$	3. Segment addition postulate
4. $AD + DC = AE + EB$	4. Substitution property of equality
5. D is the midpoint of $\overline{AC}$. E is the midpoint of $\overline{AB}$.	5. Given
6. $AD = DC$ $AE = EB$	6. Definition of midpoint
7. $2AD = 2AE$	7. Substitution property of equality
8. $AD = AE$	8. Division property of equality
9. $\overline{AD} \cong \overline{AE}$	9. Definition of congruent segments *side*
10. $\angle A \cong \angle A$	10. Congruence of angles is reflexive. *angle*
11. $\triangle DBA \cong \triangle ECA$	11. SAS
12. $\overline{DB} \cong \overline{EC}$	12. CPCTC

Therefore, the segments from the base angles of an isosceles triangle to the midpoints of the opposite sides are congruent.

CHECKING FOR UNDERSTANDING

Communicating Mathematics

Read and study the lesson to answer these questions.

1. Make a list of the ways to prove triangles congruent. How are these ways the same? How are they different? **See margin.**

2. Decide which pair(s) of the following triangles is congruent. Justify your answer. **a and d are congruent by ASA.**

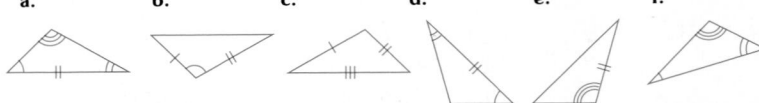

a.   b.   c.   d.   e.   f.

3. Answers may vary. Sample answers are: show they are corresponding parts of congruent triangles or show they are vertical angles.

3. List three ways to show that two angles are congruent.

4. In $\triangle DOA$, name the sides that include $\angle 10$, $\angle 11$, and $\angle 12$.
 $\overline{AD}$ and $\overline{AO}$; $\overline{DO}$ and $\overline{AO}$; $\overline{DO}$ and $\overline{DA}$

5. In $\triangle DOC$, name the angles that include $\overline{DC}$, $\overline{DO}$, and $\overline{CO}$.
 $\angle 1$ and $\angle 3$; $\angle 1$ and $\angle 2$; $\angle 2$ and $\angle 3$

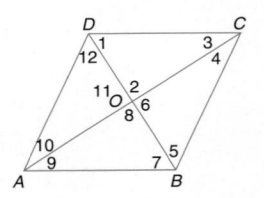

Indicate the additional pairs of corresponding parts that would have to be proved congruent in order to use the given postulate or theorem to prove the triangles congruent.

6. $\triangle ACE \cong \triangle DCE$ by SSS $\overline{AC} \cong \overline{DC}$

7. $\triangle ACB \cong \triangle CAE$ by SAS $\overline{CE} \cong \overline{AB}$

8. $\triangle ACB \cong \triangle CAE$ by AAS $\angle ABC \cong \angle CEA$

9. $\triangle ACB \cong \triangle CAE$ by ASA $\angle ACB \cong \angle CAE$

10. $\triangle ACB \cong \triangle DCE$ by AAS
10. $\angle ACB \cong \angle DCE$, $\overline{BC} \cong \overline{EC}$; $\angle ABC \cong \angle DEC$, $\overline{AC} \cong \overline{DC}$; $\angle ACB \cong \angle DCE$, $\overline{AB} \cong \overline{DE}$; or $\angle ABC \cong \angle DEC$, $\overline{BC} \cong \overline{EC}$

Prove each conclusion if possible. If not possible, state the additional information that could be given to prove the conclusion. See Solutions Manual.

11. $\overline{AB} \cong \overline{CD}$
$\overline{AB} \parallel \overline{CD}$
Therefore, $\triangle AOB \cong \triangle DOC$.

12. $\overline{AB} \parallel \overline{CD}$
Therefore, $\triangle AOB \cong \triangle DOC$.

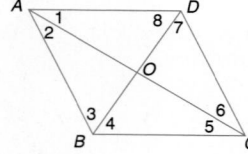

Determine which triangles in *ABCD* are congruent under the given conditions. Justify your answers. See Solutions Manual.

13. $\angle 8 \cong \angle 4$
$\overline{AD} \cong \overline{BC}$

14. $\overline{AB} \parallel \overline{DC}$
$\overline{AB} \cong \overline{DC}$

15. O is the midpoint of both $\overline{DB}$ and $\overline{AC}$.

16. If $\overline{PR}$ and $\overline{QS}$ bisect each other, write a paragraph proof to show that $\triangle PQT \cong \triangle RST$. See Solutions Manual.

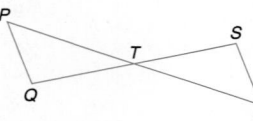

EXERCISES

Practice

A

Draw and label triangles *DEF* and *RST*. Indicate the additional pairs of corresponding parts that would have to be proved congruent in order to use the given postulate or theorem to prove the triangles congruent.

17. $\angle D \cong \angle R$ and $\overline{DE} \cong \overline{RS}$ by ASA $\angle E \cong \angle S$

18. $\angle E \cong \angle S$ and $\overline{EF} \cong \overline{ST}$ by AAS $\angle D \cong \angle R$

19. $\angle F \cong \angle T$ and $\angle D \cong \angle R$ by AAS $\overline{DE} \cong \overline{RS}$ or $\overline{EF} \cong \overline{ST}$

20. $\angle E \cong \angle S$ and $\angle F \cong \angle T$ by ASA $\overline{EF} \cong \overline{ST}$

LESSON 4-5   ANOTHER TEST FOR CONGRUENT TRIANGLES   195

RETEACHING THE LESSON

In Lesson 4-4, students were directed to make summary sheets for proving congruence by SSS, SAS, and ASA. Have the students add a summary sheet for AAS that includes careful drawings.

Practice Masters Booklet, p. 27

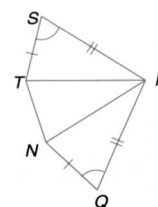

Determine which triangles are congruent under the given conditions. Justify your answers. See margin.

21.
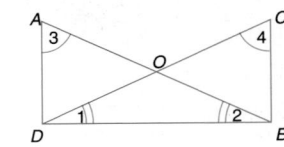

22.
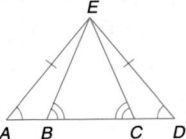

B

23. One order of steps:
3, 1, 5, 9, 8, 2, 7, 6, 4.

23. The steps in the following proof are *not* in logical order. Rearrange them in a correct sequence and give the reasons.

Given: $\overline{AB} \perp \overline{BC}$, $\overline{AE} \perp \overline{DE}$,
$\angle 1 \cong \angle 2$, $\overline{AB} \cong \overline{AE}$

Prove: $\overline{AC} \cong \overline{AD}$

Statements	Reasons
1. $\angle 3$ is a right angle.	1. ___?___ $\perp$ lines form rt. $\angle$s.
2. $\angle 1 \cong \angle 2$	2. ___?___ Given
3. $\overline{AB} \perp \overline{BC}$	3. ___?___ Given
4. $\overline{AC} \cong \overline{AD}$	4. ___?___ CPCTC
5. $\overline{AE} \perp \overline{DE}$	5. ___?___ Given
6. $\triangle ABC \cong \triangle AED$	6. ___?___ ASA
7. $\overline{AB} \cong \overline{AE}$	7. ___?___ Given
8. $\angle 3 \cong \angle 4$	8. ___?___ All rt. $\angle$s are $\cong$.
9. $\angle 4$ is a right angle.	9. ___?___ $\perp$ lines form four rt. $\angle$s.

Determine if each conclusion is valid based on the information given in the figure. Justify your answer. See margin.

24.
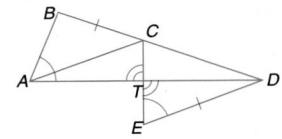

$\triangle ABC \cong \triangle DTE$

25.
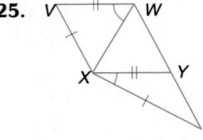

$\triangle VWX \cong \triangle YXZ$

Write a paragraph proof for each. See margin.

26. **Given:** $\angle 1 \cong \angle 2$
$\angle L \cong \angle M$

Prove: $\overline{EM} \cong \overline{AL}$

27. **Given:** $\overline{ST} \cong \overline{QN}$
$\angle S \cong \angle Q$
$\overline{PS} \cong \overline{PQ}$

Prove: $\triangle TPN$ is isosceles.

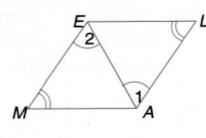

Write a two-column proof for each.

28. Given: $\overline{BC} \cong \overline{AD}$
$\overline{BD} \cong \overline{AC}$

Prove: $\angle BAC \cong \angle ABD$
See margin.

29. Prove that a segment drawn from the vertex angle of an isosceles triangle through the midpoint of the opposite side divides the triangle into two congruent triangles. **See margin.**

30. Prove that the bisector of the vertex angle of an isosceles triangle is perpendicular to the base of the triangle. **See Solutions Manual.**

Critical Thinking

31. Monty says that two triangles can be proved congruent by using AAA (angle-angle-angle). Missy disagrees. Who do you agree with? Justify your answer completely. **AAA does not prove two triangles congruent. See students' justifications.**

Applications

32. **History** It is said that Thales determined the distance from the shore to enemy Greek ships during an early war by sighting the angle to the ship from a point P on the shore, walking a distance to point Q, and then sighting the angle to the ship from that point. He then reproduced the angles on the other side of line PQ and continued these lines until they intersected. **See Solutions Manual.**

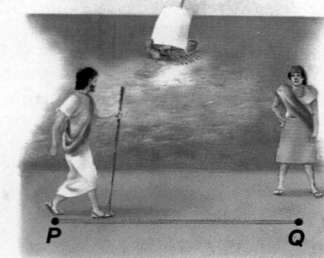

   a. How did he determine the distance to the ship in this way?

   b. Why does it work?

33. **Home Economics** Explain why the plane of an ironing board is parallel to the plane of the floor if the legs of the board bisect each other. **See Solutions Manual.**

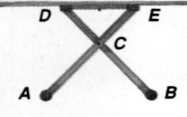

Mixed Review

34. Write a two-column proof. **(Lesson 4-4)**
Given: $\overline{PR} \cong \overline{TR}$
$\angle 1 \cong \angle 2$
$\angle P$ and $\angle T$ are right angles.
Prove: $\overline{QR} \cong \overline{SR}$ **See Solutions Manual.**

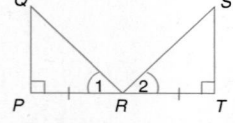

35. If $\triangle CAK \cong \triangle PIE$, which angle in $\triangle CAK$ is congruent to $\angle IPE$ in $\triangle PIE$? **(Lesson 4-3)** $\angle ACK$

36. Name five ways to prove that two lines are parallel. **(Lesson 3-4)** **See Solutions Manual.**

37. **Algebra** Find the length and the midpoint of the segment with endpoints having coordinates $(7, 4)$ and $(-3, 8)$. **(Lesson 1-4)** $2\sqrt{29}$; $(2, 6)$

Wrap-Up

38. **Journal Entry** Write a paragraph to describe the difference between the AAS theorem and ASA postulate. Give examples to show how each one is used. **See students' work.**

EXTENDING THE LESSON

Math Power: Using Reasoning

Is this statement true or false? Explain your answer.
"To prove that two triangles are congruent, you can use any two pairs of congruent, corresponding sides and a pair of corresponding, congruent angles, or you can use any two pairs of corresponding, congruent angles and a pair of corresponding, congruent sides."

The first part of the statement is not true. If two pairs of corresponding, congruent sides are given, the *included* corresponding angles must be congruent in order to prove the triangles congruent (SAS). The second part is true, since you can prove triangles congruent by ASA and by AAS.

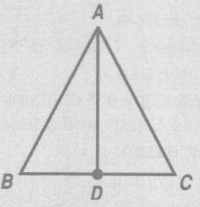
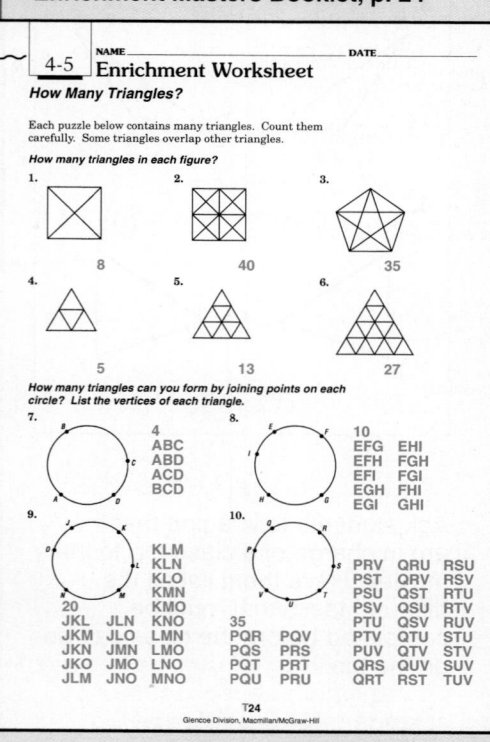

Lesson Resources

- Practice Master 4-6
- Evaluation Master, Quiz C, p. 52
- Activity Master, p. 4

 Transparency 4-6 contains the 5-Minute Check and a teaching aid for this lesson.

INTRODUCING THE LESSON

 5–Minute Check

(over Lesson 4-5)

Write a congruence statement for each pair of triangles. Which postulate or theorem proves their congruence (SSS, SAS, ASA, or AAS)?

1.

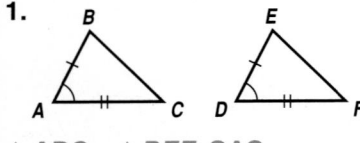

$\triangle ABC \cong \triangle DEF$; SAS

2.

$\triangle GHI \cong \triangle JKL$; ASA

3.

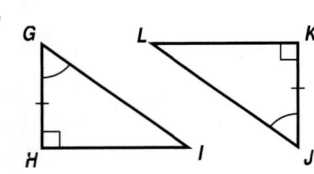

$\triangle MNP \cong \triangle QRS$; AAS

4.

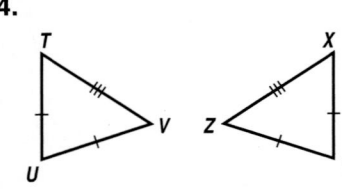

$\triangle TUV \cong \triangle XYZ$; SSS

Motivating the Lesson

Ask students to imagine that they are in charge of a class trip to the movies. Have them list all the different tasks that must be completed before the class can go on the trip. Sample answers: vote on movie to see, collect money, arrange transportation

---

4-6 Problem-Solving Strategy: Identify Subgoals

Objective After studying this lesson, you should be able to:
4-6
- solve problems by identifying and achieving subgoals.

Solving a problem is like walking a mile; it takes many small steps. Being able to identify the steps, or subgoals, that need to be accomplished to solve a problem makes solving the problem simpler.

Example 1

CONNECTION

Number Theory

What fraction of the five-digit whole numbers are divisible by 1, 2, 3, 4, and 5?

We could write out all of the five-digit numbers, determine which ones are divisible by 1, 2, 3, 4, and 5, and then find the fraction of the five-digit numbers that these numbers represent. But, that approach would be quite time consuming.

First subgoal To solve the problem efficiently, identify what kind of numbers have 1, 2, 3, 4, and 5 as factors. Numbers that have the least common multiple of 1, 2, 3, 4, and 5 as a factor also have 1, 2, 3, 4, and 5 as factors. Since the least common multiple of 1, 2, 3, 4, and 5 is 60, the five-digit numbers that have 60 as a factor are the ones we wish to identify.

Second subgoal Use a calculator to find how many five-digit whole numbers are divisible by 60.

The numbers are:

10,020,	10,080,	10,140,	...,	99,960.
60×167,	60×168,	60×169,	...,	60×1666

So, there is a multiple of 60 for each number from 167 to 1666 inclusive. Therefore, there are 1500 five-digit numbers that are divisible by 1, 2, 3, 4, and 5.

Final subgoal Find the fraction of the five-digit numbers that are divisible by 1, 2, 3, 4, and 5. Since there are 90,000 five-digit numbers, the fraction is $\frac{1500}{90,000}$ or $\frac{1}{60}$.

In geometric proofs, we often have to take several steps to complete the proof. Setting subgoals can be helpful in taking those steps.

ALTERNATE TEACHING STRATEGIES

Another example of using subgoals can be found in algebra. To solve some quadratic equations, begin by finding two binomial factors of a polynomial. Solve $x^2 - 5x + 6 = 0$.

$$x^2 - 5x + 6 = (x - 3)(x - 2)$$

So, $(x - 3)(x - 2) = 0$

$$x - 3 = 0 \quad x - 2 = 0$$
$$x = 3 \quad x = 2$$

The solutions are 2 and 3.

Ask students to write a paragraph describing a problem that can be solved by identifying one or more subgoals.

Example 2

Write a two-column proof.

Given: $\overline{KT} \perp \overline{IE}$

$\angle IKS \cong \angle ITS$

Prove: $\angle KEI \cong \angle TEI$

Plan:

Let's set some subgoals before we start the proof. Reasoning backward, we can show that $\angle KEI \cong \angle TEI$ if $\triangle KEI \cong \triangle TEI$. To prove these triangles congruent, we need to show that $\angle KIE \cong \angle TIE$ and $\overline{KI} \cong \overline{TI}$. This can be proved by showing that they are corresponding parts of congruent triangles IKS and ITS. This can be proved from the given information.

Our subgoals are:

1. Prove $\triangle IKS \cong \triangle ITS$.
2. Use CPCTC to show that $\angle KIE \cong \angle TIE$ and $\overline{KI} \cong \overline{TI}$.
3. Prove $\triangle KEI \cong \triangle TEI$.
4. Use CPCTC to show that $\angle KEI \cong \angle TEI$.

Now, use the subgoals to write the proof.

Proof:

Statements	Reasons
1. $\overline{KT} \perp \overline{IE}$	1. Given
2. $\angle ISK$ and $\angle IST$ are right angles.	2. $\perp$ lines form four rt $\angle$s.
3. $\angle ISK \cong \angle IST$	3. All rt. $\angle$s are $\cong$.
4. $\angle IKS \cong \angle ITS$	4. Given
5. $\overline{IS} \cong \overline{IS}$	5. Congruence of segments is reflexive.
6. $\triangle IKS \cong \triangle ITS$	6. AAS
7. $\angle KIE \cong \angle TIE$ $\overline{KI} \cong \overline{TI}$	7. CPCTC
8. $\overline{IE} \cong \overline{IE}$	8. Congruence of segments is reflexive.
9. $\triangle KIE \cong \triangle TIE$	9. SAS
10. $\angle KEI \cong \angle TEI$	10. CPCTC

CHECKING FOR UNDERSTANDING

Communicating Mathematics

Read and study the lesson to answer these questions.

1. Why is it helpful to identify subgoals when trying to solve a problem? It breaks the problem into smaller steps.

Teaching Tip   Ask students to compare *goal* and *subgoal* and to give examples of each.

Chalkboard Examples

For Example 1
For how many numbers less than 10,000 is the sum of their digits 4?   Subgoals: one-digit, two-digit, three-digit, and four-digit numbers
1-digit: 4
2-digits: 13, 22, 31, 40
3-digits: 103, 112, 121, 130, 202, 211, 220, 301, 310, 400
4-digits: 1003, 1012, 1021, 1030, 1102, 1120, 1111, 1201, 1210, 1300, 2002, 2011, 2020, 2101, 2110, 2200, 3001, 3010, 3100, 4000
Answer : 35

For Example 2
Write a two-column proof.
Given: $\overline{BE} \cong \overline{CE}$, $\angle BAE \cong \angle CDE$
Prove: $\angle BAD \cong \angle CDA$

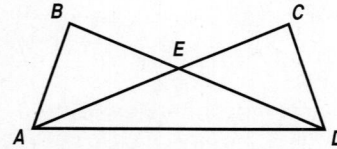

Subgoals: Prove $\triangle ABE \cong \triangle DCE$: use CPCTC *and* SAS to prove $\triangle BAD \cong \triangle CDA$; use CPCTC to prove the angles congruent.
1. $\overline{BE} \cong \overline{CE}$; $\angle BAE \cong \angle DCE$ (Given)
2. $\angle BEA \cong \angle CED$ (Vertical $\angle$s are $\cong$.)
3. $\triangle ABE \cong \triangle DCE$ (AAS)
4. $\overline{AB} \cong \overline{DC}$; $\overline{EA} \cong \overline{ED}$; $\angle ABE \cong \angle DCE$ (CPCTC)
5. $BE = CE$; $EA = ED$ (Definition of $\cong$ segments.)
6. $BE + ED = CE + EA$ (Addition prop. of equality)
7. $BD = BE + ED$; $CA = CE + EA$ (Segment Addition Postulate)
8. $BD = CA$ (Substitution)
9. $\overline{BD} \cong \overline{CA}$ (Definition of $\cong$ segments)
10. $\triangle BAD \cong \triangle CDA$ (SAS)
11. $\angle BAD \cong \angle CDA$ (CPCTC)

2. When do you anticipate using the strategy of identifying subgoals in your study of geometry? **Answers may vary. A typical answer is 2-column proof.**

3. What fraction of the five-digit whole numbers are divisible by 1, 2, 3, 4, 5, 6, and 7? $\frac{43}{18,000}$

Checking for Understanding

Exercises 1-7 are designed to help you assess students' understanding through reading, writing, speaking, and modeling. You should work through Exercises 1-3 with your students and then monitor their work on Exercises 4-7.

Closing the Lesson

Speaking Activity Ask students to define "subgoal of a problem" in their own words.

Homework Exercises

Assignment Guide

Basic: 8-16
Average: 8-16
Enriched: 8-16

Additional Answers

11. Subgoals: $\triangle ADB \cong \triangle ACB$, $\angle DAB \cong \angle CAB$.
    Statements   (Reasons)
    a. $\overrightarrow{AB} \perp$ plane BCD.   (Given)
    b. $\overline{AB} \perp \overline{DB}$; $\overline{AB} \perp \overline{CB}$
       (Definition of perpendicular plane)
    c. $\angle ABD$ and $\angle ABC$ are right angles.   ($\perp$ lines form four rt. $\angle$s.)
    d. $\angle ABD \cong \angle ABC$ (All rt. $\angle$s are $\cong$.)
    e. $\overline{DB} \cong \overline{CB}$ (Given)
    f. $\overline{AB} \cong \overline{AB}$ (Congruence of segments is reflexive.)
    g. $\triangle ABD \cong \triangle ABC$ (SAS)
    h. $\angle DAB \cong \angle CAB$ (CPCTC)

Guided Practice

Solve. Use the strategy of identifying subgoals.

4. How many whole numbers less than 1000 have digits whose sum is 8? **45**

5. Find the sum of the reciprocals of all the factors of 48. $2\frac{7}{12}$

6. Find the least positive integer having remainders of 2, 3, and 2 when divided by 3, 5, and 7 respectively. **23**

7. Identify the subgoals you would need to accomplish to complete the proof. $\triangle BCG \cong \triangle FCD$; $\overline{BG} \cong \overline{FD}$; $\triangle ABG \cong \triangle EFD$; $\angle A \cong \angle E$

   Given: $\overline{AG} \cong \overline{ED}$
   $\overline{BC} \cong \overline{FC}$
   $\overline{BG} \perp \overline{AE}$
   $\overline{FD} \perp \overline{AE}$

   Prove: $\angle A \cong \angle E$

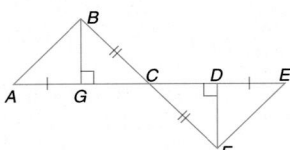

EXERCISES

Practice

Solve. Use any strategy.

8. An antique dealer bought an antique chair for $400 and sold it for $500 the following week. A month later, the dealer bought the chair back for $600 and then sold it to another dealer for $700. How much profit did the antique dealer make? **$200**

9. Find the least four-digit perfect square whose digits are all even. **4624 = 68²**

10. James invited his friends Jill and Enrico over for a cookout. His small grill is only big enough to cook two hamburgers at a time. If each hamburger must cook for 5 minutes on each side, what is the least amount of time James could take to cook all three hamburgers? **15 min**

11. Identify the subgoals you would need to accomplish to complete the proof. Then complete the proof.

    Given: $\overrightarrow{AB} \perp$ plane BCD.
    $\overline{DB} \cong \overline{CB}$

    Prove: $\angle DAB \cong \angle CAB$
    See margin.

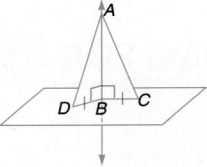

Have students work in small groups to solve the following problem using the strategy of identifying a subgoal: How many numbers less than 10,000 have the sum of their digits equal to 2 and are also divisible by 10?   **6**

Strategies

Look for a pattern.
Solve a simpler problem.
Act it out.
Guess and check.
Draw a diagram.
Make a chart.
Work backward.

14. Answers may vary. A sample answer is $123 - 4 - 5 - 6 - 7 + 8 - 9 = 100$

12. The date May 19, 1995, is represented by 5/19/95, and is called a *product date* since $5 \times 19 = 95$. Find all of the product dates in the 1990s. **See margin.**

13. All my pets are dogs except two, all are cats except two, and all are hamsters except two. How many pets do I have? **3; 1 dog, 1 cat, and 1 hamster**

14. Delete or change some '+' symbols to '−' in the equation below to make it true. *(Hint: The spacing between numbers can be changed to make greater numbers.)*

$$1 + 2 + 3 + 4 + 5 + 6 + 7 + 8 + 9 = 100$$

15. In how many ways can you roll two dice to obtain a sum divisible by 3? **12**

16. Five couples who had known each other for years were reminiscing about predictions they had made. Art, Naren, Will, Jared, and Anthony predicted who would marry Justine, Vivian, Cynthia, Kim, and Sarah. Art said that Will would marry Justine. Naren said that Anthony would marry Vivian. Will thought that Art would not marry Kim or Sarah and Anthony was sure that Naren would not marry Sarah.

  a. What marriages would have taken place if all the predictions were correct? **See margin.**

  b. It turned out that no one's prediction was right! One of the women is Anthony's sister. If we know who she is, we can tell who is really married to whom. What marriages did take place and who is Anthony's sister? **See margin.**

COOPERATIVE LEARNING PROJECT

Work in groups. Each person in the group must understand the solution and be able to explain it to any person in class.

When a billiard ball hits the cushion of a billiard table, the angle at which it rebounds has the same measure as the angle at which it hit the cushion. The billiard table shown at the right has sides that are in the ratio of 5 to 7. Copy the table and use a protractor and straightedge to draw the path of a billiard ball that is hit at a 45° angle from one corner of the table. The ball will rebound several times before ending up in one of the corners. How many times did the ball rebound before reaching a corner? Draw several other billiard tables with sides in different ratios and repeat the process. Write a formula for finding the number of rebounds on a billiard table with sides a and b units long where a and b are whole numbers with no common factors other than 1. **10; number of rebounds = $a + b - 2$**

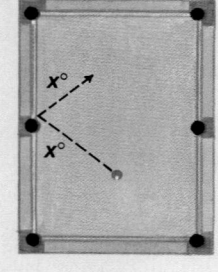

LESSON 4-6 PROBLEM-SOLVING STRATEGY: IDENTIFY SUBGOALS 201

EXTENDING THE LESSON

Math Power: Problem Solving

How many squares are there in a checkerboard? **204**

Cooperative Learning Project

This activity provides students an opportunity to *learn* things together, not just do things together. You may wish to refer to pages T6-T7 and page 162C for the various elements of cooperative groups and specific goals and strategies for using them.

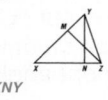

Lesson Resources

- Reteaching Master 4-7
- Practice Master 4-7
- Enrichment Master 4-7
- Evaluation Master, Quiz D, p. 52

 Transparency 4-7 contains the 5-Minute Check and a teaching aid for this lesson.

Objective After studying this lesson, you should be able to:
4-7 ■ use properties of isosceles and equilateral triangles.

Application   Jerome Taylor has been contracted by the Harper family to draw the blueprints for their A-frame house. He must find the measurements for the angles formed where the roof meets the ground. Mr. Taylor knows that the two sides of the roof are to meet at an angle of 40° at the top of the house. Based on this information, at what angle should the roof meet the ground for this house? *You will solve this problem in Example 1.*

The front of an A-frame house is shaped like an isosceles triangle. Recall that an isosceles triangle has at least two sides congruent. Another important property of an isosceles triangle is that it has *line symmetry*. That is, if you fold an isosceles triangle along the bisector of its vertex angle, the two base angles match exactly. This observation leads us to the following theorem.

INTRODUCING THE LESSON

 5-Minute Check

(over Lesson 4-6)

Solve.

1. What fraction of the three-digit numbers are multiples of 4 and 5?   **1/20**
2. What fraction of the numbers less than 100 are prime numbers?   **1/4**
3. Write a plan for a proof.
   Given: $\overline{BC} \cong \overline{EF}$, $\angle B \cong \angle E$, $\overline{AG} \cong \overline{DG}$
   Prove: $\overline{AF} \cong \overline{CD}$

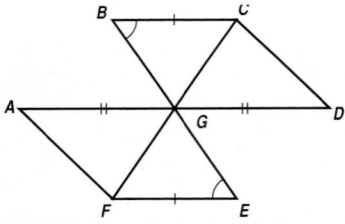

Subgoals: prove △BCG ≅ △EFG by AAS. Use CPCTC, the given statement, and vertical angles to prove △FGA ≅ △CGD. Use CPCTC to prove $\overline{AF} \cong \overline{CD}$.

Theorem 4-6 Isosceles Triangle Theorem	**If two sides of a triangle are congruent, then the angles opposite those sides are congruent.**

Proof of Theorem 4-6

Given: $\triangle PQR$
         $\overline{PQ} \cong \overline{RQ}$

Prove: $\angle P \cong \angle R$

Proof:

Statements	Reasons
1. Let S be the midpoint of $\overline{PR}$.	1. Every segment has exactly one midpoint.
2. Draw auxiliary segment QS.	2. Through any 2 pts. there is 1 line.
3. $\overline{PS} \cong \overline{RS}$	3. Definition of midpoint
4. $\overline{QS} \cong \overline{QS}$	4. Congruence of segments is reflexive.
5. $\overline{PQ} \cong \overline{RQ}$	5. Given
6. $\triangle PQS \cong \triangle RQS$	6. SSS
7. $\angle P \cong \angle R$	7. CPCTC

202   **CHAPTER 4**   **CONGRUENT TRIANGLES**

Motivating the Lesson

Have students fold a sheet of paper in half and use it to draw and cut out an isosceles triangle. Ask them to make a conjecture about angles 1, 2, 3, and 4.
∠1 ≅ ∠2 and ∠3 ≅ ∠4

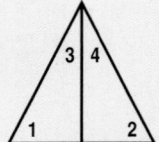

ALTERNATE TEACHING STRATEGIES

Using Investigation

You can guide students to discover that the base angles of an isosceles triangle are congruent. In Investigation 6 on page A6 of **More Investigations in Geometry,** students use measurement and manipulatives to explore isosceles triangles.

Using Reasoning

Is this statement true or false? Give reasons for your answer. "Base angles of an isosceles triangle are always acute." **True; if the base angles were right or obtuse, the sum of the measures of the angles would be greater than 180, which is impossible in a triangle.**

Example 1

APPLICATION

Construction

INVESTIGATION

You can learn more about isosceles triangles in Investigation 6 on page A6.

Find the angle that the roof of the Harper's house should make with the ground.

The base of the isosceles triangle lies on the ground, and the two sides of the roof are the legs. So the angles formed by the roof and ground are base angles and must be congruent, by the Isosceles Triangle Theorem. Also, the vertex angle of this triangle measures 40°.

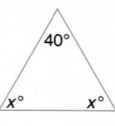

We can use the Angle Sum Theorem to determine the value of *x*. Let *x* represent the measure of each base angle.

$$x + x + 40 = 180$$
$$2x = 140$$
$$x = 70$$

The roof of the A-frame house should meet the ground at a 70° angle.

Since isosceles triangles have many applications to construction and other fields, it is important that we be able to find the measures of their angles.

Example 2

CONNECTION

Algebra

In isosceles triangle *RST*, ∠*R* is the vertex angle. If *m*∠*S* = 7*x* − 17 and *m*∠*T* = 3*x* + 35, find the measure of each angle of the triangle.

Since △*RST* is isosceles, the base angles are congruent.

$$m\angle S = m\angle T$$
$$7x - 17 = 3x + 35 \quad \text{\textit{Substitution property of equality}}$$
$$4x = 52$$
$$x = 13$$

$$m\angle S = 7x - 17 \qquad m\angle T = 3x + 35 \qquad \text{\textit{Calculating both angle}}$$
$$= 7(13) - 17 \qquad\quad = 3(13) + 35 \qquad \text{\textit{measures verifies that}}$$
$$= 74 \qquad\qquad\quad = 74 \qquad\qquad\quad \text{\textit{m}}\angle S = m\angle T.$$

$$m\angle R = 180 - m\angle S - m\angle T$$
$$= 180 - 74 - 74 \text{ or } 32$$

Thus, the measures of ∠*R*, ∠*S*, and ∠*T* are 32, 74, and 74, respectively.

An auxiliary ray is used in the proof of the following theorem, which is the converse of the Isosceles Triangle Theorem.

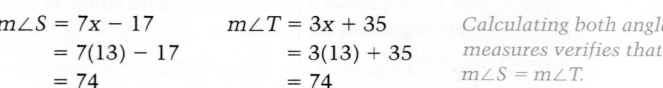

Theorem 4-7

If two angles of a triangle are congruent, then the sides opposite those angles are congruent.

Chalkboard Examples

For Example 1
If ∠*X* is the vertex angle of an isosceles triangle and m∠*X* = 52, find m∠*Y* and m∠*Z*.   64, 64

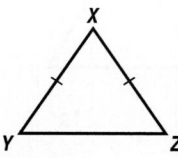

For Example 2
In isosceles triangle *DEF*, ∠*D* is the vertex angle. If m∠*E* = 2*x* + 40 and m∠*F* = 3*x* + 22, find the measure of each angle of the triangle.   m∠*D* = 28, m∠*E* = 76, m∠*F* = 76

Teaching Tip   Point out that Corollary 4-3 is an "if and only if" statement. Ask students to state this corollary another way.   **A triangle is equiangular if and only if it is equilateral.**

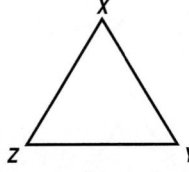
Example 3

*You will be asked to
complete the proof in
Exercise 39.*

Write a plan for a two-column proof for Theorem 4-7.

Draw an auxiliary ray that is the bisector
of ∠*ABC* and let *D* be the point
where the bisector intersects $\overline{AC}$. Show
that △*ABD* ≅ △*CBD* by AAS using the
given information and the auxiliary ray.
Then, $\overline{AB}$ ≅ $\overline{CB}$ by CPCTC.

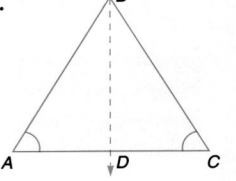

The Isosceles Triangle Theorem leads us to some interesting corollaries.
You will be asked to prove these in Exercises 38 and 37 respectively.

Corollary 4-3	**A triangle is equilateral if and only if it is equiangular.**
Corollary 4-4	**Each angle of an equilateral triangle measures 60°.**

CHECKING FOR UNDERSTANDING

Communicating Mathematics

Read and study the lesson to answer these questions.

1. Describe the special properties of an isosceles triangle. See margin.

2. isosceles

2. If two angles of △*ABC* are congruent, what kind of triangle is *ABC*?

3. Does an equilateral triangle have a line of symmetry? Explain. See margin.

4. Draw and label an isosceles triangle including the congruent parts.
   Identify the base, the legs, the vertex angle, and the base angles. See margin.

Guided Practice

For each exercise, draw △*ABC* with point *D* on $\overline{BC}$ such that the following conditions are satisfied. See Solutions Manual.

5. $\overline{AD}$ bisects ∠*BAC*, but $\overline{BD}$ and $\overline{DC}$ are *not* congruent.

6. $\overline{AD}$ ⊥ $\overline{BC}$, but $\overline{BD}$ and $\overline{DC}$ are *not* congruent.

7. $\overline{BD}$ ≅ $\overline{DC}$, but $\overline{AD}$ is *not* perpendicular to $\overline{BC}$.

8. $\overline{BD}$ ≅ $\overline{DC}$, but $\overline{AD}$ does *not* bisect ∠*BAC*.

9. If $\overline{XW}$ is the perpendicular bisector of $\overline{YZ}$ in △*XYZ* and *W* is on $\overline{YZ}$, what
   type of triangle is △*XYZ*? isosceles

10. If $\overline{XW}$ bisects both ∠*YXZ* and $\overline{YZ}$ in △*XYZ*, must △*XYZ* be isosceles?
    no

Given the following information, name two angles that must be congruent.

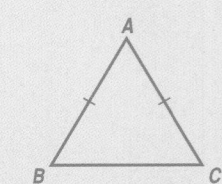

11. ∠*EAB* and ∠4
12. ∠1 and ∠2

11. $\overline{EA}$ ≅ $\overline{EB}$

12. $\overline{AD}$ ≅ $\overline{AC}$

13. $\overline{AF}$ ≅ $\overline{AG}$
    ∠5 and ∠6 or ∠ EFA and ∠ BGA

14. $\overline{FA}$ ≅ $\overline{FE}$
    ∠3 and ∠7

204   CHAPTER 4   CONGRUENT TRIANGLES

Additional Answers

1. Base angles congruent; two
   sides congruent; line
   symmetry
3. Yes; an equilateral triangle is
   isosceles, and an isosceles
   triangle has symmetry.

4.

base: $\overline{BC}$
legs: $\overline{AB}$ and $\overline{AC}$
vertex ∠: ∠*A*
base angles: ∠B and ∠C

Find the value of x.

15. 67
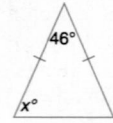
46°
x°

16. 60
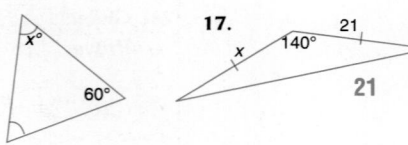
x°
60°

17.

21
140°
x
21

18. Graph $\triangle RST$ with vertices $R(4, 2)$, $S(8, 2)$, and $T(6, 6)$. Prove that $\triangle RST$ is isosceles. **See margin.**

19. Write a two-column proof. **See Solutions Manual.**

Given: $\overline{AB} \cong \overline{BC}$
Prove: $\angle 3 \cong \angle 5$

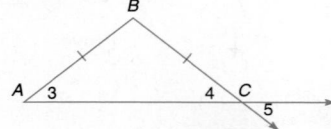
B
A 3   4 C 5

EXERCISES

Practice
A

Find the value of x.

20.
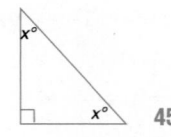
x°
x°
45

21.
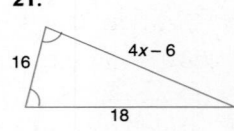
16
4x − 6
18
6

22.
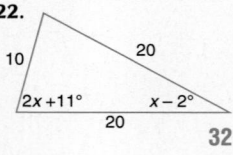
10
20
2x + 11°
x − 2°
20
32

23.
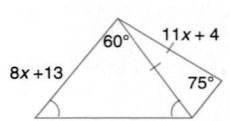
60°
11x + 4
8x + 13
75°
3

24.
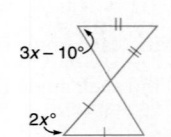
3x − 10°
2x°
25

25.
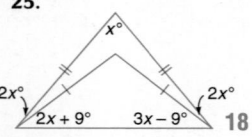
x°
2x°
2x°
2x + 9°
3x − 9°
18

State the conclusions that can be drawn from the given information. Justify your answers. See Solutions Manual.

26. $\angle 1$ and $\angle 3$ are complementary.
$\angle 2$ and $\angle 4$ are complementary.
$\angle 1 \cong \angle 2$

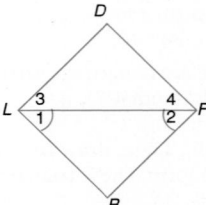
D
L 3 4 F
1 2
B

27. $\overline{TB} \cong \overline{TR}$
$\angle 1 \cong \angle 2$

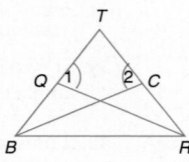
T
Q 1   2 C
B   R

LESSON 4-7 ISOSCELES TRIANGLES **205**

RETEACHING THE LESSON

Find the missing measures in each triangle.

1.
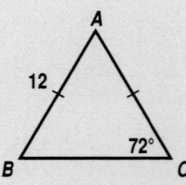
A
12
72°
B   C

$AC = 12$, m$\angle A = 36$, m$\angle B = 72$

2.
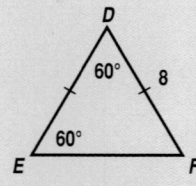
D
60°
8
60°
E   F

$DE = 8$, $EF = 8$, m$\angle F = 60$

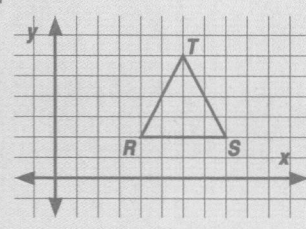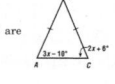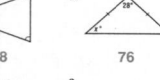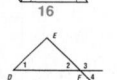

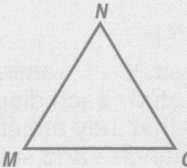
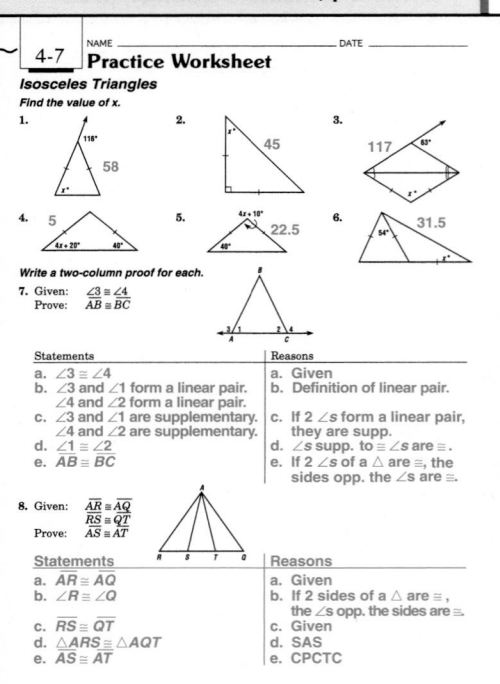
Write a two-column proof for each. See Solutions Manual.

28. **Given:** $\overline{AB} \cong \overline{BC}$
    Prove: ∠3 ≅ ∠4

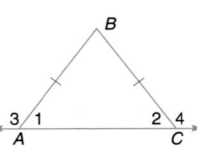

29. **Given:** $\overline{PS} \cong \overline{QR}$
    ∠3 ≅ ∠4
    Prove: ∠1 ≅ ∠2

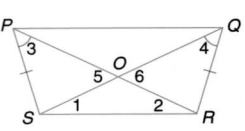

30. **Given:** $\overline{ZT} \cong \overline{ZR}$
    $\overline{TX} \cong \overline{RY}$
    Prove: ∠5 ≅ ∠7

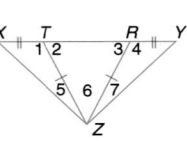

31. **Given:** △ABC is isosceles.
    $\overline{DE} \parallel \overline{AB}$, $\overline{AC} \cong \overline{BC}$
    Prove: △DEC is isosceles.

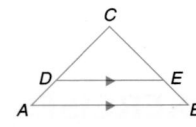

32. **Given:** ∠5 ≅ ∠6
    $\overline{GJ} \perp \overline{FH}$
    Prove: △FHJ is isosceles.

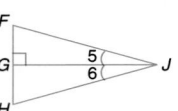

33. **Given:** $\overline{AB} \cong \overline{AC}$
    $\overline{BX}$ bisects ∠ABC
    $\overline{CX}$ bisects ∠ACB
    Prove: $\overline{BX} \cong \overline{CX}$

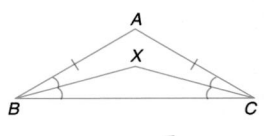
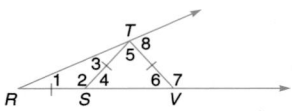

34. Find each angle measure if m∠1 = 30. See margin.
35. Find each angle measure if m∠8 = 60. See margin.

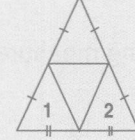

 36. △RST is an isosceles triangle with two vertices R(3, 8) and S(-2, 1). If ∠R is the vertex angle, could (8, 1) be the coordinates of T? Explain. **yes; If T is (8, 1), RS = RT.**

Write a two-column proof for each. 37. See margin.

37. Each angle of an equilateral triangle measures 60°. (Corollary 4-4)

38. A triangle is equilateral if and only if it is equiangular. (Corollary 4-3)
    Hint: Since the statement contains if and only if, the proof must show that an equilateral triangle is equiangular and that an equiangular triangle is equilateral. **See Solutions Manual.**

39. If two angles of a triangle are congruent, then the sides opposite those angles are congruent. (Theorem 4-7). **See Solutions Manual.**

Critical Thinking

40. Draw an isosceles triangle. Then, draw line segments connecting the midpoints of the sides to form a new triangle. What type of triangle is formed? Explain. **See margin.**

Additional Answer

40. Isosceles; the midpoints cut the sides of the isosceles triangle in half, so the halves will be congruent also. The small triangles, 1 and 2, can be proved congruent. This makes the small triangle isosceles by CPCTC.

41. Hang Gliding The sail of a certain type of hang glider consists of two congruent isosceles triangles joined along the keel so that a 90° angle is formed at the nose of the sail. In order to construct such a sail, what must be the measure of ∠BCD? **135**

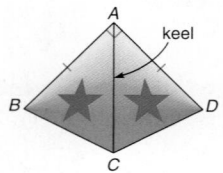

42. If the surface is level then it is horizontal. The plumb line will be vertical, so it is perpendicular to the surface. A perpendicular dropped from the vertex angle of an isosceles triangle will pass through the midpoint of the base.

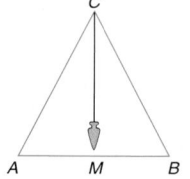

42. Carpentry Before the invention of the bubble level, carpenters used a device called a *plumb level* to verify that a surface was level. This level consisted of a frame in the shape of an isosceles triangle with the midpoint of the base (point *M* in the figure at the left) marked. A plumb line was suspended from the vertex angle. To use this instrument, the carpenter would hold it upright with the base resting on the surface to be leveled. If the surface was level, over what point on the base do you think the plumb line would hang? Explain. **point *M*; see margin.**

43. Use the BASIC program to find the measures of the base angles of an isosceles triangle which has a vertex angle of the given measure.

```
10 INPUT "ENTER THE MEASURE OF THE VERTEX ANGLE OF AN
   ISOSCELES TRIANGLE."; A
20 B = (180 − A)/2
30 "THE BASE ANGLES OF THE ISOSCELES TRIANGLE ARE EACH ";
   B; " DEGREES."
40 END
```

a. 26 **77**   b. 120 **30**   c. 32 **74**

d. 78 **51**   e. 85 **47.5**   f. 101 **39.5**

45. ∠NTI ≅ ∠NCA, ∠TIN ≅ ∠CAN, and $\overline{TN} \cong \overline{CN}$; ∠NTI ≅ ∠NCA, ∠TIN ≅ ∠CAN, and $\overline{IN} \cong \overline{AN}$; ∠NTI ≅ ∠NCA, ∠INT ≅ ∠ANC, and $\overline{TI} \cong \overline{CA}$; ∠NTI ≅ ∠NCA, ∠INT ≅ ∠ANC, and $\overline{IN} \cong \overline{AN}$; ∠TIN ≅ ∠CAN, ∠INT ≅ ∠ANC, and $\overline{TI} \cong \overline{CA}$; ∠TIN ≅ ∠CAN, ∠INT ≅ ∠ANC, and $\overline{TN} \cong \overline{CN}$

47. ∠1 ≅ ∠4 ≅ ∠5 ≅ ∠8; ∠2 ≅ ∠3 ≅ ∠6 ≅ ∠7; angles that are supplementary because the lines are parallel: ∠2 and ∠5, ∠4 and ∠6, ∠1 and ∠7, ∠3 and ∠8; angles that are supplementary because they form linear pairs: ∠1 and ∠2, ∠2 and ∠4, ∠4 and ∠3, ∠3 and ∠1, ∠5 and ∠7, ∠7 and ∠8, ∠8 and ∠6, ∠6 and ∠5.

44. △BLS ≅ △BES; ∠LBS ≅ ∠EBS; △LBU ≅ △EBU; ∠LUS ≅ ∠EUS

44. Identify the subgoals you would need to accomplish to complete the proof. **(Lesson 4-6)**

Given: $\overline{BL} \cong \overline{BE}$
        $\overline{LS} \cong \overline{ES}$

Prove: ∠LUS ≅ ∠EUS

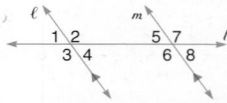

45. List combinations of congruent corresponding parts that could be used to prove that △TIN ≅ △CAN by AAS. **(Lesson 4-5)** **See margin.**

46. Algebra The measures of the angles of △MAP are x + 14, 3x + 1, and 6x − 5. Find the measures of the angles. **(Lesson 4-2)** **31, 52, 97**

47. List all of the conclusions that can be drawn from the figure. **(Lesson 3-2)** **See margin.**

48. Determine if a valid conclusion can be made from these two statements.
- If a student scores 92 or above on the Geometry test, he or she will receive an A.
- Don scored 94 on the Geometry test.

State the law of logic you used. **(Lesson 2-3)** **Don will receive an A on the Geometry test; detachment**

49. Write a five-question quiz that covers the major concepts of this lesson. **See students' work.**

LESSON 4-7   ISOSCELES TRIANGLES   207

Review the items in your portfolio. Make a table of contents of the items, noting why each item was chosen. Replace any items that are no longer appropriate.

EXTENDING THE LESSON

Math Power: Using Communication

Discuss the statement, "You need to know the measure of only one angle in an isosceles triangle in order to find the measure of all three." To what extent is this statement true?

One can find all the measures of the angles in an isosceles triangle given one measure if one also knows if that angle is a base angle or the vertex angle.

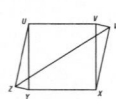

Using the Chapter Summary and Review

The Chapter Summary and Review begins with an alphabetical listing of the new terms that were presented in the chapter. Have students define each term and provide an example of it, if appropriate.

The Skills and Concepts presented in the chapter are reviewed using a side-by-side format. Encourage students to refer to the Objectives and Examples on the left as they complete the Review Exercises on the right.

The Chapter Summary and Review ends with exercises that review Applications and Connections.

CHAPTER

4 | SUMMARY AND REVIEW

VOCABULARY

After completing this chapter, you should be familiar with the following terms:

acute triangle	**164**	**165**	legs
base	**165**	**202**	line symmetry
base angles	**165**	**164**	obtuse triangle
corollary	**173**	**172**	remote interior angles
equiangular	**164**	**164**	right triangle
equilateral	**165**	**165**	scalene triangle
exterior angle	**172**	**164**	sides
hypotenuse	**165**	**165**	vertex angle
included angle	**185**	**164**	vertices
isosceles triangle	**165**		

SKILLS AND CONCEPTS

OBJECTIVES AND EXAMPLES	REVIEW EXERCISES

Upon completing this chapter, you should be able to:

- identify parts of triangles and classify triangles by their parts. **(Lesson 4-1)**

Types of Triangles

Classification by Angles	
acute	three acute angles
obtuse	one obtuse angle
right	one right angle
equiangular	three congruent angles

Classification by Sides	
scalene	no two sides congruent
isosceles	at least two sides congruent
equilateral	three sides congruent

Use these exercises to review and prepare for the chapter test.

In figure ABCDE, ∠BAE and ∠BDE are right angles and the congruent parts are indicated.

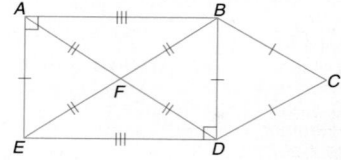

1. Name the right triangle(s). △ABE, △DBE
2. Which triangle is equilateral? △BCD
3. Which segment is opposite ∠C? $\overline{BD}$
4. Name the acute triangle(s). △AFE, △BDF, △BCD
5. Which triangles are isosceles?
6. Name the obtuse triangle(s). △ABF, △DFE
   5. △ABF, △BFD, △DFE, △AFE, △BCD

Additional Answer

25. Statements   (Reasons)
    a. *E* is the midpoint of $\overline{AC}$.
       ∠1 ≅ ∠2   (Given)
    b. $\overline{AE} ≅ \overline{CE}$ (Definition of midpoint)
    c. ∠BEC ≅ ∠DEA   (Vertical ∠s are ≅)
    d. △BEC ≅ △DEA   (ASA)
    e. ∠3 ≅ ∠4   (CPCTC)

OBJECTIVES AND EXAMPLES

- use the angle sum and exterior angle theorems. **(Lesson 4-2)**

Find the values of x and y.

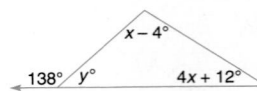

By the exterior angle theorem,
$$(x - 4) + (4x + 12) = 138$$
$$5x = 130$$
$$x = 26$$

By the angle sum theorem,
$$(x - 4) + (4x + 12) + y = 180$$
$$(26 - 4) + (4(26) + 12) + y = 180$$
$$138 + y = 180$$
$$y = 42$$

- identify congruent triangles and name corresponding parts of congruent triangles. **(Lesson 4-3)**

Definition of Congruent Triangles

Two triangles are congruent if and only if their corresponding parts are congruent.

- use SAS, SSS, and ASA postulates to test for triangle congruence. **(Lesson 4-4)**

Given: $\overline{LN}$ and $\overline{OP}$ bisect each other at M.

Prove: $\angle O \cong \angle P$

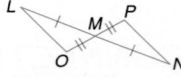

Statements	Reasons
1. $\overline{LN}$ and $\overline{OP}$ bisect each other at M.	1. Given
2. $\overline{LM} \cong \overline{MN}$ $\overline{PM} \cong \overline{MO}$	2. Definition of bisector
3. $\angle LMO \cong \angle NMP$	3. Vertical ⚞ are ≅.
4. $\triangle LMO \cong \triangle NMP$	4. SAS
5. $\angle O \cong \angle P$	5. CPCTC

REVIEW EXERCISES

In $\triangle MNO$, $\overline{MO} \perp \overline{ON}$, $\overline{OP} \perp \overline{MN}$, and $m\angle N = 37$. Find the measure of each angle.

7. $\angle OMN$ 53
8. $\angle MON$ 90
9. $\angle PON$ 53
10. $\angle MOP$ 37

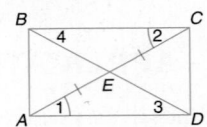

Use the information from the figure to find each measure.

11. x 120   12. w 60
13. v 60   14. r 55
15. s 55   16. t 65
17. y 25   18. z 35

Draw triangles $\triangle GHI$ and $\triangle JKL$. Label the corresponding parts if $\triangle GHI \cong \triangle JKL$. Use the figures to complete each statement.

19. $\angle L \cong \underline{?}$ $\angle I$ 22. $\angle IHG$ 24. $\angle KLJ$
20. $\overline{GI} \cong \underline{?}$ $\overline{JL}$
21. $\overline{KJ} \cong \underline{?}$ $\overline{HG}$ 22. $\angle LKJ \cong \underline{?}$
23. $\overline{LJ} \cong \underline{?}$ $\overline{IG}$ 24. $\angle HIG \cong \underline{?}$

Write a two-column proof for each. See margin.

25. **Given:** E is the midpoint of $\overline{AC}$.
$\angle 1 \cong \angle 2$
Prove: $\angle 3 \cong \angle 4$

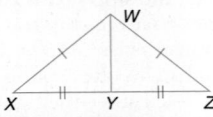

26. **Given:** $\triangle WXZ$ is isosceles.
Y is the midpoint of $\overline{XZ}$.
Prove: $\overline{YW}$ bisects $\angle XWZ$.

Alternate Review Strategy

To provide a brief in-class review, you may wish to read the following questions to the class and have them answer verbally.

1. Explain how you could identify each type of triangle.
   right   **contains one right angle**
   obtuse   **contains one obtuse angle**
   acute   **contains three acute angles**
   isosceles   **at least two sides congruent**
   equilateral   **all three sides congruent**
   scalene   **no two sides congruent**
2. The angles of a triangle measure $3x + 5$, $4x - 6$, and $x - 3$. What is the value of x?   **23**
3. An exterior angle at A of $\triangle ABC$ measures $12x$. If $m\angle B = 7x - 2$ and $m\angle C = 6x - 8$, what is the value of x?   **10**
4. If $\triangle ABC \cong \triangle DEF$, which sides and angles of the triangles are congruent?
   $\overline{AB} \cong \overline{DE}$, $\overline{AC} \cong \overline{DF}$, $\overline{BC} \cong \overline{EF}$, $\angle A \cong \angle D$, $\angle B \cong \angle E$, and $\angle C \cong \angle F$.
5. If you wanted to prove $\triangle ABC \cong \triangle XYZ$ using the SAS postulate, name three parts of each triangle you would have to prove congruent.   **Sample answer: $\overline{AB} \cong \overline{XY}$; $\angle B \cong \angle Y$; and $\overline{BC} \cong \overline{YZ}$.**
6. What theorem enabled you to prove Theorem 4-5 (AAS) using Postulate 4-3 (ASA)?   **Angle Sum Theorem (Sum of angles in a triangle is 180.)**
7. If one base angle of an isosceles triangle is $4x + 2$ and the vertex angle is $4x - 4$, what is the measure of the vertex angle?   **56**
8. If three sides of an equilateral triangle measure $4x + 5$, $7x - 16$, and $3y + 3$, what is the value of y?   **10**

A two-page Cumulative Review from the *Evaluation Masters* is shown below. It can be used to review skills and concepts presented thus far in the text. Standardized Test Practice Questions are also provided in the *Evaluation Masters*.

Evaluation Masters, pp. 53-54

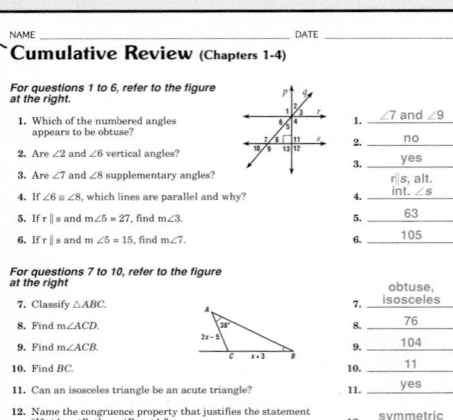

NAME _____ DATE _____

~ **Cumulative Review** (Chapters 1-4)

For questions 1 to 6, refer to the figure at the right.

1. Which of the numbered angles appears to be obtuse?
   1. ∠7 and ∠9
2. Are ∠2 and ∠6 vertical angles?
   2. no
3. Are ∠7 and ∠8 supplementary angles?
   3. yes
4. If ∠6 ≅ ∠8, which lines are parallel and why?
   4. r∥s, alt. int. ∠s
5. If r ∥ s and m∠5 = 27, find m∠3.
   5. 63
6. If r ∥ s and m∠5 = 15, find m∠7.
   6. 105

For questions 7 to 10, refer to the figure at the right

7. Classify △ABC.
   7. obtuse, isosceles
8. Find m∠ACD.
   8. 76
9. Find m∠ACB.
   9. 104
10. Find BC.
    10. 11
11. Can an isosceles triangle be an acute triangle?
    11. yes
12. Name the congruence property that justifies the statement "If ∠A ≅ ∠B, then ∠B ≅ ∠A."
    12. symmetric
13. The measure of an angle is 18 less than twice its complement. Find the measure of the angle.
    13. 54

Refer to the figure to complete each statement. Justify your answers.

14. If DC ≅ AE and ∠ACD ≅ ∠EAC, then △ _?_ ≅ △ _?_ .
    14. △ACD ≅ △ACE by SAS
15. If BD ≅ BE and ∠BDC ≅ ∠BEA, then △ _?_ ≅ △ _?_ .
    15. △BDC ≅ △BEA by ASA
16. If ∠FAC ≅ ∠FCA and DF ≅ EF, then △ _?_ ≅ △ _?_ .
    16. △ADF ≅ △ECF by SAS

53
Glencoe Division, Macmillan/McGraw-Hill

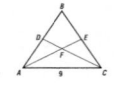

NAME _____ DATE _____

~ **Cumulative Review** (Chapters 1-4)—Continued

17. John, Joe and Jim each play an instrument. The instruments are the drums, the sax and the trombone. Joe and the drummer are in the same Geometry class. The sax player and the drummer go to Jim's house to practice. Who plays the trombone?
    17. Jim

18. The faces of a cube are numbered with consecutive numbers. Three of the numbers are shown. What are the possible sums of the numbers on all the faces of the cube?
    18. 123; 129

Write a conjecture based on the given information. Draw a figure to illustrate your conjecture.

19. Given: M is the midpoint of AB.
    19. See students' work

Write the converse of each conditional. Determine if the converse is true or false.

20. If an angle measures 128°, then it is obtuse.
    20. See students' work; false
21. If two lines have the same slope, then they are parallel and nonvertical.
    21. See students' work; true

For questions 22-25, refer to the coordinate grid.

22. Classify triangle ABC.
    22. right, scalene
23. What is the slope of any line parallel to BC?
    23. −1
24. B is the midpoint of AD. What are the coordinates of D?
    24. (−6, −3)
25. What is the length of any segment congruent to AC?
    25. √82

54
Glencoe Division, Macmillan/McGraw-Hill

210   Chapter 4

■ use AAS theorem to test for triangle congruence. **(Lesson 4-5)**

AAS

If two angles and a nonincluded side of one triangle are congruent to the corresponding two angles and side of a second triangle, the two triangles are congruent.

Write a paragraph proof for each. See margin.

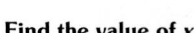

27. **Given:** KL ≅ ML
    ∠J ≅ ∠N
    ∠1 ≅ ∠2
    Prove: JK ≅ NM

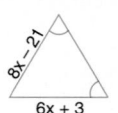

28. **Given:** JL ≅ NL
    ∠1 ≅ ∠2
    KL ≅ ML
    Prove: ∠K ≅ ∠M

■ use the properties of isosceles and equilateral triangles. **(Lesson 4-7)**

In isosceles triangle FGH, ∠H is the vertex angle. If m∠F = 5x − 6 and m∠G = 3x + 14, find the measure of each angle of the triangle.

Since △FGH is isosceles and ∠H is the vertex angle, m∠F = m∠G.

$$5x − 6 = 3x + 14 \qquad m∠F = 5x − 6$$
$$2x = 20 \qquad\qquad = 5(10) − 6$$
$$x = 10 \qquad\qquad = 44$$

$$m∠F + m∠G + m∠H = 180$$
$$44 + 44 + m∠H = 180$$
$$m∠H = 92$$

The measures of the angles are 44, 44, and 92.

Find the value of x.

29. 12
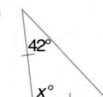

30. 96
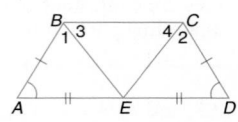

Write a two-column proof. See Solutions Manual.

31. **Given:** ∠A ≅ ∠D
    AB ≅ DC
    E is the midpoint of AD.
    Prove: ∠3 ≅ ∠4

APPLICATIONS AND CONNECTIONS

32. **Sports**   The sail for a sailboat is a right triangle. If the angle at the top of the sail measures 54°, what is the measure of the angle at the bottom? **(Lesson 4-2)** 36

33. **Number Theory**   Find a three-digit number that is a perfect square and a perfect cube. **(Lesson 4-6)** 729

34. **Navigation**   The captain of a ship uses an instrument called a *pelorus* to note the angle between the ship's path and the line from the ship to a lighthouse. The captain finds the distance that the ship travels and the change in the measure of the angle with the lighthouse as the ship progresses. When the angle with the lighthouse is twice that of the original angle, the captain knows that the ship is as far from the lighthouse as the ship has traveled since the lighthouse was first sighted. Why? **(Lesson 4-7)** See Solutions Manual.

Additional Answers

27. We are given that KL ≅ ML, ∠J ≅ ∠N, and ∠1 ≅ ∠2. Therefore, △JKL ≅ △NML by AAS. So, JK ≅ NM by CPCTC.

28. It is given that JL ≅ NL, ∠1 ≅ ∠2, and KL ≅ ML. So, △JKL ≅ △NML by SAS. Therefore, ∠K ≅ ∠M by CPCTC.

In figure *PQRST*, ∠*R* is right and the congruent parts are indicated.

1. Name the isosceles triangle(s). △*PSQ*, △*PST*
2. Which triangle is right? △*QRS*
3. Which segment of △*PTS* is opposite∠*T*? $\overline{PS}$
4. Name the triangle(s) that appear to be scalene. △*QRS*

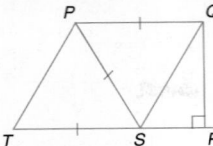

This page may be used as a test or as a review. In addition, two multiple-choice tests (Forms 1A and 1B) and two free-response tests (Forms 2A and 2B) are provided in the *Evaluation Masters*. Chapter 4 Test, Form 1A is shown below.

In the figure, $\overline{GH} \cong \overline{GL}$, $\overline{GI} \cong \overline{GK}$, $\overline{GJ} \perp \overline{HL}$ m∠3 = 30, and m∠4 = 20. Find each measure.

5. m∠8 90
6. m∠7 90
7. m∠9 60
8. m∠6 60
9. m∠2 30
10. m∠5 120
11. m∠10 120
12. m∠L 40
13. m∠H 40
14. m∠1 20

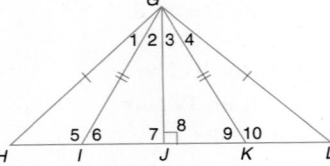

Evaluation Masters, pp. 43-44

Name the additional pairs of corresponding parts that would have to be proved congruent in order to use the given postulate or theorem to prove the triangles congruent.

15. SSS $\overline{PB} \cong \overline{RW}$
16. SAS $\overline{PB} \cong \overline{RW}$ or ∠*X* ≅ ∠*H*
17. AAS ∠*B* ≅ ∠*R* or ∠*X* ≅ ∠*H*
18. ASA ∠*X* ≅ ∠*H*

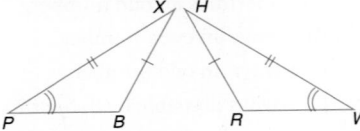

19. Find the greatest four-digit whole number with exactly three factors. 9409

20. **Given:** $\overline{AC} \perp \overline{BD}$
    ∠*B* ≅ ∠*D*
    Prove: *C* is the midpoint of $\overline{BD}$. **See Solutions Manual.**

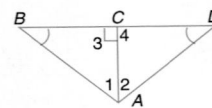

Bonus

History   When a march by Napoleon's army was blocked by a stream, a young soldier found the distance across the stream by sighting the angle to the opposite edge of the stream with the brim of his hat. He then turned and, without raising or lowering his head, sighted the point in line with the brim of his hat. He paced off the distance to this point and reported the distance across the stream. How did the soldier know the distance? Why did his method work? **See Solutions Manual.**

Test and Review Generator software is provided in Apple, IBM, and Macintosh versions. You may use this software to create your own tests or worksheets, based on the needs of your students.

The **Performance Assessment Booklet** provides an alternate assessment for evaluating student progress. An assessment for this chapter can be found on pages 7-8.

The questions on these pages may be used to help students prepare for college entrance exams such as the SAT test.

These questions require careful analysis and thorough understanding of the concepts.

These pages can be used as an overnight assignment.

After students have completed the pages, discuss how each problem can be solved, or provide copies of the solutions from the *Merrill Geometry Solutions Manual*.

College Entrance Exam Preview

Directions: Choose the one best answer. Write A, B, C, or D. You may use a calculator.

1.
B

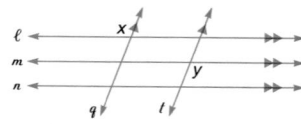

If $\ell \parallel m$ in the figure above, which of the following must be equal to 180?

I. $m\angle 3 + m\angle 5$
II. $m\angle 4 + m\angle 6$
III. $m\angle 1 + m\angle 7$
IV. $m\angle 2 + m\angle 8$
V. $m\angle 7 + m\angle 8$

(A) I and II only

(B) III and IV only

(C) V only

(D) I, II, III, and IV only

2. The sum of an odd number and an even
C number is

(A) sometimes an odd number.

(B) always an even number.

(C) always an odd number.

(D) always divisible by 3, 5, or 7.

3. If $|6x - 8| = 10$, then $x =$
B

(A) 3   (B) 3 or $-\frac{1}{3}$

(C) $\frac{1}{3}$ or -3   (D) 0

4.
A

If $\ell \parallel m \parallel n$ and $q \parallel t$, then

(A) $m\angle x = m\angle y$

(B) $m\angle x > m\angle y$

(C) $m\angle x < m\angle y$

(D) cannot determine the relationship between $m\angle x$ and $m\angle y$

5. A basket holds 65 apples. Thirteen of
D the apples are rotten. What percentage of the apples are good?

(A) 20%   (B) 52%

(C) 95%   (D) 80%

6. What is the slope of the line that passes
A through the points (-4, 8) and (3, -7)?

(A) $-\frac{15}{7}$ (B) -2

(C) -1   (D) $-\frac{7}{15}$

7. What is the average of $a + 5$, $2a - 4$,
C and $3a + 8$?

(A) $2a$ (B) $3a + 3$

(C) $2a + 3$ (C) $6a + 9$

8. Three vertices of a parallelogram are at
B (2, 1), (-1, -3), and (6, 4). The fourth vertex is at

(A) (0, 3)   (B) (3, 0)

(C) (-1, 4)   (D) (6, 1)

9. For all $x \neq 0$, $\dfrac{x^6 + x^6 + x^6}{x^3} =$
D

(A) x^6 (B) $3x^2$

(C) $x^3 + 2x^6$ (D) none of these

10. Tickets to the spring play were \$2 for
B students and \$4 for adults. A total of 250 tickets were sold. If s is the number of student tickets sold, which of the following is a formula for the total sales in dollars?

(A) $2s + 1000$

(B) $2s + 4(250 - s)$

(C) $4s + 2(250 + s)$

(D) $4s + 500$

Solve. You may use a calculator.

11. In the figure below, lines ℓ and m are parallel. List three angles, all having the same measure.

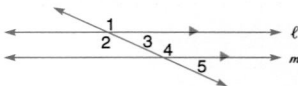

$\angle 1, \angle 2, \angle 4$

12. One hundred high school students were asked how many courses they were taking that school year. The results are recorded in the table below. What is the average number of courses that a student in this group is taking?

Number of Courses	5	6	7	8
Number of Students	9	19	52	20

6.83 courses

13. Twenty-two students have chartered a bus to travel to the championship basketball game and will split the cost equally. After 17 of the students have turned in their share, $131.75 has been collected. What is the cost of chartering the bus?

$170.50

14. A box contains 75 red, blue, and green pens. If 24% are red and 17 pens are blue, what fraction of the pens are green?

$\frac{8}{15}$

15. Mark can type 45 words per minute, and there is an average of 450 words per page. At this rate, how many hours would it take Mark to type a paper x pages long?

$\frac{x}{6}$ **hours**

CHAPTER 5
Applying Congruent Triangles

Lesson Objective Chart

Lesson (Pages)	Lesson Objectives	State/Local Objectives
5-1 (216-222)	**5-1**: Identify and use medians, altitudes, angle bisectors, and perpendicular bisectors in a triangle.	
5-2 (223-229)	**5-2**: Recognize and use tests for congruence of right triangles.	
5-3 (230-232)	**5-3**: Solve problems by working backward.	
5-4 (233-239)	**5-4A**: Use indirect reasoning and indirect proof to reach a conclusion.	
	5-4B: Recognize and apply the properties of inequalities to the measures of segments and angles.	
5-5 (240-245)	**5-5**: Recognize and use relationships between sides and angles in a triangle.	
5-6 (246-250)	**5-6**: Apply the triangle inequality theorem.	
5-7 (252-257)	**5-7**: Use the SAS Inequality and SSS Inequality in proofs and to solve problems.	

ORGANIZING THE CHAPTER

You may want to refer to the **Course Planning Calendar** on page T28.

Lesson Planning Guide / Blackline Masters Booklets

Lesson (Pages)	Pacing Chart (days) Course I	II	III	Reteaching	Practice	Enrichment	Evaluation	Technology	Lab Manual	Activities Mixed Problem Solving	Applications	Cooperative Learning Activity	Multicultural	Transparencies
5-1 (216-222)	2	2	2	p. 26	p. 30	p. 26		p. 5	pp.42-45			p. 33		5-1
5-2 (223-229)	2	2	2	p. 27	p. 31	p. 27	Quiz A, p. 65		pp.46-49		p. 19			5-2
5-3 (230-232)	1	1	1		p. 32					p. 5				5-3
5-4 (233-239)	2	2	1.5	p. 28	p. 33	p. 28	Quiz B, p. 65							5-4
5-5 (240-245)	2	2	1.5	p. 29	p. 34	p. 29	Mid-Chapter Test, p. 69						p. 5	5-5
5-6 (246-250)	1	1	1	p. 30	p. 35	p. 30	Quiz C, p. 66							5-6
5-7 (252-257)	2	1	1	p. 31	p. 36	p. 31	Quiz D, p. 66	p. 41						5-7
Review (258-260)	1	1	1	Multiple Choice Tests, Forms 1A and 1B, pp. 57-60 Free Response Tests, Forms 2A and 2B, pp. 61-64										
Test (261)	1	1	1	Cumulative Review. pp. 67-68 Standardized Tests Practice Questions, p. 70										

Course I: Chapters 1-11; Course II: Chapters 1-12; Course III: Chapters 1-13

Other Chapter Resources

Student Edition
Chapter Opener, pp. 214-215
Journal Entry, pp. 222, 257
History Connection, p. 229
Cooperative Learning Project, p. 232
Mid-Chapter Review, p. 239
History Connection, p. 245
Portfolio, p. 250
Technology, p. 251
Algebra Review, pp. 262-263
More Investigations in Geometry, pp. A6-A7
Extended Project 2, pp. B6-B9

Teacher's Classroom Resources
Transparency 5-0
Real World Applications Transparencies, 9, 10
Performance Assessment Booklet, pp. 9-10
Problem-of-the-Week Activity Cards, 12, 13, 14
Tech Prep Applications Booklet, pp. 9-10
LOGO Instruction Materials, Technology Masters pp. 19-36

Other Supplements
Flow Proof and Indirect Proof
Algebra and Geometry Overhead Manipulative Resources
Glencoe Mathematics Professional Series

Software
Test and Review Generator (Apple, IBM, and Macintosh)
Teacher's Guide for Software Resources

ENHANCING THE CHAPTER

Cooperative Learning

Planning Teaching Materials

When groups have had substantial experience and exhibit reasonable competence in cooperative-learning skills, you may not have to give much special care to how you arrange materials. However, until this stage is achieved, you should consider how to distribute material in order to communicate that the activity is to be a group and not an individual activity. One way to do this is to provide only one set of materials or one copy of the worksheet to the group. The members will quickly realize that they have to work together if they are to be successful in achieving the objective and receiving your recognition. A variation on this method is to provide each member of the group with a worksheet but tell the group that you will collect only one of them, chosen at random. This method also encourages members to help one another and to make sure that each member has and understands the correct answer. A third method, appropriate in some activities, is to give each member only part of the materials or resources required to complete the task. Thus, every member must participate if the whole group is to be successful.

Technology

The Technology Feature following Lesson 5-6 uses a BASIC program to test any three numbers to see if they may be the measures of the sides of a triangle. This is an excellent example of the use of BASIC to help make a task that can be long and tiresome very simple and short. Students are asked to use the program to check several sets of numbers and are then asked two questions regarding the program. You may wish to discuss their answers to these questions in class. Challenge students to use their own sets of numbers in the program.

Critical Thinking

The ability to evaluate data and make sound judgments or decisions involves a thorough understanding and fluency with the vocabulary and how language is used or misused. Students will enjoy applying the content of this chapter while engaging their critical-thinking skills to analyze propaganda, the most familiar type being TV advertising. For example, have students work in small groups to choose a current popular ad, state what conclusion the advertiser wants the viewer to assume, identify the data supplied to support this conclusion (if any), list additional data that is required to actually support the conclusion, and describe other equally valid conclusions that could be made based on the same data, along with an explanation.

Cooperative Learning, p. 33

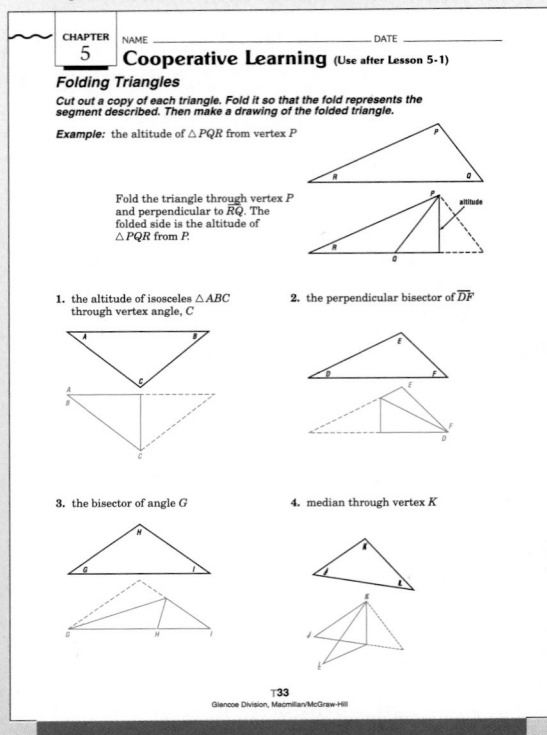

Technology, p. 41

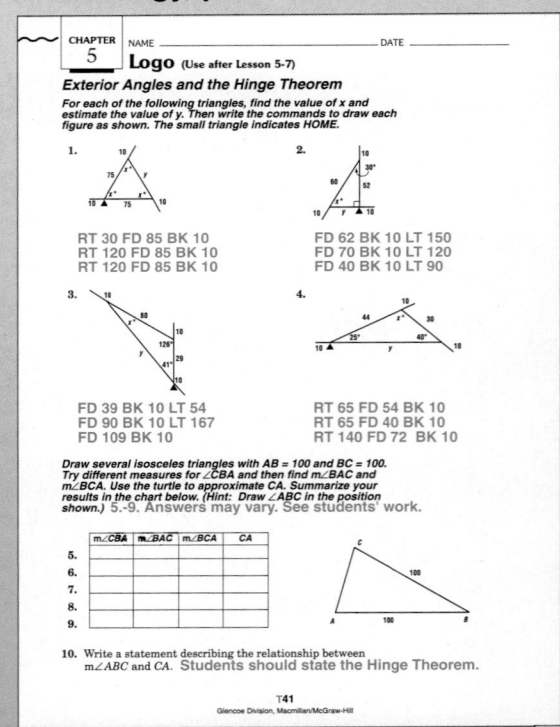

Problem of the Week Activity

The card shown below is one of three available for this chapter. It can be used as a class or small group activity.

Activity Card

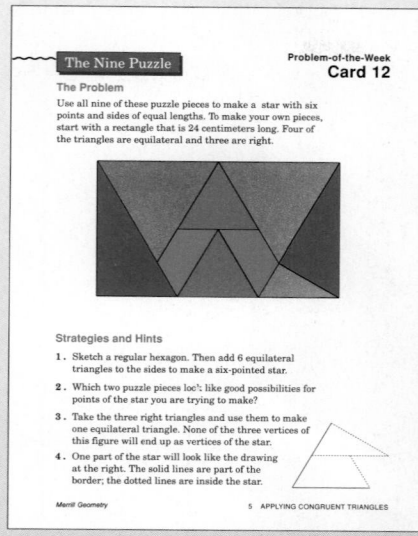

The Nine Puzzle

Problem-of-the-Week
Card 12

The Problem

Use all nine of these puzzle pieces to make a star with six points and sides of equal lengths. To make your own pieces, start with a rectangle that is 24 centimeters long. Four of the triangles are equilateral and three are right.

Strategies and Hints

1. Sketch a regular hexagon. Then add 6 equilateral triangles to the sides to make a six-pointed star.
2. Which two puzzle pieces look like good possibilities for points of the star you are trying to make?
3. Take the three right triangles and use them to make one equilateral triangle. None of the three vertices of this figure will end up as vertices of the star.
4. One part of the star will look like the drawing at the right. The solid lines are part of the border; the dotted lines are inside the star.

Merrill Geometry   5   APPLYING CONGRUENT TRIANGLES

Manipulatives and Models

The following materials may be used as models or manipulatives in Chapter 5.

- paper, pins (Lesson 5-1)
- toothpicks (Lesson 5-2)
- compass (Lesson 5-5)
- rubber bands (Lesson 5-5)
- straws, pipe cleaners, twist ties (Lesson 5-6)
- straws (Lesson 5-7)

Outside Resources

Books/Periodicals

Johnson, D. and G. Rising. *Guidelines for Teaching Mathematics.* Wadsworth Publishing Co.

Kotz, Samuel and Donna F. Stroup. *Educational Stressing - How to Cope in an Uncertain World.* Marcel Dekker, Inc.

Wilder, R. *Evolution of Mathematical Concepts: An Elementary Study.* John Wiley and Sons.

Films/Videotapes/Videodiscs

The Mechanical Universe . . . and Beyond, Part I, California Institute of Technology and the Southern California Consortium, 1-800-LEARNER

Software

Geometric Supposer: Triangles, WINGS for Learning/Sunburst, 101 Castleton St., Pleasantville, NY 10570

IBM Geodraw, EduQuest, 4111 Northside Pkwy NW, P.O. Box 2150, Atlanta, GA 30055

Multicultural

Multicultural Activity, p. 5

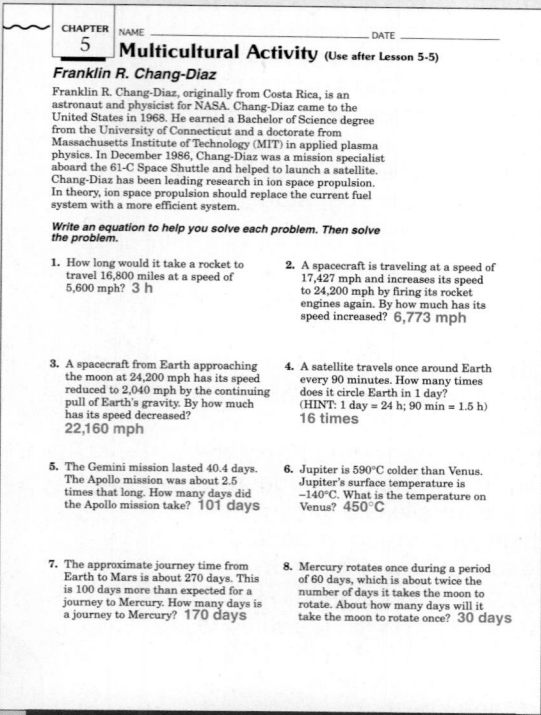

CHAPTER 5   NAME _____ DATE _____

Multicultural Activity (Use after Lesson 5-5)

Franklin R. Chang-Diaz

Franklin R. Chang-Diaz, originally from Costa Rica, is an astronaut and physicist for NASA. Chang-Diaz came to the United States in 1968. He earned a Bachelor of Science degree from the University of Connecticut and a doctorate from Massachusetts Institute of Technology (MIT) in applied plasma physics. In December 1986, Chang-Diaz was a mission specialist aboard the 61-C Space Shuttle and helped to launch a satellite. Chang-Diaz has been leading research in ion space propulsion. In theory, ion space propulsion should replace the current fuel system with a more efficient system.

Write an equation to help you solve each problem. Then solve the problem.

1. How long would it take a rocket to travel 16,800 miles at a speed of 5,600 mph? 3 h

2. A spacecraft is traveling at a speed of 17,427 mph and increases its speed to 24,200 mph by firing its rocket engines again. By how much has its speed increased? 6,773 mph

3. A spacecraft from Earth approaching the moon at 24,200 mph has its speed reduced to 2,040 mph by the continuing pull of Earth's gravity. By how much has its speed decreased? 22,160 mph

4. A satellite travels once around Earth every 90 minutes. How many times does it circle Earth in 1 day? (HINT: 1 day = 24 h; 90 min = 1.5 h) 16 times

5. The Gemini mission lasted 40.4 days. The Apollo mission was about 2.5 times that long. How many days did the Apollo mission take? 101 days

6. Jupiter is 590°C colder than Venus. Jupiter's surface temperature is −140°C. What is the temperature on Venus? 450°C

7. The approximate journey time from Earth to Mars is about 270 days. This is 100 days more than expected for a journey to Mercury. How many days is a journey to Mercury? 170 days

8. Mercury rotates once during a period of 60 days, which is about twice the number of days it takes the moon to rotate. About how many days will it take the moon to rotate once? 30 days

Lab Manual

Lab Activity, pp. 42-45

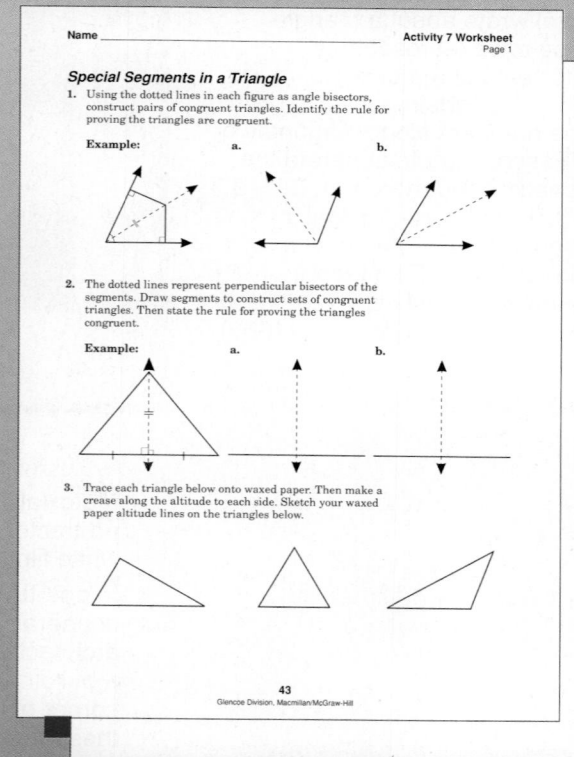

Name _____   Activity 7 Worksheet
                                        Page 1

Special Segments in a Triangle

1. Using the dotted lines in each figure as angle bisectors, construct pairs of congruent triangles. Identify the rule for proving the triangles are congruent.

Example: a.   b.

2. The dotted lines represent perpendicular bisectors of the segments. Draw segments to construct sets of congruent triangles. Then state the rule for proving the triangles congruent.

Example: a.   b.

3. Trace each triangle below onto waxed paper. Then make a crease along the altitude to each side. Sketch your waxed paper altitude lines on the triangles below.

43
Glencoe Division, Macmillan/McGraw-Hill

Using the Chapter Opener

This two-page introduction to the chapter provides students with an opportunity to see how geometry is used throughout the world in various cultures. **Transparency 5-0**, available in *The Merrill Geometry Transparency Package*, provides another full-color visual and motivational activity that you can use to engage your students in the mathematical content of the chapter.

Multicultural Notes

Thailand Of the approximately 400 Buddhist shrines in Thailand's capital, Bangkok, the most magnificent is Wat Phra Kaeo, the Temple of the Emerald Buddha. Inside the temple is a thirty-one-inch high jade statue of Buddha, the head of which is made from a single enormous emerald. The shrines feature roofs consisting of four or five colorful, overlapping triangles, which create a telescoping effect.

France In mathematics, seemingly unrelated ideas are sometimes shown to be connected in a neat, clear way. In 1644, French mathematician Blaise Pascal wrote about a triangle whose rows represent the coefficients of the binomial (a + b) raised to a certain power. The sum of the numbers along diagonals of the Pascal triangle generate the Fibonacci sequence: 1, 1, 2, 3, 5, 8, 13, and so forth. Pascal's triangular array represents a bridge between Fibonacci's sequence (published in1202) and Newton's binomial formula (1665).

Chapter Project

Materials pencil or pen, protractor, camera, black-and-white film

Procedure Organize students into cooperative groups of perspective architects. Have each group select a building and photograph a single corner of its selected building from these perspectives: (1) With the corner as the center of a circle, take photographs at eye level from different points around the circumference, maintaining the same radius each time. (2) Maintaining the same view, take two or more photographs at different distances. (3) Using one or more of the viewpoints from (1) and (2), take photographs of each viewpoint at different heights.

Make copies of each group's photographs. Have students draw lines of perspective along the top and bottom of each building face that converges at the corner. Have them extend the lines to the two

Applying Congruent Triangles

CHAPTER OBJECTIVES

In this chapter, you will:
- Identify and use the special segments in triangles.
- Prove right triangles congruent.
- Recognize and apply relationships between the sides and angles in a triangle.

GEOMETRY AROUND THE WORLD
United States

Like the geometric forms used in art, the lines and angles of beautiful buildings delight us. Besides being attractive, well-designed homes and public buildings must also be structurally sound. Making sure that buildings are sturdy and livable as well as striking is the job of technical architects such as Norma Merrick Sklarek.

Sklarek, a graduate of Columbia University School of Architecture, was the first African American woman registered as an architect in the United States. For over 30 years, she has been ensuring that a variety of buildings all over the world are safely wired, energy-efficient, and capable of withstanding decades of time.

In some cities, such as San Francisco and Tokyo, Sklarek has also had to make sure that the buildings she helps design will not collapse during earthquakes. As you have probably guessed, the practical skills of technical architects are needed whenever new buildings are erected. Sklarek has worked on a variety of projects, including office and apartment buildings, hotels, hospitals, and other public buildings, such as the U.S. Embassy in Tokyo.

GEOMETRY IN ACTION

Because of their distinct shape, triangles make what architects describe as "strong architectural statements." Basically, this means there's no way to mistake a triangle's sharp angles for any other form. Measure the angles and the sides of two small triangles in the design for a triangular-shaped building shown at the right. Are all the angles and sides the same? Are their corresponding parts congruent? **yes; yes**

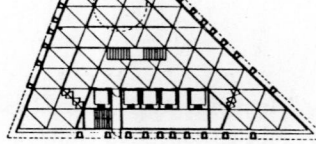

Have you ever seen a triangular-shaped building? Which rooms would be the most angular? Which rooms would have the fewest angles?

◀ *U.S. Embassy in Tokyo* Inset: *Norma Merrick Sklarek*

215

Connections and Applications

Lesson	Connections (C) and Applications (A)	Examples	Exercises
5-1	C: Algebra		12, 23, 24-25
	A: Construction		37
5-2	C: Algebra	2	19-22
	A: Construction	1	33
	C: Manufacturing		32
5-4	A: Entertainment		35
	A: Biology		39
5-5	C: Algebra	1	23, 24
	A: Genetics		31
5-6	C: Counting	1	32a, 32b
	C: Algebra	2	33 34, 47
	C: Probability		32c
	A: Construction		44
	A: Gardening		42
5-7	C: Algebra	2	8-10 18-20, 31
	A: Biology		30

vanishing points (where the lines converge). Have students draw a horizontal line connecting the two vanishing points, and measure and record the apex angles, altitude, and median of each triangle.

Ask each group to prepare a report discussing the changes in the apex angle, altitude, and median of each perspective triangle, as the viewpoint changes. Have each group present its photographs, perspective graphics, and conclusions to the class for discussion.

Resources

Lanker, Brian. *I Dream a World: Portraits of Black Women Who Changed America*. Stewart, Tabori & Chang

Boutelle, Sara Holmes. *Julia Morgan, Architect*. Abbeville Press

Kultermann, Udo. *New Direction in African Architecture*. George Braziller, Inc.

INTRODUCING THE LESSON

 5-Minute Check

(over Chapter 4)

1. In △ABC, m∠A = 2x + 5, m∠B = 3x − 15 and m∠C = 5x − 10. Find the value of x and the measure of each angle. What kind of triangle is △ABC? **20, 45, 45, 90; right isosceles**

2. Given that △DEF ≅ △GHI, complete each statement.
   a. ∠D ≅ ___ ∠G
   b. ∠E ≅ ___ ∠H
   c. ∠F ≅ ___ ∠I
   d. GH ≅ ___ DE
   e. HI ≅ ___ EF
   f. GI ≅ ___ DF

Given: △JKL and △MNO. State the postulate or theorem you could use to prove them congruent if you knew the following.

3. $\overline{JK} \cong \overline{MN}$, ∠K ≅ ∠N, and ∠L ≅ ∠O **AAS**
4. $\overline{JK} \cong \overline{MN}$, $\overline{KL} \cong \overline{NO}$, and $\overline{JL} \cong \overline{MO}$ **SSS**

Motivating the Lesson

Ask students what they think of when you say *median*. Some might say the middle of the freeway or the middle score on a test for one class. Explain what a median of a triangle is. Ask them what they think of when you say the word *altitude*. Students may say it is how high something is. Explain what an altitude of a triangle is. Do the same with *angle bisector* and *perpendicular bisector*.

Special Segments in Triangles

Objective
5-1

After studying this lesson, you should be able to:

■ identify and use medians, altitudes, angle bisectors, and perpendicular bisectors in a triangle.

Application

Almost everywhere you look there are triangles. Triangles are used to create beautiful patterns in stained-glass windows and quilts, and also in designing bridges and buildings. The Eiffel Tower is constructed with triangles because, of all the polygons, they are the most rigid.

Triangles have four types of special segments.

One kind of special segment of a triangle is called a **median.** A median connects a vertex of a triangle to the midpoint of the opposite side. For △ABC at the right, $\overline{AX}$, $\overline{BY}$, and $\overline{CZ}$ are the medians. Every triangle has three medians.

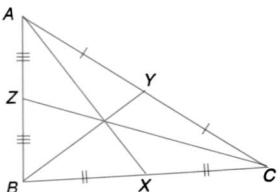

A second kind of special segment is an **altitude**. An altitude has one endpoint at a vertex of a triangle and the other on the line that contains the side opposite that vertex so that the segment is perpendicular to this line. For acute triangle DEF at the left, $\overline{DP}$, $\overline{EQ}$, and $\overline{FR}$ are the altitudes. Every triangle has three altitudes.

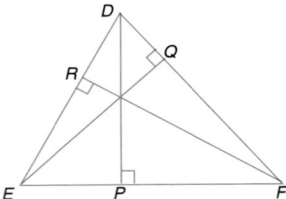

The altitudes for a right and an obtuse triangle are shown below. The legs of a right triangle are two of the altitudes. For an obtuse triangle, two of the altitudes are outside of the triangle.

One endpoint of an altitude may be a point not on the triangle.

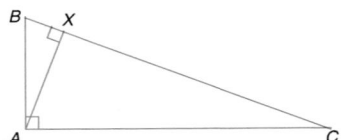

In right triangle ABC, $\overline{CA}$ is the altitude from C and $\overline{BA}$ is the altitude from B.

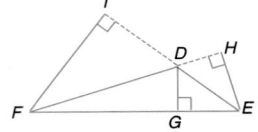

In obtuse triangle DEF, $\overline{DG}$, $\overline{EH}$ and $\overline{FI}$ are the altitudes. Notice that $\overline{EH}$ and $\overline{FI}$ are outside of △DEF.

ALTERNATE TEACHING STRATEGIES

Using Investigation

Draw an acute triangle on the chalkboard and challenge students to draw a perpendicular line from each vertex to the opposite side. Explain that they just found the altitudes of an acute triangle. Experiment with the altitudes of a right triangle and of an obtuse triangle.

Using Constructions

Have students review the Construction section on page 46, drawing $\overline{QR}$ to make a triangle. Point out that $\overline{PW}$ is an angle bisector.

Next, have them review the construction on page 58, drawing $\overline{QR}$ and $\overline{QS}$. Point out that $\overline{BQ}$ is a perpendicular bisector.

Example 1

$\triangle KCT$ has vertices $K(12, -6)$, $C(9, 2)$, and $T(2, 4)$. Determine the coordinates of point M on $\overline{KT}$ so that $\overline{CM}$ is a median of $\triangle KCT$.

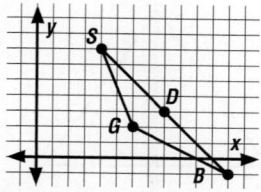

You may want to review midpoints in Lesson 1-5 and slopes of perpendicular lines in Lesson 3-5.

According to the definition of median, $\overline{CM}$ will be a median of $\triangle KCT$ if M is the midpoint of $\overline{KT}$.

$$\left(\frac{x_1 + x_2}{2}, \frac{y_1 + y_2}{2}\right) = \left(\frac{12 + 2}{2}, \frac{-6 + 4}{2}\right)$$

Substitute (12, -6) for (x_1, y_1) and (2,4) for (x_2, y_2).

$$= (7, -1)$$

The coordinates of M on $\overline{KT}$ are $(7, -1)$.

Determine if $\overline{CM}$ is an altitude of $\triangle KCT$.

For $\overline{CM}$ to be an altitude of $\triangle KCT$, $\overleftrightarrow{CM}$ must be perpendicular to $\overleftrightarrow{KT}$. This means that the product of the slopes of $\overleftrightarrow{CM}$ and $\overleftrightarrow{KT}$ must be -1.

$$\text{slope} = \frac{y_2 - y_1}{x_2 - x_1}$$

$$\text{slope of } \overleftrightarrow{CM} = \frac{2 - (-1)}{9 - 7} \qquad \text{slope of } \overleftrightarrow{KT} = \frac{-6 - 4}{12 - 2}$$

$$= \frac{3}{2} \qquad\qquad\qquad = -\frac{10}{10} \text{ or } -1$$

$$\text{product of slopes} = \frac{3}{2} \cdot (-1) \text{ or } -\frac{3}{2}$$

Since the product of these slopes is not -1, $\overleftrightarrow{CM}$ is not perpendicular to $\overleftrightarrow{KT}$. Thus, $\overline{CM}$ is not an altitude of $\triangle KCT$.

The third of the four special segments of a triangle is an **angle bisector.** An angle bisector is a segment that bisects an angle of the triangle and has one endpoint at a vertex of the triangle and the other endpoint at another point on the triangle. For $\triangle PQR$ at the right, $\overline{PX}$, $\overline{QY}$, and $\overline{RZ}$ are the angle bisectors. Since there are three angles in every triangle, every triangle has three angle bisectors.

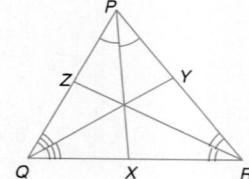

LESSON 5-1 SPECIAL SEGMENTS IN TRIANGLES 217

Chalkboard Example

For Example 1

$\triangle SGB$ has vertices $S(4, 7)$, $G(6, 2)$, and $B(12, -1)$.

a. Determine the coordinates of point J on $\overline{GB}$ so that $\overline{SJ}$ is a median of $\triangle SGB$.
   J must be the midpoint of $\overline{GB}$ for $\overline{SJ}$ to be a median.
   $$\left(\frac{x_1 + x_2}{2}, \frac{y_1 + y_2}{2}\right) =$$
   $$\left(\frac{6 + 12}{2}, \frac{2 + (-1)}{2}\right) = \left(9, \frac{1}{2}\right)$$
   The coordinates of J on $\overline{GB}$ are $(9, \frac{1}{2})$.

b. Point D has coordinates $(8, 3)$. Is $\overline{GD}$ an altitude of $\triangle SGB$?
   $\overleftrightarrow{GD}$ must be perpendicular to $\overleftrightarrow{SB}$ for $\overline{GD}$ to be an altitude.
   $$\text{slope of } \overline{GD} = \frac{3 - 2}{8 - 6} = \frac{1}{2}$$
   $$\text{slope of } \overleftrightarrow{SB} = \frac{7 - (-1)}{4 - 12} = -1$$
   Since the product of the slopes is $-\frac{1}{2}$ and not -1, $\overleftrightarrow{GD}$ is not perpendicular to $\overleftrightarrow{SB}$. Thus, $\overline{GD}$ is not an altitude of $\triangle SGB$.

Teaching Tip When drawing the four special segments of triangles discussed in this lesson, point out that each vertex and each side has *only one* of each of the segments. Have students explain why.

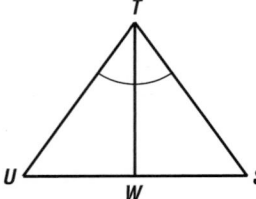
The following example illustrates how the special segments of triangles can be used to prove special properties of triangles.

Example 2

Prove the statement *If an angle bisector of a triangle is also an altitude, then the triangle is isosceles.*

Given: $\overline{BD}$ is an angle bisector of △*ABC*.
$\overline{BD}$ is an altitude of △*ABC*.

Prove: △*ABC* is isosceles.

Proof:

Statements	Reasons
1. $\overline{BD}$ is an angle bisector of △*ABC*.	1. Given
2. ∠*ABD* ≅ ∠*CBD*	2. Definition of bisector
3. $\overline{BD}$ is an altitude of △*ABC*.	3. Given
4. $\overline{BD}$ ⊥ $\overrightarrow{AC}$	4. Definition of altitude
5. ∠*ADB* and ∠*CDB* are right angles.	5. ⊥ lines form four rt. ∡.
6. ∠*ADB* ≅ ∠*CDB*	6. All rt. ∡ are ≅.
7. $\overline{BD}$ ≅ $\overline{BD}$	7. Congruence of segments is reflexive.
8. △*ADB* ≅ △*CDB*	8. ASA
9. $\overline{CB}$ ≅ $\overline{AB}$	9. CPCTC
10. △*ABC* is isosceles.	10. Definition of isosceles triangle

Now let's investigate the fourth type of special segment.

INVESTIGATION

Cut out any large acute triangle. Fold the triangle so that one vertex falls on a second vertex as shown below.

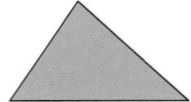 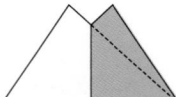

Unfold the triangle. Repeat the process with the other two pairs of vertices. What do you notice about the three folds? Each is perpendicular to a side and they all intersect in one point.

In the investigation, the folds in the triangle were the **perpendicular bisectors** of the sides of the triangle. A line or a line segment that passes through the midpoint of a side of a triangle *and* is perpendicular to that side is the *perpendicular bisector* of the side of triangle.

Perpendicular bisectors of segments have some special properties. These properties are listed in Theorems 5-1 and 5-2. You will be asked to prove these theorems in Exercises 28 and 29. Theorem 5-3 involves the bisector of an angle and will be proved in Exercise 30.

Theorem 5-1	A point on the perpendicular bisector of a segment is equidistant from the endpoints of the segment.
Theorem 5-2	A point equidistant from the endpoints of a segment lies on the perpendicular bisector of the segment.
Theorem 5-3	A point on the bisector of an angle is equidistant from the sides of the angle.
Theorem 5-4	A point in the interior of or on an angle and equidistant from the sides of an angle lies on the bisector of the angle.

CHECKING FOR UNDERSTANDING

Communicating Mathematics

1. An angle bisector bisects an angle and a perpendicular bisector bisects a side.

Read and study the lesson to answer these questions.

1. What is the difference between an angle bisector and a perpendicular bisector of a triangle?

2. Could a median be a perpendicular bisector of a side of a triangle? If so, in what type of triangle would this occur? Justify your answer. **yes; isosceles**

3. How are Theorems 5-1 and 5-2 related?
   3. Theorem 5-2 is the converse of Theorem 5-1.

Guided Practice

Complete. Refer to the figure at the right.

4. $\overline{EB}$ is a __?__ of $\triangle ABC$. **median**

5. __?__ is an altitude of $\triangle ABC$. $\overline{AD}$

6. If $\overline{CF}$ is both an angle bisector and an altitude of $\triangle ABC$, then $\triangle ABC$ is __?__. **isosceles**

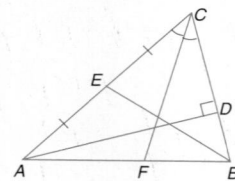

Draw and label a figure to illustrate each situation. See margin.

7. $\overline{PS}$ is a median of $\triangle PQR$ and S is between Q and R.
8. $\overline{QT}$ is an angle bisector of $\triangle PQR$ and T is between P and R.
9. $\overline{RU}$ is an altitude of $\triangle PQR$ and Q is between U and P.
10. $\overline{AC}$ and $\overline{BC}$ are altitudes of $\triangle ABC$.
11. $\overline{DX}$ is an altitude of $\triangle DEF$ and F is between E and X.

LESSON 5-1   SPECIAL SEGMENTS IN TRIANGLES   219

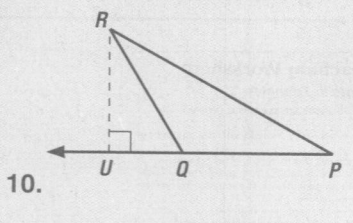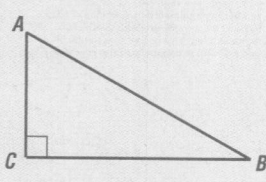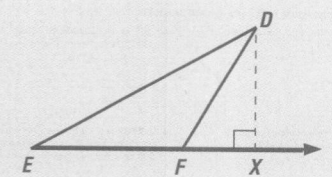
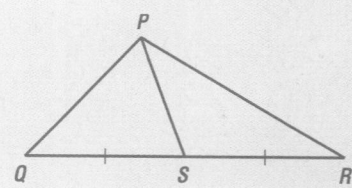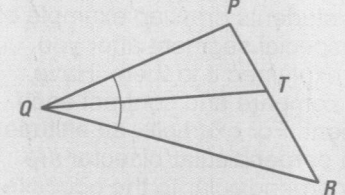

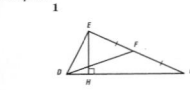 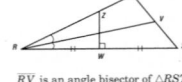
12. Answer each question if $R(3, 3)$, $S(-1, 6)$, and $T(1, 8)$ are the vertices of $\triangle RST$, and $\overline{RX}$ is a median of $\triangle RST$ with X on $\overline{ST}$.

   a. What are the coordinates of X? (0, 7)

   b. What is the length of $\overline{RX}$? 5 units

   c. What is the slope of $\overleftrightarrow{RX}$? $-\frac{4}{3}$

   d. Is $\overline{RX}$ an altitude of $\triangle RST$? Explain. no; the product of the slopes of $\overline{ST}$ and $\overline{RX}$ is not -1.

13. Write a two-column proof. See margin.

   Given: $\overline{AB} \cong \overline{CB}$
   $\overline{BD}$ is a median of $\triangle ABC$.

   Prove: $\overline{BD}$ is an altitude of $\triangle ABC$.

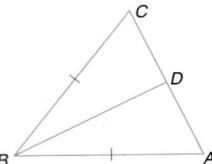

EXERCISES

Practice Draw and label a figure to illustrate each situation. See margin.

A

14. $\overline{PT}$ and $\overline{RS}$ are medians of $\triangle PQR$ and intersect at V.

15. $\overline{AD}$ is a median and an altitude of $\triangle ABC$.

16. $\overline{XM}$ is a median and an angle bisector of $\triangle XYZ$, and $\overline{ZX}$ is an altitude.

17. $\triangle DEF$ is a right triangle with right angle at F. $\overline{FG}$ is a median of $\triangle DEF$ and $\overleftrightarrow{GH}$ is the perpendicular bisector of $\overline{DE}$.

INVESTIGATION

18. For parts a–d, draw a large acute triangle that is not equilateral. Then complete the indicated construction and answer each question.

   a. Construct the three medians of the triangle. What do you notice?

   b. Construct the three altitudes of the triangle. What do you notice?

   c. Construct the three angle bisectors of the triangle. What do you notice?

   d. Construct the three perpendicular bisectors of the sides of the triangle. What do you notice?

   e. Cut out each of the triangles from parts a-d. Then place each triangle on the head of the pin at the point where the constructed lines intersect. Describe what you observe. Only the triangle from part a balances.

   f. What changes would occur if the constructions in parts a-d were done on a right triangle or an obtuse triangle, instead of an acute triangle?

18. a-d. They intersect in one point.

18.f. The perpendicular bisectors and the altitudes would intersect at a point on or outside of the triangle.

State whether each sentence is _always, sometimes,_ or _never_ true. 19. always

19. The three medians of a triangle intersect at a point inside the triangle.

20. The three angle bisectors of a triangle intersect at a point outside the triangle. never

RETEACHING THE LESSON

Have students draw an example of each special segment after you have explained it to them. Have them compare and contrast each segment. For example, an altitude and a perpendicular bisector are both perpendicular to the opposite segments; or, a perpendicular bisector must have an endpoint on the segment, while the altitude may not.

5-2 Right Triangles

Objective
5-2 · recognize and use tests for congruence of right triangles.

The America's Cup race is the most famous international yachting competition. In 1987, *Stars and Stripes* brought the America's Cup back to the United States after it had been lost to Australia in 1983. The mainsail for *Stars and Stripes*, like the mainsails for most modern sailboats, is shaped like a right triangle. The spare mainsail must be congruent to the original mainsail. *Why?* What do you need to know about the sails to determine if they are congruent?

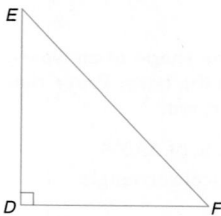

Suppose right triangle *DEF*, shown at the left, represents one of the mainsails. Since all right angles are congruent and all right triangles have a right angle, any other right triangle has at least one angle congruent to an angle in Δ*DEF*. If the corresponding legs are congruent, then the triangles will be congruent by SAS.

Theorem 5-5 LL	If the legs of one right triangle are congruent to the corresponding legs of another right triangle, then the triangles are congruent.

You will be asked to prove Theorem 5-5 in Exercise 27.

Suppose you know that the hypotenuse and an acute angle of a right triangular sail are congruent to the corresponding parts of the mainsail. Must these two sails be congruent? Since we know that the right angles are congruent, knowing that another angle and the hypotenuse are also congruent tells us that two corresponding angles and a corresponding nonincluded side are congruent. So, the triangles must be congruent by AAS.

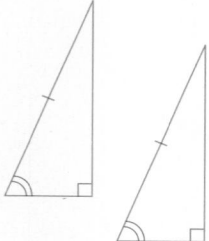

LESSON 5-2   RIGHT TRIANGLES   223

ALTERNATE TEACHING STRATEGIES

Using Exploration
Have students list all of the parts of a right triangle. Have them list all of the possible combinations of two parts; for example, they could combine a leg and an acute angle, a leg and the right angle, and so on. Have them find what combinations will prove two right triangles congruent by trying to find counterexamples or by proving the statements true.

Using Models
Have students use toothpicks to make a counterexample of the combinations of the parts of a triangle listed in this lesson. For example, have them construct two right triangles that are not congruent even though one leg is congruent to the leg of the other. Then have them try to make a counterexample of the theorems and postulate discussed in this lesson.

INTRODUCING THE LESSON

5-Minute Check
(over Lesson 5-1)

Draw and label a figure to illustrate each situation.

1. $\overline{SL}$ is an altitude of △*RST* and a perpendicular bisector of side $\overline{RT}$.

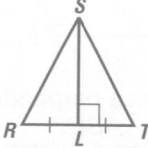

2. △*HIJ* is an isosceles triangle with vertex angle at *J*. $\overline{JN}$ is an altitude of △*HIJ*.

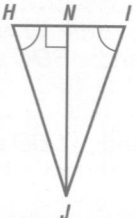

State whether each sentence is *always*, *sometimes*, or *never* true.

3. The three perpendicular bisectors of the sides of a triangle intersect at more than one point. **never**
4. The altitudes of a triangle contain the midpoints of the opposite sides. **sometimes**
5. The medians of a triangle contain the midpoints of the opposite sides. **always**

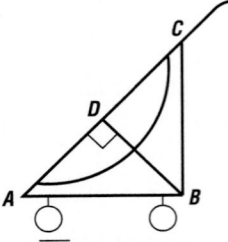
224   Chapter 5

Theorem 5-6 HA	If the hypotenuse and an acute angle of one right triangle are congruent to the hypotenuse and corresponding acute angle of another right triangle, then the two triangles are congruent.

Proof of Theorem 5-6

Given: $\triangle ABC$ and $\triangle XYZ$ are right triangles.
        $\angle A$ and $\angle X$ are right angles.
        $\overline{BC} \cong \overline{YZ}$
        $\angle B \cong \angle Y$
Prove: $\triangle ABC \cong \triangle XYZ$

Proof:

Statements	Reasons
1. $\triangle ABC$ and $\triangle XYZ$ are right triangles. $\angle A$ and $\angle X$ are right angles. $\overline{BC} \cong \overline{YZ}$; $\angle B \cong \angle Y$	1. Given
2. $\angle A \cong \angle X$	2. All rt. $\angle$s are $\cong$.
3. $\triangle ABC \cong \triangle XYZ$	3. AAS

You can use the HA Theorem in many proofs involving right triangles.

Example 1

APPLICATION
Construction

A truss for a roof is in the shape of an isosceles triangle with an altitude from the vertex angle to the base. Prove that the two right triangles formed by the altitude are congruent.

Given: $\overline{WY}$ is an altitude of $\triangle XYZ$.
        $\triangle XYZ$ is an isosceles triangle.
Prove: $\triangle XWY \cong \triangle ZWY$

Proof:

Statements	Reasons
1. $\overline{WY}$ is an altitude of $\triangle XYZ$.	1. Given
2. $\overline{WY} \perp \overline{XZ}$	2. Definition of altitude
3. $\angle XWY$ and $\angle ZWY$ are right angles.	3. $\perp$ lines form four rt. $\angle$s.
4. $\triangle XWY$ and $\triangle ZWY$ are right triangles.	4. Definition of right triangle
5. $\triangle XYZ$ is an isosceles triangle.	5. Given
6. $\overline{XY} \cong \overline{ZY}$	6. Definition of isosceles triangle
7. $\angle X \cong \angle Z$	7. If 2 sides of a $\triangle$ are $\cong$ the $\angle$s opp. the sides are $\cong$.
8. $\triangle XWY \cong \triangle ZWY$	8. HA

You have already seen that right triangles are congruent if corresponding legs are congruent (LL) or if the hypotenuses and corresponding acute angles are congruent (HA). As a third possibility, suppose you know that a leg and an acute angle of the *Stars and Stripes* mainsail are congruent to the corresponding leg and acute angle of the spare sail. Must these two sails be congruent? To see, we must consider two different cases.

Case 1
The leg is included between the acute angle and the right angle.

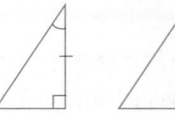

Case 2
The leg is *not* included between the acute angle and the right angle.

In both cases, the triangles are congruent. For Case 1, the triangles are congruent by ASA. For Case 2, the triangles are congruent by AAS. This observation suggests Theorem 5-7. *You will prove Theorem 5-7 in Exercise 28.*

Theorem 5-7 LA	If one leg and an acute angle of one right triangle are congruent to the corresponding leg and acute angle of another right triangle, then the triangles are congruent.

Example 2

CONNECTION
Algebra

Find the values of *x* and *y* so that △*ABC* is congruent to △*DEF*.

△*ABC* will be congruent to △*DEF* by LA if $\overline{AB} \cong \overline{DE}$ and $\angle A \cong \angle D$.

$$AB = DE \qquad m\angle D = m\angle A$$
$$15 - 2x = 5 \qquad 9y - 32 = 67$$
$$-2x = -10 \qquad 9y = 99$$
$$x = 5 \qquad y = 11$$

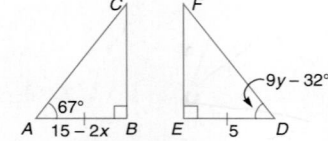

If $x = 5$, then $\overline{AB} \cong \overline{DE}$; and if $y = 11$, then $\angle A \cong \angle D$. Therefore, △*ABC* ≅ △*DEF*.

For a final application of congruent right triangles, let's look at pitching a tent. If the tent pole is perpendicular to the ground and the ground is level, then the tent pole, ground, and tent rope pulled taut from the tent pole form a right triangle. If two tent ropes of the same length are each pulled taut from tent poles of the same height, then the stakes at the end of each rope will be placed in the same spot on the ground relative to the tent poles. This situation suggests the following postulate.

LESSON 5-2 RIGHT TRIANGLES 225

Teaching Tip When discussing the theorems in this lesson, point out that they are an extension of previous theorems or postulates, such as AAS or SAS. This is because all right triangles have one angle that is congruent, namely the right angle. Thus, you only need two other parts to prove two right triangles congruent.

Teaching Tip If students are having difficulty visualizing the concepts in this lesson, have them make models of the problems.

Chalkboard Example

For Example 2
Find the values of *x* and *y* so that △*JKL* is congruent to △*MLK*.

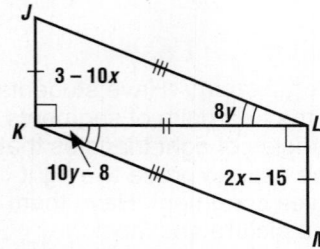

△*JKL* will be congruent to △*MLK* by LA if $\overline{JK} \cong \overline{ML}$ and $\angle JLK \cong \angle MKL$.
$$JK = ML$$
$$3 - 10x = 2x - 15$$
$$-12x = -18$$
$$x = 1.5$$
$$m\angle JLK = m\angle MKL$$
$$8y = 10y - 8$$
$$-2y = -8$$
$$y = 4$$
If $x = 1.5$, then $\overline{JK} \cong \overline{ML}$ and if $y = 4$, then $\angle JLK \cong \angle MKL$. Therefore, △*JKL* ≅ △*MLK*.

Checking for Understanding

Exercises 1-13 are designed to help you assess students' understanding through reading, writing, speaking, and modeling. You should work through Exercises 1-3 with your students and then monitor their work on Exercises 4-13.

Error Analysis

If students are having difficulty understanding why only four combinations of segments and angles can be used to prove right triangles congruent, give a counterexample to show why the other combinations will not work.

Closing the Lesson

Writing Activity Have students write the four pairs of segments and angles of right triangles that can be used to prove two right triangles congruent. Have them draw a picture and label the congruent segments or angles that would be used in the proof.

Postulate 5-1 HL	If the hypotenuse and a leg of one right triangle are congruent to the hypotenuse and corresponding leg of another right triangle, then the triangles are congruent.

CHECKING FOR UNDERSTANDING

Communicating Mathematics

Read and study the lesson to answer each question.

1. Write a sentence to explain why the tests for congruency of right triangles have only two requirements while the tests for other triangles have three. Right triangles all have a right angle in common.

2. Which of the tests for congruent triangles would you use to justify the Leg-Leg test for congruent right triangles? SAS

3. Explain to a classmate why two cases must be considered when proving Theorem 5-7 (LA). The side given may be either an included or a non-included leg.

Guided Practice

Name the theorem or postulate used to determine whether each pair of triangles is congruent. If there is not enough information write *none*.

4.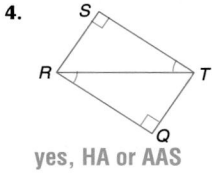
yes, HA or AAS

5.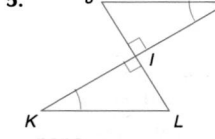
none

6.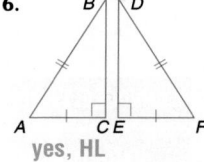
yes, HL

7.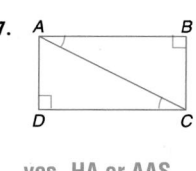
yes, HA or AAS

8.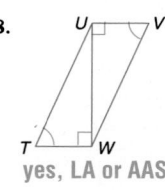
yes, LA or AAS

9.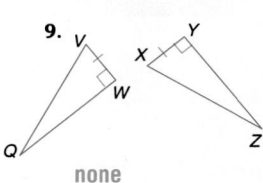
none

Find the value of *x* for each figure.

10.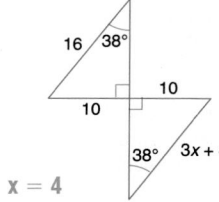
x = 4

11.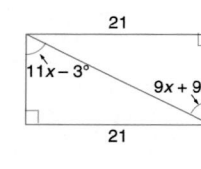
x = 6

12.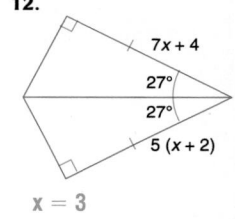
x = 3

13. Use the figure at the right to write a two-column proof.

   Given: ∠Q and ∠S are right angles.
   ∠1 ≅ ∠2

   Prove: △PQR ≅ △RSP
   See margin.

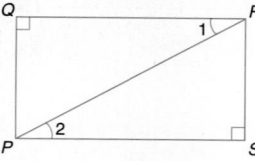

Homework Exercises

Assignment Guide
Basic: 14-25, 31-32, 34-38
Average: 16-28, 31-38
Enriched: 17-18, 21-38

Additional Answers

13. **Statements** (Reasons)
    a. ∠Q and ∠S are right angles; ∠1 ≅ ∠2 (Given)
    b. △QRP and △SPR are right triangles. (Definition of right triangles)
    c. $\overline{PR} \cong \overline{PR}$ (Congruence of segments is reflexive.)
    d. △PQR ≅ △RSP (HA)
14. Yes; LA
15. No, there is no AA or AAA congruence theorem.
16. Yes; LL
17. Yes; HA
18. Yes; HL

EXERCISES

Practice
A

For each situation, determine whether △ABC ≅ △XYZ. Justify your answer.
See margin.

14. **Given:** $\overline{BC} \cong \overline{YZ}$ and ∠A ≅ ∠X

15. **Given:** ∠A ≅ ∠X and ∠B ≅ ∠Y

16. **Given:** $\overline{AC} \cong \overline{XZ}$ and $\overline{BC} \cong \overline{YZ}$

17. **Given:** $\overline{AB} \cong \overline{XY}$ and ∠B ≅ ∠Y

18. **Given:** $\overline{AB} \cong \overline{XY}$ and $\overline{BC} \cong \overline{YZ}$

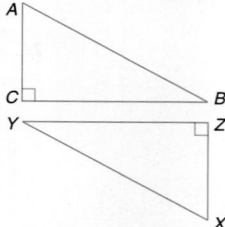

For each figure, find the values of x and y so that △DEF ≅ △PQR by the indicated theorem or postulate.

B

19. HL

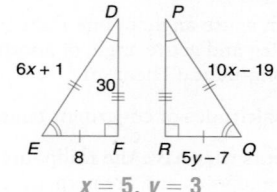

$x = 5, y = 3$

20. HA

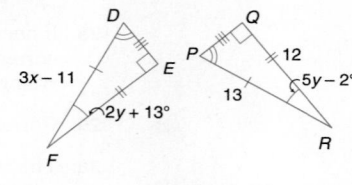

$x = 8, y = 5$

21. LA

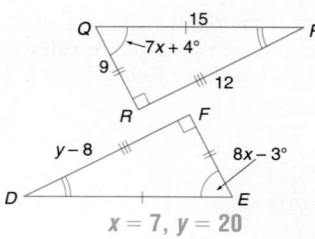

$x = 7, y = 20$

22. LL

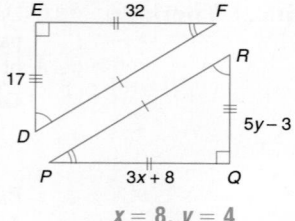

$x = 8, y = 4$

LESSON 5-2   RIGHT TRIANGLES   227

RETEACHING THE LESSON

Have students draw two triangles that are congruent by SAS. Then have them draw two right triangles that are congruent by SAS. If you take out the A for angle, you are left with SS. In a right triangle, this is the same as LL, and since all right angles are congruent, LL for right triangles is actually the same as SAS for any triangle. Do the same for the other theorems in this lesson.

Reteaching Masters Booklet, p. 27

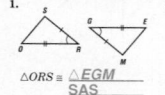
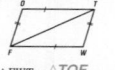
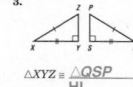
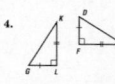

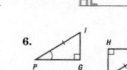

Exercise Notes

You may want students to complete Exercises 27 and 28 in class so that they see the relationship of LL to SAS and of LA to AAS.

Additional Answer

23. Statements   (Reasons)
    a. $\overline{QP} \cong \overline{SR}$; $\angle Q$ and $\angle S$ are right angles.   (Given)
    b. $\triangle RQP$ and $\triangle PSR$ are right triangles. (Definition of right triangles)
    c. $\overline{PR} \cong \overline{PR}$ (Congruence of segments is reflexive)
    d. $\triangle RQP \cong \triangle PSR$ (HL)
    e. $\angle 1 \cong \angle 2$ (CPCTC)

Practice Masters Booklet, p. 31

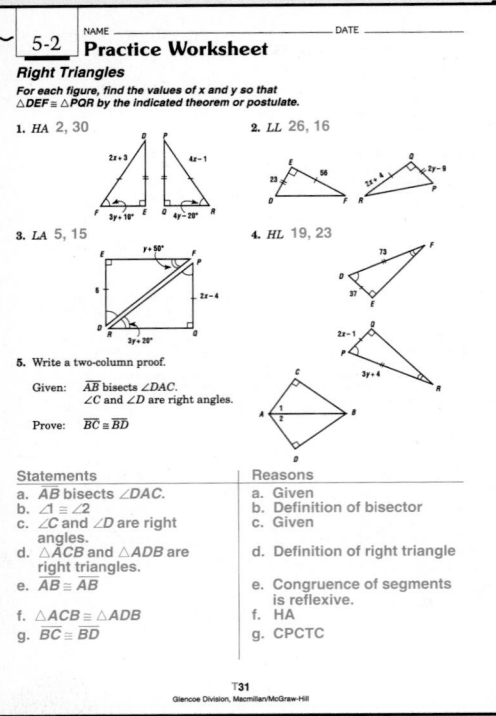

Use the figure at the right to write a two-column proof. **See margin.**

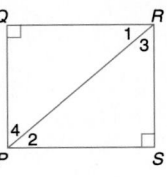

23. **Given:** $\overline{QP} \cong \overline{SR}$
    $\angle Q$ and $\angle S$ are right angles.
    Prove: $\angle 1 \cong \angle 2$

24. **Given:** $\angle Q$ and $\angle S$ are right angles.
    $\overline{QR} \parallel \overline{PS}$
    Prove: $\overline{PQ} \cong \overline{RS}$

Use the figure at the right to write a two-column proof. **See Solutions Manual.**

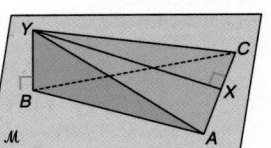

25. **Given:** $\triangle ABY$ and $\triangle CBY$ are right triangles.
    $\overline{AB} \cong \overline{CB}$
    $\overline{YX} \perp \overline{AC}$
    Prove: $\overline{AX} \cong \overline{CX}$

26. **Given:** $\overline{YX}$ is an altitude of $\triangle AYC$.
    $\angle AYX \cong \angle CYX$
    $\overline{YB} \perp$ Plane $\mathcal{M}$
    Prove: $\angle AYB \cong \angle CYB$

Draw and label a figure for each statement. List the information that is given and the statement to be proved in terms of your figure. Then write a two-column proof. **See Solutions Manual.**

27. If the legs of one right triangle are congruent to the corresponding legs of another right triangle, then the triangles are congruent. (Theorem 5-5)

28. If one leg and an acute angle of one right triangle are congruent to the corresponding leg and acute angle of another right triangle, then the triangles are congruent. (Theorem 5-7)

 29. Corresponding altitudes of congruent triangles are congruent.

30. The two segments that have the midpoint of each leg of an isosceles triangle as one endpoint and are perpendicular to the base of the triangle are congruent.

Critical Thinking   31. Using the figure at the right, write two paragraph proofs, using two different pairs of congruent right triangles. **See Solutions Manual.**

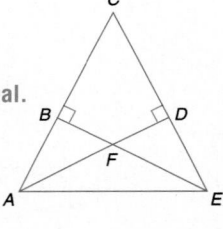

   Given: $\overline{AC} \perp \overline{BE}$
   $\overline{CE} \perp \overline{AD}$
   $\overline{AC} \cong \overline{CE}$
   Prove: $\overline{BE} \cong \overline{AD}$

Additional Answers

24. Statements   (Reasons)
    a. $\angle Q$ and $\angle S$ are right angles; $\overline{QR} \parallel \overline{PS}$ (Given)
    b. $\triangle RQP$ and $\triangle PSR$ are right triangles. (Definition of right triangles)
    c. $\angle 1 \cong \angle 2$ (Alternate Interior Angle Theorem)
    d. $\overline{PR} \cong \overline{PR}$ (Congruence of segments is reflexive.)
    e. $\triangle RQP \cong \triangle PSR$ (HA)
    f. $\overline{PQ} \cong \overline{RS}$ (CPCTC)

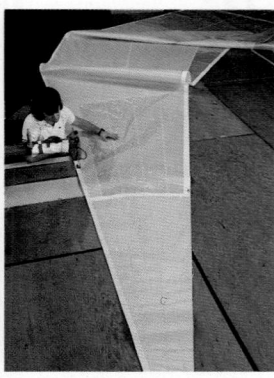

Application

32. Manufacturing Donald Owens is having a new foresail made for his boat. The old foresail is in the shape of a right triangle with the dimensions shown at the right. If the sailmaker knows that the new foresail is shaped like a right triangle, list all of the different possible sets of information that Mr. Owens could give the sailmaker so that she could verify that the new foresail is the same size and shape as the old foresail. **See margin.**

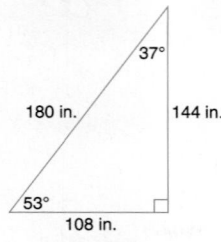

180 in.   144 in.
37°
53°
108 in.

33. Construction Four wood braces of equal length are to be used to support a deck near where the deck meets the wall of a house. One end of each brace will be attached to the bottom of the deck at the same distance from the wall. Explain why the other end of each brace will be attached to the wall at the same distance from the bottom of the deck. **See Solutions Manual.**

Mixed Review **Refer to the figure for Exercises 34-36.**

34. If X is the midpoint of $\overline{AD}$, name the additional parts of $\triangle AXC$ and $\triangle DXB$ that would have to be congruent to prove that $\triangle AXC \cong \triangle DXB$ by ASA. **(Lesson 4-5)** $\angle 6 \cong \angle 1$

35. $\angle 5$ and $\angle 4$; $\angle 1$ and $\angle 6$

35. If $\overline{AC} \parallel \overline{BD}$, which pairs of numbered angles must be congruent? **(Lesson 3-2)**

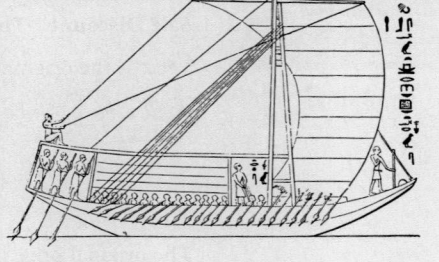

A
1 2   3 B
                4
        X
5
C   6 D

36. If $m\angle 3 = 3d + 11$, $m\angle 4 = 5d - 2$, and $m\angle ABD = 97$, find the value of d. **(Lesson 1-6)** $d = 11$

37. Write the statement *A median of a triangle bisects one side of the triangle* in if-then form. **(Lesson 2-2)** If a segment is a median of a triangle, then it bisects one side of the triangle.

Wrap-Up **38.** Write a short paragraph describing each of the tests for congruence of right triangles presented in this lesson. **See students' work.**

HISTORY CONNECTION

The oldest pictures of sailboats that have been found are on Egyptian vases made around 3200 B.C. Since Egypt had no wood strong enough for large ships, their boats were made of green papyrus stalks tied in bundles. The Nile River was perfect for shipping cargo between northern and southern Egypt since the water flows north and the wind blows from north to south. The sailors could ride the current to travel north and raise the sails to use the wind to travel south.

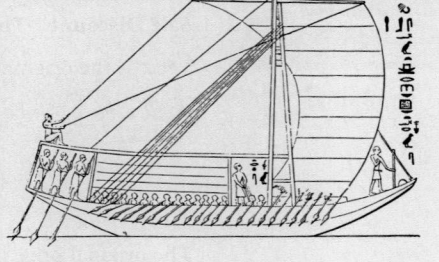

LESSON 5-2   RIGHT TRIANGLES   229

EXTENDING THE LESSON

Math Power: Reasoning

If a and b represent the length of the two legs of a right triangle and c represents the length of the hypotenuse, explain why $a + b > c$ and why $c > a$.

History Connection

The History Connection features introduce students to persons or cultures involved in the development of mathematics. You may want students to further research Egypt and the Nile River.

Additional Answer

32. legs: 108 in., 144 in.; hypotenuse and an angle: 180 in., 37° or 180 in., 53°; a leg and an angle: 108 in., 53°; 108 in., 37°; 144 in., 53°; or 144 in., 37°; hypotenuse and a leg: 180 in., 144 in. or 180 in., 108 in.

Enrichment Masters Booklet, p. 27

NAME _____ DATE _____

5-2 **Enrichment Worksheet**

Tangrams

The tangram puzzle is composed of seven pieces that form a square, as shown at the right. This puzzle has been a popular amusement for Chinese students for hundreds and perhaps thousands of years.

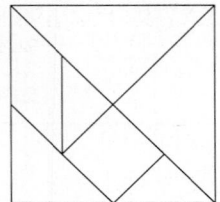

Make a careful tracing of the figure above. Cut out the pieces and rearrange them to form each figure below. Record each answer by drawing lines within each figure.

1.   2.   3.

  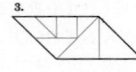

4.   5.   6.

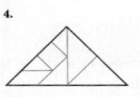  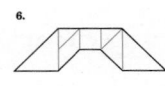

7. Create a different figure using the seven tangram pieces. Trace the outline. Then challenge another student to solve the puzzle.
See students' work.

T27
Glencoe Division, Macmillan/McGraw-Hill

Problem-Solving Strategy: Work Backward

Lesson Resources

- Practice Master 5-3
- Activity Master, p. 5

 Transparency 5-3 contains the 5-Minute Check and a teaching aid for this lesson.

INTRODUCING THE LESSON

 5-Minute Check

(over Lesson 5-2)

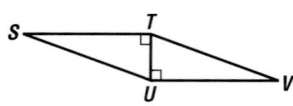

Determine whether △STU ≅ △VUT, using the given information. Justify your answer.

1. ∠S ≅ ∠V   yes, by LA
2. SU ≅ VT   yes, by HL
3. ∠STU and ∠VUT are right angles.   no

Write a two-column proof.

4. Given: ∠STU and ∠VUT are right angles. SU ≅ VT Prove: ∠S ≅ ∠V

   Statements   (Reasons)
   a. ∠STU and ∠VUT are right angles; SU ≅ VT. (Given)
   b. △STU and △VUT are right triangles. (Definition of rt. △)
   c. TU ≅ UT   (Congruence of segments is reflexive.)
   d. △STU ≅ △VUT   (HL)
   e. ∠S ≅ ∠V   (CPCTC)

Motivating the Lesson

Ask students to think of times when working backward or going backward is vital to achieving a goal. For example, how would we park a car or get out of a driveway if we did not have a reverse gear?

TEACHING THE LESSON

Teaching Tip   Once you have found the original price, work the problem forward to show students that the equations do not change.

Objective
5-3

After studying this lesson, you should be able to:
- solve problems by working backward.

Application

FYI···

Charles Babbage built the first computer and is recognized as the father of modern computers. A woman, Ada Byron Lovelace, showed him how to program it.

Mr. Dean spent $1491.21 on a personal computer from Wholesale Electronics. The computer was on sale for 25% off. In addition, Mr. Dean received 10% off of the sale price for paying in cash instead of financing his purchase. Sales tax of 5.2% was added after the discounts. Mr. Dean plans to insure his computer for its original price. For what amount should he insure the computer?

We know the discounted price, so we can work backward to find the original price.

Sales Tax   The last operation in computing the price was to add sales tax.

Let x = the price of the computer before the tax was added. Then $0.052x$ = the amount of sales tax on the computer. *5.2% = 0.052*

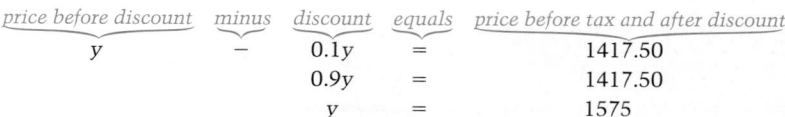

price before sales tax	plus	sales tax	equals	price after sales tax
x	+	$0.052x$	=	1491.21
		$1.052x$	=	1491.21
		x	=	1417.50

Discount for Cash   Mr. Dean's 10% off for paying cash was a discount *before* the sales tax.

Let y = the price before the 10% discount. Then $0.1y$ = the amount of the 10% discount. *10% = 0.1*

price before discount	minus	discount	equals	price before tax and after discount
y	−	$0.1y$	=	1417.50
		$0.9y$	=	1417.50
		y	=	1575

Sale Discount   The sale price was 25% off the original price.

Let z = the original price. Then $0.25z$ = the amount of the 25% discount.
25% = 0.25

original price	minus	discount	equals	price before tax and after sale discount
z	−	$0.25z$	=	1575
		$0.75z$	=	1575
		z	=	2100

The original price of the computer was $2100. Mr. Dean should insure his personal computer for $2100.

ALTERNATE TEACHING STRATEGIES

Using Applications

Have a student pretend to be the owner of a store. Have another student or students pose as customers and go into the store with questions about his or her bill that need to be answered by working backward. For example, perhaps the customer thinks she was charged too much but cannot read the purchase price on the bill.

Using Questioning

Brainstorm ideas with students where working backward is necessary to solve a problem. You can give them a list of places where they might need to work backward (in school, at home, playing sports, etc.).

CHECKING FOR UNDERSTANDING

Communicating Mathematics

1. Guess a price and find the total after discounts and sales tax. Then make a revised guess, if necessary and repeat.

Guided Practice

TAMIKO

Read and study the lesson to answer each question.

1. Describe how you could use *guess and check* to find the original price of the personal computer.

2. Describe how to check the answer to the application problem.

3. Explain how you might use working backward when writing a proof.

2. Work forward to check that $1491.21 is the total after discounts and tax on $2100.

3. Work backward from the statement to be proved to the given information.

Solve each problem by working backward.

4. On a game show, all the contestants begin with the same number of points. They are awarded points for questions answered correctly and lose points for questions answered incorrectly. Tamiko answered six 20-point questions correctly. Then she answered a 50-point question and an 80-point question incorrectly. In her final round question, Tamiko tripled her score and won with a score of 270 points. How many points did each player have at the beginning of the game? **100 points**

5. Decrease a number by 52, then multiply the result by 12, then add 20 and divide by 4. If the final result is 32, with what number did you start? **61**

6. Tom collected baseball cards for a few years before he decided to give them all away and try a new hobby. First he gave half the cards plus one extra card to Leila. Then, he gave half of what was left plus one extra card to Karl. Then, he gave half of what was left plus one extra card to Jarrod. Finally, Tom gave the remaining 74 cards to his sister, Charlene. How many baseball cards did Tom have in his collection?
606 cards

EXERCISES

Practice

Strategies

Look for a pattern.
Solve a simpler problem.
Act it out.
Guess and check.
Draw a diagram.
Make a chart.
Work backward.

Solve. Use any strategy.

7. Chicken Express sells chicken wings in boxes of 15 or 25 pieces. Ken and Julie bought seven boxes and got 125 wings for a party. How many boxes of 15 did they buy? **5**

8. The cans of soda in a soda machine cost 65¢. If the machine will accept quarters, dimes, and nickels, how many different combinations of coins must the machine be programmed to accept? **14 combinations**

9. Enrico cashed his paycheck this morning. He put half of the paycheck in the savings account for his college tuition. He then paid $20 for a concert ticket. He spent one eighth of the remaining money on pizza with friends. If Enrico had $42 left, how much was his paycheck? **$136**

LESSON 5-3 PROBLEM-SOLVING STRATEGY: WORKING BACKWARD 231

Homework Exercises

Assignment Guide

Basic: 7-12
Average: 8-13
Enriched: 9-14

Exercise Note

For Exercise 8, making a chart may help organize ideas.

Exercise Notes

For Exercise 11, the process of elimination may be the best way to solve this problem.

For Exercise 13, use the formula area = s^2, then $\frac{4}{9}s^2 = (s-5)^2$.

Practice Masters Booklet, p. 32

---

10. Continue the pattern. Explain your reasoning.
$$1^3 = 1^2 - 0^2$$
$$2^3 = 3^2 - 1^2$$
$$3^3 = 6^2 - 3^2$$
$$4^3 = \underline{\ ?\ }\ \ 10^2 - 6^2$$
$$5^3 = \underline{\ ?\ }\ \ 15^2 - 10^2$$

11. Each letter in the following equation represents a single digit. Find the digits that make the equation correct.
$ON + ON + ON + ON = GO$
O = 0, *N* = 5, *G* = 2 or *O* = 2, *N* = 3, *G* = 9

12. Shelly's little sister changed the 5 on one of Shelly's dice to a 3. She changed the 6 on the other die to a 4. Shelly rolled both the dice.
   a. How many different sums could Shelly have rolled? **10**
   b. What is the total Shelly most likely rolled? **7**

13. When the length of each side of a square is decreased by 5 units, the area of the square is $\frac{4}{9}$ of the area of the original square. What is the area of the original square? **225 square units**

14. Montgomery's Department Store is having an electronics sale. A VCR is on sale for $50 less than the list price. The store employees receive an additional 15% discount. The sales tax added to the price is 6%. If a store employee paid $198.22 for the VCR, what is the regular price? **$270**

COOPERATIVE LEARNING PROJECT

Work in groups. Each person in the group must understand the solution and be able to explain it to any person in class.

Lewis Carroll (1832-1898), the author of *Alice in Wonderland*, was very interested in logic, mathematics, and word games. One of the word games that he invented, Doublets, became very popular in his day. Many competitions in the game were sponsored by the magazine *Vanity Fair*. The object of the game is to take two different words of the same length and transform one word into the other by a series of intermediate words that differ by only one letter. Proper names are not allowed and each word should be common enough to find in a dictionary. An example is turning CAT to DOG.

CAT
COT   *Step 1: Change A to O. The new word is COT.*
DOT   *Step 2: Change C to D. The new word is DOT.*
DOG   *Step 3: Change T to G. The new word, DOG, is the desired word.*

Change TOP to HAT, make a SEED GROW, and turn WILD to TAME. What is the least number of steps it takes to change one word to another? **The number of letters that are different; sample answers are TOP → HOP → HOT → HAT; SEED → SLED → SLEW → SLOW → GLOW → GROW; WILD → WIND → WAND → WANE → SANE → SAME → TAME.**

EXTENDING THE LESSON

Math Power: Problem Solving

Have students act as owners of their own computer store. Have them figure out prices for their computers. You can give them a wholesale price and have them calculate what the list price should be. If they want to advertise a discount, will they still make a profit? Do they want to sell a lot of computers at a lower price, or do they want to sell a few computers at a higher price?

Cooperative Learning Project

This activity provides students an opportunity to *learn* things together, not just do things together. You may wish to refer to pages T6-T7 and page 214c for the various elements of cooperative groups and specific goals and strategies for using them.

5-4 Indirect Proof and Inequalities

Objectives
5-4A
- use indirect reasoning and indirect proof to reach a conclusion, and

5-4B
- recognize and apply the properties of inequalities to the measures of segments and angles.

Application

During criminal trials, defendants sometimes try to use an *alibi* to prove that they could not have committed the crime for which they are accused. An alibi is a claim that the defendant was somewhere else when the crime was committed. If the jury believes the alibi, then the defendant is proved innocent. The use of an alibi is an example of a form of **indirect reasoning.**

Direct reasoning is just an application of the Law of Detachment. You may wish to review this law in Lesson 2-3.

Up to this point, the proofs you have encountered have used direct reasoning. With direct reasoning, you start with a true hypothesis and prove that the conclusion is true. With indirect reasoning, you *assume* that the conclusion is false and then show that this assumption leads to a contradiction of the hypothesis or some other accepted fact, like a postulate, theorem, or corollary. That is, since your assumption has been proved false, the conclusion must be true.

The following steps summarize the process of indirect reasoning. You can use these steps when doing an **indirect proof.**

Steps for Writing an Indirect Proof

1. **Assume that the conclusion is false.**
2. **Show that the assumption leads to a contradiction of the hypothesis or some other fact, such as a postulate, theorem, or corollary.**
3. **Point out that the assumption must be false, and therefore, the conclusion must be true.**

Example 1

State the assumption you would make to start an indirect proof of each statement. *Do not write the proofs.*
a. $\overline{XW}$ is an altitude of $\triangle XYZ$.
b. $\triangle MNO$ is not a right triangle.
c. $m\angle A > m\angle B$

To write an indirect proof, we assume that the conclusion is false. So negate each statement.
a. $\overline{XW}$ is not an altitude of $\triangle XYZ$.
b. $\triangle MNO$ is a right triangle.
c. $m\angle A \leq m\angle B$ *Remember that if $m\angle A$ is not greater than $m\angle B$, then it could be less than or equal to $m\angle B$.*

ALTERNATE TEACHING STRATEGIES

Using Critical Thinking
Have students think of an example of indirect reasoning (other than an exam question). Have them go through steps 1-3 listed on page 233 and relate their example to the steps. Have them state the hypothesis and conclusion.

Using Logical Reasoning
You can build the chart on page 235 with students. Have them pick numbers for *a*, *b*, and *c* and then devise the statements in the chart. Have them use several examples to get an idea of what is happening. Ask students to write the statements in mathematical terms.

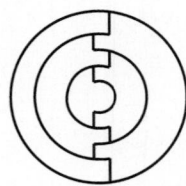

In Lesson 4-2, you learned about a relationship between exterior angles of a triangle and their remote interior angles. The following theorem is a result of this relationship and can be proven using an indirect proof.

Chalkboard Example

For the Example
State the assumption you would make to start an indirect proof of each statement. Do not write the proofs.
a. $\overline{AB}$ bisects $\angle A$. $\overline{AB}$ does not bisect $\angle A$.
b. $\triangle XTZ$ is isosceles. $\triangle XTZ$ is not isosceles.
c. $m\angle 1 < m\angle 2$. $m\angle 1 \geq m\angle 2$

Teaching Tip Relate this lesson to Lesson 5-3. In a direct proof, you solve the problem by working from the beginning or forward. In an indirect proof, you solve the problem by working backward, or by assuming the conclusion is false.

Teaching Tip Theorem 5-8 can also be proven directly. You may want to have students solve it as a project.

Theorem 5-8 *Exterior Angle* *Inequality Theorem*	**If an angle is an exterior angle of a triangle, then its measure is greater than the measure of either of its corresponding remote interior angles.**

Indirect Proof of Theorem 5-8

Given: $\angle 4$ is an exterior angle of $\triangle RST$.

Prove: $m\angle 4 > m\angle 1$
$m\angle 4 > m\angle 2$

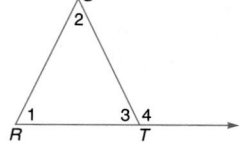

Indirect Proof:

Step 1: Make the assumption that $m\angle 4 \leq m\angle 1$ or $m\angle 4 \leq m\angle 2$.

Step 2: We will only show that the assumption $m\angle 4 \leq m\angle 1$ leads to a contradiction, since the argument for $m\angle 4 \leq m\angle 2$ uses the same reasoning.

$m\angle 4 \leq m\angle 1$, means that either $m\angle 4 = m\angle 1$ or $m\angle 4 < m\angle 1$. So, we need to consider both cases.

Case 1: If $m\angle 4 = m\angle 1$, then, since $m\angle 1 + m\angle 2 = m\angle 4$ by the Exterior Angle Theorem, we have $m\angle 1 + m\angle 2 = m\angle 1$ by substitution. Then $m\angle 2 = 0$, which contradicts the fact that the measure of an angle is greater than 0.

Case 2: If $m\angle 4 < m\angle 1$, then since $m\angle 1 + m\angle 2 = m\angle 4$ by the Exterior Angle Theorem, we have $m\angle 1 + m\angle 2 < m\angle 1$ by substitution. If $m\angle 1 + m\angle 2 < m\angle 1$, then $m\angle 2 < 0$, which contradicts the fact that the measure of an angle is greater than 0.

Step 3: In both cases, the assumption leads to the contradiction of a known fact. Therefore, the assumption that $m\angle 4 \leq m\angle 1$ must be false, which means that $m\angle 4 > m\angle 1$ must be true. Likewise, $m\angle 4 > m\angle 2$.

In the proof of Theorem 5-8, certain properties of inequalities that you encountered in algebra were used. For example, in Step 1 of the proof it was stated that if $m\angle 4 \leq m\angle 1$, then $m\angle 4 = m\angle 1$ or $m\angle 4 < m\angle 1$. This statement is an application of the *Comparison or Trichotomy Property*, which states that for any two numbers a and b, either $a > b$, $a = b$, or $a < b$. The chart at the top of the next page gives a list of properties of inequalities that you studied in algebra.

Properties of Inequality for Real Numbers

	For all numbers *a*, *b*, and *c*,
Comparison Property	$a < b$, $a = b$, or $a > b$.
Transitive Property	1. If $a < b$ and $b < c$, then $a < c$. 2. If $a > b$ and $b > c$, then $a > c$.
Addition and Subtraction Properties	1. If $a > b$, then $a + c > b + c$ and $a - c > b - c$. 2. If $a < b$, then $a + c < b + c$ and $a - c < b - c$.
Multiplication and Division Properties	1. If $c > 0$ and $a < b$, then $ac < bc$ and $\frac{a}{c} < \frac{b}{c}$. 2. If $c > 0$ and $a > b$, then $ac > bc$ and $\frac{a}{c} > \frac{b}{c}$. 3. If $c < 0$ and $a < b$, then $ac > bc$ and $\frac{a}{c} > \frac{b}{c}$. 4. If $c < 0$ and $a > b$, then $ac < bc$ and $\frac{a}{c} < \frac{b}{c}$.

The following statement can be used to define the inequality relationship between two numbers.

Definition of Inequality	For any real numbers *a* and *b*, $a > b$ if there is a positive number *c* such that $a = b + c$.

CHECKING FOR UNDERSTANDING

Communicating Mathematics

7. If two parallel lines are cut by a transversal, then alternate exterior angles are not congruent.

Read and study the lesson to answer each question. See margin.

1. Explain why the use of an alibi during a trial is an example of indirect reasoning.

2. In Lesson 2-4, the properties of equality for real numbers were presented. Compare these properties to the properties of inequality presented in this lesson. Describe the similarities and differences between them.

3. Given that $a > b$ and $c > d$, Lynn concluded that $a + b > c + d$.
   a. Find values of *a*, *b*, *c*, and *d* to show that Lynn's conclusion is not always true.
   b. Write a true inequality that results from the given information.

Guided Practice

State the assumption you would make to start an indirect proof of each statement.

4. Points *M*, *N*, and *P* are collinear. Points *M*, *N*, and *P* are not collinear.
5. Triangle *ABC* is acute. $\triangle ABC$ is right or obtuse.
6. The disk is defective. The disk is not defective.
7. If two parallel lines are cut by a transversal, then alternate exterior angles are congruent.
8. The angle bisector of the vertex angle of an isosceles triangle is also an altitude of the triangle. The angle bisector of the vertex angle of an isosceles triangle is not an altitude of the triangle.

LESSON 5-4 INDIRECT PROOF AND INEQUALITIES   235

Teaching Tip   When discussing the chart, remind students that if $c < 0$ it is a negative number, and if $c > 0$ it is a positive number. Review rules for operations using positive and negative numbers.

EVALUATING THE LESSON

Checking for Understanding

Exercises 1-17 are designed to help you assess students' understanding through reading, writing, speaking, and modeling. You should work through Exercises 1-3 with your students and then monitor their work on Exercises 4-17.

Error Analysis

Students may have difficulty understanding how an indirect proof actually proves the conclusion true. Point out that *all* possibilities are looked at, and *all* of the incorrect conclusions must be ruled out before you can say that the original conclusion is true.

Closing the Lesson

Writing Activity Have students write three mathematical statements. Have them exchange papers and write the assumptions they would make to start an indirect proof.

Additional Answers

1. The alibi provides a contradiction to being guilty—therefore, not guilty.

2. The comparison property differentiates between less than, equal to, and greater than. The symmetric and reflexive properties apply only to equalities, while the transitive property applies to inequalities as well. Addition, subtraction, multiplication, and division properties exist for both equalities and inequalities, although there is a significant difference between the multiplication and division properties for equalities and inequalities.

3a. Let $a = 2$, $b = 1$, $c = 5$, and $d = 4$. Then $a > b$ and $c > d$, but $a + b \not> c + d$ since $3 \not> 9$.

3b. If $a > b$ and $c > d$, then $a + c > b + d$.

Homework Exercises

Assignment Guide

Basic: 18-29, 34-40
Average: 18-21, 24-31, 34-40
Enriched: 18-20, 25-40
All: Mid-Chapter Review, 1-8

Additional Answers

17. Assume that $\overline{PZ}$ is a median of $\triangle PQR$. We are given that $PQ \cong PR$ and that $\angle 1 \neq \angle 2$. Since $\overline{PZ}$ is a median of $\triangle PQR$, $QZ \cong ZR$ since Z is the midpoint of $\overline{QR}$ by the definition of median. By the Isosceles Triangle Theorem, $\angle Q \cong \angle R$. Therefore, $\triangle PZQ \cong \triangle PZR$ by SAS. Then $\angle 1 \cong \angle 2$ by CPCTC. This is a contradiction of a given fact. Therefore, our assumption that $\overline{PZ}$ is a median of $\triangle PQR$ must be false, which means $\overline{PZ}$ is not a median of $\triangle PQR$.

23. Statements (Reasons)
  a. $NM \cong OM$ (Given)
  b. $\angle 2 \cong \angle N$ (Isosceles Triangle Theorem)
  c. $m\angle 1 > m\angle N$ (Exterior Angle Inequality Theorem)
  d. $m\angle 2 = m\angle N$ (Definition of congruent angles)
  e. $m\angle 1 > m\angle 2$ (Substitution prop. of equality)

24. Statements (Reasons)
  a. $SP \cong QP$ (Given)
  b. $\angle 1 \cong \angle 2$ (Isosceles Triangle Theorem)
  c. $m\angle SQR = m\angle 1 + m\angle 3$ (Angle Addition Postulate)
  d. $m\angle SQR > m\angle 1$ (Definition of inequality)
  e. $m\angle 1 = m\angle 2$ (Definition of congruent angles)
  f. $m\angle SQR > m\angle 2$ (Substitution prop. of equality)

Use the figure at the right. Complete each statement with either < or >.

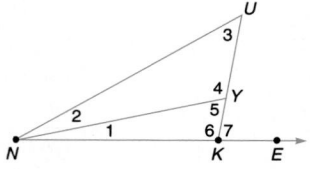

9. $m\angle UNK \underline{} m\angle 1$ >

10. $m\angle 5 \underline{} m\angle 4$ <

11. $m\angle 1 \underline{} m\angle 7$ <

12. If $m\angle 1 < m\angle 3$, then $m\angle 5 \underline{} m\angle 1$. >

Name the property of inequality that justifies each statement.

13. If $-4x < 20$, then $x > -5$. division

14. If $AB + CD > EF + CD$, then $AB > EF$. subtraction

15. If $m\angle 1 < m\angle 2$ and $m\angle 3 < m\angle 1$, then $m\angle 3 < m\angle 2$. transitive

16. If $XY \neq 2x - 25$, then $XY < 2x - 25$ or $XY > 2x - 25$. comparison

17. Write an indirect proof. **See margin.**
Given: $\overline{PQ} \cong \overline{PR}$
  $\angle 1 \neq \angle 2$
Prove: $\overline{PZ}$ is *not* a median of $\triangle PQR$.

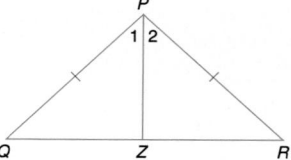

EXERCISES

Practice A

18. Complete the indirect proof in paragraph form by completing each sentence.

Through a point not on a given line, there is exactly one line perpendicular to the given line.

Given: P is a point not on line ℓ.

Prove: $\overrightarrow{PQ}$ is the only line through P perpendicular to ℓ.

18.a. $\overrightarrow{PQ}$ is not the only line through P perpendicular to ℓ. Call this line $\overrightarrow{PR}$, where R is a point on ℓ different from Q.

  a. Make the assumption that $\underline{}$.
  b. Both $\overrightarrow{PQ}$ and $\overrightarrow{PR}$ are perpendicular to ℓ because $\underline{}$. It is assumed.
  c. Since $\underline{}$, $\angle 1$ and $\angle 2$ are right angles. $\perp$ lines form four rt. $\angle$s.
  d. By $\underline{}$, $m\angle 1 = 90$ and $m\angle 2 = 90$. Definition of right angle
  e. $m\angle 1 + m\angle 2 + m\angle QPR = 180$ by $\underline{}$. The sum of the $\angle$s in a $\triangle$ is 180.
  f. By $\underline{}$, $90 + 90 + m\angle QPR = 180$. Substitution prop. of equality
  g. Therefore by $\underline{}$, $m\angle QPR = 0$. Subtraction property of equality
  h. But, $m\angle QPR > 0$ since $\underline{}$. Angle measures must be greater than 0.
  i. Therefore, our assumption is incorrect, so $\underline{}$. $\overrightarrow{PQ}$ is the only line through P perpendicular to ℓ.

Additional Answer

25. Statements (Reasons)
  a. $m\angle ABC = m\angle BCA$ (Given)
  b. $m\angle ABC = x + c$ (Angle Addition Postulate)
  c. $m\angle ABC > x$ (Definition of inequality)
  d. $m\angle BCA > x$ (Substitution prop. of equality)
  e. $m\angle ADB > m\angle BCA$ (Exterior Angle Inequality Theorem)
  f. $m\angle ADB > x$ (Transitive prop. of inequality)
  g. $y > x$ (Substitution prop. of equality)

Use the figure to complete each statement with either < or >.

19. $m\angle 6 \underline{\quad ?\quad} m\angle 4$ >
20. $m\angle 11 \underline{\quad ?\quad} m\angle 8$ <
21. $m\angle 9 \underline{\quad ?\quad} m\angle 1$ <
22. If $m\angle 10 = m\angle 13$, $m\angle 10 \underline{\quad ?\quad} m\angle 6$ <

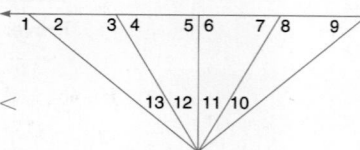

Write a two-column proof. See margin.

23. **Given:** $\triangle KNL$
    $\overline{NM} \cong \overline{OM}$
    Prove: $m\angle 1 > m\angle 2$

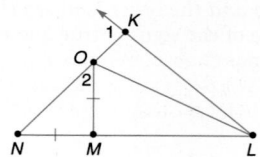

24. **Given:** $\triangle SQR$
    $\overline{SP} \cong \overline{QP}$
    Prove: $m\angle SQR > m\angle 2$

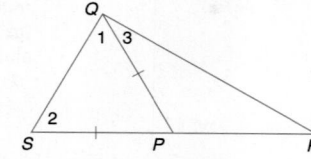

25. **Given:** $\triangle ABC$
    $m\angle ABC = m\angle BCA$
    Prove: $x < y$

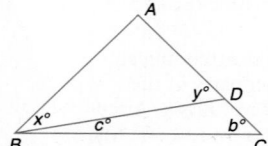

26. **Given:** $\triangle AEC$
    $\triangle CFB$
    Prove: $m\angle 4 < m\angle 1$

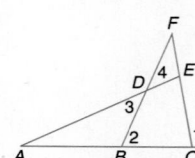

Write an indirect proof. See Solutions Manual.

27. **Given:** $\angle 2 \not\cong \angle 1$
    Prove: ℓ is not parallel to *m*.

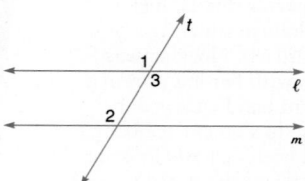

28. **Given:** $\triangle ABC$ is equilateral.
    $\triangle ABX$ is equilateral.
    $\triangle ACX$ is *not* equilateral.
    Prove: $\triangle BCX$ is *not* equilateral.

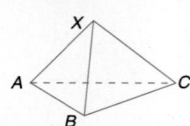

29. If two lines intersect, then they intersect in no more than one point.
30. If two sides of a triangle are *not* congruent, then angles opposite those sides are *not* congruent.
31. If no two altitudes of a triangle are congruent, then the triangle is scalene.
32. If $\overleftrightarrow{AB}$ and $\overleftrightarrow{PQ}$ are skew lines, then $\overleftrightarrow{AP}$ and $\overleftrightarrow{BQ}$ are skew lines.

RETEACHING THE LESSON

Work through the steps for writing an indirect proof using one or more examples. Make up real-world examples so that students can better comprehend the logic involved. Explain again that *all* possibilities must be looked at to prove that only one answer is possible by the process of elimination.

Additional Answer

26. **Statements (Reasons)**
    a. $m\angle 1 > m\angle 2$ and $m\angle 2 > m\angle 3$ (Exterior Angle Inequality Theorem)
    b. $\angle 3 \cong \angle 4$ (Vertical $\angle$s are $\cong$)
    c. $m\angle 3 = m\angle 4$ (Definition of congruent angles)
    d. $m\angle 2 > m\angle 4$ (Substitution prop. of equality)
    e. $m\angle 1 > m\angle 4$ (Transitive prop. of inequality)

Reteaching Masters Booklet, p. 28

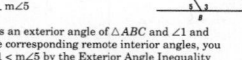

NAME _____ DATE _____

5-4 Reteaching Worksheet

Indirect Proof and Inequalities

A type of proof called **indirect proof** is sometimes used in geometry. In an indirect proof you assume the opposite of what you want to prove and show that this assumption leads to a contradiction of the original hypothesis or some other known fact, such as a postulate, theorem, or corollary.

The following theorem is called the Exterior Angle Inequality Theorem and can be proved by an indirect proof. (See page 234 in your book.)

> If an angle is an exterior angle of a triangle, then its measure is greater than the measure of either of its corresponding remote interior angles.

Example: Refer to the figure to complete the statement with either < or >.

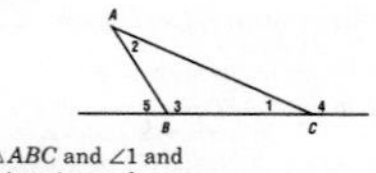

$m\angle 1 \underline{\quad ?\quad} m\angle 5$

Since $\angle 5$ is an exterior angle of $\triangle ABC$ and $\angle 1$ and $\angle 2$ are the corresponding remote interior angles, you know $m\angle 1 < m\angle 5$ by the Exterior Angle Inequality Theorem.

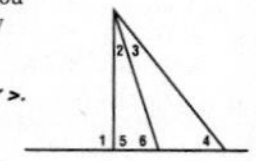

Use the figure at the right. Complete each statement with < or >.

1. $m\angle 1 \underline{\;>\;} m\angle 6$ 2. $m\angle 2 \underline{\;<\;} m\angle 1$
3. $m\angle 6 \underline{\;>\;} m\angle 3$ 4. $m\angle 4 \underline{\;<\;} m\angle 6$
5. Complete the indirect proof in paragraph form by completing each sentence. 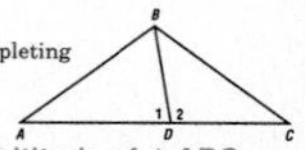
   Given: $m\angle 1 \neq m\angle 2$
   Prove: $\overline{BD}$ is not an altitude of $\triangle ABC$.
   a. In addition to the given, assume that $\underline{\overline{BD}\text{ is an altitude of } \triangle ABC}$
   b. Then $\overline{BD} \perp \overline{AC}$ by $\underline{\text{definition of altitude}}$
   c. Since $\underline{\text{perpendicular segments form four right angles}}$, $\angle 1$ and $\angle 2$ are right angles.
   d. Since all right angles are congruent, $\underline{\angle 1 \cong \angle 2}$
   e. Since $\angle 1 \cong \angle 2$, $m\angle 1 = \underline{m\angle 2}$
   f. But it is given that $\underline{m\angle 1 \neq m\angle 2}$.
   g. So our additional assumption is incorrect. Therefore, $\underline{\overline{BD}\text{ is not an altitude of } \triangle ABC}$

T28
Glencoe Division, Macmillan/McGraw-Hill

Additional Answer

33. **Statements** (Reasons)
    a. m∠X + m∠XPR + m∠XRP = 180; m∠Q + m∠QPR + m∠QRP = 180 (Angle Sum Theorem)
    b. m∠X + m∠XPR + m∠XRP = m∠Q + m∠QPR + m∠QRP (Substitution prop. of equality)
    c. m∠QPR = m∠QPX + m∠XPR; m∠QRP = m∠QRX + m∠XRP (Angle Addition Postulate)
    d. m∠X + m∠XPR + m∠XRP = m∠Q + (m∠QPX + m∠XPR) + (m∠QRX + m∠XRP) (Substitution prop. of equality)
    e. m∠X = m∠Q + (m∠QPX + m∠QRX) (Subtraction prop. of equality)
    f. m∠X > m∠Q (Definition of inequality)

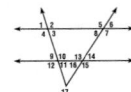

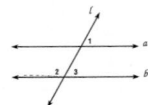

33. Write a two-column proof. See margin.

Given: X is in the interior of △PQR.

Prove: m∠X > m∠Q

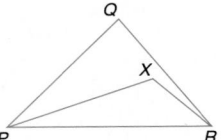

Critical Thinking

34. Use indirect reasoning and a chart to solve this problem:
A guard's prisoner is given the choice of opening one of two doors. Each door leads either to freedom or to the dungeon. A sign on the door on the right reads *This door leads to freedom and the other door leads to the dungeon.* The door on the left has a sign that reads *One of these doors leads to freedom and the other leads to the dungeon.* The guard tells the prisoner that one of the signs is true and the other is false. Which door should the prisoner choose? Why? The door on the left. If the sign on the door on the right were true, then both signs would be true. But one sign is false, so the sign on the door on the right must be false.

Application

35. **Entertainment** As a dinner party game, Mr. Block had his murder staged. Use the clues from the following scenario to determine who "killed" Mr. Block. Explain your reasoning.

Four people were attending an exclusive dinner party at the island estate of Mr. Block. After dinner, Inspector Photos and Ms. Tebbe went for a walk on the grounds. Upon returning to the house, they found that Mr. Block had been killed, shot in the back with an arrow. Mr. Sopher, who is legally blind without his glasses, told the inspector that he had been in the lounge smoking a pipe when he heard Mr. Block scream. Mrs. Bloom, with her left arm in a sling and right hand wrapped in bandages due to a recent accident, said she had been upstairs looking at paintings when she heard a scream. The security guard who is stationed in a building near the dock informed Inspector Photos that no one other than the four guests had been on the island that day.

Mr. Sopher; Photos and Tebbe each have alibis and Bloom couldn't shoot an arrow with the sling on.

Mixed Review

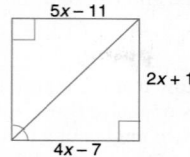

36. If R, S, and T are collinear, $RS = 13$, $ST = 2x + 7$, and $RT = 3x + 8$, which point is between the other two? Justify your answer. **(Lesson 1-4)**

37. Name the properties of equality that justify the statement *If $2x + 6 = 8$, then $x + 3 = 4$.* **(Lesson 2-4)** Distributive, Division

38. Find the value of x. Explain your reasoning. **(Lesson 5-2)** $x = 4$; The figure is a square because the two triangles are congruent.

(figure: square with sides labeled $5x - 11$ (top), $2x + 1$ (right side, diagonal), $4x - 7$ (bottom))

39. Biology A bacteria population triples in number each day. If there are 2,187,000 bacteria on the seventh day, how many bacteria were there on the first day? **(Lesson 5-3)** 3000 bacteria

Wrap-Up

40. Write an explanation of the steps used for an indirect proof that you could use to teach another student about indirect reasoning. **See students' work.**

MID-CHAPTER REVIEW

Refer to the figure at the right to answer each question.

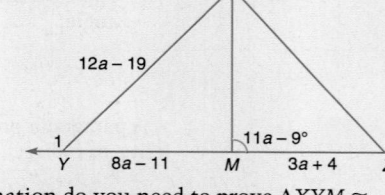

1. Find the value of a if $\overline{XM}$ is a median of $\triangle XYZ$. **(Lesson 5-1)** 3

2. Find the value of a if $\overline{XM}$ is an altitude of $\triangle XYZ$. **(Lesson 5-1)** 9

3. If $\overline{XM}$ is the perpendicular bisector of $\overline{YZ}$, is $\triangle XYM \cong \triangle XZM$? Justify your answer. **(Lesson 5-2)** yes by LL or SAS

4. If $\overline{XM}$ is an altitude of $\triangle XYZ$, what additional information do you need to prove $\triangle XYM \cong \triangle XZM$ by HL. **(Lesson 5-2)** $XY \cong XZ$ **5.** $<$; Exterior angle inequality theorem

5. Complete with either $<$ or $>$: $m\angle Z \underline{\ ?\ } m\angle 1$. Justify your answer. **(Lesson 5-4)**

6. If $YM < YX$, find all possible values of a. **(Lesson 5-4)** $a > 2$

7. Write an indirect proof for the statement *If two lines not in the same plane do not intersect, then the lines are skew.* **(Lesson 5-4)** See margin.

8. Eric, Sally, and Jon are playing a card game. They have a rule that when a player loses a hand, he or she must subtract enough points from his score to double each of the other players' scores. First Eric loses a hand, then Jon, then Sally. If each player now has 8 points, who lost the most points? **(Lesson 5-3)** Eric

---

EXTENDING THE LESSON

Math Power: Problem Solving

State the assumption you would make to start an indirect proof if the conclusion is $m\angle 1 > m\angle 2$.

$m\angle 1 \leq m\angle 2$

Mid-Chapter Review

The Mid-Chapter Review provides students with a brief review of the concepts and skills in Lessons 5-1 through 5-4. Lesson numbers are given at the end of problems or instruction lines so students may review concepts not yet mastered.

Additional Answer

Mid-Chapter Review

7. We are given that we have two lines that are noncoplanar and that do not intersect. Assume the lines are not skew. Then we have two possibilities for the lines.

Case 1: The lines intersect. This contradicts the given statement that the lines do not intersect.

Case 2: The lines are parallel. By the definition of parallel, this contradicts the given statement that the lines are noncoplanar.

In each case we are led to a contradiction. Hence, our assumption must be false and therefore, the lines are skew.

Enrichment Masters Booklet, p. 28

5-4 Enrichment Worksheet

NAME _____   DATE _____

Logic Problems

The following problems can be solved by eliminating possibilities. It may be helpful to use charts such as the one shown in the first problem. Mark an X in the chart to eliminate a possible answer.

Solve each problem.

1. Nancy, Olivia, Mario, and Kenji each has one piece of fruit in their school lunch. They have a peach, an orange, a banana, and an apple. Mario does not have a peach or a banana. Olivia and Mario just came from class with the student who has an apple. Kenji and Nancy are sitting next to the student who has a banana. Nancy does not have a peach. Which student has each piece of fruit?

	Nancy	Olivia	Mario	Kenji
Peach				
Orange				
Banana				
Apple				

Nancy-apple, Olivia-banana, Mario-orange, Kenji-peach

2. Victor, Leon, Kasha, and Sheri each play one instrument. They play the viola, clarinet, trumpet, and flute. Sheri does not play the flute. Kasha lives near the student who plays flute and the one who plays trumpet. Leon does not play a brass or wind instrument. Which student plays each instrument?

Victor-flute, Leon-viola, Kasha-clarinet, Sheri-trumpet

3. Mr. Guthrie, Mrs. Hakoi, Mr. Mirza, and Mrs. Riva have jobs of doctor, accountant, teacher, and office manager. Mr. Mirza lives near the doctor and the teacher. Mrs. Riva is not the doctor or the office manager. Mrs. Hakoi is not the accountant or the office manager. Mr. Guthrie went to lunch with the doctor. Mrs. Riva's son is a high school student and is only seven years younger than his algebra teacher. Which person has each occupation?

Mr. Guthrie-teacher, Mrs. Hakoi-doctor, Mr. Mirza-office manager, Mrs. Riva-accountant

4. Yvette, Lana, Boris, and Scott each have a dog. The breeds are collie, beagle, poodle, and terrier. Yvette and Boris walked to the library with the student who has a collie. Boris does not have a poodle or terrier. Scott does not have a collie. Yvette is in math class with the student who has a terrier. Which student has each breed of dog?

Yvette-poodle, Lana-collie, Boris-beagle, Scott-terrier

T28
Glencoe Division, Macmillan/McGraw-Hill

INTRODUCING THE LESSON

 5-Minute Check

(over Lesson 5-4)

1. State the first step in an indirect proof.   **Assume the conclusion is false.**
2. State the assumption you would make to start an indirect proof if you want to prove △*MNO* is a right triangle.   **△*MNO* is not a right triangle.**

Fill in the blank to make a true statement.

3. If $a < b$ and $b < c$, then ___.
   $a < c$
4. If $c < 0$ and $a < b$, then ___.
   $ac > bc$ and $\frac{a}{c} > \frac{b}{c}$

Motivating the Lesson

Draw an isosceles triangle on the board or overhead and review the relationship between the base angles and the sides of the triangle. Have students make conjectures about angle measures and side measures in any triangle. Have them look at right triangles or obtuse triangles to get ideas.

TEACHING THE LESSON

Teaching Tip   Theorems 5-9 and 5-10 can be summarized by saying that the shorter segment is opposite the smaller angle, and the longer segment is opposite the larger angle.

Inequalities for Sides and Angles of a Triangle

Objective
5-5

After studying this lesson, you should be able to:
■ recognize and use relationships between sides and angles in a triangle.

INVESTIGATION

You know from Chapter 4 that in a triangle if two sides are congruent then the angles opposite those sides are congruent. What is the relationship between two angles of a triangle if the sides opposite those angles are not congruent? Draw several different triangles and measure each side and angle. Describe the measure of the angle opposite the longest side of the triangle. **It is greater than the measures of the other two angles.**

The investigation leads us to Theorem 5-9.

Theorem 5-9	If one side of a triangle is longer than another side, then the angle opposite the longer side is greater than the angle opposite the shorter side.

The converse of Theorem 5-9 is also true.

Theorem 5-10	If one angle of a triangle is greater than another angle, then the side opposite the greater angle is longer than the side opposite the lesser angle.

A paragraph proof for Theorem 5-9 is given below. You will be asked to write an indirect proof for Theorem 5-10 in Exercise 28.

Proof of Theorem 5-9

Given: △*PQR*
$PQ > RQ$

Prove: $m\angle QRP > m\angle P$

Paragraph Proof:

Draw auxiliary segment *RM* so that *M* is between *P* and *Q* and $\overline{QM} \cong \overline{QR}$.

Thus, △*QMR* is isosceles, and $m\angle 1 = m\angle 2$ since if two sides of a triangle are congruent the angles opposite those sides are congruent.

240   CHAPTER 5   APPLYING CONGRUENT TRIANGLES

ALTERNATE TEACHING STRATEGIES

Using Investigation

Instruct students to draw a triangle and have them use a protractor to measure each angle and a ruler to measure each side. Have them list the angles and the sides in order from greatest to least. What do they notice about the order? **The order of the angles corresponds to the order of the opposite sides.** Does everyone's triangle fit the pattern?   **yes**

Using Modeling

Use a compass to look at angle measures of a triangle and their opposite side lengths. Use the compass legs to represent two sides of a triangle. The third side is between the compass points. Have students make conjectures about angle relationships and side lengths in triangles based on this activity and their knowledge of other triangles.

Notice that $\angle 1$ is an exterior angle of $\triangle PRM$. Since the measure of an exterior angle is greater than the measure of either of its corresponding remote interior angles, $m\angle P < m\angle 1$.

Since $m\angle 2 + m\angle 3 = m\angle QRP$ by the angle addition postulate, $m\angle 2 < m\angle QRP$ by the definition of inequality. Thus, $m\angle 1 < m\angle QRP$ by the substitution property of equality.

Finally, we can apply the transitive property of inequality to the inequalities $m\angle P < m\angle 1$ and $m\angle 1 < m\angle QRP$ to get $m\angle P < m\angle QRP$.

You can use algebra to help solve problems involving triangles.

Example 1

In $\triangle PQR$, $m\angle P = 6x + 4$, $m\angle Q = 7x + 12$, and $m\angle R = 6x - 7$. List the sides of $\triangle PQR$ in order from the longest to the shortest.

In order to compare the lengths of the sides of $\triangle PQR$, you must determine the measures of the angles in $\triangle PQR$. Since the sum of the measures of the angles of a triangle is 180, $m\angle P + m\angle Q + m\angle R = 180$.

$$m\angle P + m\angle Q + m\angle R = 180$$
$$(6x + 4) + (7x + 12) + (6x - 7) = 180$$
$$19x + 9 = 180$$
$$19x = 171$$
$$x = 9$$

$m\angle P = 6x + 4$	$m\angle Q = 7x + 12$	$m\angle R = 6x - 7$
$= 6(9) + 4$	$= 7(9) + 12$	$= 6(9) - 7$
$= 58$	$= 75$	$= 47$

Since $m\angle R < m\angle P < m\angle Q$, by Theorem 5-10, the side opposite $\angle R$ is shorter than the side opposite $\angle P$, and the side opposite $\angle P$ is shorter than the side opposite $\angle Q$. Thus, in $\triangle PQR$, $\overline{PQ}$ is shorter than $\overline{QR}$ is shorter than $\overline{PR}$. So the sides in order from longest to shortest are $\overline{PR}$, $\overline{QR}$, $\overline{PQ}$.

Check the answer by drawing $\triangle PQR$ with angles of 58°, 75°, and 47° and measuring the sides.

In the figure at the right, P is a point not on line t, and Q is the point on t such that $\overline{PQ} \perp t$. In Lesson 3-6, we defined the distance between P and t as the length of $\overline{PQ}$. At that time, it was stated, without proof, that $\overline{PQ}$ was the shortest segment from P to t. Assuming this is true, if R is any point, other than Q, on t, $\overline{PR}$ would have to be longer than $\overline{PQ}$. *Why?*

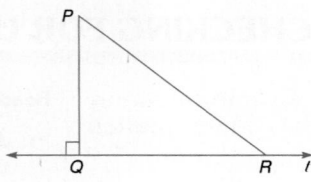

Teaching Tip Have students rewrite the paragraph proof of Theorem 5-9 as a two-column proof.

Chalkboard Example

For the Example
In $\triangle JKL$, $KL = 13x + 6$, $JL = 8x + 5$, and $JK = 7x - 7$. List the angles of $\triangle JKL$ in order from least to greatest if the perimeter of $\triangle JKL$ is 144 feet.
$$KL + JL + JK = 144$$
$$(13x + 6) + (8x + 5) + (7x - 7) = 144$$
$$28x + 4 = 144$$
$$28x = 140$$
$$x = 5$$
$$KL = 13(5) + 6$$
$$KL = 71$$
$$JL = 8(5) + 5$$
$$JL = 45$$
$$JK = 7(5) - 7$$
$$JK = 28$$
Thus, $m\angle L < m\angle K < m\angle J$ by Theorem 5-9. So the angles in order from least to greatest are $\angle L$, $\angle K$, $\angle J$.

EVALUATING THE LESSON

Checking for Understanding

Exercises 1-14 are designed to
help you assess students'
understanding through reading,
writing, speaking, and modeling.
You should work through
Exercises 1-3 with your students
and then monitor their work on
Exercises 4-14.

Closing the Lesson

Modeling Activity Have students
use toothpicks to make a triangle
and have them list the sides in
order from shortest to longest and
the angles from least to greatest.

Additional Answer

1.

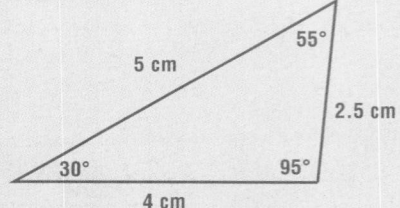

Construct a 30° angle. Then
mark off segments of 5 cm
and 4 cm on each of the rays.
Connect the endpoints of
those segments.

We will now restate our assumption about the shortest segment from a
point to a line as a theorem and show that it is true as a direct result of
Theorem 5-10.

Theorem 5-11	**The perpendicular segment from a point to a line is the shortest segment from the point to the line.**

*Proof of
Theorem 5-11*

Given: $\overline{PQ} \perp t$
$\overline{PR}$ is any segment from P to t
that is different from $\overline{PQ}$.

Prove: $PR > PQ$

Proof:

Statements	Reasons
1. $\overline{PQ} \perp t$	1. Given
2. $\angle 1$ and $\angle 2$ are right angles.	2. $\perp$ lines form four rt. $\angle$s.
3. $\angle 1 \cong \angle 2$	3. All rt. $\angle$s are $\cong$.
4. $m\angle 1 = m\angle 2$	4. Definition of congruent angles
5. $m\angle 1 > m\angle 3$	5. If an $\angle$ is an ext. $\angle$ of a Δ, then its measure is greater than the measure of either of its corr. remote int. $\angle$s.
6. $m\angle 2 > m\angle 3$	6. Substitution
7. $PR > PQ$	7. If one $\angle$ of a Δ is greater than another $\angle$, then the side opp. the greater $\angle$ is longer than the side opp. the lesser $\angle$.

The proof of Corollary 5-1 follows directly from Theorem 5-11. You will be
asked to prove the corollary in Exercise 29.

Corollary 5-1	**The perpendicular segment from a point to a plane is the shortest segment from the point to the plane.**

CHECKING FOR UNDERSTANDING

*Communicating
Mathematics*

Read and study the lesson to answer each question. See margin.

1. A triangle has angles measuring about 30°, 55°, and 95° and sides
measuring about 4 cm, 5 cm, and 2.5 cm. Draw the triangle and label the
measures of all sides and angles. Explain how to construct the triangle.

2. Justify the statement *In an obtuse triangle, the longest side is opposite the obtuse angle.*

3. Write the conclusions you can draw about △*PAL*, if

   a. *PA = PL*

   b. *m∠A > m∠L*

   c. *PA < PL.*

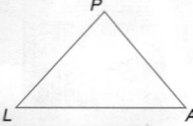

Additional Answers

2. In an obtuse triangle, there is one obtuse angle and it must be the largest angle of the triangle. The longest side must be opposite this angle.
3a. ∠A ≅ ∠L
3b. *PL > PA*
3c. m∠L < m∠A
14. Statements   (Reasons)
   a. ∠D is a right angle. (Given)
   b. m∠D = 90   (Definition of right angle)
   c. ∠F is an acute angle. (There can be at most one right or obtuse angle in a triangle.)
   d. m∠F < 90   (Definition of acute angle)

   e. m∠F < m∠D (Substitution prop. of equality)
   f. *ED < EF*   (If one ∠ of a △ is greater than another ∠ then the side opp. the greater ∠ is longer than the side opp. the lesser ∠.)

Guided Practice   **For each triangle, list the angles in order from greatest to least.**

4.
5.
6.

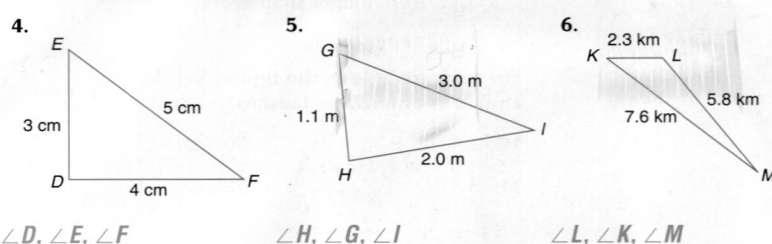

∠D, ∠E, ∠F   ∠H, ∠G, ∠I   ∠L, ∠K, ∠M

For each triangle, list the sides in order from longest to shortest.

7.
8.
9.

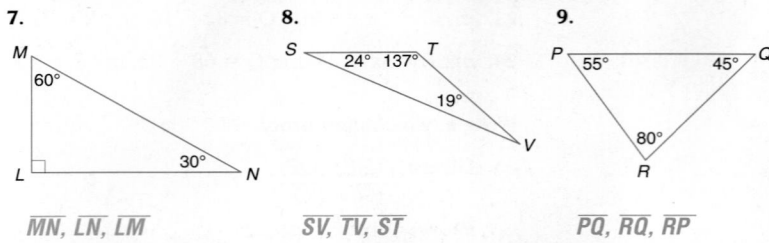

$\overline{MN}$, $\overline{LN}$, $\overline{LM}$ $\overline{SV}$, $\overline{TV}$, $\overline{ST}$ $\overline{PQ}$, $\overline{RQ}$, $\overline{RP}$

Given the angles indicated in the figure, answer each question.

10. Which side of △*PAT* is the longest? $\overline{PA}$

11. Which side of △*HPT* is the shortest? $\overline{HT}$

12. How do the two sides in Exercises 10 and 11 compare? $\overline{PA}$ is longer than $\overline{HT}$.

13. What is the longest side of the figure *PATH*? $\overline{PA}$

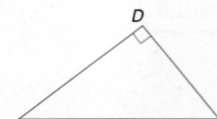

14. Write a two-column proof. See margin.
    Given: △*DEF*
            ∠*D* is a right angle.
    Prove: *EF > ED*

LESSON 5-5   INEQUALITIES FOR SIDES AND ANGLES OF A TRIANGLE   243

RETEACHING THE LESSON

Your students may have difficulty understanding that the shortest segment from a point to a line is the perpendicular segment. Have them stretch a rubber band to reach different points on a line. Where is the rubber band least taut?

Reteaching Masters Booklet, p. 29

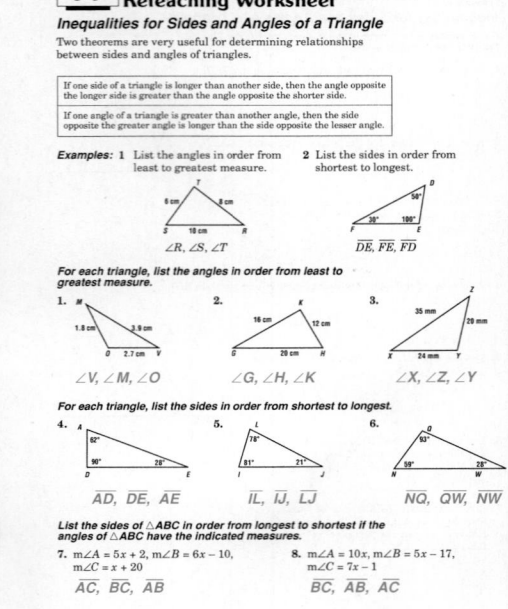

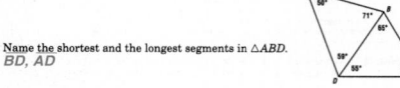

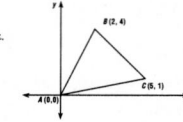

APPLYING THE LESSON

Homework Exercises

Assignment Guide

Basic: 15-26, 30-36
Average: 17-28, 30-36
Enriched: 17-18, 21-36

Exercise Notes

For Exercise 18, you can compare the lengths of segments in the three triangles because $\triangle SQT$ and $\triangle PRQ$ each have one side in common with $\triangle PSQ$.

Additional Answer

25. Statements (Reasons)
    a. $QR > QP$ (Given)
    b. $m\angle P > m\angle R$ (If one side of a $\triangle$ is longer than another side, then the $\angle$ opp. the longer side is greater than the $\angle$ opp. the shorter side.)
    c. $\overline{PR} \cong \overline{PQ}$ (Given)
    d. $\angle Q \cong \angle R$ (Isosceles Triangle Theorem)
    e. $m\angle Q = m\angle R$ (Definition of congruent angles)
    f. $m\angle P > m\angle Q$ (Substitution prop. of equality)

Practice Masters Booklet, p. 34

5-5 NAME ______ DATE ______

Practice Worksheet

Inequalities for Sides and Angles of a Triangle

For Exercises 1 to 4, refer to the figure on the right. This figure is not drawn to scale.

1. Name the shortest and the longest segments in $\triangle BCD$. $\overline{BC}$, $\overline{DC}$
2. Name the shortest and the longest segments in $\triangle ABD$. $\overline{BD}$, $\overline{AD}$
3. Find the shortest segment in the figure. $\overline{BC}$
4. How many of the segments in the figure are longer than $\overline{BD}$? 3

5. List the angles in order from least to greatest. $\angle A, \angle C, \angle B$
6. List the sides of $\triangle MNO$ in order from longest to shortest if $m\angle M = 4x + 20$, $m\angle N = 2x + 10$, and $m\angle 0 = 3x - 20$. $\overline{NO}$, $\overline{MO}$, $\overline{MN}$
7. List the angles of $\triangle KLM$ in order from least to greatest if $KL = x - 4$, $LM = x + 4$, $KM = 2x - 1$, and the perimeter of $\triangle KLM$ is 27. $\angle M, \angle K, \angle L$

T34

EXERCISES

Practice

A

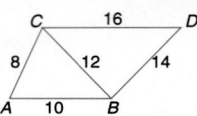

15. Name the least and greatest angles in ΔABC. $\angle CBA$; $\angle A$
16. Name the least and greatest angles in ΔBCD. $\angle D$; $\angle CBD$

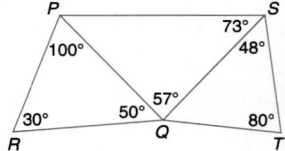

17. Find the shortest segment in the figure. This figure is not drawn to scale. $\overline{QT}$
18. How many of the segments in the figure are longer than $\overline{PS}$? 3

B

For each triangle in the figure, list the angles in order from least to greatest.

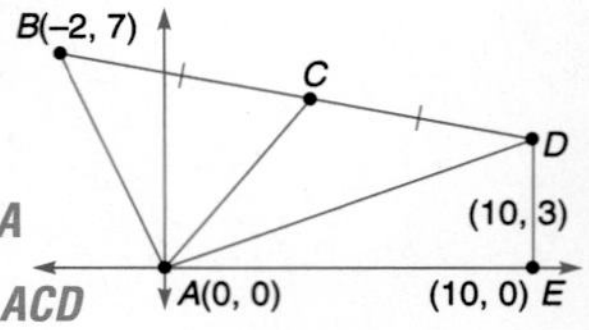

19. ΔADE $\angle EAD, \angle ADE, \angle E$
20. ΔABC $\angle CAB, \angle B, \angle BCA$
21. ΔABD $\angle ADB, \angle B, \angle BAD$
22. ΔACD $\angle CAD, \angle CDA, \angle ACD$

List the sides of ΔPQR in order from longest to shortest if the angles of ΔPQR have the indicated measures.

23. $m\angle P = 7x + 8$, $m\angle Q = 8x - 10$, $m\angle R = 7x + 6$ $\overline{QR}, \overline{PQ}, \overline{PR}$
24. $m\angle P = 3x + 44$, $m\angle Q = 68 - 3x$, $m\angle R = x + 61$ $\overline{PQ}, \overline{QR}, \overline{PR}$

Write a two-column proof. See margin.

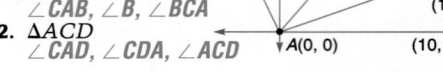

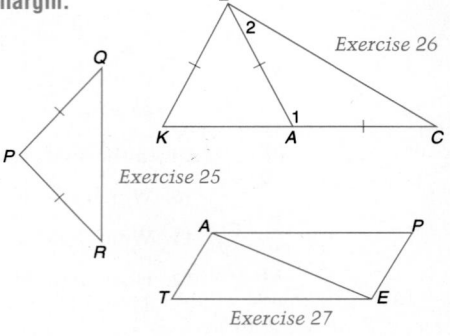

25. **Given:** $QR > QP$
    $\overline{PR} \cong \overline{PQ}$
    Prove: $m\angle P > m\angle Q$
26. **Given:** $\overline{AC} \cong \overline{AE}$
    $\overline{AE} \cong \overline{KE}$
    Prove: $m\angle 1 > m\angle 2$
27. **Given:** $TE > AE$
    $m\angle P > m\angle PAE$
    Prove: $TE > PE$

Exercise 25

Exercise 26

Exercise 27

C

28. Write an indirect proof for Theorem 5-10: If one angle of a triangle is greater than another angle, then the side opposite the greater angle is longer than the side opposite the lesser angle. See Solutions Manual.
29. Write a paragraph proof for Corollary 5-1: The perpendicular segment from a point to a plane is the shortest segment from the point to the plane. See Solutions Manual.

Additional Answers

26. Statements (Reasons)
    a. $\overline{AE} \cong \overline{KE}$ (Given)
    b. $\angle EKA \cong \angle EAK$ (Isosceles Triangle Theorem)
    c. $m\angle EKA = m\angle EAK$ (Definition of congruence)
    d. $m\angle 1 > m\angle EKA$ (Exterior Angle Inequality Theorem)
    e. $m\angle 1 > m\angle EAK$ (Substitution prop. of equality)
    f. $m\angle EAK > m\angle 2$ (Exterior Angle Inequality Theorem)
    g. $m\angle 1 > m\angle 2$ (Transitive prop. of inequality)
27. Statements (Reasons)
    a. $m\angle P > m\angle PAE$ (Given)
    b. $AE > PE$ (If one $\angle$ of a $\triangle$ is greater than another $\angle$, then the side opp. the greater $\angle$ is longer than the side opp. the lesser angle.)
    c. $TE > AE$ (Given)
    d. $TE > PE$ (Transitive prop. of inequality)

Critical Thinking   **30.** If $AB > BC > AC$ in $\triangle ABC$ and $\overline{AM}$, $\overline{BN}$, and $\overline{CO}$ are the medians of the triangle, list $\overline{AM}$, $\overline{BN}$, and $\overline{CO}$ in order from longest to shortest.
        $\overline{BN}$, $\overline{AM}$, $\overline{CO}$

Application   **31. Genetics**   The line graphed at the right represents the relation obtained by predicting the height of a son given the height of his father. Points A, B, and C each represent a particular father and son. For which pair is the prediction the worst? Justify your claim.   **C; Distance from C to the line is greatest.**

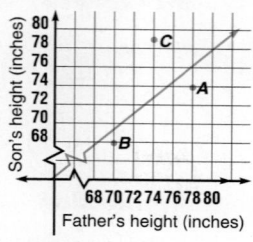

Son's height (inches) — vertical axis: 68, 70, 72, 74, 76, 78, 80
Father's height (inches) — horizontal axis: 68 70 72 74 76 78 80

Mixed Review   **32.** If B is between A and C, $AC = 33$, and $AB = 21 - 4x$, find all possible values of x. **(Lesson 5-4)** $-3 < x < \dfrac{21}{4}$

33. Given $\triangle ANT \cong \triangle TOE$, $AN = 15$, $NT = 19$, $AT = 27$, and $EO = 4x - 1$, find the value of x. **(Lesson 4-3)**   **5**

34. Draw a figure to illustrate two parallel lines with a plane perpendicular to both lines. **(Lesson 3-1)**   **See Solutions Manual.**

35. If $\angle A \cong \angle B$, $m\angle A = 7d - 1$, and $m\angle B = 11d - 53$, is $\angle B$ acute, right, or obtuse? **(Lesson 1-7)**   **right**

Wrap-Up   **36.** Write a summary of the characteristics of triangles that you have learned in this lesson. **See students' work.**

HISTORY CONNECTION

The geometry that we use and study today has its roots in surveying. The word *geometry* literally means to measure the earth. Although the purpose of surveying has remained the same, to accurately describe land, the instruments of surveying have changed over the centuries.

In A.D. 60, an Egyptian named Heron of Alexandria invented the *dioptra* for surveying and making astronomical observations. A dioptra could measure horizontal and vertical angles.

The Romans used a *groma* to measure squares and rectangles for laying out city blocks, streets, and aqueducts. A groma consists of two crosspieces mounted to swivel on a pole. Each arm of the crosspieces has a plumb-bob.

Today's surveyors use *transits* and *theodolites*. These instruments measure both angles and distances. To find a distance, surveyors measure the time it takes for light to travel from one point to another and back. Since they know the speed of light, they can find the distance the light traveled. Modern transits and theodolites use lasers to transmit the light.

LESSON 5-5   INEQUALITIES FOR SIDES AND ANGLES OF A TRIANGLE   245

EXTENDING THE LESSON

Math Power: Connections

Ask students: In an isosceles triangle, how can you tell from the angle measures if the third side is longer or shorter than the two equal sides?

If the base angles measure greater than 60, then the third side will be shorter than the two equal sides; if less than 60, then the third side will be longer; and if 60, then the triangle is equilateral.

History Connection

The History Connection features introduce students to persons or cultures who were involved in the development of mathematics. You may want students to further research surveying.

Lesson Resources

• Reteaching Master 5-6
• Practice Master 5-6
• Enrichment Master 5-6
• Evaluation Master, p. 66

 Transparency 5-6 contains the 5-Minute Check and a teaching aid for this lesson.

INTRODUCING THE LESSON

5-Minute Check

(over Lesson 5-5)

For Exercises 1-3, refer to the figure below.

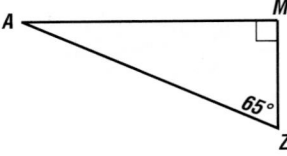

1. If m∠Z is 65, list the angles in order from least to greatest.
   ∠A, ∠Z, ∠M
2. List the sides in order from shortest to longest. $\overline{MZ}$, $\overline{MA}$, $\overline{AZ}$
3. Is $\overline{MZ}$ the shortest segment to $\overline{MA}$ from point Z? Justify your answer. **yes, because $\overline{MZ} \perp \overline{MA}$ and by Corollary 5-1, $\overline{MZ}$ must be the shortest segment.**
4. If m∠D = 9x + 14, m∠G = 4x − 2, and m∠P = 3x − 8, list the sides of △DGP in order from longest to shortest.
   $\overline{GP}$, $\overline{DP}$, $\overline{DG}$

Motivating the Lesson

Give students rubber bands and have them make a triangle with it in their fingers. Have them stretch and distort the rubber band to make different triangles. Ask them what they can say about the sides of the triangles.

Objective
5-6

After studying this lesson, you should be able to:
▪ apply the triangle inequality theorem.

Application

Jane's art class has been asked to make a variety of triangular frames for mathematical mobiles for an art show. The students are to make these frames by bending pieces of wire 100 centimeters long at two points and soldering the ends together.

Will it make any difference where along the wire Jane makes her two bends in order to create the triangular frames? Can these two points be chosen purely at random? What are the factors Jane needs to take into account before bending the wire?

INVESTIGATION

Try simulating Jane's wire bending by taking a straw and bending it in two distinct points and then putting a pin through the ends to fasten them together. Try several different combinations of bends similar to those suggested below. Will the process always form a triangle? Why or why not?

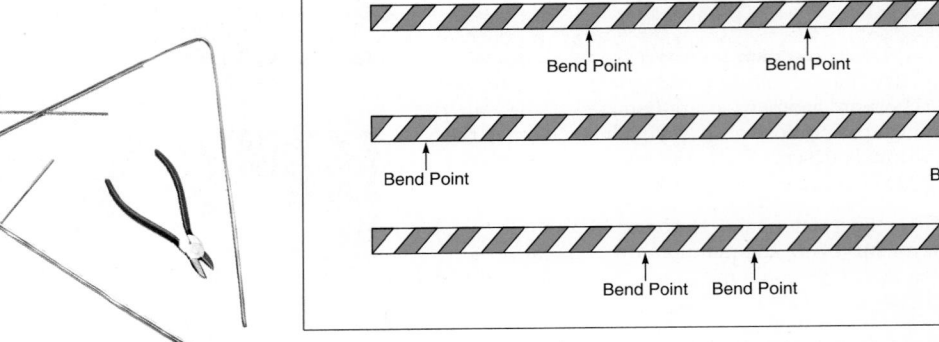

What conclusion can you draw about the lengths of the sides of triangles? One possible conclusion is stated in the following theorem.

Theorem 5-12
Triangle Inequality Theorem

The sum of the lengths of any two sides of a triangle is greater than the length of the third side.

You will be asked to prove the Triangle Inequality Theorem in Exercise 37.

ALTERNATE TEACHING STRATEGIES

Using Modeling

Have students do the investigation on page 246. They can use straws, pipe cleaners, twist ties, or any bendable sticks that can be marked. Once the students have experimented, ask them to formulate some hypotheses. When does bending the stick not form a triangle? When does it form a triangle?

Using Manipulatives

Join two twist ties at one end so that one measures 6 cm exactly and the other 10 cm exactly. Overlap the two and measure the length from the end of the shorter twist tie to the end of the longer twist tie. Stretch the ties out to make a straight line and measure from end to end. These numbers represent the range for the length of the third side.

The Triangle Inequality Theorem shows that some sets of line segments cannot be used to form a triangle, because their lengths do not satisfy the inequality.

Example 1

Mrs. Bailey, Jane's art teacher, gave Jane four pieces of copper tubing to use to make a triangular base for her mobiles. The lengths of the pieces of tubing are 2 meters, 4.5 meters, 5.8 meters, and 10.2 meters. How many different triangles could Jane make?

There are four possible ways for Jane to choose three pieces of tubing for the triangular base. She can choose the following combinations:

a. 2 m, 4.5 m, and 5.8 m

b. 2 m, 4.5 m, and 10.2 m

c. 2 m, 5.8 m, and 10.2 m

d. 4.5 m, 5.8 m, and 10.2 m

To determine if each of the four combinations can be used to form a triangle, you must test that all combinations for the lengths of the three sides satisfy the triangle inequality.

a. 2 m, 4.5 m, 5.8 m

Is $2 + 4.5 > 5.8$? *yes*

Is $2 + 5.8 > 4.5$? *yes*

Is $4.5 + 5.8 > 2$? *yes*

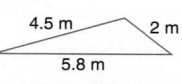

These three pieces can be used to form a triangle.

b. 2 m, 4.5 m, 10.2 m

Is $2 + 4.5 > 10.2$? *no*

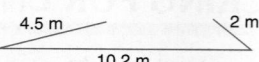

These three pieces cannot be used to form a triangle. *Why don't you need to check the other two combinations for the sides?*

c. 2 m, 5.8 m, 10.2 m

Is $2 + 5.8 > 10.2$? *no*

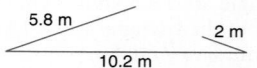

These three pieces cannot be used to form a triangle.

d. 4.5 m, 5.8 m, 10.2 m

Is $4.5 + 5.8 > 10.2$? *yes*

Is $4.5 + 10.2 > 5.8$? *yes*

Is $5.8 + 10.2 > 4.5$? *yes*

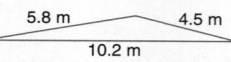

These three pieces can be used to form a triangle.

Jane can make mobiles with either of two different sets of tubing, Set A or Set D.

If the lengths of two sides of a triangle are known, then it is possible to determine the range of possible lengths for the third side.

LESSON 5-6   THE TRIANGLE INEQUALITY   247

Chalkboard Example

For Example 2
The lengths of two sides of a triangle are 8 and 13. What are the possible lengths of the third side?

$$8 + x > 13 \qquad 13 + x > 8$$
$$x > 5 \qquad\qquad x > -5$$
$$8 + 13 > x$$
$$21 > x$$

Disregard the second inequality because the measure of x must be positive. Therefore, the third side must be greater than 5 and less than 21.

EVALUATING THE LESSON

Checking for Understanding

Exercises 1-12 are designed to help you assess students' understanding through reading, writing, speaking, and modeling. You should work through Exercises 1-4 with your students and then monitor their work on Exercises 5-12.

Reteaching Masters Booklet, p. 30

Example 2

The lengths of two sides of a triangle are 6 cm and 10 cm. What are the possible lengths for the third side of this triangle?

Let x = the length of the third side.

By the Triangle Inequality Theorem, each of these inequalities must be true.

$$x + 6 > 10 \qquad x + 10 > 6$$
$$x > 4 \qquad\qquad x > -4$$

$$10 + 6 > x$$
$$16 > x \quad x < 16$$

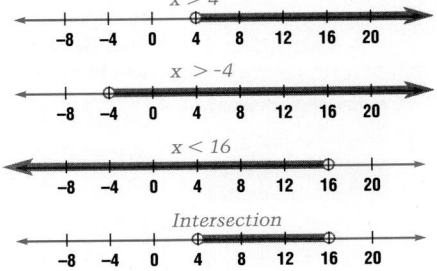

The length of the third side must fall in the range included in all three inequalities. The graphs show us that the length of the third side must be between 4 cm and 16 cm.
The possible measures can be expressed as follows: $\{x \mid 4 < x < 16\}$.

CHECKING FOR UNDERSTANDING

Communicating Mathematics

Read and study the lesson to answer each question. **See students' work.**

1. State the Triangle Inequality Theorem in your own words.

2. Give an example of a set of numbers that can be the lengths of the sides of a triangle and a set of numbers that cannot be. Use drawings or sketches to justify your reasoning. **See students' work.**

3. An isosceles triangle has a base that is 8 inches long.
   a. Are there any restrictions on how short or how long the legs of this triangle can be? **The legs can be any length greater than 4 inches.**
   b. Draw diagrams to help explain your answer. **See students' work.**

4. Two sides of a triangle are 5 cm and 13 cm long. Must 5 cm be the length of the shortest side of the triangle? Must 13 cm be the length of the longest side? Explain. **See margin.**

Guided Practice

Determine whether it is possible to draw a triangle with sides of the given measures. Write *yes* or *no*. If yes, then draw the triangle.
See students' drawings.

5. 1, 2, 5 **no**   6. 11, 10, 17 **yes**   7. 2.4, 6.8, 4.5 **yes**

The measures of two sides of a triangle are given. Between what two numbers must the measure of the third side fall?

    3 and 27   **9 and 17**   **4 and 38**
8. 12 and 15   9. 4 and 13   10. 21 and 17

11. Is it possible for the points $A(0, 0)$, $B(3, 2)$, and $C(-6, -4)$ to be the vertices of a triangle? Explain your answer. **no; the points are collinear.**

RETEACHING THE LESSON

Ask students for three numbers. Have them test these numbers to see if they can be the lengths of the sides of a triangle. Repeat this process until the students begin to grasp the idea of the Triangle Inequality Theorem.

Additional Answer

4. Let x be the length of the third side. Then $8 < x < 18$ so 5 cm must be the length of the shortest side, but 13 cm is not necessarily the length of the longest.

12. Write a two-column proof. **See margin.**

Given: $\angle B \cong \angle ACB$

Prove: $AD + AB > CD$

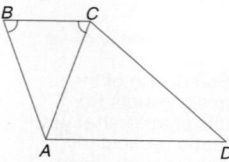

EXERCISES

Practice

Determine whether it is possible to draw a triangle with sides of the given measures. Write *yes* or *no*.

A

13. 12, 11, 17 **yes**   **14.** 1, 2, 3 **no**   **15.** 4.7, 9, 4.1 **no**

16. 2.5, 6, 6.5 **yes**   **17.** 12, 2.2, 14.3 **no**   **18.** 2.3, 12, 12.2 **yes**

19. 9, 40, 41 **yes**   **20.** 5, 100, 100 **yes**   **21.** 204, 7, 215 **no**

Two sides of a triangle are 18 and 21 centimeters in length. Determine whether each measurement can be the length of the third side.

B

22. 10 cm **yes**   **23.** 40 cm **no**   **24.** 7 cm **yes**

25. 21 cm **yes**   **26.** 3 cm **no**   **27.** 57 cm **no**

Is it possible to have a triangle with the given vertices? Write *yes* or *no*. Explain your answer.

28. $A(4, -3)$, $B(0, 0)$, $C(-4, 3)$ **no**   **29.** $D(-2, 1)$, $E(2, -1)$, $F(-6, 3)$ **no**

30. $G(-2, 4)$, $H(-6, 5)$, $I(-3, -3)$ **yes**   **31.** $J(3, -3)$, $K(8, 2)$, $L(5, 5)$ **yes**

CONNECTION
Counting

32. Answer each question, given that Victor has five straws with lengths of 3 cm, 4 cm, 5 cm, 6 cm, and 12 cm.

a. How many different triangles can Victor make with the straws? **4**

b. How many different triangles can Victor make that have a perimeter that is divisible by 3? **2**

CONNECTION
Probability

c. There are 10 different combinations of straws. What is the probability that if Victor chooses three straws at random he will be able to make a triangle? *(number of choices that will make a triangle) ÷ (total number of ways to choose 3 straws from a group of 5)* $\frac{4}{10} = \frac{2}{5}$ **or 0.4**

CONNECTION
Algebra

If the sides of a triangle have the following lengths, find all possible values for *x*.

33. $(3x + 2)$ cm, $(8x - 10)$ cm, $(5x + 8)$ cm $\{x | x > \frac{8}{3}\}$

34. $2x$ ft, $(15 - x)$ ft, $(4x - 6)$ ft $\{x | 3 < x < 7\}$

35. How many different triangles are possible if the measures of the three sides must be selected, without repetition, from the measures 1, 2, 3, and 4? **1**

Write a two-column proof for each.
See Solutions Manual.

36. Given: $MN = MQ$

Prove: $OP + ON > PQ$

C

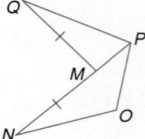

Additional Answers

12. Statements   (Reasons)

a. $\angle B \cong \angle ACB$ (Given)

b. $\overline{AB} \cong \overline{AC}$ (If two ∠s are ≅, the sides opp. the ∠s are ≅.)

c. $AB = AC$ (Definition of congruent segments)

d. $AD + AC > CD$ (Triangle Inequality)

e. $AD + AB > CD$ (Substitution prop. of equality)

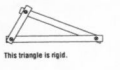
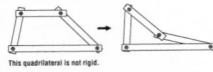
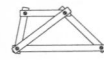
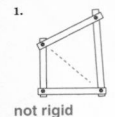

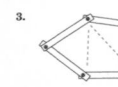

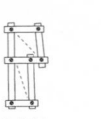
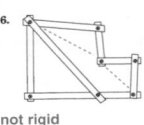

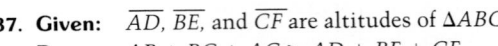

Portfolio

Select one of the assignments from this chapter that you found particularly challenging. Place it in your portfolio.

37. Given: $\overline{AD}$, $\overline{BE}$, and $\overline{CF}$ are altitudes of $\triangle ABC$.

Prove: $AB + BC + AC > AD + BE + CF$

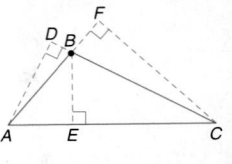

38. Write a two-column proof for the Triangle Inequality Theorem. (Theorem 5-12)

Given: $\triangle PQR$

Prove: $PQ + PR > RQ$

Hint: Draw auxiliary segment PS so that P is between S and R and $\overline{PQ} \cong \overline{PS}$. **See Solutions Manual.**

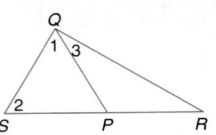

Critical Thinking

39. State and prove a theorem that compares the measure of the longest side of a quadrilateral with the measures of the other three sides. **See Solutions Manual.**

Graphing Calculator

41a. 1 in., 4 in., 4 in.; 2 in., 3 in., 4 in.; 3 in., 3 in., 3 in.

40. Choose a partner. Each partner should enter the code [INT] [(] 100 [×] [RAND] [)] in a TI-81 graphing calculator or the code [INT] [(] 100 [×] [RAN#] [)] in a Casio graphing calculator. Then each should press [ENTER] or [EXE] three times and record the random values from the display. The first person who obtains five sets of random values that are possible measures for the sides of a triangle wins the game.

Applications

41. Construction A metal rod that is 9 inches long is to be cut into three pieces and welded together to form a triangular brace for a stair step.
a. If the pieces all have an integral length, name all of the possible combinations of lengths.
b. Is the triangle with the shortest side isosceles, scalene, or equilateral?

42. Gardening Mr. and Mrs. Zellar have six old railroad ties that they would like to use to border two different triangular flower beds. They have two ties that are 3 feet long, two ties that are 5 feet long, one tie that is 7 feet long, and one tie that is 4 feet long. Can these ties be used to border two flower beds without having to cut them? If so, what are the possible dimensions of each flower bed? **Three sets of flower beds can be made: 3, 3, 5 and 4, 5, 7; 3, 3, 4 and 5, 5, 7; or 3, 5, 7 and 3, 4, 5.**

Mixed Review

41b. The shortest side is 1 in. and that triangle is 1 in., 4 in., 4 in., an isosceles triangle.

43. What is the longest segment of $\triangle XYZ$ if $m\angle X = 4n + 61$, $m\angle Y = 67 - 3n$, and $m\angle Z = n + 74$? **(Lesson 5-5)** $\overline{XZ}$

44. If $\triangle NQD$ has vertices $N(2, -1)$, $Q(-4, -1)$, and $D(-1, 3)$, describe $\triangle NQD$ in terms of its angles and sides. **(Lesson 4-1)** acute, isosceles

45. Find the slope of the line that passes through points $(6, -11)$ and $(4, 9)$. **(Lesson 3-5)** -10

46. For the following theorem, name the given and the prove statements and draw a figure. Then write a two-column proof. **(Lesson 2-6)**
If $\overline{PQ}$ bisects $\overline{AB}$ at point M, then $\overline{AM} \cong \overline{MB}$. **See Solutions Manual.**

47. Algebra The measure of an angle is 5 more than four times the measure of its complement. Find the measure of both angles. **(Lesson 1-8)** 73, 17

Wrap-Up

48. Write a sentence to describe a situation where the triangle inequality theorem may be used in daily living. **See students' work.**

250 CHAPTER 5 APPLYING CONGRUENT TRIANGLES

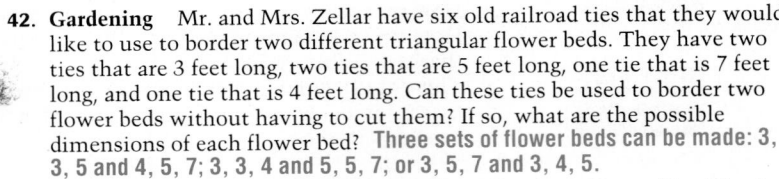

EXTENDING THE LESSON

Math Power: Connections

Tell students that the triangle inequality theorem can be rewritten as "The difference between any two sides of a triangle is less than the length of the third side." Why is this true?

(side 1) + (side 2) > side 3
(side 2) + (side 3) > side 1
(side 1) + (side 3) > side 2

If you subtract (side 1) from each side of the first inequality, (side 2) from each side of the second inequality, and (side 3) from each side of the third inequality, you get
side 2 > (side 3) − (side 1)
side 3 > (side 1) − (side 2)
side 1 > (side 2) − (side 3)

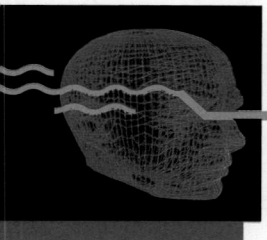

Technology
The Triangle Inequality

► **BASIC**
Geometric Supposer
Graphing calculators
LOGO
Spreadsheets

You have learned that the sum of the measures of any two sides of a triangle must be greater than the measure of the third side. You can determine whether any three numbers can be the measures of the sides of a triangle by addition. However, this process can be long and tiresome if you have several sets of numbers to check. A computer can help you complete the task in very little time.

The BASIC program below can be used to do the arithmetic necessary to test any three numbers to see if they may be the measures of the sides of a triangle. You simply enter the numbers you wish to check.

```
10 PRINT "THE TRIANGLE TESTER"
20 PRINT
30 PRINT "WHAT THREE MEASURES WOULD YOU LIKE TO TEST?"
40 PRINT "MAKE SURE THAT YOU ENTER THE MEASURES OF THE
   SIDES IN ORDER FROM LEAST TO GREATEST."
50 INPUT A, B, C
60 PRINT
70 IF A + B > C THEN 100
80 PRINT "A, B, AND C CANNOT BE THE MEASURES OF THE
   SIDES OF A TRIANGLE."
90 GOTO 110
100 PRINT "A, B, AND C CAN BE THE MEASURES OF THE SIDES OF
    A TRIANGLE."
110 END
```

EXERCISES

Use the BASIC program to determine whether the numbers given could be the measures of the sides of a triangle.

1. 4, 6, 11 no

2. 3.5, 7.75, 5.25 yes

3. 5.776, 11.845, 5.803 no

4. 389, 227, 101 no

5. What does line 70 of the program do? Check to see if the sum of the two lesser measures is greater than the greatest measure.

6. The program only checks one inequality instead of three. Why? If the sum of the two lesser measures is more than the greatest measure, then the other two inequalities will be true also.

TECHNOLOGY   251

Using Technology

Objective This optional page shows how the programming language BASIC can be used to perform mathematical computations and to enhance and extend mathematical concepts.

Teaching Suggestions

Work through each line of the program with students and explain the logic. Some of the ideas here are very important in computer programming and can give students a good understanding of what the computer is doing. After you have explained the program itself, have students check it by picking three numbers and "pretending to be the computer." Have them follow each step as the computer would and do the necessary computations. This can be used as a problem-solving strategy when programming.

Lesson Resources

- Reteaching Master 5-7
- Practice Master 5-7
- Enrichment Master 5-7
- Evaluation Master, p. 66
- Technology Master, p.41

 Transparency 5-7 contains the 5-Minute Check and a teaching aid for this lesson.

INTRODUCING THE LESSON

 5-Minute Check

(over Lesson 5-6)

Determine whether it is possible to draw a triangle with sides of the given measures.

1. 4, 5, 6   **yes**
2. 6.1, 8.3, 14.4   **no**
3. 99, 210, 310   **no**

Two sides of a triangle are 5 cm and 9 cm in length. Determine whether each measurement can be the length of the third side.

4. 3 cm   **no**
5. 13 cm   **yes**

Motivating the Lesson

Review the Triangle Inequality Theorem from the previous lesson and ask your students to relate it to two triangles. What would the triangles need to have in common to demonstrate the theorem? What would need to be different?

TEACHING THE LESSON

Teaching Tip   It may help students if you point out that in Theorems 5-13 and 5-14 the longer side is in the same triangle as the greater angle.

5-7 Inequalities Involving Two Triangles

Objective
5-7

After studying this lesson, you should be able to:
- use the SAS Inequality and SSS Inequality in proofs and to solve problems.

Application

Over the winter, Gina Salazar follows a program to stretch and strengthen different muscles in preparation for track season in the spring. One exercise to strengthen the muscles around her ankles is shown below. For this exercise, she moves one foot against the tension supplied by an elastic band.

INVESTIGATION
You can learn more about triangles in Investigation 7 on pages A6–A7.

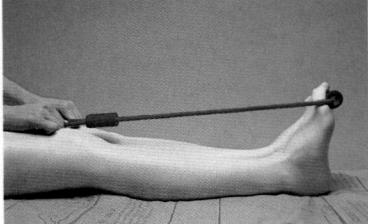
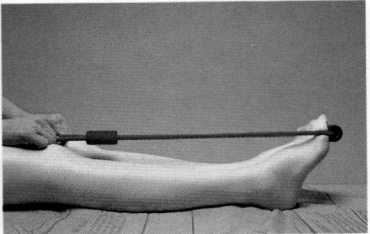

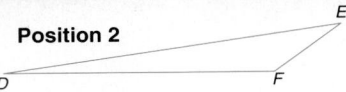

Position 1   **Position 2**

The sides that represent Gina's leg and foot have the same length in each triangle. Thus, $\overline{AC} \cong \overline{DF}$ and $\overline{BC} \cong \overline{EF}$. Because of the way Gina moves her foot, you know the measure of the angle between her leg and foot is greater in position 2 than in position 1. Also, the elastic band is longer in position 2 than in position 1. Thus, $m\angle F > m\angle C$ and $DE > AB$.

In general, it appears that as the measure of the angle between Gina's leg and foot increases, the length of the elastic band increases. Similarly, if the length of the elastic band is increased, the angle between the leg and foot increases to maintain the tension. This suggests the following two theorems.

Theorem 5-13 **SAS Inequality** **(Hinge Theorem)**	If two sides of one triangle are congruent to two sides of another triangle, and the included angle in one triangle is greater than the included angle in the other, then the third side of the first triangle is longer than the third side in the second triangle.
Theorem 5-14 **SSS Inequality**	If two sides of one triangle are congruent to two sides of another triangle and the third side in one triangle is longer than the third side in the other, then the angle between the pair of congruent sides in the first triangle is greater than the corresponding included angle in the second triangle.

ALTERNATE TEACHING STRATEGIES

Using Modeling

Have students use their hands, their elbows, and their noses as points of a triangle. Tell them to move their hands toward their nose and then away from their nose while keeping their elbow in the same place. What happens to the angle formed by their elbow as their hand moves away from their nose? What happens to the angle as their hand moves toward their nose?

Using Investigation

You can guide students to discover the SAS Inequality. In Investigation 7 on pages A6 and A7 of **More Investigations in Geometry,** students use manipulatives to explore triangle inequalities.

An indirect proof for the SSS Inequality is given below. You will be asked to write a paragraph proof for the SAS Inequality in Exercise 27.

Indirect Proof of
SSS Inequality
(Theorem 5-14)

Given: $\overline{AC} \cong \overline{DF}$
$\overline{BC} \cong \overline{EF}$
$DE > AB$

Prove: $m\angle F > m\angle C$

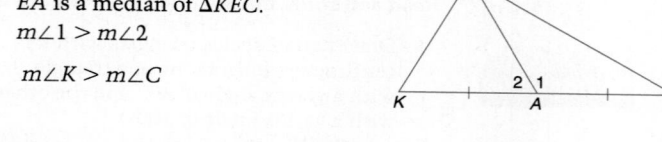

Proof:

Step 1: Assume $m\angle F \leq m\angle C$.

Step 2: If $m\angle F \leq m\angle C$, then either $m\angle F = m\angle C$ or $m\angle F < m\angle C$.

Case 1: If $m\angle F = m\angle C$, then $\triangle ABC \cong \triangle DEF$ by SAS, and $AB = DE$. *Why?*   *CPCTC*

Case 2: If $m\angle F < m\angle C$, then $AB > DE$ by SAS Inequality.

Step 3: In both cases, our assumption lead to a contradiction of the hypothesis that $DE > AB$. Therefore, the assumption that $m\angle F \leq m\angle C$ must be false, and the conclusion, $m\angle F > m\angle C$, must be true.

Examples 1 and 2 illustrate different geometric and algebraic applications of the SAS Inequality and the SSS Inequality.

Example 1

Write a two-column proof.

Given: $\overline{EA}$ is a median of $\triangle KEC$.
$m\angle 1 > m\angle 2$

Prove: $m\angle K > m\angle C$

Proof:

Statements	Reasons
1. $\overline{EA}$ is a median of $\triangle KEC$.	1. Given
2. A is the midpoint of $\overline{KC}$.	2. Definition of median
3. $\overline{KA} \cong \overline{AC}$	3. Definition of midpoint
4. $\overline{EA} \cong \overline{EA}$	4. Congruence of segments is reflexive.
5. $m\angle 1 > m\angle 2$	5. Given
6. $EC > EK$	6. SAS Inequality
7. $m\angle K > m\angle C$	7. If one side of a $\triangle$ is longer than another side, then the $\angle$ opp. the longer side is greater than the $\angle$ opp. the shorter side.

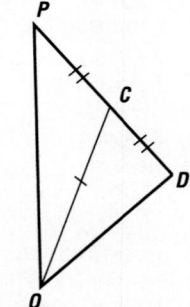

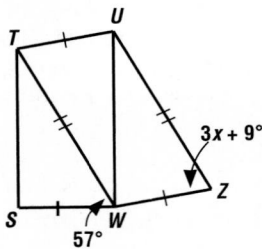
Example 2

CONNECTION
Algebra

In the figure, $\angle 1 \cong \angle 2$, $\overline{PT} \cong \overline{QR}$, and $PQ > SR$. Write two inequalities to describe the possible values for x.

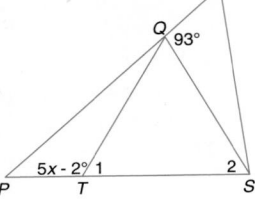

If two angles in a triangle are congruent, then the sides opposite those angles are congruent. So, since $\angle 1 \cong \angle 2$, $\overline{QS} \cong \overline{QT}$.

Since $\overline{PT} \cong \overline{QR}$, $\overline{QT} \cong \overline{QS}$, and $PQ > SR$, you know $m\angle PTQ > m\angle RQS$ by the SSS Inequality.

Since $\angle PTQ$ is an angle of a triangle, you know that $m\angle PTQ < 180$.

Use these two inequalities to describe the possible values for x.

$$
\begin{array}{ll}
m\angle PTQ > m\angle RQS & m\angle PTQ < 180 \\
5x - 2 > 93 & 5x - 2 < 180 \\
5x > 95 & 5x < 182 \\
x > 19 & x < 36.4
\end{array}
$$

The inequalities $x > 19$ and $x < 36.4$, or $19 < x < 36.4$, describe the possible values of x.

CHECKING FOR UNDERSTANDING

Communicating Mathematics

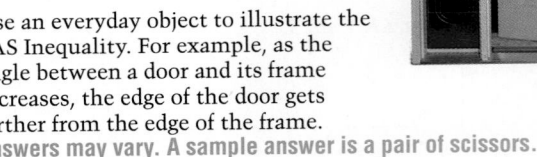

INVESTIGATION

1a. See students' work

1b. the one with a 100° vertex angle

2. Answers may vary. A sample answer is that as the angle between the edges of a hinge gets larger, the distance between the ends of the sides gets larger.

Read and study the lesson to answer each question.

1. Draw two isosceles triangles with legs 2 centimeters long. Draw one triangle with a vertex angle of 40° and the other with a vertex angle of 100°.
   a. Measure the base of each triangle.
   b. Which triangle has a longer base?
   c. What theorem does this investigation demonstrate? **SAS Inequality**

2. The SAS Inequality Theorem is subtitled the Hinge Theorem. Explain why you think it is given this name.

3. Use an everyday object to illustrate the SAS Inequality. For example, as the angle between a door and its frame increases, the edge of the door gets farther from the edge of the frame.
   Answers may vary. A sample answer is a pair of scissors.

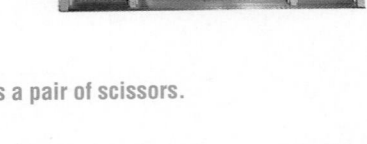

Refer to the figure at the right to write an equation or inequality relating each pair of angle measures.

4. $m\angle ALK, m\angle ALN$ $m\angle ALK < m\angle ALN$
5. $m\angle ALK, m\angle NLO$ $m\angle ALK < m\angle NLO$
6. $m\angle OLK, m\angle NLO$ $m\angle OLK > m\angle NLO$
7. $m\angle KLO, m\angle ALN$ $m\angle KLO = m\angle ALN$

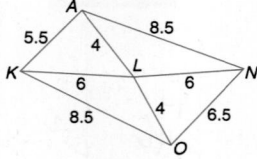

In $\triangle ABC$, M is the midpoint of $\overline{AB}$. If $m\angle 1 = 5x + 20$ and $m\angle 2 = 8x - 100$, determine which measure is greater. Justify your answers.

8. BC or AC AC
9. $m\angle B$ or $m\angle A$ $m\angle B$
10. $m\angle 1$ or $m\angle 2$ $m\angle 1$

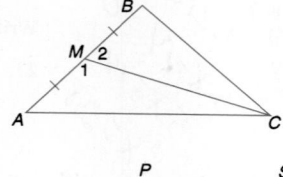

11. Write a two-column proof.
    Given: $\overline{PQ} \cong \overline{SQ}$
    Prove: $PR > SR$
    See margin.

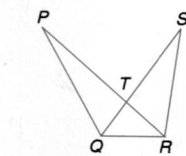

EXERCISES

Write an inequality relating each pair of measures.

12. $m\angle ADC, m\angle ADB$

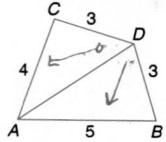

12. $m\angle ADC < m\angle ADB$

13. AB, AC $AB > AC$

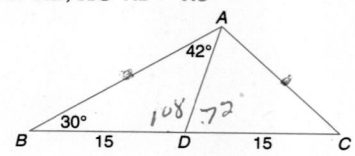

14. PT, RS $PT < RS$

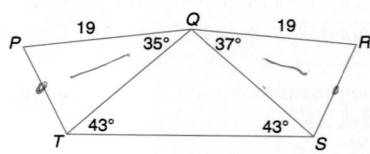

15. $m\angle 1, m\angle 2$ $m\angle 1 < m\angle 2$

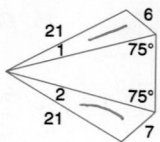

16. ZR, XR $ZR < XR$

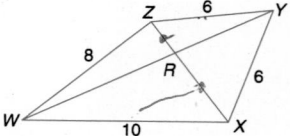

17. $m\angle DFE, m\angle DFG$

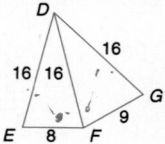

17. $m\angle DFE > m\angle DFG$

LESSON 5-7   INEQUALITIES INVOLVING TWO TRIANGLES   255

APPLYING THE LESSON

Homework Exercises

Assignment Guide
Basic: 12-23, 28-35
Average: 14-25, 28-35
Enriched: 16-35

Additional Answer

11. **Statements** (Reasons)
    a. $\overline{PQ} \cong \overline{SQ}$ (Given)
    b. $\overline{QR} \cong \overline{QR}$ (Congruence of segments is reflexive)
    c. $m\angle PQR = m\angle PQS + m\angle SQR$ (Angle Addition Postulate)
    d. $m\angle PQR > m\angle SQR$ (Definition of Inequality)
    e. $PR > SR$ (SAS Inequality)

Reteaching Masters Booklet, p. 31

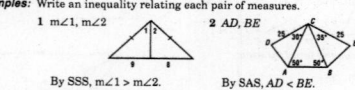

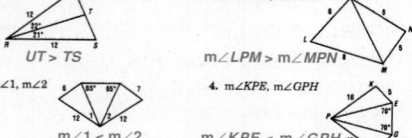

RETEACHING THE LESSON

Give each student two straws of different lengths. Have students use the straws as two sides of a triangle. As they vary the size of the angle included between the two straws have them record the measure of the angle and the measure of the distance between the other ends of the two straws (the length of the third side of the triangle). Have them predict a relationship between the angle and the third side.

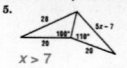

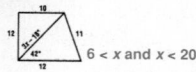

Practice Masters Booklet, p. 36

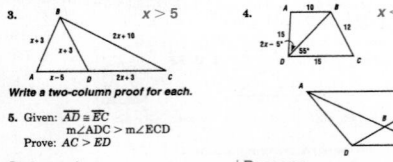
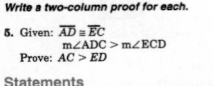

NAME _____ DATE _____
5-7 Practice Worksheet
Inequalities Involving Two Triangles
Write an inequality relating each pair of measures.
1. $m\angle PRQ$, $m\angle PRS$ 2. $m\angle ABE$, $m\angle DBC$
  $m\angle PRQ < m\angle PRS$ $m\angle ABE < m\angle DBC$

For each figure, write an inequality or pair of inequalities to describe the possible values of x.
3. $x > 5$ 4. $x < 30$

Write a two-column proof for each.
5. Given: $\overline{AD} \cong \overline{EC}$, $m\angle ADC > m\angle ECD$ Prove: $AC > ED$

Statements	Reasons
a. $\overline{AD} \cong \overline{EC}$	a. Given
b. $\overline{DC} \cong \overline{DC}$	b. Congruence of segments is reflexive.
c. $m\angle ADC > m\angle ECD$	c. Given
d. $AC > ED$	d. SAS Inequality

6. Given: D is the midpoint of $\overline{AC}$. $BC > AB$ Prove: $m\angle 1 > m\angle 2$

Statements	Reasons
a. D is the midpoint of $\overline{AC}$.	a. Given
b. $\overline{AD} \cong \overline{DC}$	b. Definition of midpoint
c. $\overline{BD} \cong \overline{BD}$	c. Congruence of segments is reflexive.
d. $\overline{BC} > \overline{AB}$	d. Given
e. $m\angle 1 > m\angle 2$	e. SSS Inequality

T36
Glencoe Division, Macmillan/McGraw-Hill

CONNECTION
Algebra

For each figure, write an inequality or pair of inequalities to describe the possible values of x.

18.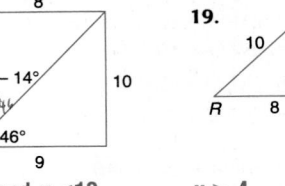
$2.8 < x$ and $x < 12$

19.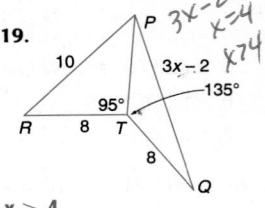
$x > 4$

20.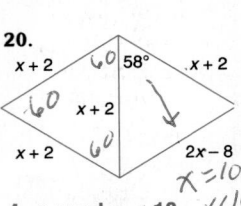
$4 < x$ and $x < 10$

(handwritten work:)
$5X-14=46$
$5X=60$
$X=12$
$5X-14=0$
$5X=14$
$X>2.8$
$X<12$
$X>2.8$
$3X-2=10$
$X=4$
$X>4$
$X=10$
$X<10$
$2X-8=0$
$2X=8$
$X>4$

Write a two-column proof.   See margin.

21. Given: $\overline{PQ} \cong \overline{RS}$
        $QR < PS$
  Prove: $m\angle 3 < m\angle 1$

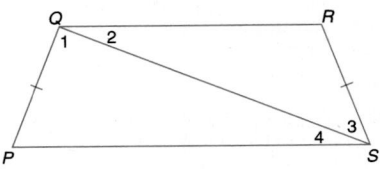

22. Given: $\overline{PR} \cong \overline{PQ}$
        $SQ > SR$
  Prove: $m\angle 1 < m\angle 2$

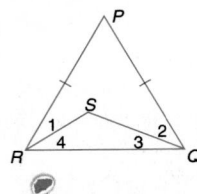

23. Given: $\triangle TER$
        $\overline{TR} \cong \overline{EU}$
  Prove: $TE > RU$

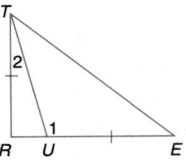

24. Given: $\overline{TU} \cong \overline{US}$
        $\overline{US} \cong \overline{SV}$
        $m\angle SVU > m\angle USV$
  Prove: $ST > UV$

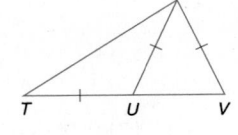

25. Given: $\overline{ED} \cong \overline{DF}$
        $m\angle 1 > m\angle 2$
        D is the midpoint of $\overline{CB}$.
        $\overline{AE} \cong \overline{AF}$
  Prove: $AC > AB$

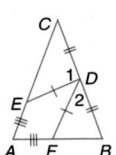

26. Given: $m\angle DBC = m\angle DCB$
        $m\angle ADB < m\angle ADC$
  Prove: $m\angle ACB < m\angle ABC$

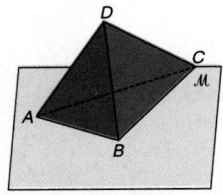

See Solutions Manual.

---

27. Write a paragraph proof for the SAS Inequality. (Theorem 5-13)

Given: $\overline{AC} \cong \overline{DF}$
$\overline{BC} \cong \overline{EF}$
$m\angle F > m\angle C$

Prove: $DE > AB$ **See Solutions Manual.**

Hint: Draw auxiliary ray FZ such that $m\angle DFZ = m\angle C$ and $ZF = BC$. Then, consider two cases: Z lies on $\overline{DE}$, and Z does not lie on $\overline{DE}$.

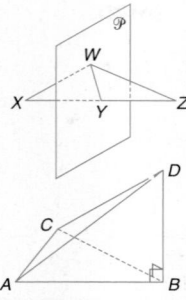

Critical Thinking

28. In the figure at the right, plane $\mathscr{P}$ bisects $\overline{XZ}$ at Y and $WZ > WX$. What can you conclude about the relation between $\overline{XZ}$ and plane $\mathscr{P}$? $\overline{XZ}$ **is not perpendicular to plane $\mathscr{P}$.**

29. In the figure at the right, $\triangle ABC$ is equilateral. Name the angle that is congruent to $\angle DCA$. Justify your answer. **See Solutions Manual.**

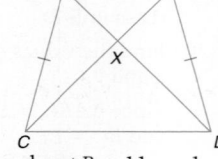

Application

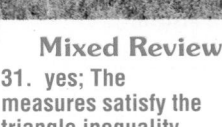

30. **Biology** In the 1970s, R. McNeill Alexander created a formula to estimate the speed (velocity) of an animal. This formula is

$$v = \frac{0.78s^{1.67}}{h^{1.17}},$$

where v is the speed of the animal in meters per second, s is the length of the animal's stride in meters, and h is the height of the animal's hip in meters. **a. 2.78 m/s, 3.08 m/s**

  a. Determine the velocity of two animals that each have a hip height of 1.08 meters and that have strides of 2.26 meters and 2.40 meters.

  b. Draw a mathematical model of the triangles formed by the two animals in Part A if one point of the triangle represents the position of each animal's hip and the other two points represent the beginning and end of each animal's stride. Then discuss how this model is related to either the SAS Inequality or the SSS Inequality. **See Solutions Manual.**

Mixed Review

31. yes; The measures satisfy the triangle inequality.

31. **Algebra** Is it possible to have a triangle with vertices $A(1, -1)$, $B(7, 7)$, $C(2, -5)$? Explain. **(Lesson 5-6)**

32. Write a two-column proof. **(Lesson 4-6)**

Given: $\overline{AC} \cong \overline{BD}$
$\overline{AD} \cong \overline{BC}$

Prove: $\triangle AXC \cong \triangle BXD$ **See Solutions Manual.**

33. If $\overline{AB} \parallel \overline{CD}$, $m\angle BAC = 3n + 32$, and $m\angle ACD = 14n - 5$, find the value of n. **(Lesson 3-3)** **9**

34. $\angle A$ and $\angle B$ are complementary. If $m\angle A = 6x + 6$ and $m\angle B = 11x - 1$, find $m\angle A$ and $m\angle B$. **(Lesson 1-8)** $m\angle A = 36$, $m\angle B = 54$

Wrap-Up

35. **Journal Entry** Write a sentence or two about the SAS Inequality and the SSS Inequality in your journal. **See students' work.**

LESSON 5-7   INEQUALITIES INVOLVING TWO TRIANGLES   257

EXTENDING THE LESSON

Math Power: Communication

The SAS Inequality Theorem is also called the Hinge Theorem. Bring in a hinge or use the hinge on a door in your classroom and have your students explain why the inequality would be called the Hinge Theorem.

Enrichment Masters Booklet, p. 31

Using the Chapter Summary and Review

The Chapter Summary and Review begins with an alphabetical listing of the new terms that were presented in the chapter. Have students define each term and provide an example of it, if appropriate.

The Skills and Concepts presented in the chapter are reviewed using a side-by-side format. Encourage students to refer to the Objectives and Examples on the left as they complete the Review Exercises on the right.

The Chapter Summary and Review ends with exercises that review Applications and Connections.

Additional Answer

8. We assume $\overline{QX}$ is a median of $\triangle PQR$. By the definition of median, X is the midpoint of $\overline{PR}$, and hence by the definition of midpoint, $\overline{PX} \cong \overline{XR}$. We are given that $\overline{QP} \cong \overline{QR}$ and we know $\overline{QX} \cong \overline{QX}$ since congruence of segments is reflexive. Therefore, $\triangle QXP \cong \triangle QXR$ by SSS and $\angle PQX \cong \angle RQX$ by CPCTC. By the definition of angle bisector, $\overline{QX}$ bisects $\angle PQR$. But this contradicts our given statement. So, our assumption must be false, and $\overline{QX}$ is not a median of $\triangle PQR$.

VOCABULARY

Upon completing this chapter, you should be familiar with the following terms:

altitude of a triangle	**216**	**233**	indirect reasoning
angle bisector of a triangle	**217**	**216**	median of a triangle
indirect proof	**233**	**218**	perpendicular bisector

SKILLS AND CONCEPTS

OBJECTIVES AND EXAMPLES	REVIEW EXERCISES

Upon completing this chapter, you should be able to:

- identify and use medians, altitudes, angle bisectors, and perpendicular bisectors of a triangle. **(Lesson 5-1)**

If $\overline{BG}$ is an altitude of $\triangle BDC$, then $\overline{BG} \perp \overline{DC}$.

If $\overline{AE}$ is a median of $\triangle ABD$, then $\overline{DE} \cong \overline{BE}$.

If $\overline{EF}$ is an angle bisector of $\triangle AED$, then $\angle 1 \cong \angle 2$.

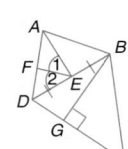

Use these exercises to review and prepare for the chapter test. 1. $m\angle BDC = m\angle BCD = 57$, $m\angle DBC = 66$
Refer to the figure to answer each question.

1. $\overline{BG}$ is an altitude and an angle bisector of $\triangle BCD$. If $m\angle DBG = 33$, find the measure of the three angles of $\triangle BCD$.

2. Find the value of x and $m\angle 2$ if $\overline{AE}$ is an altitude of $\triangle ABD$, $m\angle 1 = 3x + 11$, and $m\angle 2 = 7x + 9$. **7, 58**

3. If $\overline{AE}$ is a median of $\triangle ABD$, $DE = 3x - 14$, $EB = 2x - 1$, and $m\angle AED = 7x + 1$, is $\overline{AE}$ also an altitude of $\triangle ABD$? Explain. **no: $m\angle AED \neq 90$**

- recognize and use tests for congruence of right triangles. **(Lesson 5-2)**

Find the values of x and y.

Since $\triangle ABC \cong \triangle DEF$ by HA, $AB = DE$ and $BC = EF$.

$$AB = DE \qquad BC = EF$$
$$3x + 7 = 19 \qquad 2y - 11 = 15$$
$$3x = 12 \qquad 2y = 26$$
$$x = 4 \qquad y = 13$$

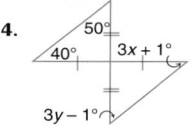

Find the values of x and y.

4.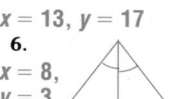

$x = 13, y = 17$

5.

$x = 11, y = 26$

6.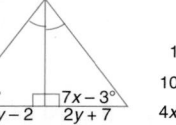

$x = 8, y = 3$

7.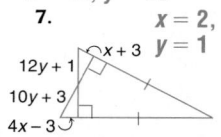

$x = 2, y = 1$

Additional Answer

9. We assume $\overline{QX}$ is not an altitude of $\triangle PQR$. This means that $\overline{QX}$ is not perpendicular to $\overline{PR}$ by the definition of altitude. So, by the definition of perpendicular, this means $\angle QXR$ is not a right angle. Therefore, $\angle QXR$ is either acute or obtuse. Since $\angle QXP$ and $\angle QXR$ form a linear pair, these two angles are supplementary. Hence, if $\angle QXP$ is acute, $\angle QXR$ is obtuse (or vice versa), by the definition of supplementary. In either case, $\angle QXP \neq \angle QXR$. But we are given that $\triangle QXP \cong \triangle QXR$, and by CPCTC this would mean $\angle QXP \cong \angle QXR$. This is a contradiction, and hence our assumption must be false. Therefore $\overline{QX}$ is an altitude of $\triangle PQR$.

OBJECTIVES AND EXAMPLES

- use indirect reasoning and indirect proof to reach a conclusion. **(Lesson 5-4)**

Steps for Writing an Indirect Proof

1. Assume that the conclusion is false.
2. Show that the assumption leads to a contradiction of the hypothesis or some other fact, such as a postulate, theorem, or corollary.
3. Conclude that the assumption must be false, and therefore the conclusion must be true.

REVIEW EXERCISES

Write an indirect proof. See margin

8. Given: $\overline{QP} \cong \overline{QR}$
$\overline{QX}$ does not bisect $\angle PQR$.
Prove: $\overline{QX}$ is not a median of ΔPQR.

9. Given: $\Delta QXP \cong \Delta QXR$
Prove: $\overline{QX}$ is an altitude of ΔPQR.

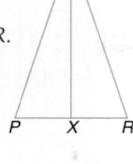

- recognize and apply the properties of inequalities to the measures of segments and angles. **(Lesson 5-4)**

Find the value of a if $AC = AB$, $AX = 16$, and $AC = 3a - 2$.

$AC = AB$
$AC = AX + XB$
$AC > AX$
$3a - 2 > 16$
$3a > 18$
$a > 6$

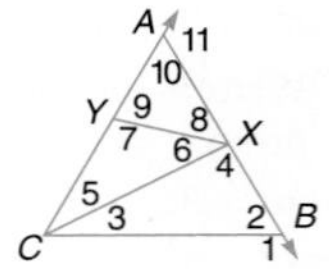

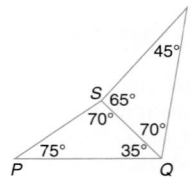

Complete each statement with < or >. Use the figure at the left.

10. $m\angle 3$ _?_ $m\angle ACB$ <
11. $m\angle 4$ _?_ $m\angle 10$ >
12. $m\angle 6$ _?_ $m\angle 11$ <
13. $m\angle 5$ _?_ $m\angle YXB$ <
14. If $m\angle 7 < m\angle 4$, then $m\angle 1$ _?_ $m\angle 8$ >

- recognize and use relationships between sides and angles in a triangle. **(Lesson 5-5)**

Find the longest segment in the figure. The figure is not drawn to scale.

The longest side of ΔPQS is the side opposite the 75° angle, $\overline{SQ}$. This side is also the shortest side of ΔQRS since it is opposite the 45° angle. Thus, the longest side is the side opposite the 70° angle in ΔQRS, $\overline{RS}$.

15. Name the shortest side in the figure at the left. $\overline{SP}$
16. List the sides of ΔABC in order from shortest to longest. $\overline{AC}$, $\overline{AB}$, $\overline{CB}$
17. List the angles of ΔBCD in order from least to greatest. $\angle D$, $\angle CBD$, $\angle BCD$
18. Write a two-column proof. See margin.
Given: $FG < FH$
Prove: $m\angle 1 > m\angle 2$

Alternate Review Strategy

To provide a brief in-class review, you may wish to read the following questions to the class and have them answer verbally.

1. Name two special segments in triangles that are perpendicular to the sides of the triangle. altitudes and perpendicular bisectors
2. If an angle and a leg of one right triangle are congruent to an angle and a leg of another right triangle, can you say that the triangles are congruent? Why? yes, by Theorem 5-7, LA
3. What is the first step in writing an indirect proof? Assume the conclusion is false.
4. If $a < b$ and $b < c$, what can you say about the relationship between a and c? $a < c$
5. What can you say about the side of a triangle opposite the angle with the smallest measure? It will be the shortest side.
6. Can lengths of 4, 9, and 13 be the lengths of the sides of a triangle? no, because $4 + 9 \not> 13$
7. State the hypothesis and the conclusion of the SSS Inequality Theorem. Hypothesis: Two sides of one triangle are congruent to two sides of another triangle and the third side of one triangle is longer than the third side of the other. Conclusion: The angle between the congruent sides in the first triangle is greater than the corresponding angle in the second triangle.

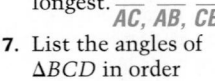

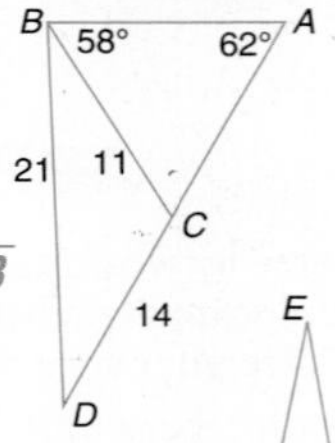

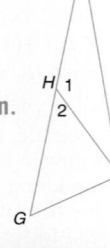

Additional Answer

18. Statements (Reasons)
   a. $FG < FH$ (Given)
   b. $m\angle FGH > m\angle 2$ (If one side of a △ is longer than another side, then the ∠ opp. the longer side is greater than the ∠ opp. the shorter side.)
   c. $m\angle 1 > m\angle FGH$ (Exterior Angle Inequality Theorem)
   d. $m\angle 1 > m\angle 2$ (Transitive prop. of inequality)

A two-page Cumulative Review from the *Evaluation Masters* is shown below. It can be used to review skills and concepts presented thus far in the text. Standardized Test Practice Questions are also provided in the *Evaluation Masters*.

Evaluation Masters, pp. 67-68

OBJECTIVES AND EXAMPLES	REVIEW EXERCISES

- apply the Triangle Inequality Theorem. **(Lesson 5-6)**

The measures of two sides of a triangle are 7 and 9. Between what two numbers is the measure of the third side?

Let x be the measure of the third side. Then by the Triangle Inequality Theorem, the following inequalities must be true.

$$x + 7 > 9 \quad x + 9 > 7 \quad 7 + 9 > x$$
$$x > 2 \qquad x > -2 \qquad 16 > x$$

Thus, the measure of the third side must be between 2 and 16.

The measures of two sides of a triangle are given. Between what two numbers is the measure of the third side?

19. 5 and 11 **6 and 16**
20. 24 and 7 **17 and 31**

Is it possible to have a triangle with the given vertices?

21. $A(-5, 12)$, $B(4, -3)$, $C(0, 0)$ **yes**
22. $D(-3, 4)$, $E(3, -5)$, $F(-1, 1)$ **no**
23. How many different triangles are possible if the measures of the three sides must be selected from the measures 2, 3, 4, and 5? **3**

- use the SAS Inequality and SSS Inequality in proofs and to solve problems. **(Lesson 5-7)**

Write an inequality relating AB and AC.

$$m\angle AXC = 75 + 18$$
$$= 93$$

$$m\angle AXB = 180 - 93$$
$$= 87$$

Since $m\angle AXC > m\angle AXB$, by SAS Inequality, $AB < AC$.

Refer to the figure to write an inequality relating each pair of measures.

24. $m\angle PNQ$, $m\angle QNR$
25. $m\angle PNS$, $m\angle RNS$
26. $m\angle NPQ$, $m\angle NRS$
27. Write a two-column proof. **See margin.**

Given: $AD = BC$
Prove: $AC > DB$

24. $m\angle PNQ < m\angle QNR$
25. $m\angle PNS < m\angle RNS$

26. $m\angle NPQ < m\angle NRS$

APPLICATIONS AND CONNECTIONS

28. **Solve by working backward.** An ice sculpture is melting at a rate of one-half its weight every one hour. After 8 hours, the sculpture weighs $\frac{5}{16}$ of a pound. How much did the sculpture weigh to begin with? **(Lesson 5-3) 80 pounds**

29. **Algebra** Find the coordinates of the point on line ℓ, whose equation is $y = 2x - 5$, that is the endpoint of the shortest segment from the origin to ℓ. **(Lesson 5-5) (2, -1)**

30. Pine City is 6 kilometers from Susanton, 9 kilometers from Blockburg, and 13 km from Leshville. Also, Susanton, Blockburg, and Leshville do not lie on a straight line. Bonnie begins in Blockburg and drives directly to Susanton, then to Leshville, and then back to Blockburg. What are the maximum and minimum distances she could have traveled on this trip? **(Lesson 5-7) maximum distance is less than 56 km, minimum distance is more than 14 km**

Additional Answer

27. **Statements   (Reasons)**
   a. $AD = BC$ (Given)
   b. $\overline{AD} \cong \overline{BC}$ (Definition of congruent segments)
   c. $\overline{BA} \cong \overline{BA}$ (Congruence of segments is reflexive.)
   d. $m\angle CBA > m\angle DAB$ (Exterior Angle Inequality Theorem)
   e. $AC > DB$ (SAS Inequality Theorem)

In $\triangle AHW$, $m\angle A = 64$ and $m\angle AWH = 36$. If $\overline{WP}$ is an angle bisector and $\overline{HQ}$ is an altitude, find each measure.

1. $m\angle AQH$ **90**   2. $m\angle AHQ$ **26**
3. $m\angle APW$ **98**   4. $m\angle HXW$ **108**

5. If $\overline{WP}$ is a median, $AP = 3y + 11$ and $PH = 7y - 5$, find AH. **46**

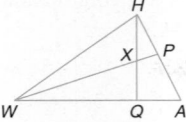

Complete each statement with < or >. Use the figure at the right.

6. $m\angle 2$ _?_ $m\angle 9$ **>**   7. $m\angle 6$ _?_ $m\angle 1$ **<**
8. If $m\angle 8 < m\angle 7$, then WX _?_ XY. **>**
9. If $MX < MZ$, then $m\angle 4$ _?_ $m\angle 5$. **<**

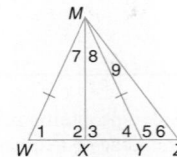

Complete each statement. Use the figure at the right.

10. If $PS > PQ$, then $m\angle PQS$ _?_ $m\angle PSQ$. **>**
11. If $m\angle SQR > m\angle SRQ$, then _?_ > _?_. **SR, SQ**
12. If $\overline{PQ} \cong \overline{PR}$ and $SQ > SR$, then _?_ _?_ $m\angle SPQ$. **$m\angle SPR$, <**
13. If $\overline{QR} \cong \overline{SR}$, $QS < PQ$, and $m\angle PRQ < m\angle PRS$, then the longest side of $\triangle PQS$ is _?_. **PS**
14. If $PS = 31$ and $SQ = 13$, then PQ is between what two numbers? **18 and 44**

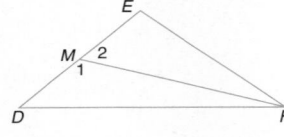

15. Find the longest segment in $\triangle ABC$ if $m\angle A = 5x + 31$, $m\angle B = 74 - 3x$, and $m\angle C = 4x + 9$. **$\overline{BC}$**

16. If the sides of a triangle have lengths of $3x + 8$ m, $5x + 2$ m and $8x - 10$ m, find all possible values for x. **$x > \frac{8}{5}$**

17. If M is the midpoint of $\overline{DE}$, $m\angle 1 > m\angle 2$, $DF = 13x - 5$, and $EF = 7x + 25$, find all possible values of x. **$x > 5$**

18. Write an indirect proof. **See Solutions Manual.**
   Given: $\overline{FM}$ is a median of $\triangle DEF$.
           $m\angle 1 > m\angle 2$
   Prove: $DF \neq EF$

Write a two-column proof. **See Solutions Manual.**

19. **Given:** $NO = QP$
             $PN > OQ$
    Prove: $MP > MO$

20. **Given:** $\overline{AD} \perp \overline{DC}$,
             $\overline{AB} \perp \overline{BC}$
             $AB = DC$
    Prove: $\overline{DC} \perp \overline{BC}$

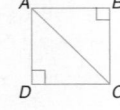

Bonus Write a two-column proof for the following statement:
If M is any point in the interior of $\triangle PQR$, then $PR + QR > PM + QM$. **See Solutions Manual.**

Using the Chapter Test

This page may be used as a test or as a review. In addition, two multiple-choice tests (Forms 1A and 1B) and two free-response tests (Forms 2A and 2B) are provided in the *Evaluation Masters*. Chapter 5 Test, Form 1A is shown below.

Evaluation Masters, pp. 57-58

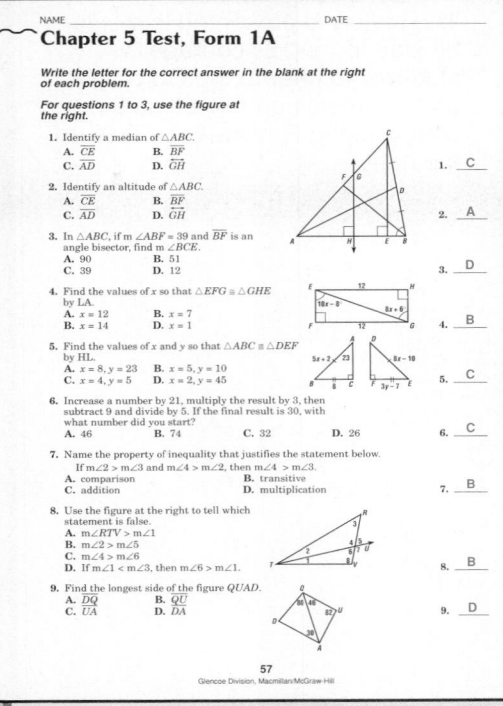

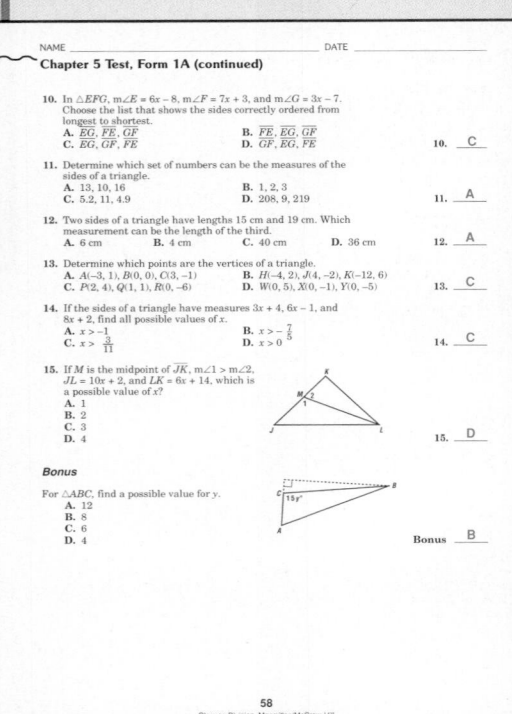

Test and Review Generator software is provided in Apple, IBM, and Macintosh versions. You may use this software to create your own tests or worksheets, based on the needs of your students.

The **Performance Assessment Booklet** provides an alternate assessment for evaluating student progress. An assessment for this chapter can be found on pages 9-10.

Using the Algebra Review

The goal of this two-page review of algebraic skills, concepts, and applications is as follows:

- It provides students a chance to review important concepts from algebra that will be useful as they study geometry.
- It gives students an opportunity to retain the concepts they learned in previous algebra courses and may need for future mathematics courses.

The review is presented in a side-by-side format. Encourage students to refer to the Objectives and Examples on the left as they complete the Review Exercises on the right.

OBJECTIVES AND EXAMPLES	REVIEW EXERCISES

■ Solve equations with variables on both sides.

$$3c + 22 = 8c - 3$$
$$3c - 3c + 22 = 8c - 3c - 3$$
$$22 + 3 = 5c - 3 + 3$$
$$\frac{25}{5} = \frac{5c}{5}$$
$$5 = c$$

Solve each equation. Check the solution.

1. $5a - 5 = 7a - 19$ **7**
2. $\frac{2}{3}x + 5 = \frac{1}{2}x + 4$ **-6**
3. $5(4 - n) = 2n - 1$ **3**
4. $2(2y - 3) = -9(y - 6) + y$ **5**

■ Solve problems involving percent of increase or decrease.

A shirt's price was decreased from $25 to $20. Find the percent of decrease.

$$\frac{r}{100} = \frac{25 - 20}{25}$$
$$r = 100\left(\frac{5}{25}\right) \text{ or } 20$$

The decrease was 20%.

Solve.

5. A skirt's price was increased from $20 to $25. Find the percent of increase. **25%**
6. The price of a half-gallon of ice cream plus 5% tax is $3.15. What is the original price of the ice cream? **$3.00**
7. A pair of jeans sells for $36 after a 25% discount. What is the original price of the jeans? **$48**

■ Solve problems involving direct variation.

If y varies directly as x, and $x = 15$ when $y = 1.5$, find x when $y = 9$.

$$\frac{x}{9} = \frac{15}{1.5} \qquad \frac{x_1}{x_2} = \frac{y_1}{y_2}$$
$$x = 9\left(\frac{15}{1.5}\right) \text{ or } 90$$

Solve. Assume that y varies directly as x.

8. If $y = 15$ when $x = 5$, find y when $x = 7$. **21**
9. If $y = 35$ when $x = 175$, find y when $x = 75$. **15**
10. If $y = 1.2$ when $x = 21$, find x when $y = 21$. **367.5**

■ Solve inequalities using multiplication or division.

$$-\frac{2m}{3} \le 10$$
$$-\frac{3}{2}\left(-\frac{2m}{3}\right) \ge -\frac{3}{2}(10)$$
$$m \ge -15$$

The direction of the inequality must be reversed because each side is multiplied by a negative number.

The solution set is $\{m | m \ge -15\}$.

Solve each inequality. Check the solution.

11. $6x \le -24$ $x \le -4$
12. $-7y \ge -91$ $y \le 13$
13. $-0.8t < -0.96$ $t > 1.2$
14. $\frac{4}{3}a < 16$ $a < 12$
15. $\frac{2}{3}k \ge \frac{2}{15}$ $k \ge \frac{1}{5}$
16. $\frac{4}{7}z > -\frac{2}{5}$ $z > -\frac{7}{10}$

OBJECTIVES AND EXAMPLES	REVIEW EXERCISES

Simplify expressions involving powers of monomials or negative exponents.

$(2x^2y^3)^3 = 2^3(x^2)^3(y^3)^3$
$= 8x^6y^9$

$\dfrac{3a^{-2}}{4a^6} = \dfrac{3}{4}(a^{-2-6}) = \dfrac{3}{4a^8}$

Simplify. Assume no denominator is equal to zero.

17. $(4a^2b)^3$ $64a^6b^3$ **18.** $(-3xy)^2(4x)^3$ $576x^5y^2$

19. $(-2c^{-2}d)^4(-3cd^2)^3$ $\dfrac{-432d^{10}}{c^5}$ **20.** $\dfrac{(3a^3b^{-1}c^2)^2}{18a^2b^3c^4}$ $\dfrac{a^4}{2b^5}$

Express numbers in scientific notation.

$3{,}600{,}000 = 3.6 \times 10^6$

$0.0021 = 2.1 \times 10^{-3}$

Express each number in scientific notation. See margin.

21. 240,000 **22.** 4,880,000,000

23. 0.000314 **24.** 0.00000187

Add or subtract polynomials.

$(4x^2 - 3x + 7) + (2x^2 + 4x)$
$= (4x^2 + 2x^2) + (-3x + 4x) + 7$
$= 6x^2 + x + 7$

$(7r^2 + 9r) - (12r^2 - 4r - 3)$
$= (7r^2 - 12r^2) + [9r - (-4r)] - (-3)$
$= -5r^2 + 13r + 3$

Find each sum or difference. See margin.

25. $(2x^2 - 5x + 7) - (3x^3 + x^2 + 2)$

26. $(x^2 - 6xy + 7y^2) + (3x^2 + xy - y^2)$

27. $(11m^2n^2 + 4mn - 6) +$
$(5m^2n^2 - 6mn + 17)$

28. $(7a^2 + 4) - (3a^2 + 2a - 6)$

Factor quadratic trinomials.

$a^2 - 3a - 4 = (a + 1)(a - 4)$

$4x^2 - 4xy - 15y^2$
$= 4x^2 + (-10 + 6)xy - 15y^2$
$= (4x^2 - 10xy) + (6xy - 15y^2)$
$= 2x(2x - 5y) + 3y(2x - 5y)$
$= (2x + 3y)(2x - 5y)$

Factor each trinomial. 29-32. See margin.

29. $y^2 + 7y + 12$ **30.** $b^2 + 5b - 6$

31. $a^2 - 10ab + 9b^2$ **32.** $2r^2 - 3r - 20$

33. $6x^2 - 5x - 6$ $(2x - 3)(3x + 2)$

34. $56m^2 - 93mn + 27n^2$
$(8m - 3n)(7m - 9n)$

Applications and Connections

35. Cartography The scale on a map is 2 cm to 5 km. Kern and Dent are 16 km apart. How far apart are they on the map? **6.4 cm**

36. Geometry For what values of d is an angle with measure $3.6d$ an acute angle? **$0 < d < 25$**

37. Sales Juanita bought sixteen 12-packs of soft drinks for the picnic. Some cost $2.79 each, and the rest cost $2.99 each. If she spent $46.04 on soft drinks, how many of each did she buy? **7 at $2.99, 9 at $2.79**

38. Travel Peter drove to work at 40 miles per hour and arrived one minute late. If he had driven at 45 miles per hour, he would have arrived one minute early. How far does Peter drive to work? **12 miles**

Additional Answers
21. 2.4×10^5
22. 4.88×10^9
23. 3.14×10^{-4}
24. 1.87×10^{-6}
25. $-3x^3 + x^2 - 5x + 5$
26. $4x^2 - 5xy + 6y^2$
27. $16m^2n^2 - 2mn + 11$
28. $4a^2 - 2a + 10$
29. $(y + 3)(y + 4)$
30. $(b + 6)(b - 1)$
31. $(a - 9b)(a - b)$
32. $(2r + 5)(r - 4)$

6 Quadrilaterals

PREVIEWING THE CHAPTER

The focus of this chapter is the classification of specific quadrilaterals and an investigation of their properties. Students begin by recognizing and defining parallelograms and identifying and proving properties of parallelograms. Next, students learn which conditions insure that a quadrilateral is a parallelogram and apply these conditions in proofs. Subsequently, students recognize properties of rectangles, squares, rhombi, and trapezoids and use these properties in proofs and other problems.

Problem-Solving Strategy Students learn to solve problems by identifying and continuing a pattern.

Lesson (Pages)	Lesson Objectives	State/Local Objectives
6-1 (266-271)	**6-1A**: Recognize and define a parallelogram.	
	6-1B: Recognize, use, and prove the properties of a parallelogram.	
6-2 (272-274)	**6-2**: Solve a problem by looking for a pattern and using the pattern to find the missing information.	
6-3 (275-280)	**6-3**: Recognize and apply the conditions that ensure that a quadrilateral is a parallelogram.	
6-4 (282-287)	**6-4A**: Recognize the properties of rectangles.	
	6-4B: Use properties of rectangles in proofs.	
6-5 (288-293)	**6-5A**: Recognize the properties of squares and rhombi.	
	6-5B: Use properties of squares and rhombi in proofs.	
6-6 (294-299)	**6-6A**: Recognize the properties of trapezoids.	
	6-6B: Use properties of trapezoids in proofs and other problems.	

Lesson Objective Chart

ORGANIZING THE CHAPTER

You may want to refer to the **Course Planning Calendar** on page T28.

Lesson Planning Guide				Blackline Masters Booklets										
	Pacing Chart (days)										Activities			
Lesson (Pages)	Course			Reteaching	Practice	Enrichment	Evaluation	Technology	Lab Manual	Mixed Problem Solving	Applications	Cooperative Learning Activity	Multicultural	Transparencies
	I	II	III											
6-1 (266-271)	2	2	2	p. 32	p. 37	p. 32					p. 20			6-1
6-2 (272-274)	1	1	1		p. 38		Quiz A, p. 79							6-2
6-3 (275-280)	2	2	1.5	p. 33	p. 39	p. 33	Quiz B, p. 79 Mid-Chapter Test, p. 83						p. 6	6-3
6-4 (282-287)	2	2	1.5	p. 34	p. 40	p. 34								6-4
6-5 (288-293)	2	1.5	1.5	p. 35	p. 41	p. 35	Quiz C, p. 80	p. 42				p. 34		6-5
6-6 (294-299)	2	1.5	1.5	p. 36	p. 42	p. 36	Quiz D, p. 80	p. 6		p. 6				6-6
Review (300-302)	1	1	1	Multiple Choice Tests, Forms 1A and 1B, pp. 71-74 Free Response Tests, Forms 2A and 2B, pp. 75-78										
Test (303)	1	1	1	Cumulative Review. pp. 81-82 Standardized Tests Practice Questions, p. 84										

Course I: Chapters 1-11; Course II: Chapters 1-12; Course III: Chapters 1-13

Other Chapter Resources

Student Edition

Chapter Opener, pp. 264-265
Cooperative Learning Project, p. 274
Journal Entry, pp. 280, 299
Technology, p. 281
Mid-Chapter Review, p. 287
Portfolio, p. 292
History Connection, p. 293
College Entrance Exam Preview, pp. 304-305
More Investigations in Geometry, pp. A7-A8
Extended Project 2, pp. B6-B9

Teacher's Classroom Resources

Transparency 6-0
Real World Applications Transparencies, 11, 12
Performance Assessment Booklet, pp. 11-12
Problem-of-the-Week Activity Cards, 15, 16, 17
Tech Prep Applications Booklet, pp. 11-12
LOGO Instruction Materials, Technology Masters pp. 19-36

Other Supplements

Flow Proof and Indirect Proof
Algebra and Geometry Overhead Manipulative Resources
Glencoe Mathematics Professional Series

Software

Test and Review Generation (Apple, IBM, and Macintosh)
Teacher's Guide for Software Resources

ENHANCING THE CHAPTER

Cooperative Learning

Explaining the Task and Providing Task Assistance

To make sure that students focus on the relevant concepts and skills throughout the session, it is important that you provide them with a clear understanding of the academic task that they are to complete. Be sure to clearly explain the objectives that are to be achieved and the procedures that students are expected to follow. Review and define pertinent concepts and, when possible, connect the task and objectives to students' previously-acquired knowledge and experience. When monitoring cooperative-learning groups as they do their work, you should resist temptation to intervene any more often than is absolutely necessary. Even when intervening, your role should be more that of an enhancer rather than an answerer. When it may be necessary to clarify instructions or review procedures and strategies, encourage the group to work its way through the problem by recalling a specific instruction you gave before the session began.

Technology

The Technology Feature following Lesson 6-3 gives a BASIC program that uses the definition of a parallelogram to determine if the coordinates of the points the user enters, name the vertices of a parallelogram. Point out to students that by using INPUT statements, the program can be used again and again by simply entering the RUN command and then entering the coordinates of the vertices of the given quadrilateral. Students are asked to change the given program by using the theorem that says that a quadrilateral with a pair of opposite sides that are congruent and parallel is a parallelogram. You may wish to ask students to change the program again by using the other tests for deciding if a quadrilateral is a parallelogram.

Critical Thinking

Grasp every opportunity to eliminate from the minds of students any notion that success in mathematics is achieved by memorizing a series of arbitrary tricks and stratagems. Utilize discussions during which students explain their reasoning, justify their responses, and relate concepts and skills to other areas of mathematics as well as to other content areas and real-life experiences. Also, encourage students to always suggest alternative procedures. When working with the content in this chapter, for example, you may wish to have students research and report on the history of quadratic equations during which they will discover that such equations were solved arithmetically by the ancient Egyptians and geometrically by Euclid.

Cooperative Learning, p. 34

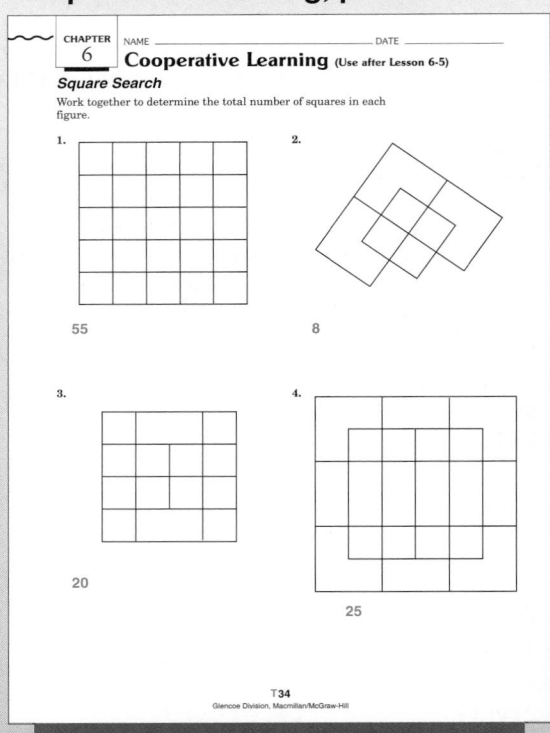

Technology, p. 6

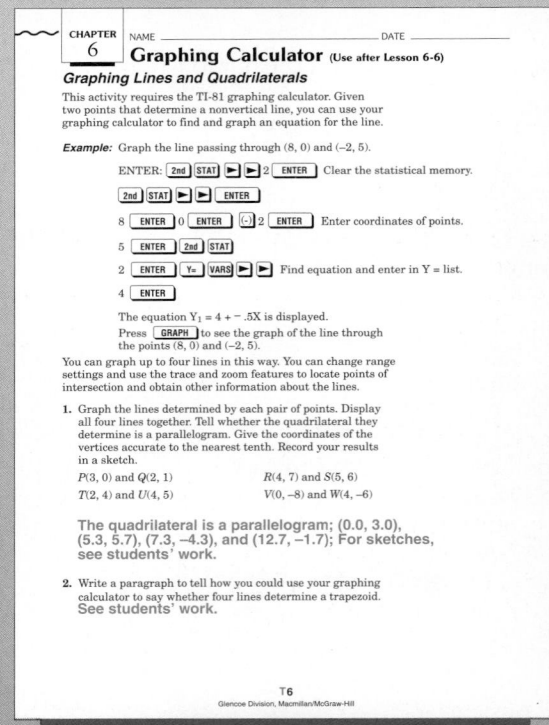

Problem of the Week Activity

The card shown below is one of three available for this chapter. It can be used as a class or small group activity.

Activity Card

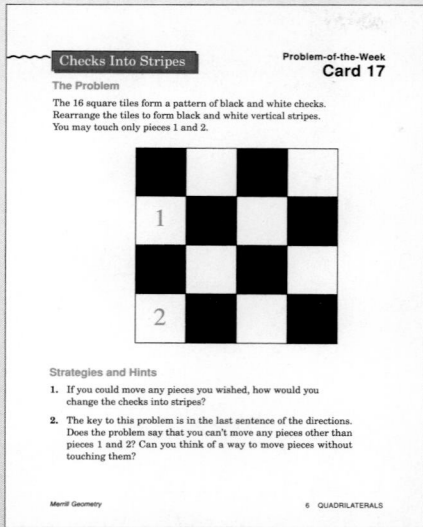

Checks Into Stripes

Problem-of-the-Week
Card 17

The Problem

The 16 square tiles form a pattern of black and white checks. Rearrange the tiles to form black and white vertical stripes. You may touch only pieces 1 and 2.

Strategies and Hints

1. If you could move any pieces you wished, how would you change the checks into stripes?

2. The key to this problem is in the last sentence of the directions. Does the problem say that you can't move any pieces other than pieces 1 and 2? Can you think of a way to move pieces without touching them?

Merrill Geometry   6 QUADRILATERALS

Manipulatives and Models

The following materials may be used as models or manipulatives in Chapter 6.

- cardboard, paper fasteners, protractor (Lesson 6-1)
- blocks (Lesson 6-2)
- straws, tape (Lesson 6-3)
- straightedge (Lesson 6-4)
- pantograph (Lesson 6-5)

Outside Resources

Books/Periodicals

Hunter, J.A.H., and Joseph S. Madachy. *Mathematical Diversions.* Dover Publications, Inc.

Lushbaugh, Warren. *Polyomineos.* Charles Scribner's Sons.

Kline, M. *Mathematics and the Physical World.* Thomas Y. Crowell.

Films/Videotapes/Videodiscs

The Emergence of Greek Mathematics, The Media Guild, 11722 Sorrento Valley Rd., Suite E, San Diego, CA 92121

Software

Geometric Supposer: Quadrilaterals, WINGS for Learning/Sunburst, 101 Castleton St., Pleasantville, NY 10570

Cabri Géometre, Brooks/Cole, Wadsworth School Group, 10 Davis Drive, Belmont, CA 94002-3098

Multicultural

Multicultural Activity, p. 6

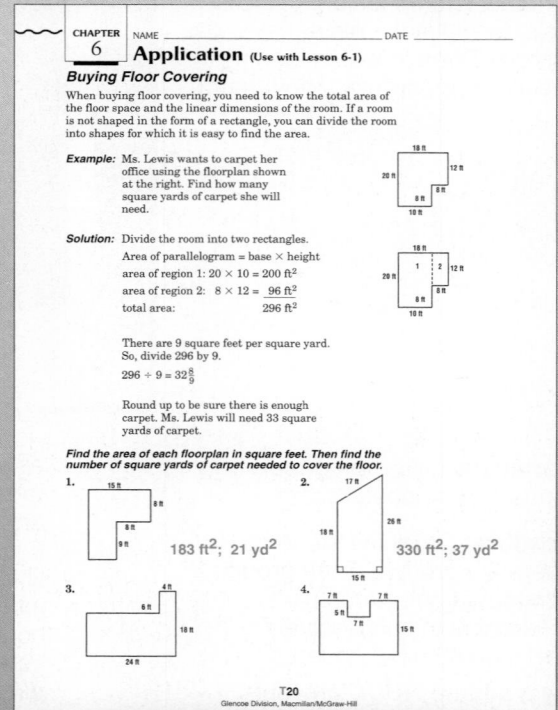

CHAPTER 6   NAME _____ DATE _____

Multicultural Activity (Use after Lesson 6-3)

Who Accomplished Which Feat?

Here is a list of prominent Hispanic and African-American people. Each was "the first" to accomplish something. To find out who accomplished which feat, solve the problems in the left-hand column. Then find your answer in the right-hand column.

1. If M is the midpoint of $\overline{RS}$ and $RM = 12$, find RS.
   Debi Thomas ___f___

2. Find $m\angle M$ in equilateral $\triangle LMN$.
   Franklin R. Chang-Diaz ___g___

3. In $\square WXYZ$, $WX = 7a - 23$ and $YZ = 49 - 5a$. Find WX.
   Martin R. Delaney ___i___

4. In $\triangle RST$, $m\angle R = 3x$, $m\angle S = 11x$, and $m\angle T = 6x$. Find $m\angle T$.
   Daniel Hale Williams ___b___

5. Find the slope of the line through $(4, 6)$ and $(2, -4)$
   Romana A. Banuela ___a___

6. If $m\angle ABC = 58$ and $\overline{DB}$ bisects $\angle ABC$, find $m\angle ABD$.
   Althea Gibson ___d___

7. In $\square ABCD$, $m\angle B = 138$. Find $m\angle C$.
   Guion "Guy" Bluford ___e___

8. Find the slope of a line perpendicular to $\overline{AB}$ with $A(3, 1)$ and $B(15, -5)$.
   Barbara Jordan ___h___

9. $\angle A$ and $\angle B$ form a linear pair. If $m\angle A = 99$, find $m\angle B$.
   Charles Drew ___j___

10. If the coordinates of M and N are -7 and 13, find the midpoint of $\overline{MN}$.
    Gracula Olivarez ___c___

(5) a. first Hispanic-American U.S. Treasurer

(54) b. African-American physician who performed the first successful heart surgery

(3) c. Hispanic-American who was the first woman to obtain a law degree from Notre Dame

(29) d. first African-American to win the U.S. Open and Wimbledon tennis tournaments

(42) e. America's first African-American astronaut

(24) f. first African-American female skater to win either a U.S. National or World title, and to go to the Olympics and win a medal

(60) g. first Hispanic-American astronaut to go into space

(2) h. first African-American woman from a Southern state to serve as a member of Congress

(19) i. first African-American officer in the United States Army

(81) j. African-American doctor who planned, established, and directed the first blood bank (during World War II)

Applications

Application, p. 20

CHAPTER 6   NAME _____ DATE _____

Application (Use with Lesson 6-1)

Buying Floor Covering

When buying floor covering, you need to know the total area of the floor space and the linear dimensions of the room. If a room is not shaped in the form of a rectangle, you can divide the room into shapes for which it is easy to find the area.

Example: Ms. Lewis wants to carpet her office using the floorplan shown at the right. Find how many square yards of carpet she will need.

Solution: Divide the room into two rectangles.
Area of parallelogram = base × height
area of region 1: $20 \times 10 = 200 \text{ ft}^2$
area of region 2: $8 \times 12 = 96 \text{ ft}^2$
total area: 296 ft^2

There are 9 square feet per square yard. So, divide 296 by 9.
$296 \div 9 = 32\frac{8}{9}$

Round up to be sure there is enough carpet. Ms. Lewis will need 33 square yards of carpet.

Find the area of each floorplan in square feet. Then find the number of square yards of carpet needed to cover the floor.

1. 183 ft^2; 21 yd^2

2. 330 ft^2; 37 yd^2

3.

4.

T20

Glencoe Division, Macmillan/McGraw-Hill

Using the Chapter Opener

This two-page introduction to the chapter provides students with an opportunity to see how geometry is used throughout the world in various cultures. **Transparency 6-0**, available in the *Merrill Geometry Package*, provides another full-color visual and motivational activity that you can use to engage your students in the mathematical content of the chapter.

Multicultural Notes

Native American   Native American art has been generally misunderstood and therefore undervalued. This art is neither realistic nor abstract; it is instead schematic and symbolic. It is subjective, dealing with dreams, visions, the imagination, and the interior life. The purpose of Native American art is primarily magical. Motifs and designs are intended to be protective, curative, and productive of good luck and prosperity.

Mexico   Rufino Tamayo (1899-1991) remains unrivaled as a painter in subtlety and delicate geometrical composition. In his murals as well as in his easel paintings, Tamayo was a leading figure in the modern art movement.

Chapter Project

Material pencil, graph paper, compass, ruler, posterboard

Procedure Organize students in cooperative groups. Each group will construct geometric progressions of successively larger, then smaller, squares.

Draw a square *ABCD* on your graph paper. Draw diagonal $\overline{BD}$. To draw a square with exactly twice the area of *ABCD*, construct a line perpendicular to $\overline{BD}$ at *B*. Using *C*

as your center and *CD* as your radius, use your compass to swing an arc of at least half of a circle. Find points *E* and *F* by extending lines *CD* and *BC* until they intersect the circle. Complete square *BDEF*. You could construct your square in any of the four directions by selecting any of the four vertices of your original square as the center of your second square. Successively larger squares are constructed by

repeating the above procedure.

To draw a square exactly half the size of *ABCD*, draw diagonals *AC* and $\overline{BD}$ intersecting at *H*. Using *B* and *A* as centers and half the diagonal as a radius, swing two arcs intersecting at *G*. Connect lines *AG* and *BG* to complete square *AGBH*.

After groups have practiced geometric progressions of enlargement and reduction, have them use progression to enlarge

Quadrilaterals

GEOMETRY AROUND THE WORLD
Russia

Do you like traditional paintings that depict things exactly as they appear in real life? Or are you drawn to more offbeat works in which the artist's idea of reality is different from what you see every day?

If you like the offbeat, you'll enjoy puzzling over the dramatic paintings of Russian artist Marc Chagall. Born in 1887, in the small Russian city of Pestkowatil, Chagall was a poor student who day-dreamed in class. Only during drawing lessons and geometry class did he sit up and take notice. Perhaps that's why Chagall's paintings contain so many distinct geometric shapes!

His family was poor, but they managed to send Chagall to an art school in the city of St. Petersburg. He later studied at another Russian art school before moving to Paris in 1913 to pursue his career as a painter.

GEOMETRY IN ACTION

Chagall's style is marked by bold colors, strong geometric shapes, and dreamlike images of floating bodies. All these are clearly evident in "Paris Through the Window," painted by Chagall when he arrived there in 1913. Chagall wears two faces in this painting—one looking out toward Paris; the other back toward Russia. How many different geometric shapes do you see in this painting? How many **quadrilaterals** make up the window?

◀ *"Paris Through the Window"*   Inset: *Marc Chagall*

Do you see the quadrilaterals in the trouser legs of Chagall's 1924 painting "Green Violinist?" What shapes are in the man's coat?

CHAPTER OBJECTIVES

In this chapter, you will:
- Recognize and use the properties of parallelograms, rhombi, rectangles, squares, and trapezoids.
- Solve problems by looking for a pattern.

Connections and Applications

Lesson	Connections (C) and Applications (A)	Examples	Exercises
6-1	C: Algebra	1	14, 26-30
	A: Physics		48
6-3	C: Algebra	1	10, 11 22-29
	A: Music		43
	A: Construction		44
6-4	C: Algebra		5-7, 22-25
	A: Building	1	
	A: Construction		40
	A: Building Material		41
	A: Sports		42
6-5	C: Algebra		10-13, 29-34
	A: Mechanics		39
6-6	C: Algebra	1, 2	9-12, 22, 26-27
	A: Agriculture		33
	A: Real Estate		34

265

and reduce squares in an artistic pattern on posterboard. Have each group present its geometric work of art to the whole class for discussion.

Resources

Greenfield, Howard. *First Impressions: Marc Chagall*. Harry N. Abrams, Inc.

Hobbs, Jack A., and Robert L. Duncan. *Arts, Ideas, and Civilization*. Prentice Hall, Inc.

Gaunt, William. *A Guide to the Understanding of Painting*. Harry N. Abrams, Inc.

INTRODUCING THE LESSON

🕐 5-Minute Check

(over Chapter 5)

Refer to the figure below for Exercises 1-2.

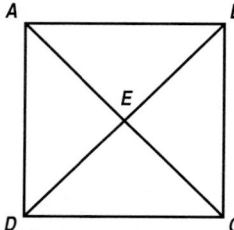

Given: $\overline{BD}$ is a perpendicular bisector of $\overline{AC}$.

1. Can you say that $\triangle AED \cong \triangle CED$?   **yes, by LL**

2. Can you say that $\triangle AED \cong \triangle CEB$?   **no**

3. If you want to prove that $m\angle C = m\angle B$ by an indirect proof, what is your assumption?   **Assume that $m\angle C < m\angle B$ or $m\angle C > m\angle B$.**

Refer to the figure below for Exercises 4-5.

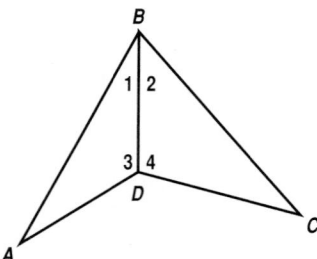

4. If $m\angle 4 > m\angle 2$, what can you say about their opposite segments?   **$BC > DC$ by Theorem 5-10**

5. If $m\angle 2 > m\angle 1$ and $\overline{AB} \cong \overline{BC}$, what can you say about the segments in the triangles?   **$DC > AD$ by the SAS Inequality Theorem**

6-1   Parallelograms

Objectives

After studying this lesson, you should be able to:

6-1A   ▪ recognize and define a parallelogram, and

6-1B   ▪ recognize, use, and prove the properties of a parallelogram.

Application

The beautiful pattern in this wooden tile is made up of **polygons**, each one with the same general shape. A polygon is a figure made up of coplanar segments, called **sides** which intersect at points called **vertices**. The sides each intersect exactly two other sides, one at each endpoint, and no two sides with a common endpoint are collinear.

FYI···

The art of making furniture and other items with inlaid wood is called marquetry. Marquetry first became popular in France in the late sixteenth century.

The polygons in the wooden tile are **quadrilaterals**, or four-sided polygons. Below are some examples and nonexamples of quadrilaterals.

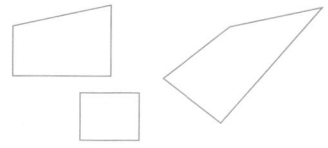

Examples

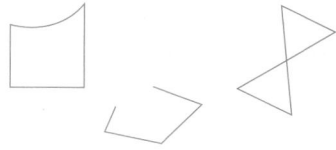

Nonexamples

We will often refer to the **diagonals** in a quadrilateral. The diagonals of a figure are the segments which connect any two nonconsecutive vertices. In quadrilateral *EFGH* at the right, the dashed line segments, $\overline{EG}$ and $\overline{FH}$, are the diagonals.

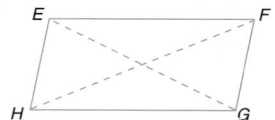

There is something else special about the quadrilaterals used in the wooden tile design. Study the pattern carefully. What do you think it is?

Parallelogram ABCD is written ▱ABCD.

The special quadrilaterals you see in the wooden tile pattern are called **parallelograms**. A parallelogram is a quadrilateral with both pairs of opposite sides parallel. The quadrilateral at the right is called parallelogram *ABCD*. The pairs of opposite sides are $\overline{AB}$ and $\overline{DC}$, and $\overline{AD}$ and $\overline{BC}$. The pairs of opposite angles are $\angle A$ and $\angle C$, and $\angle B$ and $\angle D$.

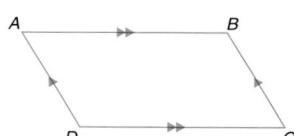

266   CHAPTER 6   QUADRILATERALS

ALTERNATE TEACHING STRATEGIES

Using Logical Reasoning

Is the following statement true or false? Write a paragraph explaining your answer. "If you know the measure of one angle in a parallelogram, you can find the measures of all four angles." **True: Since opposite angles are congruent and consecutive angles are supplementary, the measures of all four can be determined from the measure of one.**

Using Cooperative Groups

Have groups of three or four take a sheet of rectangular dot paper and divide it into several 4 by 4 arrays. Ask them to draw all possible noncongruent parallelograms that are not rectangles or rhombi. Have the groups compare their answers and the methods they used to organize their counts.

What conjectures can you make about the sides of a parallelogram? Can you develop a convincing argument or proof to show that your conjectures are correct?

| Theorem 6-1 | **Opposite sides of a parallelogram are congruent.** |

Proof of Theorem 6-1

Given: $\square PQRS$

Prove: $\overline{PQ} \cong \overline{RS}$
$\overline{QR} \cong \overline{SP}$

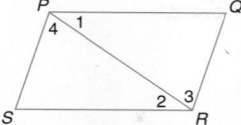

Paragraph Proof:

Draw an auxiliary segment PR and label angles 1, 2, 3, and 4 as shown. Since the opposite sides of a parallelogram are parallel, $\angle 1 \cong \angle 2$, and $\angle 3 \cong \angle 4$ because they are alternate interior angles. Since congruence of segments is reflexive, $\overline{PR} \cong \overline{PR}$. So $\triangle QPR \cong \triangle SRP$ by ASA. $\overline{PQ} \cong \overline{RS}$ and $\overline{QR} \cong \overline{SP}$ by CPCTC.

The angles of a parallelogram have a special relationship also.

Theorem 6-2	**Opposite angles of a parallelogram are congruent.**
Theorem 6-3	**Consecutive angles in a parallelogram are supplementary.**
	You will be asked to prove Theorems 6-2 and 6-3 in Exercises 41 and 42.

Example 1

DUCK is a parallelogram. Find the values of w, x, y, and z.

Since the opposite sides of a parallelogram are congruent, $x = 7$.

The opposite angles are congruent, so $z = 113$.

The consecutive angles of a parallelogram are supplementary, so $y + 113 = 180$. Therefore, $y = 67$.

$\angle KCU$ and $\angle UCS$ form a linear pair, so $m\angle KCU + m\angle UCS = 180$. The opposite angles of a parallelogram are congruent, so $m\angle KCU = 67$. Therefore, $w = 113$.

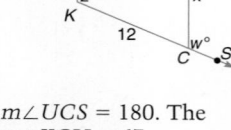

If the diagonals of a parallelogram are drawn, what appears to be true about them? Our next theorem states the relationship.

| Theorem 6-4 | **The diagonals of a parallelogram bisect each other.** |

Motivating the Lesson
Ask each student to draw three different four-sided polygons (quadrilaterals). Have the class share drawings and discuss the different types shown and their properties.

TEACHING THE LESSON

Teaching Tip   A good way to investigate parallelograms is by having students cut out examples and use paper folding to demonstrate the different properties mentioned in Theorems 6-1, 6-2, 6-3, and 6-4.

Teaching Tip   After reading the proof of Theorem 6-1, point out that the theorem could also have been proved by drawing $\overline{QS}$ instead.

Chalkboard Example

For Example 1
MATH is a parallelogram. Find the values of w, x, y, and z.

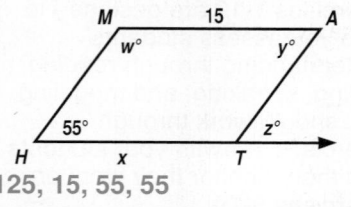

125, 15, 55, 55

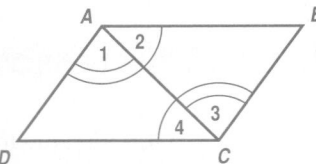

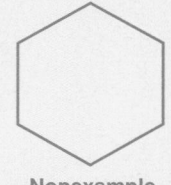

Example 2 **Write a plan for the proof of Theorem 6-4.**

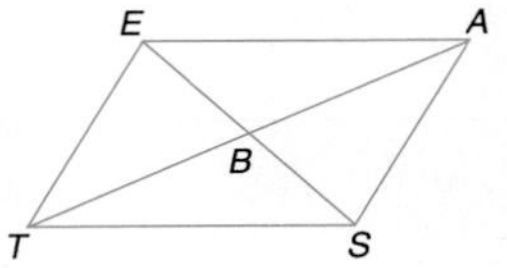

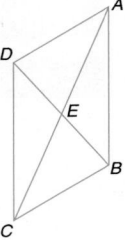

Given: $\square EAST$

Prove: $\overline{ES}$ bisects $\overline{AT}$.
$\overline{AT}$ bisects $\overline{ES}$.

Plan for Proof:

First, use the alternate interior angle theorem, and Theorem 6-1 to prove that $\Delta EBA \cong \Delta SBT$ or that $\Delta EBT \cong \Delta SBA$ by ASA. Next, show that B is the midpoint of both $\overline{ES}$ and $\overline{AT}$. Then conclude that $\overline{ES}$ bisects $\overline{AT}$ and $\overline{AT}$ bisects $\overline{ES}$, by the definition of a segment bisector.
You will be asked to complete the proof in Exercise 43.

CHECKING FOR UNDERSTANDING

Communicating Mathematics

Read and study the lesson to answer these questions. **See margin.**

1. Describe a quadrilateral and sketch an example and a nonexample.
2. Look around your classroom and name at least five different quadrilaterals you are able to find. **Answers may vary. See students' work.**
3. By definition, what is the special characteristic a quadrilateral must have in order to be a parallelogram? **both pairs of opposite sides parallel**
4. If quadrilateral *FRAC* is a parallelogram, what congruence statements can you make? $\overline{FR} \cong \overline{CA}$, $\overline{FC} \cong \overline{RA}$, $\angle F \cong \angle A$, $\angle R \cong \angle C$

Guided Practice

Complete each statement about parallelogram *ABCD* at the right. Then name the theorem or definition that justifies your answer.

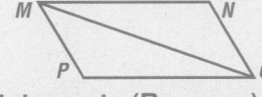

5. $\overline{AB} \parallel$ __?__ $\overline{DC}$; **definition of parallelogram**
6. $\overline{DA} \cong$ __?__ $\overline{CB}$; **Th. 6-1**
7. $\Delta ADC \cong$ __?__ ΔCBA; **SAS or SSS**
8. $\angle CDA \cong$ __?__ $\angle ABC$; **Th. 6-2**
9. $\overline{DE} \cong$ __?__ $\overline{EB}$; **Th. 6-4**
10. $\angle BAC \cong$ __?__ $\angle ACD$; **alt. int. angles th.**
11. Is quadrilateral *ABCD* a parallelogram if its vertices have coordinates $A(1, 1)$, $B(3, 6)$, $C(8, 8)$, and $D(6, 3)$? Justify your answer. **See margin.**
12. If quadrilateral *SLAM* is a parallelogram and $m\angle S = 92$, what are the measures of angles *L*, *A*, and *M*? $m\angle L = 88$, $m\angle A = 92$, $m\angle M = 88$
13. Prove that a diagonal and the sides of a parallelogram form two congruent triangles. **See margin.**
14. In $\square ABCD$, $AB = 2x + 5$, $CD = y + 1$, $AD = y + 5$, and $BC = 3x - 4$. Find the measures of the sides. $x = 13$ and $y = 30$, so $AB = CD = 31$, $AD = BC = 35$

Chalkboard Example

For Example 2
Write a plan for the proof of Theorem 6-2
Given: parallelogram *ABCD*
Prove: $\angle A \cong \angle C$, $\angle B \cong \angle D$

Draw an auxiliary segment $\overline{AC}$. Number angles as shown. By alternate interior angles and congruence of segments is reflexive, show $\triangle CDA \cong \triangle ABC$ by ASA. CPCTC lets you prove $\angle D$ and $\angle B$ congruent. In a similar way, prove the other two angles congruent.

EVALUATING THE LESSON

Checking for Understanding

Exercises 1-19 are designed to help you assess students' understanding through reading, writing, speaking, and modeling. You should work through Exercises 1-4 with your students and then monitor their work on Exercises 5-19.

Closing the Lesson

Writing Activity Ask students to draw and label a parallelogram and write which angles and segments are congruent, which segments are parallel, and which angles are supplementary.

Additional Answers

1. A quadrilateral is a four-sided closed figure in one plane.

11. slope of $\overline{AB} = \frac{1-6}{1-3} = \frac{5}{2}$

slope of $\overline{BC} = \frac{6-8}{3-8} = \frac{2}{5}$

slope of $\overline{CD} = \frac{8-3}{8-6} = \frac{5}{2}$

slope of $\overline{DA} = \frac{3-1}{6-1} = \frac{2}{5}$

Since the opposite sides have the same slope, they are parallel and *ABCD* is a parallelogram.

13. Given: parallelogram *MNOP*
Prove: $\triangle MNO \cong \triangle OPM$

Statements (Reasons)
a. *MNOP* is a parallelogram. (Given)
b. $\overline{MN} \cong \overline{OP}$, $\overline{NO} \cong \overline{PM}$ (opp. sides of a $\square$ are $\cong$.)
c. $\angle MNO \cong \angle OPM$ (opp. $\angle$s of a $\square$ are $\cong$.)
d. $\triangle MNO \cong \triangle OPM$ (SAS)

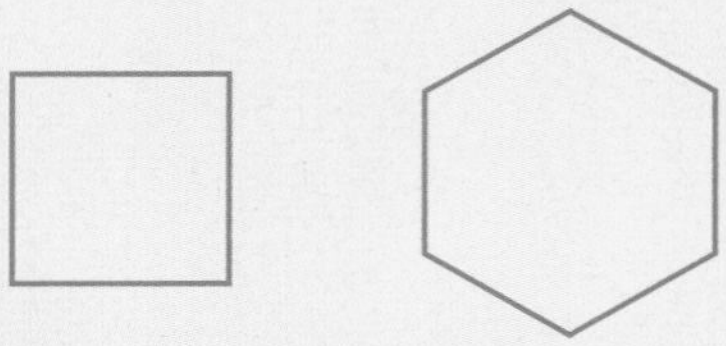

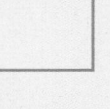

DUNK is a parallelogram. Name a theorem or definition that justifies each statement.

15. $\overline{DU} \parallel \overline{KN}$ definition of parallelogram

16. M is the midpoint of $\overline{KU}$.   Th. 6-4

17. $m\angle DUN = m\angle NKD$ Th. 6-2

18. $\angle KDU$ is a supplement of $\angle DKN$.   Th. 6-3

19. If $DU = 3x + 6$, $UN = 8y - 4$, $KN = 8x - 4$, and $KD = 2y + 14$, find the perimeter of $DUNK$.   **64**

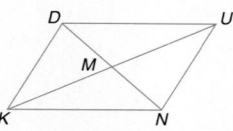

EXERCISES

Practice

EFGH is a parallelogram. Determine whether each statement must be true. If it must be true, state the theorem or definition that justifies the statement.

See margin.

20. $\overline{FE} \parallel \overline{GH}$

21. $\triangle FDE \cong \triangle HDG$

22. $\angle FGH \cong \angle FEH$

23. $\overline{FD} \cong \overline{DG}$

24. $\triangle FHE \cong \triangle GHE$

25. $DE = \frac{1}{2} EG$

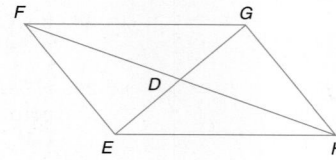

If each quadrilateral is a parallelogram, find the value of x, y, and z.

26.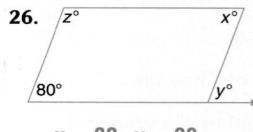

$x = 80$, $y = 80$, $z = 100$

27.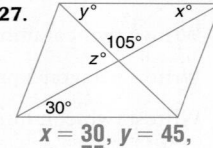

$x = 30$, $y = 45$, $z = 75$

28.

$x = 25$, $y = 35$, $z = 120$

29. Given parallelogram $PQRS$ with $m\angle P = y$ and $m\angle Q = 4y + 20$, find the measures of $\angle R$ and $\angle S$. $m\angle R = 32$, $m\angle S = 148$

30. In parallelogram $ABCD$, $m\angle C = x + 75$ and $m\angle D = 3x - 199$. Find the measure of each angle. $m\angle A = 151$, $m\angle B = 29$, $m\angle C = 151$, $m\angle D = 29$

31. Find all the possible ordered pairs for the fourth vertex of a parallelogram with vertices at $J(1, 1)$, $U(3, 4)$, and $N(7, 1)$. $(9, 4)$, $(5, -2)$, $(-3, 4)$

32. **Given:**   Parallelogram $MATH$
            $\overline{MP} \cong \overline{TQ}$

     Prove: $\overline{PH} \parallel \overline{AQ}$ See Solutions Manual.

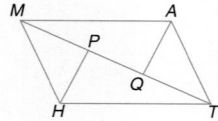

LESSON 6-1   PARALLELOGRAMS   269

APPLYING THE LESSON

Homework Exercises

Assignment Guide
Basic: 20-39, 46-56
Average: 23-42, 46-56
Enriched: 26-56

Exercise Notes

For Exercises 29-31, 38, and 39, encourage students to draw a diagram of the given information.

Additional Answers

20. true; definition of parallelogram
21. true; Theorem 6-4, vertical angles are congruent, and SAS
22. true; Theorem 6-2
23. false
24. false
25. true; Theorem 6-4

Reteaching Masters Booklet, p. 32

 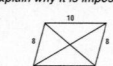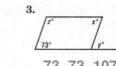
RETEACHING THE LESSON

Have students cut out two pairs of congruent strips of cardboard, one pair longer than the other. Have them use paper fasteners to attach the strips to form a parallelogram. The angles of the parallelogram are adjustable. Have students use a protractor to set one angle equal to 75° and then measure the other three angles and note their relationships to 75°.

They can reset the angle to 45° and repeat the activity.

You may also wish to have students check the diagonals with a ruler to demonstrate that the diagonals bisect each other.

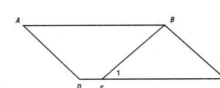
Is each quadrilateral a parallelogram? Justify your answer. See margin.

33.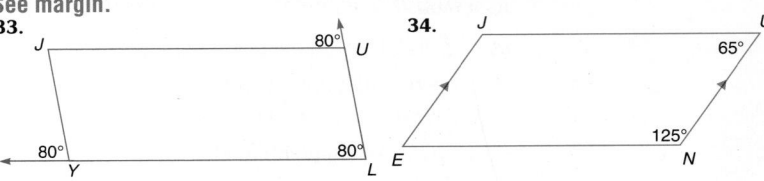

34.

Explain why it is impossible for each figure to be a parallelogram. See margin.

35.   36.   37.

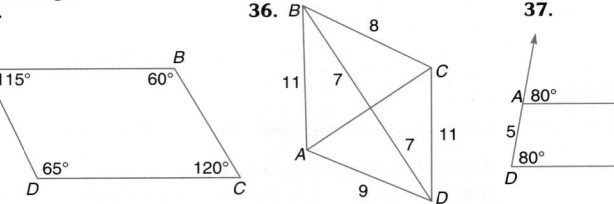

38. If *NCTM* is a parallelogram, $m\angle N = 12x + 10y + 5$, $m\angle C = 9x$, and $m\angle T = 6x + 15y$, find $m\angle M$. **45**

39. *NCSM* is a parallelogram with diagonals $\overline{NS}$ and $\overline{MC}$ that intersect at point *P*. If $NP = 4a + 20$, $NS = 13a$, $PC = a + b$, and $PM = 2b - 2$, find *CM*. **36**

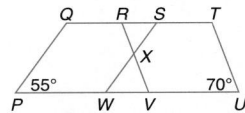

40. If *PQSW* and *RTUV* are parallelograms, find $m\angle SXR$. **55**

41. Write a two-column proof of Theorem 6-2. **See margin.**

42. Write a paragraph proof of Theorem 6-3. **See margin.**

43. Write a two-column proof of Theorem 6-4. **See Solutions Manual.**

Write a two-column proof.

44. **Given:** *PQST* is a parallelogram.
    $\overline{RP}$ bisects $\angle QPT$.
    $\overline{VS}$ bisects $\angle QST$.

    Prove: $\overline{RP} \parallel \overline{VS}$ **See Solutions Manual.**

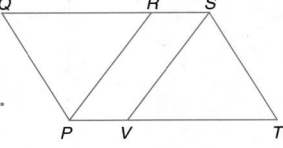

45. **Given:** *PQST* is a parallelogram.
    $\overline{RP}$ bisects $\angle QPT$.
    $\overline{VS}$ bisects $\angle QST$.

    Prove: $\overline{RP} \cong \overline{VS}$ **See Solutions Manual.**

270   CHAPTER 6   QUADRILATERALS

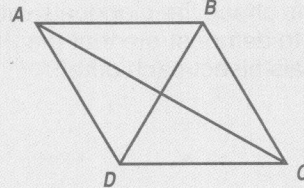

Construction

46. Construct a parallelogram with one angle congruent to the given angle and sides congruent to the given segments. **See students' work.**

Critical Thinking

47. Draw some figures to determine if the statement *If the midpoints of the sides of any quadrilateral are connected in clockwise order, they form a parallelogram* is *true* or *false*. Justify your conclusion. **true**

Applications

48. Physics Vectors are represented by line segments that have a certain length and direction. In physics, vectors are used to indicate force or motion. If two forces, *A* and *B*, are acting on an object, then the net force, or resultant vector, *R*, can be found by drawing a parallelogram. The resultant is represented by the diagonal that begins at the common endpoint of the vectors. Copy vectors *X* and *Y* and find the resultant.

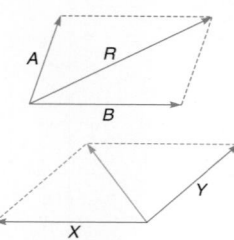

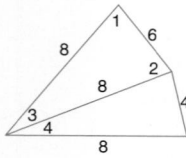

Mixed Review

49. Complete the statements with <, >, or =. **(Lesson 5-7)**

$m\angle 1 \underline{\ ?\ } m\angle 2$ =

$m\angle 3 \underline{\ ?\ } m\angle 4$ >

50. HA, LL, LA, and HL; see students' explanations.

50. Name the postulates and theorems that can be used to prove two right triangles congruent. Explain each. **(Lesson 5-3)**

51. If $\triangle DOG \cong \triangle CAT$, what segment in $\triangle CAT$ is congruent to $\overline{GO}$ in $\triangle DOG$? **(Lesson 4-3)** $\overline{TA}$

52. If $m\angle R = 90$ in $\triangle RST$, describe $\triangle RST$ as acute, obtuse, or right. Could $\triangle RST$ be isosceles? Could $\triangle RST$ be equiangular? **(Lesson 4-1)** right; yes; no

53. Find the slope of the line that passes through (-4, 8) and (3, 0). **(Lesson 3-5)** $-\frac{8}{7}$

54. Are the edge lines on a straight highway a model of lines that are intersecting, parallel, or skew? **(Lesson 3-1)** parallel

55. Write the conditional *A parallelogram is a quadrilateral with opposite sides parallel* in if-then form. **(Lesson 2-2)** If a quadrilateral has opposite sides parallel, then it is a parallelogram.

Wrap-Up

56. Summarize all the conclusions that you can draw if you know that a quadrilateral is a parallelogram. **See students' work.**

EXTENDING THE LESSON

Math Power: Problem Solving

In the figure, *ABCD* and *CDEF* are parallelograms. What is m∠*E* if m∠*A* = 57? 123

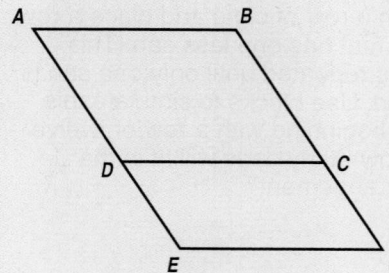

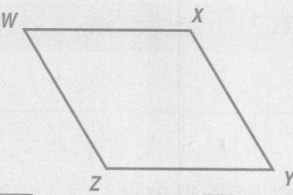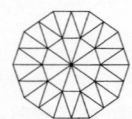
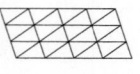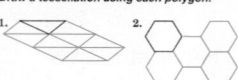
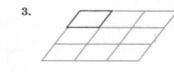
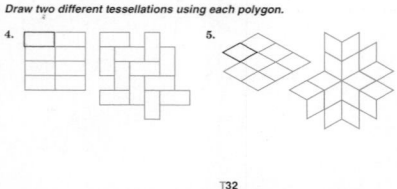

- Practice Master 6-2
- Evaluation Master, p. 79

Transparency 6-2 contains the 5-Minute Check and a teaching aid for this lesson.

INTRODUCING THE LESSON

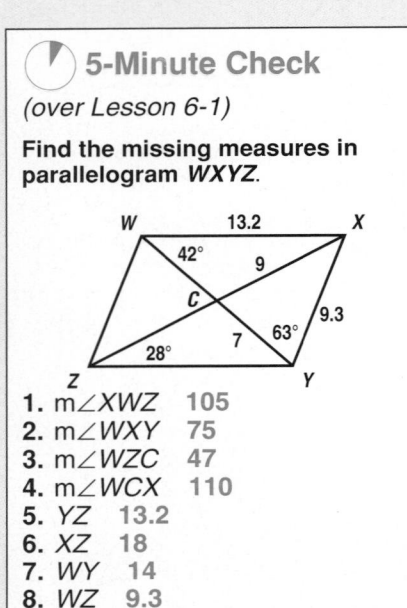

5-Minute Check

(over Lesson 6-1)

Find the missing measures in parallelogram WXYZ.

1. m∠XWZ   105
2. m∠WXY   75
3. m∠WZC   47
4. m∠WCX   110
5. YZ   13.2
6. XZ   18
7. WY   14
8. WZ   9.3

Motivating the Lesson

Teresa exercised for 10 minutes on Monday, 20 minutes on Tuesday, and 40 minutes on Wednesday. For how many minutes do you think she exercised on Thursday? Explain your answer.   **80 minutes; her pattern is to double the exercise time each day.**

TEACHING THE LESSON

Teaching Tip   Have students look carefully at one or more of Wendy's drawings and count the number of angles formed.

6-2 Problem-Solving Strategy: Look for a Pattern

Objective
6-2

After studying this lesson, you should be able to:
- solve a problem by looking for a pattern and using the pattern to find the missing information.

Application

A critical thinking problem on Wendy's geometry quiz asked her to find the number of angles formed by 10 distinct rays with a common endpoint. The figure she drew looked a little confusing, so Wendy drew some figures with fewer rays and made a table to record how many angles they formed.

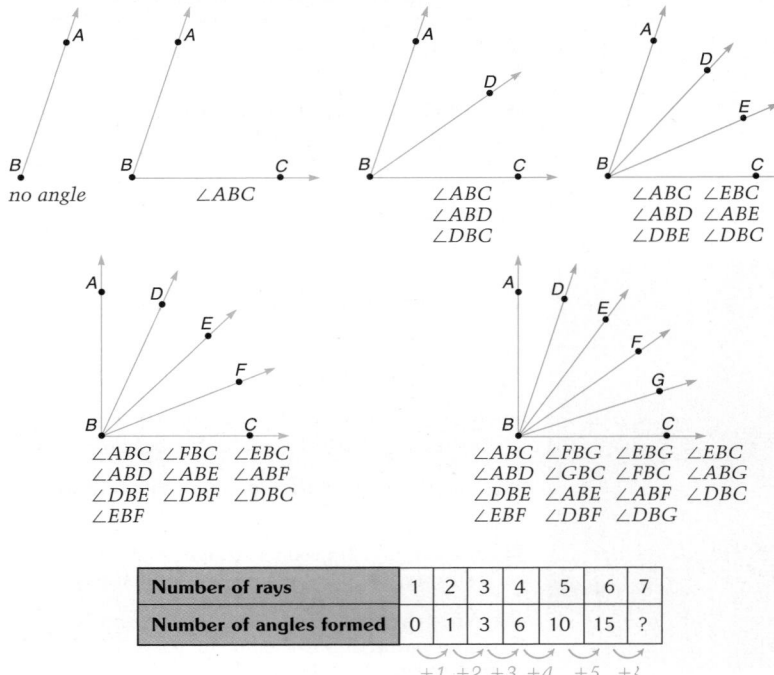

Number of rays	1	2	3	4	5	6	7
Number of angles formed	0	1	3	6	10	15	?

+1 +2 +3 +4   +5   +?

After drawing a figure with 6 rays, Wendy noticed a pattern. She conjectured that a figure with 10 rays must form 45 angles. Do you agree?

ALTERNATE TEACHING STRATEGIES

Using Manipulatives

One way to stack canned goods is to start with a row of cans and place a row above it that has one less can. This pattern is repeated until only one can is at the top. Use blocks to simulate this pattern, beginning with a row of twelve cans. How many cans will fit in the entire arrangement?   **78 cans**

Using Connections

An interesting numerical pattern that describes some phenomena in nature is the Fibonacci sequence: 1, 1, 2, 3, 5, 8, 13, 21, 34, . . .The center of a sunflower is arranged so that the ratio of the number of spirals in one direction to the number of spirals in the other direction is two consecutive Fibonacci numbers. Name the next two numbers in the sequence.   **55 and 89**

Example

CONNECTION
Algebra

What is the remainder when 3^{200} is divided by 5?

Make a table of the remainders when successive powers of 3 are divided by 5 and look for a pattern. Use the $\boxed{y^x}$ key on your calculator to find the powers of 3.

n	3^n	Remainder of $3^n \div 5$
1	$3^1 = 3$	3
2	$3^2 = 9$	4
3	$3^3 = 27$	2
4	$3^4 = 81$	1
5	$3^5 = 243$	3
6	$3^6 = 729$	4
7	$3^7 = 3187$	2
8	$3^8 = 6561$	1
9	$3^9 = 19,683$	3

The remainders of $3^n \div 5$ repeat in a pattern of four:
3, 4, 2, 1, 3, 4, 2, 1, ...

Every fourth power has a remainder of 1 when divided by 5. So since 200 is divisible by 4, $3^{200} \div 5$ has a remainder of 1.

CHECKING FOR UNDERSTANDING

Communicating Mathematics

Read and study the lesson to answer these questions.

1. How many angles are formed by 12 rays with a common endpoint? **66**

2. What is the remainder when $3^{250} \div 5$? **4**

3. Do you see a pattern in the ones' digits of successive powers of 3? **yes, 3, 9, 7, 1, 3, 9, 7, 1, …**

Guided Practice

Find the next number in each pattern.

4. 1, 2, 4, 8, 16, 32, _?_ **64**

5. 1, 2, 4, 7, 11, 16, 22, _?_ **29**

6. 6, 2, 4, 6, 2, 4, 6, 2, 4, 6, _?_ **2**

EXERCISES

Solve. Use any strategy.

7. Shina and Jeff have invited seven other couples over for a picnic. They will rent square cardtables to seat their friends for dinner. One of the cardtables can seat four people. If the tables are placed end to end to form one long table, how many must Shina and Jeff rent to seat everyone?
7 tables

LESSON 6-2   PROBLEM-SOLVING STRATEGY: LOOK FOR A PATTERN   273

Teaching Tip   If students try to find 3^{200} on a scientific calculator, they will get a number in scientific notation that has been rounded. Therefore, point out that a calculator cannot solve this problem.

Chalkboard Example

For the Example
What is the ones' digit of 9^{46}?
Make a table of powers of 9.

$9^1 = 9$	$9^5 = 59,049$
$9^2 = 81$	$9^6 = 531,441$
$9^3 = 729$	$9^7 = 4,782,969$
$9^4 = 6,561$	$9^8 = 43,046,721$

The pattern is that odd powers have a ones' digit of 9, even powers have a ones' digit of 1. Therefore, the ones' digit of 9^{46} must be 1.

EVALUATING THE LESSON

Checking for Understanding

Exercises 1-6 are designed to help you assess students' understanding through reading, writing, speaking, and modeling. You should work through Exercises 1-3 with your students and then monitor their work on Exercises 4-6.

Closing the Lesson

Writing Activity Have each student create a problem like those presented in this lesson. Have students exchange their problems for solution.

APPLYING THE LESSON

Homework Exercises

Assignment Guide

Basic: 7-13
Average: 7-13
Enriched: 7-13

RETEACHING THE LESSON

Have students work together in small groups to solve this problem. How many diagonals can be drawn in a polygon of ten sides?   **35**

Exercise Notes

For Exercises 7-9 and 12, it would be useful to draw a diagram. Exercise 12 may also be solved by acting it out (on paper).

For Exercises 7, 9, and 13, encourage students to look for a pattern.

For Exercise 10, students may use a chart.

8. The Moores used 4 miles of fencing to enclose their square 640-acre cornfield. Their neighbors, the Escaladas, bought 2 miles of fencing to enclose their square horse pasture. How many acres is the Escaladas' pasture? **160 acres**

9. Find the number of pairs of vertical angles determined by eight distinct lines passing through a point. **56 pairs**

10. At Grandma's Bakery, muffins are sold in boxes of 4, 6, or 13. Jena can buy 8 muffins by choosing two boxes of 4 muffins, but she can't buy 9 muffins with any combination of boxes. Find all of the numbers of muffins less than 25 that Jena cannot buy. **1, 2, 3, 5, 7, 9, 11, 15**

11. How many triangles are there in the figure shown at the right? *(Hint: There are more than 12 triangles.)* **47**

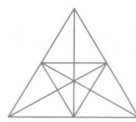

12. Nathan. He caught Tim after he ran 100 yards and there were 5 yards left to the finish line. Since Nathan runs faster, he won.

12. Nathan beat Tim by 5 yards in a 100-yard dash. The next time, Nathan evened-up the race by starting 5 yards behind Tim. If they each ran at the same rate as in the previous race, who won the second race? Explain.

13. Use your calculator to find the values of 11^2, 111^2 and 1111^2. Without calculating, use a pattern to determine the value of $11,111^2$. **123,454,321**

COOPERATIVE LEARNING PROJECT

Work in groups. Each person in the group must understand the solution and be able to explain it to any person in class.

Choose a three-digit number in which the digit in the hundreds place is greater than the digit in the ones place. Reverse the digits to form a different three-digit number and subtract the new number from the original. If necessary, add leading zeros to the difference to make it a three-digit number. Reverse the digits of the difference and add that number to the difference. What is the result? Try a few more examples. Is the result always the same? What is the result if the hundreds digit equals the ones digit? **1089; yes; 0**

EXTENDING THE LESSON

Math Power: Communication

Ask students to investigate the sums of odd numbers. When they find a pattern, ask them to write the pattern in algebraic form. One way to describe the pattern is, if x is the nth odd number, then $1 + 3 + 5 \ldots + x = n^2$.

Cooperative Learning Project

This activity provides students an opportunity to *learn* things together, not just do things together. You may wish to refer to pages T6-T7 and page 264c for the various elements of cooperative groups and specific goals and strategies for using them.

Practice Masters Booklet, p. 38

6-3 Tests for Parallelograms

Objective
6-3

After studying this lesson, you should be able to:
- recognize and apply the conditions that ensure that a quadrilateral is a parallelogram.

Application

The artist who designed this stained glass window used parallelograms and color effectively to create an unusual effect. In order for the pattern to work, it was essential that the basic components were all parallelograms. The artist had to know how to ensure that a quadrilateral is a parallelogram. There are several tests, other than the definition for a parallelogram, that she might have used.

Theorem 6-5	If both pairs of opposite sides of a quadrilateral are congruent, then the quadrilateral is a parallelogram.

Proof of Theorem 6-5

Given: $\overline{MA} \cong \overline{DE}$
$\overline{ME} \cong \overline{DA}$

Prove: *MADE* is a parallelogram.

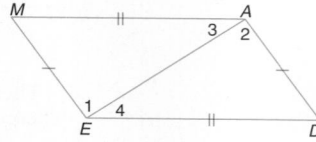

Proof:

Statements	Reasons
1. $\overline{MA} \cong \overline{DE}$ $\overline{ME} \cong \overline{DA}$	1. Given
2. $\overline{AE} \cong \overline{EA}$	2. Congruence of segments is reflexive.
3. $\triangle MAE \cong \triangle DEA$	3. SSS
4. $\angle 1 \cong \angle 2$ $\angle 3 \cong \angle 4$	4. CPCTC
5. $\overline{ME} \parallel \overline{DA}$ $\overline{MA} \parallel \overline{DE}$	5. If 2 lines are cut by a transversal and alt. int. ∠s are ≅, then the lines are ∥.
6. *MADE* is a parallelogram.	6. Definition of parallelogram

The following theorem provides another test to determine if a quadrilateral is a parallelogram. You will be asked to prove this theorem in Exercise 17.

LESSON 6-3 TESTS FOR PARALLELOGRAMS 275

6-3 Lesson Notes

Lesson Resources
- Reteaching Master 6-3
- Practice Master 6-3
- Enrichment Master 6-3
- Evaluation Master, pp. 79, 83
- Multicultural Master, p. 6

 Transparency 6-3 contains the 5-Minute Check and a teaching aid for this lesson.

INTRODUCING THE LESSON

5-Minute Check
(over Lesson 6-2)

Find the next number in each pattern.

1. 4, 2, 6, 8, 4, 2, ...   6
2. 1, 6, 4, 9, 7, 12, 10, ...   15
3. 1, 4, 9, 16, 25, 36, 49, ...   64

Solve. Look for a pattern.

4. What is the remainder when 4^{98} is divided by 5?   1
5. The numbers 1, 3, 6, and 10 are called triangular numbers because those numbers of dots can be arranged to form an equilateral triangle. Find the ninth triangular number.   45

Motivating the Lesson
Ask your students to draw $\overline{AB}$ and $\overline{CD}$ so that they both share a midpoint, *M*. Have them use a ruler to draw *ACBD*. Ask what conjecture they might make about *ABCD*. Sample answer: If you begin with two diagonals that bisect each other, you get a parallelogram.

ALTERNATE TEACHING STRATEGIES

Using Charts
Have students make a chart summarizing the ways in which a quadrilateral can be proved to be a parallelogram.

Using Problem Solving
The coordinates of three points in a plane are *A*(0, 3), *B*(–2, –1), and *C*(3, –1). Find the coordinates of *D* so that *ABCD* will form a parallelogram. (5, 3)

Teaching Tip For Theorem 6-6, students can use grid or dot paper to draw two congruent, parallel segments and then connect their endpoints. They can see that the resulting figure will always be a parallelogram.

Chalkboard Example

For the Example
The coordinates of the vertices of quadrilateral *EFGH* are *E*(6, 5), *F*(6, 11), *G*(14, 18), and *H*(14, 12). Determine if quadrilateral *EFGH* is a parallelogram.
Find the lengths of $\overline{FG}$ and $\overline{EH}$.
$FG = \sqrt{(14-6)^2 + (18-11)^2} = \sqrt{113}$
$EH = \sqrt{(14-6)^2 + (12-5)^2} = \sqrt{113}$
Find the slopes of $\overline{FG}$ and $\overline{EH}$.
slope of $\overline{FG} = \frac{18-11}{14-6} = \frac{7}{8}$
slope of $\overline{EH} = \frac{12-5}{14-6} = \frac{7}{8}$
Since two opposite sides are congruent and parallel, *EFGH* is a parallelogram.

Teaching Tip After discussing the Example, ask students how they might have used Theorem 6-5 to show that quadrilateral *ABCD* is a parallelogram. Use the distance formula on all four sides and show that both pairs of opposite sides are congruent.

Theorem 6-6	**If one pair of opposite sides of a quadrilateral are both parallel and congruent, then the quadrilateral is a parallelogram.**

We can use the distance and slope formulas to determine if the conditions of Theorem 6-6 are satisfied.

Example 1

CONNECTION
Algebra

The coordinates of the vertices of quadrilateral *ABCD* are *A*(-1, 3), *B*(2, 1), *C*(9, 2), and *D*(6, 4). Determine if quadrilateral *ABCD* is a parallelogram.

Find *BC* and *AD* to determine if this pair of opposite sides are congruent.

$BC = \sqrt{(2-9)^2 + (1-2)^2}$ or $\sqrt{50}$
$AD = \sqrt{(-1-6)^2 + (3-4)^2}$ or $\sqrt{50}$

Since $BC = AD$, $\overline{BC} \cong \overline{AD}$.

Find the slopes of $\overline{BC}$ and $\overline{AD}$ to determine if these opposite sides are parallel.

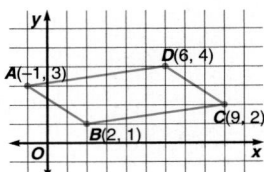

slope of $\overline{BC} = \frac{1-2}{2-9}$ or $\frac{1}{7}$
slope of $\overline{AD} = \frac{3-4}{-1-6}$ or $\frac{1}{7}$

Since the slopes $\overline{BC}$ and $\overline{AD}$ are equal, the sides are parallel. Since one pair of sides is both congruent and parallel, *ABCD* is a parallelogram by Theorem 6-6.

There are two more tests for parallelograms. You will be asked to prove Theorem 6-7 in Exercise 41.

Theorem 6-7	**If the diagonals of a quadrilateral bisect each other, then the quadrilateral is a parallelogram.**
Theorem 6-8	**If both pairs of opposite angles in a quadrilateral are congruent, then the quadrilateral is a parallelogram.**

Here is a summary of the tests to show that a quadrilateral is a parallelogram.

Show that:
1. Both pairs of opposite sides are parallel. (Definition)
2. Both pairs of opposite sides are congruent. (Theorem 6-5)
3. A pair of opposite sides are both parallel and congruent. (Theorem 6-6)
4. Diagonals bisect each other. (Theorem 6-7)
5. Both pairs of opposite angles are congruent. (Theorem 6-8)

CHECKING FOR UNDERSTANDING

Communicating Mathematics

Read and study the lesson to answer these questions.

1. Which of the tests for a parallelogram do you think the artist used to ensure that the quadrilaterals in the stained glass window design were parallelograms? Why do you think the artist chose this test? **Answers may vary. See students' work.**

Determine if each conditional is *true* or *false*. If it is false, draw a counterexample.

2. If the opposite angles in a quadrilateral are congruent, then the quadrilateral is a parallelogram. **true**

3. If two sides of a quadrilateral are congruent, then the quadrilateral is a parallelogram. **See margin.**

4. If a diagonal and the sides of quadrilateral *WXYZ* form two congruent triangles, then *WXYZ* is a parallelogram. **See margin.**

5. If a pair of consecutive angles in a quadrilateral are congruent, then the quadrilateral is a parallelogram. **See margin.**

Guided Practice

Determine if each quadrilateral must be a parallelogram. Justify your answer.
See margin.

6.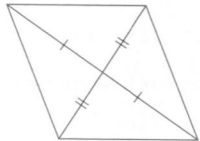

7.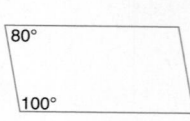

8.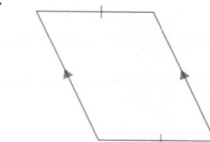

9.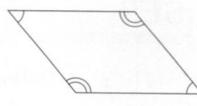

What values must *x* and *y* have in order for each quadrilateral to be a parallelogram?

10.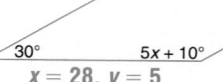
$x = 28, y = 5$

11.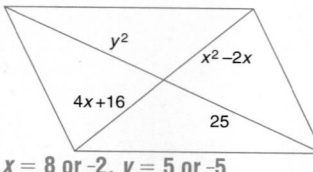
$x = 8$ or -2, $y = 5$ or -5

LESSON 6-3   TESTS FOR PARALLELOGRAMS   277

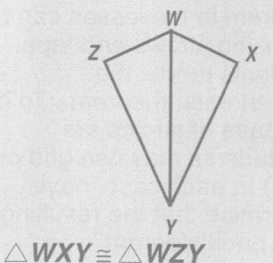

Homework Exercises

Assignment Guide

Basic: 18-35, 42-50
Average: 21-38, 42-50
Enriched: 24-50

Additional Answer

12. Find the slope of the opposite sides.

slope of $\overline{JK} = \dfrac{-2-(-2)}{3-8} = 0$

slope of $\overline{KL} = \dfrac{-2-(-4)}{8-7} = 2$

slope of $\overline{LM} = \dfrac{-4-(-6)}{7-3} = \dfrac{1}{2}$

slope of $\overline{MJ} = \dfrac{-6-(-2)}{3-3}$,

undefined

Since the slopes of opposite sides are not equal, the sides are not parallel, and *JKLM* is not a parallelogram.

Reteaching Masters Booklet, p. 33

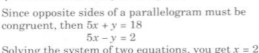

6-3 Reteaching Worksheet

Tests for Parallelograms

You can show that a quadrilateral is a parallelogram if you can show that one of the following is true.

1. Both pairs of opposite sides are parallel.
2. Both pairs of opposite sides are congruent.
3. A pair of opposite sides are both parallel and congruent.
4. Diagonals bisect each other.
5. Both pairs of opposite angles are congruent.

Example: What values must x and y have in order for the quadrilateral to be a parallelogram?

Since opposite sides of a parallelogram must be congruent, then $5x + y = 18$
$5x - y = 2$
Solving the system of two equations, you get $x = 2$ and $y = 8$.

What values must x and y have in order for each quadrilateral to be a parallelogram?

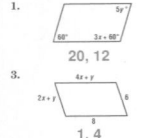

1.   20, 12

2. 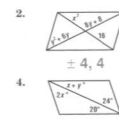   ± 4, 4

3.   1, 4

4.   12, 8

Determine if each quadrilateral must be a parallelogram. Justify your answer.

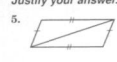

5.   yes; Both pairs of opposite sides are congruent.

6. 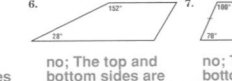   no; The top and bottom sides are parallel, but the other pair may not be.

7.    no; Top and bottom sides are not parallel.

T33
Glencoe Division, Macmillan/McGraw-Hill

Quadrilateral *JKLM* has vertices *J*(3, -2), *K*(8, -2), *L*(7, -4), and *M*(3, -6).

12. Show that *JKLM* is not a parallelogram. **See margin.**

13. Show that the quadrilateral formed by joining consecutive midpoints of the sides of *JKLM* is a parallelogram. **See Solutions Manual.**

Write a two-column proof. **See Solutions Manual.**

14. **Given:** $\triangle AEU \cong \triangle OUE$
    Prove: *AEOU* is a parallelogram.

15. **Given:** $\square PQRS$
    $\overline{XS} \cong \overline{QY}$
    Prove: *PYRX* is a parallelogram.

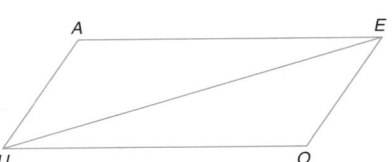

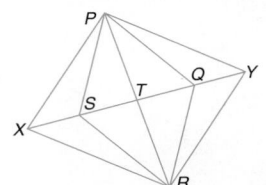

16. **Given:** $\overline{UN} \parallel \overline{KE}$
    $\angle YUK \cong \angle REN$
    Prove: *UNEK* is a parallelogram.

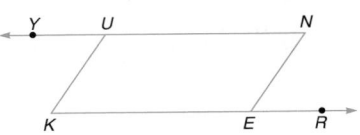

17. Write a two-column proof of Theorem 6-6.

EXERCISES

Practice

Determine if each quadrilateral must be a parallelogram. Justify your answer.
See margin.

A

18.

19.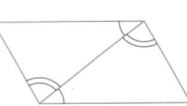

20.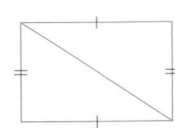

21.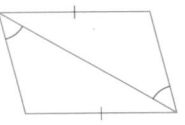

278   CHAPTER 6   QUADRILATERALS

RETEACHING THE LESSON

Each theorem in the lesson can be modeled using straws and tape. Have students model the conditions of each theorem. (To be sure that pairs of straws are parallel, students may use grid or dot paper.) In each case, have them determine that the resulting figure is a parallelogram.

Additional Answers

18. yes; Theorem 6-5
19. yes; Theorem 6-8
20. yes; opposite sides parallel
21. no

CONNECTION Algebra

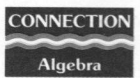

Use parallelogram *ABCD* and the given information to find each value.

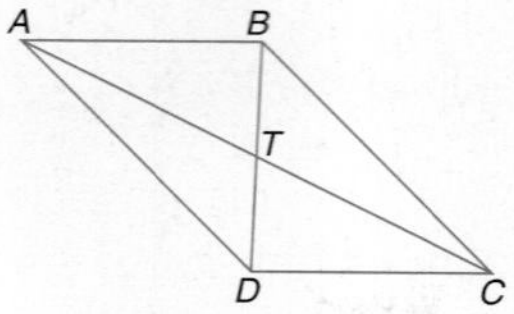

22. $m\angle ABC = 137$. Find $m\angle DAB$. 43
23. $AC = 5x - 12$ and $AT = 14$. Find x. 8
24. $AB = 6$, $BC = 9$, and $m\angle ABC = 80$. Find CD. 6
25. $BC = 4x + 7$ and $AD = 8x - 5$. Find x. 3
26. $BT = 3x + 1$ and $BD = 4x + 8$. Find x. 3
27. $m\angle BCD = 3x + 14$ and $m\angle ADC = x + 10$. Find $m\angle ADC$. 49

B

What values must x and y have in order that the quadrilateral is a parallelogram?

28.

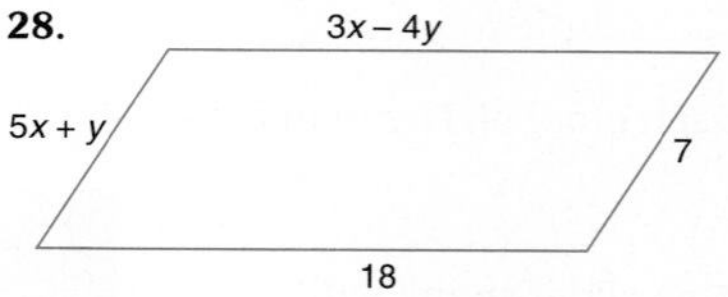

$x = 2$, $y = -3$

29.

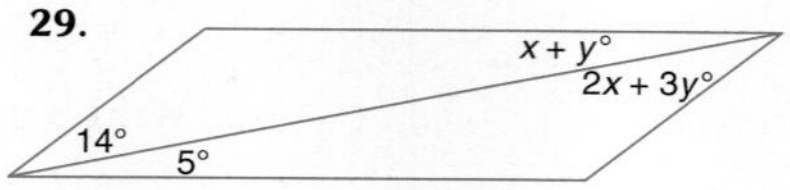

$x = 1$, $y = 4$

Determine if each statement is *true* or *false*. If false, find a counterexample. See margin.

30. A quadrilateral is a parallelogram if it has two pairs of congruent sides.
31. A quadrilateral is a parallelogram if it has one pair of congruent sides and one pair of parallel sides.

Determine whether *ABCD* is a parallelogram given each set of vertices. Explain. See Solutions Manual.

32. $A(8, 10)$, $B(16, 17)$, $C(16, 11)$, $D(8, 4)$
33. $A(8, 6)$, $B(6, 0)$, $C(4, 2)$, $D(7, 3)$
34. $A(-4, 0)$, $B(6, 0)$, $C(5, 4)$, $D(0, 4)$
35. $A(-2, 6)$, $B(2, 8)$, $C(3, 8)$, $D(-1, 3)$

36. Draw a quadrilateral that has two pairs of congruent sides, but is not a parallelogram. See margin.
37. Draw a quadrilateral that is not a parallelogram and has one pair of parallel sides and one pair of congruent sides. See margin.

Exercise Notes

For Exercise 24, extra information is given. The measure of the angle is unnecessary.

For Exercise 27, more than one step is necessary. After finding the value of x, the measure of the angle must be determined.

For Exercises 32-35, more than one method can be used.

Additional Answers

30. no; a sample drawing:

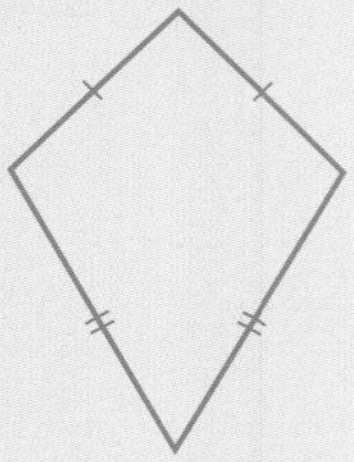

31. no; a sample drawing:

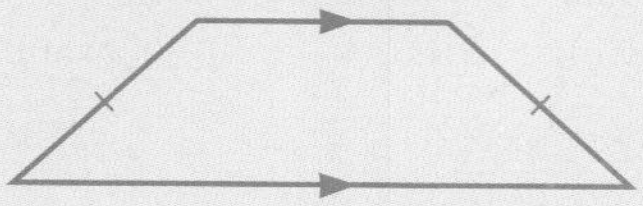

Additional Answers

36. Sample answer:

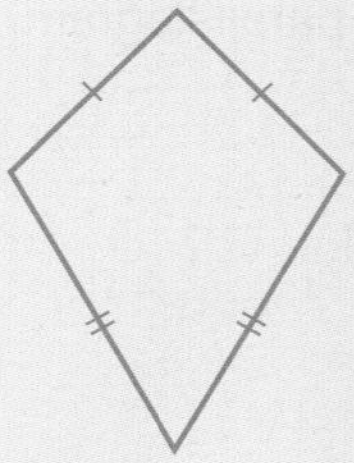

37. Sample answer:

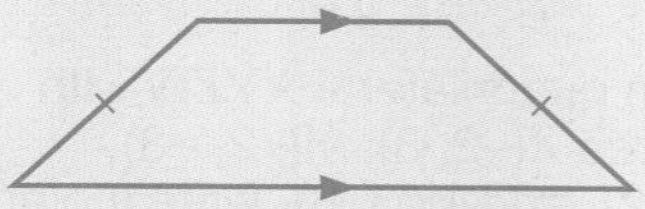

Practice Masters Booklet, p. 39

6-3 NAME ______________ DATE ______________

Practice Worksheet

Tests for Parallelograms

What values must x and y have in order for each quadrilateral to be a parallelogram?

1.

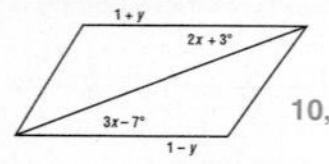

10, 0

2.

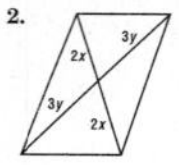

any values for x and y that are greater than 0

3. Refer to the figure at the right. $\overline{YZ}$ bisects $\angle XYK$ and $\overline{LK}$ bisects $\angle ZLM$. Also, $\angle 1 \cong \angle 2$. Is $YZLK$ a parallelogram? Explain.
yes; Opposite angles are congruent.

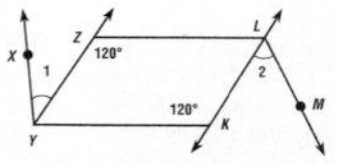

4. Refer to the figure at the right. $\overline{AC} = \overline{WV}$ and $\overline{BD} = \overline{WV}$. Also, $\overline{AB} = \overline{XY}$ and $\overline{CD} = \overline{XY}$. Is $ABCD$ a parallelogram? Explain.
yes; Both pairs of opposite sides are congruent.

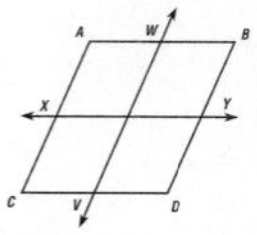

Determine whether ABCD is a parallelogram given each set of vertices. Explain.

5. $A(2, 5)$, $B(5, 9)$, $C(3, -1)$, $D(6, 3)$
yes; Opposite sides have equal lengths and are therefore congruent.

6. $A(-1, 6)$, $B(2, -3)$, $C(5, 9)$, $D(2, 7)$
no; Slope $\overline{AD} = \frac{1}{3}$ and slope $\overline{BC} = 4$, so these two opposite sides are not parallel.

T39

Enrichment Masters Booklet, p. 33

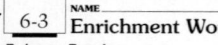

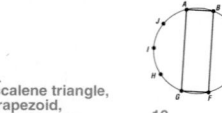
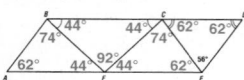

  Write a two-column proof. See Solutions Manual.

38. Given: $\square NCTM$
$\overline{NA} \cong \overline{ST}$
Prove: $ACSM$ is a parallelogram.

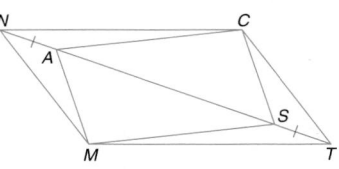

39. Given: $\triangle TWA$ is equilateral.
$TBWA$ is a parallelogram.
$TWAI$ is a parallelogram.
Prove: $\triangle IBM$ is equilateral.

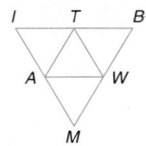

40. Given: $\triangle PQR \cong \triangle STV$
$\overline{PR} \parallel \overline{VS}$
Prove: $PRSV$ is a parallelogram.

41. Write a paragraph proof of Theorem 6-7. See Solutions Manual.

Critical Thinking

42. Explain why this glider swing will always remain parallel to the ground.
See margin.

Applications

43. Music   Explain why this keyboard stand will always remain parallel to the floor.
See margin.

44. Construction   Mr. Gallagher is building an open staircase for a new home. He has measured several three-foot support bars to hold up the handrail. If he nails the support bars to the handrail and to the edge of the staircase so that the bars are six inches apart, will the handrail be parallel to the staircase? Explain.   **yes; the opposite sides of the quadrilaterals are congruent, so they are parallelograms and opposite sides are parallel.**

Mixed Review

45. Find the next number in the pattern 2, 5, 10, 17, 26, _?_. **(Lesson 6-2)** **37**

46. The opposite angles of a parallelogram have measures of $9x + 12$ and $15x$. Find the measures of the angles. **(Lesson 6-1)** **30**

47. Could 30, 35, and 66 be the measures of the sides of a triangle? Explain. **(Lesson 5-6)** **no; Triangle inequality; 30 + 35 ≯ 66**

48. obtuse; one obtuse angle

48. The angles in a triangle have measures of $7x - 8$, $3x + 3$, and $18x - 11$. Is the triangle acute, obtuse, or right? Explain. **(Lesson 4-1)**

49. The measure of an acute angle is $18y$. What are the possible values of y? **(Lesson 1-7)** **$0 < y < 5$**

Wrap-Up

50. Journal Entry   Write a sentence in your journal about each test that you can use to prove that a quadrilateral is a parallelogram. **See students' work.**

EXTENDING THE LESSON

Math Power: Reasoning

Given quadrilateral $XYZW$ with vertices $X(-2, 3)$, $Y(-2, -3)$, $Z(3, 2)$, and $W(3, 8)$, write a plan using the fact that if the diagonals of a quadrilateral bisect each other, then the quadrilateral is a parallelogram, for a proof that $XYZW$ is a parallelogram.   The diagonals are $\overline{XZ}$ and $\overline{YW}$. If you can show that they have the same midpoint, you can show that they bisect each other. Therefore, Theorem 6-7 applies, and the figure is a parallelogram.

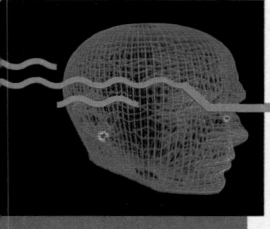

Technology
Parallelograms

► **BASIC**
Geometric Supposer
Graphing calculators
LOGO
Spreadsheets

A BASIC computer program can be written to use one of the tests for determining if a quadrilateral is a parallelogram. The program below uses the definition of a parallelogram to determine if the coordinates of the points the user enters name the vertices of a parallelogram.

```
10 REM THIS PROGRAM DETERMINES WHETHER POINTS ARE
   THE VERTICES OF A PARALLELOGRAM
20 INPUT "ENTER THE COORDINATES OF POINT A.";
   X1, Y1
30 INPUT "ENTER THE COORDINATES OF POINT B.";
   X2, Y2
40 INPUT "ENTER THE COORDINATES OF POINT C.";
   X3, Y3
50 INPUT "ENTER THE COORDINATES OF POINT D.";
   X4, Y4
60 IF (X2 - X1) = 0 THEN GOTO 80
70 M1 = (Y2 - Y1)/(X2 - X1)
80 IF (X4 - X3) = 0 THEN GOTO 110
90 M2 = (Y4 - Y3)/(X4 - X3)
100 IF M1 <> M2 THEN GOTO 200
110 IF (X3 - X2) = 0 AND (X4 - X1) = 0 AND (X2 - X1)
    = 0 THEN GOTO 200
120 IF (X3 - X2) = 0 AND (X4 - X1) = 0
    THEN GOTO 180
130 IF (X3 - X2) = 0 THEN GOTO 200
140 M3 = (Y3 - Y2)/(X3 - X2)
150 IF (X4 - X1) = 0 THEN GOTO 200
160 M4 = (Y4 - Y1)/(X4 - X1)
170 IF M3 <> M4 THEN GOTO 200
180 PRINT "ABCD IS A PARALLELOGRAM."
190 GOTO 210
200 PRINT "ABCD IS NOT A PARALLELOGRAM."
210 END
```

EXERCISES

Use the BASIC program to determine if each set of points are the vertices of a parallelogram.

1. $A(9, 7)$, $B(11, 13)$, $C(6, 12)$, $D(4, 6)$ **yes**

2. $A(-4, 1)$, $B(-3, 2)$, $C(8, 5)$, $D(6, 3)$ **no**

3. How could you change the program to determine whether a quadrilateral is a parallelogram using the theorem that says that a quadrilateral with a pair of opposite sides that are congruent and parallel is a parallelogram? **See margin.**

TECHNOLOGY   281

Using Technology

Objective This optional page shows how the BASIC programming language can be used to perform mathematical computations and to enhance and extend mathematical concepts.

Teaching Suggestions This Technology Feature uses a BASIC program to explore the conditions necessary to prove that a quadrilateral is a parallelogram.

Have students read the program to see what it is doing. Ask them how the program tests that the vertices form a parallelogram. It finds the slope of pairs of opposite sides; if each pair has equal slopes, the figure is a parallelogram.

Ask them to explain why lines 60, 110, and 120 are included. The slope of a vertical line is undefined; the program tests to see if a pair of opposite sides are both vertical. If they are, the lines are parallel.

If computers using BASIC are available, have students type in the program and try it for several quadrilaterals.

Additional Answer

3. Change lines 110-170 to use the distance formula to find the length of segments *AB* and *CD*.

Lesson Resources

- Reteaching Master 6-4
- Practice Master 6-4
- Enrichment Master 6-4

 Transparency 6-4 contains the 5-Minute Check and a teaching aid for this lesson.

5-Minute Check

(over Lesson 6-3)

Write a reason for each statement in the proof.

Given: $\triangle PRS \cong \triangle RPQ$
Prove: $PQRS$ is a parallelogram.

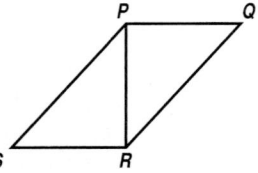

Statements (Reasons)
1. $\triangle PRS \cong \triangle RPQ$ (Given)
2. $\angle SRP \cong \angle QPR$ (CPCTC)
3. $\overline{PQ} \parallel \overline{RS}$ (If 2 lines are cut by a transversal and alt. int. $\angle$s are $\cong$, then the lines are $\parallel$.)
4. $\overline{PQ} \cong \overline{RS}$ (CPCTC)
5. $PQRS$ is a parallelogram. (If a pair of opp. sides of a quad. are $\cong$ and $\parallel$, it is a $\square$.)

Motivating the Lesson

Ask students to name five everyday objects that are rectangles. **Sample answer: walls, floors, sheets of paper, fields, windows**

6-4 Rectangles

Objectives
6-4A
6-4B

After studying this lesson, you should be able to:
- recognize the properties of rectangles, and
- use properties of rectangles in proofs.

Application

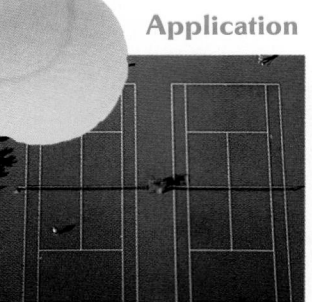

Have you ever thought about the importance of rectangles in the sports you play or enjoy watching? Without them, many of our most popular sports would be very different or maybe not even exist at all. The photographs on this page show sports that involve rectangles. How many of them do you enjoy?

A **rectangle** is a quadrilateral with four right angles. It follows that because both pairs of opposite angles are congruent, a rectangle is a parallelogram. Since a rectangle is a parallelogram, it has all the properties of a parallelogram.

The diagonals of a rectangle also have a special relationship.

Theorem 6-9	If a parallelogram is a rectangle then its diagonals are congruent.

Proof of Theorem 6-9

Given: $ABCD$ is a rectangle with diagonals $\overline{AC}$ and $\overline{BD}$.

Prove: $\overline{AC} \cong \overline{BD}$

Proof:

Statements	Reasons
1. $ABCD$ is a rectangle.	1. Given
2. $\overline{DC} \cong \overline{DC}$	2. Congruence of segments is reflexive.
3. $\overline{AD} \cong \overline{BC}$	3. Opp. sides of a $\square$ are $\cong$.
4. $\angle ADC$ and $\angle BCD$ are right angles.	4. Def. of rectangle
5. $\angle ADC \cong \angle BCD$	5. All rt. $\angle$ are $\cong$.
6. $\triangle ADC \cong \triangle BCD$	6. SAS
7. $\overline{AC} \cong \overline{BD}$	7. CPCTC

The converse of Theorem 6-9 is often used in the building trades to ensure that an angle is a right angle.

ALTERNATE TEACHING STRATEGIES

Using Discussion

Ask students to discuss whether it can be proved that a rectangle is a parallelogram, given only that a rectangle is a quadrilateral with four right angles. **Yes. Since both pairs of opposite angles are congruent, the figure is a parallelogram.**

Using Problem Solving

Place this array on the chalkboard or overhead.

```
· · · · ·
· · · · ·
· · · · ·
· · · · ·
· · · · ·
```

Have students find the total number of squares that can be drawn using the grid points as vertices.   **40**

Example 1

APPLICATION

Building

The Owens family is constructing a deck in their backyard. Mrs. Owens has laid out stakes where the corners of the deck will be as shown below. She has made sure that the opposite sides are congruent. If the diagonals are congruent, can Mrs. Owens be sure that the deck will be a rectangle?

Label the vertices M, N, O, and P. Then $\overline{MN} \cong \overline{OP}$, $\overline{MP} \cong \overline{ON}$, and $\overline{MO} \cong \overline{NP}$. We need to prove that $MNOP$ is a rectangle.

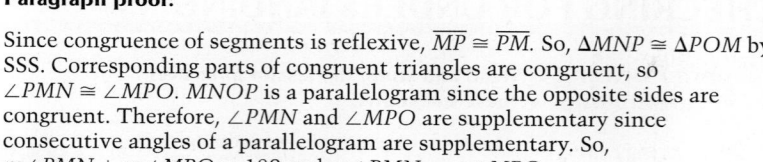

Given: $\overline{MN} \cong \overline{OP}$, $\overline{MP} \cong \overline{ON}$, $\overline{MO} \cong \overline{NP}$

Prove: $MNOP$ is a rectangle.

Paragraph proof:

Since congruence of segments is reflexive, $\overline{MP} \cong \overline{PM}$. So, $\triangle MNP \cong \triangle POM$ by SSS. Corresponding parts of congruent triangles are congruent, so $\angle PMN \cong \angle MPO$. $MNOP$ is a parallelogram since the opposite sides are congruent. Therefore, $\angle PMN$ and $\angle MPO$ are supplementary since consecutive angles of a parallelogram are supplementary. So, $m\angle PMN + m\angle MPO = 180$ and $m\angle PMN = m\angle MPO$.

By the substitution property of equality, $2m\angle PMN = 180$ so $m\angle PMN = 90$. Therefore, $\angle PMN$ and $\angle MPO$ are right angles. Since the opposite angles of a parallelogram are congruent, $\angle PON$ and $\angle MNO$ are right angles also. $MNOP$ is a rectangle.

Yes, Mrs. Owens can be sure that the layout for the deck is a rectangle if the diagonals are congruent. *This example proves the converse of Theorem 6-9.*

We can construct a rectangle using right angles and the definition of a parallelogram.

CONSTRUCTION

Construct a rectangle with a length of 5 cm and a width of 4 cm.

1. Use a straightedge to draw line ℓ. Label a point J on ℓ. With your compass set at 5 cm, place the point at J and locate point K on ℓ so that $JK = 5$. Now construct lines perpendicular to ℓ through J and through K. Label them m and n.

2. Set your compass at 4 cm. Place the compass point at J and mark off a segment on m. Using the same compass setting, place the compass at K and mark a segment on n. Label these points O and P.

3. Draw $\overline{OP}$.

Quadrilateral $JKPO$ is a parallelogram and all angles are right angles. Therefore, quadrilateral $JKPO$ is a rectangle with a length of 5 cm and a width of 4 cm.

TEACHING THE LESSON

Chalkboard Example

For the Example
Write a paragraph proof.
Given: $RECT$ is a parallelogram.
$\overline{RE} \perp \overline{RT}$
Prove: $RECT$ is a rectangle.

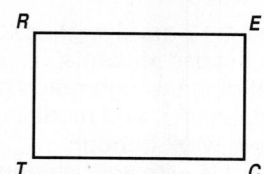

Since $\overline{RE} \perp \overline{RT}$, $\angle ERT$ is a right angle. Since $RECT$ is a parallelogram, opposite angles are congruent and consecutive angles are supplementary. Therefore, $\angle ECT$, $\angle RTC$, and $\angle REC$ are all right angles. Since all four angles are right, $RECT$ is a rectangle.

Teaching Tip For the construction, demonstrate each step using the chalkboard or overhead projector.

Teaching Tip

CHECKING FOR UNDERSTANDING

Communicating Mathematics

Read and study the lesson to answer these questions.

1. Look for examples of rectangles in the objects around you. Could the objects you see be another shape and still be effective? For example, would a circular door be as useful as a rectangular door?

2. If quadrilateral *GHIJ* is a rectangle, what can you say about its diagonals?

3. Are there any properties of a parallelogram that do not hold true for rectangles? Explain. **No, a rectangle is a parallelogram.**

4. Name two properties that hold for all rectangles, but not necessarily for all parallelograms. **diagonals congruent, all right angles**

1. Answers may vary. See students' work.
2. They bisect each other and are congruent.

Guided Practice

If quadrilateral *JKLM* is a rectangle, find the value of *x*.

5. $LP = 3x + 7$
   $MK = 26$ **2**

6. $LJ = 4x - 12$
   $KM = 7x - 36$ **8**

7. $KP = x^2$
   $PJ = 7x - 10$ **2 or 5**

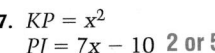

8. Construct a rectangle with sides congruent to the given segments. **See students' work.**

9. Is it true that, "If two sides of a quadrilateral are perpendicular, then the quadrilateral is a rectangle?" If not, draw a counterexample. **See margin.**

10. Show that quadrilateral *WXYZ* is a rectangle, with vertices *W*(1, 1), *X*(5, 5), *Y*(8, 2), and *Z*(4, -2). **See margin.**

284   CHAPTER 6   QUADRILATERALS

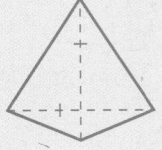
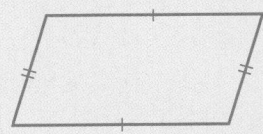
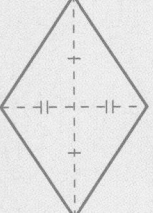

11. Write a two-column proof. **See Solutions Manual.**

Given: $\square WXYZ$
$\angle 1$ and $\angle 2$ are complementary.

Prove: $WXYZ$ is a rectangle.

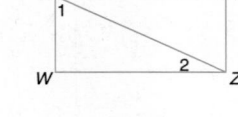

12. If quadrilateral $NCTM$ is a parallelogram, explain why quadrilateral $PQRS$ must be a rectangle. **See Solutions Manual.**

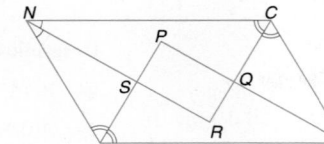

EXERCISES

Practice

Use rectangle *MATH* and the given information to solve each problem.

13. $MP = 6$, find HA. **12**

14. $MH = 8$, find AT. **8**

15. $HP = 3x$ and $PT = 18$, find x. **6**

16. $m\angle 1 = 55$, find $m\angle 2$. **62.5**

17. $m\angle 3 = 110$, find $m\angle 4$. **70**

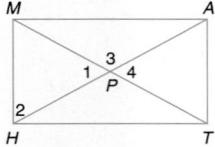

Draw a counterexample to show that each statement below is false. **See margin.**

18. If a quadrilateral has congruent diagonals, it is a rectangle.

19. If a quadrilateral has opposite sides congruent, it is a rectangle.

20. If a quadrilateral has diagonals that bisect each other, it is a rectangle.

21. Graph $J(2, -3)$, $K(-3, 1)$, $L(1, 6)$, and $M(6, 2)$.

   a. Describe two ways of determining if $JKLM$ is a rectangle. **See margin.**

   b. Is $JKLM$ a rectangle? Justify your answer. **See margin.**

CONNECTION
Algebra

Find the values of x and y in rectangle *PQRS*.

22. $PT = 3x - y$
$ST = x + y$
$TQ = 5$ $2\frac{1}{2}, 2\frac{1}{2}$

23. $PS = y$
$QR = x + 7$
$PQ = y - 2x$
$SR = x + 1$ **3, 10**

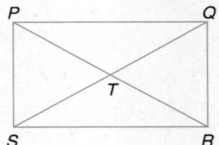

24. $PT = x + y$
$ST = 2y - 7$
$PR = -3x$ **-2, 5**

LESSON 6-4   RECTANGLES   **285**

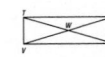

RETEACHING THE LESSON

Draw rectangle *ABCD* on the chalkboard and draw diagonals $\overline{AC}$ and $\overline{BD}$. Label $AB = 14$ and $BC = 9$. Label the point of intersection of the diagonals E, and label $AE = 8.3$. Have students find all the other measures of the rectangle. $BE = DE = CE = 8.3$, $CD = 14$, $AD = 9$

Additional Answer

21.

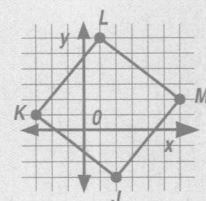

Additional Answers

38. Given: *READ* is a parallelogram. ∠*R* is a right angle.

Prove: *READ* is a rectangle.

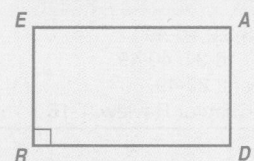

Statements   (Reasons)

a. *READ* is a parallelogram. ∠*R* is a right angle. (Given)

b. m∠*R* = 90   (Definition of right angle)

c. ∠*A* ≅ ∠*R*   (Opp. ∠s of a ▱ are ≅.)

d. m∠*A* = m∠*R*   (Definition of congruent angles)

e. m∠*A* = 90   (Substitution prop. of equality)

f. ∠*R* and ∠*E* are supplementary. ∠*R* and ∠*D* are supplementary. (Consec. ∠s in a ▱ are supp.)

g. m∠*R* + m∠*E* = 180 m∠*R* + m∠*D* = 180 (Definition of supplementary)

h. 90 + m∠*E* = 180 90 + m∠*D* = 180 (Substitution prop. of equality)

Practice Masters Booklet, p. 40

6-4 NAME _____ DATE _____

Practice Worksheet

Rectangles

Use rectangles ABCD and the given information to solve each problem.

1. If $AC = 4x - 60$ and $BD = 30 - x$, find BD.
   12

2. If $AC = 4x - 60$ and $AE = x + 5$, find EC.
   40

3. If $m∠BAC = 4x + 5$ and $m∠CAD = 5x - 14$, find $m∠CAD$.
   41

4. If $AE = 2x + 3$ and $BE = 12 - x$, find BD.
   18

5. $m∠BAC = 3x + 5$ and $m∠ACD = 40 - 2x$. Find $m∠AED$.
   52

Determine whether PQRS is a rectangle. Explain.

6. $P(2, 3)$, $Q(5, 9)$, $R(11, 6)$, $S(8, 0)$
   yes; opposite sides parallel and all right angles

7. $P(-1, 4)$, $Q(3, 6)$, $R(9, -3)$, $S(5, -5)$
   no; not all right angles

8. $P(1, 3)$, $Q(4, 7)$, $R(6, 2)$, $S(2, 4)$
   no; opposite sides not parallel

9. $P(-1, -3)$, $Q(-4, 6)$, $R(8, 10)$, $S(11, 1)$
   yes; opposite sides parallel and all right angles

10. $P(-1, -2)$, $Q(5, 2)$, $R(13, -10)$, $S(7, -14)$
    yes; opposite sides parallel and all right angles

T40
Glencoe Division, Macmillan/McGraw-Hill

286   Chapter 6

Use rectangle *MNRS* and the given information to solve each problem.
32, 58, 58

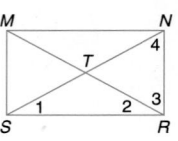

25. If m∠1 = 32, find the m∠2, m∠3, and m∠4.

26. If $ST = 14.25$, find MR. 28.5

27. If m∠*MTN* = 116, find m∠1 and m∠4. 32, 58

Determine whether *ABCD* is a rectangle. Explain.

28. $A(12, 2)$, $B(12, 8)$, $C(-3, 8)$, $D(-3, 2)$

28. yes; opposite sides parallel and all right angles

29. $A(0, -3)$, $B(4, 8)$, $C(7, -4)$, $D(11, 7)$ no; not all right angles

30. $A(4, 0)$, $B(6, -3)$, $C(8, 4)$, $D(10, 1)$ no; not all right angles

31. $A(-5, 8)$, $B(6, 9)$, $C(7, -2)$, $D(-4, -3)$
yes; opposite sides parallel and all right angles

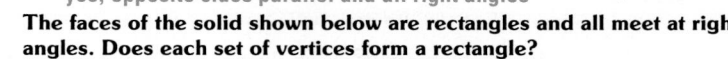 **The faces of the solid shown below are rectangles and all meet at right angles. Does each set of vertices form a rectangle?**

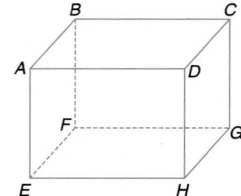

32. A, H, G, and B yes

33. A, C, E, and G yes

34. E, D, C, and F yes

35. B, D, H, and A no

36. E, H, F, and B no

37. F, C, G, and B yes

38. Prove that if one angle of a parallelogram is a right angle, then the parallelogram is a rectangle. See margin.

Critical Thinking

39. The ordered pairs $(2, 2)$, $(16, 4)$, and $(8, -4)$ are the coordinates of three of the vertices of a parallelogram. a. $(22, -2)$, $(10, 10)$, $(-6, -6)$
a. Find all possible ordered pairs for the fourth vertex.
b. Do any of these ordered pairs result in a parallelogram that is a rectangle? yes, (10, 10) does

Applications

40. Construction A cement contractor is getting ready to pour a footer for a new home. The outside dimensions of the basement walls are to be 42 feet by 56 feet. She places stakes and strings to mark the outside walls with the corners at *J*, *K*, *L*, and *M*. To make sure that quadrilateral *JKLM* is a rectangle, the contractor measures $\overline{MK}$ and $\overline{JL}$. If $MK <$ JL, describe how she should move stakes *F* and *G* to make quadrilateral *JKLM* a rectangle. Explain your answer. left

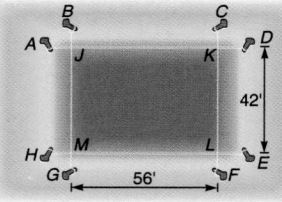

41. Building Materials Explain why the rectangle is used as the shape for bricks used in construction of walls in homes and buildings. See margin.

286   CHAPTER 6   QUADRILATERALS

Additional Answers

38. continued

i. m∠*E* = 90 m∠*D* = 90 (Subtraction prop. of equality)

j. ∠*A*, ∠*E*, and ∠*D* are right. (Definition of right angle)

k. *READ* is a rectangle. (Definition of rectangle)

41. Sample answer: Since all of the angles and the opposite sides are congruent, the bricks are interchangeable and can be installed in rows easily.

286   Chapter 6

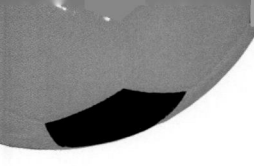

42. Sports Investigate the playing field of each sport. Is it a rectangle? If so, what are its dimensions? **See margin.**

   a. racquetball   **b.** wrestling   **c.** polo
   d. volleyball   **e.** tennis   **f.** bowling
   g. soccer   **h.** baseball   **i.** jai alai

Mixed Review

43. Determine whether quadrilateral $ABCD$ with vertices $A(9, 4)$, $B(0, -2)$, $C(-4, 6)$, and $D(5, 6)$ is a parallelogram. **(Lesson 6-3)** **no**

44. 58

44. Quadrilateral $WEST$ is a parallelogram. If $WE = 3x + 7$, $ES = 7y - 1$, $ST = 6x - 2$, and $TW = 2y + 9$, find the perimeter of $WEST$. **(Lesson 6-1)**

45. Find the slope of the line that passes through $(9, 3)$ and $(8, -4)$. **(Lesson 3-5)** **7**

46. If a quadrilateral is a rectangle, then it is a parallelogram.

46. Write *A rectangle is a parallelogram* in if-then form. **(Lesson 2-2)**

47. The West High School band is selling pizzas. Pizzas can be plain cheese or topped with any combination of pepperoni, green peppers, mushrooms, and onions. How many different pizzas are possible? **(Lesson 1-3)** **16**

Wrap-Up

48. Explain how rectangles and parallelograms are the same and how they are different. **See students' work.**

Additional Answers

42a. rectangular; 20 by 40 feet (20 feet high)
42b. circular
42c. rectangular; 300 by 200 yards
42d. rectangular; 29.5 by 59 feet
42e. rectangular; 36 by 78 feet
42f. rectangular; 62 feet $10\frac{3}{16}$ inches by 41 inches
42g. rectangular; 100 to 130 by 50 to 100 yards
42h. square infield; 90 by 90 feet
42i. rectangular; 176 by 55 feet (40 feet high)

MID-CHAPTER REVIEW

Complete each statement about parallelogram *EFGH*. Then name the theorem or definition that justifies your answer. (Lesson 6-1) See margin.

1. $\overline{GH} \parallel \underline{\ ?\ }$ **2.** $\angle GHE \cong \underline{\ ?\ }$
3. $\overline{FD} \cong \underline{\ ?\ }$ **4.** $\triangle FDE \cong \underline{\ ?\ }$
5. $\overline{EH} \cong \underline{\ ?\ }$ **6.** $\overline{GF} \parallel \underline{\ ?\ }$

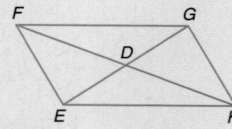

Find the next number in each pattern. (Lesson 6-2)

7. 0, 1, 3, 6, 10, 15, $\underline{\ ?\ }$ **21**
8. 1, 8, 27, 64, $\underline{\ ?\ }$ **125**
9. -1, 2, -4, 8, -16, $\underline{\ ?\ }$ **32**
10. 6, $\frac{9}{2}$, 3, $\frac{3}{2}$, 0, $\underline{\ ?\ }$ $-\frac{3}{2}$

State the definition or theorem that proves that quadrilateral *ABCD* is a parallelogram using the given information. (Lesson 6-3)

11. $\overline{AB} \parallel \overline{DC}$ and $\overline{BC} \parallel \overline{AD}$ **Definition of parallelogram**
12. $\overline{BC} \cong \overline{AD}$ and $\overline{BC} \parallel \overline{AD}$ **Theorem 6-6**
13. $\angle ABC \cong \angle ADC$ and $\angle BAD \cong \angle BCD$ **Theorem 6-8**
14. $\overline{OC} \cong \overline{OA}$ and $\overline{DO} \cong \overline{BO}$ **Theorem 6-7**

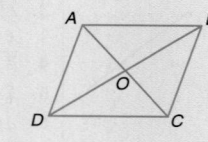

15. Write a two-column proof. **(Lesson 6-4)**

   Given: rectangle $JKLM$
               $\overline{KF} \cong \overline{MH}$
               $\overline{JE} \cong \overline{LG}$

   Prove: $EFGH$ is a parallelogram. **See Solutions Manual.**

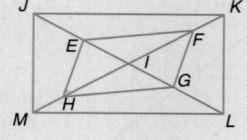

Answers for Mid-Chapter Review

1. $\overline{FE}$; definition of parallelogram
2. $\angle GFE$; Theorem 6-2
3. $\overline{HD}$; Theorem 6-4
4. $\triangle HDG$; Theorem 6-4 and SAS
5. $\overline{FG}$; Theorem 6-1
6. $\overline{HE}$; Definition of parallelogram

LESSON 6-4 RECTANGLES 287

EXTENDING THE LESSON

Math Power: Problem Solving

Given rectangle $LMNP$, $LI = 3x - 2$, $MI = 2x + 3$. Find LN.   **26**

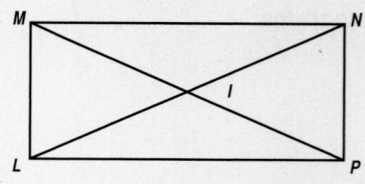

Mid-Chapter Review

The Mid-Chapter Review provides students with a brief review of the concepts and skills in Lessons 6-1 through 6-4. Lesson numbers are given at the end of problems or instruction lines so students may review concepts not yet mastered.

Enrichment Masters Booklet, p. 34

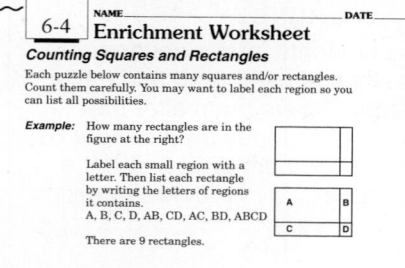

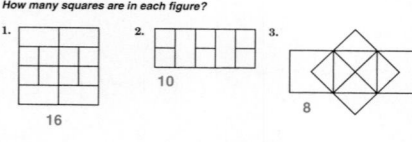

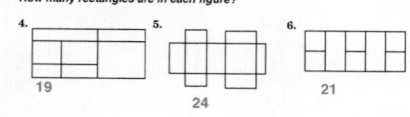

Lesson Resources

- Reteaching Master 6-5
- Practice Master 6-5
- Enrichment Master 6-5
- Evaluation Master, p. 80
- Activity Master, p. 79
- Technology Master, p. 42

 Transparency 6-5 contains the 5-Minute Check and a teaching aid for this lesson.

INTRODUCING THE LESSON

 5-Minute Check

(over Lesson 6-4)

Find the values of *v*, *w*, *x*, *y*, and *z* if *SURE* is a rectangle.

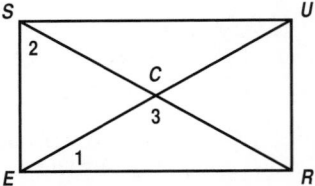

1. $SR = 4v + 2$, $EU = 6v - 8$ 5
2. $EC = 2w + 3$, $CU = 3w - 1$ 4
3. $m\angle 1 = x$, $m\angle 2 = 2x$ 30
4. $UR = 6y - 7$, $SE = 4y - 1$ 3
5. $m\angle 1 = 2z$, $m\angle 3 = 8z$ 15

Motivating the Lesson

Have students form a square from four strips of cardboard and paper fasteners. Have them alter the angles so that they are not right angles. Ask them to describe the new figure.   **It is a parallelogram with four equal sides and is called a rhombus.**

Objectives

6-5A
6-5B

After studying this lesson, you should be able to:
- recognize the properties of squares and rhombi, and
- use properties of squares and rhombi in proofs.

Application

Rhombi is the plural of rhombus.

The decorative window panes in this window are shaped like **rhombi**. A **rhombus** is a quadrilateral with four congruent sides. Therefore, since the opposite sides are congruent, a rhombus is a parallelogram. Rhombi are often used in designs for floor coverings and in many board games.

A rhombus has all of the properties of a parallelogram. The diagonals of a rhombus have two special relationships that are described in the following theorems.

Theorem 6-10	The diagonals of a rhombus are perpendicular. *You will be asked to prove this theorem in Exercise 36.*
Theorem 6-11	Each diagonal of a rhombus bisects a pair of opposite angles.

Proof of Theorem 6-11

Given: $ABCD$ is a rhombus.

Prove: Each diagonal bisects a pair of opposite angles.

Statements	Reasons
1. $ABCD$ is a rhombus.	1. Given
2. $ABCD$ is a parallelogram.	2. Definition of rhombus
3. $\angle ABC \cong \angle ADC$ $\angle BAD \cong \angle BCD$	3. Opp. $\angle$ of a $\square$ are $\cong$.
4. $\overline{AB} \cong \overline{BC} \cong \overline{CD} \cong \overline{DA}$	4. Definition of rhombus
5. $\triangle ABC \cong \triangle ADC$	5. SAS
6. $\angle 5 \cong \angle 6$ $\angle 7 \cong \angle 8$	6. CPCTC
7. $\triangle BAD \cong \triangle BCD$	7. SAS
8. $\angle 1 \cong \angle 2$ $\angle 3 \cong \angle 4$	8. CPCTC
9. Each diagonal bisects a pair of opposite angles.	9. Definition of angle bisector

288   CHAPTER 6   QUADRILATERALS

ALTERNATE TEACHING STRATEGIES

Using Charts

Have students make a chart that lists all the properties of parallelograms, rectangles, rhombi, and squares. Before they begin, ask them to think about how they will indicate properties that are shared by more than one figure.

Using Logical Reasoning

Ask students to make up four statements like the following that use the words *all* or *some*: "Some rhombi are squares." "All rectangles are parallelograms."

The characteristics of a rhombus can be helpful in solving problems.

Example 1

Use rhombus *RSTV* with *SV* = 42 to determine whether each statement is *true* or *false*. Justify your answers.

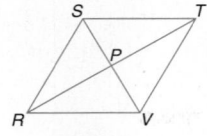

a. $RT = 42$ — generally false; The diagonals of a rhombus are not congruent unless it is a rectangle.

b. $PS = 21$ — true; The diagonals of a parallelogram bisect each other.

c. $\overline{RT} \perp \overline{SV}$ — true; The diagonals of a rhombus are perpendicular.

You can construct a rhombus with a compass and straightedge.

Construct a rhombus.

1. Draw $\overline{AD}$. Set the compass to match the length of $\overline{AD}$. You will use this compass setting for all arcs drawn.

Step 1
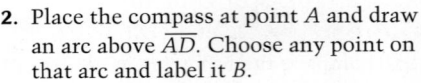

2. Place the compass at point *A* and draw an arc above $\overline{AD}$. Choose any point on that arc and label it *B*.

Step 2
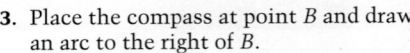

3. Place the compass at point *B* and draw an arc to the right of *B*.

4. Then place the compass at point *D* and draw an arc to intersect the arc drawn from point *B*. Label the point of intersection *C*.

Steps 3-4
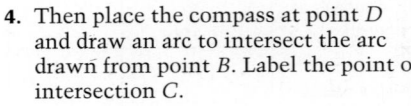

5. Use a straightedge to draw $\overline{AB}$, $\overline{BC}$, and $\overline{CD}$.

Step 5
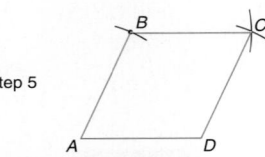

Quadrilateral *ABCD* is a rhombus since all of the sides are congruent.

When a quadrilateral is both a rhombus and a rectangle, it is a **square**. A square is a quadrilateral with four right angles and four congruent sides. You can construct a square in the same way that you constructed a rhombus, but a square must have a right angle.

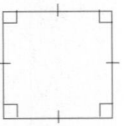

LESSON 6-5   SQUARES AND RHOMBI   289

TEACHING THE LESSON

Teaching Tip   Before reading Example 1, ask students to recall which properties of diagonals are common to all parallelograms, which are common to rectangles, and which are common to rhombi.

Chalkboard Example

For the Example
Use rhombus *DLMP* with *DM* = 26 to determine whether each statement is *true* or *false*. Justify your answers.

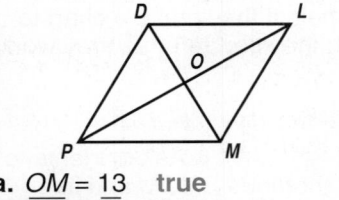

a. $OM = 13$ true
b. $\overline{MD} \cong \overline{PL}$ false
c. $m\angle DLO = m\angle LDO$ false

Teaching Tip   Have a student do the construction at the chalkboard or at the overhead projector so that the class can see each step.

Checking for Understanding

Exercises 1-13 are designed to help you assess students' understanding through reading, writing, speaking, and modeling. You should work through Exercises 1-3 with your students and then monitor their work on Exercises 4-13.

Error Analysis

Students may confuse the properties of parallelograms, rectangles, rhombi, and squares. It may help if they make a chart to which they can refer as they work.

Closing the Lesson

Writing Activity Ask students to copy rhombus *RHOM* and its diagonals.

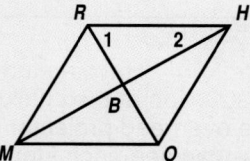

Ask them to describe how they would find the measure of ∠1 if they knew the measure of ∠2. Sample answer: Since △*RHB* is a right triangle, the acute angles are complementary. Therefore, $90 - m\angle 2 = m\angle 1$.

Additional Answers

1. A quadrilateral with four congruent sides has the opposite sides congruent. Since the opposite sides are congruent, it is a parallelogram.
2. Sample answer: Similarities: Both have opposite sides parallel and both have diagonals that bisect each other. Differences: A rhombus has diagonals that are perpendicular, all four sides are congruent, and the diagonals bisect the opposite pairs of angles.

CHECKING FOR UNDERSTANDING

Communicating Mathematics

Read and study the lesson to answer these questions. See margin.

1. A rhombus can be defined as any quadrilateral with four congruent sides. Explain why this definition is equivalent to *A rhombus is a parallelogram with four congruent sides.*

2. Compare a parallelogram and a rhombus. How are they the same? How are they different?

3. Explain the relationship between squares and rhombi. Is every rhombus a square? Is every square a rhombus?

Guided Practice

Determine whether *ABCD* is a parallelogram, rectangle, rhombus, or square. List all that apply. See margin.

4. $A(0, 1)$, $B(2, 0)$, $C(3, 2)$, $D(1, 3)$

5. $A(-1, 0)$, $B(1, 0)$, $C(3, 5)$, $D(1, 5)$

6. $A(-3, 2)$, $B(-3, 8)$, $C(12, 8)$, $D(12, 2)$

7. $A(8, 11)$, $B(2, 3)$, $C(3, 7)$, $D(9, 15)$

8. $A(-1, 8)$, $B(-6, -2)$, $C(5, 0)$, $D(10, 10)$

9. Copy and complete the following table. Determine if each quadrilateral has the given property. Write *yes* or *no*.

	Property	Parallelogram	Rectangle	Rhombus	Square
a.	The diagonals bisect each other.	yes ?	yes ?	yes ?	yes ?
b.	The diagonals are congruent.	no ?	yes ?	no ?	yes ?
c.	Each diagonal bisects a pair of opposite angles.	no ?	no ?	yes ?	yes ?
d.	The diagonals are perpendicular.	no ?	no ?	yes ?	yes ?

Use rhombus *BCDE* and the given information to solve each problem.

10. If $m\angle EBC = 132.6$, find $m\angle EBD$. 66.3

11. If $m\angle BDC = 25.9$, find $m\angle EDC$. 51.8

12. If $m\angle BEC = 2x + 10$ and $m\angle CED = 5x - 20$, find x. 10

13. If $m\angle CBD = 2x + 24$ and $m\angle EBD = x^2$, find x. 6 or -4

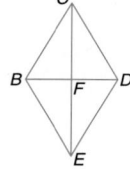

Additional Answers

3. A square is a rhombus that is also a rectangle. A rhombus is not always a square, but a square is always a rhombus.
4. square, rectangle, rhombus, parallelogram
5. parallelogram
6. rectangle, parallelogram
7. parallelogram

8. rhombus, parallelogram
14. rectangle, square
15. parallelogram, rectangle, rhombus, square
16. rhombus, square
17. parallelogram, rectangle, rhombus, square
18. square

EXERCISES

Practice

A

Name all the quadrilaterals—parallelogram, rectangle, rhombus, or square—that have each property. **See margin.**

14. All angles are congruent.

15. The opposite sides are parallel.

16. All sides are congruent.

17. The opposite sides are congruent.

18. It is equiangular and equilateral.

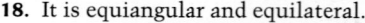

Use rhombus *BEAC* with *BA* = 26 to determine whether each statement is *true* or *false.* **Justify your answers. See margin.**

19. $CE = 26$

20. $HA = 13$

21. $\overline{BA} \perp \overline{EC}$

22. $\triangle BHE \cong \triangle AHC$

23. $m\angle BEH = m\angle EBH$

24. $\angle CBE$ and $\angle BCA$ are supplementary.

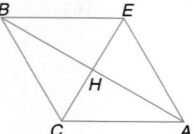

B

Determine whether *EFGH* is a parallelogram, rectangle, rhombus, or square. List all that apply. **See margin.**

25. $E(0, 1)$, $F(2, 0)$, $G(4, 4)$, $H(2, 5)$

26. $E(0, 0)$, $F(4, -3)$, $G(8, 0)$, $H(4, 3)$

27. $E(2, -3)$, $F(-3, 1)$, $G(1, 6)$, $H(6, 2)$

28. $E(0, -4)$, $F(-4, 0)$, $G(0, 4)$, $H(4, 0)$

CONNECTION
Algebra

Use rhombus *IJKL* and the given information to solve each problem. **See margin.**

29. If $m\angle 3 = 62$, find $m\angle 1$, $m\angle 4$, and $m\angle 6$.

30. If $m\angle 3 = 2x + 30$ and $m\angle 4 = 3x - 1$, find x.

31. If $m\angle 3 = 4(x + 1)$ and $m\angle 5 = 2(x + 1)$, find x.

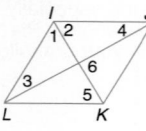

32. If *WXYZ* is a square, find $m\angle ZXY$. **45**

33. *PQMN* is a parallelogram. If $PN = 7x - 10$ and $PQ = 5x + 6$, for what value of x is *PQMN* a rhombus? **8**

34. *ABXY* is a parallelogram. If $AB = 5x + 24$ and $BX = x^2$, for what values of x is *ABXY* a rhombus? **-3 and 8**

A kite is a quadrilateral with exactly two pairs of consecutive sides congruent and no two opposite sides congruent.

35. What conjecture can you make about the diagonals of a kite? Prove your conjecture. **See Solutions Manual.**

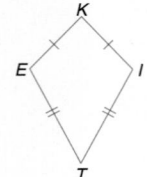

APPLYING THE LESSON

Homework Exercises

Assignment Guide

Basic: 14-31, 38-46
Average: 17-34, 38-46
Enriched: 20-46

Additional Answers

22. True, since the diagonals of a parallelogram bisect each other and all four sides of a rhombus are congruent, the triangles are congruent by SSS.

23. False, the consecutive angles of a rhombus are not congruent unless it is also a square.

24. True, the consecutive angles in a parallelogram are supplementary.

25. parallelogram, rectangle

26. parallelogram, rhombus

27. parallelogram, rectangle, rhombus, square

28. parallelogram, rectangle, rhombus, square

29. $m\angle 1 = 28$, $m\angle 4 = 62$, $m\angle 6 = 90$

30. 31

31. 14

Reteaching Masters Booklet, p. 35

6-5   **Reteaching Worksheet**

NAME _____   DATE _____

Squares and Rhombi

A rhombus is a quadrilateral with four congruent sides. A square is a quadrilateral with four right angles and four congruent sides.

The diagonals of a rhombus have two special relationships:

1. The diagonals of a rhombus are perpendicular.
2. Each diagonal of a rhombus bisects a pair of opposite angles.

Example: *ABCD* is a rhombus. If m∠*ADB* = 27, find m∠*ADC*.

Since each diagonal of a rhombus bisects a pair of opposite angles, m∠*ADC* = 2 (m∠*ADB*). So m∠*ADC* = 2 (27) or 54.

Use rhombus PQRS and the given information to solve each problem.

1. If *ST* = 13, find *SQ*. **26**

2. If m∠*PRS* = 17, find m∠*QRS*. **34**

3. Find m∠*STR*. **90**

4. If *SP* = 4x − 3 and *PQ* = 18 + x, find x. **7**

Determine whether the quadrilateral with the given vertices is a parallelogram, rectangle, rhombus, or square. List all that apply.

5. *M*(1, 5), *N*(6, 5), *O*(6, 10), *P*(1, 10)
   parallelogram, rectangle, rhombus, square

6. *W*(−4, −2), *X*(5, −2), *Y*(8, 4), *Z*(−1, 4)
   parallelogram

7. *D*(−7, 3), *E*(−2, 3), *F*(1, 7), *G*(−4, 7)
   parallelogram, rhombus

8. *R*(0, 0), *E*(10, 0), *S*(10, 5), *T*(0, 5)
   parallelogram, rectangle

T35
Glencoe Division, Macmillan/McGraw-Hill

RETEACHING THE LESSON

Have students draw diagrams to show diagonals of a parallelogram, a rectangle, a rhombus, and a square. Have them mark and discuss congruent sides and angles in each figure.

Additional Answers

19. False, the diagonals of a rhombus are not congruent unless it is also a square.

20. True, the diagonals of a parallelogram bisect each other.

21. True, the diagonals of a rhombus are perpendicular.

Additional Answer

36. Given: *ABCD* is a rhombus.
Prove: *AC* ⊥ *BD*
Statements   (Reasons)
a. *ABCD* is a rhombus.
(Given)
b. $\overline{AB} \cong \overline{BC}$ (Definition of rhombus)
c. $\overline{BD}$ bisects $\overline{AC}$ at *E*. (Diagonals of a ▱ bisect each other)
d. $\overline{AE} \cong \overline{CE}$ (Definition of bisector)
e. $\overline{BE} \cong \overline{BE}$ (Congruence of segments is reflexive)
f. △*ABE* ≅ △*CBE*   (SSS)
g. ∠*BEA* ≅ ∠*BEC*   (CPCTC)
h. ∠*BEA* and ∠*BEC* form a linear pair.   (Definition of linear pair)
i. ∠*BEA* and ∠*BEC* are supplementary   (If two ∠s form a linear pair, they are supp.)
j. m∠*BEA* + m∠*BEC* = 180 (Definition of supp.)
k. m∠*BEA* = m∠*BEC* (Definition of congruent angles)
l. 2m∠*BEA* = 180 (Substitution prop.)
m. m∠*BEA* = 90   (Division prop. of equality)
n. ∠*BEA* is a right angle. (Definition of right angle)
o. $\overline{AC} \perp \overline{BD}$ (Definition of perpendicular)

Practice Masters Booklet, p. 41

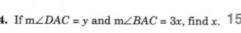
---

36. Write a two-column proof of Theorem 6-10. **See margin.**

37. Write a two-column proof. **See margin.**

Given: *ABCD* is a rhombus.
$\overline{AF} \cong \overline{BG}$
$\overline{BG} \cong \overline{CH}$
$\overline{CH} \cong \overline{DE}$
$\overline{DE} \cong \overline{AF}$

Prove: *EFGH* is a parallelogram.

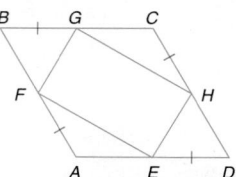

Critical Thinking

38. A line of symmetry for a figure is a line that can be drawn through the figure so that it can be folded along the line and the two halves match exactly. Draw a rhombus. How many lines of symmetry can you find? two - the diagonals

Applications

39. Mechanics   If you change the measures of the angles in a rhombus and the sides remain the same length, the sides will still be parallel. This property is useful in mechanical objects such as the car jack shown at the right. As the crank is turned, the measures of the angles at *A* and *C* become greater and those at *B* and *D* become lesser.

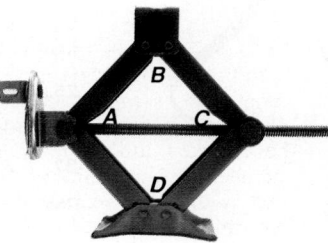

Portfolio
Select one of the constructions or proofs from this chapter that you found especially challenging. Place it in your portfolio.

a. Describe what happens to the diagonals of the rhombus as the crank is turned. *AC* becomes shorter and *BD* becomes longer.

b. What property of a rhombus ensures that the car will remain parallel to the ground as it lifts? Explain. **See margin.**

c. Could a parallelogram that is not a rhombus be used in this car jack? Why or why not? no; See reason for 39b. Since the diagonals of other parallelograms are not perpendicular, the car would remain parallel but the load would shift as the jack was raised.

Mixed Review

40. In rectangle *MNOP*, m∠1 = 32. Find m∠2, m∠3, and m∠4. **(Lesson 6-4)** 32, 58, 58

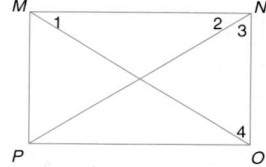

41. *ABCD* is a rectangle. If *AB* = 2x + 5, *CD* = y + 1, *AD* = y + 5, and *BC* = 3x − 4, find the measures of the sides. **(Lesson 6-1)** *AB* = 31, *BC* = 35, *CD* = 31, and *AD* = 35

42. If the sides of a triangle have measures of 3x + 2, 8x + 10, and 5x + 8, find all possible values of x. **(Lesson 5-6)** no solution

292   CHAPTER 6   QUADRILATERALS

Additional Answer

39b. The base of the jack and the plate that supports the car are parallel to the rod between points *A* and *C* and perpendicular to the diagonal $\overline{BD}$.
The diagonals of a rhombus are perpendicular. Changing the lengths of the diagonals doesn't affect the level of the car.

43. Determine whether the figure contains a pair of congruent triangles. Justify your answer. **(Lesson 5-2)** yes; LA or AAS

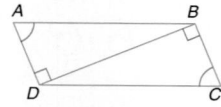

44. What algebraic property allows us to say that if $m\angle 1 = m\angle 2$ and $m\angle 2 = m\angle 3$, then $m\angle 1 = m\angle 3$? **(Lesson 2-4)** Transitive property of equality

45. Is the top of your desk best modeled by a point, a line, or a plane? **(Lesson 1-2)** plane

Wrap-Up **46.** Copy the diagram at the right. Label the regions quadrilaterals, parallelograms, rhombi, rectangles, and squares to show the relationships among the figures.

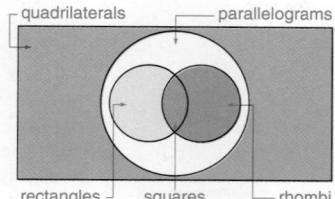

HISTORY CONNECTION

In India, geometry is used to expand the Hindu temples in a way that reflects a person's growth. During each stage of development, a body grows but remains similar to the earlier form. The temples are built beginning with the altar and then each stage of expansion adds to the structure.

When the temples are expanded, the expansion is a *gnomon*. A gnomon is any figure which when added to another figure leaves the new figure **similar** to the original. Similar figures have the same shape and a different size. For example, if a temple begins with a square altar, each consecutive step would add a shape that makes the temple into a larger square.

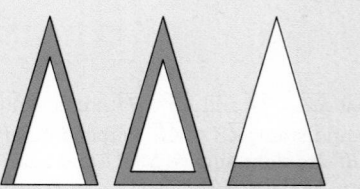

Three different ways of expanding a triangle with a gnomon.

The floor plan of a Hindu temple.

LESSON 6-5   SQUARES AND RHOMBI   293

EXTENDING THE LESSON

Math Power: Connections

A device called a pantograph is used to copy, enlarge, or reduce images. Thomas Jefferson used one at Monticello to make copies of his letters. Have students investigate pantographs and what mathematical properties are at work in the device. The pantograph creates similar figures by using congruent angles formed in parallelograms.

History Connection

The History Connection features introduce students to persons or cultures who were involved in the development of mathematics. You may want students to further research Hindu architecture or Hindu contributions to geometry.

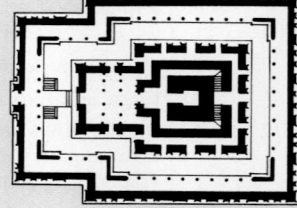

Lesson Resources

- Reteaching Master 6-6
- Practice Master 6-6
- Enrichment Master 6-6
- Evaluation Master, p. 80
- Activity Master, p. 6
- Technology Master, p. 6

 Transparency 6-6 contains the 5-Minute Check and a teaching aid for this lesson.

INTRODUCING THE LESSON

 5-Minute Check

(over Lesson 6-5)

Using P for parallelogram, R for rectangle, S for square, and Rh for rhombus, write the letters of all the quadrilaterals that have these properties.

1. perpendicular diagonals   S, Rh
2. diagonals that bisect each other   P, R, S, Rh
3. congruent diagonals   R, S
4. two pairs of congruent opposite angles   P, R, S, Rh
5. supplementary consecutive angles   P, R, S, Rh
6. diagonals that bisect opposite angles   S, Rh
7. four right angles   R, S
8. two pairs of opposite parallel sides   P, R, S, Rh

Motivating the Lesson

Ask each student to draw four quadrilaterals that are not parallelograms. Have students compare their examples and determine if any of them have special names.   Sample answers: trapezoid, kite

---

6-6   Trapezoids

Objectives

6-6A
6-6B

After studying this lesson, you should be able to:
- recognize the properties of trapezoids, and
- use the properties of trapezoids in proofs and other problems.

Application

Frank Lloyd Wright was one of the most influential American architects. He created the prairie style of homes to harmonize with the landscape. This style emphasizes horizontal lines and natural materials because Wright thought a building should "grow" from its site. The faces of the roof of the prairie style home shown at the right are shaped like **trapezoids**.

INVESTIGATION

You can learn more about trapezoids in Investigation 8 on pages A7–A8.

A trapezoid is a quadrilateral with exactly one pair of parallel sides. The parallel sides are called **bases**, and the nonparallel sides are called **legs**. ∠A and ∠D and ∠B and ∠C are pairs of **base angles**.

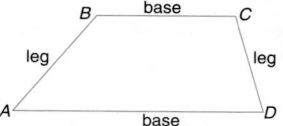

A trapezoid is an **isosceles trapezoid** if its legs are congruent. You can fold an isosceles trapezoid so that the legs coincide. What do you think is true about the base angles?

Theorem 6-12	Both pairs of base angles of an isosceles trapezoid are congruent.

Proof of Theorem 6-12

Given: $TRAP$ is an isosceles trapezoid.
$\overline{RA} \parallel \overline{TP}$
$\overline{TR} \cong \overline{PA}$

Prove: $\angle T \cong \angle P$
$\angle TRA \cong \angle PAR$

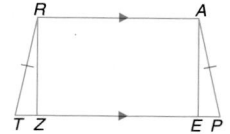

Paragraph proof:

Draw auxiliary segments so that $\overline{RZ} \perp \overline{TP}$ and $\overline{AE} \perp \overline{TP}$. Since $\overline{RA} \parallel \overline{TP}$ and parallel lines are everywhere equidistant, $\overline{RZ} \cong \overline{AE}$. Perpendicular lines form right angles, so $\angle RZT$ and $\angle AEP$ are right angles. $\triangle RZT$ and $\triangle AEP$ are right triangles by definition. Therefore, $\triangle RZT \cong \triangle AEP$ by HL. $\angle T \cong \angle P$ by CPCTC.

Since $\angle ARZ$ and $\angle RAE$ are right angles and all right angles are congruent, $\angle ARZ \cong \angle RAE$. $\angle TRZ \cong \angle PAE$ by CPCTC. So $\angle TRA \cong \angle PAR$ by angle addition.

ALTERNATE TEACHING STRATEGIES

Using Communication

Have students draw labeled diagrams to illustrate each theorem in this lesson.

Using Investigation

You can guide students to discover that in an isosceles trapezoid the base angles are congruent and the diagonals are congruent. In Investigation 8 on pages A7 and A8 of **More Investigations in Geometry,** students use measurement and construction to explore trapezoids.

Isosceles trapezoids have another unique property.

| Theorem 6-13 | **The diagonals of an isosceles trapezoid are congruent.**
You will be asked to prove this theorem in Exercise 28. |

The **median** of a trapezoid is the segment that joins the midpoints of the legs. The median has a special relationship to the bases. Draw a trapezoid and measure the bases and the median. What is their relationship?

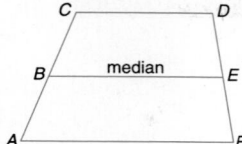

| Theorem 6-14 | **The median of a trapezoid is parallel to the bases and its measure is one half the sum of the measures of the bases.** |

You can use the lengths of the bases to find the length of the median.

Example 1

CONNECTION
Algebra

Find the length of the median $\overline{QR}$ of trapezoid *MNOP* with vertices *M*(2, -9), *N*(-1, 1), *O*(3, 8), and *P*(10, 5).

First, graph the trapezoid to find the bases.

$\overline{NO}$ and $\overline{MP}$ are the bases. Now use the distance formula to find *NO* and *MP*.

$$NO = \sqrt{(-1-3)^2 + (1-8)^2}$$
$$= \sqrt{65}$$

$$MP = \sqrt{(2-10)^2 + (-9-5)^2}$$
$$= \sqrt{260}$$

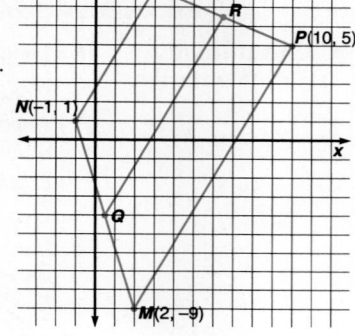

According to Theorem 6-14, the length of the median is half of the sum of the lengths of the bases, so $QR = \frac{1}{2}(NO + MP)$.

$$QR = \frac{1}{2}(NO + MP)$$
$$= \frac{1}{2}\left(\sqrt{65} + \sqrt{260}\right) \quad \text{\textit{Use your calculator.}}$$
$$\approx 12.09$$

The length of the median is approximately 12 units.
Check by finding the coordinates of the midpoints and then applying the distance formula.

Teaching Tip Point out that Theorems 6-12 and 6-13 apply only to isosceles trapezoids, while Theorem 6-14 applies to all trapezoids.

Teaching Tip After reading Theorem 6-14, have students draw a few examples of trapezoids on grid or dot paper in such a way that it is easy to count to find the lengths of the bases and median.

Chalkboard Example

For Example 1
Find the length of the median of a trapezoid with vertices *M*(0, 0), *A*(0, 3), *T*(4, 4), and *H*(4, −1).
Graph the trapezoid to find the measures of the bases.

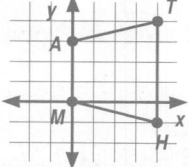

$MA = \sqrt{(0-0)^2 + (3-0)^2} = \sqrt{9} = 3$
$TH = \sqrt{(4-4)^2 + (4-(-1))^2} = \sqrt{25} = 5$
$\text{median} = \frac{3+5}{2} = 4$

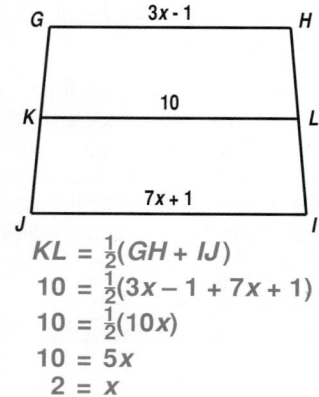
The length of the median can be used to find the lengths of the bases.

Example 2

Given trapezoid *ABCD* with median $\overline{EF}$, find the value of *x*.

EF is half the sum of *AB* and *DC*, so we can write the following equation.

$$EF = \tfrac{1}{2}(AB + DC)$$
$$21 = \tfrac{1}{2}(3x + 4 + 5x - 2) \qquad Substitution$$
$$21 = \tfrac{1}{2}(8x + 2)$$
$$21 = 4x + 1$$
$$20 = 4x$$
$$5 = x$$

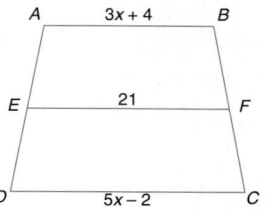

The value of *x* is 5.
Check: Is the sum of the measures of the bases twice the measure of the median?

CHECKING FOR UNDERSTANDING

Communicating Mathematics

Read and study the lesson to answer these questions.

1. Draw a trapezoid with each set of characteristics. **See margin.**
   a. both bases are shorter than the legs
   b. contains a right angle
   c. has two obtuse angles

2. Draw an isosceles trapezoid and label the legs and the bases. **See margin.**

3. If the measure of the median of a trapezoid is 15, what could the measures of the bases be? Explain. **Any two positive numbers whose sum is 30; The sum of the measures of the bases is twice the measure of the median.**

Guided Practice

ABCD is an isosceles trapezoid with bases $\overline{AD}$ and $\overline{BC}$. Use the figure and the given information to solve each problem.

4. If *BA* = 9, find *CD*. **9**
5. If *AC* = 21, find *BD*. **21**
6. If *AC* = 4*y* − 5 and *BD* = 2*y* + 3, find *AC* and *BD*. **11**
7. If *m∠BAD* = 123, find *m∠CBA*. **57**
8. If *m∠ADC* = 105, find *m∠DAB*. **105**

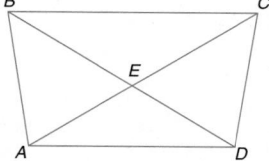

9. Find the length of the median of a trapezoid with vertices at (1, 0), (3, -1), (6, 2), and (7, 6). $\frac{9\sqrt{2}}{2} \approx$ **6.364 units**

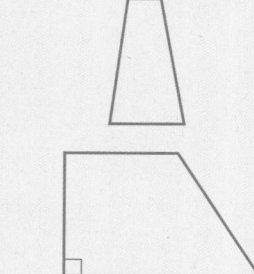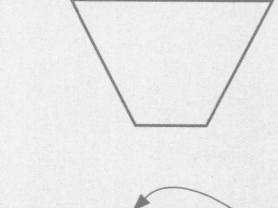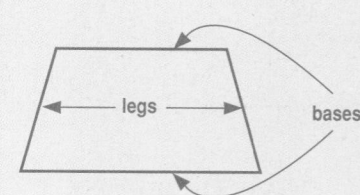

Find the value of x.

10.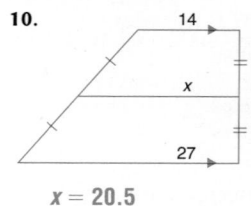
$x = 20.5$

11.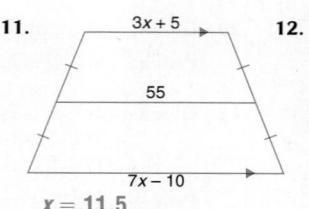
$x = 11.5$

12.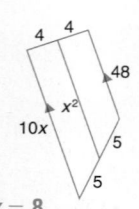
$x = 8$

EXERCISES

Practice

A

If possible, draw a trapezoid that has the following characteristics. If the trapezoid cannot be drawn, explain why. **See margin.**

13. three congruent sides

14. congruent bases

15. a leg longer than both bases

16. bisecting diagonals

17. two right angles

18. four acute angles

19. one pair of opposite angles congruent

B

PQRS is an isosceles trapezoid with bases $\overline{PS}$ and $\overline{QR}$. Use the figure and the given information to solve each problem. **21. 32.1**

20. If $PS = 20$ and $QR = 14$, find TV. **17**

21. If $QR = 14.3$ and $TV = 23.2$, find PS.

22. If $TV = x + 7$ and $PS + QR = 5x + 2$, find x. **4**

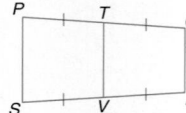

23. If $m\angle RVT = 57$, find $m\angle QTV$. **57**

24. If $m\angle VTP = a$, find $m\angle TPS$ in terms of a. **180 − a**

25. If the measure of the median of an isosceles trapezoid is 4.5, what are the possible integral measures for the bases? **1, 8; 2, 7; 3, 6; 4, 5**

26. $\overline{UR}$ is the median of a trapezoid with bases $\overline{ON}$ and $\overline{TS}$. If the coordinates of the points are $U(1, 3)$, $R(8, 3)$, $O(0, 0)$, and $N(8, 0)$, find the coordinates of T and S. **T(2, 6), S(8, 6)**

27. isosceles trapezoid; Justifications may vary.

27. What type of quadrilateral is *PQRS* if its vertices are $P(1, 3)$, $Q(-3, -1)$, $R(-2, -8)$, and $S(8, 2)$? Justify your answer.

28. Write a paragraph proof of Theorem 6-13. **See Solutions Manual.**

LESSON 6-6   TRAPEZOIDS   297

RETEACHING THE LESSON

Draw this trapezoid on the chalkboard or overhead projector. Find the missing measures with students.

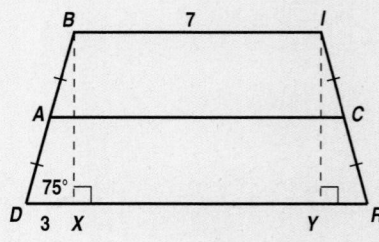

1. $m\angle IRD$ **75** **2.** YR **3**
3. DR **13** **4.** AC **10**

Additional Answer

13.

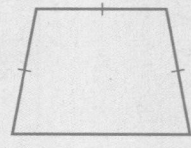

 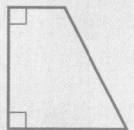
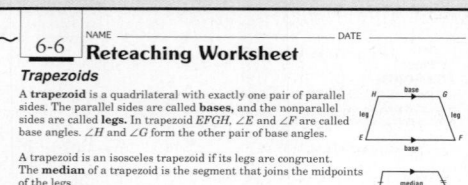

Write a two-column proof. See margin.

29. **Given:** Trapezoid *RSPT* is isosceles.
    Prove: △*RSQ* is isosceles.

30. **Given:** △*SQR* is isosceles.
    △*PQT* is isosceles.
    $\overline{TP} \parallel \overline{RS}$
    Prove: *RSPT* is an isosceles trapezoid.

31. In the figure at the right, *P* is a point not in plane 𝒜 and △*XYZ* is an equilateral triangle in plane 𝒜. Plane ℬ is parallel to plane 𝒜 and intersects $\overline{PX}$, $\overline{PY}$, and $\overline{PZ}$ in points *J*, *I*, and *K* respectively.

   a. How many trapezoids are formed? Name them. **3; *JKZX*, *IJXY*, *IKZY***

   b. If the trapezoids are isosceles, are they congruent? Justify your answer. **See margin.**

   c. Where could *P* be if none of the trapezoids are congruent? **Answers may vary.**

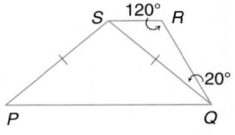

Critical Thinking

32. The figure at the right is a trapezoid with bases $\overline{SR}$ and $\overline{PQ}$. *PS* = *QS*, m∠*SRQ* = 120, and m∠*RQS* = 20. Find the measure of ∠*PSQ*. **100**

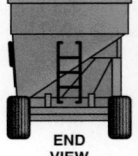

Applications

33. **Agriculture** Farmers use a gravity grain box to transport grain to a storage bin or grain elevator. The side and end views of a gravity grain box are shown below.

   a. Copy each view and label the vertices of the quadrilaterals. Describe each quadrilateral. **See margin.**
   b. Are any of the trapezoids on the grain box congruent? **See margin.**

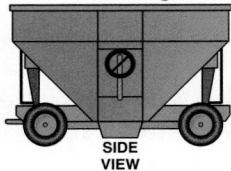

Additional Answers

31b. Yes: The bases and legs must be congruent if they are isosceles.

33a.

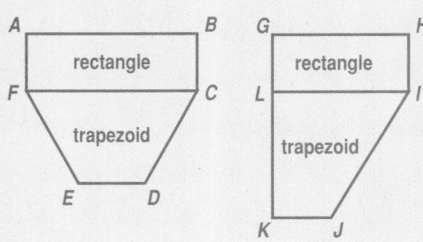

33b. Yes: *LIJK* from the end view is congruent to the trapezoid on the other end of the box.

34. Real Estate A land developer bought a parcel of land for building new homes. A scale drawing of the lots into which the land will be divided is shown at the right. $\overline{BG}$ and $\overline{CF}$ are the medians of trapezoids $ADEH$ and $BDEG$ respectively. If $c = 81$, find a, b, d, and e.
$a = 162$, $b = 81$, $d = 125$, $e = 137.5$

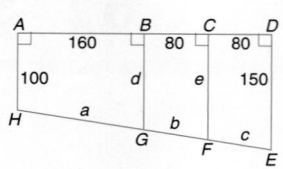

Computer

35. The BASIC computer program given below will find the measure of the median of a trapezoid $ABCD$ with legs $\overline{AB}$ and $\overline{CD}$.

```
10 INPUT "ENTER THE COORDINATES OF A"; X1, Y1
20 INPUT "ENTER THE COORDINATES OF B"; X2, Y2
30 INPUT "ENTER THE COORDINATES OF C"; X3, Y3
40 INPUT "ENTER THE COORDINATES OF D"; X4, Y4
50 X5 = (X1 + X2)/2
60 Y5 = (Y1 + Y2)/2
70 X6 = (X3 + X4)/2
80 Y6 = (Y3 + Y4)/2
90 M = SQR ((X5 - X6)^2 + (Y5 - Y6)^2)
100 PRINT "THE MEASURE OF THE MEDIAN IS "; M; "."
110 END
```

Use the program to find the measure of the median of the trapezoid with the given vertices. Round your answers to the nearest hundredth.

a. $A(3, 5)$, $B(-1, 3)$, $C(7, 5)$, $D(7, 6)$ **6.18**

b. $A(-1, 7)$, $B(8, 8)$, $C(2, 10)$, $D(-4, 8)$ **4.74**

Mixed Review

36. Determine if the statement *If a quadrilateral has all four sides congruent, then it is a square* is *true* or *false*. If false, give a counter-example. **(Lesson 6-5)** false; any rhombus that is not a square

37. Find the value of x if $\ell \parallel m$. **(Lesson 3-3)** 30

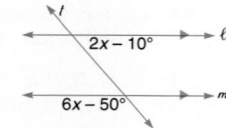

38. Determine if statement (3) follows from statements (1) and (2) by the law of detachment or the law of syllogism. If it does, state which law was used. **(Lesson 2-3)** yes; detachment

(1) If a quadrilateral has exactly two opposite sides parallel, then it is a trapezoid.

(2) $ABCD$ has exactly two opposite sides parallel.

(3) $ABCD$ is a trapezoid.

39. If $\angle B \cong \angle L$, $m\angle B = 7x + 29$, and $m\angle L = 9x - 1$, is $\angle B$ acute, right, or obtuse? **(Lesson 1-7)** obtuse

Wrap-Up

40. Journal Entry Write a few sentences about the differences and similarities between trapezoids and parallelograms in your journal. See students' work.

EXTENDING THE LESSON

Three vertices of a trapezoid *TWIN* are $T(-2, 3)$, $W(2, 3)$, and $I(6, -1)$. Find the coordinates of N if the coordinates of the endpoints of the median are $(-2, 1)$ and $(4, 1)$.
$N(-2, -1)$

Enrichment Masters Booklet, p. 36

6 | SUMMARY AND REVIEW

VOCABULARY

Upon completing this chapter, you should be familiar with the following terms:

base	**294**	**266**	quadrilateral
base angle	**294**	**282**	rectangle
diagonal	**266**	**288**	rhombus
isosceles trapezoid	**294**	**266**	sides
leg	**294**	**289**	square
median	**295**	**294**	trapezoid
polygon	**266**	**266**	vertices
parallelogram	**266**		

SKILLS AND CONCEPTS

OBJECTIVES AND EXAMPLES	REVIEW EXERCISES

Upon completing this chapter, you should be able to:

- recognize, use, and prove the properties of a parallelogram. **(Lesson 6-1)**

In $\square MNOP$, if $PQ = 8x - 16$ and $QN = 2x + 8$, find PN.

Since the diagonals of a parallelogram bisect each other, $PQ = QN$.

$$PQ = QN$$
$$8x - 16 = 2x + 8$$
$$6x = 24$$
$$x = 4$$

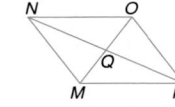

Now substitute 4 for x to find either PQ or QN.

$$PQ = 8(4) - 16 \text{ or } 16$$

$$PN = 2(PQ) \text{ or } 32$$

Use these exercises to review and prepare for the chapter test.

Complete each statement about parallelogram ABCD below. Then name the theorem or postulate that justifies your answer.

1. $\overline{BE} \cong \underline{\ ?\ } \overline{ED}$; Th. 6-4
2. $\overline{AB} \cong \underline{\ ?\ } \overline{DC}$; Th. 6-1
3. $\angle ADC \cong \underline{\ ?\ }$
4. $\overline{BC} \parallel \underline{\ ?\ }$
5. $\triangle BCD \cong \underline{\ ?\ }$
6. $\angle 1 \cong \underline{\ ?\ } \angle 2$; Th. 3-1
7. $\overline{CE} \cong \underline{\ ?\ } \overline{EA}$; Th. 6-4
8. $\angle ADC$ and $\underline{\ ?\ }$ are supplementary.
   $\angle DCB$ or $\angle DAB$; Th. 6-3
3. $\angle ABC$; Th. 6-2
4. $\overline{AD}$; Definition of $\square$
5. $\triangle DAB$; SAS, or SSS

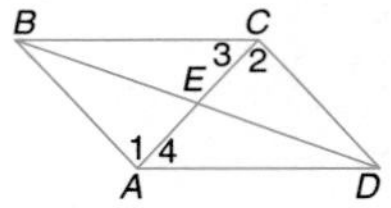

Additional Answers (left margin):

Additional Answers

9. Statements   (Reasons)
   a. $\square\ PRSV, \triangle PQR \cong \triangle STV$ (Given)
   b. $\overline{RS} \cong \overline{PV}$ (Opp. sides of a $\square$ are $\cong$.)
   c. $\overline{QS} \parallel \overline{PT}$ (Definition of parallelogram)
   d. $\overline{QR} \cong \overline{VT}$ (CPCTC)
   e. $QR + RS = QS, PV + VT = PT$ (Segment Addition Postulate)
   f. $QR + RS = PV + VT$ (Addition prop. of equality)
   g. $QS = PT$ (Substitution prop. of equality)
   h. $\overline{QS} \cong \overline{PT}$ (Definition of congruent segments)
   i. Quadrilateral $PQST$ is a parallelogram   (If a pair of opp. sides of a quad. are $\cong$ and $\parallel$, it is a $\square$.)

10. Statements   (Reasons)
    a. $\square PQST, \overline{QR} \cong \overline{TV}$ (Given)
    b. $\overline{QP} \cong \overline{ST}$ (Opp. sides of a $\square$ are $\cong$.)
    c. $\angle Q \cong \angle T$ (Opp. $\angle$s of a $\square$ are $\cong$.)
    d. $\triangle QPR \cong \triangle TSV$ (SAS)
    e. $\overline{PR} \cong \overline{VS}, \angle QRP \cong \angle TVS$ (CPCTC)
    f. $\overline{QS} \parallel \overline{PT}$ (Definition of parallelogram)
    g. $\angle TVS \cong \angle RSV$ (If 2 $\parallel$ lines are cut by a transversal, alt. int. $\angle$s are $\cong$.)

---

h. $\angle QRP \cong \angle RSV$ (Congruence of angles is transitive.)
i. $\overline{PR} \parallel \overline{VS}$ (If 2 lines are cut by a transversal and corr. $\angle$s are $\cong$, the lines are $\parallel$.)
j. Quadrilateral $PRSV$ is a parallelogram.   (If a pair of opp. sides of a quad. are $\cong$ and $\parallel$, it is a $\square$.)

- recognize the conditions that determine if a quadrilateral is a parallelogram. **(Lesson 6-3)**

If $m\angle DFG = 4y + 9$ and $m\angle FDH = 3y + 24$, find the value of y in order for $DFGH$ to be a parallelogram.

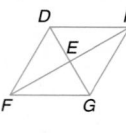

If the consecutive interior angles of a quadrilateral are supplementary, then it is a parallelogram. So, $m\angle DFG + m\angle FDH = 180$.

$$4y + 9 + 3y + 24 = 180$$
$$7y = 147$$
$$y = 21$$

- recognize and use the properties of rectangles. **(Lesson 6-4)**

Properties of a rectangle
- Opposite sides are congruent.
- Opposite angles are congruent.
- Consecutive angles are supplementary.
- Diagonals bisect each other.
- All four angles are right angles.
- Diagonals are congruent.

- recognize and use the properties of squares and rhombi. **(Lesson 6-5)**

$RHOM$ is a rhombus. If $m\angle 1 = 33$, find $m\angle 2$, $m\angle 3$, and $m\angle 4$.

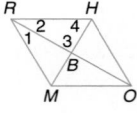

The diagonals of a rhombus bisect a pair of opposite angles, so $\angle 1 \cong \angle 2$. $m\angle 2 = 33$

The diagonals are perpendicular. So $\angle 3$ is a right angle. $m\angle 3 = 90$

In $\triangle HRB$, $m\angle 2 + m\angle 3 + m\angle 4 = 180$. Using substitution, $33 + 90 + m\angle 4 = 180$, so $m\angle 4 = 57$.

Write a two-column proof. See margin.

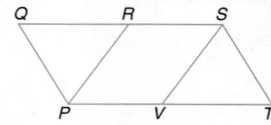
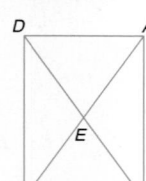

9. **Given:** $\square PRSV$
   $\triangle PQR \cong \triangle STV$
   Prove: Quadrilateral $PQST$ is a parallelogram.

10. **Given:** $\square PQST$
    $\overline{QR} \cong \overline{TV}$
    Prove: Quadrilateral $PRSV$ is a parallelogram.

If $ABCD$ is a rectangle, find the value of x.

11. $DB = 5x - 4$
    $AC = 6x - 10$ **6**
12. $m\angle DAC = 12x + 1$
    $m\angle CAB = 6x - 1$ **5**
13. $EB = 8x + 4$
    $AC = 24x - 8$ **2**
14. $AB = x^2$
    $DC = 3x - 2$ **1 or 2**
15. $m\angle BCD = 10x^2$
    $m\angle CDA = 9x^2 + 9$ **3 or -3**

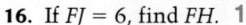

Use rhombus $FGHI$ and the given information to solve each problem.

16. If $FJ = 6$, find FH. **12**
17. If $m\angle FGJ = 23$, find $m\angle FGH$. **46**
18. Find $m\angle IJF$. **90**
19. If $HG = 4x - 1$ and $FG = 20 + x$, find x. **7**

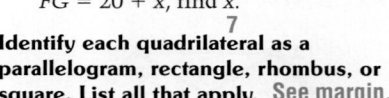

Identify each quadrilateral as a parallelogram, rectangle, rhombus, or square. List all that apply. See margin.

20. $K(2, 3)$, $L(7, 3)$, $M(5, 0)$, $N(0, 0)$
21. $P(0, 9)$, $Q(-2, 1)$, $R(2, 0)$, $S(4, 8)$
22. $T(0, 0)$, $U(6, 6)$, $V(12, 0)$, $W(6, -6)$

Additional Answers

20. parallelogram
21. rectangle, parallelogram
22. square, rhombus, rectangle, parallelogram

A two-page Cumulative Review from the *Evaluation Masters* is shown below. It can be used to review skills and concepts presented thus far in the text. Standardized Test Practice Questions are also provided in the *Evaluation Masters*.

Evaluation Masters, pp. 81-82

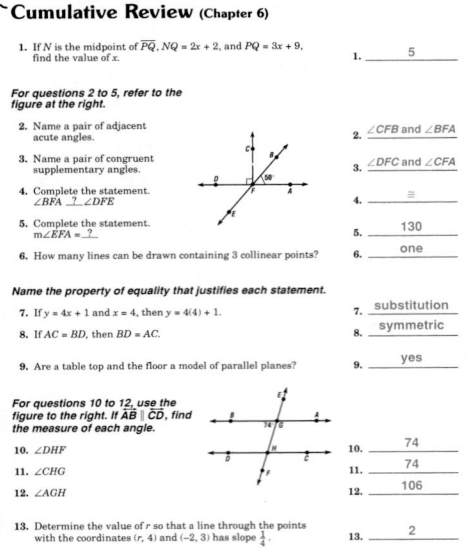

OBJECTIVES AND EXAMPLES	REVIEW EXERCISES

■ recognize and use the properties of trapezoids. **(Lesson 6-6)**

Find the measures of the numbered angles.

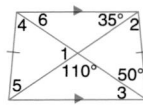

$m\angle 1 = 70 \qquad m\angle 2 = 60$
$m\angle 3 = 35 \qquad m\angle 4 = 60$
$m\angle 5 = 50 \qquad m\angle 6 = 35$

RSTW is a trapezoid with bases $\overline{RS}$ and $\overline{TW}$. Use the figure and the given information to solve each problem.

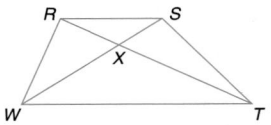

23. If $m\angle SRX = 35$, find $m\angle RTW$. **35**
24. If $m\angle RSW = 45$, find $m\angle TWS$. **45**
25. If $m\angle RTW = 47$, find $m\angle SRT$. **47**
26. If $RS = 23$ and $TW = 19$, find the measure of the median of $RSTW$. **21**
27. If $m\angle XTW = 23$ and $m\angle SXR = 127$, find $m\angle XWT$. **30**

APPLICATIONS AND CONNECTIONS

28. **Business** Jason is stacking cans of juice in a pyramid at the end of a grocery aisle. The base of the pyramid is a single row of cans and each row has one can less than the one below it. If each can is 12 centimeters tall, what is the minimum number of cans Jason could use to build a pyramid 120 centimeters tall? **(Lesson 6-2)** **55**

30. **Construction** A diagram of a bridge support is shown below. The support is an isosceles trapezoid and the cross-pieces, $\overline{AG}$ and $\overline{BG}$ are congruent. Find $m\angle ADF$. **(Lesson 6-6)** **50**

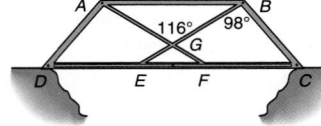

29. **Art** Tami is constructing a frame for her art project. She has two 12-inch pieces of framing material and two 16-inch pieces. If Tami cuts the ends of each piece at a 45° angle and places the congruent pieces on the opposite sides, will the frame be a rectangle? Explain. **(Lesson 6-4)** See margin.

Additional Answer

29. Yes; The corners will each have a 90° angle.

Complete each statement about parallelogram *DHGF* at the right. Then name the theorem or postulate that justifies your answer.

1. $\overline{DE} \cong \underline{\ ?\ } \ \overline{EG}$; Th. 6-4   2. $\angle FDH \cong \underline{\ ?\ } \ \angle FGH$; Th. 6-2

3. $\overline{FD} \parallel \underline{\ ?\ } \ \overline{GH}$; def. of $\square$ 4. $\triangle FDG \cong \underline{\ ?\ } \ \triangle HGD$; SAS

5. If *DHGF* is a rhombus, then $\overline{DG} \perp \underline{\ ?\ }$. $\overline{FH}$; Th. 6-10

6. If *DHGF* is a rhombus, then $\overline{DG}$ bisects $\underline{\ ?\ }$ and $\underline{\ ?\ }$.
   $\angle FDH$ and $\angle FGH$; Th. 6-11

7. The sequence 1, 1, 2, 3, 5, 8, . . . is called the *Fibonacci sequence*. Find the next four numbers in the pattern. **13, 21, 34, 55**

Determine whether *ABCD* is a parallelogram. Explain. **See Solutions Manual.**

8. $A(-2, 6)$, $B(2, 11)$, $C(3, 8)$, $D(-1, 3)$ 9. $A(-3, 7)$, $B(3, 2)$, $C(0, -1)$, $D(-6, 3)$

10. $A(7, -3)$, $B(4, -2)$, $C(6, 4)$, $D(12, 2)$ 11. $A(11, 3)$, $B(4, 2)$, $C(1, -2)$, $D(8, -1)$

Determine if each statement is *true* or *false*. If false, draw a counterexample.
See Solutions Manual for drawings.

12. If a quadrilateral has four right angles, then it is a rectangle. **true**

13. If the diagonals of a quadrilateral are perpendicular, then it is a rhombus. **false**

14. If a quadrilateral has all four sides congruent, then it is a square. **false**

15. If a quadrilateral has opposite sides congruent and one right angle, then it is a rectangle.
    true

PQRS is an isosceles trapezoid with bases $\overline{QR}$ and $\overline{PS}$. Use the figure and the given information to solve each problem.

16. If $PS = 32$ and $TV = 26$, find QR. **20**

17. If $PT = 18$, find VR. **18**

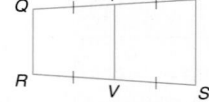

18. If $m\angle QTV = 79$, find $m\angle TVS$. **101**

19. If $QR = 9x$ and $PS = 13x$, find TV. **11x**

20. If $QR = x - 3$, $PS = 2x + 4$, and $TV = 3x - 10$, find QR, PS, and TV.
    $QR = 4$, $PS = 18$, $TV = 11$

Bonus

Given: $\square LMNP$
          $\overline{MP} \perp \overline{LN}$

Prove: *LMNP* is a rhombus. **See Solutions Manual.**

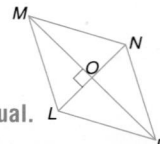

Using the Chapter Test

This page may be used as a test or as a review. In addition, two multiple-choice tests (Forms 1A and 1B) and two free-response tests (Forms 2A and 2B) are provided in the *Evaluation Masters*. Chapter 6 Test, Form 1A is shown below.

Evaluation Masters, pp. 71-72

NAME _____ DATE _____
Chapter 6 Test, Form 1A

Write the letter for the correct answer in the blank at the right of each problem.

1. If *ABCD* is a parallelogram, $m\angle A = x$, and $m\angle D = 2x - 3$, find the value of *x*.
   A. 3   B. 31   C. 61   D. 121   1. __C__

2. *XYZW* is a parallelogram with diagonals $\overline{XZ}$ and $\overline{YW}$ that intersect at point A. If $XA = 3m$, $ZA = 5m - 4$, and $YW = 10m$, find $\overline{WA}$.
   A. 2   B. 5   C. 10   D. 20   2. __C__

3. Opposite angles are always congruent in a(n)
   A. trapezoid.   B. quadrilateral.
   C. isosceles trapezoid.   D. parallelogram.   3. __D__

4. Find the next number in the pattern 8, 7, 9, 8, 10, 9, 11, __?__.
   A. 9   B. 10   C. 11   D. 12   4. __B__

5. One way to prove a quadrilateral is a parallelogram is to show that
   A. it has one pair of congruent sides.
   B. it has one pair of parallel sides.
   C. the diagonals bisect each other.
   D. the diagonals are congruent.   5. __C__

For questions 6 to 9, use parallelogram ACFG.

6. If $m\angle GAC = 112$, find $m\angle ACF$.
   A. 22   B. 68
   C. 112   D. 158   6. __B__

7. If $m\angle CAG = a + 20$ and $m\angle AGF = 2a + 10$, find $m\angle ACF$.
   A. 110   B. 70
   C. 50   D. 20   7. __A__

8. If $AG = 2x + 10$ and $CF = 5x - 2$, find *x*.
   A. $\frac{12}{7}$ B. $\frac{8}{7}$
   C. $\frac{8}{3}$ D. 4   8. __D__

9. If $AX = 4y + 3$ and $XF = 2y + 7$, find *y*.
   A. $\frac{5}{3}$ B. $\frac{2}{3}$
   C. $\frac{5}{3}$ D. $\frac{2}{3}$ 9. __B__

10. Not all rectangles have
    A. diagonals that bisect each other.
    B. diagonals that are congruent.
    C. four congruent sides.
    D. consecutive angles that are supplementary.   10. __C__

71
Glencoe Division, Macmillan/McGraw-Hill

NAME _____ DATE _____
Chapter 6 Test, Form 1A (continued)

For questions 11 to 14, use rectangle RSTU.

11. Which of the following are *not* congruent in *RSTU*?
    A. diagonals   B. all sides
    C. all angles   D. none of the above   11. __B__

12. If $m\angle 1 = 62$, find $m\angle 2$.
    A. 59   B. 31
    C. 28   D. 14   12. __C__

13. If $RX = 2y + 2x$, $XT = 3y - 1$, and $US = 28$, find the values of *x* and *y*.
    A. $x = 5$, $y = 2$ B. $x = 2$, $y = 5$
    C. $x = 4$, $y = 9$ D. $x = 9$, $y = 4$ 13. __B__

14. If $RS = 20$, $UT = x + 10$, $RU = y + 3$, and $ST = 15$, find the values of *x* and *y*.
    A. $x = 10$, $y = 12$ B. $x = 30$, $y = 18$
    C. $x = 5$, $y = 17$ D. $x = 23$, $y = 25$ 14. __A__

15. Diagonals are always perpendicular in a
    A. rectangle.   B. parallelogram.
    C. trapezoid.   D. rhombus.   15. __D__

16. A rhombus is *not* a
    A. polygon.   B. parallelogram.
    C. trapezoid.   D. quadrilateral.   16. __C__

17. If *DEFG* is a square, find $m\angle DEG$.
    A. 30   B. 45
    C. 60   D. 90   17. __B__

18. The measures of the bases of a trapezoid are 14 and 20. What is the measure of the median of this trapezoid?
    A. 17   B. 24
    C. 34   D. 68   18. __A__

19. *MNOP* is an isosceles trapezoid with $\overline{NO} \parallel \overline{MP}$. If $m\angle M = 2x$ and $m\angle P = x + 27$, find the value of *x*.
    A. 69   B. 51
    C. 27   D. 9   19. __C__

20. If *QRST* is an isosceles trapezoid, then which statement is true?
    A. $QS = RT$ B. $QS < RT$
    C. $QS > RT$ D. $QS = RT$ 20. __D__

Bonus

To construct a rhombus given the diagonals, you must first find the
A. midpoint of the diagonals.
B. length of the sides.
C. measure of all angles.
D. length of one diagonal.   Bonus __A__

72
Glencoe Division, Macmillan/McGraw-Hill

Test and Review Generator software is provided in Apple, IBM, and Macintosh versions. You may use this software to create your own tests or worksheets, based on the needs of your students.

The **Performance Assessment Booklet** provides an alternate assessment for evaluating student progress. An assessment for this chapter can be found on pages 11-12.

College Entrance Exam Preview

The questions on these pages involve comparing two quantities, one in Column A and one in Column B. In certain questions, information related to one or both quantities is centered above them.

Directions:
Write A if the quantity in Column A is greater. Write B if the quantity in Column B is greater. Write C if the quantities are equal. Write D if there is not enough information to determine the relationship.

Column A	Column B

1. B

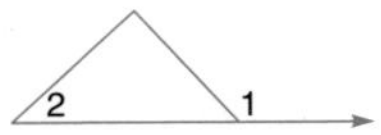

$m\angle 2$ — $m\angle 1$

2. A

$$0 < x < 1$$

$2x$ — x^2

3. C

a, b, and c are positive integers.

$\dfrac{a+b+c}{3}$ — the average of a, b, and c

4. A

$$y \neq 3$$

$2y + 1$ — $\dfrac{y^2 - 3y}{\frac{1}{2}(y-3)}$

5. D

In $\triangle ABC$, $m\angle A > m\angle B$ and $m\angle A > m\angle C$.

AC — AB

6. C

$$\ell \parallel m$$

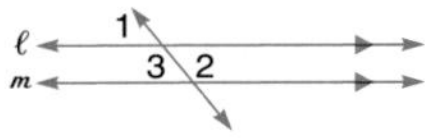

$m\angle 2 + m\angle 3 - m\angle 1$ — $m\angle 2$

Column A	Column B

7. C

The sum of the integers from 1 to 20 — 210

8. B

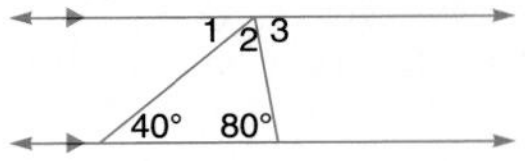

$m\angle 1$ — $m\angle 2$

9. D

$$a > 0$$

$\dfrac{1}{a}$ — a

10. D

$$x > y$$

$|x|$ — $|y|$

11. A

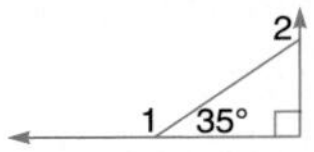

$m\angle 1$ — $m\angle 2$

12. B

$$r > 0$$
$$s < 0$$

$r + s$ — $r - s$

13. A

$$a^\star = a^3 - 1$$

$5^\star$ — $(-5)^\star$

14. B

10^{10} — $10^{11} - 10^{10}$

15. A

The largest prime factor of 858 — The largest prime factor of 2310

16. C

$$3x - 4y = -2$$
$$4x + 2y = 12$$

x — y

Solve each of the following. You may use a calculator.

17. Express the quotient $4,000,000 \div 6400$ in decimal and scientific notation.
    625; 6.25×10^2

18. Line p is parallel to line t, and lines ℓ and m intersect at point P on line t. If $\angle 1$ measures 80° and $\angle 2$ measures 30°, find the degree measure of $\angle 3$.

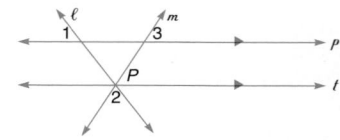

    70°

19. Write the equation of the line that passes through the points $(9, 7)$ and $(-3, 5)$ in standard form.
    $x - 6y = -33$

20. A person's optimal heart rate for exercising, h, is determined by subtracting their age, a, from 220 and then taking 75% of the result. Write a formula to represent this relation.
    $h = 0.75(220 - a)$

21. How many units apart are the points $(-11, 2)$ and $(6, 4)$ in the coordinate plane?
    $\sqrt{293} \approx 17.1$ units

22. Use the formula $d = st$ where d represents distance in miles, s represents speed in miles per hour, and t represents time in hours, to find the speed of a race car if it travels 5 miles in 2 minutes and 30 seconds. **120 mph**

TEST-TAKING TIP

Quantitative Comparisons

Even though you don't know if you are dealing with an equality or an inequality in a quantitative comparison, you can use the rules for inequalities to simplify the comparison. In algebra, you learned that you can add or subtract a quantity from both sides of an inequality without changing the direction of the inequality sign. You can also multiply or divide by positive values and maintain the direction of the inequality. Study the example below.

Column A	Column B

x is a positive integer, and
$$0 < k < 1.$$

x	$\frac{x}{k}$

Since k is a positive number, you can multiply the value in each column by k.

kx	x

Then you can divide each value by x.

k	1

Since the instructions say that $0 < k < 1$, the quantity in Column B must be greater.

Remember that multiplying or dividing by a negative number will reverse an inequality sign. *Never assume* that variables represent positive numbers if that is not stated in the instructions.

23. What are the values of x for which $\dfrac{x(x + 1)}{(x - 4)(x + 3)}$ is undefined? **4, -3**

7 Similarity

PREVIEWING THE CHAPTER

This chapter examines and compares geometric figures that have the same shape but are different sizes. The chapter begins with a discussion of proportion and applies proportions to geometric figures. The term *similar* is then introduced and defined, and similar polygons and similar triangles are investigated. Fractals are used in the investigation of similar triangles and to explain the concept of similarity. Students then use similar triangles to solve problems involving proportional parts. The chapter concludes with a look at parts of similar triangles and uses them to investigate the proportional relationships of corresponding perimeters, altitudes, angle bisectors, and medians.

Problem-Solving Strategy Students combine the strategy of *solve a simpler problem* with that of *look for a pattern* to solve what otherwise might require cumbersome and time-consuming manipulations.

Lesson Objective Chart

Lesson (Pages)	Lesson Objectives	State/Local Objectives
7-1 (308-313)	7-1: Recognize and use ratios and proportions.	
7-2 (314-320)	7-2: Apply and use the properties of proportions.	
7-3 (321-326)	7-3A: Identify similar figures.	
	7-3B: Solve problems involving similar figures.	
7-4 (328-335)	7-4A: Identify similar triangles.	
	7-4B: Use similar triangles to solve problems.	
7-5 (336-341)	7-5A: Use proportional parts of triangles to solve problems.	
	7-5B: Divide a segment into congruent parts.	
7-6 (342-348)	7-6: Recognize and use the proportional relationships of corresponding perimeters, altitudes, angle bisectors, and medians of similar triangles.	
7-7 (349-351)	7-7: Solve problems by first solving a simpler related problem.	

ORGANIZING THE CHAPTER

You may want to refer to the **Course Planning Calendar** on page T28.

Lesson Planning Guide				Blackline Masters Booklets							Activities				
Lesson (Pages)	**Pacing Chart (days)** Course			Reteaching	Practice	Enrichment	Evaluation	Technology	Lab Manual	Mixed Problem Solving	Applications	Cooperative Learning Activity	Multicultural	Transparencies
	I	**II**	**III**											
7-1 (308-313)	2	1.5	1	p. 37	p. 43	p. 37		p. 7						7-1
7-2 (314-320)	2	1.5	1.5	p. 38	p. 44	p. 38	Quiz A, p. 93				p. 21			7-2
7-3 (321-326)	2	2	1.5	p. 39	p. 45	p. 39								7-3
7-4 (328-335)	2	2	2	p. 40	p. 46	p. 40	Quiz B, p. 93 Mid-Chapter Test, p. 97		pp.50-53			p. 35		7-4
7-5 (336-341)	2	2	1.5	p. 41	p. 47	p. 41			pp.54-57					7-5
7-6 (342-348)	2	2	1.5	p. 42	p. 48	p. 42	Quiz C, p. 94	p. 43		p. 7				7-6
7-7 (349-351)	1	1	1		p. 49		Quiz D, p. 94						p. 7	7-7
Review (352-354)	1	1	1	Multiple Choice Tests, Forms 1A and 1B, pp. 85-88 Free Response Tests, Forms 2A and 2B, pp. 89-92										
Test (355)	1	1	1	Cumulative Review. pp. 95-96 Standardized Tests Practice Questions, p. 98										

Course I: Chapters 1-11; Course II: Chapters 1-12; Course III: Chapters 1-13

Other Chapter Resources

Student Edition

Chapter Opener, pp. 306-307
Astronomy Connection, p. 313
Journal Entry, pp. 313, 335
Technology, p. 327
Mid-Chapter Review, p. 335
Portfolio, p. 348
Cooperative Learning Project, p. 351
Algebra Review, pp. 356-357
More Investigations in Geometry, pp. A8-A9
Extended Project 3, pp. B10-B13

Teacher's Classroom Resources

Transparency 7-0
Real World Applications Transparencies, 13, 14
Performance Assessment Booklet, pp. 13-14
Problem-of-the-Week Activity Cards, 18, 19, 20
Tech Prep Applications Booklet, pp. 13-14
LOGO Instruction Materials, Technology Masters pp. 19-36

Other Supplements

Flow Proof and Indirect Proof
Algebra and Geometry Overhead Manipulative Resources
Glencoe Mathematics Professional Series

Software

Test and Review Generator (Apple, IBM, and Macintosh)
Teacher's Guide for Software Resources

ENHANCING THE CHAPTER

Cooperative Learning

Assigning Roles to Students

Keep in mind that past and current experiences of most students involve competitive rather than cooperative activities. Therefore, remember to be patient as well as persistent in your efforts to develop cooperative interdependence. One way to enhance group skills is to assign each student in the group a specific role. Examples of such roles include a *checker,* who makes sure all members know and can explain the responses, an *encourager,* who motivates silent or reluctant members to participate, a *praiser,* who commends members for good ideas or contributions, a *prober,* who asks questions about or calls for further clarifications of ideas that have been proposed, a *materials handler,* who obtains the necessary items for the activity and then returns them to their proper places, a *recorder,* who writes the group's ideas or answers on paper, and a *help asker,* who requests assistance from the teacher when the group needs it. Other roles may suggest themselves to you to meet certain needs of a particular activity or student. For example, a group member who has difficulty remaining quiet can be assigned the role of *noise monitor,* who uses a non-verbal signal to remind the members to quiet down.

Technology

The Technology Feature following Lesson 7-3 employs the *Geometric Supposer: Triangles* software from Sunburst. In this feature, students are asked to explore relationships in similar triangles by finding the measures of angles and segments. Students use several different sets of similar triangles to investigate these relationships. These exercises should lead students to the conclusion that a line parallel to a side of a triangle forms a triangle similar to the original triangle.

Critical Thinking

Everyday problems outside the classroom frequently require skills in divergent thinking to solve. This often is contrary to the classroom experiences of many students. For example, when faced with a problem in a classroom situation, students most often focus on what *is* the solution rather than on what *is not* the solution. To help develop divergent thinking, provide a straight-back chair as a model and have students draw it, not by drawing the chair but by drawing what is *not* the chair. They will recognize that this consists primarily of geometric figures which if drawn correctly will result in a fairly professional drawing of the chair.

Cooperative Learning, p. 35

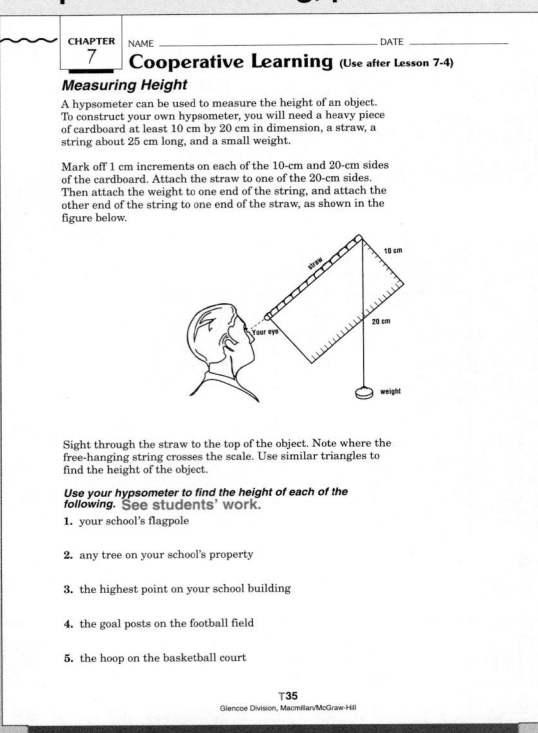

Technology, p. 43

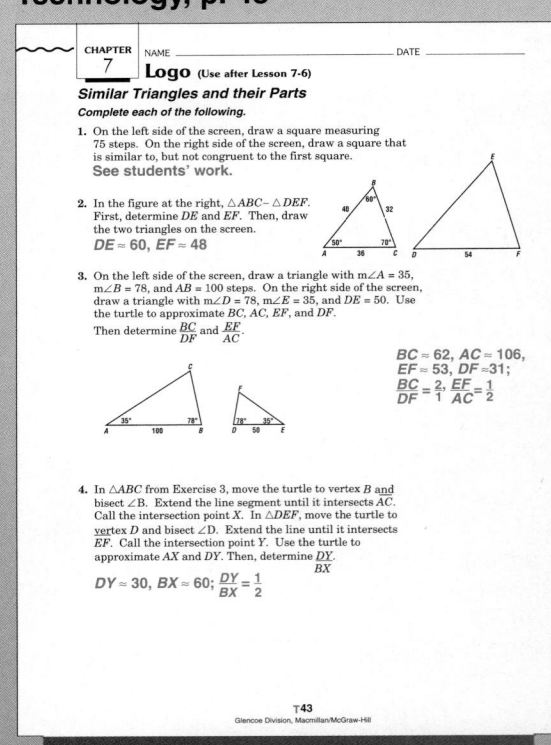

Problem of the Week Activity

The card shown below is one of three available for this chapter. It can be used as a class or small group activity.

Activity Card

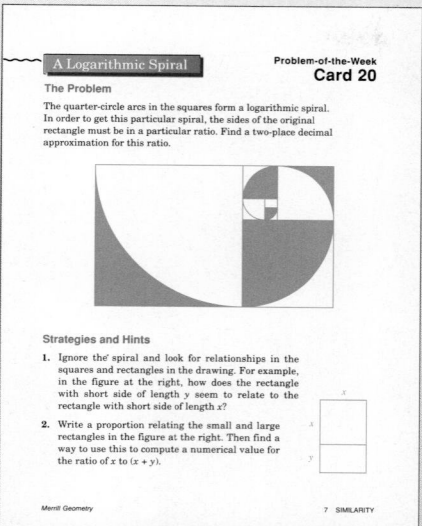

A Logarithmic Spiral

Problem-of-the-Week
Card 20

The Problem

The quarter-circle arcs in the squares form a logarithmic spiral. In order to get this particular spiral, the sides of the original rectangle must be in a particular ratio. Find a two-place decimal approximation for this ratio.

Strategies and Hints

1. Ignore the spiral and look for relationships in the squares and rectangles in the drawing. For example, in the figure at the right, how does the rectangle with short side of length *y* seem to relate to the rectangle with short side of length *x*?

2. Write a proportion relating the small and large rectangles in the figure at the right. Then find a way to use this to compute a numerical value for the ratio of *x* to (*x* + *y*).

Merrill Geometry
7 SIMILARITY

Manipulatives and Models

The following materials may be used as models or manipulatives in Chapter 7.

- tape measure (Lesson 7-1)
- map (Lesson 7-1)
- scientific calculator (Lesson 7-2)
- straightedge (Lesson 7-3)
- examples of fractals (Lesson 7-4)
- rulers, twist ties (Lesson 7-5)

Outside Resources

Books/Periodicals

Fleischmann, M., D.J. Tildesley, and R.C. Ball. *Fractals in the Natural Sciences.* Princeton University Press.

Gardner, M. *Mathematical Carnival.* Alfred A. Knopf.

Kasner, E. and J. Newman. *Mathematics and the Imagination.* Simon and Schuster.

Films/Videotapes/Videodiscs

Similarity, California Institute of Technology Bookstore, I-51, Pasadena, CA 91125

Zooms on Self-Similar Figures, International Film Bureau, Inc., 332 S. Michigan Ave., Chicago, IL 60604

Software

Geometric Super Supposer, WINGS for Learning/Sunburst, 101 Castleton, St., Pleasantville, NY 10570

Multicultural

Multicultural Activity, p. 7

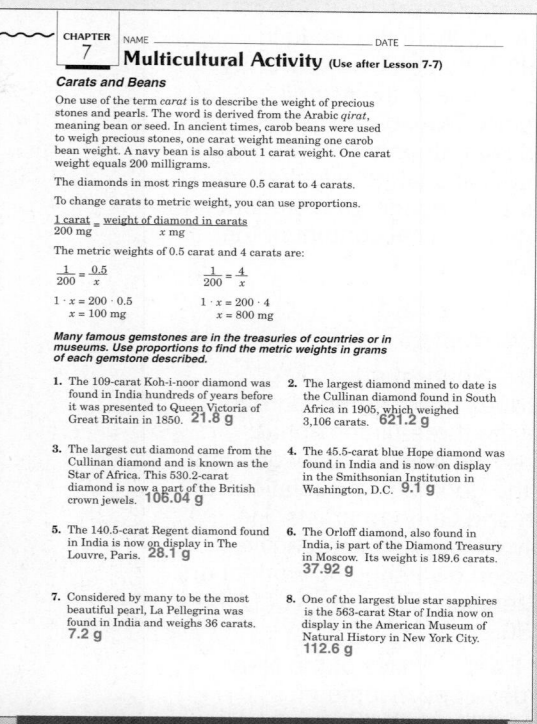

CHAPTER 7   NAME _____ DATE _____

Multicultural Activity (Use after Lesson 7-7)

Carats and Beans

One use of the term *carat* is to describe the weight of precious stones and pearls. The word is derived from the Arabic *qirat*, meaning bean or seed. In ancient times, carob beans were used to weigh precious stones, one carat weight meaning one carob bean weight. A navy bean is also about 1 carat weight. One carat weight equals 200 milligrams.

The diamonds in most rings measure 0.5 carat to 4 carats.

To change carats to metric weight, you can use proportions.

$$\frac{1 \text{ carat}}{200 \text{ mg}} = \frac{\text{weight of diamond in carats}}{x \text{ mg}}$$

The metric weights of 0.5 carat and 4 carats are:

$$\frac{1}{200} = \frac{0.5}{x} \qquad\qquad \frac{1}{200} = \frac{4}{x}$$

$$1 \cdot x = 200 \cdot 0.5 \qquad 1 \cdot x = 200 \cdot 4$$
$$x = 100 \text{ mg} \qquad\quad x = 800 \text{ mg}$$

Many famous gemstones are in the treasuries of countries or in museums. Use proportions to find the metric weights in grams of each gemstone described.

1. The 109-carat Koh-i-noor diamond was found in India hundreds of years before it was presented to Queen Victoria of Great Britain in 1850. **21.8 g**

2. The largest diamond mined to date is the Cullinan diamond found in South Africa in 1905, which weighed 3,106 carats. **621.2 g**

3. The largest cut diamond came from the Cullinan diamond and is known as the Star of Africa. This 530.2-carat diamond is now a part of the British crown jewels. **106.04 g**

4. The 45.5-carat blue Hope diamond was found in India and is now on display in the Smithsonian Institution in Washington, D.C. **9.1 g**

5. The 140.5-carat Regent diamond found in India is now on display in The Louvre, Paris. **28.1 g**

6. The Orloff diamond, also found in India, is part of the Diamond Treasury in Moscow. Its weight is 189.6 carats. **37.92 g**

7. Considered by many to be the most beautiful pearl, La Pellegrina was found in India and weighs 36 carats. **7.2 g**

8. One of the largest blue star sapphires is the 563-carat Star of India now on display in the American Museum of Natural History in New York City. **112.6 g**

Lab Manual

Lab Activity, pp. 50-53

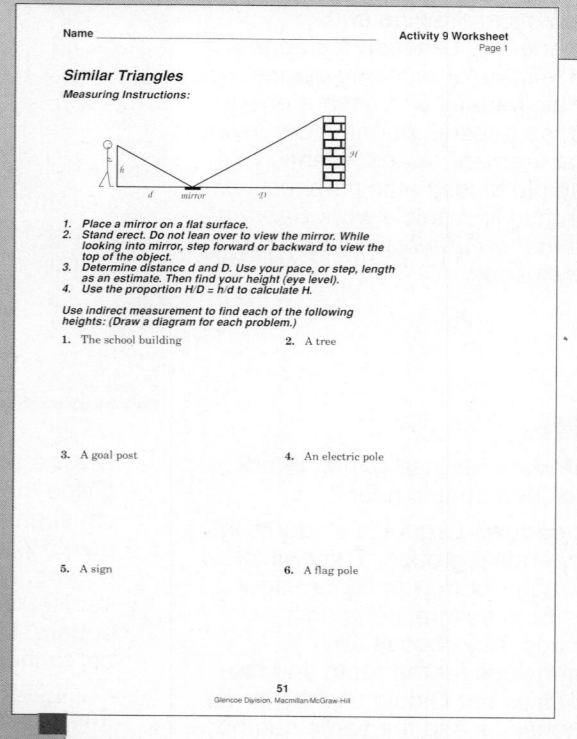

Name _____   Activity 9 Worksheet
Page 1

Similar Triangles
Measuring Instructions:

1. Place a mirror on a flat surface.
2. Stand erect. Do not lean over to view the mirror. While looking into mirror, step forward or backward to view the top of the object.
3. Determine distance d and D. Use your pace, or step, length as an estimate. Then find your height (eye level).
4. Use the proportion H/D = h/d to calculate H.

Use indirect measurement to find each of the following heights: (Draw a diagram for each problem.)

1. The school building
2. A tree

3. A goal post
4. An electric pole

5. A sign
6. A flag pole

51
Glencoe Division, Macmillan-McGraw-Hill

Using the Chapter Opener

This two-page introduction to the chapter provides students with an opportunity to see how geometry is used throughout the world in various cultures. **Transparency 7-0**, available in the *Merrill Geometry Transparency Package*, provides another full-color visual and motivational activity that you can use to engage your students in the mathematical content of the chapter.

Multicultural Notes

Spain   Spanish artist Diego Velazquez used a procedure for achieving three-dimensional perspective that was very different from the geometric calculations of Italian and German artists. He openly challenged perspective science in his intriguing work of art Las Meninas (*The Maids of Honor*) in 1656.

Near East   Artists of the Near East developed isometric perspective. With this method, parallel lines and edges recede in diagonal directions, as they do in linear perspective, but do not converge at a point. Isometric perspective is important in mechanical drawing and engineering, because the edges and lengths of receding planes remain parallel and unshortened and, as a result, permit more exact measurement. An excellent example of isometric perspective is Mahmud Muzahib's work *Babram Gur in the Turquoise Palace on Wednesday*.

Chapter Project

Materials   unlined paper, pencil, black pen, metric ruler

Procedure   Organize students into cooperative groups. They will draw a square room with square floor tiles from several perspectives. Groups may choose any dimensions for the room and the floor tiles but should use the same dimensions and the same number of tiles in all drawings.

Give these directions for the first drawing (the dimensions are only a suggestion):

Draw a square 15 cm by 15 cm; divide the bottom edge into ten 1.5 cm segments. Select a vanishing point, V, in the upper part of the square, along the central axis or vertical line of symmetry of the square. Mark points Z_1 and Z_2 10 cm to the left and to the right of V. Z_1, V, and Z_2 should be collinear and $\overleftrightarrow{Z_1 Z_2}$ should be parallel to the base of the square. Draw lines connecting each point on the bottom edge with V.

Draw lines connecting the leftmost three points with Z_2, the rightmost three points with Z_1. Draw ten horizontal lines up from the bottom edge, connecting points of intersection between lines to point V and lines to points Z_1 and Z_2. Draw a line from the upper corners of the square to point V; drop veritical lines from each of these lines to each inner corner of the floor. Draw a horizontal line between the two verticals.

Similarity

GEOMETRY AROUND THE WORLD
Germany

Have you ever wondered how artists paint three-dimensional scenes—pictures with height, width, and depth—on flat, two-dimensional canvases? They use a geometric concept called linear perspective, in which the lines of objects come together in a way that gives the viewer the illusion of depth.

One of the masters of linear perspective drawing was a German painter and wood engraver named Albrecht Dürer. Dürer, who lived from 1471 to 1528, traveled to Italy to study the visual geometry of Leonardo da Vinci. He then developed a technique to obtain linear perspective that he worked out on his canvas before he began painting. Carefully, he drew a grid of "parallel" lines receding to a vanishing point. He then created two additional points of alignment called lateral points. To these, Dürer added other geometric points and lines to guide him in providing depth to his paintings.

GEOMETRY IN ACTION

Look carefully at the copy of one of Dürer's engravings, completed in 1514. Notice how the parallel lines of the ceiling, table, and window ledge all recede to a single vanishing point just above the chair on the right. This technique is illustrated by the diagram below. What dimension did Dürer add to the engraving using this technique?

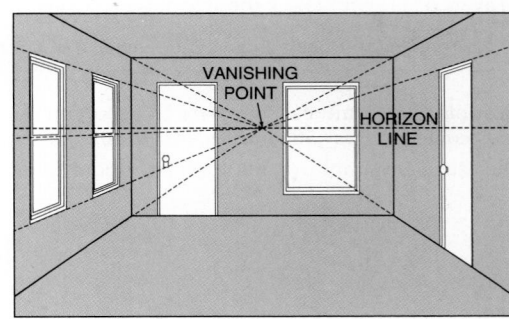

◄ *"St. Jerome in His Cell"* Inset: *Albrecht Dürer*

307

Do you see the depth in this work by Albrecht Dürer? How do you think he achieved this effect?

Connections and Applications

Suggest the following variations:
- Move the vanishing point up or down the central axis.
- Move the vanishing point to the right or left of the central axis.
- Change the distance between Z_1 and Z_2 and V, but equally on both sides.
- Locate cubes at various depths. (Hint: Review the chapter opener, especially Durer's location of the table. Align the cube edges along lines to V; align cube diagonals along lines to Z_1 and Z_2.)

Have each group compare the different perspectives of the drawings from the perspective of viewers entering each room, and present the drawings and perspective evaluation to the class.

Resources

Kemp, Martin. *The Science of Art.* Yale University Press

Pedoe, Dan. *Geometry and the Liberal Arts.* St. Martin's Press

INTRODUCING THE LESSON

5-Minute Check

(over Chapter 6)

1. In a parallelogram opposite sides and angles are
   _____. **congruent**
2. If one pair of opposite sides of a quadrilateral are congruent and parallel, then the quadrilateral is a
   _____. **parallelogram**
3. In rectangle *ABCD*, diagonal $\overline{AC}$ measures $4x + 6$, and diagonal $\overline{BD}$ measures $9x - 14$. Find the value of *x*. **4**
4. In rhombus *DEFG*, the diagonals intersect at *X*. If *DX* = 7, find *DF*. **14**
5. In trapezoid *ABCD*, $\overline{AB} \parallel \overline{CD}$. *X* is the midpoint of $\overline{DA}$ and *Y* is the midpoint of $\overline{BC}$. If *AB* = 6 and *CD* = 10, find *XY*. **8**

Motivating the Lesson

Ask students what the phrase "The average number of children in a family is 2.4" means to them. How can a family have 2.4 children? Explain that this is an average number and that a ratio was used to calculate the number.

Objective
7-1

After studying this lesson, you should be able to:
- recognize and use ratios and proportions.

Application

According to the 1990 United States census, there are about 32 people for every 10 families. This information can be expressed as the ratio 32 to 10 or $\frac{32}{10}$ or $\frac{3.2}{1}$. In other words, there were about 3.2 people per family.

A **ratio** is a comparison of two quantities. The ratio of *a* to *b* can be expressed as $\frac{a}{b}$ where *b* is not zero. The ratio can also be written as *a:b*.

Example 1

APPLICATION
Biology

Many parts of the human body have a common ratio. The students in a geometry class measured the sizes of their necks and their wrists in centimeters. The measures are displayed in the table. What is a good estimate for the ratio of the neck to the wrist?

Neck	30	33.5	31	33	34.5	35	34	32
Wrist	15	17.5	15.5	15	14	16	15	14

Neck	31	40	35	39.5	33	37.5	31	33
Wrist	15.5	17	18	16.5	15	17.5	15.5	15

Neck	34.5	42	37	42.5	35.5	39	36.5	36.5
Wrist	14	18	18	21	14.5	18	16	14.5

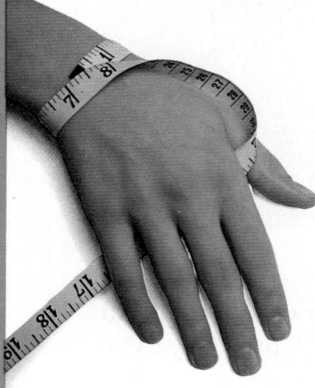

If you add all the neck sizes for the class and divide by 24, the average neck size is about 35.3 centimeters. The average wrist size is about 16.1 centimeters. Therefore the average ratio is $\frac{35.3}{16.1}$ or about 2.19. The size of their necks, on the average, is about twice the size of their wrists.

Check your neck and wrist. Is your neck about twice the size of your wrist?

Refer to the application about families. Suppose a TV report on the census stated there were 160 people for every 50 families. Is this different from the first ratio of $\frac{32}{10}$? When they are simplified, both ratios are equivalent to $\frac{3.2}{1}$.

$$\overset{\div 10}{\frac{32}{10}} = \frac{3.2}{1} \qquad \overset{\div 50}{\frac{160}{50}} = \frac{3.2}{1}$$

An equation stating that two ratios are equal is a **proportion**. So, $\frac{32}{10} = \frac{160}{50}$ is a proportion.

ALTERNATE TEACHING STRATEGIES

Using Models

Bring in a can of food and use the nutritional information to set up ratios and find proportions. Relate the ratios to one serving and also to the amount in the entire can. Use two equal ratios to demonstrate proportion to your students.

Using Charts

Have students do the experiment in Example 1 to find the class average ratio of neck size to wrist size. How does it compare to the average found in Example 1?

Every proportion has two **cross products**. In the proportion $\frac{32}{10} = \frac{160}{50}$, the cross products are 32 times 50 and 160 times 10. The cross products of a true proportion are equal. 32 and 50 are called the **extremes**, and 160 and 10 are called the **means**.

$$\frac{32}{10} = \frac{160}{50}$$

$$32(50) = 10(160)$$
$$\text{extremes} \qquad \text{means}$$
$$1600 = 1600$$

Consider the general case.

$$\frac{a}{b} = \frac{c}{d}$$
$$(bd)\frac{a}{b} = (bd)\frac{c}{d} \qquad \textit{Multiply each side by bd.}$$
$$da = bc \qquad \textit{Simplify.}$$

Equality of Cross Products	For any numbers *a* and *c* and any nonzero numbers *b* and *d*, $\frac{a}{b} = \frac{c}{d}$ if and only if *ad = bc*. *The product of the means equals the product of the extremes.*

Example 2

APPLICATION

Travel

Countries have different monetary systems. The chart at the right shows the rate of exchange for some foreign currency in terms of U.S. dollars. If a tour book costs 450 Taiwanese dollars, how much would it cost in U.S. dollars?

Foreign Currency	Rate of Exchange per U.S. Dollar
Spanish peseta	102.70
Swedish krona	5.9680
Swiss frank	1.4470
Taiwanese dollar	25.74
German mark	1.6310

Since 25.74 Taiwanese dollars can be exchanged for 1 U.S. dollar, the ratio of Taiwanese dollars to 1 U.S. dollar is $\frac{25.74}{1}$. The ratio of 450 Taiwanese dollars to *x* U.S. dollars would be written $\frac{450}{x}$, where *x* is the number of U.S. dollars. These ratios are equivalent and can be written as a proportion.

$$\frac{25.74}{1} = \frac{450}{x}$$
$$25.74x = 450 \qquad \textit{Find the cross product.}$$
$$\frac{25.74x}{25.74} = \frac{450}{25.74} \qquad \textit{Divide each side by 25.74.}$$
$$x = 17.48 \qquad \textit{Use your calculator.}$$

The book costs about $17.48 in U.S. currency.

Ratios can also be used to compare three or more numbers. The expression *a:b:c* means that the ratio of the first two numbers is *a:b*, the ratio of the last two numbers is *b:c*, and the ratio of the first and last numbers is *a:c*.

LESSON 7-1   PROPERTIES OF PROPORTIONS   309

Chalkboard Examples

For Example 1
The students in the geometry class in Example 1 measured the distance from the base of their wrists to the top of their middle finger and found the average size to be about 15.9 cm. They also measured their height and found an average height of 167 cm. What is a good estimate for the ratio of height to length of hand?
$$\frac{167}{15.9} = 10.5$$

For Example 2
Use the chart in Example 2. If a shirt costs 19.95 U.S. dollars, how much would it cost in Spanish pesetas?
$$\frac{102.70}{1} = \frac{x}{19.95}$$
$$x = 2048.87 \text{ pesetas}$$

Teaching Tip   When expressing a ratio $\frac{a}{b}$, *b* cannot be zero because you cannot divide by zero (or the denominator of a fraction cannot be zero).

Teaching Tip   When considering the general case of $\frac{a}{b} = \frac{c}{d}$, your students may wonder why the equation was multiplied by *bd*. Explain that the purpose was to eliminate the fractions.

310   Chapter 7

Chalkboard Example

For Example 3
The measures of two consecutive angles between the parallel sides of a trapezoid are 5:7. The other two consecutive angle measures between the parallel sides are 1:3. What are the measures of the angles in the trapezoid?

$5x + 7x = 180$ $y + 3y = 180$
$\quad 12x = 180$ $\quad 4y = 180$
$\quad\quad x = 15$ $\quad\quad y = 45$

The angle measures are 5(15) or 75, 7(15) or 105, 45 and 3(45) or 135.

EVALUATING THE LESSON

Checking for Understanding

Exercises 1-18 are designed to help you assess students' understanding through reading, writing, speaking, and modeling. You should work through Exercises 1-5 with your students and then monitor their work on Exercises 6-18.

Error Analysis

Remind students that they can find cross products only when there is an equals sign between the ratios.

Closing the Lesson

Writing Activity Have each student measure the distance around his or her clenched fist. How does it compare with the length of his or her foot?

Example 3

The ratio of the measures of the angles of a triangle is 3:5:7. What is the measure of each angle in the triangle?

Let $3x$, $5x$, and $7x$ represent the measures of the angles of the triangle.

$3x + 5x + 7x = 180$ *The sum of the angle measures in a triangle is 180.*
$\quad\quad\quad 15x = 180$
$\quad\quad\quad\quad x = 12$ *Divide each side by 15.*

The measures of the angles are 3(12) or 36, 5(12) or 60, and 7(12) or 84.

CHECKING FOR UNDERSTANDING

Communicating Mathematics

If there are 81 boys and 72 girls in the sophomore class, the ratio of boys to girls is $\frac{81}{72}$. Read and study the lesson to answer these questions about the proportion $\frac{81}{72} = \frac{1.125}{1}$.

1. Name the two ratios in this proportion. $\frac{81}{72}$ and $\frac{1.125}{1}$

2. Name the means. **72 and 1.125**

3. Name the extremes. **81 and 1**

4. Show that the product of the means is equal to the product of the extremes. **72 × 1.125 = 81 and 81 × 1 = 81**

5. Explain what $\frac{1.125}{1}$ represents. **There are 1.125 boys for every girl.**

Guided Practice

6. 1.013
7. 0.542
8. 1.460

Use the 1991 final standings for the American League West to find the ratios for Exercises 6-9. Express each ratio as a decimal rounded to three decimal places.

6. games won to games lost for Seattle

7. games won to games played for Chicago

8. games won to games lost for Minnesota

9. games won by Kansas City to games won by Texas **0.976**

Team	Wins	Losses
Minnesota	92	63
Chicago	84	71
Texas	82	73
Oakland	82	74
Kansas City	80	76
Seattle	78	77
California	77	79

Given $a = 3$, $b = 2$, $c = 6$, and $d = 4$, determine if each pair of ratios forms a true proportion.

10. $\frac{b}{a} \stackrel{?}{=} \frac{d}{c}$ **yes**

11. $\frac{a}{c} \stackrel{?}{=} \frac{b}{d}$ **yes**

12. $\frac{c}{b} \stackrel{?}{=} \frac{d}{a}$ **no**

13. $\frac{(a+b)}{b} \stackrel{?}{=} \frac{(c+d)}{d}$ **yes**

14. $\frac{d}{b} \stackrel{?}{=} \frac{c}{a}$ **yes**

Find the value of x using cross products.

15. $\frac{x}{3} = \frac{15}{10}$ **4.5**

16. $\frac{5}{17} = \frac{2x}{51}$ **7.5**

17. $\frac{x+1}{x} = \frac{7}{2}$ **0.4**

18. The ratio of AB to AC is equivalent to the ratio of FT to FE. If $AB = 8$, $BC = 6$, and $FT = 2$, what is FE? **3.5**

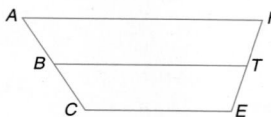

EXERCISES

Practice

Gears on bicycles are called sprocket wheels. To determine gear ratios on bicycles, you must find the ratio of the number of rear sprocket teeth to the number of front sprocket teeth. Find each ratio. Express your answer as a decimal rounded to two places.

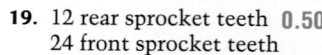

19. 12 rear sprocket teeth   **0.50**
    24 front sprocket teeth

20. 15 rear sprocket teeth
    55 front sprocket teeth   **0.27**

21. 13 rear sprocket teeth
    52 front sprocket teeth   **0.25**

22. 20 rear sprocket teeth
    30 front sprocket teeth   **0.67**

Solve each proportion using cross products.

23. $\frac{11}{24} = \frac{x}{24}$ **11**

24. $\frac{5}{8} = \frac{20}{x}$ **32**

25. $\frac{b}{3.24} = \frac{1}{8}$ **0.405**

26. $\frac{4}{n} = \frac{7}{8}$ **$\frac{32}{7}$**

27. $\frac{m+3}{12} = \frac{5}{4}$ **12**

28. $\frac{1}{3} = \frac{t}{8-t}$ **2**

$\overline{AD}$ is a median of $\triangle ABC$ shown at the right.

29. Find the ratio of BD to DC.   **$\frac{1}{1}$**

30. Find the ratio of DC to BC.   **$\frac{1}{2}$**

31. If $\triangle ABC$ is an equilateral triangle, find the ratio of $m\angle ABD$ to $m\angle ADC$.   **$\frac{2}{3}$**

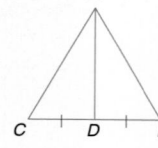

Homework Exercises

Assignment Guide
Basic: 19-36, 43-45, 48-53
Average: 22-39, 43-44, 46, 48-53
Enriched: 25-43, 46-53

Exercise Notes
For Exercises 19-22, point out that gears with a different number of rear teeth and front teeth can have the same gear ratio. For example, gears with three rear teeth and six front teeth have the same gear ratio as those described in Exercise 19.

Reteaching Masters Booklet, p. 37

RETEACHING THE LESSON

Have students think of a situation that involves ratios or proportions like batting averages from the sports page or scales on a map. Then have them set up a ratio and a proportion for some of the examples.

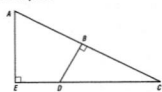

B

32. In the figure at the right, $\frac{RS}{SP} = \frac{RT}{TQ}$.
Use proportions to complete the table.

a. $RP = 5$; $TQ = 6$; $RQ = 10$
b. $RS = 36$; $RP = 81$
c. $RS = 2$; $SP = 1$; $TQ = 8$
d. $RS = 15\frac{3}{7}$; $SP = 20\frac{4}{7}$; $RQ = 84$

	RS	SP	RP	RT	TQ	RQ
a.	2	3	_?_	4	_?_	_?_
b.	_?_	45	_?_	32	40	72
c.	_?_	_?_	3	16	_?_	24
d.	_?_	_?_	36	36	48	_?_

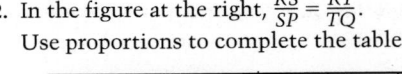

Proportions can be used to change a fraction to a percent. For example to change $\frac{5}{6}$ to a percent, you solve the proportion $\frac{5}{6} = \frac{n}{100}$. Use a proportion to change each fraction to a percent. Round your answers to the nearest tenth.

33. $\frac{3}{8}$ 37.5%

34. $\frac{5}{12}$ 41.7%

35. $\frac{13}{4}$ 325%

C

Use equality of cross products to show each of the following is true. Assume that *b* and *d* are not zero. See margin.

36. $\frac{a}{b} = \frac{c}{d}$ if $\frac{a+b}{b} = \frac{c+d}{d}$.

37. $\frac{a}{b} = \frac{c}{d}$ if $\frac{a-b}{b} = \frac{c-d}{d}$.

38. $\frac{a}{b} = \frac{c}{d}$ if $\frac{a}{b} = \frac{a+c}{b+d}$ or $\frac{c}{d} = \frac{a+c}{b+d}$.

An expression of the form $x = y = z$ means $x = y$, $y = z$, and $x = z$. Solve for *x* and *y*. See margin.

39. $8 = \frac{10}{x} = \frac{y}{5}$

40. $\frac{x-1}{x} = \frac{3}{4} = \frac{y}{y+1}$

41. Write $xy = 22$ as a proportion. See margin.

42. The ratio of the measures of two angles of an isosceles triangle is 1 to 2. What are the possible measures of the angles of the triangle? 36, 72, 72 or 45, 45, 90

Critical Thinking

43. Suppose the measures of the sides of two rectangles are proportional.
  a. Will their perimeters have an equivalent ratio? Explain. yes
  b. Will their areas have an equivalent ratio? Explain. not necessarily; only if they are congruent

Applications

44. **Carpentry** The pitch of a roof is the ratio of the rise (change in height) to the run (change in width). If a roof has a rise of 3.5 feet and a run of 10.5 feet, what is its pitch? $\frac{3.5}{10.5}$ or $\frac{1}{3}$

45. Travel Use the table on page 309 to determine how many Swedish kronas a traveler would receive for $500 in U.S. currency. **2984**

46. Banking One way to determine the strength of a bank is to calculate its capital-to-assets ratio as a percent. A strong bank should have a ratio of 4% or more. The Pilgrim National Bank has a capital of 2.3 billion dollars and assets of 52.6 billion dollars. Is it a strong bank? Explain.

46. yes; the ratio 0.044 > 0.04

47. Sports On a bike, the ratio of the number of rear sprocket teeth to the number of front sprocket teeth is equivalent to the number of rear sprocket wheel revolutions to the number of pedal revolutions. If there are 24 rear sprocket teeth and 54 front sprocket teeth, how many revolutions of the rear sprocket wheel will occur for 3 revolutions of the pedal? **about 1.3**

Mixed Review

48. Can a rectangle be a rhombus? Explain. **(Lesson 6-5)** yes; if it is a square

49. Can 19, 31, and 55 be the measures of the sides of a triangle? Explain. **(Lesson 5-6)** no; fails the triangle inequality

50. Draw and label an obtuse isosceles triangle. **(Lesson 4-1)** See margin.

51. Write *A trapezoid has exactly two opposite sides parallel* in if-then form. **(Lesson 2-2)**

51. If a quadrilateral is a trapezoid, then it has exactly two opposite sides parallel.

52. Draw opposite rays $\overrightarrow{QS}$ and $\overrightarrow{QR}$. **(Lesson 1-6)** See margin.

Wrap-Up

53. Journal Entry Write a sentence in your journal to describe one new type of problem that you learned to solve in this geometry lesson. When might you need to solve a problem like this? **See students' work.**

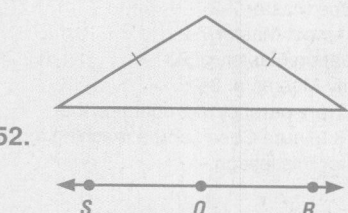
ASTRONOMY CONNECTION

The fields of astronomy and geometry are closely related. Among other things, astronomers use geometry to calculate the speeds of celestial bodies. Vera Rubin, one of only 75 women to be nominated to the National Academy of Sciences, studies the speeds of faraway galaxies.

Ms. Rubin has been studying spiral galaxies for several years at the Department of Terrestrial Magnetism in Washington, D.C. She has discovered that in spiral galaxies, the stars in the outer arms of the galaxy do not slow down like the outer planets of our solar system do. Traveling at the speeds they do, these fast-moving outer stars should fly off into space. Ms. Rubin has hypothesized that there must be some type of matter between the stars that pulls them together. She calls this *dark matter*. Research on dark matter is still being conducted. But the studies that have been completed on 200 different spiral galaxies confirm Ms. Rubin's theory.

LESSON 7-1 PROPERTIES OF PROPORTIONS 313

EXTENDING THE LESSON

Math Power: Connections

Show that if $\dfrac{a}{b} = \dfrac{c}{d} = \dfrac{e}{f}$

then $\dfrac{a}{b} = \dfrac{c}{d} = \dfrac{e}{f} = \dfrac{a+c+e}{b+d+f}$.

Set each ratio equal to x. So, $a = bx$, $c = dx$, and $e = fx$. Then, $a + c + e = (b + d + f)x$. So,

$$\dfrac{a+c+e}{b+d+f} = x = \dfrac{a}{b} = \dfrac{c}{d} = \dfrac{e}{f}$$

Astronomy Connection

Have students research spiral galaxies. They may want to write to the National Academy of Sciences for more information on Vera Rubin and her discovery of dark matter, as well as other information on spiral galaxies.

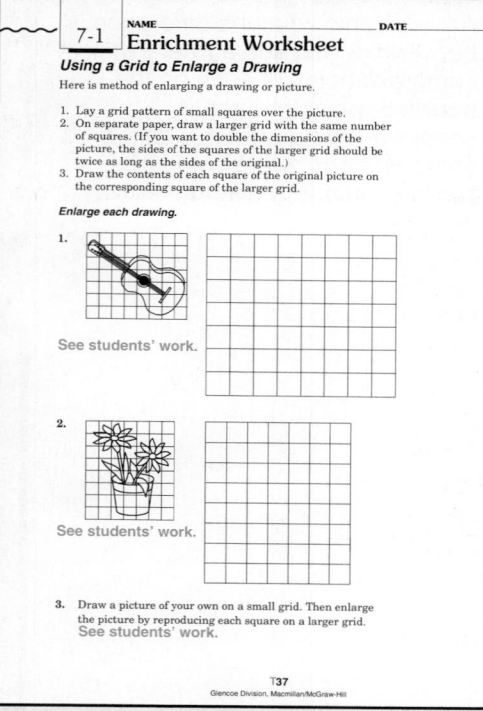

Lesson Resources

- Reteaching Master 7-2
- Practice Master 7-2
- Enrichment Master 7-2
- Evaluation Master, p. 93
- Activity Master, p. 35

 Transparency 7-2 contains the 5-Minute Check and a teaching aid for this lesson.

INTRODUCING THE LESSON

 5-Minute Check

(over Lesson 7-1)

Determine if each pair of ratios forms a proportion.

1. $\frac{2}{3} \stackrel{?}{=} \frac{16}{24}$ yes

2. $\frac{9}{11} \stackrel{?}{=} \frac{81}{88}$ no

Solve each proportion using cross products.

3. $\frac{10}{11} = \frac{11}{x}$ 12.1

4. $\frac{2}{5} = \frac{9x}{13}$ 0.58

5. $\frac{x-1}{9} = \frac{3x+2}{21}$ -6.5

Motivating the Lesson

Ask students what the difference is between a ratio and a rate. Put some examples of each on the board. Explain that a ratio compares two numbers with the same unit and a rate compares two numbers with different units.

7-2 Applications of Proportions

Objective
7-2

After studying this lesson, you should be able to:
- apply and use the properties of proportions.

Application

Suppose that you are selecting a rectangle design for the wallpaper in your room. Which of the four rectangular design shapes at the right appeals to you most?

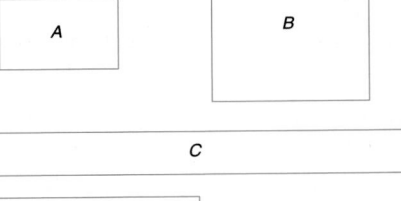

Measure the length and width of the rectangle you selected and calculate the ratio of the length to the width.

If you chose rectangle *A*, the rectangle considered most pleasing by many artists and architects, the ratio of length to width is about 1.618. This ratio is known as the *golden ratio*. Rectangles in which the ratio of their length to their width is 1.618 are called *golden rectangles*. Because of their pleasing shape, they can be found in ancient and modern architecture and in nature. Notice the number of golden rectangles in the picture of the Parthenon.

Because the ratio of length to width is the same for all golden rectangles, the measures of their corresponding sides are proportional. Rectangles *ABCD* and *PQRS* are golden rectangles.

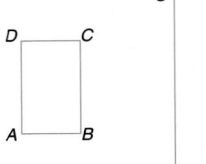

$\frac{BC}{AB} = \frac{1.618}{1}$ $\frac{QR}{PQ} = \frac{1.618}{1}$

$\frac{BC}{AB} = \frac{QR}{PQ}$ *Transitive property*

$AB \cdot QR = BC \cdot PQ$ *Cross products*

$\frac{AB \cdot QR}{QR \cdot PQ} = \frac{BC \cdot PQ}{QR \cdot PQ}$ *Division property of equality*

$\frac{AB}{PQ} = \frac{BC}{QR}$

ALTERNATE TEACHING STRATEGIES

Using Comparison

Ask students to use a straightedge to draw a rectangle. Have them measure the length and width of their rectangle. Have them calculate how closely their random rectangle matches the proportional sides of a golden rectangle.

Using Applications

Have each student bring a map into class and use it to find the distance between two points using the scale on the map, as in Example 2. Have students select the two locations themselves.

Proportions are also used with special ratios called **rates**. A rate is the ratio of two measurements that may have different types of units. For example, a race car at the Indianapolis 500 can travel 966 feet in 3 seconds and has a rate of speed of 966 feet/3 seconds or 322 feet per second.

Example 1

APPLICATION
Sports

In 1990 Arie Luyendyk set a track record for the Indianapolis 500. He averaged about 15.499 miles in 5 minutes. At this rate, how far could he travel in 1 hour?

This problem can be solved by writing and solving a proportion. Let d represent the distance he could travel in one hour. *Remember that 1 hour = 60 minutes.*

$$\frac{15.499 \text{ mi}}{5 \text{ min}} = \frac{d \text{ mi}}{60 \text{ min}}$$

$15.499 \cdot 60 = 5d$ *Cross*
$929.94 = 5d$ *products*
$185.988 = d$

At this rate, Luyendyk could travel 185.988 miles in 1 hour.

FYI···

A.J. Foyt and Al Unser, Sr. have each won the Indianapolis 500 four times.

Proportions and maps can be used to find distances between two locations.

Example 2

APPLICATION
Travel

On a map of Florida, three fourths of an inch represents 15 miles. If it is approximately 10 inches from Tampa to Jacksonville on the map, what is the actual distance in miles?

Let d represent the distance in miles from Tampa to Jacksonville.

$$\frac{0.75 \text{ in.}}{10 \text{ in.}} = \frac{15 \text{ mi}}{d \text{ mi}}$$

$0.75d = 15 \cdot 10$ *Cross products*
$0.75d = 150$
$d = 200$ *Division property of equality*

The distance from Tampa to Jacksonville is about 200 miles.

TEACHING THE LESSON

Teaching Tip When discussing rates as proportions, have students think of some examples of rates, such as miles/hour, feet/second, and so on.

Teaching Tip When discussing Example 2, point out that you can also set up the proportion as
$$\frac{0.75 \text{ in.}}{15 \text{ mi}} = \frac{10 \text{ in.}}{d \text{ mi}}.$$
Show that the cross products will be the same.

Chalkboard Examples

For Example 1
If Emerson Fittipaldi averaged 45.892 miles in 15 minutes at the Indianapolis 500, how far could he travel in 1 hour? Did he set a new track record?
$$\frac{45.892 \text{ mi}}{15 \text{ min}} = \frac{d \text{ mi}}{60 \text{ min}}$$
$$2753.52 = 15d$$
$$183.568 = d$$
He did not set a new record since 185.988 > 183.568.

For Example 2
On a map of Florida, 1 inch represents 25 miles. If it is approximately 8 inches from Tampa to Jacksonville, what is the actual distance in miles? Does this map correspond with the map in Example 2?
$$\frac{1 \text{ in.}}{8 \text{ in.}} = \frac{25 \text{ mi}}{d \text{ mi}}$$
$$d = 8 \times 25$$
$$d = 200$$
Yes, the two maps correspond.

Checking for Understanding

Exercises 1-12 are designed to help you assess students' understanding through reading, writing, speaking, and modeling. You should work through Exercises 1-3 with your students and then monitor their work on Exercises 4-12.

Closing the Lesson

Speaking Activity Have each student name a situation in which a proportion could be used. Also, have them state the units being compared in the proportion.

Additional Answers

1. Sample answer: Measure the length and the width. Then divide the length by the width. If the quotient is about 1.618, it is a golden rectangle.

3. Set up a proportion:
$$\frac{15 \text{ km}}{1 \text{ cm}} = \frac{x \text{ km}}{7.9 \text{ cm}}$$

CHECKING FOR UNDERSTANDING

Communicating Mathematics

Read and study the lesson to answer each question.

1. Explain how you would determine whether the rectangle at the right is a golden rectangle. **See margin.**

2a. **About 8.9 people in 1000 were married in 1895.**

2. **a.** The marriage rate for 1895 was 8.9. If the rate was per 1000 people, explain what this rate means.

   b. The marriage rate in 1993 was 9.2. What is the difference between the two rates? **0.3 more people per 1000 were married in 1993 than in 1895**

   c. For every 10,000 people, how many would you expect to be married in 1993? **92**

3. A map is scaled so that 1 centimeter represents 15 kilometers. Two towns are 7.9 centimeters apart on the map. Explain how to set up a proportion to determine the distance between the two towns. **See margin.**

Guided Practice

Determine which proportion can be used to solve the problem. Do not solve.

4. Find the cost of 120 pencils if 100 pencils cost $16.10. **c**

   a. $\frac{100}{16.10} = \frac{x}{120}$ **b.** $\frac{16.10}{120} = \frac{100}{x}$ **c.** $\frac{100}{16.10} = \frac{120}{x}$ **d.** $\frac{16.10}{100} = \frac{120}{x}$

5. How much in U.S. currency would you receive for $75 in Canadian currency if the exchange rate is one Canadian dollar equals $0.88 in U.S. currency?

   a. $\frac{88}{100} = \frac{x}{75}$ **b.** $\frac{100}{88} = \frac{x}{75}$ **c.** $\frac{88}{100} = \frac{75}{x}$ **d.** $\frac{100}{x} = \frac{75}{88}$ **a**

Suppose the measures of the corresponding sides of the polygons *ABCD* and *PQRS* are proportional.

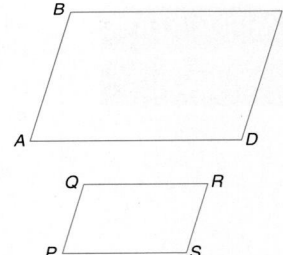

6. If $AB = 2$, $AD = 5$, and $PQ = 3$, find PS. **7.5**

7. If $RS = 4.5$, $CD = 6.23$, and $BC = 7.0$, find QR. **about 5.06**

8. If $CD = 21.7$, $DA = SP + 4$, and $SR = 14.0$, find SP. **about 7.27**

316 CHAPTER 7 SIMILARITY

Determine if the given quantities are proportional.

9. the ratio of the number of sides of a rectangle to the number of its diagonals and the ratio of the number of sides of a pentagon to the number of its diagonals **no**

10. the ratio of the number of sides of a triangle to the number of its exterior angles and the ratio of the number of sides of a hexagon to the number of its exterior angles **yes**

Use a proportion to solve each problem.

11. **Consumer Math**   The average American drinks about 4 soft drinks every 3 days. About how many soft drinks will the average person drink in a year? **487 soft drinks**

12. **Sports**   A designated hitter made 8 hits in 9 games. If she continues hitting at that rate, how many hits will she make in 108 games? **96 hits**

EXERCISES

Practice   Use the number line at the right to determine if the given ratios are equal.

 13. $\frac{CD}{CT}$ and $\frac{AC}{AT}$ **yes**

14. $\frac{BD}{BT}$ and $\frac{AD}{AT}$ **no**

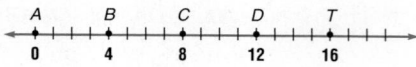

15. $\frac{AB}{AT}$ and $\frac{BC}{BT}$ **no**

Suppose the measures of corresponding sides of the polygons at the right are proportional.

16. If $AB = 4$, $AD = 8$, and $PQ = 6$, find PS. **12**

17. If $RS = 4.5$, $CD = 6.3$, and $BC = 7$, find QR. **5**

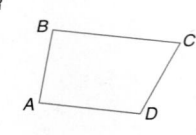

18. If $CD = 21.8$, $DA = 43.6$, and $SR = 33$, find SP. **66**

Use a proportion to solve each problem.

19. According to the National Safety Council, the death rate in the United States from motor vehicle accidents in 1992 was 15.8 per 100,000 people.

   a. In 1992 Los Angeles had a population of about 3,600,000. Approximately how many people would you estimate died from motor vehicle accidents in Los Angeles that year? **about 569 people**

   b. Based on the United States population of about 255,000,000 in 1992, about how many people would you estimate died from motor vehicle accidents in the United States in 1992? **about 40,290 people**

LESSON 7-2   APPLICATIONS OF PROPORTIONS   317

Homework Exercises

Assignment Guide

Basic: 13-24, 29-32, 37-42
Average: 15-26, 29, 32-34, 37-42
Enriched: 14, 18-29, 33-42

Exercise Notes

For Exercises 16-18 and 21-22, proportional polygons are written in the same way that congruent polygons are written. That is, the letters (or vertices) will be written in the order in which the segment and angles of each polygon correspond to each other.

20a. 24.7, 38.7, 40.0, 47.6, 11.5 (in thousands per square mile)

25. A(1, –1) and T(1, 5) or A(–5, –1) and T(–5, 5)

20. Geography The population and area of the five largest metropolitan areas in the world are given in the chart below. The population density of a city or country is the ratio of its population to its area.

Metropolitan Area	Population (thousands)	Area (square miles)
Tokyo, Japan	26,952	1089
Mexico City, Mexico	20,207	522
Sao Paulo, Brazil	18,052	451
Seoul, South Korea	16,268	342
New York City, United States	14,622	1274

   a. Find the population density of each metropolitan area. Express each ratio as a decimal rounded to one decimal place.

   b. Which area has the greatest population density? What does this mean?
   Seoul; Sample answer: On the average, there are more people living in each square mile in Seoul than in the other cities.

Suppose the measures of corresponding sides of polygons ABCD and PQRS are proportional. Round your answer to the nearest tenth.

21. If $QR = x + 3$, $PQ = 4$, $BC = x + 5$, and $AB = 5$, find BC and QR. **10; 8**

22. If $DA = x + 2$, $AB = x - 3$, $PS = 5$, and $PQ = 3$, find AB and DA. **7.5; 12.5**

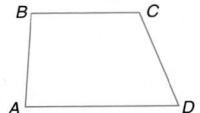
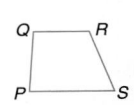

Use a proportion to solve each problem. Round your answer to the nearest tenth.

23. A 6-foot tree casts a 3.25-foot shadow. How tall is a tree that casts a 10-foot shadow at the same time of day? **about 18.5 ft**

24. Joyce Grauser has a drawing that is 20 centimeters long and 14 centimeters wide. She reduces the picture on a copying machine so that the copy is 10 centimeters wide.

   a. How long is the copy? **about 14.3 cm**

   b. What is the percentage of reduction? **about 28.6%**

25. The measures of the corresponding sides of PDRS and BATL are proportional. Given the vertices P(2, 1), D(4, 1), R(4, 5), S(2, 5), B(–2, –1), and L(–2, 5), find the possible coordinates of A and T.

INVESTIGATION

26. Draw a star inside a regular hexagon as illustrated in the diagram at the right. Find AB, BD, AD, AE, AC, and BE by measuring the segments. Find the ratios $\frac{BD}{AB}$, $\frac{AD}{AB}$, $\frac{AE}{AB}$, $\frac{AC}{AB}$, and $\frac{BD}{BE}$. Which ones represent the golden ratio? **See margin.**

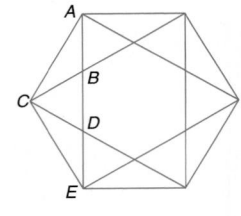

318   CHAPTER 7   SIMILARITY

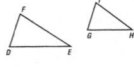

27. So far this semester, Lisa has 76 out of 90 possible points in her history class. If she gets a 100% on the next test and that raises her grade in the course to a 90%, how many points were possible on the test? **50 points**

28. The perimeter of a triangle is 72 inches and the ratio of the measures of the sides is 3:4:5. Find the measure of the sides. **18, 24, 30**

Critical Thinking

29. Statistics The headlines in a newspaper read "U.S. Crime Rate down 0.4% in 1992." Use the information at the right to determine if the headlines told the whole story. Explain your answer. **See margin.**

Year	Population	Total Crimes
1991	252,177,000	14,872,900
1992	255,082,000	14,438,200

Applications

30. Music The vibrations of the strings on a guitar produce the musical sounds. When the number of vibrations per second has a ratio of 2:1, the sounds are one octave apart. The sound from the higher octave has twice the number of vibrations as the sound from the lower octave. The number of vibrations per second is the frequency and is measured in a unit called Hertz. If the lowest string on a guitar has a frequency of 82.5 Hertz, find the frequency of a sound one octave higher. **165 Hertz**

31. Electronics One basic stereo system consists of a CD component, a receiver, and two speakers. To determine how much money you should spend on the system, one rule might be to use a ratio of 1:3:2. In other words, the receiver should cost three times as much as the CD component, and the speakers should cost twice as much as the CD component. If you have saved $1000, how would you allocate your money to buy a stereo system? **$166.67 for CD component, $500.00 for a receiver, $333.33 for speakers**

32. Astronomy Amos plans to make a scale model of Earth, the moon, and the sun. Suppose he makes the diameter of Earth 2 centimeters.

	Diameter	Distance from Earth
Earth	8000 miles	0 miles
Moon	2200 miles	240,000 miles
Sun	864,000 miles	93,000,000 miles

32a. 60 cm

a. How far away in centimeters should he place the moon from Earth?

b. How long should the diameter of the moon be? **0.55 cm**

c. How far away should he make the sun from Earth? **23,250 cm**

d. How long should the diameter of the sun be? **216 cm**

33. Art Joan Frank is a potter making a rectangular clay plaque 25 inches wide and 36 inches long. The plaque shrinks uniformly in the kiln to a 30-inch length. What is the width after the plaque shrinks? **about 20.8 in.**

Chapter 7 319

Additional Answer

29. Sample answer: The newspaper used the following method: If you find the percentage of the population involved in crime in 1991 (5.898%) and the percentage involved in 1992 (5.660%), there are 0.238% fewer people involved in crime. To find the decrease, you divide 0.238 (the change) by 5.898 (the original percentage). The percentage of decrease is about 0.4%. However, most often percentages of change are found by finding the amount of change, (in this case 14,438,200 − 14,872,900 or −434,700) and dividing by the original amount, (in this case 14,872,900). This method yields a change of $\frac{-434,700}{14,872,900}$ or about −0.03%.

Practice Masters Booklet, p. 44

7-2 **Practice Worksheet**

NAME _____ DATE _____

Applications of Proportions

Points M and N are midpoints of their respective segments.

1. Find the ratio AM to MB. $\frac{1}{1}$

2. Find the ratio AM to AB. $\frac{1}{2}$

3. If $\triangle ABC$ is an equilateral triangle, find the ratio of AM to BN. $\frac{1}{1}$

Suppose the measures of corresponding sides of $\triangle ABC$ and $\triangle DEF$ are proportional.

4. If $BC = 20$, $DE = 9$, and $EF = 15$, find AB. **12**

5. If $BC = 24$, $EF = 9$, $AC = y + 30$, and $DF = y$, find AC. **48**

6. If $AB = 5x + 3$, $BC = x + 1$, $DE = 4x$ and $EF = x$, find EF. **1**

Use a proportion to solve each problem.

7. The ratio of seniors to juniors in the Math Club is 2:3. If there are 21 juniors, how many seniors are in the club? **14 seniors**

8. A 15-foot building casts a 9-foot shadow. How tall is a building that casts a 30-foot shadow at the same time? **50 ft**

9. A photo that is 3 inches wide and 5 inches high was enlarged so that it is 12 inches wide. How high is the enlargement? **20 in.**

10. Philip has been eating 2 hamburgers every 5 days. At that rate, how many hamburgers will he eat in 30 days? **12 hamburgers**

T44

Glencoe Division, Macmillan/McGraw-Hill

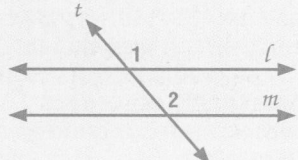
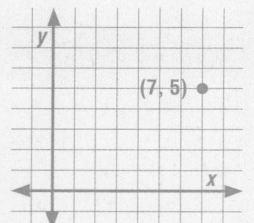
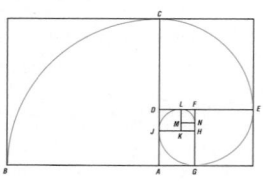

34. Baking Tim's brownie recipe called for 2 squares of chocolate to $\frac{3}{4}$ cup flour. He wants to make as much brownie mix as possible, so he uses all $6\frac{1}{2}$ squares of chocolate that are left in the package. How much flour should he use? $2\frac{7}{16}$ **cups**

35. Consumer Math Henri Rici paid $8000 for a car. After one year its value had decreased by $2000. By what percent had the car depreciated in value? **25%**

36. Travel The scale on a map is 1 centimeter to 57 kilometers. Two cities in North Dakota, Fargo and Bismark, are 4.7 cm apart on the map. What is the actual distance between these cities? **267.9 km**

Computer

37. The *Fibonacci sequence* is also related to the golden ratio. The BASIC computer program below will find the first twenty terms of the Fibonacci sequence. **See margin.**

a. Write the first twenty terms of the Fibonacci sequence.

b. Describe the relationship between the terms of the Fibonacci sequence.

c. Find the ratio between the pairs of consecutive terms of the sequence. What do you notice about these ratios?

```
10 DIM X(20)
20 X(1) = 1
30 X(2) = 1
40 PRINT "THE FIRST TWENTY
   TERMS OF THE FIBONACCI
   SEQUENCE ARE ";
   X(1); ", "; X(2);
50 FOR N = 3 TO 20
60 X(N) = X(N - 1) +
   X(N - 2)
70 PRINT ", "; X(N);
80 NEXT N
90 PRINT "."
100 END
```

Mixed Review

38. Solve the proportion $\frac{t}{18} = \frac{5}{6}$ using cross products. **(Lesson 7-1)** **15**

39. The vertex angle of an isosceles triangle measures 104°. What are the measures of the base angles? **(Lesson 4-7)** **38, 38**

40. Draw parallel lines ℓ and *m* and transversal *t* and label a pair of corresponding angles 1 and 2. **(Lesson 3-1)** **See margin.**

41. Graph the point (7, 5) on a coordinate plane. **(Lesson 1-1)** **See margin.**

Wrap-Up

42. Give three examples of how ratios, rates, and proportions are used in your environment. **See students' work.**

EXTENDING THE LESSON

Math Power: Problem Solving

Use a calculator to find the value of $x = \frac{1}{2}(\sqrt{5} - 1)$. What do you notice about the answer? What happens when you substitute this value for *x* in the polynomial $x^2 + x - 1$?   **0.61803. . .; this is the golden ratio; the value of the polynomial is zero.**

7-3 Similar Polygons

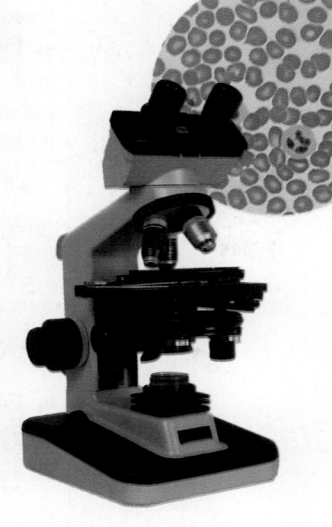

Objectives

After studying this lesson, you should be able to:

7-3A ■ identify similar figures, and

7-3B ■ solve problems involving similar figures.

Application

Research scientists use microscopes in their laboratories to study characteristics of blood cells that are not apparent to the naked eye. The microscope provides a larger view of the actual cells. When figures are the same shape but not necessarily the same size, they are called similar figures.

If the corresponding angles of two polygons are congruent and the measures of the corresponding sides are proportional, then the two polygons have the same shape. The parallelograms below are similar.

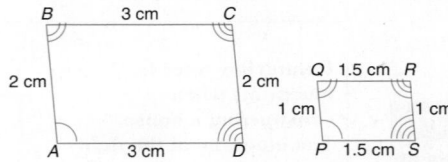

The symbol ~ means *is similar to*. We write ▱*ABCD* ~ ▱*PQRS*, which means *parallelogram ABCD is similar to parallelogram PQRS*. Just as in congruence, the order of the letters indicates the vertices that correspond. We can make the following statements about parallelograms *ABCD* and *PQRS*.

$$\angle A \cong \angle P \qquad \angle B \cong \angle Q \qquad \angle C \cong \angle R \qquad \angle D \cong \angle S$$

$$\frac{AB}{PQ} = \frac{BC}{QR} = \frac{CD}{RS} = \frac{DA}{SP} = \frac{2}{1}$$

The ratio of the lengths of two corresponding sides of two similar polygons is called the **scale factor**. The scale factor of ▱*ABCD* to ▱*PQRS* is 2.

Definition of Similar Polygons

Two polygons are similar if and only if their corresponding angles are congruent and the measures of their corresponding sides are proportional.

The properties of proportions can be used to solve problems involving similar polygons.

LESSON 7-3   SIMILAR POLYGONS   321

ALTERNATE TEACHING STRATEGIES

Using Discussion

Discuss the phrase "if and only if" with the students. Ask them what it means in the definition of similar polygons. Remind them that in a definition or theorem, the phrase "if and only if" means that the hypothesis leads to the conclusion *and* the conclusion leads to the hypothesis.

Using Examples

Copy the figures on page 321 onto the chalkboard. Ask a student to name a pair of corresponding sides. Write those sides as a ratio, substitute the values, and calculate the ratio. Do the same for another pair of corresponding sides. How does it compare to the first ratio? It will be either the same value or a reciprocal. Does order matter when listing segments in a ratio? yes

Lesson Resources

• Reteaching Master 7-3
• Practice Master 7-3
• Enrichment Master 7-3

 Transparency 7-3 contains the 5-Minute Check and a teaching aid for this lesson.

INTRODUCING THE LESSON

🕐 **5-Minute Check**

(over Lesson 7-2)

Suppose the measures of corresponding sides of polygons *ABCD* and *MNOP* are proportional.

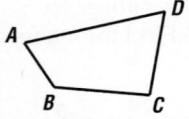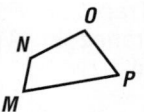

1. If *AB* = 3, *BC* = 5, and *MN* = 1, find *NO*.   **1.67**
2. If *AD* = 12, *NO* = 5, and *MP* = 8, find *BC*.   **7.5**

Use a proportion to solve.

3. The ratio of the height of a 2-year old girl to her height as an adult is 1 to 2. If a girl measures 33 inches at 2 years, how tall will she be as an adult?

$$\frac{2}{1} = \frac{x \text{ in.}}{33 \text{ in.}}$$

x = 66

She will be 66 inches tall, or 5 feet 6 inches.

Motivating the Lesson

Draw several pairs of similar polygons on the chalkboard or overhead along with several pairs of polygons that are not similar. Draw pairs of polygons that have a different number of sides. Ask students what they notice about the pairs.

Teaching Tip When discussing scale factor, point out that there is more than one scale factor for two similar polygons. For example, the scale factor of parallelogram *ABCD* to parallelogram *PQRS* is 2, and the scale factor of parallelogram *PQRS* to parallelogram *ABCD* is $\frac{1}{2}$.

Teaching Tip After defining similar polygons, you may want to ask students if all polygons of different type are similar. For example, are all rectangles similar? **no** Are all regular hexagons similar? **yes**

Chalkboard Examples

For Example 1
Trapezoid *PQRS* is similar to trapezoid *VWTU*. Find the value of *x*.

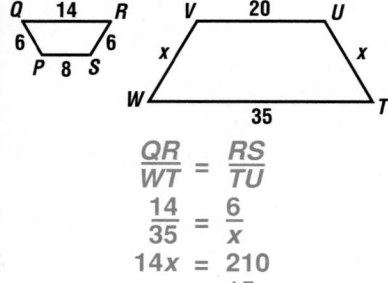

$$\frac{QR}{WT} = \frac{RS}{TU}$$
$$\frac{14}{35} = \frac{6}{x}$$
$$14x = 210$$
$$x = 15$$

For Example 2
Refer to the blueprint in Example 2. Using the proportions of similar figures, determine the dimensions of the utility room.
$$\frac{1}{16} = \frac{0.5}{w} \qquad \frac{1}{16} = \frac{0.75}{l}$$
$$w = 8 \text{ feet} \qquad l = 12 \text{ feet}$$

Example 1

Quadrilateral *PQRS* is similar to quadrilateral *ABCD*.

a. Find the value of *x*.

The corresponding sides are proportional, so we can write a proportion to find the value of *x*.

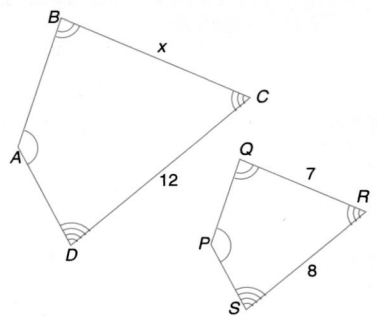

$$\frac{BC}{QR} = \frac{DC}{SR}$$
$$\frac{x}{7} = \frac{12}{8}$$
$$8x = 84 \qquad \textit{Cross products}$$
$$x = 10.5$$

The value of *x* is 10.5.

b. Find the scale factor of quadrilateral *PQRS* to quadrilateral *ABCD*.

The scale factor is the ratio of the lengths of two corresponding sides. $\overline{SR}$ and $\overline{DC}$ are two corresponding sides.

$$\text{scale factor} = \frac{SR}{DC}$$
$$= \frac{8}{12} \text{ or } \frac{2}{3}$$

The scale factor of quadrilateral *PQRS* to quadrilateral *ABCD* is $\frac{2}{3}$.

Example 2

APPLICATION

Construction

Contractors refer to blueprints when constructing a house. The blueprint at the right is similar to the floor plan of a constructed house. One inch on the blueprint represents 16 feet in the actual house. Using the properties of similar figures, determine the dimensions of the kitchen.

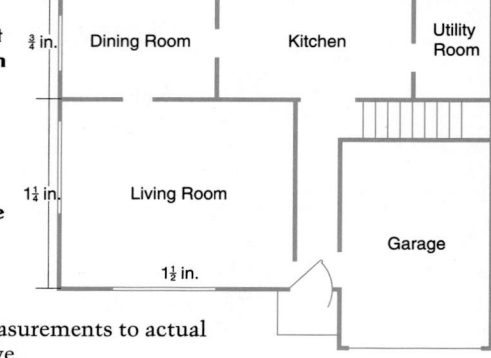

First create a proportion relating the blueprint measurements to actual measurements. Then solve.

$$\frac{\textit{blueprint measurement}}{\textit{actual measurement}} = \frac{\textit{blueprint kitchen measurement}}{\textit{actual kitchen measurement}}$$

$$\frac{1}{16} = \frac{1.25}{\ell} \qquad 1\tfrac{1}{4} = 1.25 \qquad\qquad \frac{1}{16} = \frac{0.75}{w} \qquad \tfrac{3}{4} = 0.75$$
$$\ell = 20 \qquad\qquad\qquad\qquad\qquad\qquad w = 12$$

The kitchen is 20 feet long and 12 feet wide.

CHECKING FOR UNDERSTANDING

Communicating Mathematics

2. yes; all the angles are congruent and the sides are in the ratio of 1:1.

3. no; their sides may not be congruent.

Guided Practice

Read and study the lesson to answer each question.

1. Describe the difference between congruence and similarity. **See margin.**

2. Must two congruent figures be similar? Explain.

3. Must two similar figures be congruent? Explain.

4. Are two equiangular polygons necessarily similar? Explain. **no; they may not have the same number of sides.**

List the conditions necessary for the pairs of figures to be similar. See margin.

5. $\triangle ABC \sim \triangle DEF$

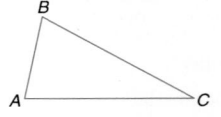 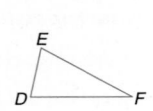

6. polygon $RSTVWX \sim$ polygon $LMNOPQ$

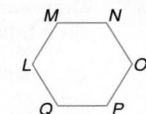

Determine whether each pair of figures is similar. Justify your answer. See margin for justification.

7.

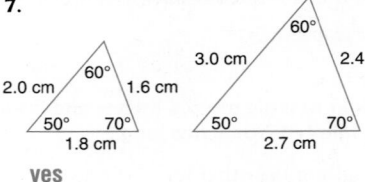

yes

8.

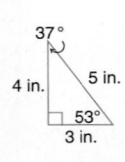

2.4 cm ... 9.2 in. ... 5 in.

no

Is each pair of figures described necessarily similar? Explain. See margin.

9. any two right triangles

10. any two congruent quadrilaterals

11. any two regular polygons

12. any two parallelograms

Given quadrilateral LEFT ~ quadrilateral CORK, find each of the following.

13. scale factor of $LEFT$ to $CORK$ $\frac{2}{3}$

14. KR **15**

15. RO **15**

16. CO **22.5**

17. **a.** perimeter of $LEFT$ **43**

   b. perimeter of $CORK$ **64.5**

   c. ratio of the perimeters of $LEFT$ and $CORK$ $\frac{43}{64.5} = \frac{2}{3}$

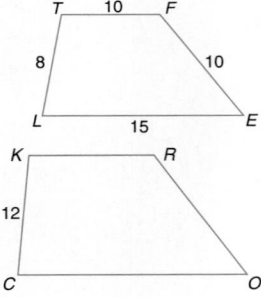

LESSON 7-3   SIMILAR POLYGONS   323

EVALUATING THE LESSON

Checking for Understanding

Exercises 1-17 are designed to help you assess students' understanding through reading, writing, speaking, and modeling. You should work through Exercises 1-4 with your students and then monitor their work on Exercises 5-17.

Closing the Lesson

Modeling Activity Give students the approximate dimensions of their school building and ask them to determine a scale factor that would allow them to get a floor plan on an $8\frac{1}{2}$-by-11-inch sheet of paper. Have students sketch the floor plan.

Additional Answers

1. Sample answer: Congruence means that two figures are exactly the same size and shape. Similarity means that two figures have the same shape, but they may be different in size.

5. $\angle A \cong \angle D$, $\angle B \cong \angle E$, $\angle C \cong \angle F$, $\frac{AB}{DE} = \frac{BC}{EF} = \frac{AC}{DF}$

6. $\angle R \cong \angle L$, $\angle S \cong \angle M$, $\angle T \cong \angle N$, $\angle V \cong \angle O$, $\angle W \cong \angle P$, $\angle X \cong \angle Q$, $\frac{RS}{LM} = \frac{ST}{MN} = \frac{TV}{NO} = \frac{VW}{OP} = \frac{WX}{PQ} = \frac{XR}{QL}$

7. Corresponding angles are congruent and $\frac{2.0}{3.0} = \frac{1.6}{2.4} = \frac{1.8}{2.7}$.

8. Corresponding angles are not congruent.

9. No, their two pairs of acute angles may not be congruent.

10. Yes, their corresponding angles are congruent, and their corresponding sides are in the ratio 1:1.

11. No, they may not have the same number of sides.

12. No, their angles may not be congruent and their sides may not be proportional.

Homework Exercises

Assignment Guide

Basic: 18-32, 34, 38-40, 43-49
Average: 19, 21-35, 38, 40-41, 43-49
Enriched: 19, 22-23, 36-38, 41-49

Additional Answers

20.

21.

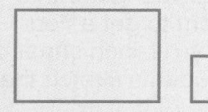

22. Impossible
23.

24.

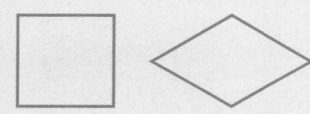

Reteaching Masters Booklet, p. 39

 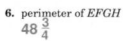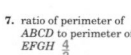
EXERCISES

Practice Two similar polygons are shown. Find the values of x and y.

A

18.

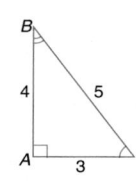

19.

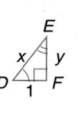 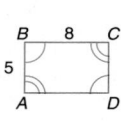 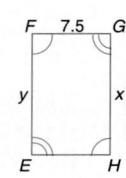

$1\frac{2}{3}, 1\frac{1}{3}$ 12, 12

B Draw and label a pair of polygons for each. If it is impossible to draw two
such figures, write *impossible*. See margin.

20. two similar isosceles triangles

21. two rectangles that are not similar

22. two equilateral triangles that are not similar

23. two regular hexagons that are similar

24. two rhombi that are not similar

25. two similar trapezoids

The legs of a right triangle are 6.2 inches and 7 inches long. The shorter leg
of a similar triangle is 17.6 inches long.

26. Find the length of the other leg of the second triangle. about 19.9 in.

27. Find the ratio of the measures of the hypotenuses. $\frac{6.2}{17.6} = \frac{31}{88}$ or about 0.35

28. Given △DEC ~ △DAB, m∠A = 25,
    m∠DCE = 80, AE = 6, AD = 10, and
    DC = 5, find each of the following.

    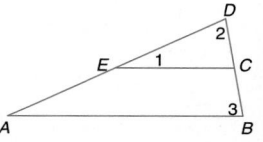

    a. m∠1 25   b. m∠2 75
    c. m∠3 80   d. DB 12.5
    e. What conclusions can be made about
       $\overline{EC}$ and $\overline{AB}$? $\frac{EC}{AB} = \frac{2}{5}$ and $\overline{EC} \parallel \overline{AB}$

29. Use grid paper and draw enlargements of each figure. Make each segment
    twice the length of the original. See Solutions Manual.

    I. 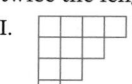   II.    III.   IV.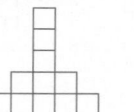

RETEACHING THE LESSON

Have each student use a
straightedge to draw and label a
polygon of any type and size. Have
them measure each side and list
the measures. Have them multiply
each measure by $\frac{1}{2}$ and use these
calculated values to construct a
similar polygon with a scale factor
of $\frac{1}{2}$.

Additional Answer

25.

30. Copy and complete each chart below, using the information from Exercise 29. **See margin.**

a.

	I	II	III	IV
Perimeter of Original	?	?	?	?
Perimeter of Enlargement	?	?	?	?

b.

	I	II	III	IV
Area of Original	?	?	?	?
Area of Enlargement	?	?	?	?

c. What conclusions can you draw from Chart **a?**

d. What conclusions can you draw from Chart **b?**

e. What would happen to the perimeters of the enlargements if the segment measures had been tripled?

f. What would happen to the area of the enlargements if the segment measures had been tripled?

g. Are the figures and their enlargements similar? **yes**

31. In order to reduce a 5-inch by 7-inch photograph, Tina uses a copy machine that reduces a document by 10%. Suppose she reduces the photo, then reduces the copy, and then reduces that copy, and so on. How many times would she have to use the copy machine in order to fit the photo into a 4-inch square? **6 times**

INVESTIGATION

Plot the given points on graph paper. Draw *RSTV* **and** $\overline{LB}$**. Find points** *M* **and** *N* **such that** *RSTV* **is similar to** *LBMN*. **See Solutions Manual for graphs.**

32. *R*(-1,0), *S*(1,0), *T*(2,3), *V*(-2,3), *L*(-3,0), *B*(3,0) **M(6,9), N(-6,9) or M(6,-9), N(-6,-9)**

33. *R*(0,4), *S*(0,0), *T*(8,0), *V*(4,6), *L*(2,0), *B*(0,0) **M(0,-4), N(3,-2) or M(0,4) N(3,2)**

Make a scale drawing of each using the given scale. See Solutions Manual.

34. A soccer field is 91 meters by 46 meters. scale: 1 mm = 1 m

35. A basketball court is 84 feet by 50 feet. scale: $\frac{1}{8}$ in. = 2 ft

36. A football field is 100 yards by 160 yards. scale: $\frac{1}{4}$ in. = 20 ft

37. A tennis court is 36 feet by 78 feet. scale: $\frac{1}{8}$ in. = 1 ft

Critical Thinking

38. Two rectangular solids are similar with ratios between the corresponding sides 3:1.

a. If you were to build a model of each using straws, would the larger solid take three times as many straws? Explain. **yes; the sides are 3:1.**

b. If you were to paint each solid, would the larger solid take three times as much paint? Explain. **no; the areas are in the ratio 9:1.**

c. Would the larger solid hold exactly three times as much water? Explain. **no; the volumes are in the ratio 27:1.**

LESSON 7-3   SIMILAR POLYGONS   325

Additional Answers

30a.

	I	II	III	IV
Perimeter of Original	16	28	20	22
Perimeter of Enlargement	32	56	40	44

30b.

	I	II	III	IV
Perimeter of Original	10	13	11	18
Perimeter of Enlargement	40	52	44	72

30c. Sample answer: The perimeters of the enlargements are twice the perimeters of the originals.

30d. Sample answer: The areas of the enlargements are four times the areas of the originals.

30e. The perimeters of the enlargements would be three times the perimeters of the originals.

30f. The areas of the enlargements would be nine times the areas of the originals.

Practice Masters Booklet, p. 45

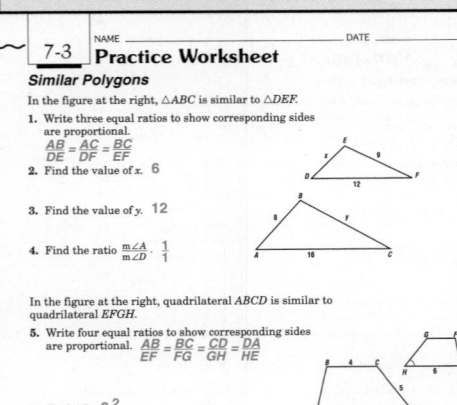

Applications

39. **Engineering**   Janis Shaull designs automobiles using scale drawings. Suppose one length on an automobile is 20 centimeters and corresponds to 2 centimeters on the drawing. Find the length on the automobile that corresponds to 9 centimeters on the drawing. 90 cm

40. **Art**   The council members of Millersville wish to honor the town's founder Clara Miller by placing a statue of Ms. Miller in the town square. They want the statue to be 8 feet tall although Ms. Miller herself was only 5 feet 2 inches tall. If her arms were 2 feet long, how long should the sculptor make the arms on the statue? about 37 in.

41. **Publishing**   Randall is working on the school yearbook. He must reduce a photo that is 4 inches wide by 5 inches long to fit in a space 3 inches wide. How long will the reduced photo be? 3.75 in.

42. **Education**   Overhead projectors project images from a transparency onto a screen so that they can be seen by many people. The scale factor of the projected image of a transparency to the transparency is 8. If the transparency is $8\frac{1}{2}$ inches by 11 inches, what are the dimensions of its image? 68 by 88 inches

Mixed Review

43. The ratio of seniors to juniors on a football team is 2:3. If there are 21 juniors, how many seniors are on the team? **(Lesson 7-2)** 14 seniors

44. What kind of quadrilateral has exactly one pair of parallel sides? **(Lesson 6-6)** trapezoid

45. If two sides of a triangle have measures of 5 and 8, what must be true about the measure of the third side? **(Lesson 5-6)** it is less than 13 and greater than 3

46. Name three different ways in which two lines can be positioned in space relative to each other. **(Lesson 3-1)** intersecting, parallel, skew

47. Rewrite the following conditional statement in if-then form. *I will wear a sweater when it is cool.* **(Lesson 2-2)** If it is cool, then I will wear a sweater.

48. An angle separates a plane into three parts. Name the parts. **(Lesson 1-6)** the angle itself, the interior, the exterior

Wrap-Up

49. Describe how you can tell if two polygons are similar. if their corresponding angles are congruent , and their corresponding sides are proportional

326   CHAPTER 7   SIMILARITY

EXTENDING THE LESSON

Math Power: Connections

If quadrilateral *NTSU* is similar to quadrilateral *JXBF* and the scale factor of quadrilateral *NTSU* to quadrilateral *JXBF* is 1, what is the scale factor of quadrilateral *JXBF* to quadrilateral *NTSU*? What can you say about the two quadrilaterals?   1; they are congruent

---

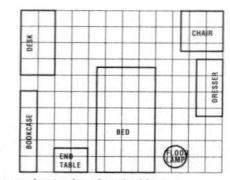
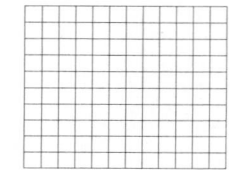

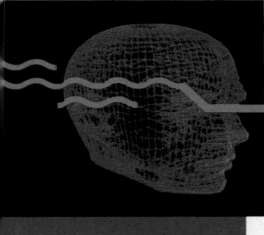

Technology
Similarity

BASIC
▶ **Geometric Supposer**
Graphing calculators
LOGO
Spreadsheets

The Geometric Supposer is a powerful tool for investigating geometric relationships. Let's use it to look at some relationships in triangles.

Begin by loading the Geometric Supposer: Triangles and drawing an acute or obtuse triangle. Your triangle will be labeled $\triangle ABC$. Choose a random point on $\overline{AB}$ by choosing *(2) Label* from the main menu, then choosing *(4) Random Point* from the Label menu. The random point will be labeled D.

Now draw a segment through D that is parallel to $\overline{BC}$. To do this choose *(1) Draw* on the main menu, then choose *(5) Parallel* from the Draw menu. Enter D as the point you wish the line to pass through and $\overline{BC}$ as the line to which it will be parallel. Define the length to intersect segments AC and AB. This parallel segment will be labeled $\overline{EF}$. *Points E and D are the same point.*

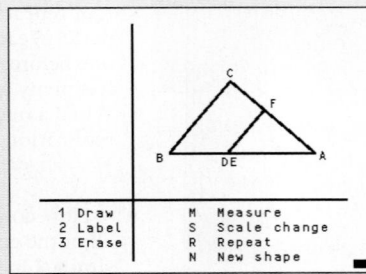

EXERCISES

Use the triangle you drew on the Geometric Supposer to answer each question. Answers for Exercises 1-3 will vary. See students' work.

1. Find the measure of each angle using the measure option.
   a. $\angle CBA$ b. $\angle BCA$ c. $\angle BAC$
   d. $\angle FEA$ e. $\angle EFA$ f. $\angle EAF$

2. Find the measure of each segment using the measure option.
   a. $\overline{AB}$ b. $\overline{AC}$ c. $\overline{BC}$
   d. $\overline{AE}$ e. $\overline{AF}$ f. $\overline{EF}$

3. Find each ratio.
   a. $\dfrac{AB}{AE}$ b. $\dfrac{AC}{AF}$ c. $\dfrac{BC}{EF}$

4. Yes; the angles are congruent and the sides are proportional.

4. Is $\triangle ABC$ similar to $\triangle AEF$? Justify your answer.

5. Draw several other triangles on the Geometric Supposer and repeat Exercises 1-4. Can you make a conjecture? A line parallel to a side of a triangle forms a triangle similar to the original triangle.

TECHNOLOGY 327

Using Technology
Objective This optional page shows how the *Geometric Supposer* can be used to investigate geometric relationships in triangles.

Teaching Suggestions
It may be easy for some students to simply press computer buttons in this lesson without understanding what is happening. Try to make sure that students follow the steps and understand the logic of the lesson by asking them what should happen next. Lead a problem-solving discussion and have students decide on the steps in the path of the solution. Make sure to define the problem you want to solve.

Students can also experiment with scale change and how it relates to similar triangles. What do they think scale change will do? How does it relate to scale factor?

Lesson Resources

- Reteaching Master 7-4
- Practice Master 7-4
- Enrichment Master 7-4
- Evaluation Master, pp. 93, 97
- Activity Master, p. 21
- Lab Manual, pp. 50-53

 Transparency 7-4 contains the 5-Minute Check and a teaching aid for this lesson.

INTRODUCING THE LESSON

🕐 5-Minute Check

(over Lesson 7-3)

Refer to the figure below. Pentagon *ABCDH* ~ pentagon *DEFGH*.

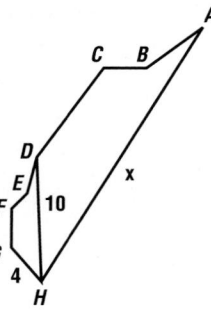

1. Find the value of *x*.

$$\frac{GH}{DH} = \frac{DH}{AH}$$

$x = 25$

2. Find the scale factor of pentagon *ABCDH* to pentagon *DEFGH*.

$$\frac{GH}{DH} = \frac{4}{10} = \frac{2}{5}$$

3. If m∠*EDH* = 12, m∠*DCB* = 96, and *BC* = 4, find m∠*GFE*, *FE*, and m∠*BAH*.   96; 1.6; 12

Motivating the Lesson

Many books on fractals and fractal geometry contain pictures of fractals. Refer students to pages 680-691 of their text for a discussion of fractals. Check a book out from the library or bring your own into class to show some examples to your students.

Objectives

7-4A
7-4B

After studying this lesson, you should be able to:
- identify similar triangles, and
- use similar triangles to solve problems.

Application

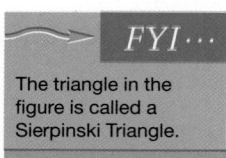

FYI···

The triangle in the figure is called a Sierpinski Triangle.

How many similar triangles are in the figure at the right? The figure is a fractal pattern. Fractals take a pattern and repeat that pattern several times. The fractal pattern on the right is of level four. There are four repeats of the large main pattern, each one smaller than the one before. Note that this pattern has many similar triangles in it. When a figure has this kind of self replication, it is called self similar. *You can learn more about fractals on pages 680–691.*

Basic Pattern

There are 200 similar triangles.

How do you know when two triangles are similar? Is it necessary to prove all of the conditions of the definition to determine whether two triangles are similar? In Chapter 4 you learned several tests to determine whether two triangles are congruent. There are also tests to determine whether two triangles are similar.

INVESTIGATION

Draw △*ABC* with m∠*C* = 45, *AC* = 5 cm and m∠*A* = 75. Then measure $\overline{BA}$ and calculate the ratio of the two sides, $\frac{CA}{BA}$. Draw a second triangle △*DEF* with m∠*F* = 45, *DF* = 8 cm, and m∠*D* = 75 and calculate the ratio of the sides $\frac{FD}{ED}$.

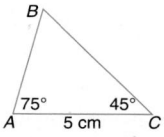

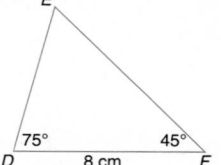

Each ratio is about 1.22. Calculate $\frac{BA}{BC}$ and $\frac{ED}{EF}$. Are these ratios the same? How about $\frac{CA}{BC}$ and $\frac{FD}{EF}$? Draw a few more triangles with the same angle measures and different side measures. Do all of the triangles appear to be similar?

The investigation leads to the following postulate.

ALTERNATE TEACHING STRATEGIES

Using Computers

Have small groups use the *Geometric Supposer* and the technology feature on page 327 to draw a triangle and a line parallel to one side within the triangle. Instruct them to make conjectures about what is necessary to prove the triangles are similar. Have them draw other triangles to test their conjectures.

Using Investigation

In the investigation on page 328, what parts of the triangles are congruent in the figures?   at least two angles Will this technique work for obtuse triangles? Will it work for right triangles?   yes Have students write a hypothesis about what is necessary to prove two triangles similar, using mathematical language and the if-then form.

Postulate 7-1 AA Similarity	**If two angles of one triangle are congruent to two angles of another triangle, then the triangles are similar.**

Example 1

In the figure, $\overline{ST} \parallel \overline{PR}$, $QS = 3$, $SP = 1$, and $TR = 1.2$. Show that $QT = 3.6$.

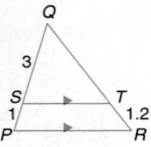

Since $\overline{ST} \parallel \overline{PR}$, $\angle QST \cong \angle QPR$ and $\angle QTS \cong \angle QRP$.

By AA Similarity, $\triangle SQT \sim \triangle PQR$. Using the definition of similar polygons, $\frac{QT}{QR} = \frac{QS}{QP}$. By the Segment Addition Postulate, $QP = QS + SP$ and $QR = QT + TR$. Substituting these values into the proportion results in the following proportion that can be solved for QT.

$$\frac{QT}{QT + TR} = \frac{QS}{QS + SP}$$

$$\frac{QT}{QT + 1.2} = \frac{3}{3 + 1} \quad \textit{Substitution property of equality}$$

$$(QT)(3 + 1) = 3(QT + 1.2) \quad \textit{Cross products}$$

$$4QT = 3QT + 3.6 \quad \textit{Distributive property}$$

$$QT = 3.6 \quad \textit{Subtraction property}$$

It is also possible to prove triangles similar by testing the measures of corresponding sides for proportionality.

Theorem 7-1 SSS Similarity	**If the measures of the corresponding sides of two triangles are proportional, then the triangles are similar.**

Proof of Theorem 7-1

Given: $\frac{PQ}{AB} = \frac{QR}{BC} = \frac{RP}{CA}$

Prove: $\triangle BAC \sim \triangle QPR$

Locate D on $\overline{AB}$ so that $\overline{DB} \cong \overline{PQ}$ and draw $\overline{DE}$ so that $\overline{DE} \parallel \overline{AC}$.

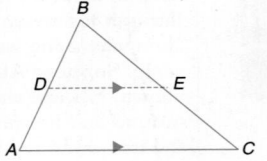 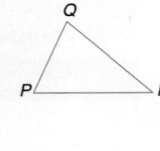

Paragraph Proof:

Since $\overline{DB} \cong \overline{PQ}$, the given proportion will become $\frac{DB}{AB} = \frac{QR}{BC} = \frac{RP}{CA}$. Since $\overline{DE} \parallel \overline{AC}$, $\angle BDE \cong \angle A$ and $\angle BED \cong \angle C$. By AA Similarity, $\triangle BDE \sim \triangle BAC$. By the definition of similar polygons, $\frac{DB}{AB} = \frac{BE}{BC} = \frac{ED}{CA}$. Using the two proportions and substitution, $\frac{QR}{BC} = \frac{BE}{BC}$ and $\frac{RP}{CA} = \frac{ED}{CA}$. This means that $QR = BE$ and $RP = ED$ or $\overline{QR} \cong \overline{BE}$ and $\overline{RP} \cong \overline{ED}$. With these congruences and $\overline{DB} \cong \overline{PQ}$, $\triangle BDE \cong \triangle QPR$ by SSS. By CPCTC, $\angle B \cong \angle Q$ and $\angle BDE \cong \angle P$. But $\angle BDE \cong \angle A$, so $\angle A \cong \angle P$. By AA Similarity, $\triangle BAC \sim \triangle QPR$.

LESSON 7-4 SIMILAR TRIANGLES 329

Teaching Tip When beginning this lesson, write the definition of similar polygons on the chalkboard or overhead. Ask students if all of those conditions need to be met to prove two triangles similar.

Chalkboard Example

For Example 1
In the figure, $\overline{AB} \parallel \overline{DE}$, $DA = 2$, $CA = 8$, and $CE = 3$. Show that $CB = 4$.

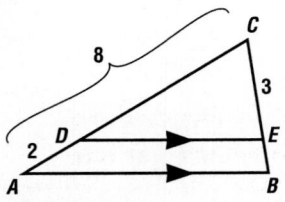

Since $\overline{AB} \parallel \overline{DE}$, $\angle CDE \cong \angle CAB$ and $\angle CED \cong \angle CBA$. Thus, $\triangle CDE \sim \triangle CAB$ by AA Similarity, and $\frac{CD}{CA} = \frac{CE}{CB}$. By the segment addition postulate, $CA = CD + DA$ and $CB = CE + EB$. By substitution, the proportion becomes

$$\frac{CD}{CD + DA} = \frac{CE}{CE + EB}$$

$$\frac{6}{8} = \frac{3}{3 + EB}$$

$$6(3 + EB) = 3 \cdot 8$$

$$18 + 6(EB) = 24$$

$$6(EB) = 6$$

$$EB = 1$$

$$CB = CE + EB$$

$$CB = 3 + 1$$

$$CB = 4$$

Teaching Tip When stating Theorem 7-1, emphasize that the conditions must be true for all three pairs of sides.

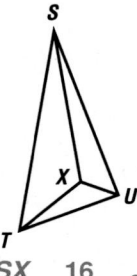
The next theorem describes another test for similarity of triangles. You will be asked to prove this theorem in Exercise 27.

Theorem 7-2 *SAS Similarity*	**If the measures of two sides of a triangle are proportional to the measures of two corresponding sides of another triangle and the included angles are congruent, then the triangles are similar.**

You can use SAS similarity to determine if two triangles are similar.

Example 2

Angle *RVU* is trisected by $\overline{VS}$ and $\overline{VT}$. If **VR = 20, VS = 25, VU = 15,** and **VT = 12,** determine which triangles in the figure are similar.

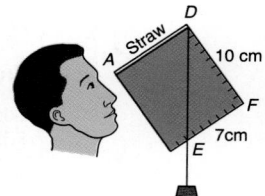

∠*RVS* ≅ ∠*SVT* ≅ ∠*TVU* since ∠*RVU* is trisected. If the corresponding sides which include the angle are proportional, then the triangles are similar. Find ratios of corresponding sides to see which ones are equivalent, thus forming a proportion.

$$\frac{VR}{VS} = \frac{20}{25} = \frac{4}{5}$$

$$\frac{VT}{VS} = \frac{12}{25}$$

$$\frac{VT}{VU} = \frac{12}{15} = \frac{4}{5}$$

Therefore, $\frac{VR}{VS} = \frac{VT}{VU}$ and $\Delta RSV \sim \Delta TUV$ by SAS Similarity.

Example 3

APPLICATION

Forestry

A hypsometer as shown at the right can be used to measure the height of a tree. Look through the straw to the top of the tree. Note where the weighted string crosses the scale. Suppose Al Henke used the readings shown. His eye was 167 cm from the ground and he was 15 m, or 1500 cm, from the tree. Find the height of the tree.

Let *x* represent the measure of the distance from eye level to the tip of the tree. If we can show that ΔDEF and ΔABC are similar, we can set up a proportion of corresponding sides and solve for *x*.

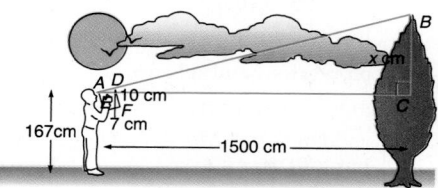

Assume that $\angle DFE$ and $\angle BCA$ are right angles. $\overline{DE} \parallel \overline{BC}$ and $\overline{AD} \parallel \overline{EF}$.

$\angle FED \cong \angle ADE$	*They are alternate interior angles.*
$\angle ADE \cong \angle ABC$	*They are corresponding angles.*
$\angle FED \cong \angle ABC$	*Congruence of angles is transitive.*
$\angle DFE \cong \angle BCA$	*All right angles are congruent.*
$\triangle DEF \sim \triangle ABC$	*AA Similarity*

Therefore, $\dfrac{BC}{EF} = \dfrac{AC}{DF}$ *Measures of corresponding sides of similar triangles are proportional.*

$$\dfrac{x}{7} = \dfrac{1500}{10}$$
$$10x = 10{,}500$$
$$x = 1050$$

The tree is $1050 + 167$ or 1217 centimeters tall. *The tree is about 12 meters tall.*

Like congruence of triangles, similarity of triangles is reflexive, symmetric, and transitive. You will prove this theorem in Exercise 29.

Theorem 7-3   **Similarity of triangles is reflexive, symmetric, and transitive.**

CHECKING FOR UNDERSTANDING

Communicating Mathematics

Read and study the lesson to answer each question. See margin.

1. Describe three ways to determine whether two triangles are similar.

2. List the tests to prove triangles are congruent and compare them to the tests to prove triangles are similar. How are the tests alike? How are they different?

3. The triangles in the figure are similar with corresponding sides of lengths a and d, c and f, and b and e. Explain why you can write the proportion $\dfrac{a}{c} = \dfrac{d}{f}$.

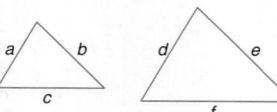

Guided Practice

4. If $\overline{LM} \parallel \overline{PT}$, name all of the congruent angles in the figure.
$\angle MLP, \angle LPT; \angle LMT, \angle MTP;$
$\angle LKM, \angle TKP; \angle LKT, \angle MKP$

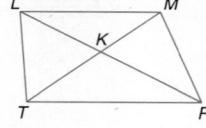

5. If $\triangle RAT \sim \triangle OFT$, name the proportional parts of the triangles.
$\overline{RA}, \overline{OF}; \overline{AT}, \overline{FT}; \overline{RT}, \overline{OT}$

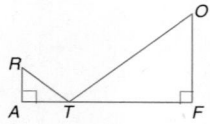

Homework Exercises

Assignment Guide

Basic: 15-26, 31-33, 35-41
Average: 17-28, 31-33, 35-41
Enriched: 17-18, 20, 22, 23-31, 34-41
All: Mid-Chapter Review, 1-7

Determine whether each pair of triangles is similar using the given information. Explain your answer.

6.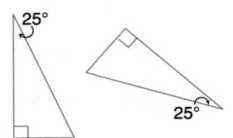

yes; AA Similarity

7.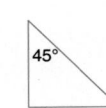

no

8.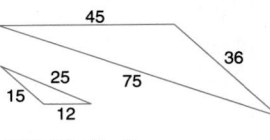

yes; SSS Similarity

9.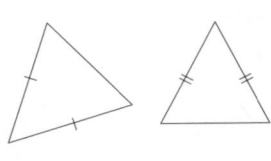

no

10.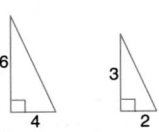

yes; SAS Similarity

11.

yes; AA Similarity

Determine if each pair of triangles is similar. If similar, state the reason and find the missing measures.

12.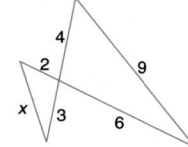

yes; SAS Similarity; $x = 4.5$

13.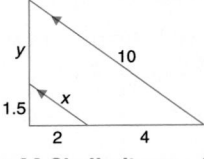

yes; AA Similarity; $x = 3\frac{1}{3}$, $y = 3$

14. One angle in a right triangle measures 25°. A second right triangle has a 65° angle. Are the two triangles similar? Explain. **yes; AA similarity**

EXERCISES

Practice

Determine whether each pair of triangles is similar using the given information. Explain your answer.

15.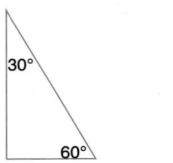

yes; AA Similarity

16.

no

17.

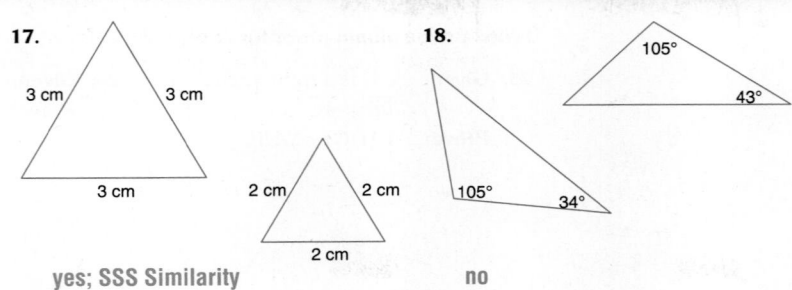

yes; SSS Similarity

18.

no

Find the value of *x*.

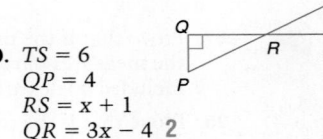

19. $QR = x + 4$
$RS = 2x + 3$
$QP = 3$
$TS = 5$ **11**

20. $TS = 6$
$QP = 4$
$RS = x + 1$
$QR = 3x - 4$ **2**

Identify the similar triangles in each figure. Explain your answer.

22. $\triangle CHB \sim \triangle DHE$
(AA Similarity)
$\triangle ACE \sim \triangle ADB$ (AA
Similarity)
$\triangle EAC \sim \triangle BHC$ (AA
Similarity)
$\triangle BAD \sim \triangle BHC$ (Th. 7-3)
$\triangle EHD \sim \triangle EAC$ (Th. 7-3)
$\triangle BAD \sim \triangle EHD$ (Th. 7-3)

21.

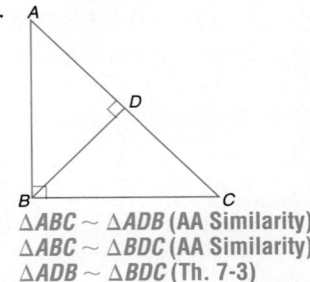

$\triangle ABC \sim \triangle ADB$ (AA Similarity)
$\triangle ABC \sim \triangle BDC$ (AA Similarity)
$\triangle ADB \sim \triangle BDC$ (Th. 7-3)

22.

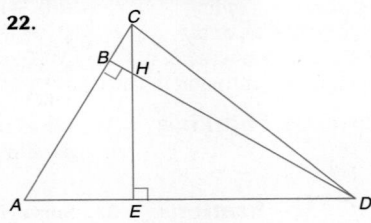

Identify the similar triangles in each figure. Explain why they are similar and find the missing measures.

23. If $\overline{BE} \parallel \overline{CD}$, find *CD*, *AC*, and *BC*.

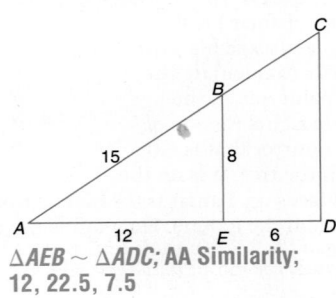

$\triangle AEB \sim \triangle ADC$; AA Similarity;
12, 22.5, 7.5

24. If *VRST* is a parallelogram, find *TC*, *SB*, and *SC*.

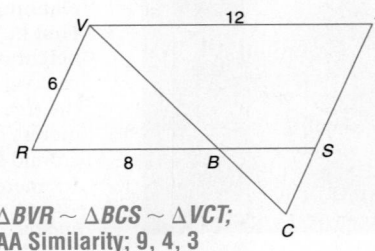

$\triangle BVR \sim \triangle BCS \sim \triangle VCT$;
AA Similarity; 9, 4, 3

LESSON 7-4   SIMILAR TRIANGLES   333

RETEACHING THE LESSON

Have each student use a
straightedge to draw a triangle.
Have them measure the sides of
the triangle and draw a similar
triangle with a scale factor of $\frac{1}{2}$.
Ask students how they know the
triangles are similar.   **because
the sides are proportional**
Explain that this is a demonstration
of SSS Similarity.

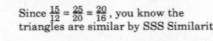
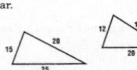
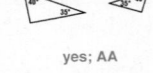
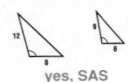
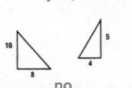
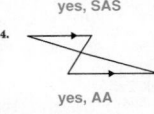

Exercise Notes

For Exercises 27-29, draw a picture of the problem situation.

For Exercise 29, prove all three parts separately to prove the theorem.

For Exercise 30a, use the distance formula.

Additional Answers

25. Statements   (Reasons)
a. ∠D is a right angle; $\overline{BE} \perp \overline{AC}$ (Given)
b. ∠EBA is a right angle. (⊥ lines form four rt. ∠s)
c. ∠D ≅ ∠EBA   (All rt. ∠s are ≅)
d. ∠A ≅ ∠A   (congruence of angles is reflexive)
e. △ADC ~ △ABE   (AA Similarity)

26. Statements   (Reasons)
a. $\overline{QS} \parallel \overline{PT}$ (Given)
b. ∠SQR ≅ ∠PTR; ∠QSR ≅ ∠TPR   (If 2 ∥ lines are cut by a transversal, alt. int. ∠s are ≅)
c. △QRS ~ △TRP   (AA Similarity)

Practice Masters Booklet, p. 46

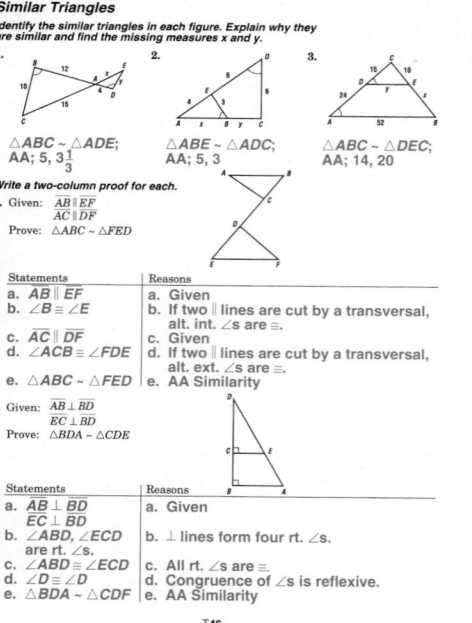

Write a two-column proof for each.   See margin.

25. Given: ∠D is a right angle.
      $\overline{BE} \perp \overline{AC}$
    Prove: △ADC ~ △ABE

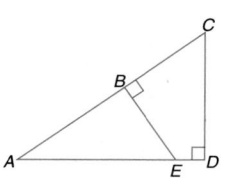

26. Given: $\overline{QS} \parallel \overline{PT}$
    Prove: △QRS ~ △TRP

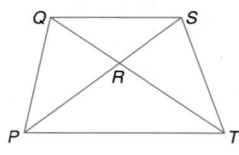

27. See Solutions Manual.

27. Prove that if the measures of two sides of a triangle are proportional to the measures of two corresponding sides of another triangle and the included angles are congruent, the triangles are similar. (Theorem 7-2)

28. Prove that if the measures of the legs of two right triangles are proportional, the triangles are similar.   See margin.

29. Prove Theorem 7-3.   See Solutions Manual.

31. One angle must be congruent to its corresponding angle and its adjacent sides must be proportional to their corresponding sides.

30. Graph △ABC and △TRC with vertices A(-2, 7), B(-2, -8), C(4, 4), R(0, -4), and T(0, 6).
    a. Prove that △ABC ~ △TRC.   See Solutions Manual.
    b. Find the ratio of the perimeters of the triangles. $\frac{3}{2}$

Critical Thinking

31. What are the minimum conditions necessary in order to have similar parallelograms?

Applications

32. **Surveying**   Leslie uses a carpenter's square to find the distance across a river. She puts the square on top of a pole which is high enough to sight along $\overline{BC}$ to point P across the river. Then she sights along $\overline{BE}$ to point Q. If QA = 2 feet and BA = 6 feet, find AP.   **18 ft**

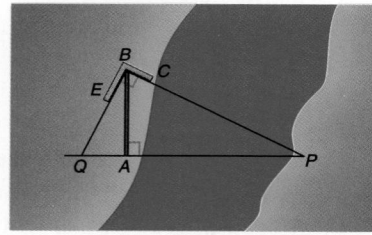

33. **Landscaping**   Lamar Presley is planning to landscape his yard. First he needs to calculate the height of a palm tree in the backyard. He sights the top of the tree in a mirror that is 6.0 meters from the tree. It is on the ground and faces up. Lamar is 0.9 meters from the mirror and his eyes are 1.8 meters from the ground. How tall is the tree? *Hint: The angle between the ground and the line of sight is congruent to the angle between the ground and the line from the mirror to the tree.*   **12 m**

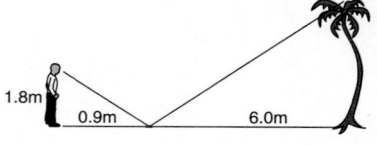

334   CHAPTER 7   SIMILARITY

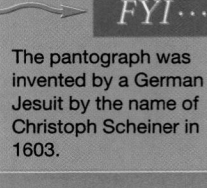

FYI ···

The pantograph was invented by a German Jesuit by the name of Christoph Scheiner in 1603.

a. △*PAB* ~ △*TCB*
SAS Similarity

34. Cartography The pantograph is an instrument that was originally used to enlarge or reduce maps. The bars are attached to form parallelogram *DCBA*. Point *P* is fixed to the drawing board and a pencil is attached at *T*. The artist traces the original picture at *B*. Suppose *PA* is 4, *CD* is 8, *CT* is 9, and *AD* is 18.

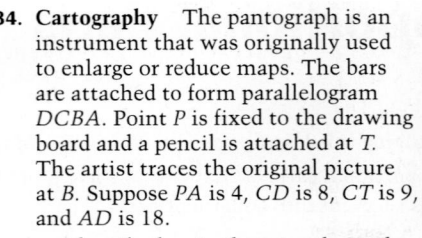
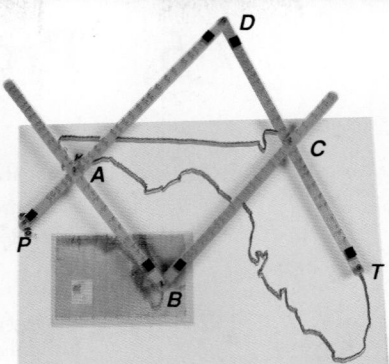

   a. Identify the similar triangles and give a reason for their similarity.

   b. What is the ratio of *PB* to *BT*? 4:9

Mixed Review

Determine whether each of the following is *true* or *false*.

35. If the corresponding sides of two polygons are proportional, the polygons are similar. **(Lesson 7-3)** false

36. Consecutive sides of a rhombus are congruent. **(Lesson 6-5)** true

37. A median of a triangle always lies in the interior of the triangle. **(Lesson 5-2)** true

38. AAS is a triangle congruence test. **(Lesson 4-5)** true

39. An isosceles triangle cannot have a right angle. **(Lesson 4-1)** false

40. Congruence of angles is transitive. **(Lesson 1-8)** true

Wrap-Up

41. Journal Entry Write a short summary of the ways you can prove two triangles are similar in your journal. Give an example of each.
See students' work.

Additional Answers

28. Given: ∠*BAC* and ∠*EDF* are right angles. $\frac{AB}{DE} = \frac{AC}{DF}$

   Prove: △*ABC* ~ △*DEF*

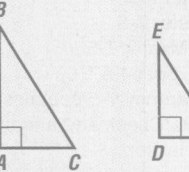

Statements (Reasons)
a. ∠*BAC* and ∠*EDF* are right angles. (Given)
b. ∠*BAC* ≅ ∠*EDF* (All rt. ∠s are ≅)
c. $\frac{AB}{DE} = \frac{AC}{DF}$ (Given)
d. △*ABC* ~ △*DEF* (SAS Similarity)

Mid-Chapter Review

5. Two polygons are similar if and only if their corresponding angles are congruent and the measures of their corresponding sides are proportional.

MID-CHAPTER REVIEW

1. Jackie's soccer team has won 12 games and lost 4. Find the ratio of wins to games played. **(Lesson 7-1)** $\frac{12}{16}$ or $\frac{3}{4}$

2. How many U.S. dollars would you receive for 3000 Italian lira if the exchange rate is 1350 lira for each U.S. dollar? **(Lesson 7-2)** about $2.22

3. If Teresa's car gets 29 miles per gallon, how many gallons of gas will she need to drive from Chicago to Bozeman, Montana, and back, a round trip of 2700 miles? **(Lesson 7-2)** about 93.1 gal

4. Find the value of *x* if $\frac{x}{5} = \frac{x-1}{3}$. **(Lesson 7-2)** 2.5

5. Define similar polygons. **(Lesson 7-3)** See margin.

6. One angle in a right triangle is 37°. A second right triangle has an angle that is 53°. Are the two triangles similar? Explain. **(Lesson 7-4)** yes; AA Similarity

7. Shelia claims that all right triangles are similar. David disagrees. Who is correct? Explain. **(Lesson 7-4)** David; the right angles are congruent, but the other two pairs of angles may not be.

LESSON 7-4 SIMILAR TRIANGLES 335

EXTENDING THE LESSON

Math Power: Problem Solving

In the Sierpinski Triangle on page 328, count and record the number of yellow triangles of each size, beginning with the largest in the middle and ending with the smallest size. What do you notice about these numbers? 1, 3, 9, 27; each one is 3 times the previous

Mid-Chapter Review

The Mid-Chapter Review provides students with a brief review of the concepts and skills in Lessons 7-1 through 7-4. Lesson numbers are given at the end of problems or instruction lines so students may review concepts not yet mastered.

Enrichment Masters Booklet, p. 40

7-4 Enrichment Worksheet
NAME _____ DATE _____

Ratio Puzzles with Triangles

If you know the perimeter of a triangle and the ratios of the sides, you can find the lengths of the sides.

Example: The perimeter of a triangle is 84 units. The sides have lengths *r*, *s*, and *t*. The ratio of *s* to *r* is 5:3, and the ratio of *t* to *r* is 2:1. Find the length of each side.

Since both ratios contain *r*, rewrite one or both ratios to make *r* the same. You can write the ratio of *t* to *r* as 6:3. Now you can write a three-part ratio.
r:*s*:*t* = 3:5:6

There is a number *x* such that *r* = 3*x*, *s* = 5*x*, and *t* = 6*x*. Since you know the perimeter, 84, you can use algebra to find the lengths of the sides.

$$r + s + t = 84$$
$$3x + 5x + 6x = 84$$
$$14x = 84$$
$$x = 6$$

So, *r* = 18, *s* = 30, and *t* = 36.
3*x* = 18, 5*x* = 30, 6*x* = 36

Find the lengths of the sides of each triangle.

1. The perimeter of a triangle is 75 units. The sides have lengths *a*, *b*, and *c*. The ratio of *b* to *a* is 3:5, and the ratio of *c* to *a* is 7:5. Find the length of each side.
a = 25, *b* = 15, *c* = 35

2. The perimeter of a triangle is 88 units. The sides have lengths *d*, *e*, and *f*. The ratio of *e* to *d* is 3:1, and the ratio of *f* to *e* is 10:9. Find the length of each side.
d = 12, *e* = 36, *f* = 40

3. The perimeter of a triangle is 91 units. The sides have lengths *p*, *q*, and *r*. The ratio of *p* to *r* is 3:1, and the ratio of *q* to *r* is 5:2. Find the length of each side.
p = 42, *q* = 35, *r* = 14

4. The perimeter of a triangle is 68 units. The sides have lengths *g*, *h*, and *j*. The ratio of *j* to *g* is 2:1, and the ratio of *h* to *g* is 5:4. Find the length of each side.
g = 16, *h* = 20, *j* = 32

5. Write a problem similar to those above involving ratios in triangles.
See students' work.

40
Glencoe Division, Macmillan/McGraw-Hill

Chapter 7 335

- Reteaching Master 7-5
- Practice Master 7-5
- Enrichment Master 7-5
- Lab Manual, pp. 54-57

 Transparency 7-5 contains the 5-Minute Check and a teaching aid for this lesson.

INTRODUCING THE LESSON

 5-Minute Check

(over Lesson 7-4)

Refer to the figures below.

1. Are the triangles similar?
   yes
2. Explain why or why not.
   SSS Similarity

Refer to the figure below.
$\overline{QN} \parallel \overline{RP}$.

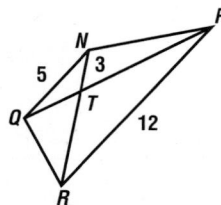

3. Identify the similar triangles
   △QNT ~ △PRT
4. Explain why the triangles are similar.   **AA Similarity**
5. Find TR.
   $$\frac{NT}{NQ} = \frac{TR}{PR}$$
   $$\frac{3}{5} = \frac{TR}{12}$$
   $$5(TR) = 36$$
   $$TR = 7.2$$

7-5 Proportional Parts

Objectives
After studying this lesson, you should be able to:
- 7-5A   ■ use proportional parts of triangles to solve problems, and
- 7-5B   ■ divide a segment into congruent parts.

Application

Why are triangles often used in buildings? One reason is the rigid nature of a triangle. Triangles are used to brace boards in roofs, to support telephone wires, and to provide the structure of bridges. In the picture at the right, each horizontal support is the base of a triangle. Each support is parallel to the others. The following theorem states that since the supports are parallel, the triangles formed are similar.

Theorem 7-4 *Triangle* *Proportionality*	**If a line is parallel to one side of a triangle and intersects the other two sides in two distinct points, then it separates these sides into segments of proportional lengths.**

Proof of Theorem 7-4

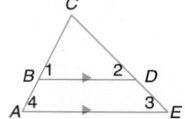

Given: $\overline{BD} \parallel \overline{AE}$

Prove: $\dfrac{BA}{CB} = \dfrac{DE}{CD}$

Paragraph Proof:

Since $\overline{BD} \parallel \overline{AE}$, $\angle 4 \cong \angle 1$ and $\angle 3 \cong \angle 2$. Then by AA Similarity, $\triangle ACE \sim \triangle BCD$. From the definition of similar polygons, $\dfrac{CA}{CB} = \dfrac{CE}{CD}$. Since B is between A and C, $CA = BA + CB$, and since D is between C and E, $CE = DE + CD$. Substituting, we get

$$\frac{BA + CB}{CB} = \frac{DE + CD}{CD}$$
$$\frac{BA}{CB} + \frac{CB}{CB} = \frac{DE}{CD} + \frac{CD}{CD}$$
$$\frac{BA}{CB} + 1 = \frac{DE}{CD} + 1 \qquad \textit{Substitution property of equality}$$
$$\frac{BA}{CB} = \frac{DE}{CD} \qquad \textit{Subtraction property of equality}$$

Likewise, proportional parts of a triangle can be used to prove the converse of Theorem 7-4. You will be asked to prove this theorem in Exercise 34.

336   CHAPTER 7   SIMILARITY

ALTERNATE TEACHING STRATEGIES

Using Manipulatives

Make a sector compass as shown on page 337 using two rulers that each have a hole punched in the middle. Put the rulers on top of each other and use a rubber band to tie them together. Draw a segment on the chalkboard that can be measured with this sector compass and construct a segment that is some multiple of the length of the original segment.

Using Computers

Use the *Geometric Supposer* and the technology feature on page 327 to draw a triangle with a segment parallel to one side, inside the triangle. Use the measure feature to calculate the scale factor for the two triangles. Have students set up and calculate as many ratios as possible for the segments and formulate conjectures about similar triangles in such situations.

If a line intersects two sides of a triangle and separates the sides into corresponding segments of proportional lengths, then the line is parallel to the third side.

Example 1

In the figure $CA = 15$, $CE = 3$, $DA = 8$, and $BA = 10$. Determine if $\overline{ED} \parallel \overline{CB}$.

From the segment addition postulate, $CA = CE + EA$ and $BA = BD + DA$. Now substitute the known measures.

$$CA = CE + EA \qquad BA = BD + DA$$
$$15 = 3 + EA \qquad 10 = BD + 8$$
$$12 = EA \qquad 2 = BD$$

To show $\overline{ED} \parallel \overline{CB}$, we must show that $\frac{EA}{CE} = \frac{DA}{BD}$. From the information above, $\frac{EA}{CE} = \frac{12}{3}$ and $\frac{DA}{BD} = \frac{8}{2}$. Since $\frac{12}{3} = \frac{8}{2}$, $\frac{EA}{CE} = \frac{DA}{BD}$. Therefore, by Theorem 7-5, $\overline{ED} \parallel \overline{CB}$.

The theorems about the proportionality of triangles can be used to solve practical problems.

Example 2

APPLICATION
History

The sector compass was an instrument used in the seventeenth and eighteenth centuries. It was perfected by Galileo and was used to solve a variety of problems. A sector compass consisted of two arms fastened at one end by a pivot joint. A scale was marked on each arm as shown in the diagram. To draw a segment two fifths of the length of a given segment, the 100-marks are placed at the endpoints of the given line. A segment drawn between the two 40-marks is two fifths of the length of the given segment. Why?

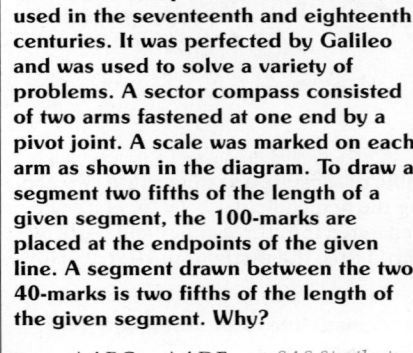

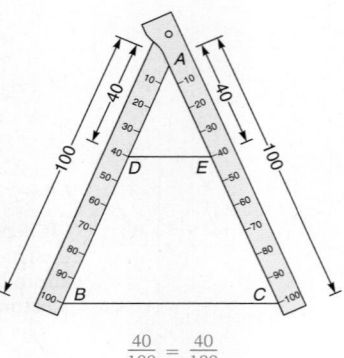

$$\frac{40}{100} = \frac{40}{100}$$

$$\triangle ABC \sim \triangle ADE \qquad \textit{SAS Similarity}$$
$$\frac{AD}{AB} = \frac{DE}{BC} \qquad \textit{Definition of similar polygons}$$
$$\frac{40}{100} = \frac{DE}{BC} \qquad \textit{Substitution property of equality}$$
$$\frac{2}{5} = \frac{DE}{BC}$$
$$\frac{2}{5} BC = DE \qquad \textit{Multiplication property of equality}$$

The proof of the following theorem is based on Theorems 7-4 and 7-5. You will be asked to complete the proof of this theorem in Exercise 35.

LESSON 7-5   PROPORTIONAL PARTS   337

TEACHING THE LESSON

Chalkboard Examples

For Example 1
In the figure, $CA = 10$, $CE = 2$, $DA = 6$, and $BA = 12$. Determine if $\overline{ED} \parallel \overline{CB}$.

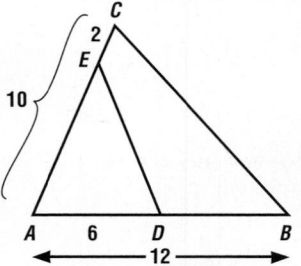

From the segment addition postulate, $CA = CE + EA$ and $BA = BD + DA$. Substitute the known measures.

$$10 = 2 + EA \qquad 12 = BD + 6$$
$$8 = EA \qquad 6 = BD$$

If $\frac{EA}{CE} = \frac{DA}{BD}$, then $\overline{ED} \parallel \overline{CB}$.

But, $\frac{EA}{CE} = \frac{8}{2}$ and $\frac{DA}{BD} = \frac{6}{6}$.

Since $\frac{8}{2} \neq \frac{6}{6}$, $\frac{EA}{CE} \neq \frac{DA}{BD}$, and $\overline{ED}$ is not parallel to $\overline{CB}$.

For Example 2
How can you use a sector compass to draw a segment three times the length of a given segment? Verify your answer.
Sample answer: Place the 30-marks at the endpoints of the given segment. Then draw a segment connecting the two 90-marks. This segment will be three times the original segment. Since $\triangle ABC \sim \triangle ADE$, $\frac{AB}{AD} = \frac{BC}{DE}$
$$\frac{90}{30} = \frac{BC}{DE}$$
$$3DE = BC$$

Additional Answers

1. Sample answer: $\overline{AB}$ and $\overline{CD}$ are divided proportionally if $\dfrac{AE}{EB} = \dfrac{CF}{FD}$.

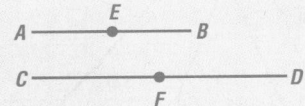

2.

Sample answers:
$\dfrac{a}{b} = \dfrac{c}{d}$, $\dfrac{a}{c} = \dfrac{b}{d}$

3. If a line intersects two sides of a triangle and separates the sides into segments of proportional lengths, then the line is parallel to the third side.

4. if it is parallel to the third side

5. if the endpoints of the segment are the midpoints of the two sides

17.

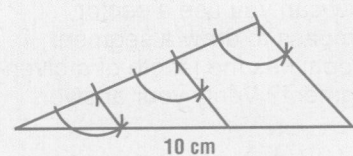

10 cm

Theorem 7-6	A segment whose endpoints are the midpoints of two sides of a triangle is parallel to the third side of the triangle and its length is one-half the length of the third side.

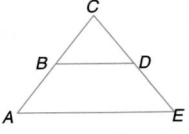

In $\triangle ACE$, suppose that B is the midpoint of $\overline{AC}$ and D is the midpoint of $\overline{CE}$. By Theorem 7-6, $\overline{BD} \parallel \overline{AE}$ and $BD = \frac{1}{2}AE$. This relationship can also be expressed $2BD = AE$.

Three or more parallel lines separate transversals into proportional parts as stated in the next two corollaries.

Corollary 7-1	If three or more parallel lines intersect two transversals, then they cut off the transversals proportionally.
Corollary 7-2	If three or more parallel lines cut off congruent segments on one transversal then they cut off congruent segments on every transversal.

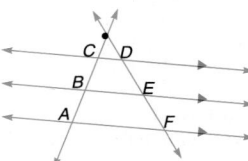

In the figure at the left, $\overleftrightarrow{CD} \parallel \overleftrightarrow{BE} \parallel \overleftrightarrow{AF}$. The transversals $\overleftrightarrow{AC}$ and $\overleftrightarrow{FD}$ have been separated into proportional segments. Sample proportions are listed below.

$$\frac{CB}{BA} = \frac{DE}{EF} \text{ ; } \frac{CA}{DF} = \frac{BA}{EF} \text{ ; } \frac{AC}{BC} = \frac{FD}{ED}$$

It is possible to separate a segment into two congruent parts by constructing the perpendicular bisector of a segment. However, a segment cannot be separated into three congruent parts by constructing perpendicular bisectors. To do this, the method illustrated below is used.

CONSTRUCTION

A similar method can be used for any given number of congruent parts.

Separate a segment into three congruent parts.

1. Copy $\overline{AB}$ and draw $\overrightarrow{AM}$.

2. With a compass point at A, mark off an arc on $\overrightarrow{AM}$ at X. Then construct $\overline{XY}$ and $\overline{YZ}$ so that $\overline{AX} \cong \overline{XY} \cong \overline{YZ}$.

3. Draw $\overline{ZB}$. Then construct lines through Y and X that are parallel to $\overline{ZB}$. Call P and Q the intersection points on $\overline{AB}$.

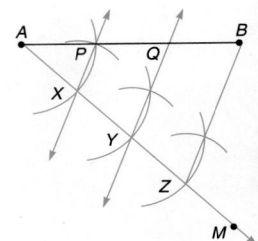

Because parallel lines cut off congruent segments on transversals, $\overline{AP} \cong \overline{PQ} \cong \overline{QB}$.

CHECKING FOR UNDERSTANDING

EVALUATING THE LESSON

Checking for Understanding

Exercises 1-17 are designed to help you assess students' understanding through reading, writing, speaking, and modeling. You should work through Exercises 1-5 with your students and then monitor their work on Exercises 6-17.

Error Analysis

The language of some of the theorems and corollaries in this lesson can be confusing. Use pictures to help students sort the information and write down the necessary given information and what the theorem is proving.

Closing the Lesson

Speaking Activity Draw a picture similar to the figure in Example 1 on the chalkboard or overhead. Go around the room and have each student name parts of the two triangles that are either congruent or proportional to each other. Have them justify their statements.

Reteaching Masters Booklet, p. 41

Communicating Mathematics

Read and study the lesson to answer each question. **See margin.**

1. Explain what it means to separate two segments proportionally.

2. Draw and label two segments that are separated proportionally. Then write several different true proportions.

3. In Chapter 3, you learned how to prove lines parallel by using special angle relationships. What other method can be used to prove lines are parallel?

A segment is drawn from one side to another in a triangle. **See margin.**

4. Under what conditions will it separate the side proportionally?

5. When will the measure of that segment be half the length of the third side?

Guided Practice

In the figure $\overline{BD} \parallel \overline{AE}$. Determine whether each statement is *true* or *false*. If it is false, explain why.

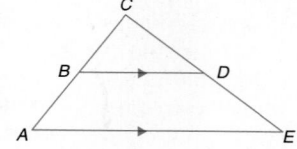

6. $\frac{BC}{ED} = \frac{AB}{CD}$ false 7. $\frac{AB}{BC} = \frac{DE}{CD}$ true

8. $\frac{CB}{CD} = \frac{CA}{CE}$ true 9. $\frac{BA}{DE} = \frac{CA}{CE}$ true

In $\triangle BAT$, determine whether $\overline{ML} \parallel \overline{BA}$ under the given conditions.

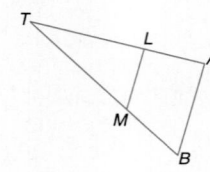

10. $\frac{TM}{MB} = \frac{TL}{LA}$ yes 11. $\frac{BA}{MB} = \frac{ML}{LA}$ no

12. $\frac{TB}{MB} = \frac{TA}{LA}$ yes 13. $\frac{TM}{ML} = \frac{TB}{BA}$ yes

Find the value of x.

14. 15. 16.

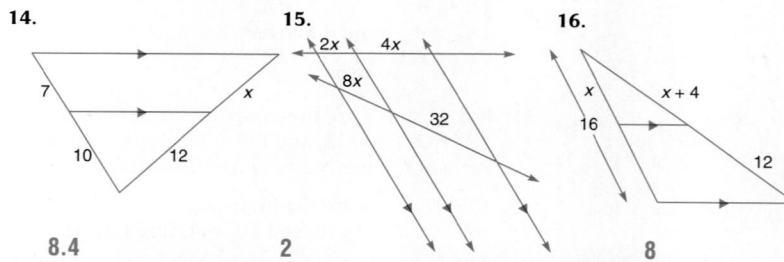

8.4 2 8

17. Draw a segment 10 centimeters long. Separate the segment into three congruent parts. **See margin.**

LESSON 7-5 PROPORTIONAL PARTS 339

RETEACHING THE LESSON

Review some of the terminology contained in the theorems of this lesson, for example, parallel, midpoints, transversal. Go through the theorems word by word (or phrase by phrase) and draw a picture illustrating the meaning of the word (or phrase). The final picture should be an illustration of the theorem.

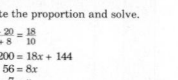 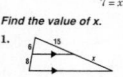 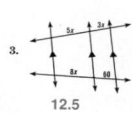
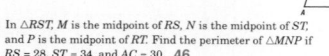

Additional Answers

33.

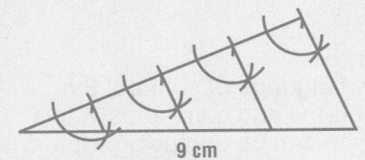

9 cm

34. Given: $\dfrac{DB}{AD} = \dfrac{EC}{AE}$
Prove: $\overline{DE} \parallel \overline{BC}$

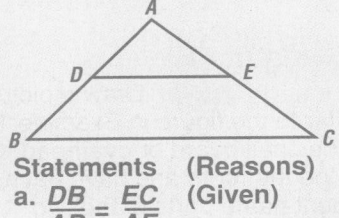

Statements	(Reasons)
a. $\dfrac{DB}{AD} = \dfrac{EC}{AE}$	(Given)

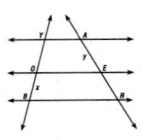

EXERCISES

In the figure at the right, $\overleftrightarrow{YA} \parallel \overleftrightarrow{OE} \parallel \overleftrightarrow{BR}$. Complete each statement.

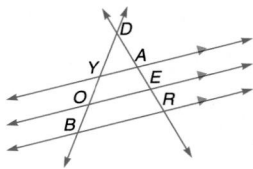

18. $\dfrac{YO}{OB} = \dfrac{AE}{?}$ **ER**   **19.** $\dfrac{YB}{OB} = \dfrac{?}{ER}$ **AR**

20. $\dfrac{?}{AE} = \dfrac{YB}{YO}$ **AR**   **21.** $\dfrac{DY}{YO} = \dfrac{DA}{?}$ **AE**

22. $\dfrac{DR}{?} = \dfrac{DB}{YB}$ **AR**   **23.** $\dfrac{?}{AE} = \dfrac{DO}{YO}$ **DE**

Find the value of *x* and *y*.

24.

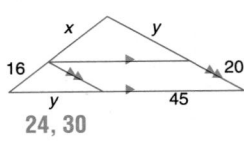

24, 30

25.

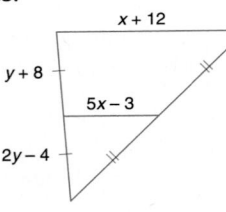

2, 12

26.

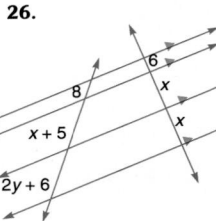

15, 7

Using the figure at the right, determine the value of *x* that would make $\overline{PQ} \parallel \overline{DF}$ under each set of conditions.

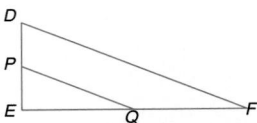

27. EQ = 3
    DP = 12
    QF = 8
    PE = x + 2 **2.5**

28. DE = 12
    PE = 7
    EQ = x + 3
    QF = x - 3 **18**

Using the figure at the right, determine the value of *x* under each set of conditions.

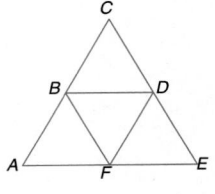

29. $\overline{BD} \parallel \overline{AE}$
    AB = 6
    DE = 8
    DC = 4
    BC = x **3**

30. $\overline{AC} \parallel \overline{DF}$
    DC = 7
    DE = 5
    FA = 8
    FE = x $\frac{40}{7}$

31. If *B*, *D*, and *F* are the midpoints of sides $\overline{CA}$, $\overline{CE}$, and $\overline{AE}$ respectively, *BD* = 7, *BF* = 12, and *DF* = 16, find the perimeter of △*AEC*. What is the ratio of the perimeter of △*BDF* to the perimeter of △*AEC*? **70; 1:2**

32. If *B*, *D*, and *F* are the midpoints of sides $\overline{CA}$, $\overline{CE}$, and $\overline{AE}$ respectively, *BD* = 8, *CA* = 10, and *DE* = 4, find *DF*, *AE*, and *BF*. **5, 16, 4**

33. Draw a segment that is 9 centimeters long. By construction, separate the segment into four congruent parts. **See margin.**

---

b. $\dfrac{AD + DB}{AD} = \dfrac{AE + EC}{AE}$
   (Addition prop. of equality)

c. $AB = AD + DB$, $AC = AE + EC$
   (Segment Addition Postulate)

d. $\dfrac{AB}{AD} = \dfrac{AC}{AE}$ (Substitution prop. of equality)

e. $\angle A \cong \angle A$ (Congruence of angles is reflexive)

f. $\triangle ADE \cong \triangle ABC$ (SAS Similarity)

g. $\angle ADE \cong \angle ABC$ (Definition of similar polygons)

h. $\overline{DE} \parallel \overline{BC}$ (If 2 lines are cut by a transversal and corr. $\angle$s are $\cong$, then the lines are $\parallel$.)

Write a two-column proof for each.

34. If a line intersects two sides of a triangle and separates the sides into corresponding segments of proportional lengths, then the line is parallel to the third side. (Theorem 7-5) **See margin.**

35. A segment whose endpoints are the midpoints of two sides of a triangle is parallel to the third side of the triangle and its length is one-half the length of the third side. (Theorem 7-6) **See Solutions Manual.**

36. Draw a segment. Then separate the segment into segments whose ratios are 2 to 3. **See margin.**

37. Given $A(2, 3)$ and $B(8,12)$, find P such that P separates $\overline{AB}$ into two parts with a ratio of 2 to 1. **(4, 6) or (6, 9)**

38. In $\triangle ABC$, $\overline{MN}$ divides sides $\overline{AC}$ and $\overline{AB}$ proportionally. If the coordinates are $A(3, 7)$, $M(0, 10)$, and $N(8, 22)$ and if $\frac{AM}{MC} = \frac{3}{1}$, find the coordinates of B and C. **$B(9\frac{2}{3}, 27)$, $C(-1, 11)$**

Critical Thinking

39. Draw any quadrilateral $RSTV$ and connect the midpoints, A, B, C, and D, of each side in order. Determine what kind of figure $ABCD$ will be. Use the information from this lesson to prove your claim. **See margin.**

Applications

40. **Tourism**   There are 44 steps to get to the first level of a monument if you enter at the west door and 33 steps to get to the second level. If you enter at the east door, there are 52 steps to get to the first level. **See margin.**
    a. Draw a sketch of the monument.
    b. Which side must be steeper? How do you know?
    c. How many steps are there to get to the second level on the east side?

41. **Real Estate**   In Forest Park, the home lots are laid out as shown at the right. What is the individual frontage of each lot on Piano Drive if the total frontage on the drive for the five lots is known to be 432 feet? **See margin.**

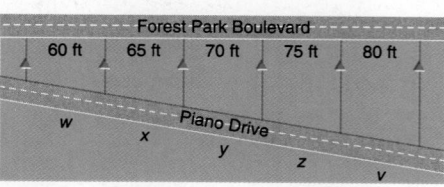

42. **History**   How could the sector compass be used to find 35% of 10? **See margin.**

Mixed Review
43. 25 cm

43. Two triangles are similar and their corresponding sides are in a ratio of 3:5. What is the measure of a side in the second triangle that corresponds to a side that measures 15 centimeters in the first triangle? **(Lesson 7-4)**

44. In $\triangle PQR$, $PQ > PR > QR$. List the angles in $\triangle PQR$ in order from greatest to least. **(Lesson 5-6)** $\angle R$, $\angle Q$, $\angle P$

45. The angles in a triangle have measures $7x - 1$, $18x + 2$, and $5x + 10$. Is the triangle acute, obtuse, or right? **(Lesson 4-1)** **obtuse**

46. Find the slope of the line that passes through the points with coordinates $(-22, 14)$ and $(8, -21)$. **(Lesson 3-5)** $-\frac{7}{6}$

47. Which property of algebra justifies the statement If $5x - 1 = 8$, then $5x = 9$? **(Lesson 2-4)** **Addition property of equality**

Wrap-Up

48. Write a five-question quiz for this lesson. **See students' work.**

EXTENDING THE LESSON

Math Power: Connections

Using the figure underneath Theorem 7-6 on page 338, draw the angle bisector of $\angle C$, the altitude of $\triangle ACE$ from point C, and the median of $\triangle ACE$ from point C. What relationship does $\overline{BD}$ have to these segments? $\overline{BD}$ **bisects all three segments.**

Additional Answers

36.

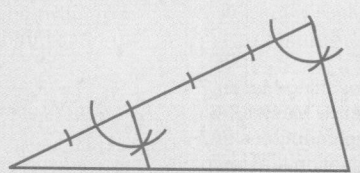

39. **Parallelogram. Draw diagonal $\overline{SV}$. $\overline{AD}$ and $\overline{BC}$ are parallel to $\overline{SV}$ and therefore parallel to each other. AD and BC are equal to $\frac{1}{2} SV$ and therefore $AD = BC$. Since $\overline{AD} \parallel \overline{BC}$ and $\overline{AD} \cong \overline{BC}$, $ABCD$ is a parallelogram.**

40a.

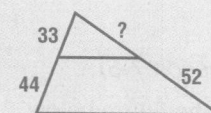

40b. **west side**
40c. **39 steps**
41. $w = 74.1$ ft, $x = 80.2$ ft, $y = 86.4$ ft, $z = 92.6$ ft, $v = 98.7$ ft
42. **Draw a line 10 units long. Place 100-marks at the endpoints. Draw a line between the 35-marks. The length of the new line will be 35% of the length of the original line.**

Enrichment Masters Booklet, p. 41

Lesson Resources

- Reteaching Master 7-6
- Practice Master 7-6
- Enrichment Master 7-6
- Evaluation Master, p. 94
- Activity Master, p. 7
- Technology Master, p.43

 Transparency 7-6 contains the 5-Minute Check and a teaching aid for this lesson.

INTRODUCING THE LESSON

5-Minute Check

(over Lesson 7-5)

Refer to the figure below.

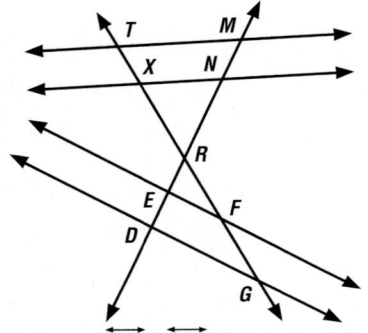

Assume $\overleftrightarrow{TM} \parallel \overleftrightarrow{XN}$. Determine if each statement is true or false.

1. $\dfrac{TX}{TR} = \dfrac{MN}{MR}$ **2.** $\dfrac{TR}{TX} = \dfrac{MR}{NR}$

    true   false

Determine whether $\overline{EF} \parallel \overline{DG}$ under the given condition.

3. $\dfrac{EF}{RE} = \dfrac{DG}{RF}$ **4.** $\dfrac{RE}{EF} = \dfrac{RD}{DG}$

    no   no

Solve.

5. Assume $\overleftrightarrow{TM} \parallel \overleftrightarrow{XN}$. If $RN = 5$, $MN = 3$, and $TX = 6$, find the value of RX.

   $\dfrac{5}{3} = \dfrac{RX}{6}$ $RX = 10$

Motivating the Lesson

Draw two similar triangles whose sides have a common ratio of 2 on the chalkboard or overhead. Have students make conjectures about the relationship of the perimeters of the two triangles. *They are proportional to the lengths of the corresponding sides.*

Objective
7-6

After studying this lesson, you should be able to:

- recognize and use the proportional relationships of corresponding perimeters, altitudes, angle bisectors, and medians of similar triangles.

Application

Two triangular jogging paths are laid out in a park as in the figure. One route is for those who like to jog a shorter path. A second path, similar in shape, is for those who like to jog a longer path. The dimensions of the inner path are 400 meters, 500 meters, and 300 meters. The longest side of the outer path is 1000 meters. Will a jogger on the outer path run twice as far as one on the inner path?

FYI...

To keep your feet warm while you jog, wear a hat. Eighty percent of your body heat escapes through your head.

The jogging paths are similar. Thus, there is a common ratio r such that $r = \dfrac{a}{e} = \dfrac{c}{g} = \dfrac{b}{f}$.

So, $re = a$, $rg = c$, and $rf = b$.

Let P_1 represent the perimeter of the shorter path and P_2 represent the perimeter of the longer path.

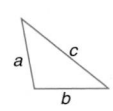 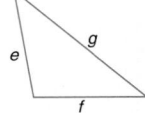

$$P_1 = a + b + c$$
$$P_1 = re + rg + rf \qquad \text{\textit{Substitution property of equality}}$$
$$P_1 = r(e + g + f) \qquad \text{\textit{Distributive property}}$$
$$P_1 = rP_2 \qquad\qquad P_2 = e + g + f$$
$$\frac{P_1}{P_2} = r$$

Therefore, $\dfrac{P_1}{P_2} = \dfrac{a}{e} = \dfrac{c}{g} = \dfrac{b}{f}$.

This proves that the perimeters of two similar triangles are proportional to the measures of the corresponding sides. This is stated in Theorem 7-7 below.

Theorem 7-7 *Proportional* *Perimeters*	**If two triangles are similar, then the perimeters are proportional to the measures of corresponding sides.**

ALTERNATE TEACHING STRATEGIES

Using Investigation

You can guide students to discover the relationship between the areas of two similar triangles. In Investigation 9 on pages A8 and A9 of **More Investigations in Geometry,** students use a graphing calculator program to explore the areas of similar triangles.

Using Cooperative Groups

Have each group draw two similar triangles, measure the sides to find the perimeters, and examine the ratios of perimeters and sides. Have them draw a median, angle bisector, and an altitude for each triangle. Have each group formulate conjectures about the ratios of segments and the sides in similar triangles.

Example 1

In the figure $\triangle RST \sim \triangle WVU$. If $UV = 500$, $VW = 400$, $UW = 300$, and $ST = 1000$, find the perimeter of $\triangle RST$.

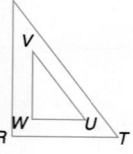

Let x represent the perimeter of $\triangle RST$.
The perimeter of $\triangle UVW = 500 + 400 + 300$ or 1200 units.

$$\frac{\text{perimeter of } \triangle UVW}{x} = \frac{VU}{ST} \qquad \textit{Proportional perimeters}$$

$$\frac{1200}{x} = \frac{500}{1000} \qquad \textit{Substitution property of equality}$$

$$x = 2400$$

The perimeter of $\triangle RST$ is 2400 units.

When two triangles are similar, the measures of their corresponding sides are proportional. What about the measures of their corresponding altitudes, medians, and angle bisectors? The following theorem states one relationship.

Theorem 7-8

If two triangles are similar, then the measures of the corresponding altitudes are proportional to the measures of the corresponding sides.

Proof of Theorem 7-8

Given: $\triangle ABC \sim \triangle PQR$
$\overline{BD}$ is an altitude of $\triangle ABC$.
$\overline{QS}$ is an altitude of $\triangle PQR$.

Prove: $\dfrac{BD}{QS} = \dfrac{BA}{QP}$

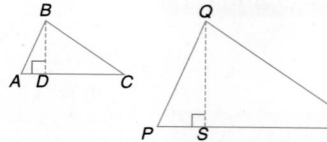

Paragraph Proof:

Since $\triangle ABC \sim \triangle PQR$ and since $\angle A$ and $\angle P$ are corresponding angles, $\angle A \cong \angle P$. Since $\overline{BD}$ is an altitude of $\triangle ABC$, $\overline{BD} \perp \overline{AC}$ and $\angle BDA$ is a right angle. Likewise, since $\overline{QS}$ is an altitude of $\triangle PQR$, $\overline{QS} \perp \overline{PR}$ and $\angle QSP$ is a right angle. So $\angle BDA \cong \angle QSP$ and $\triangle ABD \sim \triangle PQS$ by AA Similarity. Thus, $\dfrac{BD}{QS} = \dfrac{BA}{QP}$.

Likewise, the measures of corresponding angle bisectors are proportional. Using the figure below, if $\triangle RST \sim \triangle EFG$, then $\angle S \cong \angle F$ and $\angle SRT \cong \angle FEG$. If $\overline{RV}$ and $\overline{EH}$ bisect $\angle SRT$ and $\angle FEG$, then $\angle SRV \cong \angle FEH$. By AA similarity, $\triangle RSV \sim \triangle EFH$ and $\dfrac{RV}{EH} = \dfrac{RS}{EF}$.

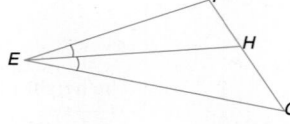

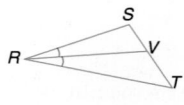

Chapter 7   343

Chalkboard Example

For Example 1
In the figure $\triangle ABD \sim \triangle ADC$. If $AD = 16$, $AC = 31$, and $DC = 23$, find the perimeter of $\triangle ABD$.

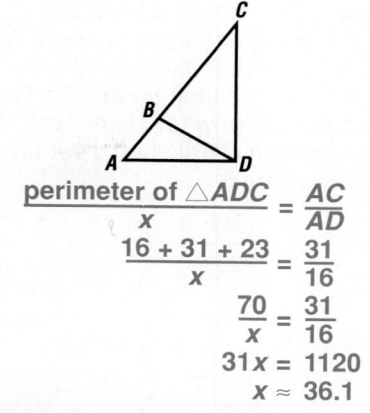

$$\frac{\text{perimeter of } \triangle ADC}{x} = \frac{AC}{AD}$$

$$\frac{16 + 31 + 23}{x} = \frac{31}{16}$$

$$\frac{70}{x} = \frac{31}{16}$$

$$31x = 1120$$

$$x \approx 36.1$$

Teaching Tip   Theorem 7-8 also states that $\dfrac{BD}{QS} = \dfrac{BC}{QR}$ and that $\dfrac{BD}{QS} = \dfrac{AC}{PR}$.

In addition, you can choose any altitude; the ratios will stay the same.

This leads us to the following theorem.

Theorem 7-9	If two triangles are similar, then the measures of the corresponding angle bisectors of the triangles are proportional to the measures of the corresponding sides.

The following theorem states the relationship between the medians of two similar triangles. You will prove this theorem in Exercise 29.

Theorem 7-10	If two triangles are similar, then the measures of the corresponding medians are proportional to the measures of the corresponding sides.

The theorem about the relationships of special segments in similar triangles can be used to solve practical problems.

Example 2

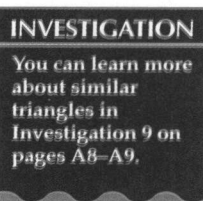

INVESTIGATION
You can learn more about similar triangles in Investigation 9 on pages A8–A9.

As a project for her photography class, Carol Page made a camera from a box. Suppose the film is 1.8 centimeters from the lens and the person being photographed is 360 centimeters from the camera. Find the height of the image on the film if the height of the person is 260 centimeters.

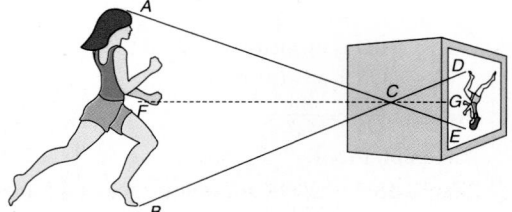

The dashed lines are the altitudes of $\triangle ABC$ and $\triangle EDC$.

Let h = the height of the image on the film. Assume that $\overline{AB} \parallel \overline{DE}$.

Since they are alternate interior angles, $\angle BAC \cong \angle DEC$ and $\angle ABC \cong \angle EDC$. Therefore, $\triangle ABC \sim \triangle EDC$ by AA Similarity.

The measures of the corresponding altitudes of similar triangles are proportional to the measures of corresponding sides.

$$\frac{AB}{FC} = \frac{ED}{GC}$$

$$\frac{260}{360} = \frac{h}{1.8} \qquad \textit{Substitution property of equality}$$

$$360h = 468$$

$$h = 1.3$$

The height of the image on the film is 1.3 centimeters.

Angle bisectors of a triangle have an additional property involving ratios.

Theorem 7-11 Angle Bisector Theorem	An angle bisector in a triangle separates the opposite side into segments that have the same ratio as the other two sides.

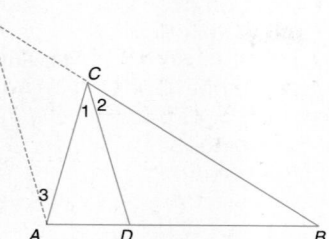

$\overline{CD}$ is the bisector of $\angle ACB$ of $\triangle ABC$. According to Theorem 7-11, $\frac{AD}{DB} = \frac{AC}{BC}$.

To prove this, construct a line through point A parallel to $\overline{DC}$ and meeting $\overrightarrow{BC}$ at E. You can prove that $\frac{AD}{DB} = \frac{EC}{BC}$ and $CA = CE$. You will complete this proof in Exercise 30.

CHECKING FOR UNDERSTANDING

Communicating Mathematics

Read and study the lesson to answer each question.

1. Draw two similar obtuse triangles and draw the medians to the longest sides. Write a statement about the medians. **See margin.**

2. Draw two similar right triangles and draw the altitude to each hypotenuse. Write a statement about the altitudes. **See margin.**

3. Tom uses the figure at the right and Theorem 7-8 to conclude $\frac{BD}{BC} = \frac{AE}{AC}$. Is he right? Why or why not? **only if △ABC is equiangular**

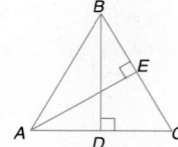

Guided Practice

In the figures at the right, $\triangle EFG \sim \triangle QRS$, $\overline{GH}$ bisects $\angle EGF$, and $\overline{ST}$ bisects $\angle QSR$. Determine whether each statement is *true* or *false*.

4. $\frac{HG}{TS} = \frac{EF}{QR}$ **true**   5. $\frac{TS}{HG} = \frac{RQ}{FG}$ **false**

6. $\frac{TS}{HG} = \frac{SQ}{GE}$ **true**   7. $\frac{FG}{RS} = \frac{HG}{TS}$ **true**

Additional Answers

1.

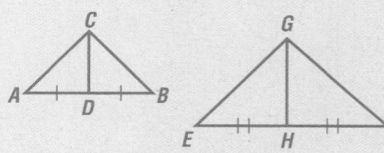

$$\frac{CD}{GH} = \frac{AB}{EF} = \frac{BC}{FG} = \frac{AC}{EG}$$

2.

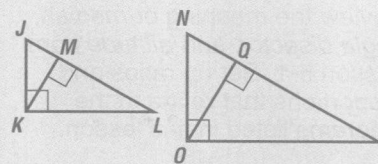

$$\frac{KM}{OQ} = \frac{JK}{NO} = \frac{KL}{OP} = \frac{LJ}{PN}$$

Checking for Understanding

Exercises 1-10 are designed to help you assess students' understanding through reading, writing, speaking, and modeling. You should work through Exercises 1-3 with students and then monitor their work on Exercises 4-10.

Error Analysis

Students may have difficulty setting up the ratios with the correct corresponding sides. Have them mark which sides correspond in the figure or write down which sides correspond before writing the ratios. It may also be helpful to redraw triangles separately when they overlap in the original figure.

Closing the Lesson

Writing Activity Draw a triangle on the chalkboard or overhead. Have each student copy the figure and use it to demonstrate one of the theorems in this lesson. Have them write the given information and what is to be proved, based upon the figure.

Homework Exercises

Assignment Guide

Basic: 11-25, 32-33, 36-42
Average: 14-28, 32, 34, 36-42
Enriched: 14-16, 18, 20-21, 23-32, 35-42

Find the value of x.

8.

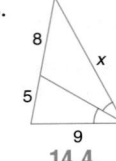

14.4

9.

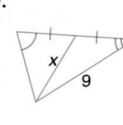 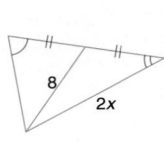

6

10. Suppose $\triangle PQR \sim \triangle ABC$. If $PR = 1.8$, $AC = 1.2$, and the perimeter of $\triangle ABC$ is 3.4, find the perimeter of $\triangle PQR$. **5.1**

EXERCISES

Practice

A

In the figure at the right $\triangle ABC \sim \triangle PQR$, $\overline{BD}$ is an altitude of $\triangle ABC$, and $\overline{QS}$ is an altitude of $\triangle PQR$. Determine whether each statement is *true* or *false*. Justify your answer. **See Solutions Manual for justifications.**

11. $\frac{BD}{QS} = \frac{AB}{PQ}$ true **12.** $\frac{AD}{PS} = \frac{QR}{BC}$ false

13. $\frac{QP}{AB} = \frac{BD}{QS}$ false **14.** $\frac{QR}{BC} = \frac{QS}{BD}$ true

15. $\frac{BD}{QS} = \frac{AC}{PR}$ true **16.** $\frac{AB}{BD} = \frac{PQ}{QS}$ true

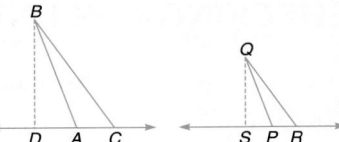

B

In the figure at the right, $\triangle ABC \sim \triangle DEF$, $\overline{AR} \cong \overline{RC}$, and $\overline{DS} \cong \overline{SF}$. Find the value of x.

17. $AC = 20$
$DF = 12$
$ES = 5$
$BR = x$ $8\frac{1}{3}$

18. $BC = x + 2$
$BR = x - 5$
$ES = 6$
$EF = 16$ **9.2**

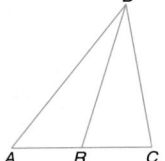 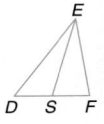

Find the value of x.

19.

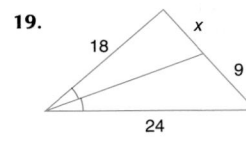

6.75

20.

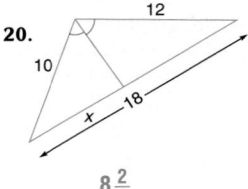

$8\frac{2}{11}$

21.

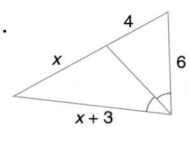

6

RETEACHING THE LESSON

Review the meaning of *median*, *angle bisector*, and *altitude* from Lesson 5-1. Set up ratios and proportions that relate to the theorems listed in this lesson.

22. In the figure at the right, $\triangle WXY \sim \triangle JKL$, $\overline{XZ}$ is a median of $\triangle WXY$, and $\overline{KM}$ is a median for $\triangle JKL$. If $XZ = 4$, $WZ = 3$, $JL = x + 2$, and $KM = 2x - 5$, find JM. **3.375**

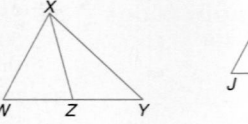
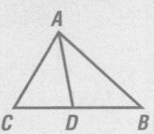
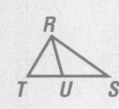

23. In the figure at the right, $\triangle ABC \sim \triangle DEF$, $\overline{AX}$ and $\overline{DY}$ are altitudes. Using the measures given, find DY. **3 or $\frac{1}{3}$**

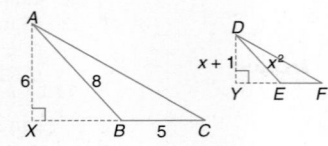

24. In the figure at the right, $\triangle STU \sim \triangle WZY$. If the perimeter of $\triangle STU$ is 30 units, find the value of x. **6**

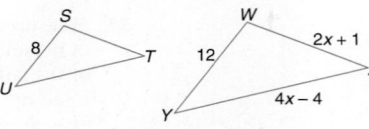

25. In the figure at the right, $\overline{UR}$ bisects $\angle VUS$, and $\overline{VS} \parallel \overline{WR}$. If $US = 5$, $WR = 15$, $UV = 10$, and $VS = 12$, find VT and UW. **8; 18.75**

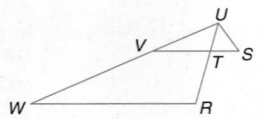

26. Suppose $\triangle LMN \sim \triangle XYZ$. If the perimeter of $\triangle LMN$ is 7.6 units, $LM = 3.0$, $MN = 2.8$, and $XY = 2.7$, find XZ. **1.62**

27. If the bisector of an angle of a triangle bisects the opposite side, what is the ratio of the measures of the other two sides of the triangle? **$\frac{1}{1}$**

28. The measures of the sides of a triangle are 10, 14, and 16. Find the measures of the segments formed where the bisector of the largest angle meets the opposite side. **$6\frac{2}{3}$, $9\frac{1}{3}$**

Write a paragraph proof for each.

29. If two triangles are similar, then the measures of the corresponding medians are proportional to the measures of the corresponding sides. (Theorem 7-10) **See margin.**

30. An angle bisector in a triangle separates the opposite side into segments that have the same ratio as the other two sides. (Theorem 7-11) **See Solutions Manual.**

31. In the figure at the right, $\overline{SV}$ bisects $\angle RST$, $\overline{RA} \cong \overline{RV}$, and $\overline{BT} \cong \overline{VT}$. Make and prove a conjecture about quadrilateral $ABTR$. **See Solutions Manual.**

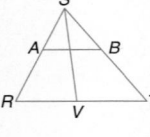

Critical Thinking

32. In the figure at the right, $\triangle ABC$ is a right triangle. $\overline{CD}$ is an altitude to the hypotenuse $\overline{AB}$. Make and prove a conjecture about the relationship of x, y, and z. **See Solutions Manual.**

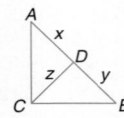

Additional Answers

29. Given: $\triangle ABC \sim \triangle RST$
    $\overline{AD}$ is a median of $\triangle ABC$
    $\overline{RU}$ is a median of $\triangle RST$
    Prove: $\dfrac{AD}{RU} = \dfrac{AB}{RS}$

We are given that $\triangle ABC \sim \triangle RST$, $\overline{AD}$ is a median of $\triangle ABC$, and $\overline{RU}$ is a median of $\triangle RST$. So, by the definition of median, $CD = DB$ and $TU = US$. According to the definition of similar polygons, $\dfrac{AB}{RS} = \dfrac{CB}{TS}$.

$CB = CD + DB$ and $TS = TU + US$ by the segment addition postulate. Substituting,

$\dfrac{AB}{RS} = \dfrac{CD + DB}{TU + US}$

$\dfrac{AB}{RS} = \dfrac{DB + DB}{US + US}$

$\dfrac{AB}{RS} = \dfrac{DB}{US}$

$\angle B \cong \angle S$ by the definition of similar polygons, and $\triangle ABD \sim \triangle RSU$ by SAS Similarity. Therefore, $\dfrac{AD}{RU} = \dfrac{AB}{RS}$ by the definition of similar polygons.

Practice Masters Booklet, p. 48

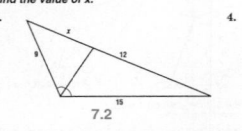
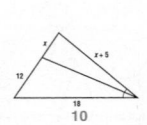
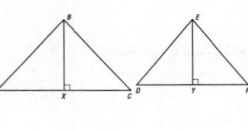

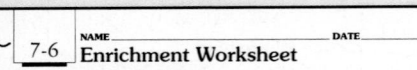
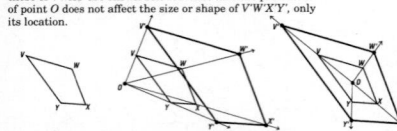
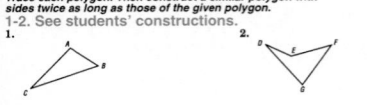
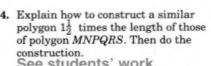
 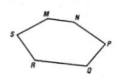
Applications

33. 0.78 cm

33. **Photography** Ron is having his senior portrait taken. Suppose Ron is 300 centimeters from a camera lens and the film is 1.3 centimeters from the lens. If Ron is 180 centimeters tall, how tall is his image on the film?

34. **Photography** Suppose the film is 1.3 centimeters from a camera lens and can have an image no more than 4.5 centimeters tall. If a person in front of the lens is 180 centimeters tall, how far from the lens can he be for a full length picture? 52 cm

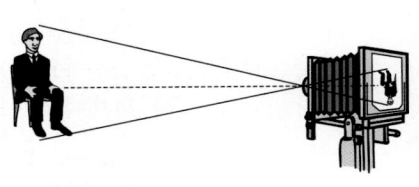

35. **Measurement** Sally estimates Steve's height by holding a ruler in front of herself and lining up the top of the ruler with his head and the bottom of the ruler with his feet. She is 12 feet away from Steve when the ruler is lined up. If the ruler is 1 foot long and she is holding it 2 feet from her eyes, how tall is Steve? 6 ft

Mixed Review

In the figure at the right $\overline{DF} \parallel \overline{BC}$, $AD = 3$, $DB = 6$, $AF = 4$, and $BC = 15$. Find each measure. (Lesson 7-5)

36. FC 8   37. DF 5

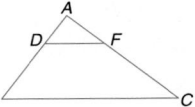

For each exercise state as many conclusions as you can using the figure and the given information. See margin.

38. Given: $\overline{MP} \cong \overline{MQ}$
    $\angle 1 \cong \angle N$
    (Lesson 4-7)

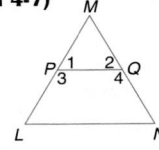

39. Given: $\overline{PR} \perp \overline{RS}$
    $\angle 2 \cong \angle 3$
    $\angle 1 \cong \angle 4$
    (Lesson 4-2)

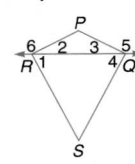

40. Given: $\angle F$ and $\angle 2$ and $\angle C$ and $\angle 1$ are complementary.
    (Lesson 3-2)

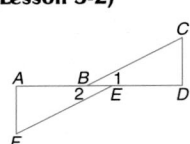

41. Given: $\overline{AB} \perp \overline{AD}$
    $\overline{BC} \perp \overline{CD}$
    $\angle 2 \cong \angle 4$
    (Lesson 1-8)

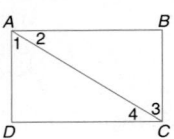

Portfolio

Select your favorite word problem from this chapter. Attach a note explaining why it is your favorite.

Wrap-Up

42. Write an application problem using the concepts you learned in this lesson. Be sure to include the answer to your problem. See students' work.

EXTENDING THE LESSON

Math Power: Reasoning

Determine if the areas of two similar triangles are proportional in any way. If so, find a proportion.

Let A_1 = area of smaller triangle
A_2 = area of larger triangle
r = common ratio
$A_1 = \frac{1}{2} bh$.

By Theorem 7-8, the measures of the corresponding altitudes are proportional to the measures of the corresponding bases. The base of the larger triangle is rb, and the altitude of the larger triangle is rh. So $A_2 = \frac{1}{2}(rb)(rh)$ or $A_2 = \frac{1}{2} bh(r^2)$. Substituting, we obtain the equation $A_2 = A_1(r^2)$, or

$$\frac{A_2}{A_1} = r^2.$$

Problem-Solving Strategy: Solve a Simpler Problem

Objective
7-7

After studying this lesson, you should be able to:
- solve problems by first solving a simpler related problem.

When you are working on a complicated or unfamiliar problem, it is often helpful to solve a similar problem first. Set aside the original problem to solve a simpler, similar problem. Then, use the strategy that worked on that simpler problem to attack the original problem.

Example 1

CONNECTION

Number Theory

Find the sum of the series 1 + 3 + 5 + . . . + 995 + 997 + 999.

Adding all of these numbers directly, even with a calculator, would be time consuming.

Let's look at a simpler problem.

$$S = 1 + 3 + 5 + 7 + 9 + 11$$

Notice that pairs of addends have a sum of 12.

$$S = 1 + 3 + 5 + 7 + 9 + 11$$

There are three such pairs. So, the sum is 3(12) or 36. *Check by adding the numbers with a calculator.*

Now, try this strategy on the original problem.

$$S = 1 + 3 + 5 + . . . + 995 + 997 + 999$$

Each sum is 1000, and since there are 500 odd numbers between 1 and 999 inclusive, there are 250 pairs. So, the sum is 250(1000) or 250,000.

You can use the problem-solving strategy of solving a simpler problem to solve geometry problems as well.

LESSON 7-7   PROBLEM-SOLVING STRATEGY: SOLVE A SIMPLER PROBLEM   349

7-7 Lesson Notes

Lesson Resources

- Practice Master 7-7
- Evaluation Master, p. 94
- Multicultural Master, p. 7

Transparency 7-7 contains the 5-Minute Check and a teaching aid for this lesson.

INTRODUCING THE LESSON

🕐 5-Minute Check
(over Lesson 7-6)

**Refer to the figure below.
Assume △AFD ~ △BEC**

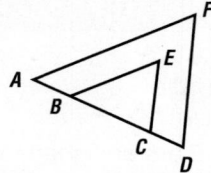

1. If $AB = 1$, $BC = 6$, $CD = 3$, and $AF = 14$, find BE.   **8.4**
2. If $\overline{EL}$ is an altitude for △BEC and $\overline{FM}$ is an altitude for △AFD, is it true that $\frac{EL}{BC} = \frac{FM}{AD}$? Why or why not?
   yes, by Theorem 7-8
3. If $\overline{EL}$ bisects ∠E and $\overline{FM}$ bisects ∠F, is it true that $\frac{EL}{FM} = \frac{BD}{AC}$? Why or why not?
   no, because $\overline{BD}$ and $\overline{AC}$ are not corresponding sides
4. If $\overline{EL}$ is a median of △BEC and $\overline{FM}$ is a median of △AFD, is it true that $\frac{EL}{FM} = \frac{BL}{AM}$?   **yes**

ALTERNATE TEACHING STRATEGIES

Using Cooperative Groups

Assign each group the problem in Example 1 and have them try to solve it themselves. Have each group find the sum of a different series. Have students compare solution strategies once each group has found a solution.

Using Problem Solving

Example 1 can also be simplified by looking at the sum of the first five numbers, then looking at the sum of the next five numbers, and so on. Doing so, you get the series 25 + (25 + 50(1)) + (25 + 50(2)) + . . .+ (25 + 50(98)) + (25 + 50(99)). Factoring out 25, you obtain 25[1 + 3 + 5 + . . .+ 198 + 199]. Repeating the process gives 25[25[25[1 + 3 + 5 + 7]]] = 250,000.

Motivating the Lesson

Ask some students how far it is from their house to school. Ask them how they calculated their answer. Discuss some of the ways to solve the problem, such as using an odometer on a car or using the scale on a map.

Chalkboard Examples

For Example 1
Find the sum of the series $S = 1 + 2 + 3 + \ldots + 997 + 998 + 999$. **Pairing the numbers as in Example 1, the pairs again sum to 1000. There are 499 pairs, and the number 500 has no pair. So the sum is $499(1000) + 500 = 499{,}500$.**

For Example 2
How many diagonals can be drawn for a polygon with 15 sides? **90**

Checking for Understanding

Exercises 1-5 are designed to help you assess students' understanding through reading, writing, speaking, and modeling. You should work through Exercises 1-3 with your students and then monitor their work on Exercises 4-5.

Closing the Lesson

Speaking Activity Ask each student to name a situation in which solving a simpler problem would be helpful.

Homework Exercises

Assignment Guide

Basic: 6-10
Average: 7-11
Enriched: 8-12

Exercise Notes

For Exercise 6, a chart or table might be helpful.

Example 2 | **How many diagonals can be drawn for a polygon with 12 sides?**

Let's draw several polygons with less than 12 sides. We will use a table to record the number of sides and the number of diagonals for each polygon.

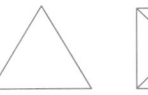 

Number of Sides	3	4	5	6	7	8	9	10	11	12
Number of Diagonals	0	2	5	9	14					

+2 +3 +4 +5

The pattern indicates that there are 54 diagonals in a polygon with 12 sides.

CHECKING FOR UNDERSTANDING

Communicating Mathematics

Read and study the lesson to answer these questions.

1. Describe how to use the problem-solving strategy to solve a simpler problem in your own words. **See students' work.**

2. with a complicated or unfamiliar problem

2. When is the strategy of solving a simpler problem useful?

3. What is the sum of the whole numbers from 1 to 200 inclusive? **20,100**

Guided Practice

Solve each problem by solving a simpler problem.

4. How many line segments would you need to draw to connect 75 points if each point had to be connected to every other point? **2775 segments**

5. In your sock drawer, you have 12 electric blue socks, 22 midnight blue socks, 18 sky blue socks, 6 periwinkle blue socks, 14 navy blue socks, 7 baby blue socks, 8 sapphire blue socks, and one aqua blue sock. How many socks must you pull from the drawer to ensure that you have a pair that matches? Explain your answer. **9 socks**

EXERCISES

Solve. Use any strategy.

6. Kara has 23 coins in her change purse. The change is worth one dollar. What combinations of coins might Kara have? **See margin.**

350　CHAPTER 7　SIMILARITY

RETEACHING THE LESSON

Ask a student to think of a problem and tell it to the class. It does not necessarily have to be a math problem. Discuss which problem-solving strategies could be used. Discuss whether using the strategy of solving a simpler problem would be helpful.

Strategies

Look for a pattern.
Solve a simpler problem.
Act it out.
Guess and check.
Draw a diagram.
Make a chart.
Work backward.

7. Use the following clues to discover the year of the completion of the first transcontinental railroad in the United States. **1869**
   - The hundreds and the tens digits are even.
   - The ones digits is one greater than the hundreds digit.
   - The sum of the digits is 24.

8. The number 10 has four divisors, namely 1, 2, 5, and 10. Find the least whole number with exactly five divisors. **16**

9. In the Fuji Japanese Restaurant, guests are served at large tables that surround the grill where the food is prepared. Bowls of rice are to be shared by two people. Three people share a bowl of vegetables, and four people share a bowl of an entree. If there are twenty-six bowls on a table, how many guests are seated at the table? **24 guests**

10. Two pots of soup are placed at the end of the salad bar at the Western Ranger Steakhouse. While Wendy was checking to see which pot was vegetable soup and which was chili, she accidentally put a ladle full of chili into the vegetable soup pot. After she realized her mistake, Wendy mixed up the soup in the vegetable soup pot and poured a ladle full of the mixture into the chili pot. Does the vegetable soup pot have more or less chili in it than the chili pot has vegetable soup? **They have the same amount.**

11. Find the sum of the series $\frac{1}{2} + \left(\frac{1}{3} + \frac{2}{3}\right) + \left(\frac{1}{4} + \frac{2}{4} + \frac{3}{4}\right) + \left(\frac{1}{5} + \frac{2}{5} + \frac{3}{5} + \frac{4}{5}\right) + \ldots + \left(\frac{1}{100} + \frac{2}{100} + \frac{3}{100} + \ldots + \frac{99}{100}\right)$. **See margin.**

12. The Healthstyle Athletic Club is having a special offer of $75 off the regular price for a one-year membership. Marc's family will receive an additional 10% discount after the $75 because his mother's employer has a corporate membership. Adding unlimited tennis privileges to the membership raises the price 5% to $463.05. What is the regular price of a one-year membership at the club? **$565**

COOPERATIVE LEARNING PROJECT

Work in groups. Each person must understand the solution and be able to explain it to any person in the class.

Jenny and Michelle were getting ready to go to a costume party dressed as Tweedledee and Tweedledum. Their costumes were identical, so Michelle wanted to pull four socks of the same color from the pile of socks in their closet. Since they were in a hurry, she grabbed enough socks to guarantee that there would be four of the same color. If the pile of socks contained red, yellow, and blue socks, how many did Michelle grab? If there had been n sisters needing the same color of socks, how many would Michelle need to grab? **10; 3(2n − 1) + 1**

LESSON 7-7   PROBLEM-SOLVING STRATEGY: SOLVE A SIMPLER PROBLEM   351

EXTENDING THE LESSON

Math Power: Problem Solving

How many diagonals can be drawn for a polygon with n sides?

$$\frac{n(n-3)}{2}$$

Cooperative Learning Project

This activity provides students an opportunity to *learn* things together, not just do things together. You may wish to refer to pages T6-T7 and page 306c for the various elements of cooperative groups and specific goals and strategies for using them.

Exercise Notes

For Exercise 9, make a chart with the number of people in one column and the number of bowls on the table in another column.

For Exercise 12, try working backward.

Additional Answers

6. There are six possible combinations: 1 half-dollar, 1 quarter, 1 nickel, and 20 pennies; 2 quarters, 1 dime, 5 nickels, and 15 pennies; 1 quarter, 5 dimes, 2 nickels, and 15 pennies; 1 quarter, 1 dime, 11 nickels, and 10 pennies; 5 dimes, 8 nickels, and 10 pennies; or 1 dime, 17 nickels, and 5 pennies.

11. The series of fractions simplifies to
$$\frac{1}{2} + 1 + \frac{3}{2} + 2 + \ldots + \frac{99}{2}.$$
So, find half of the sum of the series $1 + 2 + 3 + \ldots + 99$. $1 + 2 + 3 + \ldots + 99 = 49(100) + 50$ or 4950, since there are 49 pairs of addends with a sum of 100, and 50 has no match. The sum of the series of fractions is $\frac{4950}{2} = 2475$.

Practice Masters Booklet, p. 49

The Chapter Summary and Review begins with an alphabetical listing of the new terms that were presented in the chapter. Have students define each term and provide an example of it, if appropriate.

The Skills and Concepts presented in the chapter are reviewed using a side-by-side format. Encourage students to refer to the Objectives and Examples on the left as they complete the Review Exercises on the right.

The Chapter Summary and Review ends with exercises that review Applications and Connections.

CHAPTER 7 | SUMMARY AND REVIEW

VOCABULARY

Upon completing this chapter, you should be familiar with the following terms:

cross products **309**   **308** ratio
proportion **308**   **321** similar polygons
rate **315**

SKILLS AND CONCEPTS

OBJECTIVES AND EXAMPLES	REVIEW EXERCISES

Upon completing this chapter, you should be able to:

Use these exercises to review and prepare for the chapter test.

- recognize and use ratios and proportions. **(Lesson 7-1)**

Write the cross products for each proportion and solve.

To solve the equation $\frac{x}{4} = \frac{27}{6}$, find the cross products.

$$\frac{x}{4} = \frac{27}{6}$$
$$6x = 4 \cdot 27$$
$$6x = 108$$
$$x = 18$$

1. $\frac{5}{x} = \frac{2}{3}$ **7.5**   2. $\frac{x}{9} = \frac{7}{15}$ **4.2**

3. $\frac{1}{x} = \frac{5}{x+5}$ **1.25**   4. $\frac{n+4}{3} = \frac{5n-3}{8}$ $\frac{41}{7}$

Determine if each statement is *true* or *false*.

5. If $\frac{a}{b} = \frac{c}{d}$, then $\frac{a}{b} = \frac{d}{c}$. **false**

6. If $\frac{a}{b} = \frac{c}{d}$, then $\frac{a+b}{b} = \frac{c+d}{d}$. **true**

- apply and use the properties of proportions. **(Lesson 7-2)**

A telephone pole casts a 36-foot shadow. Nearby a 6-foot man casts an 8-foot shadow. To find the height of the telephone pole, write a proportion.

$$\frac{x}{36} = \frac{6}{8}$$
$$8x = 6 \cdot 36$$
$$8x = 216$$
$$x = 27 \qquad \text{The pole is 27 feet tall.}$$

The measures of corresponding sides of $\triangle ABC$ and $\triangle XYZ$ below are proportional.

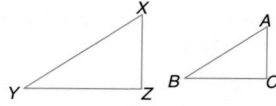

7. If $AB = 7$, $AC = 6$, and $XZ = 8$, find XY. $9\frac{1}{3}$

8. If $BC = 7$, $AC = 6$, and $XZ = 14$, find YZ. $16\frac{1}{3}$

Additional Answers

13. Statements   (Reasons)
   a. isosceles trapezoid $PQRS$; $\overline{QR} \parallel \overline{PS}$ (Given)
   b. $\overline{QP} \cong \overline{RS}$ (Definition of isosceles trapezoid)
   c. $\overline{RQ} \cong \overline{RQ}$ (Congruence of segments is reflexive)
   d. $QP = RS$, $RQ = RQ$ (Definition of congruent segments)
   e. $\frac{RQ}{RQ} = 1$, $\frac{QP}{RS} = 1$ (Division prop. of equality)
   f. $\frac{RQ}{RQ} = \frac{QP}{RS}$ (Substitution prop. of equality)
   g. $\frac{RP}{QS} = \frac{RS}{QP}$ (Given)
   h. $\angle PQR \cong \angle SRQ$ (Base $\angle$s of an iso. trap. are $\cong$.)
   i. $\triangle PQR \sim \triangle SRQ$ (SAS Similarity)

use proportions to solve problems involving similar figures. (Lesson 7-3)

$\square QRST \sim \square MNOP$

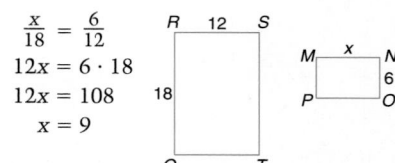

$\dfrac{x}{18} = \dfrac{6}{12}$

$12x = 6 \cdot 18$

$12x = 108$

$x = 9$

Determine whether each statement is *true* or *false*.

9. All congruent triangles are similar. true

10. All similar triangles are congruent.
    false

In the figure below $\triangle ABC \sim \triangle GFE$.

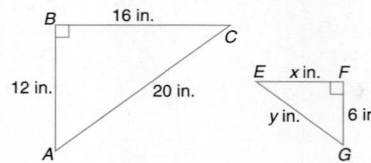

11. Find x. 8   12. Find y. 10

---

identify similar triangles. (Lesson 7-4)

There are three ways to prove that two triangles are similar.

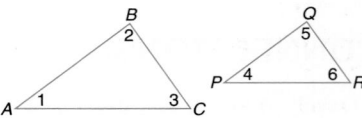

AA Similarity	$\angle 1 \cong \angle 4, \angle 3 \cong \angle 6$
SSS Similarity	$\dfrac{AB}{PQ} = \dfrac{BC}{QR} = \dfrac{CA}{RP}$
SAS Similarity	$\dfrac{AB}{PQ} = \dfrac{AC}{PR}, \angle 1 \cong \angle 4$

Write a two-column proof for each. See margin.

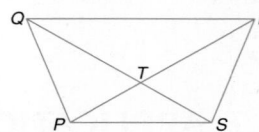

13. **Given:** $\dfrac{RP}{QS} = \dfrac{RS}{QP}$
    $\overline{QR} \parallel \overline{PS}$
    isosceles trapezoid $PQRS$
    Prove: $\triangle PQR \sim \triangle SRQ$

14. **Given:** $\overline{QR} \parallel \overline{PS}$
    Prove: $\dfrac{QT}{TS} = \dfrac{TR}{PT}$

---

use proportional parts of triangles to solve problems. (Lesson 7-5)

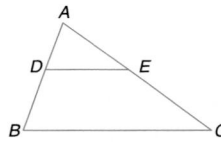

If $\overline{DE} \parallel \overline{BC}$, then $\dfrac{AD}{DB} = \dfrac{AE}{EC}$.

Use the figure and the given information to find the value of x.

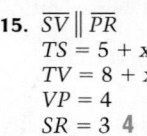

15. $\overline{SV} \parallel \overline{PR}$
    $TS = 5 + x$
    $TV = 8 + x$
    $VP = 4$
    $SR = 3$ 4

16. $\overline{RT} \parallel \overline{QV}$
    $TV = 7.29$
    $PV = x$
    $PQ = 9$
    $QR = 27$ 2.43

CHAPTER 7   353

Additional Answer

14. Statements   (Reasons)
    a. $\overline{QR} \parallel \overline{PS}$ (Given)
    b. $\angle RQT \cong \angle PST, \angle QRT \cong \angle SPT$ (Alternate Interior Angle Theorem)
    c. $\triangle QRT \sim \triangle SPT$ (AA Similarity)
    d. $\dfrac{QT}{TS} = \dfrac{TR}{PT}$
       (Definition of similar polygons)

A two-page Cumulative Review from the *Evaluation Masters* is shown below. It can be used to review skills and concepts presented thus far in the text. Standardized Test Practice Questions are also provided in the *Evaluation Masters*.

Evaluation Masters, pp. 95-96

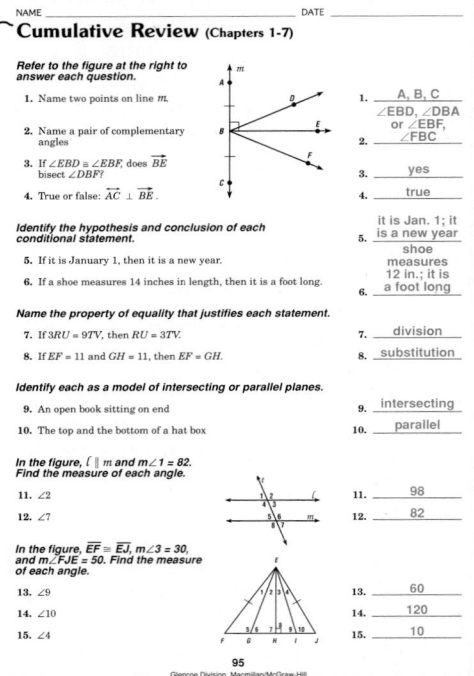

■ use the proportional relationships of corresponding perimeters, altitudes, angle bisectors, and medians of similar triangles. **(Lesson 7-6)**

$\triangle ABC \sim \triangle PQR$

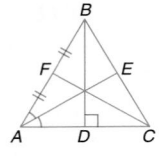
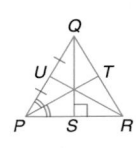

Perimeter	$\dfrac{AB + BC + CA}{PQ + QR + RP} = \dfrac{CA}{RP}$	
Altitude	$\dfrac{BD}{QS} = \dfrac{BA}{QP}$	
Angle bisector	$\dfrac{AE}{PT} = \dfrac{CA}{RP}$	
Median	$\dfrac{CF}{RU} = \dfrac{CA}{RP}$	

Find each of the following.

17. If $\triangle ABC \sim \triangle XYZ$, find YN.

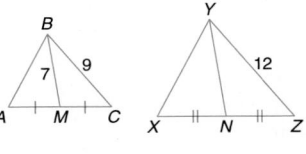

$9\frac{1}{3}$

18. If $\triangle STV \sim \triangle PQM$, find the perimeter of $\triangle PQM$.

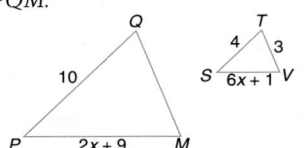

27.5

APPLICATIONS AND CONNECTIONS

19. Probability If the probability of rolling a sum of 7 with 2 dice is $\frac{1}{6}$, how many sums of 7 would you expect to get if you rolled the dice 174 times? **(Lesson 7-2)** 29

20. Travel A map is scaled so that 1 centimeter represents 15 kilometers. How far apart are two towns if they are 7.9 centimeters apart on the map? **(Lesson 7-2)** 118.5 km

21. Drafting A proportional divider is a drafting instrument which is used to enlarge or reduce a drawing. A screw at T keeps $\overline{AT} \cong \overline{TC}$ and $\overline{DT} \cong \overline{TB}$. $\overline{AB}$ and $\overline{CD}$ can be set so they are divided proportionally at T in any desired ratio. How would you adjust the dividers in order to enlarge a design in the ratio 7 to 4? **(Lesson 7-4)**
$AT = TC = 4$ and $DT = TB = 7$

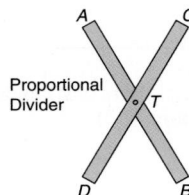

Proportional Divider

22. Hobbies A twin-jet airplane especially suited for medium-range flights has a length of 78 meters and a wingspan of 90 meters. If a scale model is made with a wingspan of 36 centimeters, find its length. **(Lesson 7-3)** 31.2 cm

23. Solve this problem by solving a simpler problem. Find the units digit of 2^{125}. **(Lesson 7-7)** 2

1. If $\frac{a}{b} = \frac{x}{y}$, which one of the following statements is *not* true? **b**

   a. $ay = bx$ b. $\frac{a+x}{b+y} = \frac{a}{b} + \frac{x}{y}$ c. $\frac{b}{a} = \frac{y}{x}$ d. $\frac{y}{b} = \frac{x}{a}$

Solve each proportion.

2. $\frac{x}{28} = \frac{60}{16}$ **105**

3. $\frac{21}{1-x} = \frac{7}{x}$ **0.25**

4. $\frac{14}{21} = \frac{18}{x}$ **27**

5. A recipe for preparing material to be dyed calls for four parts alum to one part washing soda. How much washing soda should be used for 150 grams of alum? **37.5 g**

Determine whether each statement is *true* or *false*.

6. All equilateral triangles are similar. **true**   7. All regular hexagons are similar. **true**

8. All isosceles triangles are similar. **false**   9. All rhombuses are similar. **false**

Determine if each pair of triangles is similar. Write *yes* or *no*. If they are similar, give a reason.

10. 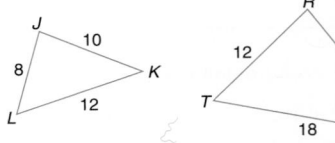   11.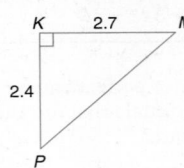

yes; SSS Similarity   **yes; SAS Similarity**

Use the figure at the right and the given information to find the value of x.

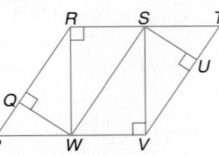

12. $\triangle RWP \sim \triangle VST$
    $PW = x$ $SU = 5$
    $QW = 1$ $ST = x + 5$ $1\frac{1}{4}$

13. $\triangle WRS \sim \triangle VUS$
    $SW = 3$ $SV = 2$
    $RS = 1\frac{1}{3}$ $SU = x + \frac{2}{3}$ $\frac{2}{9}$

Complete each of the following.

14. **Given:** $\triangle ABC \sim \triangle RSP$
    D is the midpoint of $\overline{AC}$.
    Q is the midpoint of $\overline{PR}$.
    Prove: $\triangle SPQ \sim \triangle BCD$ **See Solutions Manual.**

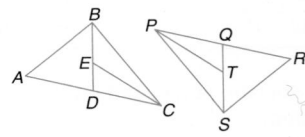

15. Use similar triangles to find the distance across the river. **36 mi**

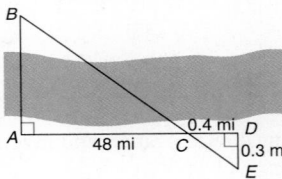

Bonus The measures of the sides of one triangle are 5, 7, and 10. The measures of the sides of another triangle are 21, 15, and 30. Find the ratio of the areas of the triangles. **1:9**

Using the Chapter Test

This page may be used as a test or as a review. In addition, two multiple-choice tests (Forms 1A and 1B) and two free-response tests (Forms 2A and 2B) are provided in the *Evaluation Masters*. Chapter 7 Test, Form 1A is shown below.

Evaluation Masters, pp. 85-86

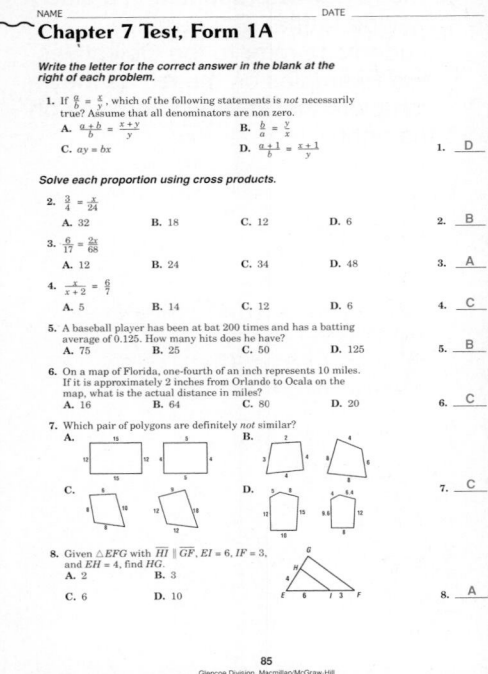

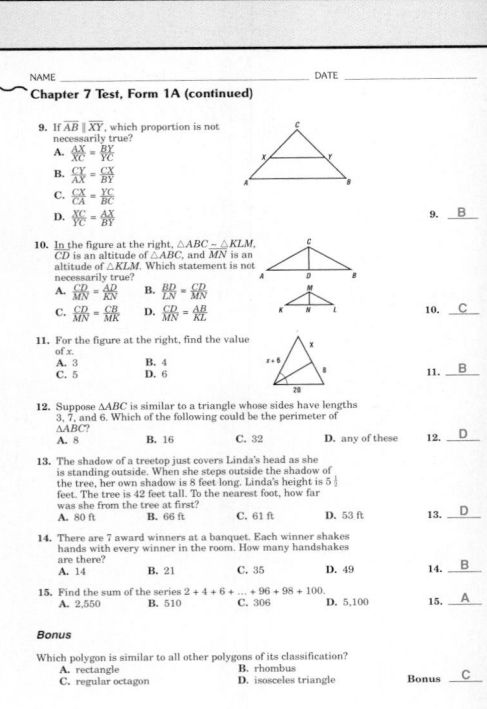

Test and Review Generator software is provided in Apple, IBM, and Macintosh versions. You may use this software to create your own tests or worksheets, based on the needs of your students.

The **Performance Assessment Booklet** provides an alternate assessment for evaluating student progress. An assessment for this chapter can be found on pages 13-14.

Using the Algebra Review

The goal of this two-page review of algebraic skills, concepts, and applications is as follows:

- it provides students a chance to review important concepts from algebra that will be useful as they study geometry.
- it gives students an opportunity to retain the concepts they learned in previous algebra courses and may need for future mathematics courses.

The review is presented in a side-by-side format. Encourage students to refer to the Objectives and Examples on the left as they complete the Review Exercises on the right.

Additional Answers

1. $7x^3y + 28x^2y^2 - 56xy^3$
2. $10x^2 - 19x + 63$
3. $-2x^3 + 56x^2 - 9x$
4. $r^2 + 4r - 21$
5. $3x^2 + 13x - 10$
6. $12n^2 - 7n - 12$
7. $6x^2 + 25xy - 9y^2$
8. $a^3 + a^2 - 27a + 28$
9. $(x + 9)^2$
10. $2(4n - 5)^2$
11. $\frac{1}{4}\left(n + \frac{3}{2}\right)\left(n - \frac{3}{2}\right)$
12. $3x(x + 8)(x - 8)$
15. $\frac{x}{4y^2 z}$;
   excluded values: $x = 0$, $y = 0$, $z = 0$
16. z; excluded values: $z = 3$
17. $\frac{a - 5}{a - 2}$;
   excluded values: $a = -5$, or 2
18. $\frac{x + 3y}{x(x - 6y)}$;
   excluded values: $x = 0$, $x = -7y$, $x = 6y$

OBJECTIVES AND EXAMPLES	REVIEW EXERCISES

■ Multiply a polynomial by a monomial.

$x^2(x + 2) + 3(x^3 + 4x^2)$
$= (x^3 + 2x^2) + (3x^3 + 12x^2)$
$= (x^3 + 3x^3) + (2x^2 + 12x^2)$
$= 4x^3 + 14x^2$

Simplify. See margin.

1. $7xy(x^2 + 4xy - 8y^2)$
2. $x(3x - 5) + 7(x^2 - 2x + 9)$
3. $4x^2(x + 8) - 3x(2x^2 - 8x + 3)$

■ Multiply a polynomial by a polynomial.

$(3x - 2)(x + 2)$
$= 3x(x) + 3x(2) + (-2)(x) + (-2)(2)$
$= 3x^2 + 6x - 2x - 4$
$= 3x^2 + 4x - 4$

Find each product. See margin.

4. $(r - 3)(r + 7)$
5. $(x + 5)(3x - 2)$
6. $(4n + 3)(3n - 4)$
7. $(2x + 9y)(3x - y)$
8. $(a - 4)(a^2 + 5a - 7)$

■ Factor perfect square trinomials and binomials that are the difference of squares.

$16a^2 - 24a + 9$
$= (4a)^2 - 2(4a)(3) + (3)^2$
$= (4a - 3)^2$

$25 - 4y^2 = (5)^2 - (2y)^2$
$= (5 - 2y)(5 + 2y)$

Factor each polynomial. 9-12. See margin.

9. $x^2 + 18x + 81$
10. $32n^2 - 80n + 50$
11. $\frac{n^2}{4} - \frac{9}{16}$
12. $3x^3 - 192x$
13. $16p^2 - 81r^4$ $(4p - 9r^2)(4p + 9r^2)$
14. $54b^3 - 72b^2g + 24bg^2$ $6b(3b - 2g)^2$

■ Simplify rational expressions.

$\frac{x + y}{x^2 + 3xy + 2y^2} = \frac{x + y}{(x + y)(x + 2y)}$
$= \frac{1}{x + 2y}$

Simplify. State the excluded values of the variables. See margin.

15. $\frac{3x^2y}{12xy^3z}$
16. $\frac{z^2 - 3z}{z - 3}$
17. $\frac{a^2 - 25}{a^2 + 3a - 10}$
18. $\frac{x^2 + 10xy + 21y^2}{x^3 + x^2y - 42xy^2}$

■ Identify the domain, range, and inverse of a relation.

State the domain, range, and inverse of $\{(3, 5), (2, 6), (-5, 6)\}$.
Domain: $\{3, 2, -5\}$ Range: $\{5, 6\}$
Inverse: $\{(5, 3), (6, 2), (6, -5)\}$

State the domain, range, and inverse of each relation. See margin.

19. $\{(-2, -1), (-1, 0), (0, 2)\}$
20. $\{(-3, 5), (-3, 6), (4, 5), (4, 6)\}$
21. $\{(4, 1), (4, -2), (4, 7), (4, -1)\}$

Additional Answers

19. Domain: $\{-2, -1, 0\}$
    Range: $\{-1, 0, 2\}$
    Inverse: $\{(-1, -2), (0, -1), (2, 0)\}$
20. Domain: $\{-3, 4\}$
    Range: $\{5, 6\}$
    Inverse: $\{(5, -3), (6, -3), (5, 4), (6, 4)\}$
21. Domain: $\{4\}$
    Range: $\{-2, -1, 1, 7\}$
    Inverse: $\{(1, 4), (-2, 4), (7, 4), (-1, 4)\}$

- Solve inequalities involving more than one operation.

$$14c \geq 6c + 48$$
$$14c - 6c \geq 6c - 6c + 48$$
$$\frac{8c}{8} \geq \frac{48}{8}$$
$$c \geq 6$$

The solution set is $\{c \,|\, c \geq 6\}$.

Solve each inequality. Check the solution.

22. $7x - 12 < 30$ $\{x \,|\, x < 6\}$
23. $4y - 11 \geq 8y + 7$ $\{y \,|\, y \leq -\frac{9}{2}\}$
24. $4(n - 1) < 7n + 8$ $\{n \,|\, n > -4\}$
25. $\frac{3}{10}(4 - d) \leq -\frac{4}{5}\left(\frac{1}{5}d + 2\right)$ $\{d \,|\, d \geq 20\}$

- Solve problems involving inverse variation.

If y varies inversely as x, and $y = 24$ when $x = 30$, find x when $y = 10$.

$$30 \cdot 24 = x \cdot 10 \quad x_1y_1 = x_2y_2$$
$$720 = 10x$$
$$72 = x$$

Solve. Assume that y varies inversely as x.

26. If $y = 28$ when $x = 42$, find y when $x = 56$. **21**
27. If $y = 35$ when $x = 175$, find y when $x = 75$. $\frac{245}{3}$ **or 81.$\overline{6}$**
28. If $y = 2.7$ when $x = 8.1$, find x when $y = 3.6$ **6.075**

- Solve equations for a specified variable.

Solve the equation $\frac{x + 1}{a} = b$ for x.

$$a\left(\frac{x + 1}{a}\right) = a(b)$$
$$x + 1 - 1 = ab - 1$$
$$x = ab - 1$$

Solve for x.

29. $\frac{x + y}{c} = d$ $cd - y$
30. $5(2a + x) = 3b$ $\frac{3b - 10a}{5}$
31. $\frac{ax - 3}{2} = 7b - 6$ $\frac{14b - 9}{a}$
32. $\frac{2x - a}{3} = \frac{a + 3b}{4}$ $\frac{7a + 9b}{8}$

Applications and Connections

33. **Employment** Ahmed's wages vary directly as the number of days he works. If his wages for 5 days are $26, how much would they be for 12 days? **$62.40**

34. **Geometry** The measure of the area of a rectangle is $25x^2 - 9$. Find the measure of its perimeter. **20x**

35. **Photography** To get a rectangular photo to fit into a rectangular frame, Leo had to trim a 1-inch strip from each side of the photo. In all, he trimmed off 46 square inches. If the photo is 3 inches longer than it is wide, what were its original dimensions? **14 in. by 11 in.**

36. **Banking** Sara budgets between $3 and $4 a month to spend on bank checking charges. Her bank charges $1.75 a month plus $0.08 per check. How many checks can Sara write each month and still meet her budget? **between 16 and 28 checks**

Right Triangles and Trigonometry

PREVIEWING THE CHAPTER

In this chapter, students explore special relationships that exist in right triangles and apply trigonometry to many different kinds of problems. Students begin by identifying the relationships between parts of a right triangle and the altitude to the hypotenuse. Next, they use the Pythagorean theorem and identify and use the properties of 45°-45°-90° and 30°-60°-90° triangles. These concepts are followed by the presentation of trigonometric ratios. Using the law of sines and the law of cosines to find missing measures in triangles concludes Chapter 8.

Problem-Solving Strategy Students learn to consider alternatives and choose the appropriate strategy for solving a problem.

Lesson Objective Chart

Lesson (Pages)	Lesson Objectives	State/Local Objectives
8-1 (360-364)	**8-1A**: Find the geometric mean between a pair of numbers.	
	8-1B: Solve problems using relationships between parts of a right triangle and the altitude to its hypotenuse.	
8-2 (365-370)	**8-2**: Use the Pythagorean Theorem and its converse.	
8-3 (371-375)	**8-3**: Use the properties of 45°-45°-90° and 30°-60°-90° triangles.	
8-4 (376-382)	**8-4A**: Express trigonometric ratios as fractions or decimals.	
	8-4B: Recognize trigonometric relationships from right triangles.	
	8-4C: Use a calculator to find values of trigonometric ratios or measures of angles.	
8-5 (384-388)	**8-5A**: Recognize angles of depression or elevation.	
	8-5B: Use trigonometry to solve problems.	
8-6 (389-393)	**8-6**: Use the law of sines to solve triangles.	
8-7 (394-398)	**8-7**: Solve triangles and problems using the law of cosines.	
8-8 (399-401)	**8-8**: Choose the appropriate strategy for solving a problem.	

ORGANIZING THE CHAPTER

You may want to refer to the **Course Planning Calendar** on page T28.

Lesson Planning Guide / Blackline Masters Booklets

Lesson (Pages)	Pacing Chart (days) Course I	II	III	Reteaching	Practice	Enrichment	Evaluation	Technology	Lab Manual	Mixed Problem Solving	Applications	Cooperative Learning Activity	Multicultural	Transparencies
8-1 (360-364)	2	2	1.5	p. 43	p. 50	p. 43		p. 44						8-1
8-2 (365-370)	2	1.5	1.5	p. 44	p. 51	p. 44	Quiz A, p.107		pp.58-61			p. 36		8-2
8-3 (371-375)	2	1.5	1	p. 45	p. 52	p. 45								8-3
8-4 (376-382)	2	2	1.5	p. 46	p. 53	p. 46	Quiz B, p.107 Mid Chapter Test, p.111						p. 8	8-4
8-5 (384-388)	2	2	1.5	p. 47	p. 54	p. 47			pp.62-65		p. 22			8-5
8-6 (389-393)	1.5	1.5	1.5	p. 48	p. 55	p. 48	Quiz C, p. 108	p. 8						8-6
8-7 (394-398)	1.5	1.5	1.5	p. 49	p. 56	p. 49								8-7
8-8 (399-401)	1	1	1		p. 57		Quiz D, p. 108			p. 8				8-8
Review (402-404)	1	1	1	Multiple Choice Tests, Forms 1A and 1B, pp. 99-102 Free Response Tests, Forms 2A and 2B, pp. 103-106										
Test (405)	1	1	1	Cumulative Review. pp. 109-110 Standardized Tests Practice Questions, p. 112										

Course I: Chapters 1-11; Course II: Chapters 1-12; Course III: Chapters 1-13

Other Chapter Resources

Student Edition
Chapter Opener, pp. 358-359
Journal Entry, pp. 364, 388
Mid-Chapter Review, p. 382
Technology, p. 383
Portfolio, p. 398
Cooperative Learning Project, p. 401
College Entrance Exam Preview, pp. 406-407
More Investigations in Geometry, p. A9-A10
Extended Project 3, pp. B10-B13

Teacher's Classroom Resources
Transparency 8-0
Real World Applications Transparencies, 15, 16, 17
Performance Assessment Booklet, pp. 15-16
Problem-of-the-Week Activity Cards, 21, 22, 23
Tech Prep Applications Booklet, pp. 15-16

Other Supplements
Algebra and Geometry Overhead Manipulative Resources
Glencoe Mathematics Professional Series

Software
Test and Review Generator (Apple, IBM, and Macintosh)
Teacher's Guide for Software Resources

ENHANCING THE CHAPTER

Cooperative Learning

Intervening to Teach Cooperative-Learning Skills

In many of their other activities, both inside and outside of school, students are required to compete more often than to cooperate. Therefore, it may require some time and attention for students to develop positive group skills. Experienced researchers recommend that only a few of these skills be taught each semester. Each new skill should be clearly defined before the session begins and skills that were introduced earlier reviewed. Then, after the session begins, the teacher should monitor the groups and intervene when appropriate. Once students recognize the need for the skill, they only need help with developing it. This involves the teacher including examples of expected behavior when the skill is first defined and then offering appropriate guidance and feedback as students practice the skill during their cooperative-learning sessions. After each session, provide time for the students to discuss and assess their behaviors. To motivate the discussion, ask each group to list the two things they did better this time than the last time and the one thing they plan to do better the next time.

Technology

The Technology Feature following Lesson 8-4 uses a graphing calculator to help students find the tangent ratio of an angle. Students are shown that the tangent ratio of an angle is simply the slope of a line. Therefore, by finding the slope of a line, the measure of the angle the line forms with a horizontal can be found. After completing the exercises found in the feature, you may wish to encourage students to write their own equations to graph in order to find the measure of the angle the line forms with a horizontal.

Critical Thinking

Students will live and work in a world that provides them with easy access to powerful personal computers and software programs that provide interactive processes for finding and understanding solutions to business problems. Such programs require the user to employ higher-level thinking skills for successful implementation. As part of their preparation for this world, students should be given opportunities not only to answer but also to ask "What if" questions. Use the problems in this chapter to provide opportunities for students to create new conditions, including reversals in which instead of finding the solution, the student gives a different solution and asks how the conditions must be changed to achieve the given results.

Cooperative Learning, p. 36

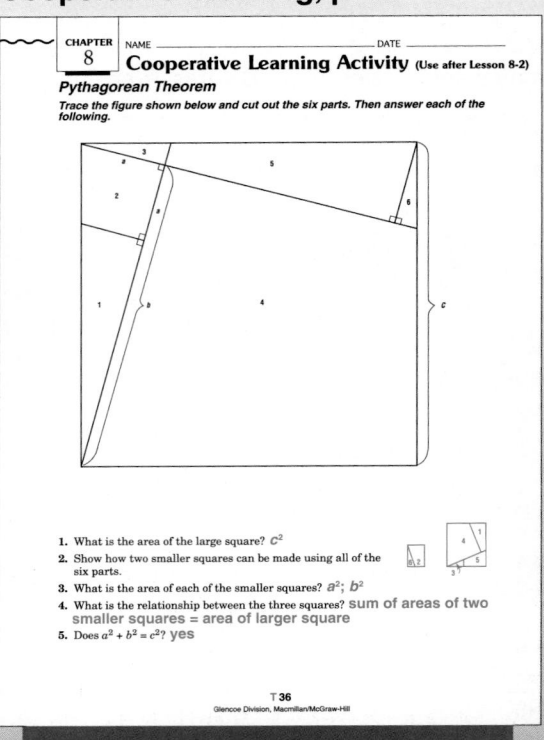

Technology, p. 8

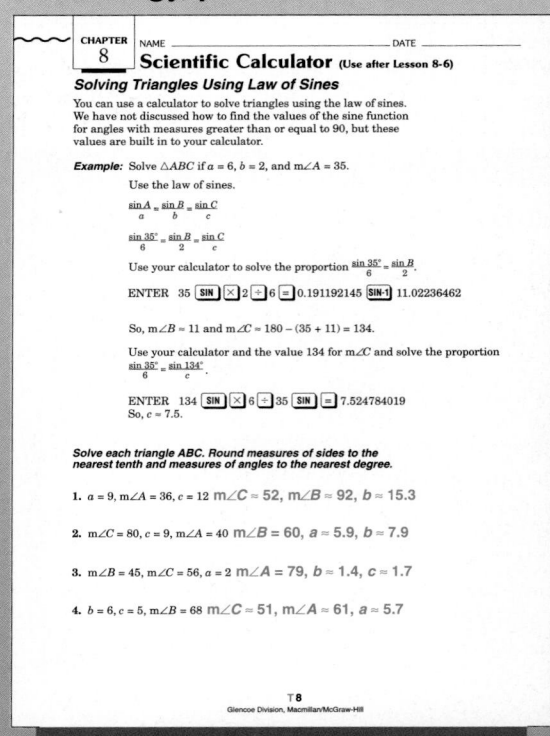

Problem of the Week Activity

The card shown below is one of three available for this chapter. It can be used as a class or small group activity.

Activity Card

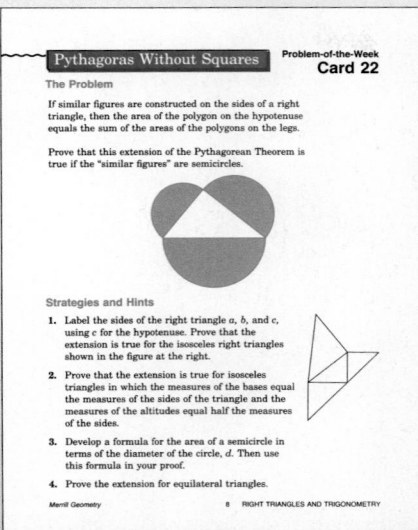

Manipulatives and Models

The following materials may be used as models or manipulatives in Chapter 8.

- dot paper (Lesson 8-1)
- grid paper (Lesson 8-2)
- photos from architectural magazine (Lesson 8-2)
- ruler (Lesson 8-3)
- scientific calculator (Lesson 8-4)
- hypsometer (Lesson 8-5)
- compass, straightedge (Lesson 8-7)

Outside Resources

Books/Periodicals

Gardner, Martin, *Mathematical Puzzles.* Thomas Y. Crowell Company.

Lasserre, F. *The Birth of Mathematics in the Age of Plato.* American Research Council.

Thompson, J.E. *Trigonometry for the Practical Worker.* Van Nostrand.

Films/Videotapes/Videodiscs

The Theorem of Pythagoras, California Institute of Technology Bookstore, I-51, Pasadena, CA 91125

Trigonometry, Access Network, 295 Midpark Way SE, Calgary, Alberta, Canada T2X 2A8

Software

The Geometer's Sketchpad, Key Curriculum Press, 2512 Martin Luther King Jr. Way, P.O. Box 2304, Berkeley, CA 94702

Geo Explorer, Scott, Foresman, 1900 E. Lake Ave., Glenview, IL 60025-9881

Multicultural

Multicultural Activity, p. 8

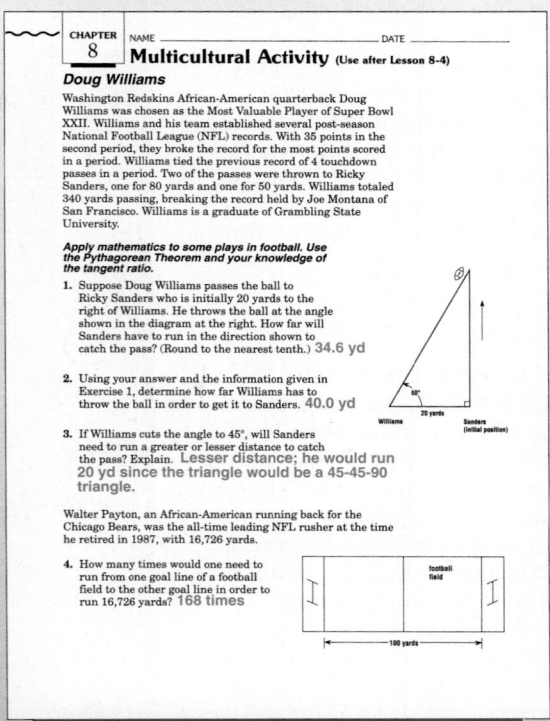

Lab Manual

Lab Activity, pp. 62-65

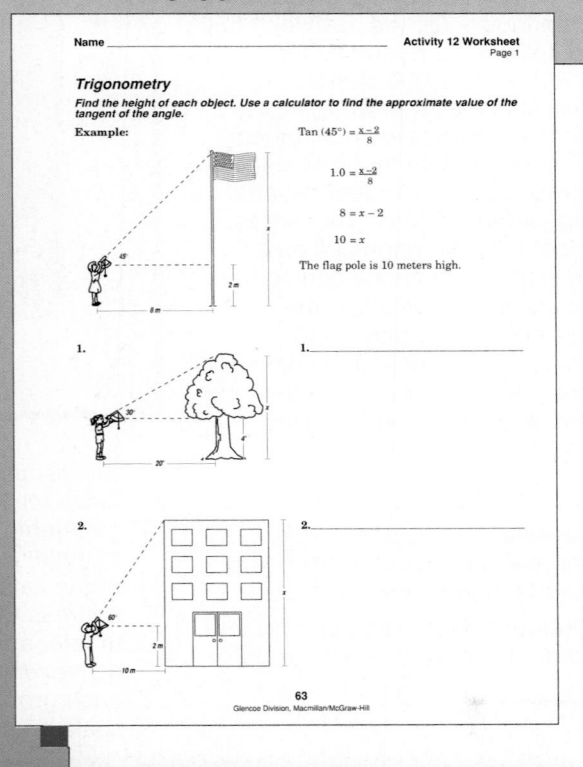

Using the Chapter Opener

This two-page introduction to the chapter provides students with an opportunity to see how geometry is used throughout the world in various cultures. **Transparency 8-0**, available in the *Merrill Geometry Transparency Package*, provides another full-color visual and motivational activity that you can use to engage your students in the mathematical content of the chapter.

Multicultural Notes

India Examples of some of the earliest forms of stone sculpture can be found in India. Prior to the second century B.C., sculptures of memorable persons, events, and decorative designs were carved only in wood. Between the second and third centuries B.C., craftsmen working on domed Buddhist temples, or *stupas*, began applying wood carving techniques to stone to create decorative railings and gateways.

Polynesia Easter Island, one of the most isolated places in the Pacific Ocean, is about 2,300 miles west of the coast of Chile. It was home to a population of mysterious sculptors. Between 690 and 1650 A.D., Easter Islanders carved some 1,000 statues or *moai*, plus altars, or *ahu*, of precisely engineered masonry on which to stand them. Most of the statues are 12 to 15 feet tall and weigh about 20 tons. The largest is 32 feet tall and weighs 90 tons. The stone giants were carved from volcanic rock from along the slopes of the volcano Rano Raraku. The giant statues have immense heads, no legs, long arms, and large, round bellies.

Chapter Project

Materials Pencil, paper, ruler, compass, protractor, posterboard, colored markers, modeling clay

Procedure Organize students into cooperative groups. Each group will discuss and sketch several ideas for a sculpture based on geometric shapes, especially the triangle, for a governing body or organization. The group should address the geographical setting, theme, and message to be conveyed by the sculpture. Have each group draw its sculpture to scale on posterboard, using accurate measurements of all geometric shapes. Each group should prepare a written proposal for funding of the sculpture to the organization, including the design and its description. Groups should build a scale model of the sculpture from modeling clay and other building materials. Each group should present its

Right Triangles and Trigonometry

GEOMETRY AROUND THE WORLD
Mexico

Unlike paintings, which have two dimensions, sculptures have three: length, width, and depth. Most of us are satisfied to simply look at paintings. But, because they have depth and are made of interesting materials, we usually want to touch sculptures.

Some sculptures are so tiny they can fit in your hand. Others, like "The Sculptured Space," an outdoor, public sculpture in Satellite City, Mexico, are enormous. "The Sculptured Space" was designed by a team of six sculptors headed by Helen Escobedo.

It is an environmental sculpture formed by a natural earth material called lava, produced by erupting volcanoes. Escobedo and her team of sculptors surrounded existing petrified lava with 64 concrete triangular prisms arranged in a circle. Each prism is 4 meters high, and the entire sculpture is 120 meters in diameter. There is no other sculpture like it!

GEOMETRY IN ACTION

Geometry is one of the oldest branches of mathematics. The word is derived from the Greek words *geo* meaning "earth," and *metria* meaning "measurement." You can use geometry to find missing measures for one prism in "The Sculptured Space." The shape of one prism is shown below. After you study Lesson 8-2, you will be able to find the length of the base. **The length is about 9.1 meters.**

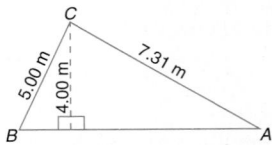

◀ *"The Sculptured Space"*

Using the people for scale, how tall does each prism in "The Sculptured Space" appear to be? **about 14 feet**

CHAPTER OBJECTIVES

In this chapter, you will:
- Find the geometric mean between two numbers.
- Use the Pythagorean Theorem and its converse.
- Recognize and use trigonometric relationships from right triangles.
- Solve triangles and problems using the law of sines and the law of cosines.

Connections and Applications

Lesson	Connections (C) and Applications (A)	Examples	Exercises
8-1	A: Measurement	2	
	C: Algebra		35
	A: Science		36
8-2	A: Construction	1	40
	A: Sports		39
	A: History		41
	A: Zoology		48
8-3	A: Architecture	2	
	A: Auto Repair		36
	A: Painting		37
8-4	A: Navigation	3	52
	A: Aviation	5	53
	A: Electronics		54
8-5	A: Aviation	1	
	A: Fire Fighting	2	
	A: Aerospace	3	
	A: Travel		34
	A: Physics		35
	A: Meteorology		36
8-6	A: Gardening	2	
	A: Aviation		30
	A: Surveying		31, 32
8-7	A: Aviation	2	36
	A: Navigation		35
	A: Sports		37

proposal to the class, which acts as the directors of the organization. The group should attempt to convince the class to provide the funding needed to build its sculpture. Have the class vote on the funding of each group's proposal.

Resources

Suzuki, Makoto. *Modern Mexican Architecture.* Process Architecture Publishing Company

Escobedo, Helen. *Mexican Monuments: Strange Encounters.* Abbeville Press

Damaz, Paul F. *Art in Latin American Architecture.* Reinhold Publishing Corporation

Lesson Resources

- Reteaching Master 8-1
- Practice Master 8-1
- Enrichment Master 8-1
- Technology Master, p. 44

 Transparency 8-1 contains the 5-Minute Check and a teaching aid for this lesson.

INTRODUCING THE LESSON

5-Minute Check

(over Chapter 7)

1. Solve $\frac{10}{t} = \frac{6}{t-1}$ using cross products. **$t = 2.5$**

2. If two similar parallelograms have a scale factor of 4.5 and one angle of the larger parallelogram measures 65°, what is the measure of the corresponding angle in the smaller parallelogram? **65°**

Refer to the figure below.

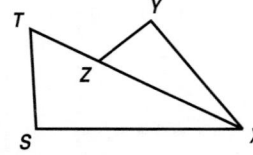

3. If $\overline{TX}$ bisects $\angle SXY$ and $\angle S \cong \angle Y$, can you say the two triangles are similar? Why or why not? **yes, the AA Similarity**

4. If $\triangle STX \sim \triangle YZX$, $TZ = 3$, $ZX = 7$, $TS = 6$, and $SX = 14$, what is the perimeter of $\triangle YZX$? **21**

Motivating the Lesson

Ask students to examine these proportions:

$\frac{3}{6} = \frac{6}{12}$ $\frac{4}{8} = \frac{8}{16}$ $\frac{11}{22} = \frac{22}{44}$

What do these proportions have in common? **The numerator of one ratio is the same as the denominator of the other.**

8-1 The Geometric Mean

Objectives
After studying this lesson, you should be able to:
- 8-1A ■ find the geometric mean between a pair of numbers, and
- 8-1B ■ solve problems using relationships between parts of a right triangle and the altitude to its hypotenuse.

Application

The shell of the chambered nautilus offers an example of right triangle relationships in nature. The segments shown allow us to approximate the spiral. The relationship among the segments in the spiral is a **geometric mean**.

The geometric mean between two positive numbers a and b is the positive number x where $\frac{a}{x} = \frac{x}{b}$. By cross multiplying, we see that $x^2 = ab$ or $x = \sqrt{ab}$.

Example 1

Find the geometric mean between 12 and 18.

Let x represent the geometric mean.

$$\frac{12}{x} = \frac{x}{18} \qquad \textit{Definition of geometric mean}$$
$$x^2 = 216 \qquad \textit{Cross multiply.}$$
$$x = \sqrt{216} \qquad \textit{Take the square root of each side.}$$
$$x \approx 14.7 \qquad \textit{Use a calculator to find an approximation.}$$

The geometric mean between 12 and 18 is about 14.7.

The geometric mean is useful when studying relationships between the sides of a right triangle and its altitude. When the altitude to the hypotenuse of a right triangle is drawn, two similar triangles are formed. In the figure at the right, altitude $\overline{QS}$ separates $\triangle PQR$ into two smaller triangles that are similar to each other and also to $\triangle PQR$. This can be proved as a theorem.

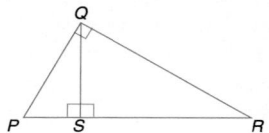

Theorem 8-1

If the altitude is drawn from the vertex of the right angle of a right triangle to its hypotenuse, then the two triangles formed are similar to the given triangle and to each other.

ALTERNATE TEACHING STRATEGIES

Using Manipulatives

Using grid or dot paper, have students draw a right triangle with an altitude from the right angle. Have them draw the triangle again, labeling the interior of each angle with its vertex letter. Then have them cut out the first triangle and cut along the altitude. Students can position the smaller models so that similarity to the larger triangle is more apparent.

Using Cooperative Groups

In groups of three, have students create problems based on the theorems of this lesson. Have them prepare an answer sheet for the problems. Groups can then exchange their problems for solution and use the answer sheets to check and discuss answers.

Proof of Theorem 8-1

Given: $\angle PQR$ is a right angle.
$\overline{QS}$ is an altitude of $\triangle PQR$.

Prove: $\triangle PSQ \sim \triangle PQR$
$\triangle PQR \sim \triangle QSR$
$\triangle PSQ \sim \triangle QSR$

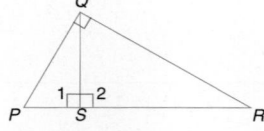

Proof:

Statements	Reasons
1. $\angle PQR$ is a right angle. $\overline{QS}$ is an altitude of $\triangle PQR$.	1. Given
2. $\overline{QS} \perp \overline{RP}$	2. Definition of altitude
3. $\angle 1$ and $\angle 2$ are right angles.	3. $\perp$ lines form 4 rt. $\angle$s.
4. $\angle 1 \cong \angle PQR$ $\angle 2 \cong \angle PQR$	4. All rt. $\angle$s are $\cong$.
5. $\angle P \cong \angle P$ $\angle R \cong \angle R$	5. Congruence of angles is reflexive.
6. $\triangle PSQ \sim \triangle PQR$ $\triangle PQR \sim \triangle QSR$	6. AA Similarity
7. $\triangle PSQ \sim \triangle QSR$	7. Similarity of triangles is transitive.

In the figure above, $\triangle PSQ \sim \triangle QSR$. So, $\frac{PS}{QS} = \frac{QS}{SR}$ because corresponding sides of similar triangles are proportional. Thus, QS is the geometric mean between PS and SR. This is stated in the theorem below.

Theorem 8-2

The measure of the altitude drawn from the vertex of the right angle of a right triangle to its hypotenuse is the geometric mean between the measures of the two segments of the hypotenuse.

You will be asked to prove Theorem 8-2 in Exercise 33.

Example 2

The geometric mean can be used to estimate hard-to-measure distances.

To find the height of the tree in her backyard, Lori held a book near her eye so that the top and bottom of the tree were in line with the edges of the cover. If Lori's eye is 5 feet off the ground and she is standing approximately 14 feet from the tree, how tall is the tree? Assume that the tree is perpendicular to the ground and that the edges of the cover of the book are at right angles.

Draw a diagram of the situation. $\overline{EL}$ is the altitude drawn from the right angle of $\triangle ETB$.

Using Theorem 8-2, we can write the equation below.

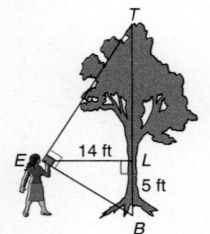

$$\frac{TL}{EL} = \frac{EL}{LB}$$
$$\frac{TL}{14} = \frac{14}{5} \qquad \textit{EL = 14, LB = 5}$$
$$5TL = 196 \qquad \textit{Cross multiply.}$$
$$TL = 39.2$$

The tree is approximately $39.2 + 5$ or 44.2 feet tall.

Chalkboard Example

For Example 1
Find the geometric mean between 3 and 45.
$$\frac{3}{x} = \frac{x}{45}$$
$$x^2 = 135$$
$$x = \sqrt{135}$$
$$x \approx 11.6$$

Teaching Tip The geometric mean can be called the mean proportional.

Chalkboard Example

For Example 2
Find *GH* in the figure below.

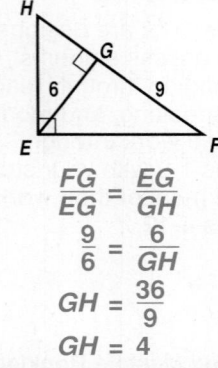

$$\frac{FG}{EG} = \frac{EG}{GH}$$
$$\frac{9}{6} = \frac{6}{GH}$$
$$GH = \frac{36}{9}$$
$$GH = 4$$

Teaching Tip For each of the theorems in this lesson, it may help students to draw diagrams and use colored pencils to outline the segments involved.

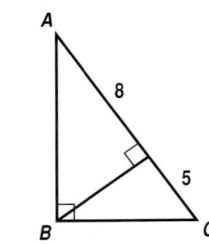

The altitude to the hypotenuse of a right triangle determines another relationship between segments.

Theorem 8-3	If the altitude is drawn to the hypotenuse of a right triangle, then the measure of a leg of the triangle is the geometric mean between the measures of the hypotenuse and the segment of the hypotenuse adjacent to that leg. *You will prove this theorem in Exercise 34.*

Example 3

Find the values of x and y.

According to Theorem 8-3, we can write the following proportions.

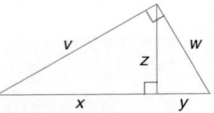

$\frac{AD}{AB} = \frac{AB}{AC}$ $\frac{DC}{BC} = \frac{BC}{AC}$

$\frac{3}{x} = \frac{x}{12}$ $\frac{9}{y} = \frac{y}{12}$ $AB = x, AD = 3, DC = 9, AC = 12, BC = y$

$x^2 = 36$ $y^2 = 108$ *Cross multiply.*

$x = 6$ $y = \sqrt{108}$ or about 10.4

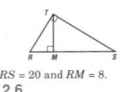
CHECKING FOR UNDERSTANDING

Communicating Mathematics

Read and study the lesson to answer these questions.

1. Describe how you would find the geometric mean between 6 and 10. If x is the geometric mean, $\frac{6}{x} = \frac{x}{10}$.

2. In the figure at the right, z is the geometric mean between __?__ and __?__. **x, y**

3. In the figure at the right, __?__ is the geometric mean between $(x + y)$ and x. **v**

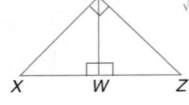

Guided Practice

Find the geometric mean between each pair of numbers.

4. 4 and 25 **10**   5. 15 and 3   6. 2 and 10

7. 7 and 22   8. $\frac{1}{2}$ and $\frac{2}{3}$ 9. 8 and 5 $\sqrt{40} \approx 6.3$

5. $\sqrt{45} \approx 6.7$ 6. $\sqrt{20} \approx 4.5$ 7. $\sqrt{154} \approx 12.4$ 8. $\frac{1}{\sqrt{3}} \approx 0.6$

10. Name three pairs of similar triangles in the figure at the right. $\triangle XYZ \sim \triangle XWY$; $\triangle XYZ \sim \triangle YWZ$; $\triangle XWY \sim \triangle YWZ$

RETEACHING THE LESSON

Complete each statement about $\triangle ABC$.

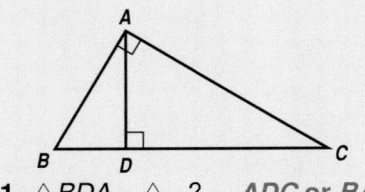

3. $\frac{BD}{?} = \frac{AD}{DC}$ **AD**

4. $\frac{BD}{AB} = \frac{AB}{?}$ **BC**

5. $\frac{DC}{?} = \frac{?}{BC}$ **AC and AC**

1. $\triangle BDA \sim \triangle$?   **ADC or BAC**

2. $\frac{BD}{AD} = \frac{AB}{?}$ **AC**

Find the values of x and y.

11.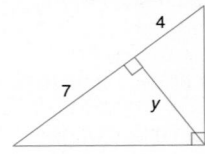

$\sqrt{44} \approx 6.6,$
$\sqrt{28} \approx 5.3$

12.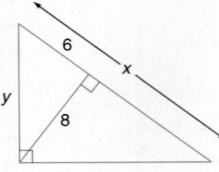

$16\frac{2}{3},\ 10$

EXERCISES

Practice

A

Find the geometric mean between each pair of numbers.

13. 3 and 5 $\sqrt{15} \approx 3.9$

14. 4 and 6 $\sqrt{24} \approx 4.9$

15. $\frac{1}{4}$ and 9 $\frac{3}{2}$

16. 4 and $\frac{1}{9}$ $\frac{2}{3}$

17. $\frac{3}{8}$ and $\frac{8}{3}$ 1

18. $\frac{2}{3}$ and $\frac{1}{3}$ $\frac{\sqrt{2}}{3} \approx 0.5$

B

Use the figure below and the given information to solve each problem.

19. $AD = 5$ and $DC = 9$. Find BD. $\sqrt{45} \approx 6.7$

20. Find BD if $DC = 12$ and $AD = 3$.   6

21. If $AD = 3$ and $DC = 10$, find BD. $\sqrt{30} \approx 5.5$

22. Find AB if $AC = 8$ and $AD = 3$. $\sqrt{24} \approx 4.9$

23. $DA = 4$ and $DC = 4$. Find BA. $\sqrt{32} \approx 5.7$

24. If $AD = 3$ and $DC = 4$, find BC. $\sqrt{28} \approx 5.3$

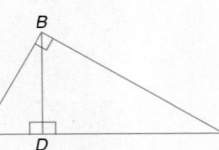

Find the values of x and y.

25.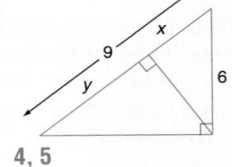

4, 5

26.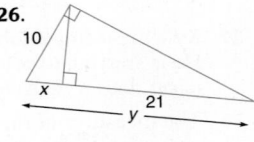

4, 25

27.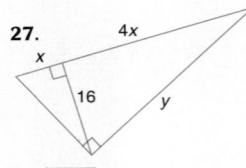

$8,\ \sqrt{1280} \approx 35.8$

28.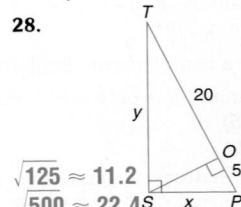

$\sqrt{125} \approx 11.2$
$\sqrt{500} \approx 22.4$

29.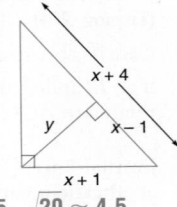

$5,\ \sqrt{20} \approx 4.5$

30.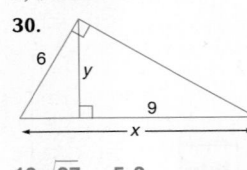

$12, \sqrt{27} \approx 5.2$

LESSON 8-1   THE GEOMETRIC MEAN   363

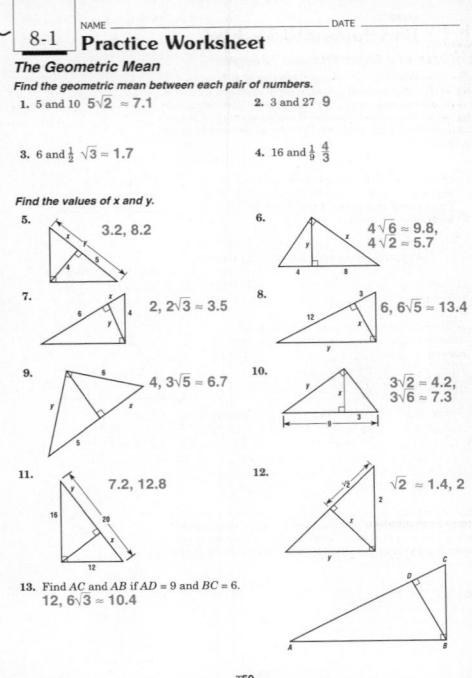

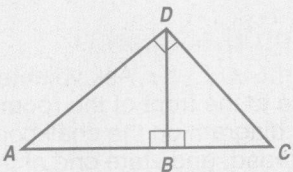
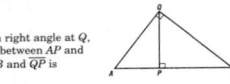
31. $VQ = 6$, $QR = 4$, $\angle PVR$ is right, and $\overline{VQ}$ is an altitude of $\triangle PVR$. Find PQ, PR, PV, and VR. **$PQ = 9$, $PR = 13$, $PV = 3\sqrt{13}$, $VR = 2\sqrt{13}$**

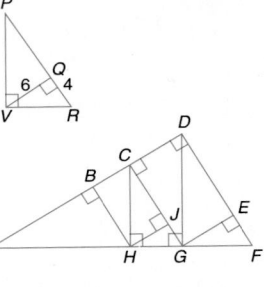

32. If $AF = 15$, $AD = 12$, and $DF = 9$ in the figure at the right, find AG, GF, DG, EF, CD, CG, and BC. **$AG = 9.6$, $GF = 5.4$, $DG = 7.2$, $EF = 3.24$, $CD = 4.32$, $CG = 5.76$, $BC = 2.7648$**

33. Write a paragraph proof of Theorem 8-2. **See margin.**

34. Write a two-column proof of Theorem 8-3. **See Solutions Manual.**

Critical Thinking

35. **Algebra** The arithmetic mean between two positive numbers a and b is $\dfrac{a+b}{2}$. Show algebraically that the arithmetic mean between two numbers is greater than the geometric mean. *(Hint: Use the problem-solving strategy of working backward.)* **See Solutions Manual.**

Application

36. **Science** The shape of the shell of the chambered nautilus can be modeled by a geometric mean. Consider the sequence of segments $\overline{OA}$, $\overline{OB}$, $\overline{OC}$, $\overline{OD}$, $\overline{OE}$, $\overline{OF}$, $\overline{OG}$, $\overline{OH}$, $\overline{OI}$, and $\overline{OJ}$. The length of each of these segments is the geometric mean between the lengths of the preceding segment and the succeeding segment. Explain. *(Hint: Consider $\triangle FGH$.)* **See margin.**

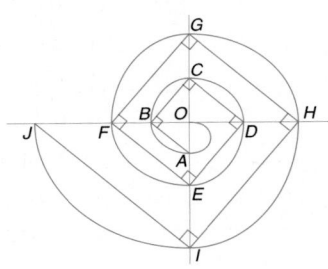

Mixed Review

37. Kyle must finish John Steinbeck's *The Pearl* and write a report by Friday. He is starting to read page 71 and the book ends on page 197. How many pages does Kyle have yet to read? **(Lesson 7-7) 127 pages**

38. The measures of the angles in $\triangle AND$ are in the ratio 4:8:12. What are the measures of the angles? **(Lesson 4-2) 30, 60, 90**

39. Name the property that allows us to say that $7(9 + 13) = 7(9) + 7(13)$. **(Lesson 2-4) Distributive property**

40. Can an obtuse angle have a complement? Explain. **(Lesson 1-8) See margin.**

41. If A, B, and C are collinear and B is between A and C, how are AB and BC related to AC? **(Lesson 1-5) $AB + BC = AC$**

Wrap-Up

42. **Journal Entry** Write two sentences about what you learned about geometric mean in your journal. **See students' work.**

EXTENDING THE LESSON

Math Power: Problem Solving

Find the area of $\triangle QRS$.
$18\sqrt{3}$ or about 31.2

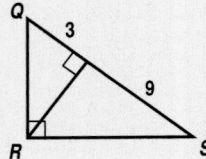

Additional Answers

36. $\triangle FGH$ is a right triangle. $\overline{OG}$ is the altitude from the vertex of the right angle to the hypotenuse of that triangle. So, by Theorem 8-2, OG is the geometric mean between OF and OH and so on.

40. No: Complementary angles have measures with a sum of 90, and the measure of an obtuse angle is greater than 90.

The Pythagorean Theorem

Objective
8-2

After studying this lesson, you should be able to:
- use the Pythagorean Theorem and its converse.

Application

Marcus and his father are building a garage behind their house. A section of the side wall is six feet wide and eight feet high. Marcus is using the **Pythagorean Theorem** to find the length for the brace for this section of wall. *You will solve this problem in Example 1.*

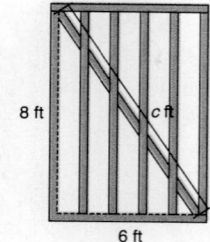

8 ft   c ft

6 ft

The concepts behind the Pythagorean Theorem have been studied and used for thousands of years. A Chinese manuscript from about 1000 B.C. that illustrates the theorem has been found. Despite this fact, the theorem is named for Pythagoras, a Greek mathematician from the sixth century who is said to have been the first to write a proof of the theorem. Many proofs of the Pythagorean Theorem exist today. United States President James Garfield presented his own proof of the theorem in 1876.

Theorem 8-4 **Pythagorean** **Theorem**	**In a right triangle, the sum of the squares of the measures of the legs equals the square of the measure of the hypotenuse.** *If c is the measure of the hypotenuse, and a and b are the measures of the legs, then $a^2 + b^2 = c^2$.*

Proof of Pythagorean Theorem

Given: right $\triangle ABC$
Prove: $a^2 + b^2 = c^2$

Proof:

Let h be the measure of the altitude drawn from C to $\overline{AB}$. Theorem 8-3 states that two geometric means now exist.

$$\frac{c}{a} = \frac{a}{x} \quad \text{and} \quad \frac{c}{b} = \frac{b}{y}$$
$$a^2 = cx \quad \text{and} \quad b^2 = cy \qquad \textit{Cross multiply.}$$

Add the equations.

$$a^2 + b^2 = cx + cy$$
$$a^2 + b^2 = c(x + y) \qquad \textit{Factor.}$$
$$a^2 + b^2 = c^2 \qquad \textit{Since c = x + y, substitute c for (x + y).}$$

LESSON 8-2   THE PYTHAGOREAN THEOREM   365

Using Applications

The steps and front walk of the Millers' house are being repaired. Mr. Miller wants to use a piece of plywood as a temporary ramp from the front door to a spot on the sidewalk 6 meters from the base of the house. If the doorway is 1.5 meters up from the ground, how long must the plywood ramp be?   **6.2 m**

Using Connections

The Pythagorean Theorem provides a way of producing segments with irrational lengths. A right triangle with legs measuring 1 unit each has a hypotenuse that measures $\sqrt{2}$ units. How could you draw a segment that measures $\sqrt{3}$ units?   **Draw a right triangle with one leg measuring 1 unit and the other measuring $\sqrt{2}$ units.**

Lesson Resources

- Reteaching Master 8-2
- Practice Master 8-2
- Enrichment Master 8-2
- Evaluation Master, p. 107
- Activity Master, p. 36
- Lab Manual, pp. 58-61

Transparency 8-2 contains the 5-Minute Check and a teaching aid for this lesson.

INTRODUCING THE LESSON

⏱ 5-Minute Check
(over Lesson 8-1)

Find the geometric mean between each pair of numbers.

1. 4 and 10 $\sqrt{40}$ or 6.3
2. 3 and 12   6
3. 2 and 50   10

Find the missing measures in $\triangle EFG$, given $EH = 4$ and $HG = 9$.

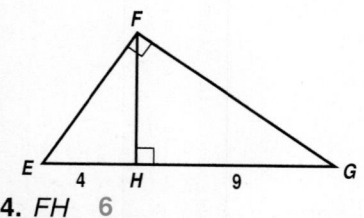

4. *FH*   6
5. *EF* $\sqrt{52}$ or 7.2
6. *FG* $\sqrt{117}$ or 10.8

Motivating the Lesson

Have each student draw a right triangle on grid paper. Have them draw a square on each side so that one side of the square is a side of the triangle. Have them cut out the three squares, cut the two smaller squares into pieces, and arrange them so that they cover the larger square.

TEACHING THE LESSON

Teaching Tip   In the proof for Theorem 8-4, point out that this is an example of using an auxiliary line to help with a proof.

Example 1

APPLICATION
Construction

Find the length of the brace Marcus needs for the section of wall that is 6 feet wide and 8 feet high.

Draw a diagram of the situation.

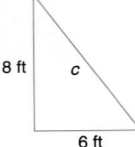

The legs of the right triangle measure 6 feet and 8 feet. We wish to find the length of the hypotenuse. Use the Pythagorean Theorem.

$$a^2 + b^2 = c^2 \qquad \text{\itshape Pythagorean Theorem}$$
$$6^2 + 8^2 = c^2 \qquad \text{\itshape a = 6 and b = 8}$$
$$36 + 64 = c^2$$
$$100 = c^2$$
$$10 = c \qquad \text{\itshape Take the square root of each side. c cannot be -10 since it represents a measure.}$$

The brace needs to be 10 feet long.

Suppose the square of the measure of the longest side of a triangle *does not* equal the sum of the squares of the measures of the other two sides. Then the triangle is *not* a right triangle. This principle, the converse of the Pythagorean Theorem, is used by carpenters when *squaring up* corners of buildings.

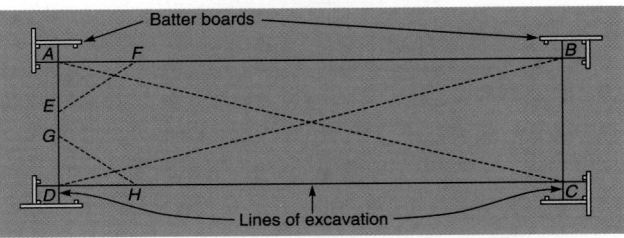

In the figure above, rectangle *ABCD* represents the lines of excavation for the foundation of a house. Since $3^2 + 4^2 = 5^2$, 3, 4, and 5 are measures of the sides of a right triangle. Therefore, from point *D* carpenters can measure 3 feet to point *G* and 4 feet to point *H*. If $\overline{GH}$ measures 5 feet, then they are assured that the corner forms a right angle. The corner is said to be *squared up*.

Theorem 8-5 *Converse of the Pythagorean Theorem*	**If the sum of the squares of the measures of two sides of a triangle equals the square of the measure of the longest side, then the triangle is a right triangle.** *You will prove this theorem in Exercise 37.*

Together, the Pythagorean Theorem and its converse are useful tools for solving right triangle problems.

Example 2

Determine whether a triangle with sides of 11.5 meters, 16.1 meters, and 20.7 meters is a right triangle.

The measure of the longest side of the triangle is 20.7 meters. Use the converse of the Pythagorean Theorem. Then find the value of each side of the equation.

$$16.1^2 + 11.5^2 \stackrel{?}{=} 20.7^2$$
$$259.21 + 132.25 \stackrel{?}{=} 428.49 \quad \text{\textit{Use a calculator.}}$$
$$391.46 \neq 428.49$$

Since $391.46 \neq 428.49$, the triangle cannot be a right triangle.

CHECKING FOR UNDERSTANDING

Communicating Mathematics

Read and study the lesson to answer these questions.

1. State the Pythagorean Theorem in your own words. When does the Pythagorean Theorem hold true? **See margin.**

2. Look through architecture magazines in your school or public library. Find photographs of structures that appear to contain right triangles. Choose one and measure the sides of the triangle. Do they indicate that the triangle is a right triangle? **Answers may vary.**

3. Write an equation that can be solved to find the length of the hypotenuse of a right triangle whose legs are 9 meters and 22 meters long. Solve your equation. $9^2 + 22^2 = x^2; \sqrt{565} \approx 23.8$

Guided Practice

Determine whether a triangle with sides having the given measures is a right triangle.

4. 5, 10, 12 **no**   5. 0.27, 0.36, 0.45 **yes**   6. 1, 2, 3 **no**

7. 9, 40, 41 **yes**   8. 10, 13, 17 **no**   9. 25, 60, 65 **yes**

Use the Pythagorean Theorem to find each missing measure.

10.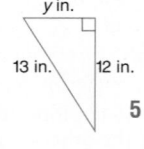
y in.
13 in.   12 in.
5

11.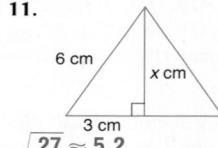
6 cm   x cm
3 cm
$\sqrt{27} \approx 5.2$

12.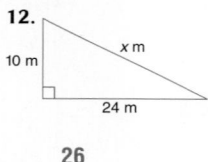
x m
10 m
24 m
26

13. The measures of the sides of a right triangle are $x + 9$, $x + 2$, and $x + 10$. Find the value of x. **3**

14. A picket fence is to have a gate 42 inches wide. The gate is 54 inches high. Find the length of a diagonal brace for the gate to the nearest inch.

15. A pleasure boat on Lake Erie sails 3 miles due north, 4 miles due east, and then 5 miles due south. To the nearest tenth of a mile, how far is the boat from its starting point? **4.5 miles**

14. **68 in.**

EXERCISES

Practice **A** Determine whether a triangle with sides having the given measures is a right triangle.

16. 12, 16, 20 **yes**
17. 1.6, 3.0, 3.4 **yes**
18. 3.87, 4.47, 5.91 **no**
19. 6, 8, 10 **yes**
20. 25, 20, 15 **yes**
21. 18, 34, 39 **no**

B Find the value of *x*. Round your answer to the nearest tenth.

22. 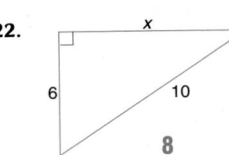 **8**

23. 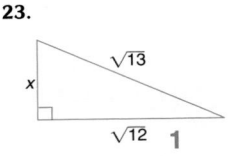 **1**

24. 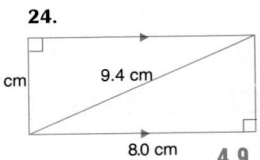 **4.9**

25. 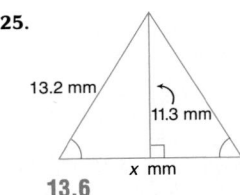 **13.6**

26. 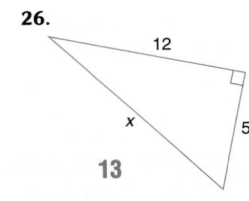 **13**

27. 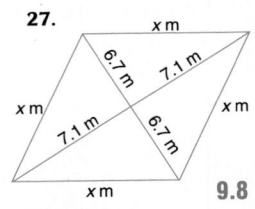 **9.8**

28. In a right triangle, the measures of the legs are 8 and $x + 7$, and the measure of the hypotenuse is $x + 10$. Find the value of *x*. $\frac{13}{6}$

29. The diagonals of a rhombus measure 30 cm and 16 cm. Use the properties of a rhombus and the Pythagorean Theorem to find the perimeter of the rhombus. **68 cm**

30. Use the triangle at the right to find $a + b + c$. **41**

31. *ABCD* is an isosceles trapezoid. If $AB = 8$, $AC = 34$, and $EF = 30$, find the perimeter of *ABCD*.
$32 + 4\sqrt{241}$ units or about 94.1 units

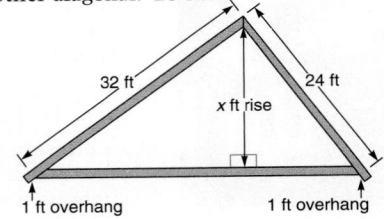

32. A diagonal of a rhombus is 48 cm long, and a side of the rhombus is 26 cm long. Find the length of the other diagonal. **20 cm**

33. The rafters of a roof truss are perpendicular to each other. One rafter is 24 feet long and the other is 32 feet long, *not* counting the overhang. Find the rise of the roof. **19.2 ft**

RETEACHING THE LESSON

Have students answer these questions about △*LMN*. Round answers to the nearest tenth.

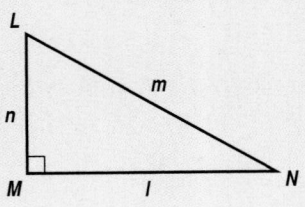

1. If $l = 8$ and $n = 12$, find *m*.   14.4
2. Find *l* if $n = 3$ and $m = 9$.   8.5
3. Find *n* if $l = 4$ and $m = 6$.   4.5
4. If $m = 50$ and $n = 40$, find *l*.   30
5. If $l = 18$ and $n = 24$, can $m = 42$?   no

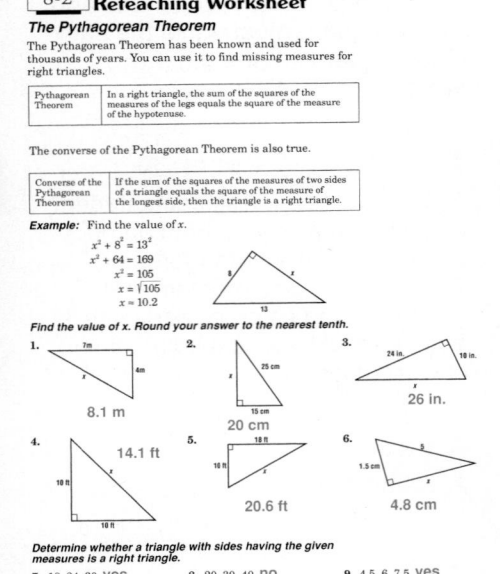

34. Draw a right triangle with vertices $A(0, a)$, $C(0, 0)$, and $B(b, 0)$ on a coordinate plane. Use the Pythagorean Theorem to derive the formula for the distance between A and B. **See margin.**

35. In a carton with rectangular sides, all pairs of intersecting edges are perpendicular. What is the length of the longest fishing rod that will fit inside the carton shown at the right? **13 feet**

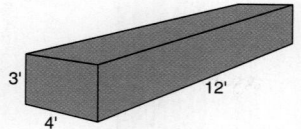

36. Explain why the drawing at the right is an illustration of the Pythagorean Theorem.

37. Write a paragraph proof of the converse of the Pythagorean Theorem. **See margin.**

36. The sum of the areas of the two smaller squares, a^2 and b^2, is equal to the area of the larger square, c^2.

Critical Thinking

38a. See students' work.

38. Draw three different acute triangles and three different obtuse triangles. Label the measure of the longest side of each triangle c and the measures of the other two sides a and b. Measure each side in centimeters.
  a. Calculate c^2 and the sum of a^2 and b^2 for each triangle.
  b. Compare your results and make a conjecture from your experiments.
     for acute triangles, $a^2 + b^2 > c^2$; for obtuse triangles, $a^2 + b^2 < c^2$

Applications

39. Sports June is making a ramp to try out her car for the pinewood derby. The ramp support forms a right angle. The base is 12 feet long and the height is 5 feet. What length of plywood does she need to complete the ramp? **13 ft**

40. Construction A stair stringer is a board that supports stairs. Suppose a set of stairs is to rise 8 feet over a length of 15 feet. Find the length of the stair stringer to the nearest foot. **17 ft**

41. History James Garfield is the only United States president to have published a mathematical proof. Research his proof in a book on the history of mathematics. What did Garfield use as the basis of his proof? **the area of a trapezoid**

Computer

A **Pythagorean triple** is a group of three whole numbers that satisfy the equation $a^2 + b^2 = c^2$, where c is the greatest number. The BASIC program below uses a procedure for finding Pythagorean triples that was developed by Euclid around 320 B.C.

```
 10 FOR X = 2 TO 6
 20 FOR Y = 1 TO 5
 30 IF X <= Y THEN GOTO 80
 40 A = INT(X^2 - Y^2 + 0.5)
 50 B = 2 * X * Y
 60 C = INT(X^2 + Y^2 + 0.5)
 65 IF A > B THEN PRINT B; " "; A; " "; C: GOTO 80
 70 PRINT A; " "; B; " "; C
 80 NEXT Y
 90 NEXT X
100 END
```

LESSON 8-2   THE PYTHAGOREAN THEOREM   369

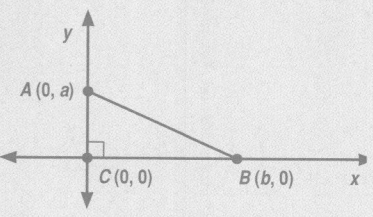
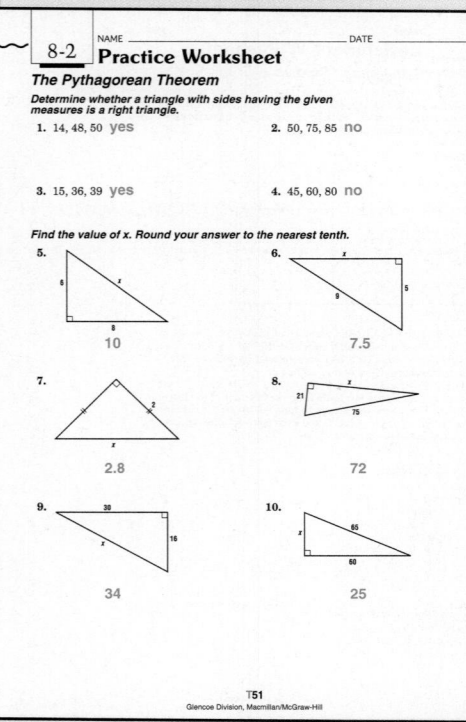

Additional Answer
37. Given: $\triangle ABC$ with sides of measure a, b, and c, where $a^2 + b^2 = c^2$
Prove: $\triangle ABC$ is a right triangle.

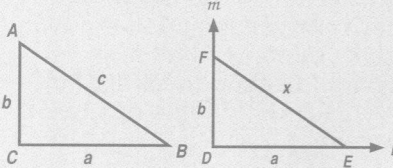

Draw $\overline{DE}$ on line ℓ with measure equal to a. At D, draw line $m \perp \overline{DE}$. Locate point F on m so that $DF = b$. Draw $\overline{FE}$ and call its measure x. Because $\triangle FED$ is a right triangle, $a^2 + b^2 = x^2$. But $a^2 + b^2 = c^2$, so $x^2 = c^2$ or $x = c$. Thus, $\triangle ABC \cong \triangle FED$ by SSS. This means $\angle C \cong \angle D$. Therefore, $\angle C$ must be a right angle, making $\triangle ABC$ a right triangle.

Run the BASIC program to generate a list of Pythagorean triples. Use the list to answer each question.

42. Notice that both (3, 4, 5) and (6, 8, 10) are Pythagorean triples. Since (6, 8, 10) = (3 · 2, 4 · 2, 5 · 2), these two triples are said to be part of a *family*. Since the numbers 3, 4, and 5 have no common factors except 1, (3, 4, 5) is called a *primitive triple*. List all of the members of the (3, 4, 5) family that are generated by the BASIC program. **(3, 4, 5), (6, 8, 10), (12, 16, 20), (24, 32, 40), (27, 36, 45)**

43. A geometry student made the conjecture that if three whole numbers are a Pythagorean triple, then their product is divisible by 60.

  a. Does this conjecture hold true for each triple that is printed by the BASIC program? **yes**

  b. Change the values in lines 10 and 20 of the program to generate more triples. Does the conjecture hold true for these triples? **yes**

  c. Do you think the conjecture is true for all Pythagorean triples? Justify your answer. **Answers may vary. The conjecture is true.**

  d. Are all sets of three whole numbers whose product is 60 Pythagorean triples? Explain. **no; 1, 2, and 30 have a product of 60, but $1^2 + 2^2 \neq 30^2$.**

Mixed Review

44. Find the geometric mean between 9 and 15. **(Lesson 8-1)** $3\sqrt{15}$

45. The bases of a trapezoid are 8 meters and 22 meters long. Find the length of the median of the trapezoid. **(Lesson 6-6)** **15 m**

46. Which lines are parallel if $\angle 2 \cong \angle 4$ and $\angle 3 \cong \angle 5$? Justify your answer. **(Lesson 3-3)** $\overrightarrow{XT} \parallel \overrightarrow{WY}; \overrightarrow{TZ} \parallel \overrightarrow{SY}$

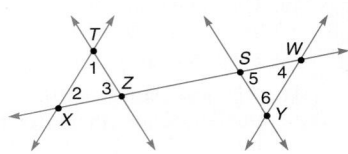

47. The measures of the legs of an isosceles triangle are $8x - 9$ and $6x - 1$. Find the value of x. **(Lesson 4-7)** **4**

48. Zoology If possible, write a valid conclusion. State the law of logic that you used. **(Lesson 2-3)**

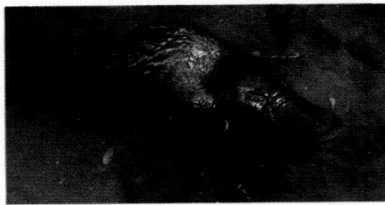

- A *monotreme* is a mammal that lays eggs.
- A duck-billed platypus is a monotreme.

A duck-billed platypus is a mammal that lays eggs; syllogism

Wrap-Up

49. Research Find three proofs of the Pythagorean Theorem by investigating the topic in your library. **See students' work.**

370   CHAPTER 8   RIGHT TRIANGLES AND TRIGONOMETRY

EXTENDING THE LESSON

Math Power: Communication

In ancient Egypt, builders would use a rope that had knots tied at 3 units, 7 units, and 12 units from one end. Write a paragraph explaining how you think they used such a rope to form right angles.

If stakes are placed in the ground at the end of the rope, at the 3-unit mark, and at the 7-unit mark and the 12-unit mark is brought back to the end of the rope, a 3-4-5 triangle has been formed.

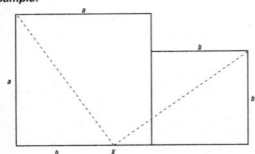 

8-3 Special Right Triangles

Objective
8-3

After studying this lesson, you should be able to:
- use the properties of 45°-45°-90° and 30°-60°-90° triangles.

Application

Baseball has been called the "great American pastime." It has been popular since the early 1800s. A professional baseball diamond is shaped like a square and has baselines that are 90 feet long. If the first baseman forces a runner out, how far will he have to throw the ball to make a double play at third? We can find the answer to this question by finding the length of a diagonal of a square with sides 90 feet long.

The diagonal of a square and the sides of the square form two isosceles right triangles, or 45°-45°-90° triangles. We can use the Pythagorean Theorem to find the length of the diagonal.

$$d^2 = 90^2 + 90^2 \quad \text{\textit{Pythagorean Theorem}}$$
$$d^2 = 8100 + 8100$$
$$d = \sqrt{16{,}200} \text{ or about } 127.3$$

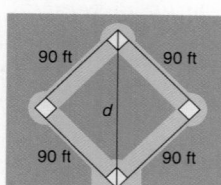

So, the first baseman would have to throw the ball about 127 feet to third base.

Let's look at the general case of a square to learn more about a 45°-45°-90° triangle.

$$d^2 = s^2 + s^2 \quad \text{\textit{Pythagorean Theorem}}$$
$$d^2 = 2s^2$$
$$d = s\sqrt{2}$$

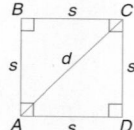

This proves the following theorem.

Theorem 8-6

In a 45°-45°-90° triangle, the hypotenuse is $\sqrt{2}$ times as long as a leg.

ALTERNATE TEACHING STRATEGIES

Using Modeling

Have students draw an isosceles right triangle with legs measuring 1 inch. Have them use their rulers to find that the length of the hypotenuse is approximately $1\frac{7}{16}$ inches. Using a calculator, $1\frac{7}{16} \approx 1.4$, which is close to $\sqrt{2}$. Have them repeat the activity for the altitude of an equilateral triangle with sides measuring 2 inches.

Using Calculators

The diagonal of a square measures 3.4 cm. How can you use a calculator to find the length of a side of the square to the nearest tenth? **Since the diagonal measures $s\sqrt{2}$, solve $3.4 = s\sqrt{2}$. Enter**

The result will be 2.4041631, which to the nearest tenth, is 2.4.

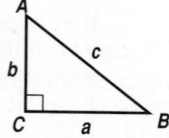

Teaching Tip After Example 1, point out that $\sqrt{2} \approx 1.414$. To check answers by estimating, think "a little less than $1\frac{1}{2}$ times."

Chalkboard Example

For Example 1
Find the value of *x*.

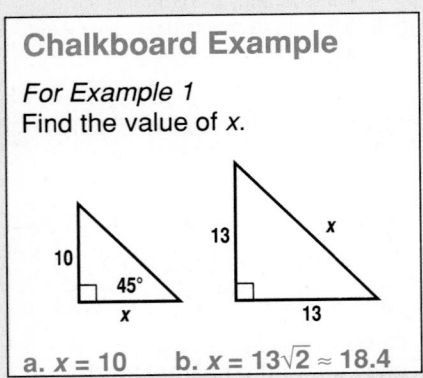

a. *x* = 10   b. *x* = 13√2 ≈ 18.4

Teaching Tip After reading Theorem 8-7, point out that $\sqrt{3} \approx 1.732$. For estimating purposes, think about its value as being about $1\frac{3}{4}$.

Example 1

Find the value of *x*.

a.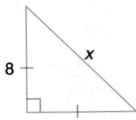

b.

Since the two base angles are congruent, the triangle is isosceles. Therefore, *x* = 8.

According to Theorem 8-6, the hypotenuse is $\sqrt{2}$ times as long as a leg. So, $x = 8\sqrt{2}$ or about 11.3.

There is a special relationship in a $30° \text{-} 60° \text{-} 90°$ triangle also.

If we draw an altitude from any vertex of an equilateral triangle, the triangle is separated into two congruent $30° \text{-} 60° \text{-} 90°$ triangles. Using the Pythagorean Theorem, it is possible to derive a formula relating the lengths of the sides to each other.

Let *s* = the measure of a side.
Let *a* = the measure of the altitude.

△PTQ and △RTQ are $30° \text{-} 60° \text{-} 90°$ triangles.

$s^2 = a^2 + \left(\frac{s}{2}\right)^2$ *Pythagorean Theorem*

$a^2 = s^2 - \left(\frac{s}{2}\right)^2$ *Solve for a.*

$a^2 = \frac{3s^2}{4}$

$a = \frac{s\sqrt{3}}{2}$

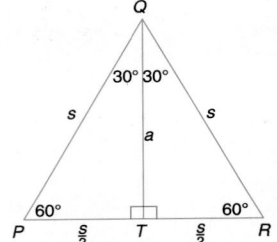

So in the $30° \text{-} 60° \text{-} 90°$ triangle, the measures of the sides are $\frac{s}{2}$, $\frac{s\sqrt{3}}{2}$, and *s*. This proves the following theorem.

Theorem 8-7

In a $30° \text{-} 60° \text{-} 90°$ triangle, the hypotenuse is twice as long as the shorter leg and the longer leg is $\sqrt{3}$ times as long as the shorter leg.

---

372   CHAPTER 8   RIGHT TRIANGLES AND TRIGONOMETRY

Example 2

APPLICATION
Architecture

A geodesic dome is made up of faces shaped like equilateral triangles. If a side of a triangle on a dome is 7 feet long, find the length of an altitude.

$\triangle ABC$ is one of the triangles. Draw $\overline{AD}$ perpendicular to $\overline{BC}$. $\triangle ADB$ is a $30°$-$60°$-$90°$ triangle.

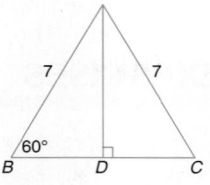

$AB = 2(BD)$	*The hypotenuse is twice the shorter leg.*
$7 = 2(BD)$	*Substitution*
$3.5 = BD$	*Division property*
$AD = \sqrt{3}\,(BD)$	*The longer leg is $\sqrt{3}$ times the shorter leg.*
$AD = \sqrt{3}\,(3.5)$	*Substitution*

The altitude is $\sqrt{3}\,(3.5)$ or about 6.1 feet.   *Check this result using the Pythagorean Theorem.*

CHECKING FOR UNDERSTANDING

Communicating Mathematics

Read and study the lesson to answer these questions.

1. If the measure of a leg of a $45°$-$45°$-$90°$ triangle is l, then the measure of the hypotenuse is __?__. $\ell\sqrt{2}$

2. The measure of the shorter leg of a $30°$-$60°$-$90°$ triangle is s. The measure of the longer leg is __?__, and the measure of the hypotenuse is __?__. $s\sqrt{3}$; $2s$

3. The measure of the long leg of a $30°$-$60°$-$90°$ triangle is 14. Write expressions for the measures of the shorter leg and the hypotenuse.
shorter leg $= \dfrac{14\sqrt{3}}{3}$ or about 8.08; hypotenuse $= 2\left(\dfrac{14\sqrt{3}}{3}\right)$ or about 16.17

Guided Practice

Find x and y.

4.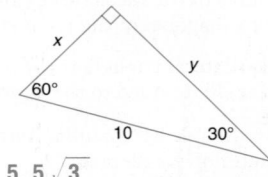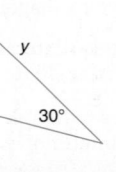

$5, 5\sqrt{3}$

5.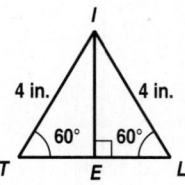

$16, 8\sqrt{3}$

The length of a side of a square is given. Find the length of a diagonal of each square.

6. 1 ft   7. 31.2 m   8. $4\frac{2}{3}$ yd

6. $\sqrt{2} \approx 1.4$ ft
7. $31.2\sqrt{2} \approx 44.1$ m
8. $\dfrac{14\sqrt{2}}{3} \approx 6.6$ yd

LESSON 8-3   SPECIAL RIGHT TRIANGLES   373

RETEACHING THE LESSON

Find the missing measures in $\triangle ABC$.

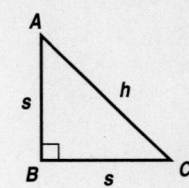

1. $s = 6$ $h = 6\sqrt{2} \approx 8.5$
2. $h = 8\sqrt{2}$ $s = 8$
3. $s = 4.1$ $h = 4.1\sqrt{2} \approx 5.8$
4. $h = 3.7\sqrt{2}$ $s = 3.7$

Find the missing measures in $\triangle DEF$.

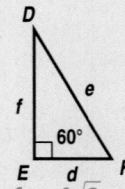

5. $d = 4$ $f = 4\sqrt{3} \approx 6.9$, $e = 8$
6. $e = 10$ $d = 5$, $f = 5\sqrt{3} \approx 8.7$
7. $f = 7\sqrt{3}$ $d = 7$, $e = 14$
8. $d = 9$ $f = 9\sqrt{3} \approx 15.6$, $e = 18$

Chalkboard Example

For Example 2
Tiles in the shape of equilateral triangles are used to cover a countertop. The side of each tile measures 4 inches. Find the height of each tile.
In $\triangle TIL$ draw the altitude *IE*. $\triangle TIE$ is a $30° - 60° - 90°$ triangle.

TI = 4 inches, so *TE* = 2 inches.
IE = $2\sqrt{3} \approx 3.5$ inches

EVALUATING THE LESSON

Checking for Understanding

Exercises 1-12 are designed to help you assess students' understanding through reading, writing, speaking, and modeling. You should work through Exercises 1-3 with your students and then monitor their work on Exercises 4-12.

Reteaching Masters Booklet, p. 45

8-3 **Reteaching Worksheet**
NAME _____ DATE _____

Special Right Triangles

Two special kinds of right triangles are the $45°$-$45°$-$90°$ triangle and the $30°$-$60°$-$90°$ right triangle.

In a $45°$-$45°$-$90°$ triangle, the hypotenuse is $\sqrt{2}$ times as long as a leg.

In a $30°$-$60°$-$90°$ triangle, the hypotenuse is twice as long as the shorter leg and the longer leg is $\sqrt{3}$ times as long as the shorter leg.

Example: Find the value of x.

1.   2.

Since the triangle is a $45°$-$45°$-$90°$ triangle, the hypotenuse is $\sqrt{2}$ times as long as the leg.
So $x = 5\sqrt{2}$ or about 7.1.

Since the triangle is a $30°$-$60°$-$90°$ triangle, the hypotenuse is twice as long as the shorter leg.
So $x = 2(8)$ or 16.

Find the value of x.

1. 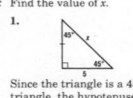   2. 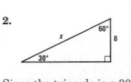   3.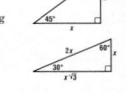

$6\sqrt{2} \approx 8.5$ mm   12 mm $12\sqrt{2} \approx 17.0$ yd

4. 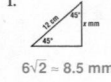   5.   6.

$9\sqrt{3} \approx 15.6$ ft $1.9\sqrt{3} \approx 3.3$ cm $20\sqrt{2} \approx 28.3$ ft

7. Find the perimeter of the triangle shown at the right.
$60 + 20\sqrt{3} \approx 94.6$ cm

T45
Glencoe Division, Macmillan/McGraw-Hill

Chapter 8   373

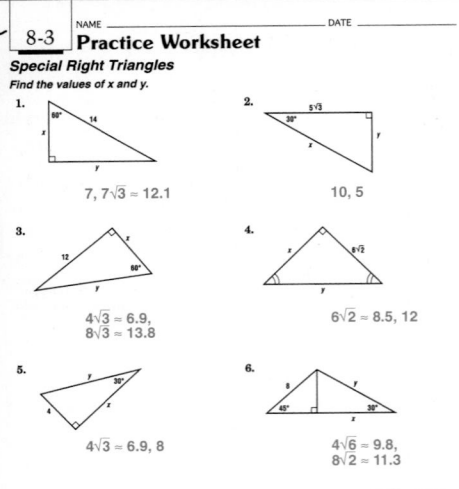

The length of a side of an equilateral triangle is given. Find the length of an altitude of each triangle.

9. 4 ft $2\sqrt{3} \approx 3.5$ ft

10. 27.4 m $13.7\sqrt{3} \approx 23.7$ m

11. $\frac{2}{3}$ yd   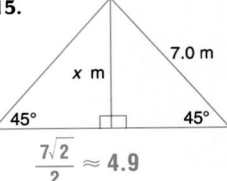 $\frac{\sqrt{3}}{3} \approx 0.6$ yd

12. The perimeter of an equilateral triangle is 24 units. Find the length of an altitude of the triangle. $4\sqrt{3} \approx 6.9$ units

EXERCISES

Practice   **Find the value of x.**

A

13.
$3\sqrt{3} \approx 5.2$

14.
$5\sqrt{2} \approx 7.1$

15.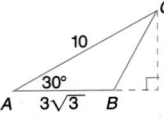
$\frac{7\sqrt{2}}{2} \approx 4.9$

16.
$3\sqrt{2} \approx 4.2$

17.
$7.5\sqrt{3} \approx 13$

18.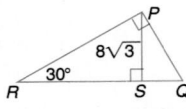
$10.4\sqrt{3} \approx 18.0$

B

19. In the triangle at the right, $AC = 10$, $AB = 3\sqrt{3}$, and $m\angle A = 30$. Find BC.
$\sqrt{37} \approx 6.083$

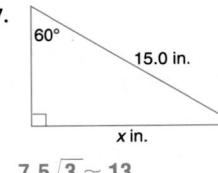

20. Find the perimeter of $\triangle PQR$ shown at the right. $48 + 16\sqrt{3} \approx 75.713$ units

21. The sum of the squares of the measures of all sides of a rectangle is 1458. Find the measure of a diagonal of the rectangle.   27

22. An altitude of an equilateral triangle is 5.2 meters long. Find the perimeter of the triangle rounded to the nearest tenth.   18.0 meters

23. $12 + 12\sqrt{3}$ or about 32.8 units

23. The diagonals of a rectangle are 12 units long and intersect at an angle of 60°. Find the perimeter of the rectangle.

24. In $\triangle RST$ shown at the right, $RT = 10\sqrt{3}$. Find RS and VS. $RS = 20\sqrt{3} \approx 34.641$; $VS = 20$

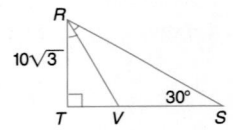

25. Find the length of the altitude of an equilateral triangle whose perimeter is 42 centimeters. $\sqrt{147} \approx 12.1$ cm

Use the figure at the right to find each measure.

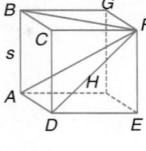

26. u $\sqrt{2}$
27. v $\sqrt{3}$
28. w 2
29. x $\sqrt{5}$
30. y $\sqrt{6}$
31. z $\sqrt{7}$

 Suppose each edge of the cube measures s units.

32. Develop a formula for the distance from A to F in terms of s. $AF = s\sqrt{3}$

33. Find $m\angle BFD$. $m\angle BFD = 60$

34. Prove Theorem 8-6. **See margin.**

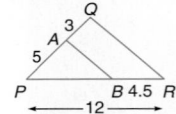

Critical Thinking

35. A stop sign is to be made from a square piece of sheet metal. The largest stop sign that can be cut from the square has sides that are each 1 foot long. How long are the sides of the square? $1 + \sqrt{2} \approx 2.4$ ft

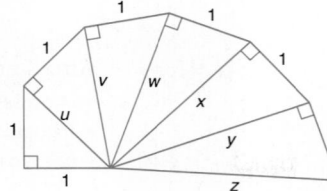

Applications

36. **Auto Repair** A mechanic working on a car needs to remove a hexagonal nut to remove the carburetor. One side of the nut is 6 millimeters long. How wide should the opening of the wrench be to fit the nut? *Hint: A hexagon is made up of six equilateral triangles.* $6\sqrt{3}$ or about 10.4 mm

Mixed Review

37. **Painting** A painter leans a ten-foot ladder against the house she is to paint. The foot of the ladder is 3 feet from the house. How far above the ground does the ladder touch the house? **(Lesson 8-2)** about 9.5 feet

38. $PA = 5$, $AQ = 3$, $PR = 12$, and $BR = 4.5$. Is $\triangle BPA \sim \triangle RPQ$? Justify your answer. **(Lesson 7-5) yes; SAS Similarity**

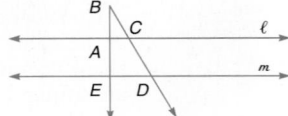

39. The base of an isosceles triangle is 18 inches long. If the legs are $3y + 21$ and $10y$ inches long, find the perimeter of the triangle. **(Lesson 4-7) 78 in.**

40. Write a paragraph proof. **(Lesson 3-3) See margin.**

Given: $m\angle BAC = 90$
$m\angle ABC = 30$
$m\angle EDC = 60$

Prove: ℓ is parallel to m.

Wrap-Up

41. Write two sentences to describe the relationships for the special right triangles you learned in this lesson. **See students' work.**

EXTENDING THE LESSON

Math Power: Problem Solving

A regular hexagon is composed of six equilateral triangles. Find the perimeter of the hexagon if its apothem measures 8 cm. (The apothem is the altitude of one of the equilateral triangles.)
$32\sqrt{3} \approx 55.4$

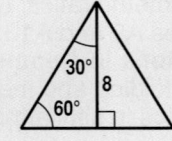

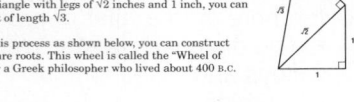
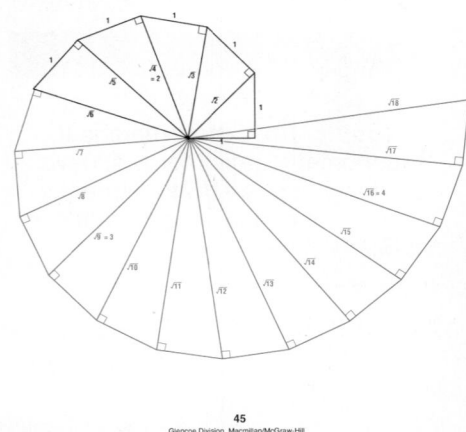

INTRODUCING THE LESSON

 5-Minute Check

(over Lesson 8-3)

Find the measure of the diagonal of each square.

1. $s = 3$ $3\sqrt{2} \approx 4.2$
2. $s = 7$ $7\sqrt{2} \approx 9.9$
3. $s = 4.5$ $4.5\sqrt{2} \approx 6.4$

Solve.

4. The shorter leg of a 30° - 60° - 90° triangle measures 6 cm. What are the measures of the other two sides? $6\sqrt{3}$ or about 10.4 cm, 12 cm
5. The hypotenuse of a 30° - 60° - 90° triangle measures 20 inches. Find the measures of the other two sides.   10 in., $10\sqrt{3}$ or about 17.3 in.

Motivating the Lesson

Ask students what they know about surveying. Discuss the need for more than a ruler or protractor to find distances across rivers and valleys and to the tops of mountains.

TEACHING THE LESSON

Teaching Tip   After reading the trigonometric ratios for $\angle A$, have students use $\triangle ABC$ to name the sine, cosine, and tangent ratios for $\angle B$. $\frac{b}{c}, \frac{a}{c}, \frac{b}{a}$

8-4   Trigonometry

Objectives

After studying this lesson, you should be able to:

- 8-4A ▪ express trigonometric ratios as fractions or decimals,
- 8-4B ▪ recognize trigonometric relationships from right triangles, and
- 8-4C ▪ use a calculator to find values of trigonometric ratios or measures of angles.

Application

When the Egyptians first used a sundial around 1500 B.C., they were using **trigonometry**. Trigonometry means triangle measurement.

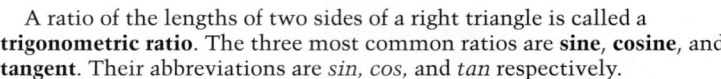

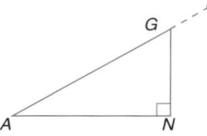

The figure at the left is a model of how a sundial works. As the sun, *S*, shines on a fixed staff, represented by $\overline{GN}$, it casts a shadow. $\overline{AN}$ represents the shadow. Since *GN* is a constant, the length of $\overline{AN}$ varies with the measure of $\angle A$. The Egyptians understood that $\frac{GN}{AN}$ is a function of the measure of $\angle A$. We will define this function as the tangent of $\angle A$.

A ratio of the lengths of two sides of a right triangle is called a **trigonometric ratio**. The three most common ratios are **sine**, **cosine**, and **tangent**. Their abbreviations are *sin*, *cos*, and *tan* respectively.

> **FYI···**
>
> A mnemonic can help you remember the trigonometric ratios. The first letters in the following rhyme represent the letters in the ratios.
> Some Old Horse Caught A Horse Taking Oats Away.
>
> $sin\ A = \frac{opposite}{hypotenuse}$
> $cos\ A = \frac{adjacent}{hypotenuse}$
> $tan\ A = \frac{opposite}{adjacent}$

$$\sin A = \frac{\text{side opposite } \angle A}{\text{hypotenuse}} = \frac{a}{c}$$

$$\cos A = \frac{\text{side adjacent to } \angle A}{\text{hypotenuse}} = \frac{b}{c}$$

$$\tan A = \frac{\text{side opposite } \angle A}{\text{side adjacent to } \angle A} = \frac{a}{b}$$

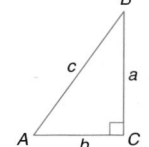

Trigonometric ratios are related to the acute angles of a right triangle, not the right angle. The value of a trigonometric ratio depends *only* on the measure of the angle. It does not depend on the size of the triangle.

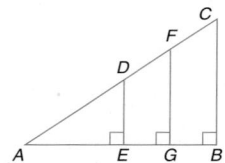

Consider the three overlapping triangles at the right. They are all right triangles that share a common angle, $\angle A$. So the triangles are similar by AA. If we use $\triangle ADE$, $\sin A = \frac{DE}{AD}$, in $\triangle AFG$, $\sin A = \frac{FG}{AF}$, and in $\triangle ACB$, $\sin A = \frac{CB}{AC}$. Because the triangles are similar, the ratios are equal. That is, $\frac{DE}{AD} = \frac{FG}{AF} = \frac{CB}{AC}$. *Recall that in similar triangles, corresponding sides are proportional.*

376   CHAPTER 8   RIGHT TRIANGLES AND TRIGONOMETRY

ALTERNATE TEACHING STRATEGIES

Using Investigation

You can guide students to discover the trigonometric ratios. In Investigation 10 on pages A9 and A10 of **More Investigations in Geometry,** students use paper folding and measurement to explore ratios in similar right triangles.

Using Applications

A surveyor wants to measure the width of a river at point *A*. She has placed stakes 100 feet apart on the far side of the river and is standing at point *A*. Her instrument tells her that m$\angle BAC = 27$ and m$\angle ABC = 90$. How wide is the river?
196.3 ft

Example 1

INVESTIGATION

You can learn more about trigonometric ratios in Investigation 10 on pages A9–A10.

Find sin M, cos M, tan M, sin N, cos N, and tan N. Express each ratio as a fraction and as a decimal.

$\sin M = \frac{ON}{MN} = \frac{8}{10}$ or 0.800

$\cos M = \frac{MO}{MN} = \frac{6}{10}$ or 0.600

$\tan M = \frac{ON}{MO} = \frac{8}{6}$ or $1.\overline{3}$

$\sin N = \frac{OM}{MN} = \frac{6}{10}$ or 0.600

$\cos N = \frac{ON}{MN} = \frac{8}{10}$ or 0.800

$\tan N = \frac{MO}{ON} = \frac{6}{8}$ or 0.750

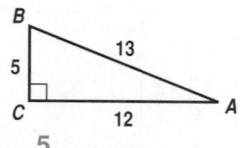

Applications of trigonometry will often require that you find a decimal approximation of a trigonometric ratio. You can use your scientific calculator to obtain approximations of trigonometric ratios. *If you do not have a scientific calculator, use the table on page 694.*

Example 2

Find each value using your calculator. *Set your calculator in degree mode.*

a. sin 75°

ENTER: 75 [SIN] 0.9659258

sin 75° ≈ 0.9659.

b. cos 65°

ENTER: 65 [COS] 0.4226182

cos 65° ≈ 0.4226.

There are many practical applications of trigonometry. You can use the ratios to find a missing measure of a right triangle.

Example 3

APPLICATION

Navigation

The *Princess III* is sailing to the Hawaiian Islands. As the ship crosses the equator, its instruments indicate that it is headed on a course that forms a 13° angle with the equator. How far will the ship be from the equator after it has traveled 90 miles on this course?

Draw a diagram of the situation.

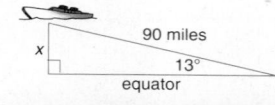

The distance from the equator can be found using the sine ratio.

$\sin 13° = \frac{x}{90}$ $\sin = \frac{opposite}{hypotenuse}$

$90 \sin 13° = x$

Use your calculator to find the distance.

ENTER: 90 [×] 13 [SIN] [=] 20.245595

The *Princess III* will be about 20.2 miles from the equator after it travels 90 miles on this course.

LESSON 8-4   TRIGONOMETRY   377

Chalkboard Examples

For Example 1
Find sin A, cos A, tan A, sin B, cos B, and tan B. Express each ratio as a fraction and as a decimal.

$\sin A = \frac{5}{13} \approx 0.385$

$\cos A = \frac{12}{13} \approx 0.923$

$\tan A = \frac{5}{12} \approx 0.417$

$\sin B = \frac{12}{13} \approx 0.923$

$\cos B = \frac{5}{13} \approx 0.385$

$\tan B = \frac{12}{5} \approx 2.4$

For Example 2
Find each value to four decimal places using a calculator.
a. sin 43°   0.6820
b. cos 84°   0.1045

For Example 3
A 16-foot ladder is propped against a building. The angle it forms with the ground is 55°. How far up the side of the building does the ladder reach?

$\sin 55° = \frac{x}{16}$

$x = $ [16] [×] [55] [sin] [=]

$= 13.106433$
The ladder reaches about 13.1 feet.

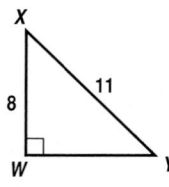
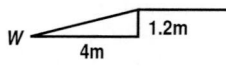
Trigonometric ratios can be used to find the measures of the acute angles in a right triangle when you know the measures of two sides of the triangle. You must determine which ratio involves the two sides of the triangle whose measures you know. Then, use the inverse capabilities of your calculator to find the measure of the angle.

Example 4

Find the approximate measure of ∠E.

We know the measure of the leg adjacent to ∠E and the measure of the hypotenuse. The cosine ratio relates these two measures.

$\cos E = \dfrac{EF}{DE}$ $\cos = \dfrac{adjacent}{hypotenuse}$

$= \dfrac{5}{14}$

Now use a calculator to find the measure of ∠E to the nearest degree.

ENTER: 5 ÷ 14 = INV COS 69.075168   *The INV key followed by COS finds the angle for which the cosine function has the value $\dfrac{5}{14}$.*

$m\angle E \approx 69$

Example 5

APPLICATION

Aviation

Don Bates is flying a plane from Memphis to Little Rock. One minute after takeoff, his altitude is 2.8 miles and he has traveled 7.5 ground miles from the airport. If he has been climbing steadily since takeoff, what is the measure of the angle that Mr. Bates' plane makes with the ground?

We can use the tangent ratio to find the measure of the angle.

$\tan y = \dfrac{2.8}{7.5}$ $\tan = \dfrac{opposite}{adjacent}$

$\tan y \approx 0.3733333$ *Use a calculator.*

$y \approx 20.47228$

The angle that the plane's path makes with the ground measures about 20°.

CHECKING FOR UNDERSTANDING

Communicating Mathematics

Read and study the lesson to answer these questions.
  3. sin *A* = cos *B*   4. They are reciprocals.
1. What does trigonometry mean? triangle measurement

2. In the triangle below, ___?___ is opposite ∠A and ___?___ is adjacent to ∠A. $\overline{BC}$, $\overline{AC}$

3. Use the triangle at the right to explain the relationship between sin *A* and cos *B*.

4. How are tan *A* and tan *B* related?

Guided Practice

Find the indicated trigonometric ratio as a fraction and as a decimal rounded to the nearest thousandth. **See margin.**

5. sin A
6. cos A
7. tan A
8. sin B
9. cos B
10. tan B

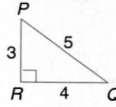

State the trigonometric ratio that corresponds to each value and angle given.

11. $\frac{3}{4}$; $\angle Q$ tan Q
12. $\frac{4}{5}$; $\angle Q$ cos Q
13. $\frac{4}{5}$; $\angle P$ sin P
14. $\frac{4}{3}$; $\angle P$ tan P

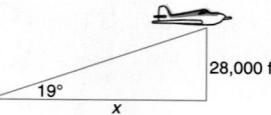

Use your calculator to find the value of each ratio to the nearest thousandth.

15. sin 10° **0.174**
16. cos 36° **0.809**
17. tan 38° **0.781**

Use your calculator to find the measure of each angle to the nearest degree.

18. sin A = 0.105 $m\angle A = 6$
19. tan S = 0.702 $m\angle S = 35$
20. cos C = 0.898 $m\angle C = 26$

21. A jet takes off and rises at an angle of 19° with the ground until it hits 28,000 feet. How much ground distance is covered in miles? *(5280 feet = 1 mile)*
about 15.4 miles

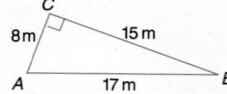

EXERCISES

Practice

Find the indicated trigonometric ratio as a fraction and as a decimal rounded to the nearest thousandth. **See margin.**

22. sin A
23. sin B
24. tan A
25. cos B
26. cos E
27. tan F

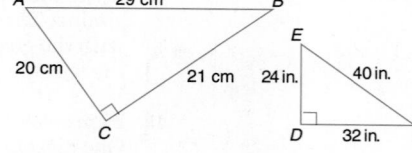

State the trigonometric ratio that corresponds to each value and angle given.

28. $\frac{\sqrt{3}}{3}$; $\angle C$ tan C
29. $\frac{1}{2}$; $\angle T$ cos T
30. $\frac{\sqrt{3}}{2}$; $\angle T$ sin T
31. $\sqrt{3}$; $\angle T$ tan T

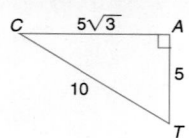

LESSON 8-4 TRIGONOMETRY 379

B Draw a 30°-60°-90° triangle. Find each ratio. State your answers as fractions.

32. $\sin 60°$ $\dfrac{\sqrt{3}}{2}$ **33.** $\cos 60°$ $\dfrac{1}{2}$ **34.** $\tan 60°$ $\sqrt{3}$

35. $\sin 30°$ $\dfrac{1}{2}$ **36.** $\cos 30°$ $\dfrac{\sqrt{3}}{2}$ **37.** $\tan 30°$ $\dfrac{\sqrt{3}}{3}$

Find the value of x. Round measures of segments to the nearest tenth and angle measures to the nearest degree.

38.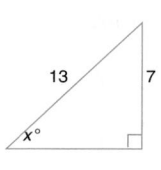
33

39.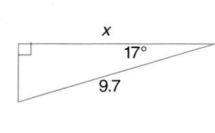
9.3

40.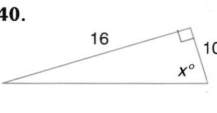
58

Find the values of x and y. Round measures of segments to the nearest tenth and angle measures to the nearest degree.

41.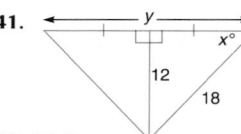
42, 26.8

42.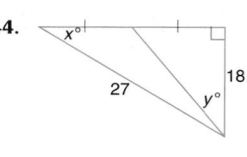
22.7, 44.6

43.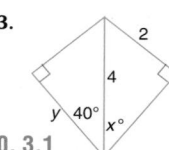
30, 3.1

C **44.**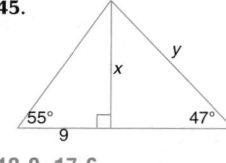
42, 29

45.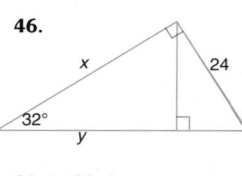
12.9, 17.6

46.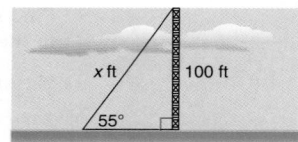
38.4, 32.6

Solve. Make a drawing.

47. A guy wire is attached to a 100-foot tower that is perpendicular to the ground. The wire makes an angle of 55° with the ground. What is the length of the wire? **about 122 feet**

48. Each side of a rhombus is 30 units long. One diagonal makes a 25° angle with a side. What is the length of each diagonal to the nearest tenth of a unit? **25.4 and 54.4 units**

49. An isosceles trapezoid has an altitude 25 inches long. One of the base angles measures 35°. Find the length of the legs of the trapezoid. **about 43.6 in.**

50. In $\triangle XYZ$, $\angle Z$ is a right angle. If $\sin X = \dfrac{3}{4}$, find $\tan Y$. $\dfrac{\sqrt{7}}{3} \approx 0.88$

380   CHAPTER 8   RIGHT TRIANGLES AND TRIGONOMETRY

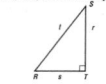

RETEACHING THE LESSON

Form groups of three or four students. Have each group use string and some chairs to outline a right triangle on the floor. Have them use a ruler and a protractor to find the measure of one side and one acute angle.

Have two members use the appropriate trigonometric ratio to find the measure of another side. Have the other member(s) check by actually measuring the side. Repeat the activity for the third side of the triangle, with students switching roles within the group.

Critical Thinking

51. Use a calculator to find the sine, cosine, and tangent of several acute angle measures to make conjectures.

   a. When is $\cos A > \sin A$? **when $m\angle A < 45$**

   b. When is $\cos A = \sin A$? **when $m\angle A = 45$**

   c. Describe the value of $\tan A$ when $m\angle A > 45$. **$\tan A > 1$**

   d. Describe the range of values for $\cos A$ and $\sin A$. **$0 \le \sin A \le 1$, $0 \le \cos A \le 1$**

Applications

52. Navigation A ship travels east from Port Lincoln 24 miles before turning north. When the ship becomes disabled and radios for help, the rescue boat needs to know the fastest route to the ship. The rescue boat navigator finds that the shortest route from Port Lincoln to the ship is 48 miles long. At what angle off of due east should the rescue boat travel to take the shortest route to the ship? **60°**

53. Aviation A jet airplane begins a steady climb of 15° and flies for two miles. What was its change in altitude in feet? *(5280 ft = 1 mile)* **about 2733 feet**

54. Electronics The power in watts that is absorbed by an AC circuit is given by $P = IV \cos\theta$, where I is the current in amps, V is the voltage, and the Greek letter θ (theta) is the measure of the phase angle. Use your calculator to find the power absorbed by a circuit if its current is 2 amps, its voltage is 120 volts, and its phase angle measures 67°. Round your answer to the nearest thousandth. **93.775 watts**

Mixed Review

55. A 30°-60°-90° triangle has a shorter leg that is 8 units long. Find the lengths of the hypotenuse and the longer leg. **(Lesson 8-3)** **16 units; $8\sqrt{3}$ or about 13.9 units**

56. Find the values of x and y. **(Lesson 8-1)**
$\sqrt{104} \approx 10.2$, $\sqrt{65} \approx 8.1$

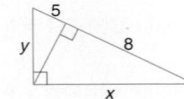

57. Determine whether $\overline{CD} \parallel \overline{BE}$. Explain your reasoning. **(Lesson 7-5)** **no;**

$AB = 9.6$
$AC = 15.0$
$AE = 6.8$
$AD = 10.0$

$\dfrac{AB}{AC} \ne \dfrac{AE}{AD}$

58. The bases of an isosceles trapezoid measure 10 inches and 22 inches. Find the length of the median of the trapezoid. **(Lesson 6-6)**
16 in.

59. Determine whether the statement "The diagonals of a rectangle bisect the opposite angles" is *true* or *false*. Justify your answer. **(Lesson 6-4)**
False; the diagonals of a rhombus bisect opposite angles.

Practice Masters Booklet, p. 53

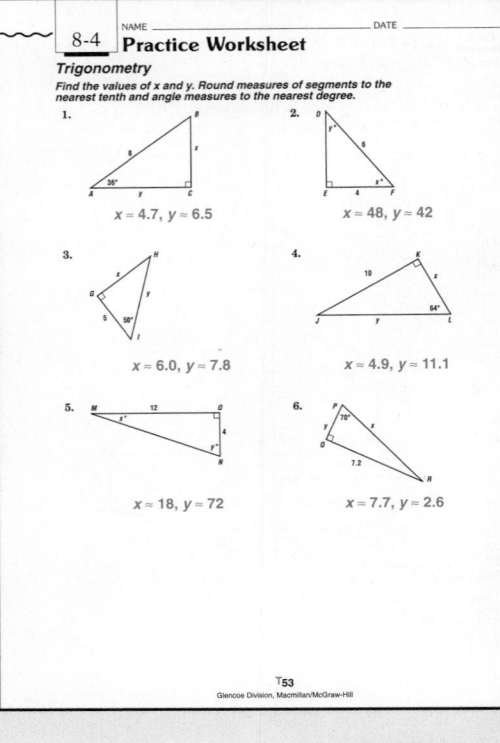

60. △*GAL* and △*IAL* satisfy the SSS Inequality. That is, $\overline{GA} \cong \overline{AI}$, $\overline{AL} \cong \overline{AL}$, and $GL < IL$. It follows that $m\angle 1 < m\angle 2$.

63. $\sin Y = \dfrac{XZ}{YZ}$

$\cos Y = \dfrac{XY}{YZ}$

$\tan Y = \dfrac{XZ}{XY}$

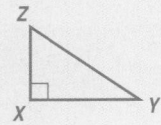

Enrichment Masters Booklet, p. 46

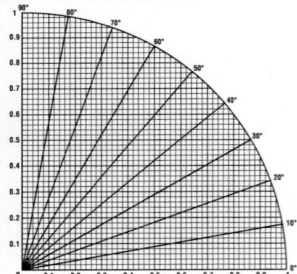

```
8-4   NAME_____ DATE_____
      Enrichment Worksheet
Sine and Cosine of Angles
The following diagram can be used to obtain approximate values
for the sine and cosine of angles from 0° to 90°. The radius of the
circle is 1. So, the sine and cosine values can be read directly
from the vertical and horizontal axes.
```

Example: Find approximate values for sin 40° and cos 40°. Consider the triangle formed by the segment marked 40°, as illustrated by the shaded triangle at the right.

$\sin 40° = \dfrac{a}{c} \approx \dfrac{0.64}{1}$ or 0.64 $\cos 40° = \dfrac{b}{c} \approx \dfrac{0.77}{1}$ or 0.77

1. Use the diagram above to complete the chart of values.

x°	0°	10°	20°	30°	40°	50°	60°	70°	80°	90°
sin x°	0	0.17	0.34	0.5	0.64	0.77	0.87	0.94	0.98	1
cos x°	1	0.98	0.94	0.87	0.77	0.64	0.5	0.34	0.17	0

2. Compare the sine and cosine of two complementary angles (angles whose sum is 90°). What do you notice?
The sine of an angle is equal to the cosine of the complement of the angle.

T 46
Glencoe Division, Macmillan/McGraw-Hill

382   Chapter 8

---

60. Write a paragraph proof. **(Lesson 5-7)** See margin.

Given: $\overline{GA} \cong \overline{AI}$
$GL < IL$

Prove: $m\angle 1 < m\angle 2$

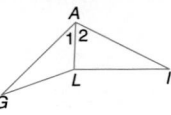

61. Find the value of *x*. **(Lesson 3-2)** 100

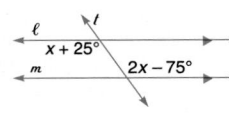

62. Two vertical angles have measures of $7x + 12$ and $4x + 42$. Find *x*. **(Lesson 2-7)** 10

Wrap-Up   **63.** Draw triangle *XYZ* with right angle *X*, and label the vertices. Write a ratio for sin *Y*, cos *Y*, and tan *Y*. **See margin.**

MID-CHAPTER REVIEW

Use right triangle *GHJ* and the given information to solve each problem. **(Lesson 8-1)**

1. Find *HK* if $GK = 8$ and $KJ = 14$. $\sqrt{112} \approx 10.6$

2. If $GJ = 15$ and $GK = 9$, find *GH*. $\sqrt{135} \approx 11.6$

3. $GK = 4$ and $KJ = 7$. Find *HJ*. $\sqrt{77} \approx 8.8$

4. Find *HG* if $KG = 8$ and $KJ = 8$. $\sqrt{128} \approx 11.3$

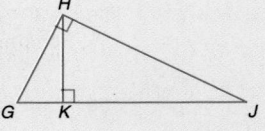

Determine whether a triangle with sides having the given measures is a right triangle. **(Lesson 8-2)**

5. 12, 16, 20 yes

6. 2.2, 2.4, 3.3 no

7. $1, \sqrt{2}, \sqrt{3}$ yes

8. $\sqrt{3}, \sqrt{4}, \sqrt{5}$ no

9. 1.6, 3.0, 3.4 yes

10. 15, 20, 25 yes

11. The length of an altitude of an equilateral triangle is $12\sqrt{3}$ units. Find the perimeter of the triangle. **(Lesson 8-3)** 72 units

12. $8\sqrt{2} \approx 11.3$ cm

12. Find the length of a diagonal of a square if a side is 8 centimeters long. **(Lesson 8-3)**

13. A 16-foot ladder is leaning against a house. It touches the bottom of a window that is 12 feet 6 inches above the ground. What is the measure of the angle that the ladder forms with the ground? Round your answer to the nearest degree. **(Lesson 8-4)** 51°

382   CHAPTER 8   RIGHT TRIANGLES AND TRIGONOMETRY

EXTENDING THE LESSON

Math Power: Connections
Determine how many different ratios can be written using the measures of the sides of a right triangle. What is the probability that a ratio chosen at random is the sine of an acute angle of the triangle? 6; $\dfrac{2}{3}$

Mid-Chapter Review
The Mid-Chapter Review provides students with a brief review of the concepts and skills in Lessons 8-1 through 8-4. Lesson numbers are given at the end of problems or instruction lines so students may review concepts not yet mastered.

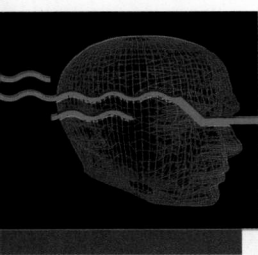

Technology
Tangent Ratio

BASIC
Geometric Supposer
▶ **Graphing calculators**
LOGO
Spreadsheets

Using Technology

Objective This optional page shows how to use a graphing calculator to relate the tangent of an angle to the slope of a line.

Teaching Suggestions

Have students examine the graph of $\triangle PQR$ carefully. They will recognize $\overline{QR}$ as the opposite side of $\angle P$ and $\overline{PR}$ as the adjacent side. Ask a volunteer to explain how $\overline{QR}$ and $\overline{PR}$ relate to the slope of $\overleftrightarrow{PQ}$. $\overline{QR}$ is the same as the difference of the y values; $\overline{PR}$ is the same as the difference of the x values.

When using the graphing calculator for the exercises, the angles to be considered will be easier to see if students also graph a horizontal line that intersects the line at the y-axis. For example, for Exercise 1, use
$$y_1 = 8x + 4$$
$$y_2 = 4$$
Since for Exercise 3 the y-intercept is 0, no other line is necessary.

The tangent ratio of an angle is the slope of a line. Consider the graph of $\overleftrightarrow{PQ}$ below.

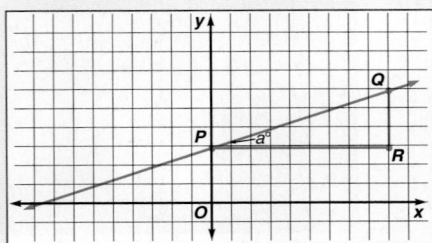

An angle with measure a is formed at P by a horizontal line and the portion of line PQ that is to the right of a vertical line, in this case the y-axis. You can find the measure of the angle using the tangent ratio for $\triangle PQR$.

$$\tan a = \frac{QR}{PR}$$

$$\tan a = \frac{3}{9} \qquad QR = 3, PR = 9$$

$$a \approx 18.4°$$

The slope of a line is given by the formula $m = \frac{y_2 - y_1}{x_2 - x_1}$, where (x_1, y_1) and (x_2, y_2) are the coordinates of two points on the line. Find the slope of $\overleftrightarrow{PQ}$ given the points $P(0, 3)$ and $Q(9, 6)$.

$$m = \frac{y_2 - y_1}{x_2 - x_1}$$

$$= \frac{6 - 3}{9 - 0} \text{ or } \frac{3}{9} \qquad (x_1, y_1) = P(0, 3); (x_2, y_2) = Q(9, 6)$$

Notice that $\tan a = m$. The vertical change, $y_2 - y_1$, is the same as the length of the side opposite, QR, and the horizontal change, $x_2 - x_1$, is the same as the length of the side adjacent, PR. So, the slope of $\overleftrightarrow{PQ}$ is the same as the tangent of the angle formed by $\overleftrightarrow{PQ}$ and a horizontal line.

EXERCISES

Graph each equation on your graphing calculator. Then find the slope of the line and the measure of the angle the line forms with a horizontal to the nearest degree.

1. $y = 8x + 4$

8; 83

2. $4x - 6y = 9$

$\frac{2}{3}$; 34

3. $y = \frac{2}{5}x$ $\frac{2}{5}$; 22

- Reteaching Master 8-5
- Practice Master 8-5
- Enrichment Master 8-5
- Activity Master, p. 22
- Lab Manual, pp. 62-65

 Transparency 8-5 contains the 5-Minute Check and a teaching aid for this lesson.

INTRODUCING THE LESSON

 5-Minute Check

(over Lesson 8-4)

State the trigonometric ratio that corresponds to each value and angle.

1. $\frac{7}{25}$, $\angle Y$ sin Y

2. $\frac{24}{7}$, $\angle X$ tan X

3. $\frac{24}{25}$, $\angle Y$ cos Y

4. $\frac{7}{25}$, $\angle X$ cos X

5. $\frac{7}{24}$, $\angle Y$ tan Y

Motivating the Lesson

Discuss how to use trigonometry to find the height of the school building.

TEACHING THE LESSON

Chalkboard Example

For Example 1

A surveyor is 130 feet from a tower. The angle of elevation to the top is 32°. The surveyor's instrument is 4.75 feet above the ground. Find the height.

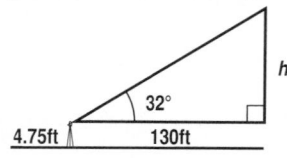

$\tan 32° = \frac{h}{130}$, $h \approx 81.23$ feet

Tower height is 85.98 feet

Objectives
8-5A
8-5B

After studying this lesson, you should be able to:
- recognize angles of depression or elevation, and
- use trigonometry to solve problems.

Application

The airport meteorologists keep close tabs on the weather to help ensure that airplanes can fly safely. One of the things that they watch is the cloud ceiling. The cloud ceiling is the lowest altitude at which solid cloud is present. If the cloud ceiling is below a certain level, usually about 61 meters, airplanes are not allowed to take off or land.

One way that meteorologists can find the cloud ceiling at night is to shine a searchlight that is located a fixed distance from their office vertically onto the clouds. Then they measure the **angle of elevation** to the spot of light on the cloud. The angle of elevation to the spot is the angle formed by the line of sight to the spot and a horizontal segment. Using this information and some trigonometry, the cloud ceiling can be determined.

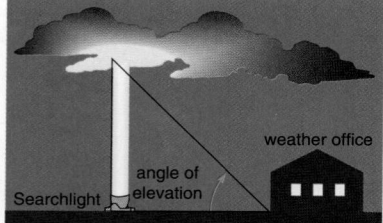

Example 1

A searchlight located 200 meters from a weather office is turned on. If the angle of elevation to the spot of light on the clouds is 35°, how high is the cloud ceiling?

Draw a diagram.

Let c represent the cloud ceiling.

$\tan 35° = \frac{c}{200}$ $tan = \frac{opposite}{adjacent}$

$200 \tan 35° = c$ *Multiply each side by 200.*

Use a calculator to find c.

ENTER: 200 ⊠ 35 TAN = 140.04151

The ceiling is about 140 meters. *With this ceiling, airplanes can take off and land.*

ALTERNATE TEACHING STRATEGIES

Using Modeling

A hypsometer measures angles of elevation. Students can make one with straw, cardboard, string, and a paper clip as shown below. Have them use a protractor to mark the angles.

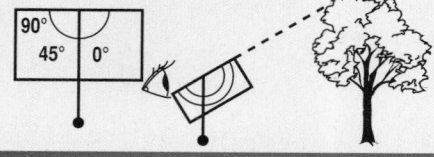

Using Discussion

Ask students to brainstorm and list as many situations as they can think of in which a measurement can be found using an angle of elevation or an angle of depression.

A person on a tower or on a cliff must look down to see an object below. This person's line of sight forms an **angle of depression** with a horizontal line.

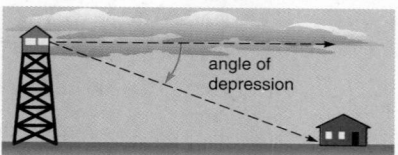
angle of depression

Example 2

APPLICATION

Fire Fighting

A fire is sighted from a fire tower in Wayne National Forest. The ranger found that the angle of depression to the fire is 22°. If the tower is 75 meters tall, how far is the fire from the base of the tower?

Let d represent the distance from the fire to the base of the fire tower.

The segments with measure d are parallel, and the line of sight is a transversal. So, by alternate interior angles, the angle between the ground and the line of sight measures 22°.

$$\tan 22° = \frac{75}{d}$$

$$d = \frac{75}{\tan 22°}$$

$$d \approx \frac{75}{0.4040}$$

$$d \approx 185.63$$

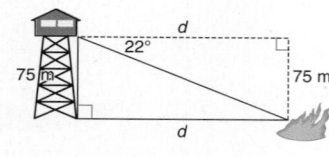

The fire is about 186 meters from the base of the tower.

Angles of depression or elevation to two different objects can be used to find the distance between those objects.

Example 3

APPLICATION

Aerospace

The lunar lander, *Eagle*, traveled aboard *Apollo 11* and descended to the surface of the moon on July 20, 1969. Before sending *Eagle* to the surface of the moon, *Apollo 11* orbited the moon three miles above the surface. At one point in the orbit, the onboard guidance system measured the angles of depression to the near and far edges of a large crater. The angles measured 25° and 18°. Find the distance across the crater.

Draw a diagram.

Let f be the distance to the far edge of the crater and n be the distance to the near edge.

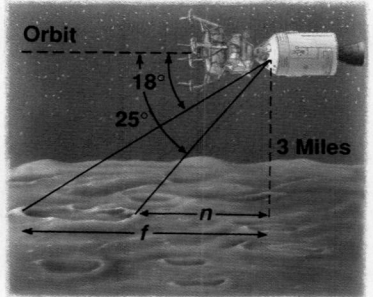

Orbit
18°
25°
3 Miles
n
f

$$\tan 18° = \frac{3}{f} \qquad \tan 25° = \frac{3}{n}$$

$$f = \frac{3}{\tan 18°} \qquad n = \frac{3}{\tan 25°}$$

$$f \approx \frac{3}{0.3249} \qquad n \approx \frac{3}{0.4663}$$

$$f \approx 9.2 \qquad n \approx 6.4$$

The distance across the crater is 9.2 − 6.4 or about 2.8 miles.

Teaching Tip   Before Example 2, ask students to demonstrate an angle of depression with their eyes, by looking straight ahead and then down to a point on the floor.

Chalkboard Examples

For Example 2
A plane is 3 miles above ground. The pilot sights the airport at an angle of depression of 15°. What is the ground distance between the plane and the airport?

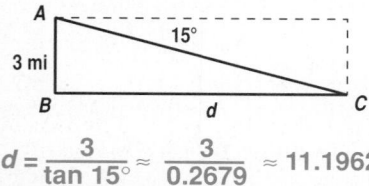

A
15°
3 mi
B
d
C

$$d = \frac{3}{\tan 15°} \approx \frac{3}{0.2679} \approx 11.1962$$
The distance is about 11.2 miles.

For Example 3
A satellite is 25 miles above a river. An observer notes an angle of depression of 40° to the near side of the river and 37° to the far side. How wide is the river?

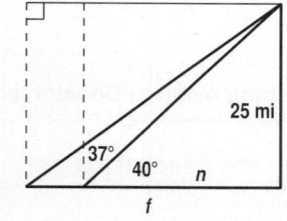

25 mi
37°
40°
n
f

$$n = \frac{25}{\tan 40°} \approx \frac{25}{0.8391} \approx 29.8$$

$$f = \frac{25}{\tan 37°} \approx \frac{25}{0.7536} \approx 33.2$$

$$f - n = 33.2 - 29.8 = 3.4 \text{ mi}$$

Teaching Tip   In Example 2, point out that 75 meters is the measure of the side opposite the angle of depression.

EVALUATING THE LESSON

Checking for Understanding

Exercises 1-15 are designed to help you assess students' understanding through reading, writing, speaking, and modeling. You should work through Exercises 1-3 with your students and then monitor their work on Exercises 4-15.

Additional Answer

3. It depends on what information is given.

If you are given:	Use:
opposite, hypotenuse	sin
opposite, adjacent	tan
adjacent, hypotenuse	cos

8. $\sin 15° = \dfrac{QR}{37}$; 9.6

9. $\sin 47° = \dfrac{10}{PQ}$; 13.7

10. $\cos 16° = \dfrac{13.4}{PQ}$; 13.9

11. $\tan 72° = \dfrac{13}{QR}$; 4.2

12. $\tan 74° = \dfrac{PR}{33.6}$; 117.2

13. $\cos 24° = \dfrac{43.7}{PQ}$; 47.8

Reteaching Masters Booklet, p. 47

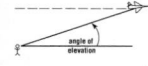
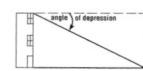

8-5 NAME _____ DATE _____
Reteaching Worksheet
Application: Using Trigonometry

Many problems in daily life can be solved by using trigonometry. Often such problems involve an **angle of elevation** or an **angle of depression**.

Example: The angle of elevation from point A to the top of a cliff is 38°. If point A is 80 feet from the base of the cliff, how high is the cliff?

Let x represent the height of the cliff.
Then $\tan 38° = \frac{x}{80}$.

80 tan 30° = x

Use a calculator set for the degree mode to find x.
ENTER: 80 × 30 TAN = 46.188021
The cliff is about 46 feet high.

Solve each problem. Round measures of segments to the nearest hundredth and measures of angles to the nearest degree.

1. From the top of a tower, the angle depression to a stake on the ground is 72°. The top of the tower is 80 feet above ground. How far is the stake from the foot of the tower? **25.99 ft**

2. A tree 40 feet high casts a shadow 58 feet long. Find the measure of the angle of elevation of the sun. **35°**

3. A ladder leaning against a house makes an angle of 60° with the ground. The foot of the ladder is 7 feet from the foot of the house. How long is the ladder? **14 ft**

4. A balloon on a 40-foot string makes an angle of 50° with the ground. How high above the ground is the ballon if the hand of the person holding the balloon is 6 feet above the ground? **36.64 ft**

47
Glencoe Division, Macmillan/McGraw-Hill

CHECKING FOR UNDERSTANDING

Communicating Mathematics

Read and study the lesson to answer these questions.

1. Make a drawing and write a few sentences to explain what is meant by an angle of elevation. **See students' work.**

2. Give an example of how one might use an angle of depression to measure something that you cannot measure directly. **See students' work.**

3. How do you decide whether to use sin, cos, or tan when you are finding the measure of an acute angle in a right triangle? Explain. **See margin.**

Guided Practice

Name the angles of elevation and depression in each figure.

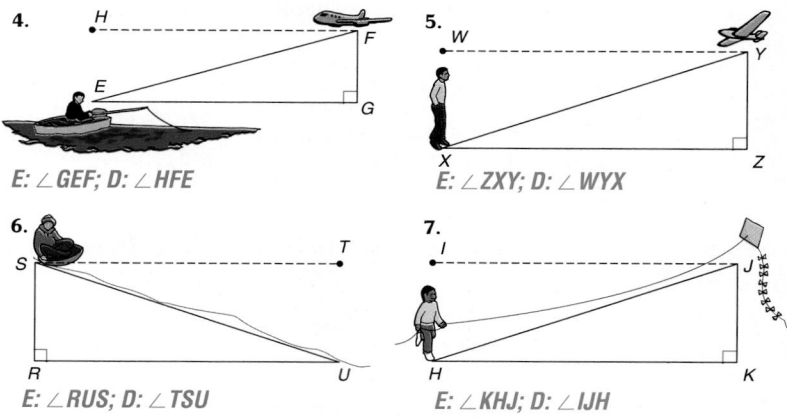

4.
E: ∠GEF; D: ∠HFE

5.
E: ∠ZXY; D: ∠WYX

6.
E: ∠RUS; D: ∠TSU

7.
E: ∠KHJ; D: ∠IJH

State an equation that would enable you to solve each problem. Then solve. Round answers to the nearest tenth. **See margin.**

8. Given $m\angle P = 15$ and $PQ = 37$, find QR.

9. Given $m\angle P = 47$ and $QR = 10$, find PQ.

10. Given $PR = 13.4$ and $m\angle P = 16$, find PQ.

11. Given $m\angle Q = 72$ and $PR = 13$, find QR.

12. Given $QR = 33.6$ and $m\angle Q = 74$, find PR.

13. Given $PR = 43.7$ and $m\angle P = 24$, find PQ.

14. A surveyor is standing 100 meters from a bridge. She determines that the angle of elevation to the top of the bridge is 35°. The surveyor's eye level is 1.45 meters above the ground. Find the height of the bridge. Round your answer to the nearest hundredth. **71.47 meters**

15. A ladder leaning against the side of a house forms an angle of 65° with the ground. The foot of the ladder is 8 feet from the building. Find the length of the ladder to the nearest foot. **19 feet**

RETEACHING THE LESSON

Show students the two figures at the right. For each, ask them to write a word problem that uses either angle of elevation or angle of depression. Have them write the solution to their problems.

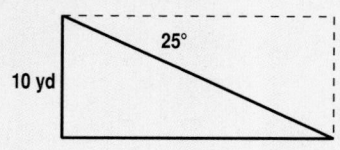

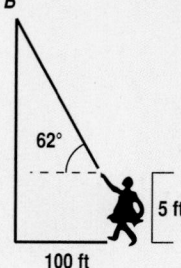

EXERCISES

Practice

A

Use the figures below to find each measure. Round your answers to the nearest whole number.

16. $m\angle Y$ **63**   17. $m\angle X$ **27**

18. $m\angle Z$ **90**   19. XY **61**

20. $m\angle U$ **90**   21. UV **2**

22. WV **7**   23. $m\angle W$ **19**

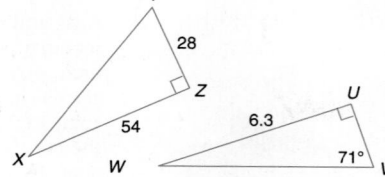

B

Solve each problem. Round measures of segments to the nearest hundredth and measures of angles to the nearest degree.

24. A surveyor is 100 meters from a building. He finds that the angle of elevation to the top of the building is 23°. If the surveyor's eye level is 1.55 meters above the ground, find the height of the building. **44.00 m**

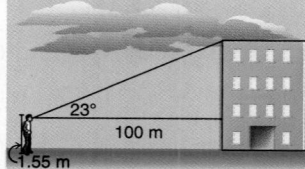

25. To secure a 500-meter radio tower against high winds, guy wires are attached to a ring 5 meters from the top of the tower. The wires form a 15° angle with the tower. Find the distance from the tower to the guy wire anchor in the ground. **132.63 meters**

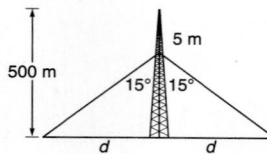

26. Mary is flying a kite on a 50-meter string. The string is making a 50° angle with the ground. How high above the ground is the kite? **38.30 meters**

27. Bill Owens is an architect designing a new parking garage for the city. The floors of the garage are to be 10 feet apart. The exit ramps between each pair of floors are to be 75 feet long. What is the measurement of the angle of elevation of each ramp? **8°**

28. From the top of a lighthouse, the angle of depression to a buoy is 25°. If the top of the lighthouse is 150 feet above sea level, find the distance from the buoy to the foot of the lighthouse. **321.68 feet**

29. At a certain time of day, the angle of elevation of the sun is 44°. Find the length of a shadow cast by a building 30 meters high. **31.07 meters**

30. A trolley car track rises vertically 40 feet over a horizontal distance of 630 feet. What is the angle of elevation of the track? **4°**

31. Danica is in the observation area of Sears Tower in Chicago overlooking Lake Michigan. She sights two sailboats going due east from the tower. The angles of depression to the two boats are 42 degrees and 29 degrees. If the observation deck is 1,353 feet high, how far apart are the boats? **938.22 feet**

LESSON 8-5   APPLICATION: USING TRIGONOMETRY   387

Error Analysis

In exercises about angles of depression, students may mistake the height they are given for the adjacent side of the angle of depression. Have them make diagrams as in Example 2 that clearly show which triangle is being used.

Closing the Lesson

Writing Activity Have each student make up one problem that uses angle of elevation and one problem that uses angle of depression. Each problem should be accompanied by a solution that includes a diagram.

APPLYING THE LESSON

Homework Exercises

Assignment Guide
Basic: 16-28, 33-41
Average: 18-30, 33-41
Enriched: 20-41

Practice Masters Booklet, p. 54

8-5   NAME _____ DATE _____

Practice Worksheet

Application: Using Trigonometry

Solve each problem. Round measures of segments to the nearest hundredth and measures of angles to the nearest degree.

1. A 20-foot ladder leans against a wall so that the base of the ladder is 8 feet from the base of the building. What angle does the ladder make with the ground? 66°

2. A 50-meter vertical tower is braced with a cable secured at the top of the tower and tied 30 meters from the base. What angle does the cable form with the vertical tower? 31°

3. At a point on the ground 50 feet from the foot of a tree, the angle of elevation to the top of the tree is 53°. Find the height of the tree. 66.35 ft

4. From the top of a lighthouse 210 feet high, the angle of depression of a boat is 27°. Find the distance from the boat to the foot of the lighthouse. The lighthouse was built at sea level. 412.15 ft

5. Richard is flying a kite. The kite string makes an angle of 57° with the ground. If Richard is standing 100 feet from the point on the ground directly below the kite, find the length of the kite string. 183.61 ft

6. An airplane rises vertically 1000 feet over a horizontal distance of 1 mile. What is the angle of elevation of the airplane's path? 11°

T 54

Glencoe Division, Macmillan/McGraw-Hill

---

32. Joe is standing on top of Marina Towers looking at the Leo Burnett World Headquarters building across the Chicago River. It is 880 feet between buildings. Joe finds the angle of elevation to the top of the Burnett building to be 8 degrees and the angle of depression to the ground level to be 20 degrees. How tall is the Burnett building to the nearest foot? **444 feet**

Critical Thinking

33. A fly and an ant are in one corner of a rectangular box. The end of the box is 4 inches by 6 inches and the diagonal across the bottom of the box makes an angle of 21.8° with the longer edge of the box. There is food in the corner opposite the insects.

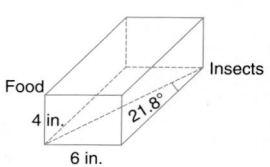

a. What is the shortest distance the fly must fly to get to the food? **about 16.6 in.**

b. What is the shortest distance the ant must crawl to get to the food? **about 19.9 in.**

Applications

34. **Travel** A ship sails due north from its home port for 90 kilometers. It then turns east for 40 kilometers before turning north again to sail for 70 kilometers. How far is the ship from its home port? **164.92 km**

35. **Physics** A pendulum 50 centimeters long is moved 40° from the vertical. How far did the tip of the pendulum rise? **11.7 cm**

36. **Meteorology** Two weather observation stations are 7 miles apart. From Station 1, the angle of elevation to a weather balloon between the stations is 35°. From Station 2, the angle of elevation to the balloon is 54°. Find the altitude of the balloon to the nearest tenth of a mile. *(Hint: Find the distance from Station 2 to the point directly below the balloon.)* **3.2 miles**

Mixed Review

37. Find cos A, sin A, and tan A. State each as a fraction and a decimal rounded to the nearest thousandth. **(Lesson 8-4)**

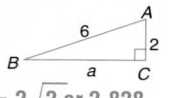

$\cos A = \frac{1}{3}$ or 0.333; $\sin A = \frac{2\sqrt{2}}{3}$ or 0.943; $\tan A = 2\sqrt{2}$ or 2.828

38. A Georgia map is drawn so that 1 centimeter represents 20 miles. If Savannah and Atlanta are 12.7 centimeters apart on the map, how far apart are the cities? **(Lesson 7-1)** **254 miles**

39. *RSTV* is a rhombus with *PT* = 7.6. Find *RT*. **(Lesson 6-5)** **15.2**

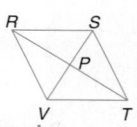

40. Write a two-column proof. **(Lesson 5-1)** **See margin.**

Given: $\overline{CI} \cong \overline{MI}$
$\overline{IT}$ is a median of $\triangle CIM$.

Prove: $\angle CIT \cong \angle MIT$

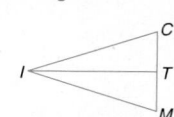

Wrap-Up

41. **Journal Entry** Write your own application problem that involves trigonometry. Provide the solution with the problem. **See students' work.**

EXTENDING THE LESSON

Math Power: Problem Solving

A surveyor finds the angle of elevation to the top of a tree to be 20°. She then moves directly towards the tree to a point 100 feet closer to the tree and finds the angle of elevation to be 30°. How far from the tree was she for the second reading? If her transit was 5 feet from the ground for both readings, how tall was the tree? **about 171 feet; about 104 feet**

Law of Sines

Objective 8-6

After studying this lesson, you should be able to:
- use the law of sines to solve triangles.

Application

A triangular flower bed has one side 8 feet long and one side 11 feet long. The angle opposite the 11-foot side measures 87 °. What are the measures of the other side and angles? *You will solve this problem in Example 2.*

You can use trigonometric functions to solve problems like this that involve triangles that are *not* right triangles. One of the ways is by using the **law of sines**.

Law of Sines

Let △*ABC* be any triangle with *a*, *b*, and *c* representing the measures of sides opposite angles with measures *A*, *B*, and *C* respectively. Then,

$$\frac{\sin A}{a} = \frac{\sin B}{b} = \frac{\sin C}{c}.$$

Plan for Proof of Law of Sines

△*ABC* is a triangle with an altitude from *C* that intersects $\overline{AB}$ at *D*. Let *h* represent the measure of $\overline{CD}$. Since △*ACD* and △*BCD* are right triangles, we can find sin *A* and sin *B*.

$$\sin A = \frac{h}{b} \qquad \sin B = \frac{h}{a}$$
$$b \sin A = h \qquad a \sin B = h$$

$b \sin A$	$=$	$a \sin B$ *Substitution*
$\frac{\sin A}{a}$	$=$	$\frac{\sin B}{b}$ *Divide each side by ab.*

The proof can be completed by using a similar technique with another altitude to show that $\frac{\sin A}{a} = \frac{\sin B}{b} = \frac{\sin C}{c}$.

Finding the measures of all the angles and sides of a triangle is called **solving the triangle**. The law of sines can be used to solve a triangle in the following cases.

1. You are given the measures of two angles and any side of a triangle.
2. You are given the measures of two sides and an angle opposite one of these sides of the triangle.

ALTERNATE TEACHING STRATEGIES

Using Communication

Have students write a paragraph explaining how the law of sines can be used to solve a triangle. They should mention what parts of the triangle must be given for the law of sines to apply.

Using Reasoning

A triangle has the given measures.

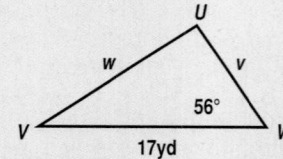

What other measure is needed for the triangle to be solvable by the law of sines? *w*, m∠*V*, or m∠*U*

Lesson Resources

- Reteaching Master 8-6
- Practice Master 8-6
- Enrichment Master 8-6
- Evaluation Master, p. 108
- Technology Master, p.8

 Transparency 8-6 contains the 5-Minute Check and a teaching aid for this lesson.

INTRODUCING THE LESSON

⏱ 5-Minute Check

(over Lesson 8-5)

Refer to the figure below. Find each measure to the nearest whole number.

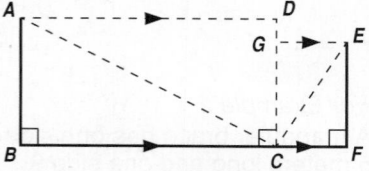

1. *AB* = 10 m, m∠*DAC* = 27. Find *BC*.   **20 m**
2. m∠*BCA* = 35, *BC* = 25 yards. Find *AB*.   **18 yd**
3. m∠*FCE* = 54, *CF* = 6 miles. Find *EF*.   **8 mi**
4. *EF* = 120 feet, m∠*GEC* = 63. Find *CF*.   **61 ft**

Motivating the Lesson

Ask students to find representations of triangles in the classroom that are not right triangles. Then have them think of examples of such outside the classroom.

TEACHING THE LESSON

Teaching Tip After reading the plan for the proof of the law of sines as far as it has been given, develop with students the plan for the rest of the proof.

Teaching Tip Bear in mind that the ambiguous case in which the law of sines yields 0 or 2 solutions has not been presented in this text, and that such situations have been avoided in the exercises.

Chalkboard Exercises

For Example 1

Solve $\triangle XYZ$ if $m\angle Z = 39$, $m\angle Y = 88$, and $y = 70$.

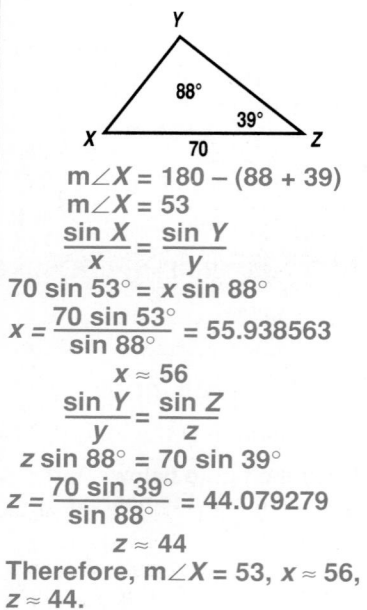

$m\angle X = 180 - (88 + 39)$
$m\angle X = 53$
$\dfrac{\sin X}{x} = \dfrac{\sin Y}{y}$
$70 \sin 53° = x \sin 88°$
$x = \dfrac{70 \sin 53°}{\sin 88°} = 55.938563$
$x \approx 56$
$\dfrac{\sin Y}{y} = \dfrac{\sin Z}{z}$
$z \sin 88° = 70 \sin 39°$
$z = \dfrac{70 \sin 39°}{\sin 88°} = 44.079279$
$z \approx 44$
Therefore, $m\angle X = 53$, $x \approx 56$, $z \approx 44$.

For Example 2

A triangular brace has one side 5 meters long and one side 9 meters long. The angle opposite the 9-meter side measures 70°. Find the measures of the other side and angles.

$\dfrac{\sin A}{a} = \dfrac{\sin C}{c}$
$\dfrac{\sin 70°}{9} = \dfrac{\sin C}{5}$
$\dfrac{5 \sin 70°}{9} = \sin C$
$0.5220515 = \sin C$
$31.46995998 = m\angle C$
$31 \approx m\angle C$
$m\angle B = 180 - (70 + 31)$
$m\angle B = 79$
$\dfrac{\sin A}{a} = \dfrac{\sin B}{b}$
$\dfrac{\sin 70°}{9} = \dfrac{\sin 79°}{b}$
$b = \dfrac{9 \sin 79°}{\sin 70°} = 9.4016325$
$b \approx 9$
Therefore, $m\angle C \approx 31$, $m\angle B \approx 79$, $b \approx 9$.

Example 1

Solve $\triangle RPQ$ if $m\angle R = 50$, $m\angle P = 67$, and $r = 10$.

First find $m\angle Q$.

$m\angle P + m\angle Q + m\angle R = 180$ *The sum of the angles*
$67 + m\angle Q + 50 = 180$ *in a triangle is 180.*
$m\angle Q = 63$

Next, use the law of sines.

$\dfrac{\sin P}{p} = \dfrac{\sin Q}{q} = \dfrac{\sin R}{r}$ *Law of sines*
$\dfrac{\sin 67°}{p} = \dfrac{\sin 63°}{q} = \dfrac{\sin 50°}{10}$ *Substitution*

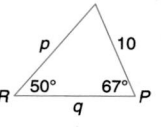

Write two proportions, each involving only one variable.

$\dfrac{\sin 67°}{p} = \dfrac{\sin 50°}{10}$ $\dfrac{\sin 63°}{q} = \dfrac{\sin 50°}{10}$
$10 \sin 67° = p \sin 50°$ *Cross products.* $10 \sin 63° = q \sin 50°$
$\dfrac{10 \sin 67°}{\sin 50°} = p$ $\dfrac{10 \sin 63°}{\sin 50°} = q$
$12.0 \approx p$ $11.6 \approx q$

Therefore, $m\angle Q = 63$, $p \approx 12.0$, and $q \approx 11.6$.

Example 2 asks you to solve a triangle given the measures of two sides and an angle opposite one of those sides.

Example 2

APPLICATION
Gardening

A triangular flower bed has one side 8 feet long and one side 11 feet long. The angle opposite the 11-foot side measures 87°. Find the measures of the other side and angles.

Draw a diagram.

Use the law of sines.

$\dfrac{\sin A}{a} = \dfrac{\sin 87°}{11} = \dfrac{\sin C}{8}$

We can solve for $m\angle C$.

$\dfrac{\sin 87°}{11} = \dfrac{\sin C}{8}$
$8 \sin 87° = 11 \sin C$ *Cross products.*
$\dfrac{8 \sin 87°}{11} = \sin C$

Use your calculator to find $m\angle C$.

ENTER: 8 ⊠ 87 SIN ÷ 11 = INV SIN 46.575101
$m\angle C \approx 47$

Additional Answers

1.

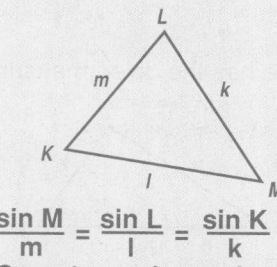

$\dfrac{\sin M}{m} = \dfrac{\sin L}{l} = \dfrac{\sin K}{k}$

3. Case 1: you know the measures of two angles and any side of a triangle; case 2: you know the measure of two sides and an angle opposite one of the known sides of the triangle.

Since the sum of the measures of the angles in a triangle is 180, we can find $m\angle A$.

$$m\angle A + m\angle B + m\angle C = 180$$
$$m\angle A + 87 + 47 \approx 180$$
$$m\angle A \approx 46$$

Now solve for a.

$$\frac{\sin 46°}{a} = \frac{\sin 87°}{11}$$
$$11 \sin 46° = a \sin 87°$$
$$\frac{11 \sin 46°}{\sin 87°} = a$$

Use your calculator to find a.

ENTER: 11 $\times$ 46 $\boxed{\text{SIN}}$ $\div$
87 $\boxed{\text{SIN}}$ $\boxed{=}$ 7.9235968

$a \approx 8$

The missing angle measures are 47° and 46°, and the missing side measures 8 feet.

CHECKING FOR UNDERSTANDING

Communicating Mathematics

Read and study the lesson to answer these questions.

See margin.

1. Draw $\triangle KLM$ and state the relationships known from the law of sines.

2. What kind of triangles can be solved using the law of sines? **non-right triangles**

3. There are two different cases when it is appropriate to use the law of sines. What are they? **See margin.**

Guided Practice

Use the given information about $\triangle ABC$ to write an equation that could be used to find each unknown value. Draw $\triangle ABC$ and mark it with the given information. See Solutions Manual.

4. If $b = 4.7$, $m\angle A = 22$, and $m\angle B = 49$, find a.

5. If $b = 10$, $a = 14$, and $m\angle A = 50$, find $m\angle B$.

6. If $m\angle A = 40$, $m\angle B = 60$, and $a = 20$, find b.

7. If $c = 12$, $b = 16$, and $m\angle B = 42$, find $m\angle C$.

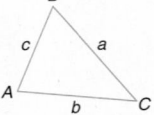

LESSON 8-6   LAW OF SINES   391

RETEACHING THE LESSON

Refer to the figure to complete each statement.

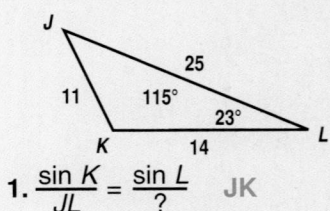

1. $\dfrac{\sin K}{JL} = \dfrac{\sin L}{?}$ **JK**

2. $\dfrac{\sin J}{KL} = \dfrac{?}{JK}$ **sin L**

3. $\dfrac{\sin 115°}{?} = \dfrac{\sin 23°}{?}$ **25, 11**

4. $\dfrac{\sin ?}{14} = \dfrac{\sin ?}{25}$ **42°, 115°**

5. $\dfrac{\sin 23°}{?} = \dfrac{\sin ?}{14}$ **11, 42°**

Teaching Tip   After Example 2, have students check the reasonableness of their answers. Is the longest side opposite the largest angle?

EVALUATING THE LESSON

Checking for Understanding

Exercises 1-12 are designed to help you assess students' understanding through reading, writing, speaking, and modeling. You should work through Exercises 1-3 with your students and then monitor their work on Exercises 4-12.

Error Analysis

Since the calculations are complex when applying the law of sines, there are many chances for error. Even with a calculator, a number or function may not be entered properly. Therefore, encourage students to estimate and check the reasonableness of their answers.

Reteaching Masters Booklet, p. 48

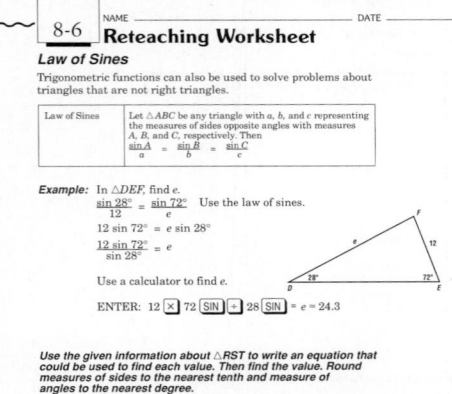

Chapter 8   391

Closing the Lesson

Speaking Activity Draw a triangle on the chalkboard or overhead and give measures for two angles and one side of the triangle. Have volunteers explain how to solve the triangle. Repeat for a triangle for which you give the measures of two sides and one angle opposite one of these sides.

APPLYING THE LESSON

Homework Exercises

Assignment Guide

Basic: 13-24, 29-36
Average: 15-26, 29-36
Enriched: 17-36

Additional Answers

8. $m\angle A = 52$, $b \approx 100.2$, $c \approx 90.4$
9. $m\angle B \approx 34$, $c \approx 11.4$, $m\angle C \approx 40$
10. $b \approx 8.9$, $c \approx 10.2$, $m\angle C = 74$
11. $m\angle C = 80$, $a \approx 13.1$, $b \approx 17.6$
13. $\dfrac{\sin 53°}{a} = \dfrac{\sin 61°}{2.8}$; 2.6

Solve each triangle *ABC*. **Round measures of sides to the nearest tenth and angle measures to the nearest degree.** See margin.

8. $m\angle B = 70$, $m\angle C = 58$, $a = 84$
9. $a = 17$, $b = 10$, $m\angle A = 106$
10. $a = 8$, $m\angle A = 49$, $m\angle B = 57$
11. $m\angle A = 40$, $m\angle B = 60$, $c = 20$

12. An isosceles triangle has a base of 22 centimeters and a vertex angle of 36°. Find its perimeter. **93.2 cm**

EXERCISES

Practice

Use the given information about $\triangle ABC$ to write an equation that could be used to find each value. Then find the value. See margin.

13. If $b = 2.8$, $m\angle A = 53$, and $m\angle B = 61$, find a.
14. If $b = 36$, $c = 12$, and $m\angle B = 98$, find $m\angle C$.
15. If $m\angle A = 70$, $m\angle B = 23$, and $c = 2.2$, find a.
16. If $m\angle C = 55$, $a = 9$, and $c = 11$, find $m\angle A$.

Solve each triangle *ABC*. **Round measures of sides to the nearest tenth and measures of angles to the nearest degree.** See margin.

17. $m\angle C = 70$, $c = 8$, $m\angle A = 30$
18. $a = 10$, $c = 25$, $m\angle C = 124$
19. $m\angle A = 29$, $m\angle B = 62$, $c = 11.5$
20. $m\angle C = 35$, $a = 7.5$, $c = 24$
21. $m\angle B = 36$, $m\angle C = 119$, $b = 8$
22. $m\angle B = 47$, $m\angle C = 73$, $a = 0.9$
23. $b = 20$, $c = 9.2$, $m\angle B = 103$
24. $a = 12$, $b = 14$, $m\angle B = 95$

25. A house is built on a triangular plot of land. Two sides of the plot are 160 feet long and they meet at an angle of 85°. If a fence is to be built around the property, how much fencing material is needed? **about 536 feet**

26. The longest side of a triangle is 34 feet. The measures of two angles of the triangle are 40 and 65. Find the lengths of the other two sides. **about 22.6 ft, 31.9 ft**

27. A ship is sighted at sea from two observation points on the coastline that are 30 miles apart. The angle formed by the coastline and the line between the ship and the first observation point measures 34°. The angle formed by the coastline and the line between the ship and the second observation point measures 45.6°. How far is the ship from the first observation point? **21.8 miles**

28. The 35-foot flagpole in front of the Stevenson High School stands on a uniformly sloped mound. When the angle of elevation of the sun is 37.2°, the shadow of the pole ends at the base of the mound. If the mound rises at an angle of 6.7°, find the length of the shadow. **54.9 feet**

392   CHAPTER 8   RIGHT TRIANGLES AND TRIGONOMETRY

Additional Answers

14. $\dfrac{\sin 98°}{36} = \dfrac{\sin C}{12}$; 19
15. $\dfrac{\sin 87°}{2.2} = \dfrac{\sin 70°}{a}$; 2.1
16. $\dfrac{\sin 55°}{11} = \dfrac{\sin A}{9}$; 42
17. $m\angle B \approx 80$, $a \approx 4.3$, $b \approx 8.4$
18. $m\angle A \approx 19$, $m\angle B \approx 37$, $b \approx 18.1$

19. $m\angle C = 89$, $a \approx 5.6$, $b \approx 10.2$
20. $m\angle A \approx 10$, $m\angle B \approx 135$, $b \approx 29.6$
21. $a \approx 5.8$, $m\angle A = 25$, $c \approx 11.9$
22. $\angle A = 60$, $b \approx 0.8$, $c \approx 1.0$
23. $m\angle C \approx 27$, $m\angle A \approx 50$, $a \approx 15.7$
24. $m\angle A \approx 59$, $m\angle C \approx 26$, $c \approx 6.2$

Critical Thinking

29. Does the law of sines hold true for the acute angles of right triangles? Justify your answer. **See margin.**

Applications

30. **Aviation** Two airplanes leave Port Columbus International Airport at the same time. Each plane flies at a speed of 310 miles per hour. One flies in the direction 60° east of north. The other flies in the direction 40° east of south.
    a. Draw a diagram of the situation. **See margin.**
    b. How far apart are the planes after 3 hours? **1196 miles**

31. **Surveying** The support for a powerline that stands on top of a hill is 60 feet tall. A surveyor stands at a point on the hill and observes that the angle of elevation to the top of the support measures 42° and to the base of the support measures 18°. How far is the surveyor from the base of the support? **109.6 feet**

Mixed Review

32. **Surveying** A surveyor is 100 meters from the base of a dam. The angle of elevation to the top of the dam measures 26°. The surveyor's eye-level is 1.73 meters above the ground. Find the height of the dam to the nearest hundredth of a meter. **(Lesson 8-5)** **50.50 meters**

33. In the figure below, $\triangle XYZ \sim \triangle XWV$. The perimeter of $\triangle XYZ$ is 34 inches, and the perimeter of $\triangle XWV$ is 14 inches. If $WV = 4$, find YZ. **(Lesson 7-6)** **about 9.7**

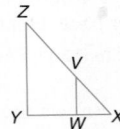

34. Use a compass and straightedge to construct a square with sides 6 centimeters long. **(Lesson 6-5)** **See students' work.**

35. Write a two-column proof. **(Lesson 4-6)**
    Given: $\overline{AB} \perp \overline{BD}$
    $\overline{DE} \perp \overline{DB}$
    $\overline{DB}$ bisects $\overline{AE}$.
    Prove: $\angle A \cong \angle E$ **See Solutions Manual.**

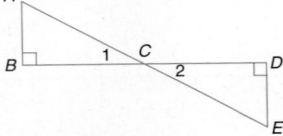

Wrap-Up

36. Draw a triangle to represent each of the two cases where it is appropriate to use the law of sines to solve a triangle. For each case, set up the proportions you would use to solve the triangle. **See students' work.**

LESSON 8-6   LAW OF SINES   393

EXTENDING THE LESSON

Math Power: Reasoning
Refer to the figure.

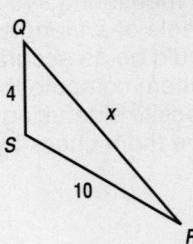

If $x = \dfrac{10 \sin 120°}{\sin 41°}$, what is $m\angle Q$?   **41**

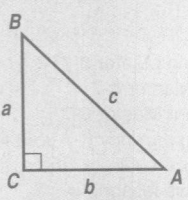
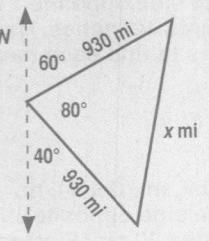

INTRODUCING THE LESSON

 5-Minute Check

(over Lesson 8-6)

In △**ABC**, m∠**A** = 52, the side opposite ∠**A** measures 15 inches, and the side opposite ∠**B** measures 12 inches. Use the law of sines to find each measure.

1. m∠B   39
2. m∠C   89
3. c   19

In △**DEF**, m∠**D** = 64, m∠**E** = 29, and the side opposite ∠**F** measures 20 cm. Find each measure.

4. m∠F   87
5. d   18
6. e   10

Motivating the Lesson

Ask students to recall what information about a triangle they need in order to solve it using the law of sines. Ask them to think of situations in which the law of sines could not be used.

TEACHING THE LESSON

Teaching Tip   In the law of cosines, ask students to look for patterns that will help them remember the equations. For example, the statement that begins "a^2 =" uses cos A.

Objective
8-7

After studying this lesson, you should be able to:
- solve triangles and problems using the law of cosines.

Application

stride angle

Hope runs for the Grandview High School cross country team and hopes to participate in an upcoming city marathon. Recently she read of a study of runners' strides in an issue of *Runners' World*. According to the study, marathon runners run most efficiently with a *stride angle* of about 100°. The stride angle is the largest angle formed by the leading and trailing legs. Hope decided to determine if she could be running more efficiently.

A coaching staff usually uses sophisticated video equipment and computer graphics to measure a runner's stride angle. But since none of this equipment was available, Hope decided to use trigonometry to make an estimate.

First, Hope measured her legs and found that they are each 34 inches long. Next, she needed to find the length of one pace. A pace is the distance between the place where one foot is placed and where the other foot comes down. To find her pace, Hope counted the number of steps she took while running 100 yards. She took 72 steps, so each pace was $\frac{100}{72}$ yards or about 50 inches.

Hope knows the lengths of the three sides of the triangle formed by her legs and one pace. Now she can use the **law of cosines** to find the measure of her stride angle.

The law of cosines allows us to solve a triangle when the law of sines cannot be used.

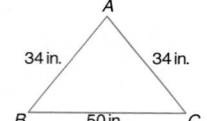

| **Law of Cosines** | Let △*ABC* be any triangle with *a*, *b*, and *c* representing the measures of sides opposite angles with measures *A*, *B*, and *C* respectively. Then, the following equations hold true. |

$$a^2 = b^2 + c^2 - 2bc \cos A$$
$$b^2 = a^2 + c^2 - 2ac \cos B$$
$$c^2 = a^2 + b^2 - 2ab \cos C$$

ALTERNATE TEACHING STRATEGIES

Using Critical Thinking

Is the following statement true or false? Explain your answer. "Using the law of cosines, the law of sines, or both, a triangle can be solved if any three of its measures are known."   **False: The measure of at least one side must be given.**

Using Manipulatives

Have the students verify the law of cosines by actually measuring two sides and the included angle of a triangle. Measurements should be as accurate as possible. Have them compute the measure of the opposite side using the law of cosines. Have them check by measuring the side.

To find the measure of Hope's stride angle, let $b = 34$, $c = 34$, and $a = 50$. We need to find $m\angle A$.

$$a^2 = b^2 + c^2 - 2bc \cos A$$
$$50^2 = 34^2 + 34^2 - 2(34)(34) \cos A \qquad \textit{Substitute}$$
$$2500 = 1156 + 1156 - 2312 \cos A$$
$$188 = -2312 \cos A$$
$$-0.0813 = \cos A$$
$$94.7 \approx A \qquad \textit{Use your calculator.}$$

Hope's stride angle is about 95°. So, she should take longer strides to run more efficiently. *How much longer should her stride be?* **about 2 inches**

The law of cosines can be used to solve a triangle in the following cases.

1. To find the measure of the third side of any triangle if the measures of the two sides and the included angle are given.

2. To find the measure of an angle of a triangle if the measures of the three sides are given.

Example 1

Solve $\triangle ABC$ where $m\angle A = 35$, $b = 16$, and $c = 19$. Round the measures of sides to the nearest hundredth and the measures of angles to the nearest tenth of a degree.

Draw and label the triangle.

Now, determine a using the law of cosines.

$$a^2 = b^2 + c^2 - 2bc \cos A \qquad \textit{Law of cosines}$$
$$a^2 = 16^2 + 19^2 - 2(16)(19) \cos 35° \qquad \textit{A = 35, b = 16, c = 19}$$
$$a^2 \approx 118.96$$
$$a \approx 10.91$$

Next use the law of sines to determine a second angle.

$$\frac{\sin A}{a} = \frac{\sin B}{b} \qquad \textit{Law of sines}$$
$$\frac{\sin 35°}{10.91} = \frac{\sin B}{16} \qquad \textit{A = 35, a} \approx \textit{10.91, b = 16}$$
$$16 \sin 35° = 10.91 \sin B \qquad \textit{Cross products.}$$
$$\sin B \approx 0.8412$$
$$B \approx 57.3$$

Finally, determine the measure of the third angle.

$$m\angle A + m\angle B + m\angle C = 180$$
$$35 + 57.3 + m\angle C \approx 180 \qquad \textit{m}\angle\textit{A = 35, m}\angle\textit{B} \approx \textit{57.3}$$
$$m\angle C \approx 87.7$$

So, $a \approx 10.91$, $m\angle B \approx 57.3$, and $m\angle C \approx 87.7$.

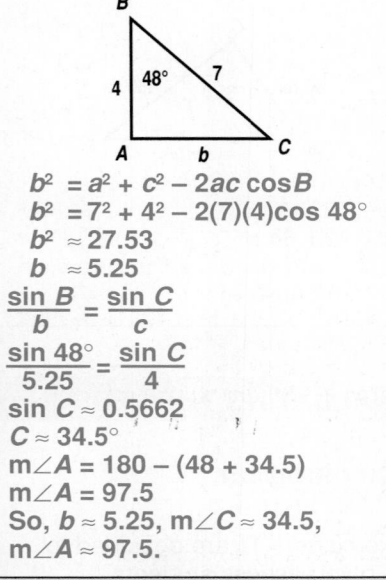

Chalkboard Example

For Example 1
Solve $\triangle ABC$ where $m\angle B = 48$, $a = 7$, and $c = 4$. Round the measures of sides to the nearest hundredth and the measures of angles to the nearest tenth of a degree.

$$b^2 = a^2 + c^2 - 2ac \cos B$$
$$b^2 = 7^2 + 4^2 - 2(7)(4)\cos 48°$$
$$b^2 \approx 27.53$$
$$b \approx 5.25$$
$$\frac{\sin B}{b} = \frac{\sin C}{c}$$
$$\frac{\sin 48°}{5.25} = \frac{\sin C}{4}$$
$$\sin C \approx 0.5662$$
$$C \approx 34.5°$$
$$m\angle A = 180 - (48 + 34.5)$$
$$m\angle A = 97.5$$
So, $b \approx 5.25$, $m\angle C \approx 34.5$, $m\angle A \approx 97.5$.

Teaching Tip When reading Example 1, have students check the calculations with their own calculators, to verify that they know the correct key sequence.

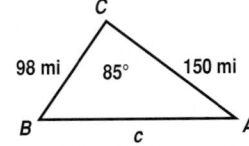

Example 2

APPLICATION
Aviation

Kristin Burrows is flying from Orlando to Miami, a distance of about 220 miles. In order to avoid bad weather, she starts her flight 12 degrees off course and flies on this course for 75 miles. How far is she from Miami?

First, draw a diagram that represents the situation.

Since you know two sides and the included angle of the triangle, use the law of cosines.

$a^2 = b^2 + c^2 - 2bc\cos A$
$a^2 = 220^2 + 75^2 - 2(220)(75)\cos 12°$ *m∠A = 12, b = 220, and c = 75*
$a^2 \approx 21746.13$
$a \approx 147.47$

Ms. Burrows is about 147 miles from Miami.

CHECKING FOR UNDERSTANDING

Communicating Mathematics

Read and study the lesson to answer these questions.   See Solutions Manual

1. Describe the two cases when it is appropriate to use the law of cosines.

2. Create a problem with a minimum of given information for which you would use the law of cosines. Solve the problem. **See students' work.**

3. Compare and contrast the cases where you would use the law of sines, the law of cosines, and the trigonometric ratios, sine, cosine, and tangent, to solve a triangle. **See Solutions Manual.**

Guided Practice

Determine whether the law of sines or the law of cosines should be used first to solve each triangle. Then solve each triangle. Round measures of sides to the nearest tenth and measures of angles to the nearest degree. See margin.

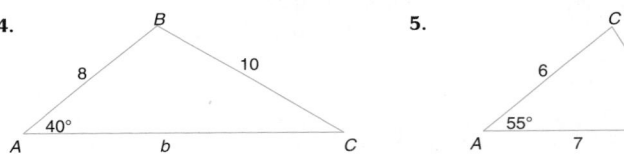

4.
5.

Sketch each triangle described and determine whether the law of sines or the law of cosines should be used first to solve the triangle. Then solve each triangle. Round measures of sides to the nearest tenth and measures of angles to the nearest degree. **See margin.**

6. $a = 14, c = 21, m\angle B = 60$
7. $a = 14, b = 15, c = 16$
8. $m\angle A = 51, a = 40, c = 35$
9. $a = 5, b = 6, c = 7$
10. $a = 140, b = 185, m\angle B = 66$
11. $a = 21.5, b = 13, m\angle C = 78$

EXERCISES

Practice

Determine whether the law of sines or the law of cosines should be used first to solve each triangle described below. Then solve each triangle. Round the measures of sides to the nearest tenth and the measures of angles to the nearest degree. **See margin.**

12. $m\angle A = 40, m\angle C = 70, c = 4$
13. $a = 11, b = 10.5, m\angle C = 35$
14. $a = 11, b = 17, m\angle B = 42$
15. $m\angle A = 56, m\angle C = 26, c = 12.2$

B

Solve each triangle described below. **See Solutions Manual.**

16. $a = 51, b = 61, m\angle B = 19$
17. $a = 5, b = 12, c = 13$
18. $a = 20, c = 24, m\angle B = 47$
19. $m\angle A = 40, m\angle B = 59, c = 14$
20. $a = 345, b = 648, c = 442$
21. $m\angle A = 29, b = 5, c = 4.9$
22. $a = 8, m\angle A = 17, m\angle B = 71$
23. $c = 10.30, a = 21.50, b = 16.71$
24. $m\angle A = 29, b = 7, c = 14.1$
25. $a = 8, b = 24, c = 18$

26. Two sides of a triangular plot of land have lengths of 400 feet and 600 feet. The angle formed by those sides measures 46.3°. Find the perimeter of the plot to the nearest foot. **1434 feet**

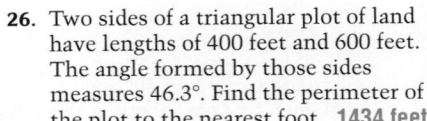
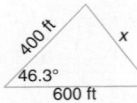

27. The measures of the sides of a triangle are 6.8, 8.4, and 4.9. Find the measure of the smallest angle to the nearest degree. **36**

28. The sides of a parallelogram are 55 cm and 71 cm long. Find the length of each diagonal if the larger angle measures 106°. **about 101.1 cm, 76.9 cm**

C 29. Circle Q has a radius of 15 centimeters. Two radii, $\overline{QA}$ and $\overline{QB}$, form an angle of 123°. Draw a diagram of the situation and find the length of $\overline{AB}$ to the nearest centimeter. **See Solutions Manual for drawing; 26 cm**

30. The sides of a triangle are 50 meters, 70 meters, and 85 meters long. Find the measure of the angle opposite the longest side to the nearest degree. **89**

31. A 40-foot television antenna stands on top of a building. From a point on the ground, the angles of elevation to the top and bottom of the antenna measure 56° and 42° respectively. How tall is the building? **61.9 ft**

Additional Answers

6. law of cosines; $b \approx 18.5$, $m\angle A \approx 41$, $m\angle C \approx 79$
7. law of cosines; $m\angle A \approx 54$, $m\angle B \approx 59$, $m\angle C \approx 67$
8. law of sines; $m\angle C \approx 43$, $m\angle B \approx 86$, $b \approx 51.3$
9. law of cosines; $m\angle A \approx 44$, $m\angle B \approx 56$, $m\angle C \approx 80$
10. law of sines; $m\angle A \approx 44$, $m\angle C \approx 70$, $c \approx 190.3$
11. law of cosines; $c \approx 22.7$, $m\angle A \approx 68$, $m\angle B \approx 34$

Closing the Lesson

Writing Activity Have students make up a problem about a triangle for which they must use the law of cosines. Have them include a solution.

APPLYING THE LESSON

Homework Exercises

Assignment Guide
Basic: 12-27, 33-43
Average: 14-29, 33-43
Enriched: 18-43

Additional Answers

12. law of sines; $a \approx 2.7$, $m\angle B = 70, b \approx 4.0$
13. law of cosines; $c \approx 6.5$, $m\angle A \approx 76, m\angle B \approx 69$
14. law of sines; $m\angle A \approx 26$, $m\angle C \approx 112, c \approx 23.6$
15. law of sines; $a \approx 23.1$, $m\angle B = 98, b \approx 27.6$

Practice Masters Booklet, p. 56

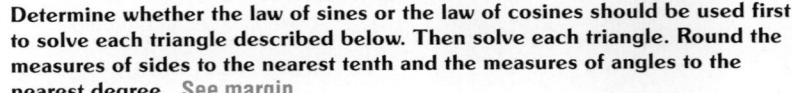

8-7 Practice Worksheet

Law of Cosines

Solve each triangle ABC described below. Round lengths of sides to the nearest tenth and measures of angles to the nearest degree.

1. $a = 16, b = 20, m\angle B = 40$
   $m\angle A \approx 31$
   $m\angle C \approx 109$
   $c \approx 29.4$
2. $a = 10, b = 15, c = 12$
   $m\angle A \approx 42$
   $m\angle B \approx 85$
   $m\angle C \approx 53$
3. $a = 42, c = 60, m\angle B = 58$
   $m\angle A \approx 43$
   $m\angle C \approx 79$
   $b \approx 51.9$
4. $m\angle A = 60, m\angle B = 72, c = 9$
   $m\angle C \approx 48$
   $a \approx 10.5$
   $b \approx 11.5$
5. $a = 7, b = 12, c = 15$
   $m\angle A \approx 27$
   $m\angle B \approx 52$
   $m\angle C \approx 101$
6. $m\angle A = 43, b = 23, c = 26$
   $m\angle B \approx 60$
   $m\angle C \approx 77$
   $a \approx 18.2$
7. $a = 16, m\angle A = 23, m\angle B = 87$
   $m\angle C \approx 70$
   $b \approx 40.9$
   $c \approx 38.5$
8. $c = 15.6, a = 12.9, b = 18.4$
   $m\angle A \approx 44$
   $m\angle B \approx 80$
   $m\angle C \approx 57$

T56
Glencoe Division, Macmillan/McGraw-Hill

Additional Answers

34. $a^2 = (b-x)^2 + h^2$
$= b^2 - 2bx + x^2 + h^2$
$= b^2 - 2bx + c^2$
$= b^2 - 2b(c \cos A) + c^2$
$= b^2 + c^2 - 2bc \cos A$

42. We are given that $\overline{AB} \cong \overline{BC}$. So $\angle 1 \cong \angle 2$ since if two sides of a triangle are congruent, then the angles opposite those sides are congruent. $\angle 1$ and $\angle 3$, and $\angle 2$ and $\angle 4$ form linear pairs. The angles in a linear pair are supplementary, so $\angle 1$ and $\angle 3$ are supplementary and $\angle 2$ and $\angle 4$ are supplementary. If two angles are supplementary to the same or to congruent angles, then they are congruent. So $\angle 3 \cong \angle 4$.

Enrichment Masters Booklet, p. 49

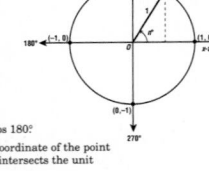

---

32. A ship at sea is 70 miles from one radio transmitter and 130 miles from another. The angle formed by the signals measures 130°. How far apart are the transmitters? **about 183 miles**

Critical Thinking

33. In $\triangle ABC$, $m\angle A = 50$, $m\angle B = 70$, and $m\angle C = 60$. Is it possible to find the measures of the sides of $\triangle ABC$ using either the law of sines, the law of cosines, or the trigonometric ratios? If it is possible, then find the sides. If it is not possible, then explain why not. **It is not possible because there are many triangles that have angles with these measures.**

34. Justify the $a^2 = b^2 + c^2 - 2bc \cos A$ portion of the law of cosines by using the Pythagorean Theorem for $\triangle BDC$. *(Hint: $\cos A = \frac{x}{c}$, so $x = c \cos A$.)* **See margin.**

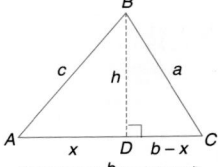

Applications

35. **Navigation**   Two ships, the *Western Princess* and the *Hoggatt Bay*, left Savannah at 10:00 A.M. The *Princess* traveled 30° north of east at a speed of 24 knots. The *Hoggatt Bay* traveled 15° east of south at a speed of 18 knots. How far apart will the ships be at noon? *(1 knot = 1 nautical mile per hour)* **about 67 nautical miles**

36. **Aviation**   Eli Cooley flew his plane 900 kilometers north before turning 15° clockwise. He flew 1150 kilometers in that direction and then landed. How far is Mr. Cooley from his starting point? **about 2032.7 km**

37. **Sports**   In golf, a *slice* is a shot to the right of its intended path (for a right-handed player) and a *hook* is off to the left. Peg's drive from the third tee is a 180-yard slice 12° from the path straight to the cup. If the tee is 240 yards from the cup, how far does Peg's ball lie from the cup? **about 74 yards**

Mixed Review

Portfolio

Review the items in your portfolio. Make a table of contents of the items, noting why each item was chosen. Replace any items that are no longer appropriate.

38. Two angles of a triangle measure 40° and 56°. If the longest side of the triangle is 38 cm long, find the length of the shortest side. Round your answer to the nearest hundredth. **(Lesson 8-6)** **24.56 cm**

39. Find the geometric mean between 8 and 18. **(Lesson 8-1)** **12**

40. In square $LMNP$, $LN = 3x - 2$ and $MP = 2x + 3$. Find LN. **(Lesson 6-5)** **13**

41. Is it possible to have a triangle with vertices at $K(5, 8)$, $L(0, -4)$, and $M(-1, 1)$? Explain your answer. **(Lesson 5-6)** **yes; the lengths of the segments satisfy the triangle inequality**

42. Write a paragraph proof. **(Lesson 4-7)**

    Given: $\overline{AB} \cong \overline{BC}$

    Prove: $\angle 3 \cong \angle 4$ **See margin.**

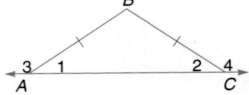

Wrap-Up

43. Write three questions that could be used for a quiz on this lesson. Be sure to provide the answers to your questions. **See students' work.**

EXTENDING THE LESSON

Math Power: Reasoning

Have students name a distance or an angle in the vicinity of the school that can be found by the law of cosines. Have them describe the problem and how the necessary measurements could be obtained.

Problem-Solving Strategy: Decision-Making

Objective 8-8

After studying this lesson, you should be able to:
▪ choose the appropriate strategy for solving a problem.

Most problems can be solved in more than one way. Choosing the most efficient way is often not obvious. When deciding which problem-solving strategy to use, ask yourself these questions.

▪ Is the problem similar to one I have solved before? If so, what strategy worked best on that problem?

▪ What problem-solving strategies do I know? Does one of these seem appropriate?

▪ Does the problem itself suggest a strategy? Does the given information or the unknown imply which strategy will work best? For example, does it ask for several answers? Then listing the possibilities is probably a good strategy to try.

Application

Simon cashed his paycheck and deposited half of the money in his savings account. He gave his sister the $20 he had borrowed and then spent $5 on lunch. After spending $\frac{1}{5}$ of the remaining money on a movie ticket, Simon had $12 left. How much was Simon's paycheck?

Look over the list of problem-solving strategies on the next page. Many of these strategies may work. We could solve a simpler problem, act it out, guess and check, or work backward. We could also write equations for each step and solve for the amount of Simon's paycheck.

Looking at the problem itself, we see that we are given the final amount of money and are asked the beginning amount. Based on this information, working backward seems to be the most appropriate strategy.

Simon had $12 after spending $\frac{1}{5}$ of the remaining money on a movie ticket, so $12 is $\frac{4}{5}$ of that amount. Before buying the movie ticket, Simon had $15 since $\frac{4}{5}$ of 15 is 12.

There was $15 left after Simon paid his sister and had lunch. So, he had 15 + 20 + 5 or $40 before then.

Half of Simon's paycheck went into his savings account and the other half, $40, remained. So, Simon's paycheck was 2 · $40 or $80.

LESSON 8-8   PROBLEM-SOLVING STRATEGY: DECISION-MAKING   399

ALTERNATE TEACHING STRATEGIES

Using Communication
Ask students to make up a problem for which drawing a diagram would be a good strategy and another problem for which guess and check would be a good strategy. Have them write each problem on a separate sheet of paper with a complete explanation of the solution on the back of the sheet.

Using Connections
Ask students to describe three methods for finding the height of a nearby tree, pole, or building.

Lesson Resources
• Practice Master 8-8
• Evaluation Master, p. 108
• Activity Master, p. 8

 Transparency 8-8 contains the 5-Minute Check and a teaching aid for this lesson.

INTRODUCING THE LESSON

🕐 5-Minute Check
(over Lesson 8-7)

In △**ABC**, m∠C = 75, *a* = 8, and *b* = 7. Find each measure to the nearest whole number.

1. *c*   9
2. m∠A   59
3. m∠B   46

In △**DEF**, m∠F = 120, d = 10, and e = 18. Find each measure to the nearest whole number.

4. *f*   25
5. m∠E   39
6. m∠D   21

Motivating the Lesson
Ask students to recall real-life situations in which there is more than one way to do something properly.   **Sample answers: different routes to school, different ways of cooking**

TEACHING THE LESSON

Teaching Tip   After reading the top of page 399, you may want to ask students to list as many problem-solving strategies as they can.

Chalkboard Example

For the Example
Linda has 5 coins worth 51 cents. What coins does she have?   **1 quarter, 2 dimes, 1 nickel, and 1 penny**

Checking for Understanding

Exercises 1-4 are designed to help you assess students' understanding through reading, writing, speaking, and modeling. You should work through Exercises 1-2 with your students and then monitor their work on Exercises 3-4.

Closing the Lesson

Writing Activity Ask students to write a paragraph about problem-solving techniques they have found to be most helpful.

Homework Exercises

Assignment Guide

Basic: 5-14
Average: 5-14
Enriched: 5-14

Exercise Notes

For Exercises 5 and 8, solve by looking for a pattern.

For Exercises 6 and 10, solve by guess and check or making a chart.

For Exercise 7, solve by acting it out.

For Exercise 9, solve by working backward.

CHECKING FOR UNDERSTANDING

Communicating Mathematics

Read and study the lesson to answer these questions.

1. Is there always only one way to solve a problem? No, but there is usually one way that is more efficient than the others.
2. How can you decide which problem-solving strategy is the best one to try? Use experience with other problems and the way they were solved and look at the wording of the problem.

Guided Practice

3. look for a pattern, act it out, make a chart; 220 cans
7. Start both timers. When the 3-minute timer runs out, start boiling the spaghetti. When after 4 minutes the 7-minute timer runs out, start it over and cook for 7 more minutes.

List the problem-solving strategies that you could use to solve each problem. Then choose the best strategy and solve.

3. The pyramid of cans shown at the right has four layers with a total of 20 cans. How many cans are there in a similar pyramid of ten layers?

4. A quarter remains still while a second quarter is rolled around it without slipping. How many times does the second coin rotate around its own axis? act it out, draw a diagram; twice

EXERCISES

Strategies

Look for a pattern.
Solve a simpler problem.
Act it out.
Guess and check.
Draw a diagram.
Make a chart.
Work backward.

Solve. Use any strategy.

5. Find the next term in the sequence 0, 2, 10, 42, 170, 682. Describe the pattern. 2730; multiply the previous term by 4 and add 2

6. What is the least number of coins you can have and be able to pay for any purchase that is less than $1? 9; 1 half-dollar, 1 quarter, 2 dimes, 1 nickel, and 4 pennies

7. You have a seven-minute and a three-minute egg timer. How could you time the boiling of spaghetti for eleven minutes?

8. Find the next number in the sequence. 3, 6, 11, 18, 27. Describe the pattern. $38 = n^2 + 2$

9. Mrs. Sterling's will states that three fourths of her estate will be left to her son, and $24,000 will go to her niece. Half of the remainder will go to her church. One third of the money remaining after the church donation will go to her alma mater and the remaining $4000 will pay Mrs. Sterling's attorney. How much is Mrs. Sterling's estate worth? $144,000

Review the list of strategies on page 400. Ask students to describe a type of problem that lends itself to solution by the use of each of the strategies. Have students share their experiences using various strategies.

10. Complete the multiplication problem at the right. Each digit 1-9 is used exactly once. **One solution is 297 × 18 = 5346.**

$$2\ \blacksquare\ \blacksquare$$
$$\times\ \underline{1\ \blacksquare}$$
$$5\ \blacksquare\ \blacksquare\ \blacksquare$$

11. The area of the bottom of a Health One Cereal box is 95 cm². The area of a side is 140 cm² and the area of the front is 532 cm². What is the volume of the box in cubic centimeters? **2660 cm³**

12. A square results when the length of a rectangle is reduced by 20% and the width is increased by 20%. How does the area of the rectangle compare to the area of the square? Express your answer as a percentage. **The area of the square is 96% of the area of the rectangle.**

13. There are between 50 and 100 stores in the Valley View Mall. Exactly 20 percent of the stores are shoe stores, and exactly one-seventh of the stores are toy stores. Determine how many stores there are in the mall. Explain your solution. **70; It is the only number divisible by 5(20% = $\frac{1}{5}$) and 7 between 50 and 100.**

14. The average height of the players of the Palatine High School boys basketball team is 6 feet 3 inches. The average height of the varsity players is 6 feet 8 inches, and the average height of the junior-varsity players is 6 feet. What fraction of the basketball team are varsity players? **$\frac{3}{8}$**

Exercise Notes
For Exercises 11 and 12, use a diagram.

For Exercises 13 and 14, use a simpler problem or guess and check.

COOPERATIVE LEARNING PROJECT

Work in groups. Each person in the group must understand the solution and be able to explain it to any person in class.

If the length of a side of a square is s, then the area of the square is $A = s \cdot s$ or s^2. In the diagram at the right, the area of square H is 64 square units and the area of square F is 49 square units. Find the areas of the other seven squares. **A-324, B-196, C-16, D-100, E-225, G-1, I-81**

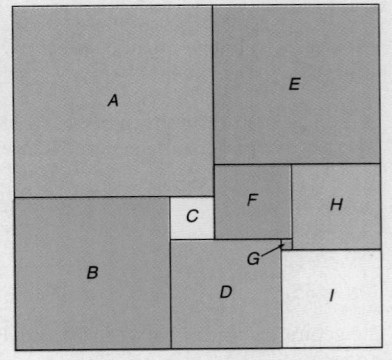

LESSON 8-8   PROBLEM-SOLVING STRATEGY: DECISION-MAKING   401

EXTENDING THE LESSON

Math Power: Reasoning
There are 215 people in a chess tournament. Participants will be paired, and the winners in each game will advance to more rounds until one person is declared chess champ. How many separate games must be played to determine the champ?   **214**

Cooperative Learning Project
This activity provides students an opportunity to *learn* things together, not just do things together. You may wish to refer to pages T6-T7 and page 358c for the various elements of cooperative groups and specific goals and strategies for using them.

Practice Masters Booklet, p. 57

VOCABULARY

Upon completing this chapter, you should be familiar with the following terms:

angle of depression	**385**	**365**	Pythagorean Theorem
angle of elevation	**384**	**376**	sine
cosine	**376**	**376**	tangent
geometric mean	**360**	**376**	trigonometric ratio
law of cosines	**394**	**376**	trigonometry
law of sines	**389**		

SKILLS AND CONCEPTS

OBJECTIVES AND EXAMPLES	REVIEW EXERCISES

Upon completing this chapter, you should be able to:

■ find the geometric mean between two numbers. **(Lesson 8-1)**

Find the geometric mean between 28 and 44. Let x represent the geometric mean.

$\dfrac{28}{x} = \dfrac{x}{44}$ *Definition of geometric mean*

$x^2 = 1232$ *Cross products*

$x = \sqrt{1232}$

$x \approx 35.1$

The geometric mean between 28 and 44 is $\sqrt{1232}$ or about 35.1.

Use these exercises to review and prepare for the chapter test.

Find the geometric mean for each pair of numbers.   **2.$\sqrt{243} \approx 15.6$**

1. 12 and 27   **18**   **2.** 9 and 27

3. 60 and 52   **4.** 20 and 75

5. 1 and 4   **2**   **6.** 13 and 39

7. 99 and 121   **8.** 8 and 6

9. m and n $\sqrt{mn}$ **10.** $4p$ and $16p$ **$8p$**

3. $\sqrt{3120} \approx 55.9$ **4.**$\sqrt{1500} \approx 38.7$

6.$\sqrt{507} \approx 22.5$ **7.** $\sqrt{11{,}979} \approx 109.4$ **8.**$\sqrt{48} \approx 6.9$

402   Chapter 8

Using the Chapter Summary and Review

The Chapter Summary and Review begins with an alphabetical listing of the new terms that were presented in the chapter. Have students define each term and provide an example of it, if appropriate.

The Skills and Concepts presented in the chapter are reviewed using a side-by-side format. Encourage students to refer to the Objectives and Examples on the left as they complete the Review Exercises on the right.

The Chapter Summary and Review ends with exercises that review Applications and Connections.

- solve problems involving relationships between parts of a right triangle and an altitude. **(Lesson 8-1)**

If $\triangle ABC$ is a right triangle with altitude $\overline{BD}$, then the following relationships hold true.

$$\frac{AD}{BD} = \frac{BD}{DC}$$

$$\frac{AC}{BC} = \frac{BC}{DC}$$

$$\frac{AC}{AB} = \frac{AB}{AD}$$

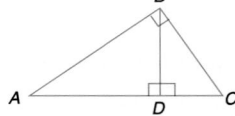

Use right triangle *KLM* and the given information to solve each problem.
See margin.

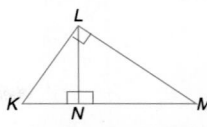

11. Find LN if $KN = 4$ and $NM = 6$.

12. Find KL if $KM = 18$ and $KN = 4$.

13. Find LM if $KN = 7$ and $NM = 3$.

14. Find LK if $KN = \frac{1}{3}$ and $NM = \frac{1}{4}$.

15. Find KM if $LM = 19$ and $NM = 14$.

16. Find KN if $LK = 0.6$ and $KM = 1.5$.

- use the Pythagorean Theorem and its converse. **(Lesson 8-2)**

A right triangle has a hypotenuse 61 inches long and a leg 11 inches long. Find the length of the other leg.

$$a^2 + b^2 = c^2$$
$$a^2 + 11^2 = 61^2$$
$$a^2 + 121 = 3721$$
$$a^2 = 3600$$
$$a = 60$$

The other leg is 60 inches long.

Find the measure of the hypotenuse of a right triangle with legs of the given measure. Round your answers to the nearest tenth.

17. 7.1, 6.7 **9.8**   **18.** 9.4, 8.0 **12.3**

19. 8.0, 15.0 **17.0**   **20.** 94, 88 **128.8**

Determine whether a triangle with sides having the given measures is a right triangle.

21. 9, 21, 23 **no**   **22.** 4, 7.5, 8.5 **yes**

23. 17, 144, 145 **yes**   **24.** 19, 24, 30 **no**

- use the properties of 30°-60°-90° and 45°-45°-90° triangles. **(Lesson 8-3)**

In a 45°-45°-90° triangle, the hypotenuse is $\sqrt{2}$ times as long as a leg.

In a 30°-60°-90° triangle, the hypotenuse is twice as long as the shorter leg and the longer leg is $\sqrt{3}$ times as long as the shorter leg.

Find the value of *x*.

25.

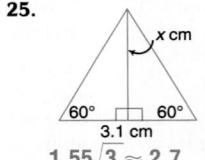

$1.55\sqrt{3} \approx 2.7$

26.

$3\sqrt{2} \approx 4.2$

27.

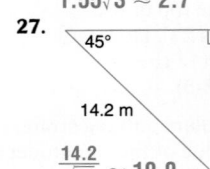

$\frac{14.2}{\sqrt{2}} \approx 10.0$

28.

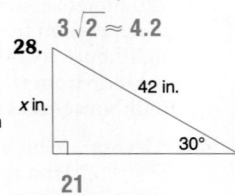

21

Alternate Review Strategy
To provide a brief in-class review, you may wish to read the following questions to the class and have them answer verbally.

1. What is the geometric mean between 5 and 15?
   $\sqrt{75} \approx 8.66$
2. In right $\triangle QRS$, $\overline{QT}$ is the altitude to the hypotenuse. What is the measure of $\overline{QT}$ if the segments of the hypotenuse measure 8 cm and 20 cm? $\sqrt{160}$ **or 12.6 cm**
3. The legs of a right triangle measure 7 inches and 10 inches. Find the length of the hypotenuse to the nearest tenth. **12.2 inches**
4. Can a right triangle have sides of 2.5 mm, 2 mm, and 1.5 mm long? **yes**
5. The legs of an isosceles right triangle measure 6 cm each. Find the length of the hypotenuse to the nearest tenth. **8.5 cm**
6. The side of an equilateral triangle measures 9 meters. Find the length of its altitude.
   $4.5\sqrt{3} \approx$ **7.8 m**
7. In a right triangle, the side opposite $\angle Y$ measures 14 cm, and the hypotenuse measures 20 cm. Find m$\angle Y$. $\approx$ **44**
8. In $\triangle ABC$, m$\angle A = 24$, m$\angle B = 47$, and $a = 9$ inches. Find b.
   $\approx$ **16 in.**
9. In $\triangle ABC$, m$\angle B = 62$, $a = 10$, and $c = 14$. Find b. $\approx$ **12.8**
10. Use any combination of mathematical symbols and exactly four 4's to make an expression with a value of 7.
    Sample answer: $44 \div 4 - 4$

Additional Answers

11. $LM = \sqrt{24} \approx 4.9$
12. $KL = \sqrt{72} \approx 8.5$
13. $LM = \sqrt{30} \approx 5.5$
14. $KL = \frac{\sqrt{7}}{6} \approx 0.4$
15. $KM \approx 25.8$
16. $KN = 0.24$

A two-page Cumulative Review from the *Evaluation Masters* is shown below. It can be used to review skills and concepts presented thus far in the text. Standardized Test Practice Questions are also provided in the *Evaluation Masters*.

Evaluation Masters, pp. 109-110

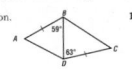

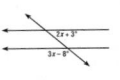

(Cumulative Review worksheet pages 109 and 110, Glencoe Division, Macmillan/McGraw-Hill)

OBJECTIVES AND EXAMPLES	REVIEW EXERCISES

■ find and use trigonometric ratios.
(Lesson 8-4)

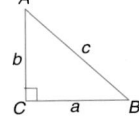

$$\sin A = \frac{a}{c}$$

$$\cos A = \frac{b}{c}$$

$$\tan A = \frac{a}{b}$$

Find the indicated trigonometric ratio as a fraction and as a decimal rounded to the nearest thousandth. See margin.

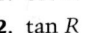
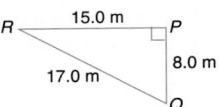

29. $\sin Q$
30. $\tan Q$
31. $\cos R$
32. $\tan R$

■ use the law of sines to solve triangles.
(Lesson 8-6)

According to the law of sines,

$$\frac{\sin A}{a} = \frac{\sin B}{b} = \frac{\sin C}{c}$$

Use the law of sines to solve each △ABC. See margin.
33. $m\angle B = 46, m\angle C = 83, b = 65$
34. $a = 80, b = 10, m\angle A = 65$
35. $a = 4.2, b = 6.8, m\angle B = 22$

■ use the law of cosines to solve triangles.
(Lesson 8-7)

According to the law of cosines,

$$a^2 = b^2 + c^2 - 2bc \cos A$$
$$b^2 = a^2 + c^2 - 2ac \cos B$$
$$c^2 = a^2 + b^2 - 2ab \cos C$$

Use the law of cosines to solve each △ABC. See margin.
36. $m\angle C = 55, a = 8, b = 12$
37. $a = 44, c = 32, m\angle B = 44$
38. $m\angle C = 78, a = 4.5, b = 4.9$
39. $a = 6, b = 9, c = 8$

Applications and Connections

40. Recreation Dana is flying a kite whose string is making a 70° angle with the ground. The kite string is 65 meters long. How far is the kite above the ground? **(Lesson 8-5)** about 61 m

41. Transportation A railroad track rises 30 feet for every 400 feet of track. What is the measure of the angle the track makes with the horizontal? **(Lesson 8-5)** about 4°

42. Navigation The top of a lighthouse is 120 meters above sea level. The angle of depression from the top of the lighthouse to a ship is 23°. How far is the ship from the foot of the lighthouse? **(Lesson 8-5)** about 283 m

43. Aviation Jim Paul flew his airplane 1000 kilometers north before turning 20° clockwise and flying another 700 kilometers. How far is Mr. Paul from his starting point? **(Lesson 8-7)** about 1675 km

44. Algebra Which problem-solving strategies might you use to find the remainder for $5^{100} \div 7$? Find the value of the remainder for $5^{100} \div 7$. **(Lesson 8-8)** Answers may vary. A typical answer is look for a pattern; 2

Additional Answers

29. $\frac{15}{17} \approx 0.882$

30. $\frac{15}{8} = 1.875$

31. $\frac{15}{17} \approx 0.882$

32. $\frac{8}{15} \approx 0.533$

33. $m\angle A = 51, c \approx 89.7, a \approx 70.2$

34. $m\angle B \approx 7, m\angle C \approx 108, c \approx 83.9$

35. $m\angle A \approx 13, m\angle C \approx 145, c \approx 10.4$

36. $c \approx 9.9, m\angle A \approx 41, m\angle B \approx 84$

37. $b \approx 30.6, m\angle A \approx 89, m\angle C \approx 47$

38. $c \approx 5.9, m\angle A \approx 48, m\angle B \approx 54$

39. $m\angle A \approx 41, m\angle B \approx 79, m\angle C \approx 60$

Find the geometric mean for each pair of numbers.

1. 3 and 12 **6**

2. 5 and 4 $\sqrt{20} \approx$ **4.5**

3. 28 and 56 $28\sqrt{2} \approx$ **39.6**

Use the figure below and the given information to solve each problem. Round your answers to the nearest tenth.

4. Find QS if $PS = 8$ and $SR = 5$. **6.3**

5. Find QP if $SP = 9.5$ and $SR = 3$. **10.9**

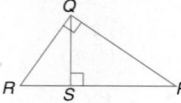

Find the measure of the hypotenuse of a right triangle with legs of the given measures. Round your answers to the nearest tenth.

6. 39, 80 **89**

7. 1.5, 11.2 **11.3**

8. 6.9, 7.2 **10.0**

9. 14.7, 18.1 **23.3**

Find the value of x.

10. 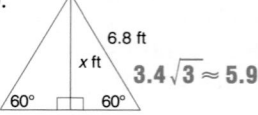 6.8 ft, x ft, 60°, 60° $3.4\sqrt{3} \approx$ **5.9**

11. 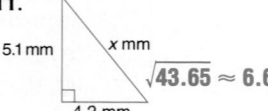 5.1 mm, x mm, 4.2 mm $\sqrt{43.65} \approx$ **6.6**

12. 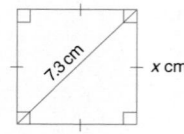 7.3 cm, x cm $\dfrac{7.3}{\sqrt{2}} \approx$ **5.2**

Find the indicated trigonometric ratio as a fraction and as a decimal rounded to the nearest thousandth. **See margin.**

13. $\sin A$

14. $\tan B$

15. $\cos A$

16. $\tan A$

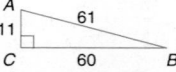 A, 61, 11, C, 60, B

17. **Fire Fighting** A fire fighter's 36-foot ladder leans against a building. The top of the ladder touches the building 28 feet above the ground. What is the measure of the angle the ladder forms with the ground? **about 51**

18. The longest side of a triangle is 30 centimeters long. Two of the angles have measures of 45 and 79. Find the measures of the other two sides and the remaining angle. **sides: 21.6, 25.3; angle: 56**

19. **Gemology** A jeweler is making a sapphire earring in the shape of an isosceles triangle with sides 22, 22, and 28 millimeters long. What is the measure of the vertex angle? **about 79**

20. **Algebra** Which problem-solving strategy might you use to find the fraction of the odd whole numbers less than 100 that are perfect squares? Find the fraction. **Answers may vary. A typical answer is make a list;** $\dfrac{5}{50}$ **or** $\dfrac{1}{10}$

Bonus Find $\sin A$, $\cos A$, and $\tan A$. **See Solutions Manual.**

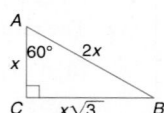 A, 60°, $2x$, x, C, $x\sqrt{3}$, B

Test and Review Generator software is provided in Apple, IBM, and Macintosh versions. You may use this software to create your own tests or worksheets, based on the needs of your students.

The **Performance Assessment Booklet** provides an alternate assessment for evaluating student progress. An assessment for this chapter can be found on pages 15-16.

Additional Answers

13. $\sin A = \dfrac{60}{61} \approx 0.984$

14. $\tan B = \dfrac{11}{60} \approx 0.183$

15. $\cos A = \dfrac{11}{61} \approx 0.180$

16. $\tan A = \dfrac{60}{11} \approx 5.455$

Using the Chapter Test

This page may be used as a test or as a review. In addition, two multiple-choice tests (Forms 1A and 1B) and two free-response tests (Forms 2A and 2B) are provided in the *Evaluation Masters*. Chapter 8 Test, Form 1A is shown below.

Evaluation Masters, pp. 99-100

NAME _____ DATE _____

Chapter 8 Test, Form 1A

Write the letter for the correct answer in the blank at the right of each problem.

1. Find the geometric mean between 5 and 9.
   A. 45   B. $\sqrt{45}$ C. 7   D. $22\frac{1}{2}$ 1. __B__

For questions 2 to 4, refer to the figure at the right.

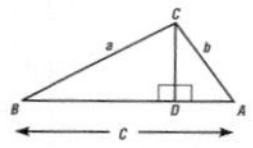

2. If $CD = 12$ and $AD = 9$, find BD.
   A. 16   B. 9   C. $6\sqrt{3}$ D. 4   2. __A__

3. If $AD = 9$ and $AB = 25$, find AC.
   A. $\sqrt{15}$ B. 3.26   C. 8.3   D. 15   3. __D__

4. If $a = 24$ and $c = 26$, find b.
   A. 35.4   B. 50   C. 10   D. 25   4. __C__

5. Determine which set of numbers can be the measures of the sides of a right triangle.
   A. 3, 5, 7   B. 13, 14, 15   C. 15, 36, 39   D. 5, 10, 13   5. __C__

6. In a right triangle, the measures of the legs are 9 and $x + 8$, and the measure of the hypotenuse is $x + 9$. Find the value of x.
   A. 32   B. 12   C. 64   D. 15   6. __A__

7. The length of a rectangle is 2 cm, and the width is 1 cm. Find the length of a diagonal.
   A. 3 cm   B. $\sqrt{5}$ cm   C. 25 cm   D. $\sqrt{3}$ cm   7. __B__

8. The measure of each leg of an isosceles right triangle is 3. Find the measure of the hypotenuse.
   A. $2\sqrt{3}$ B. $\frac{3\sqrt{3}}{2}$ C. $3\sqrt{2}$ D. $\frac{2\sqrt{3}}{3}$ 8. __C__

9. The measure of an altitude of an equilateral triangle is $4\sqrt{3}$. Find the perimeter.
   A. 24   B. $12 + 4\sqrt{3}$ C. $12\sqrt{3}$ D. 36   9. __A__

10. Find the length of a diagonal of a cube that has edges of length 6 in.
    A. $6\sqrt{5}$ in.   B. $3\sqrt{6}$ in.   C. $6\sqrt{3}$ in.   D. 6 in.   10. __C__

99
Glencoe Division, Macmillan/McGraw-Hill

NAME _____ DATE _____

Chapter 8 Test, Form 1A (continued)

For questions 11 and 12, refer to the figure at the right.

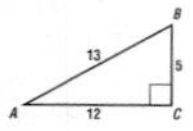

11. Find $\sin A$.
    A. $\frac{5}{12}$ B. $\frac{5}{13}$ C. $\frac{12}{13}$ D. $\frac{12}{5}$ 11. __B__

12. Find $m\angle B$ to the nearest degree.
    A. 22   B. 24   C. 67   D. 76   12. __C__

13. In $\triangle RST$, R is the right angle. If $\cos T = \frac{4}{5}$, find $\tan S$.
    A. $\frac{5}{4}$ B. $\frac{3}{4}$ C. $\frac{4}{3}$ D. $\frac{4}{5}$ 13. __C__

14. Sam is flying a kite on a 40-meter string. The angle of elevation of the kite measures 35°, and Sam's hand is 1.8 m above the ground. About how high is the kite off the ground.
    A. 21.1 m   B. 22.9 m   C. 23.7 m   D. 24.7 m   14. __D__

15. In $\triangle ABC$, $a = 7$, $b = 5$, and $m\angle A = 42$. Find $m\angle B$ to the nearest degree.
    A. 21   B. 29   C. 70   D. 109   15. __B__

16. In $\triangle ABC$, $m\angle A = 54$, $m\angle B = 68$, and $c = 21$. Find b to the nearest whole unit.
    A. 19   B. 23   C. 25   D. 29   16. __B__

17. In $\triangle ABC$, $a = 12$, $b = 16$, and $m\angle C = 78$. Find c to the nearest tenth of a unit.
    A. 79.8   B. 50.1   C. 28.5   D. 17.9   17. __D__

18. The measures of the sides of a triangle are 10, 7, and 9. Find the measure of the largest angle to the nearest degree.
    A. 13   B. 76   C. 61   D. 43   18. __B__

19. Choose the most efficient strategy for solving the following problem.
    What is the remainder when 3^{16} is divided by 4?
    A. look for a pattern   B. draw a diagram
    C. work backwards   D. make a chart   19. __A__

20. Solve the problem in question 19.
    A. 0   B. 1   C. 2   D. 3   20. __B__

Bonus

$\triangle PQR$ is a right triangle with acute angles P and R. If $\tan P = \frac{b}{a}$, what is the value of $\sin R$?
    A. $\frac{1}{\sqrt{10}}$ B. $\frac{3}{\sqrt{10}}$ C. $\frac{1}{3}$ D. 3   Bonus __B__

100
Glencoe Division, Macmillan/McGraw-Hill

The questions on these pages may be used to help students prepare for college entrance exams such as the SAT test. These questions require careful analysis and a thorough understanding of the concepts.

These pages can be used as an overnight assignment.

After students have completed the pages, discuss how each problem can be solved, or provide copies of the solutions from the *Merrill Geometry Solutions Manual*.

College Entrance Exam Preview

Directions: Choose the one best answer. Write A, B, C, or D. You may use a calculator.

1. In $\triangle ABC$, $AB = 8$ and $BC = 12$. Which one of the following cannot be the measure of $\overline{AC}$?

D

(A) 5   (B) 8

(C) 12   (D) 20

2. $\dfrac{1}{x} - \dfrac{2}{y} =$

B

(A) $-\dfrac{1}{xy}$ (B) $\dfrac{y - 2x}{xy}$

(C) $\dfrac{-1}{x - y}$ (D) $\dfrac{1}{y - x}$

3.

C

If $\overline{AE} \parallel \overline{BD}$, $AB = 10$, $BC = x$, $ED = x + 3$, and $DC = x + 6$, then $x =$

(A) 6   (B) 7

(C) 12   (D) 15

4. The graph of $2x - y - 8 = 0$ crosses the x-axis at $x =$

A

(A) 4   (B) 8

(C) -2   (D) -4

5. If $x - \dfrac{2}{x - 3} = \dfrac{x - 1}{3 - x}$, then $x =$

C

(A) 3 or -1   (B) 3 or -3

(C) -1   (D) 3

6. Find all a such that $|-a| = 7$.

C

(A) 7   (B) -7

(C) 7 and -7   (D) no such a exists

7. If $\triangle ACB \cong \triangle STU$, then

D

     I. $\overline{AB} \cong \overline{SU}$

     II. $\angle C \cong \angle S$

     III. $\overline{AC} \cong \overline{TS}$

(A) I only

(B) II only

(C) III only

(D) I and III only

8.

A

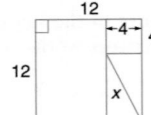

Which inequality gives the best approximation for x?

(A) $8 < x < 9$ (B) $9 < x < 10$

(C) $10 < x < 11$ (D) $11 < x < 12$

9. The measures of the sides of four triangles are given. Which one is not a right triangle?

C

(A) 5, 12, 13   (B) 8, 15, 17

(C) 12, 15, 18   (D) 9, 40, 41

10. The ninth term of the sequence 5, 6, 8, 11, 15, 20, 26, 33, . . . is

D

(A) 60   (B) 51

(C) 48   (D) 41

11. @ is defined so that $x @ y = x^2 + xy$. The value of $8 @ 2$ is

B

(A) 20   (B) 80

(C) 48   (D) -12

12. The ratio of $\dfrac{1}{3}$ to $\dfrac{5}{12}$ is

A

(A) 4 to 5   (B) 1 to 4

(C) 5 to 4   (D) 5 to 36

Solve each of the following. You may use a calculator.

13. Kelsey has taken four tests in English class this semester. Her scores were 82, 81, 79, and 87. A student must have a test average of 85 to receive a B in the class. What must Kelsey score on the next test to receive a B? **96**

14. In the figure below, $\overline{AB}$ and $\overline{CD}$ are parallel line segments. Find the area of trapezoid $ABCD$. **76 square units**

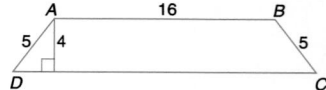

15. Right triangles ABC and DEF are similar. If $BC = 9$, $AC = 21$, and $EF = 24$, find DF. **56 units**

16. Mr. Pearson can wash his car in 30 minutes. His daughter Jan can do the job in 20 minutes. How long will it take them to wash the car if they work together? **12 minutes**

17. $^*x$ is defined as $^*x = x^2 + 5x$. Find the value of $^*5 - {}^*(-1)$. **54**

18. One tenth of the water in a fish bowl evaporates in the first day after it is filled. The second day, one-twelfth of the remaining water evaporates. What fraction of the original amount of water remains after the second day? $\dfrac{33}{40}$

19. The corner is cut from a rectangular piece of cardboard as shown below. Find the area of the remaining cardboard. **162 square inches**

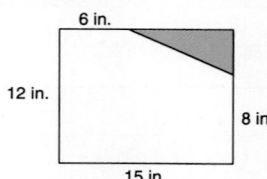

20. Two cars leave from the same place at 8:45 A.M. If both cars travel in the same direction, one car travels at 55 mph, and the other travels at 62 mph, how far apart are they at 11:15 A.M.? **17.5 miles**

C H A P T E R

9

Circles

PREVIEWING THE CHAPTER

Beginning by defining the parts of a circle, the chapter proceeds by observing relationships among lines, circles, and the coordinate plane. Students analyze the relationships among parts of a circle and between arcs and angles. Arcs and chords are then examined, and theorems about these relationships are introduced. Inscribed angles and their measures are investigated next, followed by a discussion of tangents. After some work with constructions, the chapter concludes with an application of the properties of chords, secants, and tangents.

Problem-Solving Strategy Students learn that solving problems can be facilitated when the data is organized and presented *in a graph*.

Lesson Objective Chart

Lesson (Pages)	Lesson Objectives	State/Local Objectives
9-1 (410-415)	**9-1A**: Name parts of circles.	
	9-1B: Determine relationships between lines and circles.	
	9-1C: Write an equation of a circle in the coordinate plane.	
9-2 (416-421)	**9-2A**: Recognize major or minor arcs or semicircles.	
	9-2B: Find the measures of arcs and central angles.	
9-3 (422-427)	**9-3**: Recognize and use relationships between arcs, chords, and diameters.	
9-4 (428-433)	**9-4A**: Recognize and find the measure of inscribed angles.	
	9-4B: Use properties of inscribed figures.	
9-5 (434-439)	**9-5**: Use properties of tangents to solve problems.	
9-6 (440-446)	**9-6**: Find the measure of angles formed by intersecting secants and tangents in relation to intercepted arcs.	
9-7 (447-453)	**9-7**: Use properties of chords, secants, and tangents to solve problems.	
9-8 (455-457)	**9-8**: Solve problems by using graphs.	

ORGANIZING THE CHAPTER

You may want to refer to the **Course Planning Calendar** on page T28.

Lesson Planning Guide / Blackline Masters Booklets

Lesson (Pages)	Course I	Course II	Course III	Reteaching	Practice	Enrichment	Evaluation	Technology	Lab Manual	Mixed Problem Solving	Applications	Cooperative Learning Activity	Multicultural	Transparencies
9-1 (410-415)	1.5	1.5	1	p. 50	p. 58	p. 50		p. 45						9-1
9-2 (416-421)	1.5	1.5	1.5	p. 51	p. 59	p. 51	Quiz A, p.121				p. 23			9-2
9-3 (422-427)	2	2	1.5	p. 52	p. 60	p. 52						p. 37		9-3
9-4 (428-433)	2	1.5	1.5	p. 53	p. 61	p. 53	Quiz B, p.121 Mid Chapter Test, p.125		pp.66-69					9-4
9-5 (434-439)	2	1.5	1.5	p. 54	p. 62	p. 54								9-5
9-6 (440-446)	2	2	1.5	p. 55	p. 63	p. 55	Quiz C, p. 122						p. 9	9-6
9-7 (447-453)	2	2	1.5	p. 56	p. 64	p. 56		p. 9						9-7
9-8 (455-457)	1	1	1		p. 65		Quiz D, p. 122			p. 9				9-8
Review (458-460)	1	1	1	Multiple Choice Tests, Forms 1A and 1B, pp. 113-116 Free Response Tests, Forms 2A and 2B, pp. 117-120										
Test (461)	1	1	1	Cumulative Review. pp. 123-124 Standardized Tests Practice Questions, p. 126										

Course I: Chapters 1-11; Course II: Chapters 1-12; Course III: Chapters 1-13

Other Chapter Resources

Student Edition

Chapter Opener, pp. 408-409
Journal Entry, pp. 415, 427
History Connection, p. 421
Mid-Chapter Review, p. 433
Portfolio, p. 453
Technology, p. 454
Cooperative Learning Project, p. 457
Algebra Review, pp. 462-463
More Investigations in Geometry, p. A10
Extended Project 3, pp. B10-B13

Teacher's Classroom Resources

Transparency 9-0
Real World Applications Transparencies, 18, 19
Performance Assessment Booklet, pp. 15-16
Problem-of-the-Week Activity Cards, 24, 25, 26
Tech Prep Applications Booklet, pp. 15-16
LOGO Instruction Materials, Technology Masters pp. 19-36

Other Supplements

Algebra and Geometry Overhead Manipulative Resources
Glencoe Mathematics Professional Series

Software

Test and Review Generator (Apple, IBM, and Macintosh)
Teacher's Guide for Software Resources

ENHANCING THE CHAPTER

Cooperative Learning

Specifying Desired Student Behaviors and Monitoring that Behavior

To make sure that students exhibit the group skills required for a successful cooperative-learning experience, you should clearly define the expected behaviors at the outset. Initially, skills will include the more obvious, such as "stay with your group," "use quiet voices," and "take turns when speaking." As groups begin to operate more effectively, add other expected behaviors, such as "criticize ideas, not people," "encourage everyone to participate," "use names and look at other members when speaking," "paraphrase statements made by others," "ask for elaboration," "probe by asking in-depth questions," "check to make sure every member understands and can explain the material," and so on. Group-learning sessions are not opportunities for the teacher to relax and, in fact, often require more diligence and self-control of the teacher than other modes of instruction. The teacher should spend the time observing the groups as they work to identify problems they are having with the assignment and in working cooperatively. Keeping a written record of the observations made can provide the teacher with a useful guide for planning future activities, for assigning roles to different students, for defining additional goals to be achieved, and for conducting conferences with individual students or their parents.

Technology

The Technology Feature following Lesson 9-7 employs the *Geometric Supposer: Circles* software from Sunburst to investigate some relationships in circles. Students are led through a series of steps to investigate products that are called *the power of the point*. Students are asked to use the results of their investigations to answer several questions about the power of a point.

Critical Thinking

Complementing Bloom's research (1956) that led to his taxonomy is the research done by Williams (1969) in which he identified eight student behaviors involving creative thinking: the four cognitive factors are *fluency, flexibility, originality,* and *elaboration*; and the four affective factors are *risk taking, complexity, curiosity,* and *imagination.* Brainstorming activities, creative problem writing, paraphrasing and elaboration, making and testing predictions, justifying conclusions, and seeking many alternatives are just some ways to encourage positive behavior. Remember that all such behaviors are cultivated best when students are encouraged to explore, express different opinions, and define ideas in a nonjudgmental environment.

Cooperative Learning, p. 37

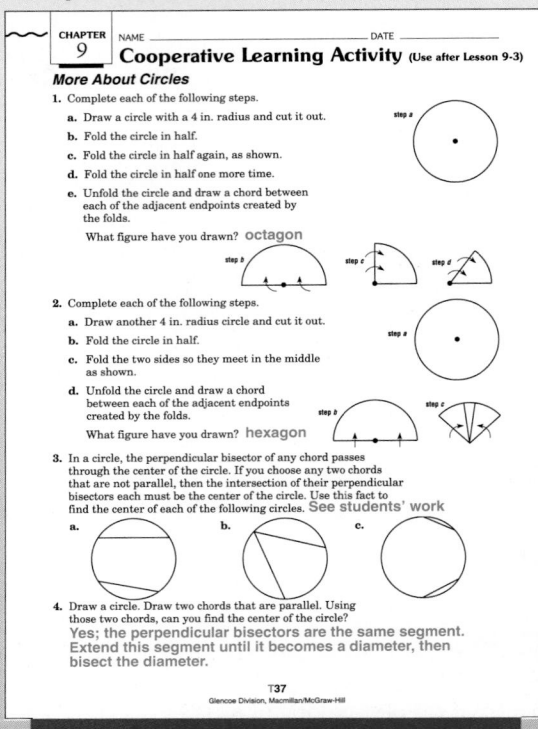

Technology, p. 45

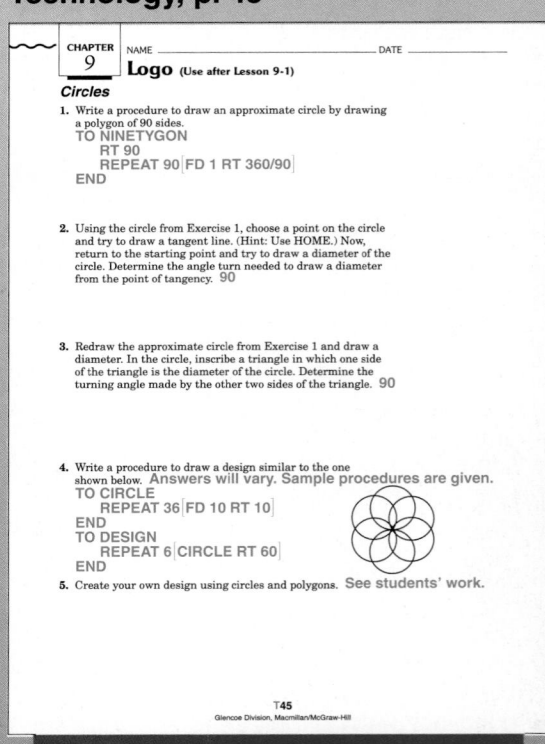

Problem of the Week Activity

The card shown below is one of three available for this chapter. It can be used as a class or small group activity.

Activity Card

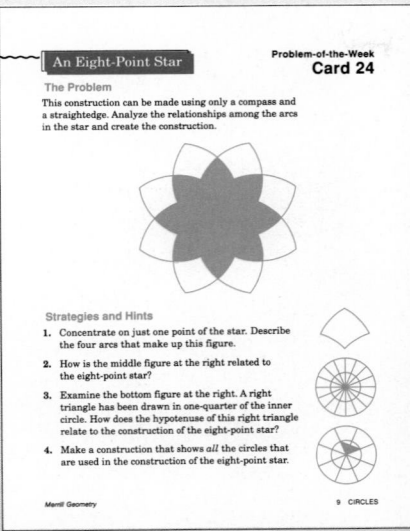

An Eight-Point Star

Problem-of-the-Week
Card 24

The Problem

This construction can be made using only a compass and a straightedge. Analyze the relationships among the arcs in the star and create the construction.

Strategies and Hints

1. Concentrate on just one point of the star. Describe the four arcs that make up this figure.

2. How is the middle figure at the right related to the eight-point star?

3. Examine the bottom figure at the right. A right triangle has been drawn in one-quarter of the inner circle. How does the hypotenuse of this right triangle relate to the construction of the eight-point star?

4. Make a construction that shows *all* the circles that are used in the construction of the eight-point star.

Merrill Geometry   9 CIRCLES

Manipulatives and Models

The following materials may be used as models or manipulatives in Chapter 9.

- string, chalk (Lesson 9-1)
- compass, straightedge (Lesson 9-3)
- protractor (Lesson 9-4)
- carpenter's square (Lesson 9-5)

Outside Resources

Books/Periodicals

Brandes, Louis G. *Geometry Can Be Fun.* Weston Walch.

O'Daffer, P. and S. Clemens. *Geometry: An Investigative Approach.* Addison-Wesley Publishing Co.

Reid, C. *A Long Way from Euclid.* Thomas Y. Crowell.

Films/Videotapes/Videodiscs

Circles, Semicircles, Ellipses, Coronet Instructional Films, 108 Wilmot Dr., Deerfield, IL 60015

Probability, TV Ontario/USA, 143 W. Franklin St., Suite 206, Chapel Hill, NC 27514

The Story of Pi, California Institute of Technology Bookstore, I-51, Pasadena, CA 91125

Software

Geometric Supposer: Circles, WINGS for Learning/Sunburst, 101 Castleton St., Pleasantville, NY 10570

Multicultural

Multicultural Activity, p. 9

CHAPTER 9 — NAME _____ DATE _____

Multicultural Activity (Use after Lesson 9-6)

The National Census

Every 10 years, the United States government studies its population trends by conducting a national census. The census gives us many facts about our country, such as the rate at which various ethnic groups are growing, our educational achievements, nuclear family trends, and the jobs of the future.

According to the 1990 census, the total population of the United States was estimated to be 251,367,000. Of this, 17.5 million, or about 7% of all Americans, were counted as Hispanic. A Hispanic was defined as someone of Spanish origin. The majority of American Hispanics live in metropolitan areas. African-Americans were counted at 28.5 million, or about 11% of all Americans.

Use the information in the table below for the exercises that follow.

THE 10 MOST-POPULATED STATES OF THE UNITED STATES (1990 Census)

State	Population	% Hispanic	Total Hispanic	% African-American	Total African-American
California	29,627,000	19.8	5,866,000	7.0	2,074,000
Texas	17,973,000	20.5	3,684,000	10.6	1,910,000
New York	17,789,000	10.6	1,886,000	15.4	2,733,000
Florida	13,098,000	8.4	1,100,000	11.9	1,565,000
Pennsylvania	11,806,000	1.3	153,000	9.3	1,102,000
Illinois	11,622,000	6.5	755,000	15.3	1,775,000
Ohio	10,792,000	1.0	108,000	10.5	1,136,000
Michigan	9,314,000	1.7	158,000	13.3	1,243,000
New Jersey	7,971,000	7.2	574,000	12.9	1,025,000
North Carolina	6,777,000	0.6	41,000	20.5	1,392,000

1. Calculate the total Hispanic population of each state. Round to the nearest thousand. **See chart.**

2. Calculate the percent of African-Americans in each state. Round to the nearest tenth of a percent. **See chart.**

3. Name the state above that had the most Hispanics. **California**

4. Use the library to find information on how the data above compares with the 1980 census. Make a circle graph that shows a breakdown of the population by ethnic origin. **See students' work.**

Lab Manual

Lab Activity, pp. 66-69

Name _____   Activity 13 Worksheet
                                                   Page 1

Inscribed Angles

1. Discuss the measures of the central angles in the figures below with your partner.

   a.   b.   c.   d.

2. Connect the endpoints of the intercepted arcs in the figures of question 1, and record the measures of the other two angles.

   a. _____   b. _____

   c. _____   d. _____

3. Model the figure below on your geoboard and complete the following:

   measure of AB = _____

   measure of BC = _____

   measure of AC = _____

   How do the arc measures compare to the measures of their respective central angles?

4. Model two congruent inscribed angles on your geoboard.

   What is true about their intercepted arcs? _____

   Compare your model with your partner's design. Are they the same? _____

   List possible conclusions from your models. _____

67
Glencoe Division, Macmillan/McGraw-Hill

Using the Chapter Opener

This two-page introduction to the chapter provides students with an opportunity to see how geometry is used throughout the world in various cultures. **Transparency 9-0**, available in the *Merrill Geometry Transparency Package*, provides another full-color visual and motivational activity that you can use to engage your students in the mathematical content of the chapter.

Multicultural Notes

North America and Greenland
The Igluligarjumiut Eskimos of Canada cut hard-packed snow into blocks with a long knife. The blocks are laid against one another in a spiral until a circular, dome-shaped igloo is constructed. Gaps are filled in with loose snow. The interior walls may be covered with skins, which permits the interior to be heated to a comfortable 15° Celsius without melting the structure.

Central Asia The Kazakhs are the largest ethnic group in Central Asia. Prior to Soviet control, they lived in circular tents, called *yurts*. The walls of a yurt are based on collapsible trellises about four feet high, enclosing a circular area about 20 feet in diameter. The roof is a shallow dome tied to the wall of trellises and supported by stakes. Wool felt covers the framework.

Chapter Project

Materials posterboard, glue, 12 lids from small jars, 2 larger lids, dried beans

Procedure Organize students into cooperative groups or pairs to construct and play an African game, *wari*. Have students collect 12 small metal or plastic lids and two larger lids. Have them glue two rows of six lids to posterboard and one large lid at each end of the two rows.

Two players face each other and begin the game of wari by placing four beans in each of their six lids. A player's territory includes the six lids in the row on his or her side and the large lid at the right. Players take turns scooping up all the beans from any cup on their side and "sowing" one bean in

each cup in a counter clockwise direction, begining with the cup adjoining the empty one. If a player drops the last bean in an enemy cup containing only one or two beans, he or she captures the two or three beans in the cup, as well as all the beans in all enemy cups that have only two or three beans, going clockwise in an unbroken sequence. The captured beans are placed in the large lid at the player's right.

Circles

CHAPTER OBJECTIVES

In this chapter, you will:
- Write equations of circles in the coordinate plane.
- Find the measures of arcs and angles in circles.
- Use properties of chords, tangents, and secants to solve problems.
- Solve problems by using graphs.

GEOMETRY AROUND THE WORLD
Kenya

What shape is your home or apartment? If you're like most Americans, its shape is basically square or rectangular. The sharp angles that characterize our buildings aren't the only home designs around, however. If you were a member of the Kikuyu, Zulu, or any of several other African tribes, your house would be round.

Because you probably haven't seen one, a circular home may sound strange. However, in areas where building materials are scarce, as they are in many parts of Africa, the circle design makes perfect sense. Why? Of all the closed geometric shapes, a circle encompasses the greatest area within a given perimeter. For this reason, U.S. architects often use a variation of a circular design called a geodesic dome to cover sports stadiums and other large public spaces.

Can you guess what geometric pattern was used to lay out the design of many African villages? A circle! Many old Zulu towns were built in a circle of 1400 round structures four or five buildings deep.

GEOMETRY IN ACTION

Like the Zulu, the Kikuyu, who live in the foothills of Mount Kenya, build comfortable, sturdy, round homes with thatched roofs. Before erecting their homes, the Kikuyu mark a circle 14 feet in diameter on the ground. Then they dig 19 holes for roof-supporting posts equal distances apart, with a wider space allowed for the door.

Turn to Lesson 9-1 of this chapter and use what you learn to write the equation for the circle of a Kikuyu home. Assume that the center of the circle is at (0, 0). $x^2 + y^2 = 49$

Because their homes are round, Kikuyu children who misbehave never have to stand in the corner!

◀ *Kikuyu village*   Inset: *Member of Zulu tribe*

409

Connections and Applications

Lesson	Connections (C) and Applications (A)	Examples	Exercises
9-1	A: Agriculture	1	
	A: Crafts		51
	A: Smart Shopping		52
9-2	C: Statistics	1	66
	A: Food		63
	A: Engineering		64
	A: Teaching		65
9-3	A: Entertainment	1	
	A: Food		42
	A: Crafts		43-44
9-4	A: Carpentry	2	
	A: Engineering		55
9-5	A: Aerospace	1	
	C: Algebra		40
	A: Agriculture		42
	A: Literature		43
9-6	A: Recreation	2	
	A: Navigation		57
9-7	A: Mechanics	1	
	A: Carpentry		36
	A: Space		37
	A: Water Management		38
	A: Architecture		39

The game ends when one player captures at least twenty-five beans or an opponent's cups are all empty. A few final beans circulating endlessly around the board are divided between the two players, each going to the player who is moving it.

Have the class discuss strategies for playing and winning wari. Consider holding wari tournaments. To make more permanent game boards, tack the lids to plywood.

Resources

Denyer, Susan. *African Traditional Architecture*. Africana Publishing Company

Zaslavsky, Claudia. *Africa Counts*. Lawrence Hill and Company

Guidoni, Enrico. *Primitive Architecture*. Harry N. Abrams, Inc.

INTRODUCING THE LESSON

 5-Minute Check

(over Chapter 8)

Solve. Round answers to the nearest tenth.

1. One leg of a right triangle measures 4 inches. The hypotenuse measures 8 inches. Find the length of the other leg.   **6.9 in.**
2. Find the geometric mean between 8 and 25.
   $\sqrt{200} \approx$ **14.1**
3. In right $\triangle RED$, m$\angle R = 51$ and the hypotenuse measures 200 yards. Find the length of the side opposite $\angle R$.   **155.4 yd**
4. In $\triangle ABC$, m$\angle A = 71$, $b = 20$, and $c = 15$. Find a.
   20.7
5. In $\triangle ABC$ above, find m$\angle B$.
   66.0

Motivating the Lesson

Draw a circle and an ellipse or oval on the chalkboard or overhead. Ask students if the two figures are circles. What is the difference between an ellipse and a circle? In a circle, all points on the circle are the same distance from the center.

9-1 Parts of Circles

Objectives

After studying this lesson, you should be able to:
9-1A ▪ name parts of circles,
9-1B ▪ determine relationships between lines and circles, and
9-1C ▪ write an equation of a circle in the coordinate plane.

Application

To irrigate the fields shown in the photograph, water is sprayed from pipes that rotate about central points. Circular patterns result. All the points along the edge of a field are the same distance from the center. Each edge forms a **circle**.

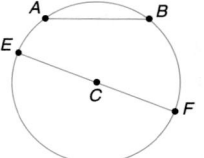

A circle is the set of all points in a plane that are a given distance from a given point in the plane called the **center**. A circle is named by its center. The circle above is called circle C. This is symbolized $\odot C$.

A **chord** of a circle is a segment that has its endpoints on the circle. $\overline{AB}$ is a chord of $\odot C$.

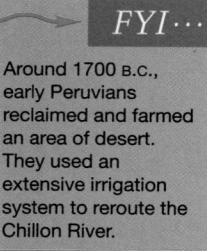

FYI···

Around 1700 B.C., early Peruvians reclaimed and farmed an area of desert. They used an extensive irrigation system to reroute the Chillon River.

A **diameter** of a circle is a chord that contains the center of the circle. $\overline{EF}$ is a diameter of $\odot C$. A **radius** of a circle is a segment with one endpoint at the center of the circle and the other endpoint on the circle. $\overline{EC}$ and $\overline{CF}$ are radii of $\odot C$. *Radii is the plural of radius.*

It follows from the definition of a circle that all the radii of a circle are congruent. Also, all diameters of a circle are congruent.

You should recall that the measure of the diameter, d, is twice the measure of the radius, r. Formulas that relate these measures are

$$d = 2r \text{ and } r = \frac{1}{2}d \text{ or } r = \frac{d}{2}.$$

Example 1

APPLICATION

Agriculture

If the spray of water in the photograph at the top of the page can reach 90 feet, what is the diameter of each circle in the photograph?

$d = 2r$
$d = 2 \cdot 90$ *Substitute 90 for r.*
$d = 180$

The diameter of each circle is 180 feet.

ALTERNATE TEACHING STRATEGIES

Using Manipulatives

Tie a string around a piece of chalk and use it to draw circles on the chalkboard. Hold the string down with your thumb or finger and pull the string tight with the chalk. Now use the chalk to draw a circle. Ask students to explain what the length of the string represents.   **the radius**

Using Experimentation

Have students experiment with tangent lines of two circles. If two circles intersect in one point, how many common external tangents will they have?   **two** How many common internal tangents will they have?   **one** If the circles intersect in two points, how many common external tangents will they have?   **two** How many common internal tangents will they have?   **none**

Example 2

Find the radius and the diameter of the circle shown at the right.

$\odot C$ has center at (3, 4). The circle contains points A(3, 10), B(3, -2), L(-3, 4), and M(9, 4). Chord $\overline{LM}$ is a diameter since it contains the center C. $\overline{LM}$ has a length of 12 units. *Why?*

Therefore, the diameter is 12 units long, and the radius must be 6 units long.

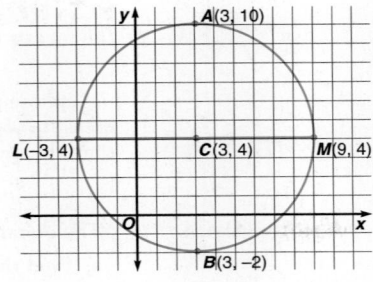

You can use the distance formula to write an equation for a circle given its center and radius. The circle at the right has its center at (-1, 4) and a radius of 5 units. Let $P(x, y)$ be any point on C. Then $\overline{CP}$ is a radius of the circle. The distance between $P(x, y)$ and C(-1, 4) is 5 units.

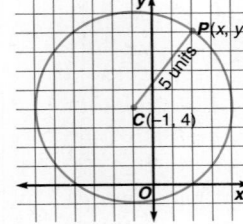

$$PC = 5$$
$$\sqrt{(x - (-1))^2 + (y - 4)^2} = 5 \qquad \textit{Distance formula}$$
$$(x + 1)^2 + (y - 4)^2 = 25 \qquad \textit{Square each side.}$$

Thus, an equation for the circle with center at (-1, 4) and a radius of 5 units is $(x + 1)^2 + (y - 4)^2 = 25$.

Standard Equation of a Circle	**In general, an equation for a circle with center at (h, k) and a radius of r units is $(x - h)^2 + (y - k)^2 = r^2$.**

Example 3

Write an equation for a circle with center at (2, -3) and a diameter of 10 units.

Since $d = 10$, it follows that $r = 5$.

$$(x - h)^2 + (y - k)^2 = r^2 \qquad \textit{General equation of a circle}$$
$$(x - 2)^2 + (y - (-3))^2 = 5^2 \qquad \textit{(h, k) = (2, -3); r = 5}$$
$$(x - 2)^2 + (y + 3)^2 = 25$$

An equation for the circle is $(x - 2)^2 + (y + 3)^2 = 25$.

A circle separates a plane into three parts. The parts are the **interior**, the **exterior**, and the **circle** itself.

Chalkboard Example

For Example 1
If the diameter of each circle at the top of page 410 is 220 feet, how far can the spray of water reach?   110 ft

Teaching Tip Remind students that in this textbook the words *diameter* and *radius* are used to refer to the lengths of these segments as well as to the segments themselves.

Teaching Tip Before stating the general equation of a circle, review the distance formula (Lesson 1-4, page 25).

Chalkboard Examples

For Example 2
Find the radius and diameter of the circle below. $r = 4$, $d = 8$

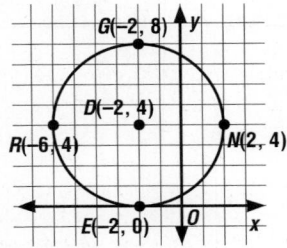

For Example 3
Write an equation for a circle having the given center and diameter measure.
a. (6, 0), 12 $(x - 6)^2 + y^2 = 36$
b. $(-\frac{1}{4}, 6)$, $\sqrt{18}$

$$(x + \frac{1}{4})^2 + (y - 6)^2 = \frac{9}{2}$$

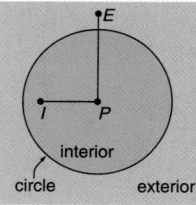

Suppose point I is in the interior of circle P. The measure of the segment joining I to P is less than the measure of the radius; that is, $IP < r$.

Suppose point E is in the exterior of circle P. The measure of the segment joining E to P is greater than the measure of the radius; that is, $EP > r$.

Chalkboard Example

For Example 4
The equation of $\odot L$ is $(x + 3)^2 = 8 - (y - 3)^2$.
a. Find the radius and the coordinates of the center, L.
$r = 2\sqrt{2}$, L (–3, 3)
b. Use the distance formula to determine if $M(-1, 4)$ is on $\odot L$, in its interior, or in its exterior. $LM = \sqrt{5} \approx 2.236$. Since $2.236 < 2\sqrt{2}$, M lies in the interior of L.
c. Sketch the graph of $\odot L$ and point M to verify the location of M.

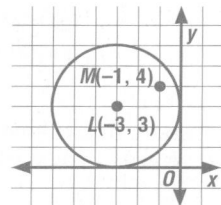

Example 4

The equation of $\odot Q$ is $x^2 + (y + 2)^2 = 16$.

a. Find the radius and the coordinates of the center, Q.

The equation for a circle with center at (h, k) and a radius r units long is $(x - h)^2 + (y - k)^2 = r^2$. The equation for $\odot Q$ can be expressed as $(x - 0)^2 + (y - (-2))^2 = 4^2$. So, the radius is 4 units long and the coordinates of Q are (0, -2).

b. Use the distance formula to determine if $T(4, 3)$ is on $\odot Q$, in its interior, or in its exterior.

$$QT = \sqrt{(4 - 0)^2 + (3 - (-2))^2}$$
$$= \sqrt{16 + 25}$$
$$= \sqrt{41}$$
$$\approx 6.4$$

Since the radius is 4 and $QT \approx 6.4$, $QT > r$. Therefore, T lies in the exterior of $\odot Q$.

c. Sketch the graph of $\odot Q$ and T to verify the location of point T.

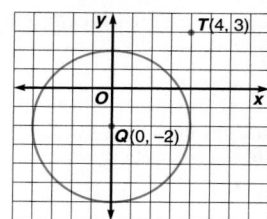

T is in the exterior of $\odot Q$.

A line in the plane of a circle can intersect the circle in one of two ways. A line can intersect a circle in exactly one point. Such a line is called a **tangent** to the circle. In the figure at the right, line ℓ intersects $\odot C$ in exactly one point, T, and is a tangent to $\odot C$.

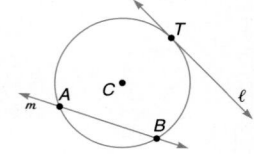

A line can also intersect a circle in exactly two points. Such a line is called a **secant** of the circle. A secant of a circle contains a chord of the circle. In the figure, line m contains the chord $\overline{AB}$ and is a secant of $\odot C$.

Additional Answers

1. **No: A is the center of the circle but it is not on the circle.**

2. **The point stays in one place and is the center of the circle. The tip of the pencil moves around the point, always at the same distance from the point.**

3. **Both tangents and secants are lines that intersect a circle. A tangent intersects a circle in one point, and a secant intersects a circle in two points.**

4a. **The radius is $\sqrt{6}$, because the general equation for a circle is $(x - h)^2 + (y - k)^2 = r^2$.**

4b. **K (–5, 0)**

A line that is tangent to two circles in the same plane is called a **common tangent** of the two circles. There are two types of common tangents.

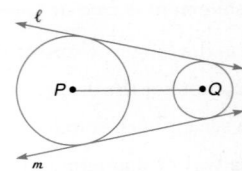

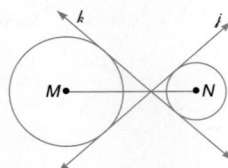

A common tangent that does not intersect the segment whose endpoints are the centers of the circles is a **common external tangent**. In the figure above, lines ℓ and m are common external tangents to $\odot P$ and $\odot Q$.

A common tangent that intersects the segment whose endpoints are the centers of the circles is a **common internal tangent**. In the figure above, lines j and k are common internal tangents to $\odot M$ and $\odot N$.

CHECKING FOR UNDERSTANDING

Communicating Mathematics

Read and study the lesson to answer these questions. See margin.

1. In $\odot A$, is A a part of the circle? Explain your answer.
2. A compass can be used to draw circles. Explain why this works.
3. Compare tangents and secants. How are they alike and/or different?
4. Consider $\odot K$, with equation $(x + 5)^2 + y^2 = 6$.
   a. Is the radius 36 or $\sqrt{6}$? Explain your answer.
   b. What are the coordinates of K?

Guided Practice

Refer to the figure at the right.

5. Name the center of $\odot P$. **P**
6. Name three radii of the circle. $\overline{PD}, \overline{PB}, \overline{PC}$
7. Name a diameter. $\overline{DB}$
8. Name a chord. $\overline{EA}$ or $\overline{DB}$
9. Name a tangent. $\overleftrightarrow{HB}$
10. Name a secant. $\overleftrightarrow{EA}$ or $\overleftrightarrow{BD}$
11. Name two points in the interior of the circle. **G, P**
12. Name two points in the exterior of the circle. **F, H**
13. Name five points that lie on the circle. **A, B, C, D, E**
14. If $PC = 6$, find DB. **12**

Determine the coordinates of the center and the measure of the radius for each circle whose equation is given.

15. $(x + 2)^2 + (y + 7)^2 = 81$
    $(-2, -7), r = 9$

16. $(x + 5)^2 + (y - 7)^2 = 100$
    $(-5, 7), r = 10$

LESSON 9-1 PARTS OF CIRCLES 413

RETEACHING THE LESSON

Review the terminology given in this lesson—circle, center, diameter, radius, chord, secant, tangent, common internal tangent, and common external tangent. Have students state the definition in their own words to see if they understand it.

EVALUATING THE LESSON

Checking for Understanding

Exercises 1-16 are designed to help you assess students' understanding through reading, writing, speaking, and modeling. You should work through Exercises 1-4 with your students and then monitor their work on Exercises 5-16.

Error Analysis

When discussing the equation for a circle, $(x - h)^2 + (y - k)^2 = r^2$, students may have difficulty remembering that the center is (h, k) and not $(-h, -k)$. Remind them that to find the distance between two points (the center and a point on the circle), you must subtract the coordinates.

Closing the Lesson

Speaking Activity Go around the room and have each student state an important aspect relating to one of the terms or equations in this lesson.

Reteaching Masters Booklet, p. 50

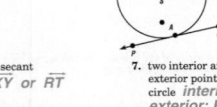

9-1 Reteaching Worksheet

Parts of Circles

A **circle** is the set of all points in a plane that are a given distance from a given point in the plane called the **center**. Various parts of a circle are labeled in the figure at the right. In the coordinate plane, an equation for a circle with center at (h, k) and a radius of r units is $(x - h)^2 + (y - k)^2 = r^2$.

Example: Determine the coordinates of the center and the measure of the radius for the circle whose equation is

$(x + 5)^2 + (y - 4)^2 = 36$.

$(x - h)^2 + (y - k)^2 = r^2$ General equation of a circle
$(x - (-5))^2 + (y - 4)^2 = 6^2$ $(h, k) = (-5, 4), r = 6$

The center is at $(-5, 4)$, and the measure of the radius is 6.

Use the figure at the right to name the following.

1. the center of $\odot S$ S
2. three radii of the circle
   SR, SM, ST
3. a diameter
   RT
4. a chord
   XY, or RT
5. a tangent
   PQ
6. a secant
   XY or RT
7. two interior and two exterior points of the circle interior: S, A exterior: P, Q

The coordinates of the center and the measure of the radius of a circle are given. Write an equation of the circle.

8. $(4, -2), 5$ $(x - 4)^2 + (y + 2)^2 = 25$

9. $(0, 3), 12$ $x^2 + (y - 3)^2 = 144$

10. Sketch the graph of $(x - 4)^2 + (y + 1)^2 = 9$.

T50
Glencoe Division, Macmillan/McGraw-Hill

APPLYING THE LESSON

Homework Exercises

Assignment Guide

Basic: 17-35, 38, 41, 45, 50-51, 53-60
Average: 18-21, 23-36, 39, 42-43, 45-46, 48, 50, 52-60
Enriched: 19-31, 34-37, 40, 43-44, 46-50, 52-60

Practice

A Determine whether each statement is *true* or *false*.

17. A diameter of a circle is the longest chord of the circle. true
18. A radius of a circle is a chord of the circle. false
19. A chord of a circle is a secant of the circle. false
20. A secant of a circle is always a diameter of the circle. false
21. Two radii of a circle always form a diameter of the circle. false
22. A radius of a circle is tangent to the circle. false

If *r* is the measure of the radius and *d* is the measure of the diameter, find each missing measure.

23. $r = 3.8$, $d = \underline{\ ?\ }$ 7.6   24. $d = 3.5$, $r = \underline{\ ?\ }$ 1.75   25. $r = \frac{x}{2}$, $d = \underline{\ ?\ }$ x

B The coordinates of the center and the measure of the radius of a circle are given. Write an equation of the circle. 29. $x^2 + y^2 = 14$

26. (0, 0), 5   27. (0, 0), 7   28. (3, 4), 6   29. (0, 0), $\sqrt{14}$
26. $x^2 + y^2 = 25$ 27. $x^2 + y^2 = 49$ 28. $(x - 3)^2 + (y - 4)^2 = 36$

Sketch the graph of the circle whose equation is given. Label the center, *C*, and the measure of the radius, *r*, on each graph. See margin.

30. $(x - 7)^2 + (y + 5)^2 = 4$ 31. $(x + 3)^2 + (y + 6)^2 = 49$

$\odot P$ has a radius of 5 units, and $\odot T$ has a radius of 3 units. Complete each statement.

32. If $QR = 1$, then $RT = \underline{\ ?\ }$. 2
33. If $PT = 7$ and $\overline{SP}$ and $\overline{ST}$ are drawn, the perimeter of $\triangle PST = \underline{\ ?\ }$. 15 units
34. $\overline{AR}$ is a $\underline{\ ?\ }$ of $\odot P$. diameter
35. $QT = \frac{1}{2} \underline{\ ?\ }$. QB
36. If $QR = 1.5$, then $AQ = \underline{\ ?\ }$. 8.5
37. If $QR = 1$, then $AB = \underline{\ ?\ }$. 15

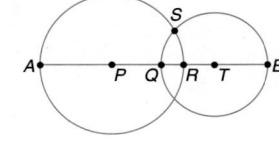

D is in the interior of $\odot C$, *A* is in the exterior of $\odot C$, and *B* is on $\odot C$. Replace each ● with <, >, or = to make a true statement.

38. CD ● CB <   39. CA ● CD >   40. CA ● CB >

Given $\odot T$ with equation $(x - 3)^2 + (y + 4)^2 = 25$, determine if each point is on the circle, in its interior, or in its exterior.

C
41. $M(-2, -3)$ 42. $A(-1, 2)$ 43. $H(6, 0)$ 44. $T(3, -4)$
    exterior   exterior   on the circle   interior

Practice Masters Booklet, p. 58

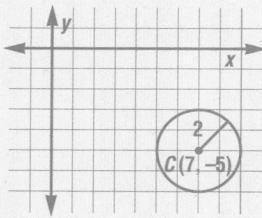
Additional Answers

30.

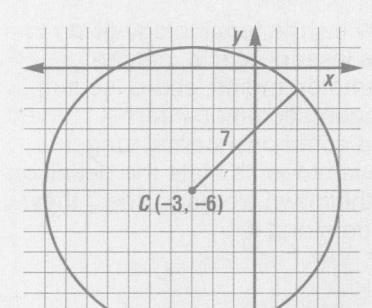

31.

Draw two different circles that have common tangents as described.
See Solutions Manual.

45. one common internal tangent and two common external tangents

46. no common internal tangents and two common external tangents

47. no common internal tangents and one common external tangent

Write an equation for each circle described.

48. $(x + 4)^2 +$
$(y + 7)^2 = 36$

48. The diameter is 12 units long and the center is at (-4, -7).

49. A diameter has its endpoints at (2, 7) and (-6, 15). $(x + 2)^2 + (y - 11)^2 = 32$

Critical Thinking

50. For any whole number, n, draw $2n$ radii equally spaced in a circle. Let any secant cut the sections formed by the radii into nonoverlapping regions. What will be the maximum number of such regions formed within the circle? Express your answer in terms of n. *(Hint: Use the problem-solving strategy of drawing a diagram.)* $3n + 1$

Applications

51. **Crafts** Heath is making a stained glass window. In order to cut out a circle of glass, he uses the tool at the right. Point P is the pivot point, and point A is the tip of the cutter. If he wants a circle with diameter of $10\frac{1}{2}$ inches, what length should he make $\overline{PA}$? $5\frac{1}{4}$ in.

52. **Smart Shopping** Some passenger vans use P 215/75 R14 tires. Have you ever wondered what these numbers indicate?

> P stands for passenger.
> 215 represents a tire thickness of 215 mm.
> 75 is 75% of the 215, which is the width of the tread.
> R means it's a radial tire.
> 14 is the diameter of the wheel rim in inches.

Suppose a car has tires labeled P175/65 R15. Find the width of the tread in millimeters and the radius of the wheel rim in inches. 113.75 mm; 7.5 in.

Mixed Review

53. How many odd perfect squares are between 0 and 1000? **(Lesson 8-8)** 16

Determine whether each statement is *true* or *false*.

54. The diagonals of an isosceles trapezoid are congruent. **(Lesson 6-6)** true

55. The diagonals of a parallelogram are congruent. **(Lesson 6-1)** false

56. If two sides of a triangle are congruent, then the angles opposite those sides are congruent. **(Lesson 4-7)** true

57. If two parallel lines are cut by a transversal, then two consecutive interior angles are congruent. **(Lesson 3-3)** false

58. If a conditional is true, then its converse is true. **(Lesson 2-2)** false

59. If two angles are supplementary, then one of the two angles is acute. **(Lesson 1-9)** false

Wrap-Up

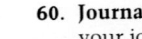

60. **Journal Entry** Write a summary of the main concepts of this lesson in your journal. See students' work.

EXTENDING THE LESSON

Math Power: Connections

Is the graph of a circle a function? Why or why not? If not, how can you make it a function? No, it is not a function. Sample answer: Because there is more than one y value for some of the x values, and it fails the vertical line test. If you use the diameter parallel to the x axis to divide the circle in half, each semicircle formed is a function by itself.

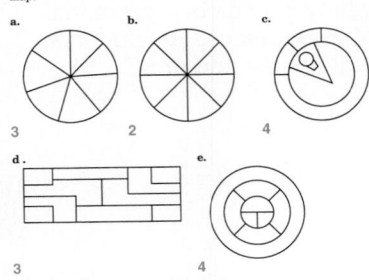

Lesson Resources

• Reteaching Master 9-2
• Practice Master 9-2
• Enrichment Master 9-2
• Evaluation Master, p. 121
• Activity Master, p. 23

 Transparency 9-2 contains the 5-Minute Check and a teaching aid for this lesson.

INTRODUCING THE LESSON

 5-Minute Check

(over Lesson 9-1)

⊙*Q* has the equation $(x - 2)^2 + (y + 8)^2 = 9$.

1. Find the radius *r*. *r* = 3
2. Find the coordinates of the center. (2, −8)
3. Find the diameter *d*. *d* = 6
4. Is the point *R*(3, −5) on ⊙*Q*, in its interior, or in its exterior? **in its exterior**
5. Sketch the graph of ⊙*Q* with point *S* (8, -5). Draw line *l* tangent to *Q* through point *S* and line *m*, a secant line of *Q*, through point *S*.

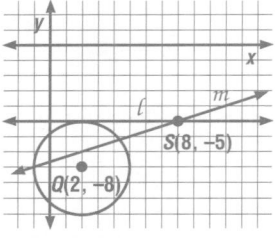

Motivating the Lesson

Ask students how they would cut a pie into five or six even pieces. Or how they would cut a pizza into eight even pieces. Relate this to central angles and arcs.

<table>
<tr><td>9-2</td><td></td></tr>
</table>

9-2 Angles and Arcs

Objectives

After studying this lesson, you should be able to:

9-2A ▪ recognize major or minor arcs or semicircles, and
9-2B ▪ find the measures of arcs and central angles.

Application

Circle graphs are often used to compare parts of a whole. The student newspaper staff of Stevenson High School reports that of the 16 girls on the girls' varsity softball team, about 6% are freshmen, 19% are sophomores, 31% are juniors, and 44% are seniors. They wish to display these results using a circle graph. However they are not sure how to accurately measure and draw the graph. Luckily, one of the staff artists is taking geometry. He remembers that each part of the circle graph is defined by an angle whose vertex is the center of the circle. Such an angle is called a **central angle.** *You will construct the circle graph in Example 1.*

FYI · · ·

The Hi Ho Brakettes, a women's fast-pitch softball team from Stratford, Connecticut, won 20 United States National Championships between 1958 and 1988.

A central angle separates a circle into **arcs.** An arc is an unbroken part of a circle. For example, in the figure below, ∠*APB* is a central angle of ⊙*P*. Points *A* and *B* and all points of the circle interior to ∠*APB* form a **minor arc** called arc *AB*. This is written $\overparen{AB}$. Points *A* and *B* and all points of the circle exterior to ∠*APB* form a **major arc** called $\overparen{ACB}$.

words	arc *AB*	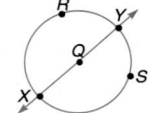	arc *ACB*	*words*
symbols	$\overparen{AB}$		$\overparen{ACB}$	*symbols*

$\overparen{AB}$ and $\overparen{BA}$ name the same minor arc.

Three letters are needed to name a major arc. Why?

A and *B* are the endpoints of $\overparen{AB}$ and $\overparen{ACB}$.

The endpoints of a segment containing the diameter of a circle separate the circle into two arcs called **semicircles.**

$\overparen{XRY}$ and $\overparen{XSY}$ are semicircles.

Arcs are measured by their corresponding central angles.

The measure of arc *LO* is 90. *words*

$m\overparen{LO} = 90$ *symbols*

Recall that a complete rotation about a given point measures 360. Therefore, the measure of $\overparen{LNO}$ is $360 - m\overparen{LO}$, or 270.

ALTERNATE TEACHING STRATEGIES

Using Experimentation

Have each student use a compass to draw a circle on a piece of paper. Have them draw five radii anywhere in the circle. Have them use a protractor to measure each angle created by the radii. What is the total measure of all of the angles in each student's circle? **360** Have students form hypotheses based on this experiment.

Using Models

Bring in an example of a circle graph from a magazine or newspaper to show students. Have them analyze the data given in the graph. Create examples and have them use the graph to draw conclusions. For example, give them a total number for the data represented and ask them to calculate the number that each section of the graph represents.

Definition of Arc Measure	The measure of a minor arc is the measure of its central angle. The measure of a major arc is 360 minus the measure of its central angle. The measure of a semicircle is 180.

Example 1

CONNECTION

Statistics

Draw a circle graph of the data given in the lesson introduction.

In a circle graph, the artist knows that the sum of the measures of the central angles should be 360. So, the central angle for each class should be the appropriate percentage of 360.

Freshmen: 6% of 360 = 21.6
Sophomores: 19% of 360 = 68.4
Juniors: 31% of 360 = 111.6
Seniors: 44% of 360 = 158.4

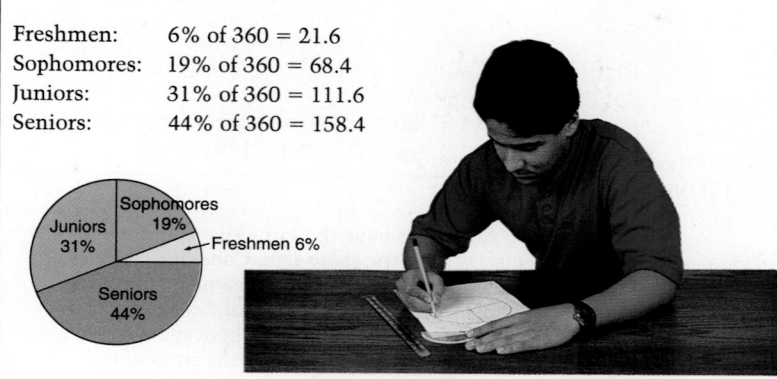

Use a protractor to measure and draw each central angle.

Chalkboard Example

For Example 1
A landfill in Jackson County was analyzed and it was found to contain 6% disposable diapers, 9% aluminum or metal, 15% plastic, 16% leaves and grass, and 54% paper. Draw a circle graph of the data.
Diapers: 6% of 360 = 21.6
Aluminum/metal: 9% of 360 = 32.4
Plastic: 15% of 360 = 54.0
Grass/leaves: 16% of 360 = 57.6
Paper: 54% of 360 = 194.4

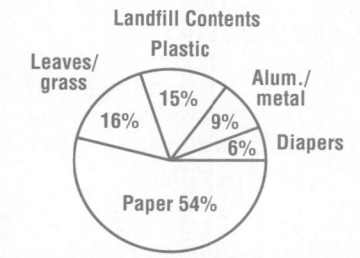

Adjacent arcs are arcs of a circle that have exactly one point in common. As with adjacent angles, the measures of adjacent arcs can be added to find the measure of the arc formed by the adjacent arcs.

In $\odot C$ at the right, $\overarc{PQ}$ and $\overarc{QR}$ are adjacent arcs and $\overarc{PQR}$ is formed by $\overarc{PQ}$ and $\overarc{QR}$.

$$m\overarc{PQ} + m\overarc{QR} = m\overarc{PQR}$$
$$110 + 120 = m\overarc{PQR}$$
$$230 = m\overarc{PQR}$$

$m\overarc{PQ} = 110,$
$m\overarc{QR} = 120$

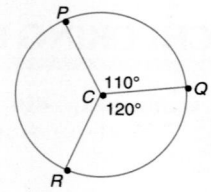

This result suggests the following postulate.

Postulate 9-1 Arc Addition Postulate	The measure of an arc formed by two adjacent arcs is the sum of the measures of the two arcs. That is, if Q is a point on $\overarc{PR}$, then $m\overarc{PQ} + m\overarc{QR} = m\overarc{PQR}$.

LESSON 9-2   ANGLES AND ARCS   417

Teaching Tip To begin a circle graph, draw a horizontal line from the center to the edge of the circle. Use this as one side of the first angle measure. Then go around the circle counterclockwise and use the leg of the previous angle as the base of the angle you are drawing.

Chalkboard Example

For Example 2
In $\odot Q$, $\overline{AC}$ is a diameter and $m\angle CQD = 40$. Find $m\widehat{CD}$, $m\widehat{CAD}$, $m\widehat{AD}$, and $m\widehat{DCA}$.

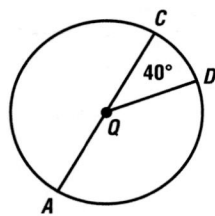

Since $\angle CQD$ is a central angle and its measure is 40, $m\widehat{CD} =$ 40. Since $\widehat{CAD}$ is the major arc for $\angle CQD$, it follows that $m\widehat{CAD} = 360 - m\widehat{CD}$, or 320. By the arc addition postulate, $m\widehat{CD} + m\widehat{AD} = m\widehat{ADC}$. Because $m\widehat{ADC} = 180$, this gives $40 + m\widehat{AD} = 180$, or $m\widehat{AD}$ = 140. Since $\widehat{DCA}$ is a major arc for $\angle AQD$ and $m\angle AQD =$ 140, $m\widehat{DCA} = 360 - 140 = 220$.

EVALUATING THE LESSON

Checking for Understanding

Exercises 1–17 are designed to help you assess students' understanding through reading, writing, speaking, and modeling. You should work through Exercises 1–5 with your students and then monitor their work on Exercises 6–17.

Example 2

In $\odot P$, $m\angle APB = 30$ and $\overline{AC}$ is a diameter. Find $m\widehat{AB}$, $m\widehat{ACB}$, $m\widehat{BC}$, and $m\widehat{BAC}$.

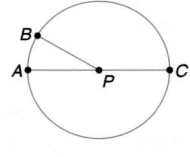

$m\widehat{AB}$ Since $\angle APB$ is a central angle and $m\angle APB = 30$, it follows that $m\widehat{AB} = 30$.

$m\widehat{ACB}$ Since $\widehat{ACB}$ is the major arc for $\angle APB$, it follows that $m\widehat{ACB} = 360 - m\widehat{AB}$. Since $m\widehat{AB} = 30$, $m\widehat{ACB} = 360 - 30$ or 330.

$m\widehat{BC}$ By the arc addition postulate, $m\widehat{AB} + m\widehat{BC} = m\widehat{ABC}$. Since $m\widehat{AB} = 30$, and $\widehat{ABC}$ is a semicircle, the following holds.
$$30 + m\widehat{BC} = 180$$
$$m\widehat{BC} = 150$$

$m\widehat{BAC}$ Since $\widehat{BAC}$ is a major arc for $\angle BPC$ and $m\angle BPC = 150$, $m\widehat{BAC} = 360 - 150$ or 210.

All circles have the same shape, but not all circles have the same size. **Concentric circles** are circles that lie in the same plane, have the same center, and have radii of different lengths. An example of this concept is a circular target. The edges of the rings of the target illustrate concentric circles.

As the rings of the target show, circles with radii of different lengths are not congruent. Two circles are congruent if their radii are congruent. Two arcs of one circle are congruent if they have the same measure.

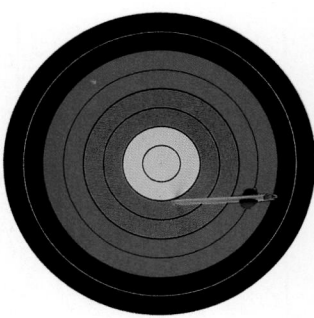

CHECKING FOR UNDERSTANDING

Communicating Mathematics

In $\odot R$ at the right, $\overline{JC}$ is a diameter. Read and study the lesson to answer these questions.

1. Name a minor arc. $\widehat{TC}$ or $\widehat{JT}$

2. Name a semicircle. Explain how you know that it is a semicircle. $\widehat{JTC}$; $\overline{JC}$ is a diameter.

3. Name a central angle. $\angle CRT$ or $\angle TRJ$

4. If $m\widehat{JT} = 123$, explain how to find $m\widehat{JCT}$. Then find $m\widehat{JCT}$. Subtract 123 from 360; 237.

5. Is the measure of a minor arc greater or less than 180? Explain. See margin.

418   CHAPTER 9   CIRCLES

Additional Answer

5. less than 180; because the minor arc contains all the points of a circle that are in the interior of an angle

In ⊙M, m∠BMC = 40, m∠CMD = 90, and $\overline{AC}$ and $\overline{BE}$ are diameters. Determine whether each arc is a minor arc, a major arc, or a semicircle. Then find the measure of each arc.

6. minor; 140
7. major; 320
8. semicircle; 180
9. semicircle; 180
10. major; 310
11. major; 270
12. major; 230
15. minor; 130

6. $\overset{\frown}{AB}$	7. $\overset{\frown}{ECA}$	8. $\overset{\frown}{BAE}$
9. $\overset{\frown}{BDE}$	10. $\overset{\frown}{DCE}$	11. $\overset{\frown}{CBD}$
12. $\overset{\frown}{DAB}$	13. $\overset{\frown}{AE}$	14. $\overset{\frown}{BC}$
15. $\overset{\frown}{BD}$	16. $\overset{\frown}{BDC}$	17. $\overset{\frown}{AD}$

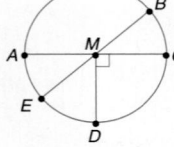

13. minor; 40
14. minor; 40
16. major; 320
17. minor; 90

EXERCISES

Practice

In ⊙P, m∠WPX = 28, m∠ZPY = 38, and $\overline{WZ}$ and $\overline{XV}$ are diameters. Find each measure.

18. m$\overset{\frown}{YZ}$ 38	19. m$\overset{\frown}{WX}$ 28	20. m∠VPZ 28
21. m$\overset{\frown}{XWY}$ 246	22. m$\overset{\frown}{VZ}$ 28	23. m$\overset{\frown}{VWX}$ 180
24. m$\overset{\frown}{ZVW}$ 180	25. m∠VPW 152	26. m$\overset{\frown}{WYZ}$ 180
27. m$\overset{\frown}{ZXW}$ 180	28. m∠XPY 114	29. m$\overset{\frown}{XY}$ 114

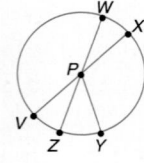

In ⊙C, m∠BCY = 2x, m∠BCQ = 4x + 15, m∠QCX = 2x + 5, and $\overline{XY}$ and $\overline{AB}$ are diameters. Find each value or measure.

30. x 20	31. m$\overset{\frown}{BY}$ 40	32. m$\overset{\frown}{BQ}$ 95
33. m$\overset{\frown}{QA}$ 85	34. m$\overset{\frown}{QX}$ 45	35. m$\overset{\frown}{YQ}$ 135
36. m∠YCQ 135	37. m∠QCA 85	38. m$\overset{\frown}{BX}$ 140
39. m∠BCX 140	40. m$\overset{\frown}{XA}$ 40	41. m$\overset{\frown}{XYA}$ 320

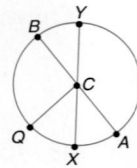

Determine whether each statement is *true* or *false*.

42. If m$\overset{\frown}{AB}$ = 32 and m$\overset{\frown}{XY}$ = 32, then $\overset{\frown}{AB}$ ≅ $\overset{\frown}{XY}$. false

43. If $\overset{\frown}{AB}$ ≅ $\overset{\frown}{XY}$ and m$\overset{\frown}{AB}$ = 32, then m$\overset{\frown}{XY}$ = 64. false

44. Two congruent circles have congruent radii. true

45. All radii of a circle are congruent radii. true

46. Two concentric circles always have congruent radii. false

47. If two circles have the same center, they are congruent. false

48. If two central angles are congruent, then their corresponding minor arcs are congruent. false

49. If two minor arcs are congruent, then their corresponding central angles are congruent. true

LESSON 9-2   ANGLES AND ARCS   419

RETEACHING THE LESSON

Draw several circles on the chalkboard or overhead with central angles drawn and labeled. Ask each student to name a central angle, minor arc, or major arc of a circle.

Closing the Lesson

Modeling Activity Have students use a compass to draw a circle on a piece of paper. Using the center as the vertex for each angle, have them draw angles of 62°, 37°, 94°, 55°, and 112° within the circle. Have them label their circles and name a central angle, the minor arc of that angle, and the major arc of that angle.

APPLYING THE LESSON

Homework Exercises

Assignment Guide

Basic: 19-41 odd, 42-47, 50-55, 59, 62-64, 67-74
Average: 18-40 even, 43-48, 51-56, 60, 62, 64-65, 67-74
Enriched: 18-40 even, 44-49, 52-58, 61-62, 65-74

Reteaching Masters Booklet, p. 51

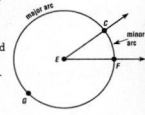

9-2 Reteaching Worksheet

Angles and Arcs

An angle whose vertex is at the center of a circle is called a **central angle**. A central angle separates a circle into two arcs called a **major arc** and a **minor arc.** In the circle at the right, ∠CEF is a central angle. Points C and F and all points of the circle interior to ∠CEF form a minor arc called arc CF. This is written $\overset{\frown}{CF}$. Points C and F and all points of the circle exterior to ∠CEF form a major arc called $\overset{\frown}{CGF}$.

Arcs are measured by their corresponding central angles. The arcs determined by a diameter are called semicircles and have measures of 180.

Example: In ⊙P, m∠APB = 42 and $\overline{AC}$ is a diameter. Find m$\overset{\frown}{AB}$, m$\overset{\frown}{ACB}$, and m$\overset{\frown}{BC}$.

Since ∠APB is a central angle and m∠APB = 42, then m$\overset{\frown}{AB}$ = 42.
m$\overset{\frown}{ACB}$ = 360 − m$\overset{\frown}{AB}$ = 360 − 42 = 318
m$\overset{\frown}{BC}$ = 180 − m$\overset{\frown}{AB}$ = 180 − 42 = 138

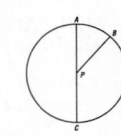

In ⊙P, m∠SPT = 51, m∠NPR = 29, and $\overline{SN}$ and $\overline{MT}$ are diameters. Find each measure.

1. m $\overset{\frown}{NR}$ 29
2. m$\overset{\frown}{ST}$ 51
3. m∠MPN 51
4. m$\overset{\frown}{TSR}$ 260
5. m $\overset{\frown}{MN}$ 51
6. m$\overset{\frown}{MST}$ 180
7. m$\overset{\frown}{NMS}$ 180
8. m$\overset{\frown}{MPS}$ 129
9. m $\overset{\frown}{SRN}$ 180
10. m$\overset{\frown}{NTS}$ 180
11. m∠TPR 100
12. m$\overset{\frown}{RT}$ 100

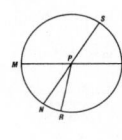

T51
Glencoe Division, Macmillan/McGraw-Hill

Exercise Notes

For Exercise 59, △OPQ is isosceles, so its base angles are congruent.

For Exercise 60, draw radius $\overline{AC}$. It also equals 1. Use the Pythagorean Theorem to find one side of the square.

For Exercise 62, △ABC and △CDE are isosceles, so their base angles are congruent.

Additional Answer

66. bean soup 28.8°, chicken soup 115.2°, tomato soup 36°, vegetable soup 180°

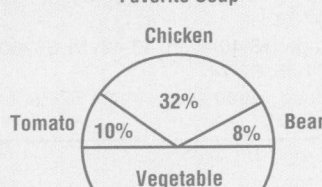

Favorite Soup

Chicken 32%
Tomato 10%
Bean 8%
Vegetable 50%

9-2 **Practice Worksheet**
NAME _____ DATE _____

Angles and Arcs

In ⊙P, m∠1 = 140 and AC is a diameter. Find each measure.

1. m∠2 40

2. m*BC* 40

3. m*AB* 140

4. m*ABC* 180

In ⊙P, m∠2 = m∠1, m∠2 = 4x + 35, m∠1 = 9x + 5, and BD and AC are diameters. Find each value or measure.

5. x 6   11. m*EB* 121

6. m*AE* 59   12. m∠CPB 118

7. m*ED* 59   13. m*CB* 118

8. m∠3 62   14. m*CEB* 242

9. m*AB* 62   15. m*DC* 62

10. m*EC* 121   16. m*CEA* 180

17. Sketch three concentric circles and a fourth circle that intersects each of the other three, with the total number of intersection points being four.

T59
Glencoe Division, Macmillan/McGraw-Hill

In the figure, *A* is the center of two concentric circles with radii $\overline{AQ}$ and $\overline{AR}$, m∠SAR = 32, and m∠RAW = 112. Find each measure.

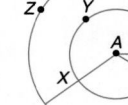

50. m$\widehat{SR}$ 32   51. m$\widehat{TX}$ 144   52. m$\widehat{SW}$ 144

53. m$\widehat{TQ}$ 32   54. m$\widehat{XQ}$ 112   55. m$\widehat{WR}$ 112

56. m$\widehat{TYX}$ 216   57. m$\widehat{SZW}$ 216

58. yes, if they are in circles with radii of different lengths

58. Can two arcs have the same measure but not be congruent? Explain.

59. If m$\widehat{PQ}$ = 120, find m∠Q. 30

60. If AE = 1, find the measure of each side of square ABCD.

$\frac{\sqrt{2}}{2} \approx 0.71$

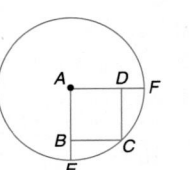

61. If *B* is a point on a semicircle XBY with $\overline{AB} \perp \overline{XY}$ at point *A*, XA = $2\frac{1}{12}$, and AY = 12, find BY. **13**

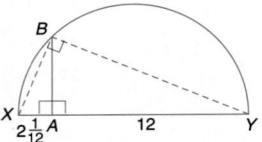

Critical Thinking

62. Find m∠ECB + m∠ACD. **230**

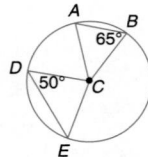

Applications

63. **Food**   Wayne cuts a pie into 6 congruent pieces. What is the measure of the central angle of each piece? **60**

64. **Engineering**   Allison Hsu designs bicycles. She designs a wheel with 30 evenly spaced spokes. Suppose the spokes are numbered consecutively from 1 through 30. Find the measure of the central angle formed by spokes 1 and 14. **156**

65. **Teaching**   Mr. Yant is a physical education teacher. He directs the students to form a circle and count off. If the students are evenly spaced around the circle and student number 12 is directly across from student number 35, how many students are in the circle? **46**

66. **Statistics**   The cafeteria staff surveyed the students of Middletown High School to determine which type of soup is the students' favorite. 8% prefer bean soup, 32% prefer chicken soup, 10% prefer tomato soup, and 50% prefer vegetable soup. Determine the central angle measures needed to accurately construct a circle graph using the data. Then draw an appropriate graph. **See margin.**

67. Write an equation for the circle with center at (1, 2) and radius of 3 units. **(Lesson 9-1)** $(x - 1)^2 + (y - 2)^2 = 9$

68. Find the value of x if the triangles below are similar. **(Lesson 7-6)** 4.5

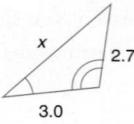
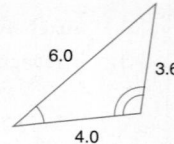

69. Find the next number in the sequence 11, 9, 7, 5, 3, 1, -1. Describe the pattern. **(Lesson 6-2)** -3, subtract 2 from the previous term

70. A median of $\triangle ABC$ separates side $\overline{BC}$ of the triangle into segments $\overline{BD}$ and $\overline{DC}$. If $CD = x + 7$ and $BD = 2x - 1$, what is the value of x? **(Lesson 5-1)** 8

71. obtuse triangles have one obtuse angle and all the angles in an acute triangle are acute

71. Describe the difference between obtuse and acute triangles. **(Lesson 4-1)**

72. Write "Concentric circles have the same center" in if-then form. **(Lesson 2-2)** If circles are concentric, then they have the same center.

73. Find the distance between A(-11, 6) and B(-3, 7). **(Lesson 1-4)** $\sqrt{65} \approx 8.1$

Wrap-Up

74. Write three questions that could be used as a quiz over this lesson. See students' work.

HISTORY CONNECTION

Around 4500 B.C., the people who lived in Iberia, the peninsula on which Spain and Portugal are now located, built large circular tombs. These tombs, called *dolmens*, are constructed of giant stones each weighing up to 30 tons! It would take about 170 people to lift a stone this size.

The interior chambers of the dolmens that have been excavated reveal engraved and painted decorations around the walls and contain tools and pottery. Archaeologists have learned a great deal about our ancestors from these structures. But they have not yet learned why the dolmens were constructed.

LESSON 9-2   ANGLES AND ARCS   **421**

EXTENDING THE LESSON

Math Power: Connections

You can represent the data in Example 1 using other types of graphs. Have your students think of other ways to represent the data and draw an example.

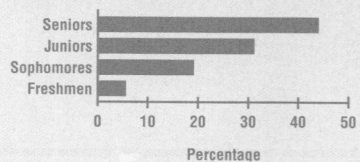

History Connection

The History Connection features introduce students to persons or cultures who were involved in the development of mathematics. You may want students to further research archaeology or the history of the people of Iberia.

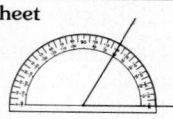

INTRODUCING THE LESSON

 5-Minute Check

(over Lesson 9-2)

Refer to the figure. *O* is the center of both circles. $\overline{AD}$ is a diameter, m∠*AOB* = 22, and ∠*DOC* is a right angle. Find each measure.

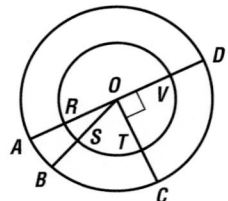

1. m$\widehat{AD}$		180
2. m$\widehat{ST}$		68
3. m∠*DOS*		158
4. m$\widehat{TVR}$		270
5. m$\widehat{CDA}$		270

Motivating the Lesson

Have students draw a circle and a central angle. Have them connect the two endpoints of the minor arc with a straight line. Point out that this is a chord of the circle. Have students draw a secant line through the circle. Point out that a chord is also formed here.

9-3 Arcs and Chords

Objective
9-3

After studying this lesson, you should be able to:
■ recognize and use relationships between arcs, chords, and diameters.

Application

The seats of a small Ferris wheel in the children's section of an amusement park move in a circular pattern. The diameter of this circle is 12 feet. The seats are connected with 6-foot steel bars. What is the length of the support bars that connect the center of the Ferris wheel with the midpoint of the bars? The geometric concepts in this lesson will help you answer this question in Example 1.

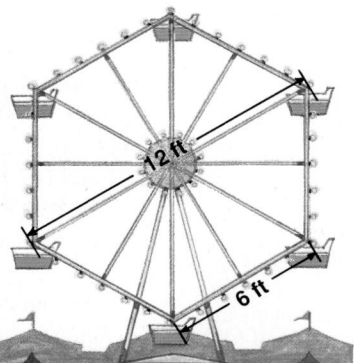

FYI···

The 2 largest Ferris wheels are located in Japan. Each one has 46 cars and can accommodate 384 riders.

When a minor arc and a chord have the same endpoints, we call the arc the **arc of the chord.** For example, in the figure at the right, $\widehat{PQ}$ is the arc of $\overline{PQ}$.

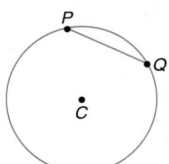

A diameter that is perpendicular to a chord has a special relationship to the chord and its arc.

Theorem 9-1

In a circle, if a diameter is perpendicular to a chord, then it bisects the chord and its arc.

Proof of Theorem 9-1

Given: ⊙*P*
$\overline{AB} \perp \overline{TK}$

Prove: $\overline{AR} \cong \overline{BR}$
$\widehat{AK} \cong \widehat{BK}$

Paragraph Proof:

Draw auxiliary radii $\overline{PA}$ and $\overline{PB}$. Since all radii of a circle are congruent, $\overline{PA} \cong \overline{PB}$. $\overline{PR} \cong \overline{PR}$ because congruence of segments is reflexive. Therefore, $\triangle ARP \cong \triangle BRP$ by HL. Thus, $\overline{AR} \cong \overline{BR}$ and ∠1 ≅ ∠2 by CPCTC. Thus, $\widehat{AK} \cong \widehat{BK}$ by the definition of congruent arcs.

ALTERNATE TEACHING STRATEGIES

Using Discovery

Have students draw two or three circles and two chords in each circle. Have them use a ruler to find the midpoints of the chords and make diameters in each circle by connecting the center with the midpoint of a chord.

What relationship does the diameter have to the chord? **They are perpendicular.** Have students formulate conclusions from their discovery.

Using Critical Thinking

Have students draw a circle with center C and one chord. Have them construct the perpendicular bisector of the chord. Have students formulate conclusions about the figure. **The perpendicular bisector of a chord goes through the center of the circle. The arc of the chord is bisected.**

Example 1

APPLICATION

Entertainment

Find the length of the support bar, $\overline{FC}$, in the Ferris wheel.

Consider just one section of the Ferris wheel. $\overline{FA} \cong \overline{FB}$ because they are radii of the same circle. Since C is the midpoint of $\overline{AB}$, $\overline{BC} \cong \overline{AC}$. $\overline{FC} \cong \overline{FC}$ since congruence of segments is reflexive. So, $\triangle FBC \cong \triangle FAC$ by SSS. Thus, $\angle FCB \cong \angle FCA$. $\angle FCB$ and $\angle FCA$ are also supplementary, so they are right angles. We can use the Pythagorean Theorem to find x.

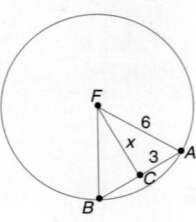

Since the diameter of the circle is 12 feet long, $FA = 6$. The steel bar represented by $\overline{BA}$ is 6 feet long. By Theorem 9-1, $AC = 3$.

$$(FC)^2 + (AC)^2 = (FA)^2 \quad \text{\textit{Pythagorean Theorem}}$$
$$x^2 + 3^2 = 6^2 \quad \text{\textit{Substitute x for FC, 3 for AC, and 6 for FA.}}$$
$$x^2 + 9 = 36$$
$$x = \sqrt{27} \text{ or about } 5.2$$

The length of the support bar is about 5.2 feet.

In a circle, a chord that is the perpendicular bisector of another chord is a diameter. The justification for the following construction is based on this relationship.

CONSTRUCTION

Locate the center of a given circle.

1. Draw any circle and two nonparallel chords. Label the chords $\overline{PQ}$ and $\overline{RS}$.

2. Construct the perpendicular bisectors for each chord. Call them ℓ and m. Call C the intersection of ℓ and m. Then C is the center of the circle because ℓ and m contain diameters of the circle.

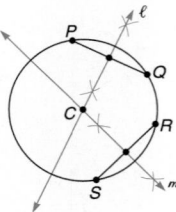

Chords and their arcs are related in the following way.

Theorem 9-2	In a circle or in congruent circles, two minor arcs are congruent if and only if their corresponding chords are congruent.

LESSON 9-3 ARCS AND CHORDS 423

TEACHING THE LESSON

Teaching Tip When discussing Theorem 9-2, remind students that "if and only if" means that the theorem and its converse are true.

Chalkboard Example

For Example 1

If the diameter of the circle in the giant ferris wheel at the amusement park is 56 feet, and the seats are connected with 6-foot steel bars, find the length of the support bar of the giant ferris wheel.

Let the length of the support bar be x.

$$x^2 + (\tfrac{1}{2}(6))^2 = (28)^2$$

$x \approx 27.8$ feet

The support bar is about 28 feet long.

Teaching Tip For Example 2, you can find the value of x in another way.

Since $\overline{QY}$ and $\overline{QL}$ are radii, they are congruent. Also, $BY = 8$ and $CL = 8$ by Theorem 9-1, so $\overline{BY} \cong \overline{CL}$. Thus, $\triangle QCL \cong \triangle QBY$ by HL, and $\overline{QB} \cong \overline{QC}$ by CPCTC. Therefore, $x = 6$.

Chalkboard Example

For Example 2
Use $\odot P$ to find the value of x.
$\overline{AB} \cong \overline{AC}$.

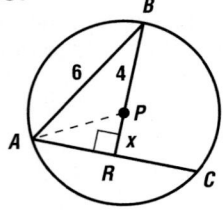

Draw radius $\overline{PA}$. $AC = 6$, so $AR = 3$. $PA = 4$ since all radii are congruent. Using the Pythagorean Theorem,
$x^2 + 3^2 = 4^2$
$x^2 = 7$
$x = \sqrt{7} \approx 2.65$

EVALUATING THE LESSON

Checking for Understanding

Exercises 1-14 are designed to help you assess students' understanding through reading, writing, speaking, and modeling. You should work through Exercises 1-4 with your students and then monitor their work on Exercises 5-14.

The proof of this theorem is based on congruent triangles. You will be asked to complete the proof in Exercise 36.

Proof of part of Theorem 9-2

Prove that if two arcs of a circle are congruent, then their corresponding chords are congruent.

Given: $\odot C$
$\overset{\frown}{AB} \cong \overset{\frown}{PQ}$

Prove: $\overline{AB} \cong \overline{PQ}$

Paragraph Proof:

Draw radii $\overline{AC}$, $\overline{BC}$, $\overline{PC}$, and $\overline{QC}$ and segments $\overline{AB}$ and $\overline{PQ}$. Since all radii of a circle are congruent, $\overline{AC} \cong \overline{PC}$ and $\overline{BC} \cong \overline{QC}$. $\overset{\frown}{AB} \cong \overset{\frown}{PQ}$ and the measure of an arc is the measure of its central angle, so $\angle ACB \cong \angle PCQ$. Therefore, $\triangle ACB \cong \triangle PCQ$ by SAS and $\overline{AB} \cong \overline{PQ}$ by CPCTC.

Example 2

Use $\odot Q$ below to find the value of x.

Draw radii $\overline{QL}$ and $\overline{QY}$. Since $\overline{QC} \perp \overline{JL}$, $CL = 8$. *Why?*

$\triangle CLQ$ is a right triangle, so use the Pythagorean Theorem to find QL.

$(QC)^2 + (CL)^2 = (QL)^2$ *Pythagorean Theorem*
$6^2 + 8^2 = (QL)^2$ *Substitute 6 for QC*
$36 + 64 = (QL)^2$ *and 8 for CL.*
$100 = (QL)^2$
$10 = QL$

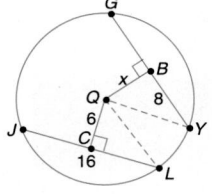

If $QL = 10$, then $QY = 10$. *Why?*

Use the Pythagorean Theorem with right triangle QBY to solve for x.

$x^2 + (BY)^2 = (QY)^2$ *Pythagorean Theorem*
$x^2 + 8^2 = 10^2$ *Substitute 8 for BY*
$x^2 + 64 = 100$ *and 10 for QY.*
$x^2 = 36$
$x = 6$

Notice that chords $\overline{JL}$ and $\overline{GY}$ in Example 2 are congruent. Notice also that $\overline{QC} \cong \overline{QB}$; that is, the chords are the same distance from the center Q. This leads to the next theorem, which you will be asked to prove in Exercises 37 and 38.

Theorem 9-3

In a circle or in congruent circles, two chords are congruent if and only if they are equidistant from the center.

424   CHAPTER 9   CIRCLES

CHECKING FOR UNDERSTANDING

Communicating Mathematics

Read and study the lesson to answer these questions about ⊙P. See margin.

1. Explain why △PAB is isosceles.
2. Explain what is meant by the term *arc of the chord*. Use the figure to give an example of an arc of a chord.
3. If $\overline{PM} \perp \overline{AB}$, state as many conclusions as you can.
4. If $\overline{AB} \cong \overline{CD}$, state as many conclusions as you can.

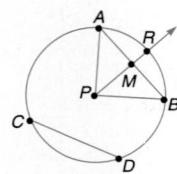

Guided Practice

5. Theorem 9-2
6. Theorem 9-2
7. Theorem 9-3
8. Theorem 9-1
9. Theorem 9-1
10. Theorem 9-3
11. Theorem 9-1

Name the theorem that justifies each statement.

5. If $\overline{BC} \cong \overline{AD}$, then $\overset{\frown}{BC} \cong \overset{\frown}{AD}$.
6. If $\overset{\frown}{BC} \cong \overset{\frown}{AD}$, then $\overline{BC} \cong \overline{AD}$.
7. If $\overline{BC} \cong \overline{AD}$, then $PQ = PR$.
8. If $\overline{PF} \perp \overline{AD}$, then $\overset{\frown}{AF} \cong \overset{\frown}{FD}$.
9. If $\overline{PQ} \perp \overline{BC}$, then $\overline{BQ} \cong \overline{QC}$.
10. If $PQ = PR$, then $\overline{CB} \cong \overline{DA}$.
11. If $\overline{FX} \perp \overline{AD}$, then $\overset{\frown}{AX} \cong \overset{\frown}{XD}$.

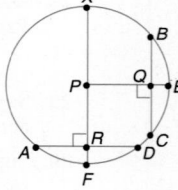

In each figure, *O* is the center of the circle. Find each measure.

12. *AC* **14**

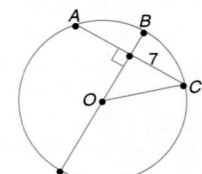

13. *m$\overset{\frown}{JK}$* **75**

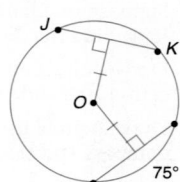

14. *ON* **10**

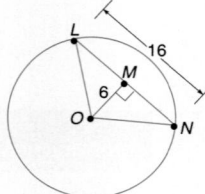

EXERCISES

Practice

In ⊙A, $\overline{SY} \perp \overline{QT}$ and $\overline{YS}$ and $\overline{ZR}$ are diameters.

15. Name a segment congruent to $\overline{VT}$. $\overline{QV}$
16. Name the midpoint of $\overset{\frown}{QT}$. S
17. Name the midpoint of $\overline{TQ}$. V
18. Name an arc congruent to $\overset{\frown}{ST}$. $\overset{\frown}{QS}$
19. Name an arc congruent to $\overset{\frown}{QY}$. $\overset{\frown}{YT}$
20. Name a segment congruent to $\overline{RZ}$. $\overline{SY}$
21. Which segment is longer, $\overline{WA}$ or $\overline{VA}$? $\overline{WA}$
22. Which segment is shorter, $\overline{QT}$ or $\overline{YS}$? $\overline{QT}$
23. If *W* is the midpoint of $\overline{QV}$, is *R* the midpoint of $\overset{\frown}{QS}$? no

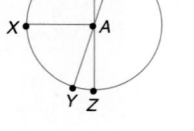

LESSON 9-3   ARCS AND CHORDS   425

RETEACHING THE LESSON

Have students take the three theorems in this lesson and rewrite them as five theorems in if-then form. You may also want to ask them to write the converse of Theorem 9-1 in if-then form to make six theorems. Have them draw a picture for each theorem and write the given information as well as what the theorem is proving.

Error Analysis

In Theorem 9-1, make sure students understand that the segment must be a diameter in order to bisect a chord and its arc. Draw examples of circles that contain two perpendicular chords that are not congruent or bisected.

Closing the Lesson

Writing Activity Have students write the converse of Theorems 9-1, 9-2, and 9-3.

APPLYING THE LESSON

Homework Exercises

Assignment Guide

Basic: 15-35, 41-42, 45-50
Average: 18-37, 41, 43, 45-50
Enriched: 18-23, 25-27, 30-41, 44-50

Additional Answers

1. $\overline{PA}$ and $\overline{PB}$ are congruent because they are both radii of ⊙P, and therefore △PAB is isosceles.
2. The arc of a chord is the arc that has the same endpoints as a chord. $\overset{\frown}{AB}$ is the arc of chord $\overline{AB}$; $\overset{\frown}{CD}$ is the arc of chord $\overline{CD}$.
3. $\overline{AM} \cong \overline{MB}$; $\overset{\frown}{AR} \cong \overset{\frown}{RB}$; △APM ≅ △BPM; ∠APR ≅ ∠BPR
4. $\overline{AB} \cong \overline{CD}$; $\overline{AB}$ and $\overline{CD}$ are equidistant from point *P*.

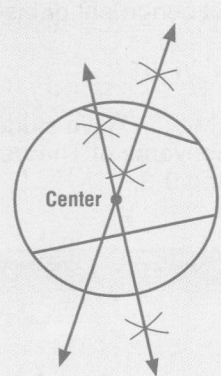
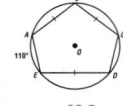
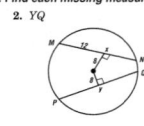
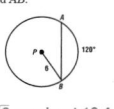 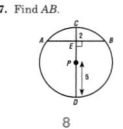
In each figure, O is the center of the circle. Find each measure.

24. m$\widehat{ST}$ **65**

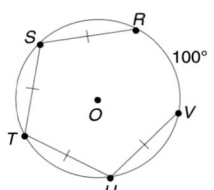

25. DF **16**

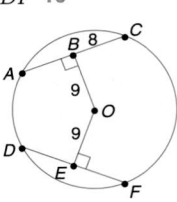

26. JL **8**

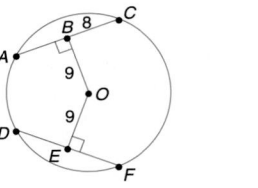

 27. If $\overline{AB} \cong \overline{CD}$, is $\widehat{AB}$ congruent to $\widehat{CD}$? Explain your answer. **See margin.**

28. If $\overline{AB} \cong \overline{XY}$, is $\widehat{AB}$ congruent to $\widehat{XY}$? Explain your answer. **See margin.**

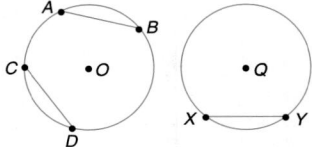

29. Suppose a chord of a circle is 10 inches long and is 12 inches from the center of the circle. Find the length of the radius. **13 in.**

30. Suppose a chord of a circle is 18 centimeters long and is 12 centimeters from the center of the circle. Find the length of the radius. **15 cm**

31. Suppose the diameter of a circle is 20 centimeters long and a chord is 16 centimeters long. Find the distance between the chord and the center of the circle. **6 cm**

32. Suppose the diameter of a circle is 10 inches long and a chord is 6 inches long. Find the distance between the chord and the center of the circle. **4 in.**

33. Draw a circle and two noncongruent chords. Which chord is closer to the center, the shorter chord or the longer chord? **longer chord**

 CONSTRUCTION

34. Draw a circle by tracing around a glass or other circular object. Use a compass and straightedge to find the center of the circle. **See margin.**

35. $\overline{MN} \cong \overline{PQ}$, MN = 7x + 13, and PQ = 10x − 8. Find PS. **31**

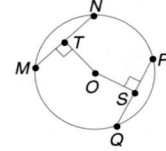

 36. In a circle, if two chords are congruent, then their corresponding minor arcs are congruent. (Theorem 9-2) Draw a diagram and write a paragraph proof. **See margin.**
See Solutions Manual.

37. In a circle, if two chords are equidistant from the center, then they are congruent. (Theorem 9-3) Draw a diagram and write a paragraph proof.

Solutions Manual.
38. In a circle, if two chords are congruent, then they are equidistant from the center. (Theorem 9-3) Draw a diagram and write a paragraph proof. **See**

39. Find the length of a chord that is the perpendicular bisector of a radius of length 20 units in a circle. **20 √3 or about 34.6 units**

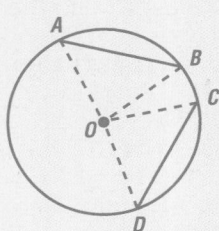

40. Circles O and P, with radii 20 and 34 units, respectively, intersect at points A and B. If the length of $\overline{AB}$ is 32 units, find OP. **42**

Critical Thinking

41. Given two circles that intersect in two points, what is the minimum number of chords you would need to construct the centers of both circles? Explain your answer. **See margin.**

Applications

42. Food Thelma is barbecuing chicken. The grill on her barbecue is in the shape of a circle with a diameter of 54 centimeters. The horizontal wires are supported by 2 wires that are 12 centimeters apart as shown in the figure. If the grill is symmetrical, what is the length of each support wire? **about 52.65 cm**

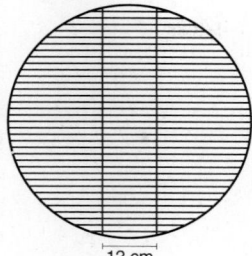

12 cm

43. Crafts Jonah plans to decoupage a picture on a circular piece of wood. He wants the picture to be able to stand freely on a shelf so he cuts along a chord of the circle to form a flat bottom. If the radius of the circle is 4 inches and the chord is 5 inches long, find the height of the final product. **about 7.1 in.**

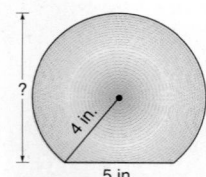

? 4 in.

5 in.

44. Crafts Tina is making a turning tray in wood shop. She has a circular piece of wood cut and sanded. Now she needs to find the center of the circle so that she can attach it to the base. Explain how she can find the center of the circle. **See margin.**

Mixed Review

45. In $\odot Q$, $\overline{AB}$ is a diameter and $\overline{QC}$ is perpendicular to $\overline{AB}$. If $m\angle CQM = 15$ and $m\angle BQN = 18$, find $m\widehat{MN}$. **(Lesson 9-2) 57**

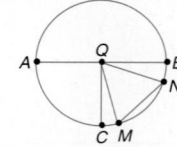

46. Find the geometric mean between 9 and 21. **(Lesson 8-1)** $\sqrt{189} \approx 13.7$

47. Draw a segment that is 11 centimeters long. Then by construction separate the segment into three congruent parts. **(Lesson 7-5) See Solutions Manual.**

48. Name the property of equality that justifies the statement "If $7x = 21$, then $x = 3$." **(Lesson 2-4) Division or multiplication prop. of equality**

49. C is between A and B. If $BC = 12$ and $BA = 17$, find CA. **(Lesson 1-4) 5**

Wrap-Up

50. Journal Entry Write a paragraph in your journal about what you think is the most important thing you learned in this lesson. How do you think this knowlege will help you in your further studies? **See students' work.**

LESSON 9-3 ARCS AND CHORDS **427**

EXTENDING THE LESSON

Math Power: Problem Solving

Extend Theorem 9-1 to show that the major arcs of a chord are also bisected if a diameter is perpendicular to the chord.
Using the figure for the proof of Theorem 9-1, draw segments $\overline{AT}$ and $\overline{BT}$. By Theorem 9-1, $\overline{AR} \cong \overline{BR}$. Also, $\overline{RT} \cong \overline{RT}$ since congruence of segments is reflexive. Since $\angle ART$ and $\angle BRT$ are right angles by Theorem 2-8, we can say $\triangle ART \cong \triangle BRT$ by LL. Therefore, $\overline{AT} \cong \overline{BT}$ by CPCTC. So, by Theorem 9-2, $\widehat{AT} \cong \widehat{BT}$.

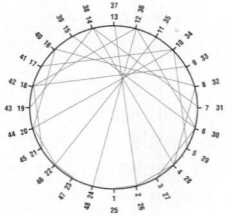

INTRODUCING THE LESSON

🕐 5-Minute Check

(over Lesson 9-3)

In circle B, $\overline{KN} \perp \overline{JL}$, and $\overline{KN}$ and $\overline{JP}$ are diameters.

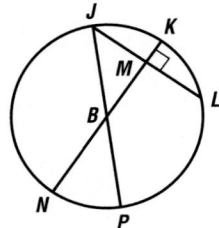

1. Name a segment congruent to $\overline{JM}$. $\overline{ML}$
2. Name an arc congruent to $\overset{\frown}{KL}$. $\overset{\frown}{JK}$
3. Name an arc congruent to $\overset{\frown}{JN}$. $\overset{\frown}{LN}$
4. Name a segment congruent to $\overline{JB}$. $\overline{KB}$, $\overline{BN}$, or $\overline{BP}$
5. Name the midpoint of $\overline{JL}$. M

Motivating the Lesson

Ask students what an inscription is, or what it means to inscribe something. **Sample answer: writing on something, like a piece of jewelry.**

Relate this to an inscribed angle, which is "an angle written on a circle," or an angle whose vertex lies on the circle.

TEACHING THE LESSON

Teaching Tip   When discussing the three cases for Theorem 9-4, draw a figure for each case.

Objectives
9-4A
9-4B

After studying this lesson, you should be able to:
▪ recognize and find the measures of inscribed angles, and
▪ use properties of inscribed figures.

Earlier in this chapter, you studied central angles. Recall that these are angles whose vertices are at the center of the circle and whose sides intersect the circle.

Another type of angle connected with circles is an inscribed angle. An **inscribed angle** is an angle whose vertex is on the circle and whose sides contain chords of the circle. We say that $\angle ABC$ intercepts $\overset{\frown}{AC}$. $\overset{\frown}{AC}$ is called the **intercepted arc** of $\angle ABC$. Notice that vertex B must be on the circle.

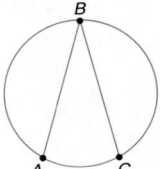

INVESTIGATION

Using a compass, draw a circle. Then with a straightedge, draw a central angle of convenient size. Then draw several inscribed angles that intercept the same arc as the central angle. Use a protractor to measure the central angle and each of the inscribed angles. How is the measure of each of the inscribed angles related to the measure of the central angle?

Repeat this investigation using a different size circle and a different size central angle.

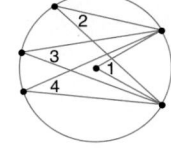

∠1 is the central angle. ∠2, ∠3, and ∠4 are the inscribed angles. All the angles intercept the arc shown in red.

This investigation leads us to the following theorem.

Theorem 9-4

If an angle is inscribed in a circle, then the measure of the angle equals one-half the measure of its intercepted arc.

There are three cases that we must consider when writing a proof of this theorem.

Case 1:   The center of the circle lies on one of the rays of the angle.
Case 2:   The center of the circle is in the interior of the angle.
Case 3:   The center lies in the exterior of the angle.

We will complete the proof for Case 1. You will be asked to complete the proofs for Cases 2 and 3 in Exercises 49 and 50, respectively.

ALTERNATE TEACHING STRATEGIES

Using Investigation

Have students complete the investigation on page 428. Have them draw conclusions based on the measures of the angles. **Sample answer: If an inscribed angle and a central angle intercept the same arc, then the measure of the inscribed angle is one-half the measure of the central angle.**

Using Modeling

Have students cut a rubber band and tape the ends to cardboard. Stretch the rubber band to form an angle, mark the vertex, and sketch the angle formed. Measure the angle and one of the legs of the angle. Stretch the rubber band until one leg is twice the measure of the original. Measure the angle. Compare the two measures. Relate this to inscribed angles in circles.

Proof of Theorem 9-4 Case 1

Given: $\angle PRQ$ inscribed in $\odot T$

Prove: $m\angle PRQ = \frac{1}{2}m\widehat{PQ}$

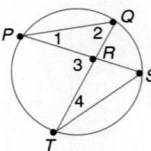

Paragraph Proof:

The center, T, lies on $\overline{RP}$. Draw radius $\overline{TQ}$ and let $m\angle PRQ = x$. Since $\angle PTQ$ is a central angle, $m\widehat{PQ} = m\angle PTQ$. Since $\overline{TQ}$ and $\overline{TR}$ are radii, $\triangle TQR$ is isosceles and $m\angle TQR = x$. By the Exterior Angle Theorem, $m\angle PTQ = 2x$. Therefore, $m\widehat{PQ} = 2x$ and $m\angle PRQ = \frac{1}{2}m\widehat{PQ}$.

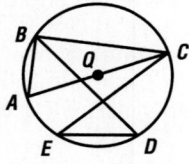
Example 1

In the figure at the right, $m\widehat{PQ} = 112$, $m\widehat{QS} = 54$, and $m\widehat{ST} = 88$. Find $m\angle 1$, $m\angle 2$, $m\angle 3$, and $m\angle 4$.

Since there are $360°$ in a circle, the sum of the measures of arcs $\widehat{PQ}$, $\widehat{QS}$, $\widehat{ST}$, and $\widehat{TP}$ must be 360.

$$m\widehat{PQ} + m\widehat{QS} + m\widehat{ST} + m\widehat{TP} = 360$$
$$112 + 54 + 88 + m\widehat{TP} = 360$$
$$m\widehat{TP} = 106$$

$$m\angle 1 = \frac{1}{2}(m\widehat{QS}) \qquad\qquad m\angle 2 = \frac{1}{2}(m\widehat{TP})$$
$$= \frac{1}{2}(54) \qquad\qquad\qquad = \frac{1}{2}(106)$$
$$= 27 \qquad\qquad\qquad\qquad = 53$$

$$m\angle 3 = m\angle 1 + m\angle 2 \qquad m\angle 4 = \frac{1}{2}(m\widehat{QS})$$
$$= 27 + 53 \qquad\qquad\qquad = \frac{1}{2}(54)$$
$$= 80 \qquad\qquad\qquad\qquad = 27$$

In Example 1, $m\angle 1 = m\angle 4$, which illustrates the first of the following theorems. The proofs of these theorems are based on Theorem 9-4 and you will be asked to prove them in Exercises 51 and 52.

Theorem 9-5	**If two inscribed angles of a circle or congruent circles intercept congruent arcs or the same arc, then the angles are congruent.**
Theorem 9-6	**If an inscribed angle of a circle intercepts a semicircle, then the angle is a right angle.**

Example 2

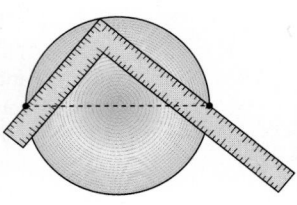

Carpentry

A carpenter needs to find the center of a circular pattern of a parquet floor. How can he find the center of the circle using only a carpenter's square?

First position the carpenter's square so that the vertex of the right angle of the square is on the circle and the square forms an inscribed angle. Since the inscribed angle is a right angle, the measure of the intercepted arc is 180. So, the points where the square crosses the circle are the ends of a diameter (Theorem 9-6). Mark these points and draw the diameter. Draw another diameter using the same method. The point where the two diameters intersect is the center of the circle.

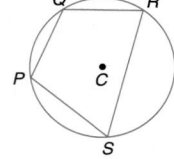

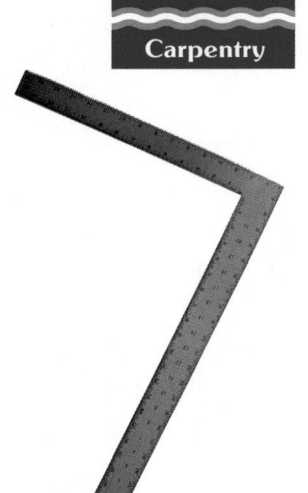

A polygon is an **inscribed polygon** if each of its vertices lies on a circle. The polygon is said to be inscribed in the circle. In the figure, quadrilateral *PQRS* is inscribed in ⊙*C*. The opposite angles of an inscribed quadrilateral are related in a special way.

| Theorem 9-7 | **If a quadrilateral is inscribed in a circle, then its opposite angles are supplementary.** |

You will be asked to prove this theorem in Exercise 53.

CONSTRUCTION

Construct a circle so that a given triangle *ABC* is inscribed in it.

1. Construct perpendicular bisectors for two sides, $\overline{AB}$ and $\overline{AC}$. Call their intersection *P*.

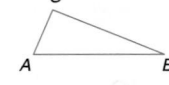

2. Using *P* as a center and *PA* as the measure of the radius, draw ⊙*P*. Then △*ABC* is inscribed in ⊙*P*.

   $$PA = PB = PC$$

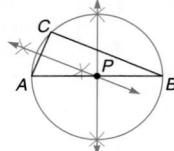

What is the relationship between the perpendicular bisector of a chord and the center of a circle? What kind of segments in a circle do the sides of △*ABC* represent?

The center lies on the perpendicular bisector. The sides of △*ABC* are chords.

430   CHAPTER 9   CIRCLES

CHECKING FOR UNDERSTANDING

Communicating Mathematics

Read and study the lesson to answer these questions. In the figure, $\overline{CD}$ is a diameter of $\odot A$.

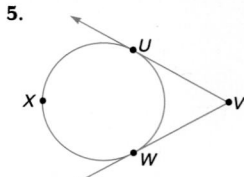

1. If $m\widehat{BC} = 42$, find $m\angle 1$. **21**

2. Explain why $m\angle 1 = m\angle 2$. **See margin.**

3. What type of triangle is $\triangle BCD$? Explain your answer. **See margin.**

4. Ms. O'Connor, a geometry teacher, tells her class that $m\widehat{DE} = 36$. One student claims $m\angle DFE = 36$ and then changes his mind and says that $m\angle DFE = 18$. Explain why both responses are incorrect. **See margin.**

Guided Practice

5. no; vertex not on circle

6. yes; vertex on circle and sides are chords

7. no; one side not a chord

Determine whether each angle is an inscribed angle. Explain your answer.

5. 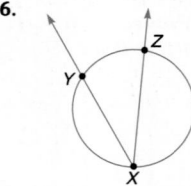   6.   7.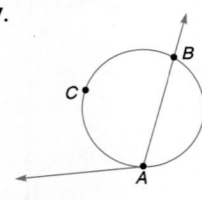

Quadrilateral *UTSK* is inscribed in a circle. Find each measure.

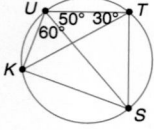

8. $m\widehat{KS}$ **120**   9. $m\angle KTS$ **60**   10. $m\widehat{UK}$ **60**

11. $m\angle USK$ **30**   12. $m\angle TSK$ **70**   13. $m\angle TSU$ **40**

14. $m\widehat{UT}$ **80**   15. $m\widehat{TS}$ **100**   16. $m\angle TKS$ **50**

17. Draw an acute triangle. Inscribe the triangle in a circle. **See students' work.**

EXERCISES

Practice

In $\odot X$, $\overline{AB} \parallel \overline{DC}$, $m\widehat{BC} = 94$, and $m\angle AXB = 104$. Find each measure.

18. $m\widehat{AB}$ **104**   19. $m\angle BAC$ **47**   20. $m\angle BDC$ **47**

21. $m\angle BCA$ **52**   22. $m\angle ADB$ **52**   23. $m\angle ADC$ **99**

24. $m\angle XAB$ **38**   25. $m\angle ABX$ **38**   26. $m\angle ACD$ **47**

27. $m\angle BCD$ **99**   28. $m\angle DEC$ **86**   29. $m\angle AED$ **94**

30. $m\angle EAD$ **34**   31. $m\widehat{DC}$ **68**   32. $m\angle BAD$ **81**

33. $m\angle DBC$ **34**   34. $m\widehat{AD}$ **94**   35. $m\angle ABD$ **47**

LESSON 9-4   INSCRIBED ANGLES   431

RETEACHING THE LESSON

Draw a large circle with a number of inscribed angles. Make sure some of them intercept the same arc. Label the points and ask students to name an inscribed angle. Then have them name an inscribed angle congruent to the first angle, if one exists. Assign measures to some of the arcs or angles and have students find the measures of some of the inscribed angles.

Additional Answers

45. Yes; yes; the perpendicular bisectors of the sides of the triangle intersect inside the triangle. The center of the circle is the point at which the bisectors intersect.

46. 90, 90, 90, 90; opposite angles of a quadrilateral inscribed in a circle are supplementary and the consecutive angles of a parallelogram are supplementary. So, each angle must have a measure of 90.

47. Draw $\overline{MT}$. Since $\overline{MH} \parallel \overline{AT}$, $\angle HMT \cong \angle MTA$ and $m\angle HMT = m\angle MTA$. But $m\angle HMT = \frac{1}{2} m\widehat{HT}$ and $m\angle MTA = \frac{1}{2} m\widehat{AM}$. Therefore, $\frac{1}{2} m\widehat{HT} = \frac{1}{2} m\widehat{AM}$ and $m\widehat{HT} = m\widehat{AM}$. The arcs are in the same circle, so $\widehat{AM} \cong \widehat{HT}$.

48. Since $\overline{AY}$ bisects $\angle XAZ$, $m\angle XAY = m\angle YAZ$. $m\angle XAY = \frac{1}{2} m\widehat{XY}$ and $m\angle YAZ = \frac{1}{2} m\widehat{YZ}$. Therefore, $\frac{1}{2} m\widehat{XY} = \frac{1}{2} m\widehat{YZ}$ and $m\widehat{XY} = m\widehat{YZ}$. Therefore Y bisects $\widehat{XZ}$.

49. $m\angle PRQ = m\angle PRK + m\angle KRQ$
$= \frac{1}{2}(m\widehat{PK}) + \frac{1}{2}(m\widehat{KQ})$
$= \frac{1}{2}(m\widehat{PK} + m\widehat{KQ})$
$= \frac{1}{2} m\widehat{PQ}$

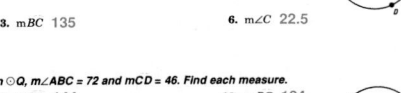

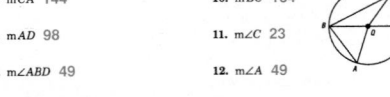

Quadrilateral GHIJ is inscribed in the circle, $m\angle GHI = 2x$, $m\angle HGJ = 2x - 10$, and $m\angle IJG = 2x + 10$. Find each measure.

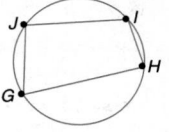

36. $m\angle GHI$ 85   **37.** $m\angle IJG$ 95   **38.** $m\angle HGJ$ 75

39. $m\angle JIH$ 105   **40.** $m\widehat{JGH}$ 210   **41.** $m\widehat{GHI}$ 190

42. $m\widehat{GJI}$ 170   **43.** $m\widehat{JIH}$ 150

See students' work.

44. Draw an obtuse triangle. Inscribe the triangle in a circle.

45. Suppose an acute triangle is inscribed in a circle. Can the center of the circle be in the interior of the triangle? Must it be in the interior of the triangle? Explain your answer.   See margin.

46. A parallelogram is inscribed in a circle. What are the measures of the angles of the parallelogram? Explain your reasoning.   See margin.

Write a paragraph proof for each.   See margin.

47. Given: $\overline{MH} \parallel \overline{AT}$
Prove: $\widehat{AM} \cong \widehat{HT}$
(Hint: Draw $\overline{MT}$.)

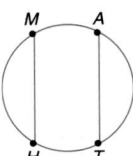

48. Given: inscribed $\angle XAZ$
$\overline{AY}$ bisects $\angle XAZ$.
Prove: Y bisects $\widehat{XZ}$.

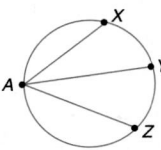

Study the proof for Case 1 of Theorem 9-4. In Case 2 and Case 3, $\overline{PR}$ is not a diameter. To prove Cases 2 and 3, draw diameter $\overline{KR}$ and use Case 1 of Theorem 9-4, the Angle Addition Postulate, and the Arc Addition Postulate.   See margin.

49. Case 2
Given: T lies inside $\angle PRQ$.
Prove: $m\angle PRQ = \frac{1}{2} m\widehat{PQ}$

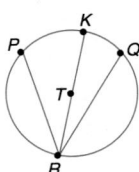

50. Case 3
Given: T lies outside $\angle PRQ$.
Prove: $m\angle PRQ = \frac{1}{2} m\widehat{PQ}$

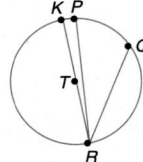

51. Prove that if two inscribed angles of a circle intercept congruent arcs, then the angles are congruent. (Theorem 9-5)   See Solutions Manual.

52. Prove that if an angle is inscribed in a semicircle, then the angle is a right angle. (Theorem 9-6)   See Solutions Manual.

53. Prove that if a quadrilateral is inscribed in a circle, then the opposite angles of the quadrilateral are supplementary. (Theorem 9-7)   See Solutions Manual.

Additional Answer

50. $m\angle PRQ = m\angle QRK - m\angle PRK$
$= \frac{1}{2}(m\widehat{QK}) - \frac{1}{2}(m\widehat{PK})$
$= \frac{1}{2}(m\widehat{QK} - m\widehat{PK})$
$= \frac{1}{2} m\widehat{PQ}$

Critical Thinking

54. An equilateral triangle *XYZ* is inscribed in ⊙*O*, point *A* bisects $\widehat{XY}$, and point *B* bisects $\widehat{XZ}$. What do you know about quadrilateral *ABZY*? Explain. **See margin.**

Application

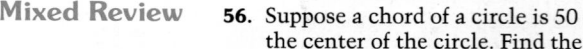

55. **Engineering**   The Reuleaux Triangle is used in the rotor design of the Wankel engine of some Mazda cars. A Reuleaux Triangle is drawn by starting with an equilateral triangle, *ELY*. Then $\widehat{EY}$, $\widehat{YL}$, and $\widehat{LE}$ are drawn using *L*, *E*, and *Y* respectively as centers.
    a. Find $m\widehat{EMY}$. **60**
    b. Suppose the Reuleaux Triangle is inscribed in a circle. Find $m\widehat{ENY}$. **120**

Mixed Review

56. Suppose a chord of a circle is 50 centimeters long and 60 centimeters from the center of the circle. Find the radius of the circle. **(Lesson 9-3)** **65 cm**

57. Can 6, 9, and 11 be the measures of the sides of a right triangle? Explain your answer. **(Lesson 8-2)** **no, $6^2 + 9^2 \neq 11^2$**

58. Are two squares always similar? Explain. **(Lesson 7-3)**

59. The median of a trapezoid is 18 inches long. If one base is 29 inches long, what is the length of the other base? **(Lesson 6-6)** **7 inches**

60. Identify the hypothesis and the conclusion of the conditional *If an angle is inscribed in a semicircle, then the angle is a right angle.* **(Lesson 2-2)**

61. Graph the points *A*(7, 4) and *B*(-3, 1) on a coordinate plane. Find the measure of $\overline{AB}$. **(Lesson 1-4)** **See margin.**
    60. **See margin.**

Wrap-Up

62. Explain the difference between a central angle and an inscribed angle of a circle. If a central angle and an inscribed angle intercept the same arc, how are their measures related? **See Solutions Manual.**

58. Yes, all angles 90° and the sides are proportional.

~~~ MID-CHAPTER REVIEW ~~~

1. Draw a diagram of a circle *O* with a tangent $\overline{AB}$ and a secant $\overline{BC}$. **(Lesson 9-1)**
See Solutions Manual.

In ⊙*C*, $m\angle 1 = m\angle 2 = 32$ and *CD* = 6. $\overline{AE}$ and $\overline{BF}$ are diameters. Find each measure. **(Lesson 9-2)**

2. *BF* **12**
3. $m\widehat{AFE}$ **180**
4. $m\widehat{AD}$ **64**
5. $m\widehat{AF}$ **148**
6. $m\widehat{DE}$ **116**
7. $m\angle 4$ **116**

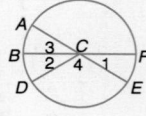

8. Suppose the diameter of a circle is 10 centimeters long and a chord is 8 centimeters long. Find the distance between the chord and the center of the circle. **(Lesson 9-3)** **3 cm**

Equilateral triangle *ABC* is inscribed in ⊙*Q* and ⊙*Q* has a radius of 12 units. (Lesson 9-4)

9. Find the length of each side. **about 20.8 units**

10. Find the distance from each vertex of the triangle to the center of the circle. **12 units**

11. Find $m\widehat{AB}$. **120**

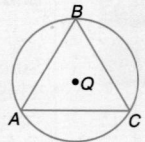

LESSON 9-4   INSCRIBED ANGLES   433

EXTENDING THE LESSON

Math Power: Reasoning

Students can work alone or in groups for this activity. Have them name some polygons that can always be inscribed in a circle and some polygons that cannot be inscribed in a circle.   **Sample answer: Any triangle and any polygon with every angle congruent; a rhombus cannot be inscribed.**

Mid-Chapter Review

The Mid-Chapter Review provides students with a brief review of the concepts and skills in Lessons 9-1 through 9-4. Lesson numbers are given at the end of problems or instruction lines so students may review concepts not yet mastered.

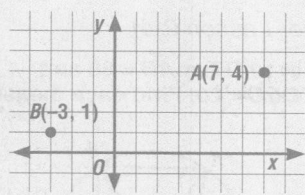
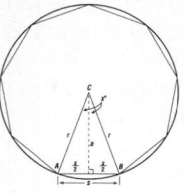

INTRODUCING THE LESSON

 5-Minute Check

(over Lesson 9-4)

Refer to ⊙T. m$\overparen{AB}$ = 68 and m∠DBC = 26. Find each measure.

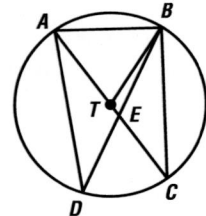

1. m∠BTC   112
2. m∠ADB   34
3. m$\overparen{DC}$ 52
4. m$\overparen{AD}$ 128
5. m∠BAD   82

Motivating the Lesson

Draw a circle and label the center. Draw a ray with its endpoint on the edge and the rest of it in the exterior of the circle. (Do not draw the ray tangent to the circle.) Ask the students if the ray in the picture is tangent to the circle. Why or why not?   No, because if you extend the ray beyond the endpoint, the line formed would intersect the circle in two points.

9-5 Tangents

Objective 9-5

After studying this lesson, you should be able to:

- use properties of tangents to solve problems.

Application

Duane has a tether ball that is attached to a rope. As he walks to the park, he twirls the ball in a circle. When he lets go of the rope, the ball flies off in a path that is tangent to its original circular path.

As you learned in Lesson 9-1, a tangent is a line in the plane of a circle that intersects the circle in exactly one point. Segments and rays that are contained in the tangent and intersect the circle are also said to be tangent to the circle.

In the figure, S is the center of the circle and T is the **point of tangency**. X is in the exterior of the circle, and $\overline{ST}$ is a radius. Thus $SX > ST$. A similar inequality holds for any point in the exterior of the circle.

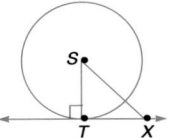

The shortest segment from a point to a line is a perpendicular segment. Thus, $\overline{ST} \perp \overleftrightarrow{TX}$. This leads to Theorem 9-8, which you will prove in Exercise 37.

Theorem 9-8	**If a line is tangent to a circle, then it is perpendicular to the radius drawn to the point of tangency.**

You can apply Theorem 9-8 to solve practical problems.

Example 1

APPLICATION
Aerospace

A spacecraft is 3000 kilometers above Earth's surface. If the radius of Earth is about 6400 kilometers, find the distance between the spacecraft and the horizon.

Since $\overline{SH}$ is a tangent segment, $\overline{SH} \perp \overline{EH}$ by Theorem 9-8. Therefore, $\triangle SHE$ is a right triangle. We can use the Pythagorean Theorem to find the distance between the spacecraft and the horizon.

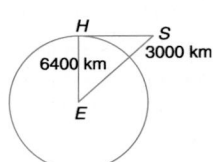

ALTERNATE TEACHING STRATEGIES

Using Investigation

You can guide students to discover that the two tangent segments from a point outside of a circle are congruent. In Investigation 11 on page A10 of **More Investigation in Geometry,** students use construction and measurement to explore tangent segments.

Using Cooperative Groups

After discussing Theorems 9-8 through 9-10, divide the class into three groups and assign each group one of the constructions in this lesson. Have each group follow the instructions and learn how to construct the desired figure. When every student understands how to construct the group's figure, have one member of each group explain the construction to the class.

$EH = 6400$, and $SE = 3000 + 6400$ or 9400

$$\begin{aligned}(EH)^2 + (SH)^2 &= (SE)^2 \quad \text{\textit{Pythagorean Theorem}}\\ 6400^2 + (SH)^2 &= 9400^2 \quad \text{\textit{Substitute 6400 for EH and 9400 for SE.}}\\ 40{,}960{,}000 + (SH)^2 &= 88{,}360{,}000\\ (SH)^2 &= 47{,}400{,}000\\ SH &\approx 6885\end{aligned}$$

The distance from the spacecraft to the horizon is about 6885 kilometers.

The converse of Theorem 9-8 is also true and provides a method for identifying tangents to a circle.

Theorem 9-9	**In a plane, if a line is perpendicular to a radius of a circle at the endpoint on the circle, then the line is a tangent of the circle.**

CONSTRUCTION

Construct a line tangent to a given circle P at a point A on the circle.

1. Draw $\overrightarrow{PA}$.

2. Construct ℓ through A and perpendicular to $\overrightarrow{PA}$. Line ℓ is tangent to $\odot P$ at A.

Since ℓ is perpendicular to radius $\overline{PA}$ at its endpoint, A, on the circle, then line ℓ is tangent to $\odot P$. (Theorem 9-9)

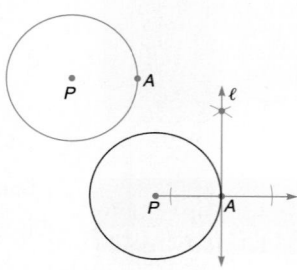

The following construction shows how to construct a tangent from a point outside the circle.

CONSTRUCTION

Construct a line tangent to a given circle C through a point A outside the circle.

1. Draw $\overline{AC}$.

2. Construct the perpendicular bisector of $\overline{AC}$. Call this line ℓ. Call X the intersection of ℓ and $\overline{AC}$.

3. Using X as the center, draw a circle with radius measuring XC. Call D and E the intersection points of the two circles.

4. Draw $\overrightarrow{AD}$. Then $\overrightarrow{AD}$ is tangent to $\odot C$.

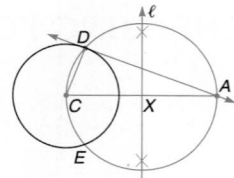

$\overrightarrow{AD}$ is a tangent to $\odot C$ if $\overrightarrow{AD} \perp \overline{DC}$. How do you know $\angle CDA$ is a right angle? **It is inscribed in a semicircle.**

LESSON 9-5 TANGENTS 435

Chalkboard Example

For the Example
If a spacecraft needs to eject its outer fuel tanks when it is 5000 km above Earth's surface, how far will it be from the horizon at the time it ejects its fuel tanks? The radius of Earth is about 6400 km.
$(6400)^2 + x^2 = (6400 + 5000)^2$
$x^2 = 89{,}000{,}000$
$x \approx 9433.98$
The spacecraft will be about 9434 km from the horizon.

Teaching Tip For the constructions in this lesson, you may want to review how to construct perpendicular lines (Lesson 1-9, page 58) and angle bisectors (Lesson 1-7, page 46).

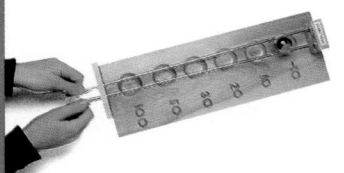

In the picture at the left, the ball bearing game demonstrates that it is possible to have two tangents to a circle from the same exterior point.

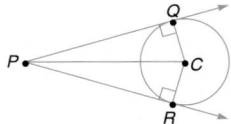

Note that $\overrightarrow{PQ}$ and $\overrightarrow{PR}$ are both tangent to $\odot C$. Also $\overline{PQ}$ and $\overline{PR}$ are **tangent segments.** By drawing $\overline{PC}$, two right triangles are formed. These triangles are congruent by *HL*, which leads us to the following theorem. You will be asked to prove this theorem in Exercise 38.

| **Theorem 9-10** | If two segments from the same exterior point are tangent to a circle, then they are congruent. |

EVALUATING THE LESSON

Checking for Understanding

Exercises 1-12 are designed to help you assess students' understanding through reading, writing, speaking, and modeling. You should work through Exercises 1-3 with your students and then monitor their work on Exercises 4-12.

Error Analysis

Two of the three constructions in this lesson may be confusing the first time through. Have students complete a number of constructions using different-size figures, and ask them to explain the importance of each step as they go along.

Closing the Lesson

Speaking Activity Have a student give the first step in completing one of the constructions discussed in this lesson. Going around the room, have the next student give the next step, and so on until the construction has been explained. Do the same for the other two constructions.

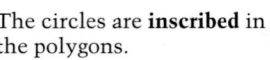

INVESTIGATION

You can learn more about tangent segments in Investigation 11 on page A10.

A polygon is a **circumscribed polygon** if each side of the polygon is tangent to a circle. The following two statements are equivalent.

The polygons are circumscribed about the circles.

The circles are **inscribed** in the polygons.

CONSTRUCTION

Construct a circle inscribed in a given triangle *ABC*.

1. Construct the angle bisectors of $\angle A$ and $\angle C$. Extend the bisectors to meet at point *X*.

2. Construct a line from *X* perpendicular to $\overline{AC}$. Label the intersection of the perpendicular line and $\overline{AC}$, *Y*.

3. Setting the compass length equal to *XY*, draw $\odot X$.

$\odot X$ is inscribed in $\triangle ABC$. Point *X* is called the **incenter.**

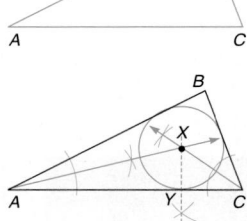

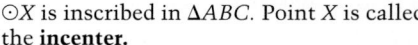

CHECKING FOR UNDERSTANDING

Communicating Mathematics

Read and study the lesson to answer these questions.
See margin for explanations.

1. How many tangents can be drawn to a circle through a point outside the circle? Explain your answer. **2**

2. How many tangents can be drawn to a circle through a point inside the circle? Explain your answer. **0**

3. How many tangents can be drawn to a circle through a point on the circle? Explain your answer. **1**

Additional Answers

1. A tangent can be drawn to each "side" of the circle from the point outside of the circle.

2. A tangent cannot pass through a point inside the circle.

3. Only one line can be drawn perpendicular to the endpoint of a radius.

Identify each polygon as circumscribed, inscribed, or neither.

4.
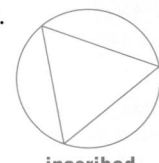
inscribed

5.
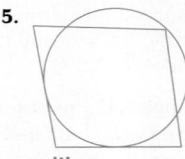
neither

6.
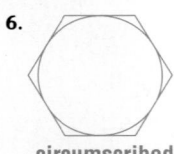
circumscribed

Find the measure of x. Assume that C is the center of the circle.

7.
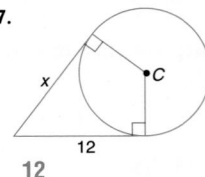
12
12

8.
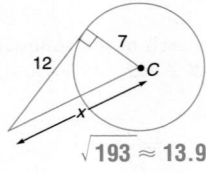
12
7
$\sqrt{193} \approx 13.9$

9.
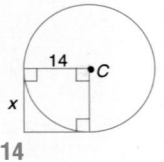
14
x
14

10.
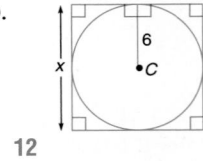
6
x
12

11.
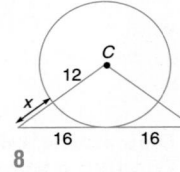
C
12
x
16   16
8

12.
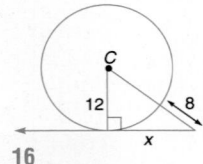
C
12
x
16

EXERCISES

Practice

A

In the figure, $\overline{AB}$ and $\overline{CD}$ both are tangent to $\odot P$ and $\odot Q$. Also $AP = 8$, $BQ = 5$, and $m\angle CPE = 45$. Find the measure of each of the following.

13. $\overset{\frown}{CE}$ 45   14. $\angle PCG$ 90   15. $\angle CGP$ 45

16. $\overline{CG}$ 8   17. $\angle QDC$ 90   18. $\angle FGD$ 45

19. $\angle FQD$ 45   20. $\overset{\frown}{DF}$ 45   21. $\overline{DQ}$ 5

22. $\overline{DG}$ 5   23. $\overline{DC}$ 13   24. $\overline{PG}$ $8\sqrt{2} \approx 11.3$

25. $\overline{GQ}$ 26. $\overline{PQ}$ 27. $\overline{AB}$ $\sqrt{329} \approx 18.1$
    $5\sqrt{2} \approx 7.1$ $13\sqrt{2} \approx 18.4$

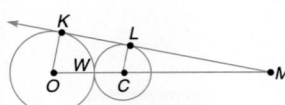
8
A
P
45°
C
E
G F
D
B
Q
5

Two circles are tangent if they share one point. In the figure at the right, $\odot O$ and $\odot C$ are tangent at W, and $\overrightarrow{MK}$ is tangent to $\odot O$ at K and to $\odot C$ at L. **See margin.**

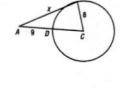
K   L
W
O   C   •M

28. What is true about $\overline{OK}$ and $\overline{CL}$? Explain your answer.

29. What is true about $\triangle OKM$ and $\triangle CLM$? Explain your answer.

LESSON 9-5   TANGENTS   437

RETEACHING THE LESSON

Review Theorems 9-8 through 9-10 with students and draw a figure to represent each theorem. Write the given information and what is being proved. Have students investigate some of the logic behind the theorems and explain it in their own words.

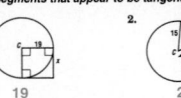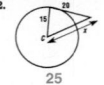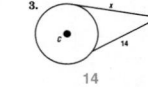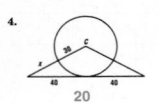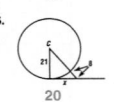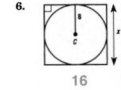

438   Chapter 9

Exercise Notes

For Exercises 30-32, apply Theorem 9-10.

For Exercise 39, remind students that in an indirect proof you assume the opposite of the conclusion and work toward a contradiction of the given information.

Additional Answers

33. *TB* = *TS* and *TA* = *TR* (If two segments from the same exterior point are tangent to a circle, then they are congruent.)
TA − *TB* = *TR* − *TS* (Substitution prop. of equality)
AB = *RS*

34. *AT* = *RT* and *TB* = *TS* (If two segments from the same exterior point are tangent to a circle, then they are congruent.)
AT + *TB* = *RT* + *TS* (Addition prop. of equality)
AB = *RS*

Practice Masters Booklet, p. 62

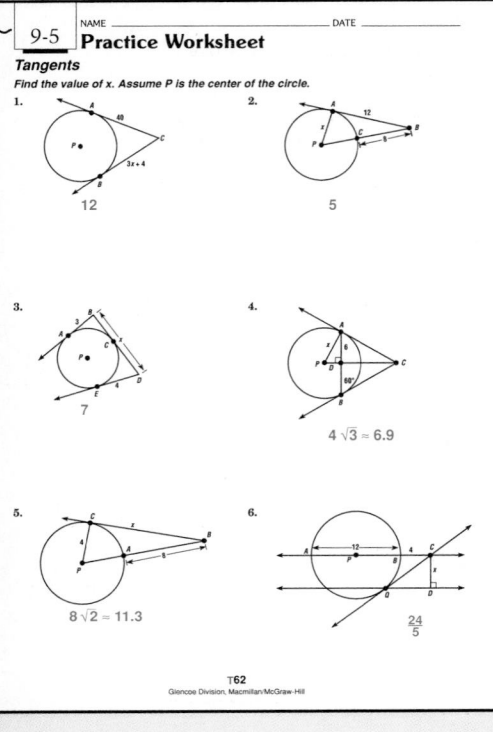

B In the figure at the right, △*ABC* is circumscribed about the circle.

30. Suppose the perimeter of △*ABC* is 42 units, *BX* = 6, and *CX* = 7. Find *AB* and *AC*. **14; 15**

31. Suppose the perimeter of △*ABC* is 50 units, *AZ* = 10, and *CX* = 12. Find *BC*. **15**

32. Suppose the perimeter of △*ABC* is 48 units, *CY* = 9.5, and *AZ* = 6. Find *BZ*. **8.5**

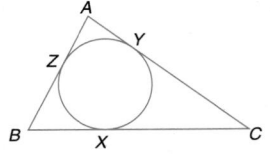

In each of the following, the lines are tangent to the circles. Explain why *AB* = *RS*. **See margin.**

33.
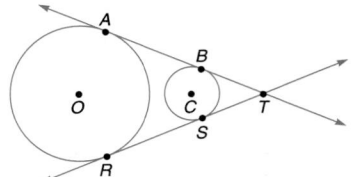

34.
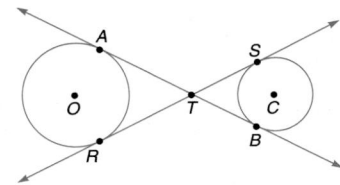

CONSTRUCTION

35. Draw a circle. Label the center *P*. Locate a point on the circle. Label it *A*. Construct a tangent to ⊙*P* at *A*. **See margin.**

36. Draw a circle. Label the center *Q*. Draw a point exterior to the circle. Label it *B*. Construct a tangent to ⊙*Q* containing *B*. **See margin.**

C Write a paragraph proof for each.

37. If a line is tangent to a circle, then it is perpendicular to the radius drawn to the point of tangency. (Theorem 9-8) **See margin.**

38. If two segments from the same exterior point are tangent to a circle, then they are congruent. (Theorem 9-10) **See Solutions Manual.**

39. Write an indirect proof.

Given: $\ell \perp \overline{AB}$
$\overline{AB}$ is a radius of ⊙*A*.

Prove: ℓ is tangent to ⊙*A*.
(Theorem 9-9) **See Solutions Manual.**

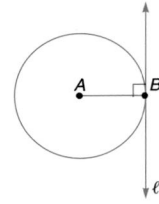

CONNECTION
Algebra

40. The graphs of *x* = 4 and *y* = −1 are both tangent to a circle that has its center in the fourth quadrant and a diameter of 14 units.
a. Write an equation of the circle. $(x - 11)^2 + (y + 8)^2 = 49$
b. Draw a graph of the circle and the tangents. **See Solutions Manual.**

Additional Answer

35.
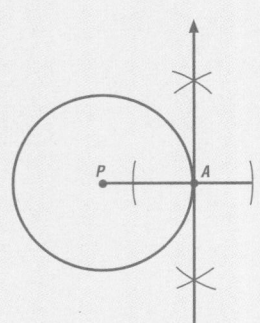

36.

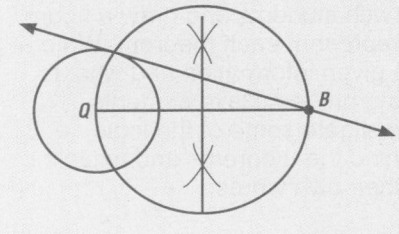

Critical Thinking

41. A circle is inscribed in a triangle whose sides are 9 centimeters, 14 centimeters, and 17 centimeters long. If P separates the 14-centimeter side into segments whose ratio is $x{:}y$ with $x < y$, find the values of x and y. **3, 11**

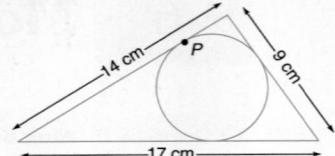

Applications

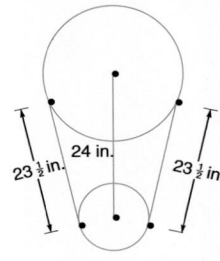

42. Agriculture The distance between the centers of the two wheels on the belt pulley system of a tractor is 24 inches. The length of the belt between the two wheels is $23\frac{1}{2}$ inches. Find the radius of each wheel if the radius of the larger wheel is twice the radius of the smaller wheel. **about 4.9 in.; 9.7 in.**

43. Literature In your own words, explain the meaning of the following poem. **See margin.**

We are, all of us, alone
Though not uncommon
In our singularity.

Touching,
We become tangent to
Circles of common experience,
Co-incident,
Defining in collective tangency
Circles
Reciprocal in their subtle
Redefinition of us.

In tangency
We are never less alone,
But no longer

Only.   by Gene Mattingly

Mixed Review

44. If the measure of inscribed angle ABC is 42, what is the measure of the intercepted arc AC? **(Lesson 9-4) 84**

45. Find the perimeter of a rhombus whose diagonals are 30 inches and 16 inches long. **(Lesson 8-2) 68 in.**

46. One right triangle has an acute angle measuring 67°, and a second right triangle has an acute angle measuring 23°. Are the triangles similar? Explain. **(Lesson 7-4) yes; AA Similarity**

47. Can a median of a triangle also be an altitude? If so, what type of triangle is it? **(Lesson 5-1) yes; isosceles**

48. Find the slope of a line that passes through the points $(2, -9)$ and $(0, 3)$. **(Lesson 3-5) -6**

Wrap-Up

49. Write three questions that could be used as a quiz over this lesson. Be sure to include the answers to your questions. **See students' work.**

LESSON 9-5 TANGENTS 439

EXTENDING THE LESSON

Math Power: Reasoning

In two nonintersecting circles, will the points of tangency of a common internal tangent ever be the same as the points of tangency of a common external tangent? Why or why not?   No, because there is only one line tangent to a given point on a circle.

Additional Answers

37. Given: $\overleftrightarrow{CA}$ is tangent to the circle at A.
Prove: $\overline{XA} \perp \overleftrightarrow{CA}$

Pick any point on $\overleftrightarrow{CA}$ other than A and call it B. Draw $\overline{XB}$. From the definition of tangent, we know that $\overleftrightarrow{CA}$ intersects $\odot X$ at exactly one point, A, and that B lies in the exterior of $\odot X$. Therefore, $XA < XB$. Thus, since $\overline{XA}$ is the shortest segment from X to $\overleftrightarrow{CA}$, it follows that $\overline{XA} \perp \overleftrightarrow{CA}$.

43. Sample answer: Everyone is their own person, an individual and alone. However, each person touches the lives of others, just as a tangent touches a circle in one place. Each person is changed by his or her relationships with others but is still alone.

Enrichment Masters Booklet, p. 54

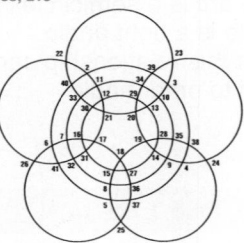

9-5 Enrichment Worksheet

Magic Circles

Study the circles at the right. Their intersection points are labeled with numbers. The sum of the numbers for each circle equals the sum for each of the other circles. Such circles are called **magic circles**.

Each circle has a sum of 14.

1. Is the set of circles below a set of magic circles? If you answer yes, identify the sum.
yes; 215

2. Label the intersection points for the circles at the right to obtain magic circles.
Answers may vary. A possible answer is shown.

T54
Glencoe Division, Macmillan/McGraw-Hill

Chapter 9   439

Lesson Resources

- Reteaching Master 9-6
- Practice Master 9-6
- Enrichment Master 9-6
- Evaluation Master, p. 122
- Multicultural Master, p. 9

 Transparency 9-6 contains the 5-Minute Check and a teaching aid for this lesson.

INTRODUCING THE LESSON

5-Minute Check

(over Lesson 9-5)

Find each measure. *AF* = 6, *BJ* = 3, and m∠*HAG* = 60.

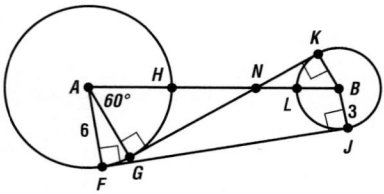

1. m∠*ANG* 30
2. m∠*KBN* 60
3. *GN* $6\sqrt{3} \approx 10.39$
4. *LK* 60

Motivating the Lesson

Draw a circle with a diameter and a tangent at one of the endpoints of the diameter. Ask if there is a relationship between the angle formed by the diameter and the tangent and the intercepted arc of that angle.   **Yes, the angle measure is one-half the measure of the arc.** This can be said because the arc is a semicircle and the angle is a right angle. Suggest that this relationship can be extended to other angle measures.

TEACHING THE LESSON

Teaching Tip When using the picture of one secant and one tangent on page 440, $\overparen{PR}$ may not look like an intercepted arc. Reviewing the definition may help.

9-6   More Angle Measures

Objective 9-6

After studying this lesson, you should be able to:
- find the measures of angles formed by intersecting secants and tangents in relation to intercepted arcs.

Application

Lines intersecting the circular patterns of a stained glass window demonstrate that many different angle relationships exist. The location of the vertex of the angle determines the relationship between the measure of the angle and its intercepted arcs.

FYI···

The first stained glass window was made for the Saint Sophia Cathedral in A.D. 535.

In Lesson 9-4, you studied the relationship between the measures of intercepted arcs and inscribed angles. The inscribed angle relationship can be extended to any angle that has its vertex on the circle. This includes angles formed by two secants or a secant and a tangent.

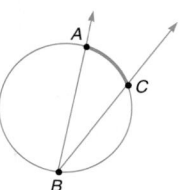

two secants

$$m\angle ABC = \frac{1}{2}m\overparen{AC}$$

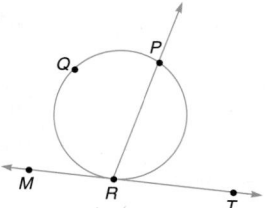

one secant, one tangent

$$m\angle PRT = \frac{1}{2}m\overparen{PR}$$

$$m\angle MRP = \frac{1}{2}m\overparen{PQR}$$

The relationship is stated in Theorem 9-11. You will prove this theorem in Exercise 55.

Theorem 9-11

If a secant and a tangent intersect at the point of tangency, then the measure of each angle formed is one-half the measure of its intercepted arc.

However, this lesson is primarily concerned with the measures of angles with vertices not on the circle.

440   CHAPTER 9   CIRCLES

ALTERNATE TEACHING STRATEGIES

Using Diagrams

Have students draw two intersecting lines on a piece of paper. On another piece of paper, have them draw a circle. Have them place one sheet of paper on top of the other and sketch the intersection of the two figures. How can students find the measure of one of the angles?

Using Modeling

With the students, make a list of the possible combinations of two intersecting lines (tangents and secants) in a circle. Then make two vertical angles out of sticks, pencils or pipe cleaners. Draw a circle on the board or overhead and ask students to demonstrate an example of each situation.

Example 1

If $m\widehat{MH} = 60$ and $m\widehat{AT} = 140$, find $m\angle 1$.

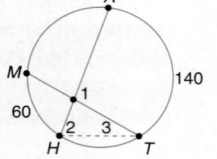

Notice that the vertex of $\angle 1$ is inside the circle. Draw $\overline{HT}$.

$$m\angle 1 = m\angle 2 + m\angle 3 \qquad \textit{Exterior Angle Theorem}$$
$$= \frac{1}{2}m\widehat{AT} + \frac{1}{2}m\widehat{MH} \qquad \textit{Theorem 9-4}$$
$$= \frac{1}{2}(140) + \frac{1}{2}(60) \qquad m\widehat{AT} = 140, \; m\widehat{MH} = 60$$
$$= 70 + 30$$
$$= 100$$

$\angle 1$ measures $100°$.

Example 1 illustrates Theorem 9-12. You will be asked to prove this theorem in Exercise 51.

Theorem 9-12	If two secants intersect in the interior of a circle, then the measure of an angle formed is one-half the sum of the measures of the arcs intercepted by the angle and its vertical angle.

In the circle at the right, two secants intersect inside the circle.

So, $m\angle 1 = \frac{1}{2}(m\widehat{MH} + m\widehat{AT})$

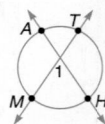

Theorem 9-13 states the relationship between the angles and the intercepted arcs when the vertex of the angle is on the exterior of the circle.

Theorem 9-13	If two secants, a secant and a tangent, or two tangents intersect in the exterior of a circle, then the measure of the angle formed is one-half the positive difference of the measures of the intercepted arcs.

There are three cases that need to be considered. You will prove these cases in Exercises 52, 53, and 54.

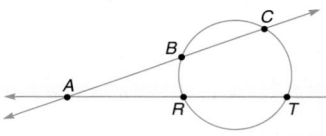

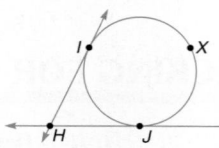

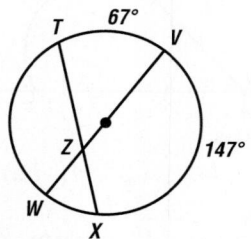

Case 1: two secants
$m\angle CAT = \frac{1}{2}(m\widehat{CT} - m\widehat{BR})$

Case 2: a secant and a tangent
$m\angle FDG = \frac{1}{2}(m\widehat{FG} - m\widehat{EG})$

Case 3: two tangents
$m\angle IHJ = \frac{1}{2}(m\widehat{IXJ} - m\widehat{IJ})$

Chalkboard Example

For Example 1
Refer to the figure below. If $m\widehat{TV} = 67$ and $m\widehat{VX} = 147$, find $m\angle WZX$.

Since $\overline{VW}$ is a diameter of $\odot Q$, $m\widehat{VX} + m\widehat{XW} = 180$. So, $m\widehat{XW} = 33$. $m\angle WZX = \frac{1}{2}(67 + 33) = 50$.

For Example 2

Alice is playing golf and her ball has landed behind a bush. If $m\widehat{AB} = 86$ and $m\widehat{AC} = 184$, find $m\angle AGB$. What does this tell Alice about her next shot?

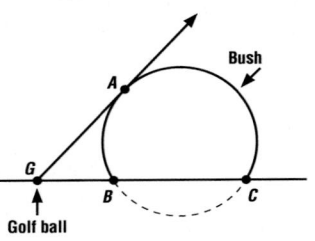

Bush

A

G

B

C

Golf ball

$m\angle AGB = \frac{1}{2}(184 - 86)$

$m\angle AGB = 49$

The angle of Alice's next shot must be greater than 49°.

For Example 3

$\overline{QU}$ and $\overline{UA}$ are tangent to $\odot T$ and $m\widehat{QA} = 80$. Find the value of *x*.

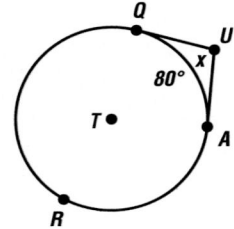

Q

U

x

80°

T

A

R

$m\angle QUA = \frac{1}{2}(m\widehat{QRA} - m\widehat{QA})$

$x = \frac{1}{2}(280 - 80)$

(why does $m\widehat{QRA} = 280$?)

$x = \frac{1}{2}(200)$

$= 100$

Checking for Understanding

Exercises 1-12 are designed to help you assess students' understanding through reading, writing, speaking, and modeling. You should work through Exercises 1-3 with your students and then monitor their work on Exercises 4-12.

Example 2

APPLICATION

Recreation

To start a game of pool, 10 balls are placed in a rack as shown below. The rack is tangent to the 9-ball at two points. If a circle represents the ball, find the measure of each arc whose endpoints are the points of tangency.

The rack is an equilateral triangle, so $m\angle A = 60$. The sides of the rack are tangent to the 9-ball at *M* and *N*. Let $m\widehat{MN} = x$. Then the measure of the corresponding major arc, $\widehat{MON}$, is $360 - x$.

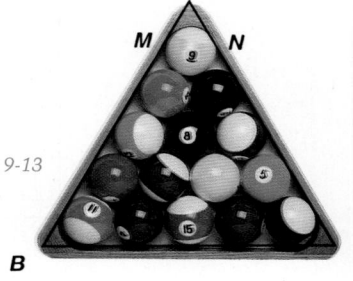

$m\angle A = \frac{1}{2}(m\widehat{MON} - m\widehat{MN})$ *Theorem 9-13*

$m\angle A = \frac{1}{2}[(360 - x) - x]$

$60 = \frac{1}{2}[360 - 2x]$

$60 = 180 - x$

$x = 120$

The measures of the two arcs are 120 and $360 - 120$ or 240.

Example 3

$\overleftrightarrow{TN}$ is tangent to $\odot Q$ at *A* and $m\widehat{AB} = 124$. Find $m\angle BAN$.

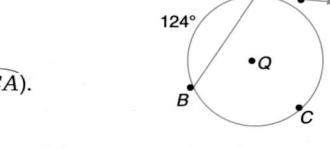

The vertex of $\angle BAN$ is on $\odot Q$. By Theorem 9-11, $m\angle BAN = \frac{1}{2}(m\widehat{BCA})$. So, first find $m\widehat{BCA}$.

$m\widehat{AB} + m\widehat{BCA} = 360$ *The sum of the measures of a minor arc and its major arc is 360.*

$124 + m\widehat{BCA} = 360$ $m\widehat{AB} = 124$

$m\widehat{BCA} = 236$

$m\angle BAN = \frac{1}{2}(m\widehat{BCA})$

$= \frac{1}{2}(236)$ or 118

The measure of $\angle BAN$ is 118.

CHECKING FOR UNDERSTANDING

Communicating Mathematics

Read and study the lesson to answer these questions.
See margin.

1. Draw examples of the three ways two secants can intersect; in the circle, on the circle, and outside the circle. Explain how to find the measures of the angles in each case.

Additional Answer

1. Sample answer:

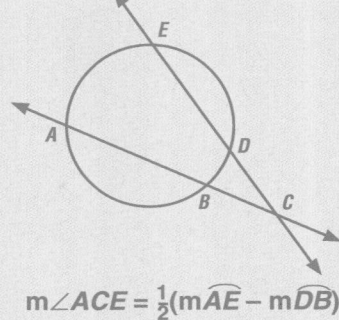

$m\angle ACE = \frac{1}{2}(m\widehat{AE} - m\widehat{DB})$

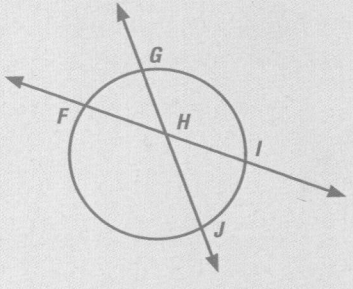

$m\angle IHJ = \frac{1}{2}(m\widehat{JI} + m\widehat{GF})$

2. How are inscribed angles and angles formed by a secant and a tangent at the point of tangency alike? How are they different?

3. When you are finding the measure of an angle whose vertex is outside of the circle, how do you know which arc measure to subtract from which arc measure?

Guided Practice

For each circle, measurements of certain arcs are given. Find the measure of each numbered angle. Assume lines that appear to be tangent are tangent.

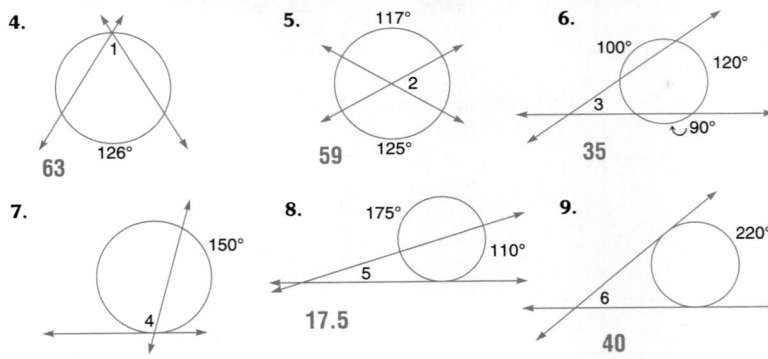

4. 63 (1, 126°)

5. 59 (117°, 2, 125°)

6. 35 (100°, 3, 120°, 90°)

7. 105 (150°, 4)

8. 17.5 (175°, 5, 110°)

9. 40 (220°, 6)

For each figure, write an equation in terms of *x* and the given measures. Then solve for *x*. Assume lines that appear to be tangent are tangent.

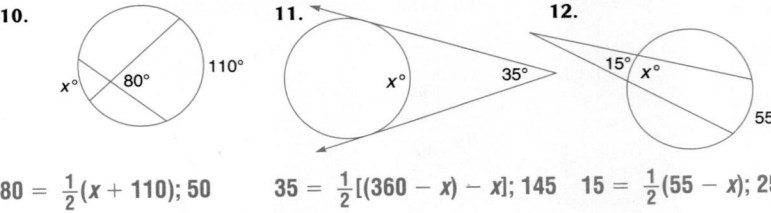

10. $80 = \frac{1}{2}(x + 110)$; 50

11. $35 = \frac{1}{2}[(360 - x) - x]$; 145

12. $15 = \frac{1}{2}(55 - x)$; 25

EXERCISES

Practice

In the figure, $m\widehat{BC} = 84$, $m\widehat{CD} = 38$, $m\widehat{DE} = 64$, $m\widehat{EF} = 60$, and $\overleftrightarrow{AB}$ and $\overleftrightarrow{AF}$ are tangents. Find each measure.

13. $m\widehat{BF}$ 114
14. $m\widehat{BDF}$ 246
15. $m\angle 1$ 66
16. $m\widehat{BFC}$ 276
17. $m\angle 2$ 138
18. $m\angle GBC$ 42
19. $m\widehat{BFE}$ 174
20. $m\angle 3$ 87
21. $m\angle 4$ 49
22. $m\angle 5$ 131
23. $m\widehat{FBC}$ 198
24. $m\angle 6$ 69
25. $m\widehat{FBD}$ 236
26. $m\angle 7$ 118
27. $m\angle 8$ 38

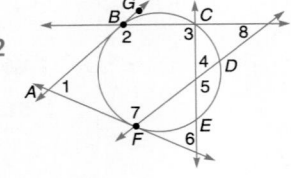

LESSON 9-6 MORE ANGLE MEASURES 443

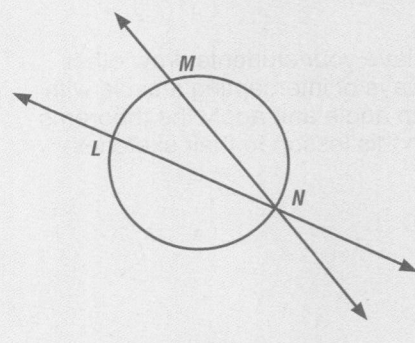

$m\angle LNM = \frac{1}{2}m\widehat{LM}$

Additional Answer

51. Given: Secants $\overleftrightarrow{AC}$ and $\overleftrightarrow{BD}$ intersect at X inside $\odot P$.
Prove: $m\angle AXB = \frac{1}{2}(m\widehat{AB} + m\widehat{CD})$

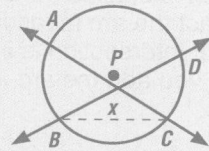

We are given that secants $\overleftrightarrow{AC}$ and $\overleftrightarrow{BD}$ intersect at X inside $\odot P$. Draw $\overline{BC}$. Because an angle inscribed in a circle has the measure of $\frac{1}{2}$ the measure of its intercepted arc, $m\angle XBC = \frac{1}{2}m\widehat{CD}$ and $m\angle XCB = \frac{1}{2}m\widehat{AB}$. By the Exterior Angle Theorem, $m\angle AXB = m\angle XCB + m\angle XBC$. By substitution, $m\angle AXB = \frac{1}{2}m\widehat{AB} + \frac{1}{2}m\widehat{CD}$. Then by use of the distributive property, $m\angle AXB = \frac{1}{2}(m\widehat{AB} + m\widehat{CD})$.

Reteaching Masters Booklet, p. 55

9-6

NAME ____ DATE ____

Reteaching Worksheet

More Angle Measures

If both sides of an angle intersect a circle, you can express it's measure in terms of associated arc measures.

- If a secant and a tangent intersect at the point of tangency, then the measure of each angle formed is one-half the measure of its intercepted arc.
- If two secants intersect in the interior of a circle, then the measure of an angle formed is one-half the sum of the measures of the arcs intercepted by the angle and its vertical angle.
- If two secants, a secant and a tangent, or two tangents intersect in the exterior of a circle, then the measure of the angle formed is one-half the positive difference of the measures of the intercepted arcs.

Example: Find the measure of $\angle MPN$.

From the last theorem above, you know
$m\angle MPN = \frac{1}{2}m(\widehat{MN} - \widehat{RS})$.
$= \frac{1}{2}(34 - 18)$
$= \frac{1}{2}(16)$ or 8

For each figure, measures of certain arcs are given. Find the measure of each numbered angle. Assume lines that appear to be tangent are tangent.

1. 2. 3.

46 67 15

For each figure, write an equation in terms of x and the given measures. Then solve for x. Assume lines that appear to be tangent are tangent.

4. 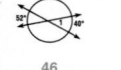 5. 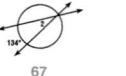 6.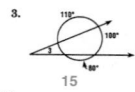

$100 = \frac{1}{2}(x+130); 70$ $50 = \frac{1}{2}[(360-x)-x]; 130$ $20 = \frac{1}{2}(70-x); 30$

T55
Glencoe Division, Macmillan/McGraw-Hill

444 Chapter 9

In the figure, $m\angle 1 = 2x$, $m\angle 1 = m\angle 2$, $m\widehat{RYT} = 4x + 4$, $m\widehat{YT} = 3x - 20$, $m\angle 4 = 3x + 14$, and $\overleftrightarrow{ST}$ and $\overleftrightarrow{SR}$ are tangents. Find each value or measure.

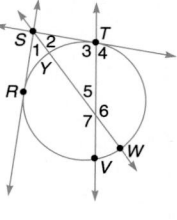

28. x 22
29. $m\angle 1$ 44
30. $m\widehat{RV}$ 108
31. $m\angle 2$ 44
32. $m\widehat{RYT}$ 92
33. $m\widehat{TRV}$ 200
34. $m\widehat{YT}$ 46
35. $m\widehat{YR}$ 46
36. $m\angle 5$ 36
37. $m\widehat{TW}$ 134
38. $m\widehat{RW}$ 134
39. $m\angle 6$ 144
40. $m\angle 4$ 80
41. $m\widehat{TWV}$ 160
42. $m\widehat{YV}$ 154
43. $m\widehat{VW}$ 26
44. $m\angle 3$ 100
45. $m\angle 7$ 144

46. In the figure below, find $m\angle CED$. 18.75

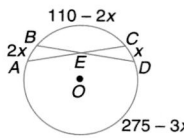

47. In the figure, $\overleftrightarrow{AD}$ passes through the center of $\odot O$. If $m\widehat{SB} = 120$, $m\widehat{AB} = 2(m\widehat{RS})$, and $m\widehat{CD} = 35$, find $m\widehat{UV}$. 15

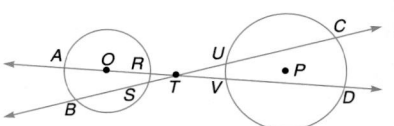

48. In the figure, $\overrightarrow{BT}$ and $\overrightarrow{BP}$ are tangent to the circle. Find the values of x, y, and z.
$x = 100$, $y = 114$, $z = 106$

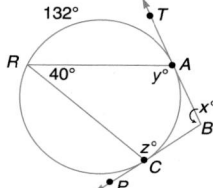

49. In the figure, $\overrightarrow{AC}$ and $\overrightarrow{AS}$ are tangent to the circle. Find the values of x, y, and z.
$x = 46$, $y = 64$, $z = 40$

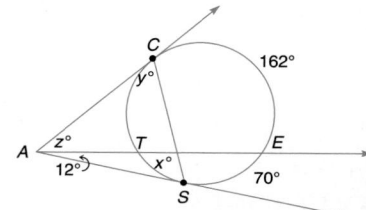

50. In a circle, chords $\overline{AC}$ and $\overline{BD}$ meet at P. If $m\angle CPB = 115$, $m\widehat{AB} = 6x + 16$, and $m\widehat{CD} = 3x - 12$, find x, $m\widehat{AB}$, and $m\widehat{CD}$. $x = 14$, $m\widehat{AB} = 100$, $m\widehat{CD} = 30$

Write a paragraph proof for each. See margin.

51. If two secants intersect in the interior of a circle, then the measure of an angle formed is one-half the sum of the measures of the arcs intercepted by the angle and its vertical angle. (Theorem 9-12)

444 CHAPTER 9 CIRCLES

RETEACHING THE LESSON

Review the two ways of finding angle measures that previously have been discussed.   If the angle is a central angle, then its measure is equal to the measure of its intercepted arc; if the angle is an inscribed angle, then it is one-half the measure of its intercepted arc.

Have your students draw other ways of intercepting a circle with an angle and apply the theorems in this lesson to their sketches.

52. Case 1 of Theorem 9-13

Given: $\overleftrightarrow{AC}$ and $\overleftrightarrow{AT}$ are secants to the circle.

Prove: $m\angle CAT = \frac{1}{2}(m\widehat{CT} - m\widehat{BR})$

(Hint: Draw $\overline{CR}$.)

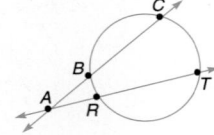

53. Case 2 of Theorem 9-13

Given: $\overrightarrow{DG}$ is a tangent to the circle.
$\overrightarrow{DF}$ is a secant to the circle.

Prove: $m\angle FDG = \frac{1}{2}(m\widehat{FG} - m\widehat{GE})$

(Hint: Draw $\overline{FG}$.)

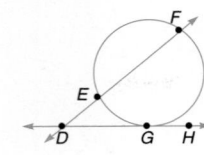

54. Case 3 of Theorem 9-13

Given: $\overrightarrow{HI}$ and $\overrightarrow{HJ}$ are tangents to the circle.

Prove: $m\angle IHJ = \frac{1}{2}(m\widehat{IXJ} - m\widehat{IJ})$

(Hint: Draw $\overline{IJ}$.)

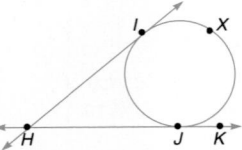

55. Write a paragraph proof of Theorem 9-11. You must prove the theorem for three cases: an acute angle, a right angle, and an obtuse angle. **See Solutions Manual.**

Critical Thinking

56. In the figure, $\overrightarrow{DA}$ and $\overrightarrow{DB}$ are tangent to the circle. What is the value of $x + y$? Explain your reasoning. **See Solutions Manual.**

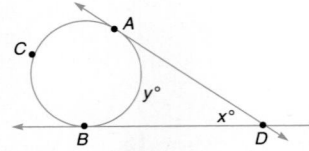

Application

57. Navigation In order to avoid dangerous rocks and shallow waters, a captain must steer the ship around what the sailors call the *danger circle*. Two lighthouses help to locate this danger circle. The measure of an inscribed angle that cuts the arc defined by the lighthouses is published on navigation charts.

a. If the measure of the angle formed by the lighthouses with the ship as the vertex is less than the published measure, is the ship safe? Why or why not? **See Solutions Manual.**

b. If the measure of the angle formed by the lighthouses with the ship as the vertex is greater than the published measure, is the ship safe? Why or why not? **See Solutions Manual.**

Additional Answer

52. We are given that $\overleftrightarrow{AC}$ and $\overleftrightarrow{AT}$ are secants to a circle. Draw $\overline{CR}$: $m\angle CRT = \frac{1}{2}m\widehat{CT}$; $m\angle ACR = \frac{1}{2}m\widehat{BR}$ because the measure of an inscribed angle equals $\frac{1}{2}$ the measure of the intercepted arc. By the Exterior Angle Theorem, $m\angle CRT = m\angle ACR + m\angle CAT$. Then by substitution, $\frac{1}{2}m\widehat{CT} = \frac{1}{2}m\widehat{BR} + m\angle CAT$, and by the subtraction property of equality, $\frac{1}{2}m\widehat{CT} - \frac{1}{2}m\widehat{BR} = m\angle CAT$. Finally, by the distributive property of equality, $\frac{1}{2}(m\widehat{CT} - m\widehat{BR}) = m\angle CAT$.

Additional Answers

53. We are given that $\overrightarrow{DG}$ is a tangent to a circle, and $\overrightarrow{DF}$ is a secant to that circle. Draw $\overline{FG}$: $m\angle DFG = \frac{1}{2}m\widehat{GE}$; $m\angle FGH = \frac{1}{2}m\widehat{FG}$ because the measure of an inscribed angle equals $\frac{1}{2}$ the measure of the intercepted arc. By the Exterior Angle Theorem, $m\angle FGH = m\angle DFG + m\angle FDG$. Then by substitution $\frac{1}{2}m\widehat{FG} = \frac{1}{2}m\widehat{GE} + m\angle FDG$, and by the subtraction property, $\frac{1}{2}m\widehat{FG} - \frac{1}{2}m\widehat{GE} = m\angle FDG$. By the distributive property, $\frac{1}{2}(m\widehat{FG} - m\widehat{GE}) = m\angle FDG$.

54. We are given that $\overleftrightarrow{HI}$ and $\overleftrightarrow{HJ}$ are tangents to a circle. Draw $\overline{IJ}$: $\frac{1}{2}m\angle IJK = \frac{1}{2}m\widehat{IJ}$ and $m\angle HIJ = \frac{1}{2}m\widehat{IJ}$ because the measure of an inscribed angle equals $\frac{1}{2}$ the measure of the intercepted arc. By the Exterior Angle Theorem, $m\angle IJK = m\angle HIJ + m\angle IHJ$. Then by substitution $\frac{1}{2}m\widehat{IXJ} = \frac{1}{2}m\widehat{IJ} + m\angle IHJ$, and by the subtraction property of equality, $\frac{1}{2}m\widehat{IXJ} - \frac{1}{2}m\widehat{IJ} = m\angle IHJ$. Finally, by the distributive property of equality, $\frac{1}{2}(m\widehat{IXJ} - m\widehat{IJ}) = m\angle IHJ$.

Practice Masters Booklet, p. 63

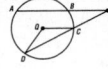
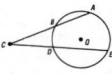
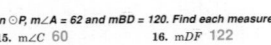
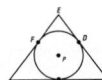

Additional Answer

64.

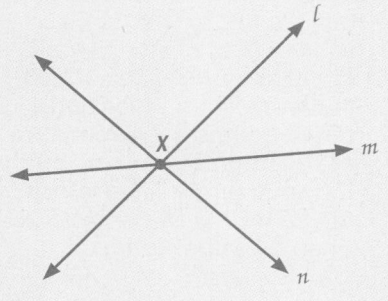

58. What can you say about a line in the plane of a circle that is perpendicular to a radius of the circle at its endpoint that is on the circle? **(Lesson 9-5)**
It is a tangent to the circle.

59. Solve the proportion $\frac{x}{5} = \frac{7}{2}$. **(Lesson 7-1)** 17.5

60. Can 7, 9, and 11 be the measures of the sides of a triangle? **(Lesson 5-6)** yes

61. The base angles of an isosceles triangle have measures $7x - 3$ and $4x + 12$. What is the measure of the vertex angle? **(Lesson 4-7)** 116

62. Find the value of x. **(Lesson 4-7)** 50

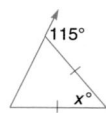

63. Congruence of angles is reflexive.

63. What guarantees that $\angle B \cong \angle B$? **(Lesson 2-7)**

64. Draw and label a diagram that shows lines ℓ, m, and n that intersect at point X. **(Lesson 1-2)** See margin.

Wrap-Up

65. Draw six circles. Use each circle to show a different way an angle can be drawn such that its sides intercept arcs of the circle. Explain how the measure of each angle is related to the measures of intercepted arcs of the circle. **See Solutions Manual.**

Looking Ahead
Algebra Review

You will need to use the quadratic formula in the next lesson. Use the quadratic equation to solve each equation.

Example: $x^2 - 8x - 4 = 0$

$$x = \frac{-b \pm \sqrt{b^2 - 4ac}}{2a}$$

$$= \frac{-(-8) \pm \sqrt{(-8)^2 - 4(1)(-4)}}{2(1)} \qquad a = 1, b = -8, c = -4$$

$$= \frac{8 \pm \sqrt{64 + 16}}{2}$$

$$= \frac{8 \pm \sqrt{80}}{2}$$

$$= \frac{8 \pm 4\sqrt{5}}{2} \qquad \textit{Simplify the radical.}$$

$$x = 4 + 2\sqrt{5} \text{ or } 4 - 2\sqrt{5}$$

$$x \approx 8.47 \text{ or } -0.47$$

The solution set is $\{4 + 2\sqrt{5}, 4 - 2\sqrt{5}\}$.

66. $x^2 - 7x - 8 = 0$ 8, -1

67. $3x^2 + 14x = 5$ $\frac{1}{3}$, -5

68. $n^2 - 13n - 32 = 0$
$\frac{13 + 3\sqrt{33}}{2}, \frac{13 - 3\sqrt{33}}{2}$

69. $-4y^2 + 13 = -16y$
$\frac{4 - \sqrt{29}}{2}, \frac{4 + \sqrt{29}}{2}$

Enrichment Masters Booklet, p. 55

NAME_____   DATE_____

9-6 **Enrichment Worksheet**

Tangent Circles

Two circles in the same plane are **tangent circles** if they have exactly one point in common. Tangent circles with no common interior points are **externally tangent**. If tangent circles have common interior points, then they are **internally tangent**. Three or more circles are **mutually tangent** if each pair of them is tangent.

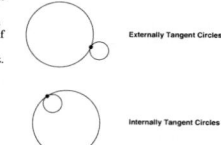

Externally Tangent Circles

Internally Tangent Circles

1. Make sketches to show all possible positions of three mutually tangent circles.

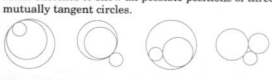

2. Make sketches to show all possible positions of four mutually tangent circles.

3. Make sketches to show all possible positions of five mutually tangent circles.

4. Write a conjecture about the number of possible positions for n mutually tangent circles if n is a whole number greater than four.

Possible answer: For $n > 4$, there are $\frac{n}{2}$ positions if n is even and $\frac{1}{2}(n + 1)$ positions if n is odd.

T55
Glencoe Division, Macmillan/McGraw-Hill

EXTENDING THE LESSON

Math Power: Reasoning

Suppose you had three segments intersecting a circle and all three segments intersected each other at one point. How many different possibilities or cases would you need to look at if you were going to prove theorems similar to the ones in this lesson involving angle measures?   6

9-7 Special Segments in a Circle

Objective

9-7

After studying this lesson, you should be able to:
- use properties of chords, secants, and tangents to solve problems.

Lesson Resources
- Reteaching Master 9-7
- Practice Master 9-7
- Enrichment Master 9-7
- Technology Master, p. 9

Transparency 9-7 contains the 5-Minute Check and a teaching aid for this lesson.

Application

An escape wheel from an antique grandfather clock has been broken and only part of the gear remains. In order to replace it, a tool and die maker needs to know the radius of the original wheel. *You will solve this problem in Example 1.*

You will learn about special relationships involving segments of chords, secants, and tangents that will help you solve this and other problems. Similar triangles can be used to prove these relationships.

In the figure, $\overline{AC}$ is separated into $\overline{AE}$ and $\overline{EC}$. $\overline{BD}$ is separated into $\overline{BE}$ and $\overline{ED}$. Study these products.

$$AE \cdot EC = 2 \cdot 6 \qquad BE \cdot ED = 3 \cdot 4$$
$$= 12 \qquad\qquad = 12$$

This is an application of Theorem 9-14.

INTRODUCING THE LESSON

5-Minute Check

(over Lesson 9-6)

Refer to the figure below.
$m\widehat{JK} = 5x - 5$, $m\widehat{KM} = 6x - 12$,
$m\widehat{JN} = 13x + 11$, $m\angle 2 = 9x + 6$,
and $\overleftrightarrow{NO}$ is a tangent. Find each value or measure.

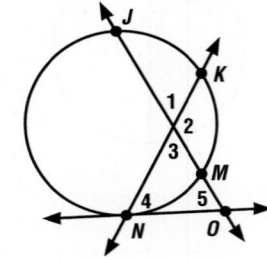

1. x 13
2. $\widehat{NM}$ 54
3. $m\angle 3$ 57
4. $m\angle 4$ 60
5. $m\angle 5$ 63

Theorem 9-14

If two chords intersect in a circle, then the products of the measures of the segments of the chords are equal.

Proof of Theorem 9-14

Given: $\overline{AC}$ and $\overline{BD}$ intersect at E.

Prove: $AE \cdot EC = BE \cdot ED$

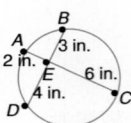

Proof:

Statements	Reasons
1. Draw $\overline{AD}$ and $\overline{BC}$ forming $\triangle DAE$ and $\triangle CBE$.	1. Through any 2 pts. there is 1 line.
2. $\angle A \cong \angle B$ $\angle D \cong \angle C$	2. If 2 inscribed $\angle s$ of a $\odot$ intercept the same arc, then the $\angle s$ are $\cong$.
3. $\triangle DAE \sim \triangle CBE$	3. AA similarity
4. $\dfrac{AE}{BE} = \dfrac{ED}{EC}$	4. Definition of similar polygons
5. $AE \cdot EC = BE \cdot ED$	5. Cross products

LESSON 9-7 SPECIAL SEGMENTS IN A CIRCLE 447

ALTERNATE TEACHING STRATEGIES

Using Investigation

Have each student complete the investigation on page 448. After everyone has a complete set of measurements, list them all in a chart on the chalkboard or overhead. Calculate the products of the segments given in the text. Help students to formulate a conjecture about the products.

Using Cooperative Groups

Draw a circle on the chalkboard or overhead that contains two chords that intersect at some point other than the center. Give measurements for three of the four segments and ask each group to find the measure of the fourth segment. Write a proportion using ratios of sides. Have the groups compare their solutions to the proof on page 447.

Motivating the Lesson

Have students inscribe a triangle in a circle. Give measures for each side of the triangle. Have them draw a median, an altitude, or an angle bisector of the triangle and extend it until it becomes a chord of the circle. Ask them to look at the special segment drawn and the side of the triangle that it intersects. How would they find the measure of each of the four segments formed?

Teaching Tip   Before discussing Theorem 9-15, take some time to make sure students understand what secant segments and external secant segments are.

Chalkboard Example

For Example 1
A mechanic needs to know the radius of a rotor to find the correct size for a new part for a car. However, he can measure only part of the rotor without taking the engine apart. If he measures a segment of 6 inches and the distance from the midpoint to the arc is 1.5 inches, what is the radius of the rotor?

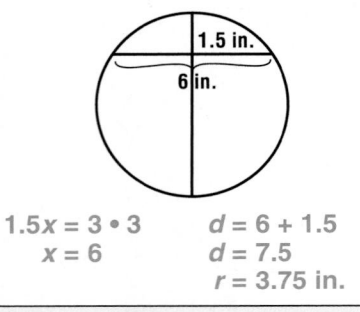

$$1.5x = 3 \cdot 3 \qquad d = 6 + 1.5$$
$$x = 6 \qquad\qquad d = 7.5$$
$$\qquad\qquad\qquad r = 3.75 \text{ in.}$$

Example 1

APPLICATION

Mechanics

How can the tool and die maker find the radius of the escape wheel of the clock?

First, measure the length of the chord across the ends of the broken piece. Suppose the chord measures 10 millimeters. Then find the midpoint of the chord and the distance to the arc. Suppose this measure is 4 millimeters.

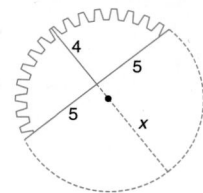

$$4 \cdot x = 5 \cdot 5 \qquad \textit{Theorem 9-14}$$
$$4x = 25$$
$$x = 6\tfrac{1}{4}$$

The diameter of the circle measures $4 + 6\frac{1}{4}$ or $10\frac{1}{4}$ millimeters. The radius measures $\frac{1}{2}(10\frac{1}{4})$ or $5\frac{1}{8}$ millimeters.

In the figure at the right, both $\overline{RP}$ and $\overline{RT}$ are called **secant segments**. As with all secants, they contain chords of the circle. The parts of these segments that are exterior to the circle are called **external secant segments**. In the figure, $\overline{RQ}$ and $\overline{RS}$ are external secant segments.

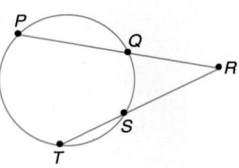

Draw a figure like the one shown above and use a ruler to measure RQ, RP, RS, and RT. Find the products $RQ \cdot RP$ and $RS \cdot RT$. How are they related? Draw several other figures and make a conjecture.

This investigation leads us to Theorem 9-15.

Theorem 9-15

If two secant segments are drawn to a circle from an exterior point, then the product of the measures of one secant segment and its external secant segment is equal to the product of the measures of the other secant segment and its external secant segment.

Plan for Proof of Theorem 9-15

To prove Theorem 9-15, start with a figure like the one shown above. Draw $\overline{PS}$ and $\overline{TQ}$. Then show that $\triangle PSR \sim \triangle TQR$. Write the proportion, $\frac{RQ}{RS} = \frac{RT}{RP}$, and find its cross product, $RQ \cdot RP = RS \cdot RT$. *You will be asked to complete this proof in Exercise 33.*

The segments formed by a tangent and a secant also have a special relationship.

The figure shows a tangent segment, $\overline{XY}$, and a secant segment, $\overline{YW}$, drawn to a circle from an exterior point, Y. If you draw $\overline{XW}$ and $\overline{XZ}$, triangles $\triangle YXZ$ and $\triangle YWX$ are formed. $m\angle YXZ = \frac{1}{2} m\widehat{XZ}$ and $m\angle XWZ = \frac{1}{2} m\widehat{XZ}$, so $\angle YXZ \cong \angle XWZ$. $\angle Y \cong \angle Y$ since congruence of angles is reflexive. Therefore, $\triangle YXZ \sim \triangle YWX$ by AA similarity.

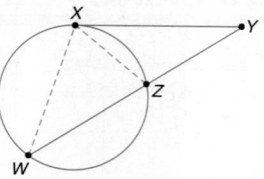

$$\frac{XY}{YW} = \frac{YZ}{XY} \qquad \textit{Definition of similarity}$$

$$XY^2 = YW \cdot YZ \qquad \textit{Cross products}$$

This leads us to Theorem 9-16. You will prove this theorem in Exercise 34.

Theorem 9-16	**If a tangent segment and a secant segment are drawn to a circle from an exterior point, then the square of the measure of the tangent segment is equal to the product of the measures of the secant segment and its external secant segment.**

Example 2

In the figure, $\overline{BC}$ is a tangent segment. Find the value of x.

$$AC \cdot DC = (BC)^2 \qquad \textit{Theorem 9-16}$$
$$(x + 6.6)x = 8^2$$
$$x^2 + 6.6x = 64$$
$$x^2 + 6.6\,x - 64 = 0$$

Use the Quadratic Formula.

$$x = \frac{-b \pm \sqrt{b^2 - 4ac}}{2a}$$

$$x = \frac{-6.6 \pm \sqrt{(6.6)^2 - 4(1)(-64)}}{2(1)} \qquad a = 1, b = 6.6, c = -64$$

$$= \frac{-6.6 \pm \sqrt{43.56 + 256}}{2}$$

$$\approx \frac{-6.6 \pm 17.3}{2}$$

$$\approx 5.35 \text{ or } -11.95$$

x is approximately 5.35.   *Why is -11.95 not used?*

Chalkboard Example

For Example 2
Refer to the figure below. $\overline{RT}$ is a tangent segment. Find the value of x.

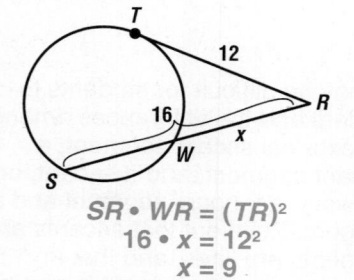

$$SR \bullet WR = (TR)^2$$
$$16 \bullet x = 12^2$$
$$x = 9$$

Communicating Mathematics

Read and study the lesson to answer these questions. See margin.

1. Describe the difference between a secant segment and an external secant segment. Use the diagram at the right to give an example of each.

2. Two secants segments are drawn to a circle from an external point. Use the figure to explain the relationship involving the secant segments and exterior secant segments.

3. Define tangent segment. Use the diagram to give an example of a tangent segment.

4. A tangent segment and a secant segment are drawn to a circle from an exterior point. Describe the relationship involving the tangent segment, the secant segment, and the external secant segment.

5. Draw a circle. Draw two intersecting chords in the circle. Label the point of intersection and write an equation involving the segments.

Guided Practice

State the equation you would use to find the value of x. Assume segments that appear to be tangent are tangent. Then find the value of x.

6.
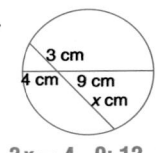
3 cm
4 cm 9 cm
x cm

$3x = 4 \cdot 9; 12$

7.
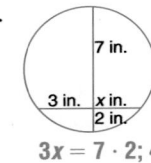
7 in.
3 in. x in.
2 in.

$3x = 7 \cdot 2; 4\frac{2}{3}$

8.
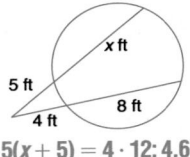
x ft
5 ft
4 ft 8 ft

$5(x+5) = 4 \cdot 12; 4.6$

9.
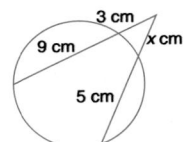
5 m   3 m
4 m
x m

$4(x + 4) = 3 \cdot 8; 2$

10.
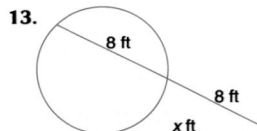
20 km
10 km   x km

$10(x+10) = 20^2; 30$

11.
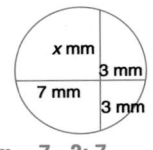
x mm
3 mm
7 mm
3 mm

$3x = 7 \cdot 3; 7$

12. $x(x + 5) = 3 \cdot 12; 4$

13. $x^2 = 8 \cdot 16; 8\sqrt{2} \approx 11.31$

12.
3 cm
9 cm   x cm
5 cm

13.
8 ft
8 ft
x ft

14.
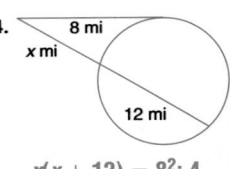
8 mi
x mi
12 mi

$x(x + 12) = 8^2; 4$

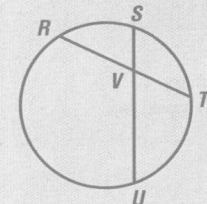

EXERCISES

Practice   Find the value of *x*. Assume segments that appear to be tangent are tangent.

A

15.
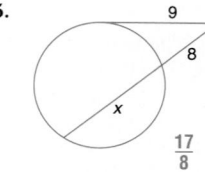
$\frac{17}{8}$

16.
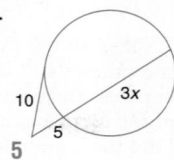
5

17.
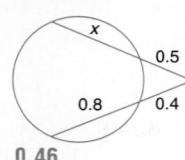
0.46

18.
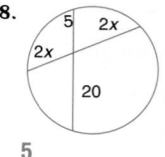
5

19.
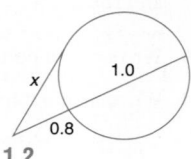
1.2

20.
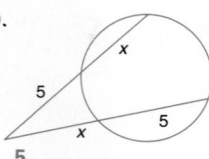
5

21.
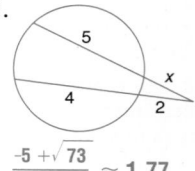
$\frac{-5 + \sqrt{73}}{2} \approx 1.77$

22.
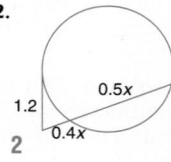
2

23.
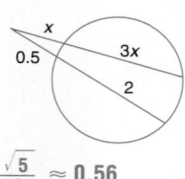
$\frac{\sqrt{5}}{4} \approx 0.56$

B

In the figure, $\overline{AB}$ is a tangent segment. Round each answer to the nearest tenth.

24. If $FH = 6$, $HD = 2$, and $HE = 3$, find CH.   **4.0**

25. If $AD = 16$, $FD = 8$, and $AG = 6$, find GC.   **15.3**

26. If $AC = 21$, $AF = 8$, and $FD = 8$, find AG.   **6.1**

27. If $CH = 20$, $EH = 10.5$, and $DH = 8$, find FH.   **26.3**

28. If $AF = 16$, $FH = 6$, and $DH = 2$, find BA.   **19.6**

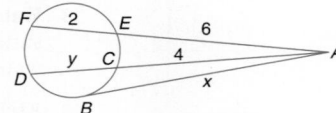

Find each value.

29. $\overleftrightarrow{TU}$ is tangent to the circle and $\overline{RT}$ is perpendicular to $\overline{TU}$. Find *x*.   **12.25**

30. $\overleftrightarrow{AB}$ is tangent to the circle. Find *x* and *y*. $\sqrt{48} \approx$ **6.9; 8**

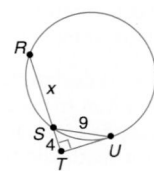

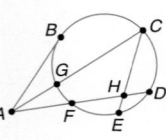

RETEACHING THE LESSON

Have students draw one figure for all three theorems discussed in this lesson. Have them write an equation for each theorem relating the measures of the segments in their pictures. Ask them to check each equation by measuring the segments involved in the equations and finding the products.

Closing the Lesson

Writing Activity Draw and label figures relating to each of the three theorems discussed in this lesson. For each figure, have students write equations involving the segments of the circle that relate to particular theorems.

APPLYING THE LESSON

Homework Exercises

Assignment Guide
Basic: 15-29, 35-37, 40-50
Average: 18-32, 35, 37-38, 40-50
Enriched: 18-23, 26-35, 38-50

Reteaching Masters Booklet, p. 56

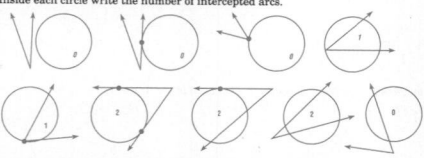

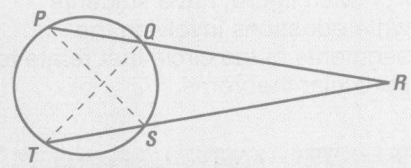
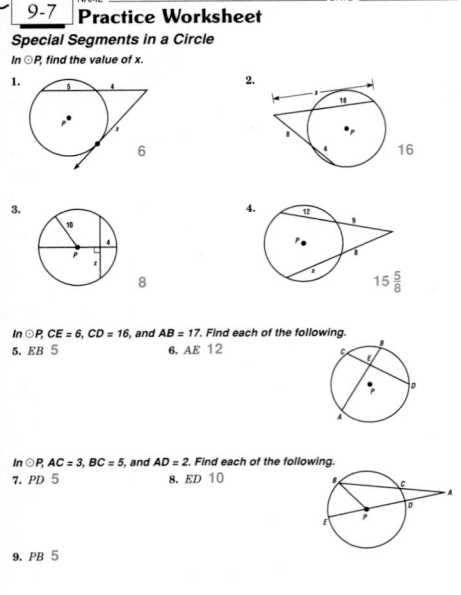

31. Your geometry teacher asks you to draw a circle through points *L*, *M*, and *N*. The measures are indicated in the figure. Find the measure of the radius of the circle you will draw. $\sqrt{51.25} \approx$ **7.16**

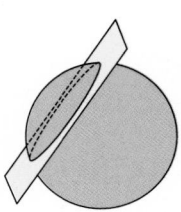

32. A sphere is cut by a plane. The radius of the sphere is 12 units long. The distance between the plane and the farthest point of the dome cut by the plane is 5 units. Find the length of the radius of the circle formed by the intersection of the sphere and the plane. $\sqrt{95} \approx$ **9.7 units**

33. Write a two-column proof of Theorem 9-15. **See margin.**

34. Write a paragraph proof of Theorem 9-16. **See margin.**

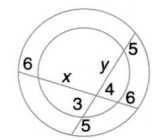

Critical Thinking   **35.** The figure shows two concentric circles. Find the values of *x* and *y*. **x = 30, y = 40**

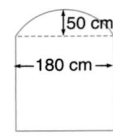

Applications   **36. Carpentry**   An arch over a door is 50 centimeters high and 180 centimeters wide. Find the length of the radius of the arch. **106 cm**

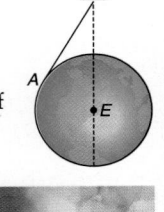

37. Space   The spaceshuttle *Discovery* (S) is 150 miles above Earth (⊙E). What is the length of its longest line of sight ($\overline{SA}$) to Earth? The diameter of Earth is about 8000 miles long. **about 1106 mi**

38. Water Management   Water is flowing through a pipe. The width of the surface of the water is 50 centimeters and the maximum depth of the water is 20 centimeters. How long is the diameter of the pipe? **51.25 cm**

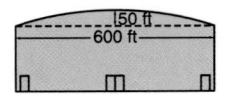

39. Architecture   An architect is designing a new domed stadium. The outside diameter of the stadium measures 600 feet. If the center of the dome is 50 feet higher than the sides of the stadium, how long is the radius of the sphere that forms the dome? **925 ft**

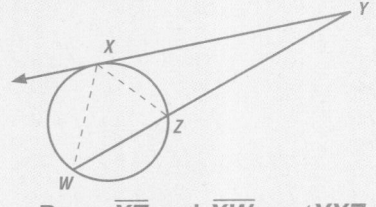

Computer
The BASIC program below will find the measure of a segment in a circle. If you know the measures of $\overline{AE}$, $\overline{EB}$, and $\overline{CE}$, the program will find the measure of $\overline{ED}$.

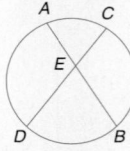

```
10  PRINT "ENTER THE MEASURES OF
    SEGMENTS AE, EB, AND CE."
20  INPUT A, E, C
30  D = (A*E)/C
40  PRINT "THE MEASURE OF SEGMENT ED IS "; D; "."
```

Portfolio

Select an item from this chapter that shows your creativity. Place it in your portfolio.

Use the BASIC program to find the measure of $\overline{ED}$ for each situation.

40. $AE = 8$, $EB = 6$, $CE = 3$ **16**

41. $AE = 9$, $EB = 2$, $CE = 7$ **about 2.6**

42. $AE = 10$, $EB = 30$, $CE = 18$ **about 16.7**

43. $AE = 0.32$, $EB = 0.69$, $CE = 0.22$ **about 1**

44. How could you change the BASIC program to find the measure of $\overline{AE}$ if you know the measures of $\overline{AB}$, $\overline{AC}$, and $\overline{AD}$? **See margin.**

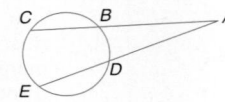

Mixed Review

45. Find $m\angle ABC$. **(Lesson 9-6)** **25**

46. Find $m\angle ECD$. **(Lesson 9-4)** **25**

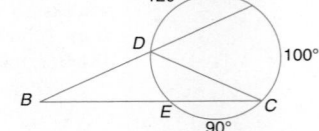

47. A 15-foot ladder leaning against a wall makes a 62° angle with the ground. If the ladder is moved so that the angle is 70°, how far did the top of the ladder move up the wall? **(Lesson 8-4)** **about 0.85 ft or 10.2 in.**

48. **See margin.**

48. Could a trapezoid have a right angle? If so, draw one. **(Lesson 6-6)**

49. Lines ℓ and m are cut by a transversal t, and $\angle 1$ and $\angle 2$ are corresponding angles. If $m\angle 1 = 4x + 3$ and $m\angle 2 = 8x - 7$, what is the value of x if ℓ and m are parallel? **(Lesson 3-4)** **2.5**

Wrap-Up

50. Your friend is trying to help you find the value of x in the figure at the right. Your friend works the problem as follows:

$$4 \cdot 10 = 8x$$
$$40 = 8x$$
$$5 = x$$

Is your friend correct? Write a paragraph explaining to your friend why the work is right or wrong. **See margin.**

LESSON 9-7   SPECIAL SEGMENTS IN A CIRCLE   453

EXTENDING THE LESSON

Math Power: Reasoning

Following Theorem 9-15, can you say that if two secant segments are drawn from an exterior point, then the product of the measures of one secant segment and its chord in the circle is equal to the product of the measures of the other secant segment and its

chord in the circle? Why or why not?   **No, because their parts are not proportional. If you used the proof involving similar triangles, the chords in the secant segments are not corresponding parts.**

Additional Answers

44. Change line 10 to ask for *AB*, *AC*, and *AD*. Change *ED* in 40 to *AE*.

48. yes

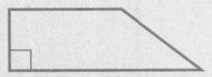

50. The friend is wrong. The measure of the exterior secant segment times the measure of the secant segment equals the measure of the other exterior secant segment times the measure of the other secant segment.

Enrichment Masters Booklet, p. 56

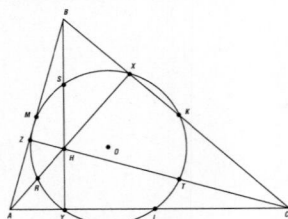

9-7 Enrichment Worksheet

The Nine-Point Circle

The figure below illustrates a surprising fact about triangles and circles. Given any $\triangle ABC$, there is a circle that contains all of the following nine points:

(1) the midpoints K, L, and M of the sides of $\triangle ABC$

(2) the points X, Y, and Z, where $\overline{AX}$, $\overline{BY}$, and $\overline{CZ}$ are the attitudes of $\triangle ABC$

(3) the points R, S, and T which are the midpoints of the segments $\overline{AH}$, $\overline{BH}$, and $\overline{CH}$ that join the vertices of $\triangle ABC$ to the point H where the lines containing the altitudes intersect.

1. On a separate sheet of paper, draw an obtuse triangle ABC. Use your straightedge and compass to construct the circle passing through the midpoints of the sides. Be careful to make your construction as accurate as possible. Does your circle contain the other six points described above? **For constructions, see students' work.; yes**

2. In the figure you constructed for exercise 1, draw $\overline{RK}$, $\overline{SL}$, and $\overline{TM}$. What do you observe? **The segments intersect at the center of the nine-point circle.**

T56
Glencoe Division, Macmillan/McGraw-Hill

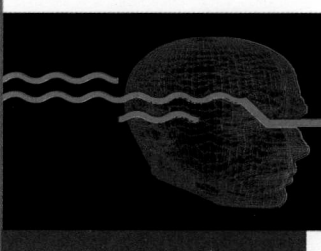

Technology

Circles

The Geometric Supposer is a powerful tool for investigating geometric relationships. Let's use it to look at some relationships in circles.

Begin by loading The Geometric Supposer: Circles and drawing any circle. Your circle will be labeled ⊙A. Choose *(2) Label* from the main menu, then choose *(4) Random Point* from the Label menu. Plot a random point outside of the circle by choosing *(3)* from this menu. The point will be labeled B.

Now draw two segments through B that are secants to circle A. To do this, choose *(1) Draw* on the main menu, then choose *(2)* for a line through point B. Define the length as intersecting the circle by choosing *(3)* from this menu. Repeat the process to draw a second segment. Your screen will show a drawing like the one at the right.

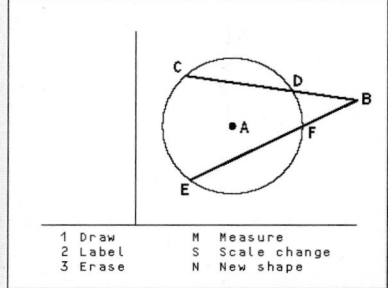

EXERCISES

Use the circle you drew on the Geometric Supposer to answer each question. Answers for Exercises 1-3 will vary. See students' work.

1. Find the measure of each segment using the measure option.
   a. $\overline{BD}$ b. $\overline{BC}$
   c. $\overline{BF}$ d. $\overline{BE}$

2. Use the measures you found in Exercise 1 to find each product.
   a. $(BD)(BC)$ b. $(BF)(BE)$

3. Draw a third secant, $\overline{BG}$, through the point B. Then, find the measure of each segment and the product of their measures.
   a. $\overline{BH}$ b. $\overline{BG}$ c. $(BH)(BG)$

4. The products you found are called the *power of the point B*. Does it appear that the power of the point is the same for every secant drawn from a given point? **yes**

5. Will the power of any point outside of the circle be the same as the power of point B? Draw other random points and secants to investigate. **no**

Problem-Solving Strategy: Using Graphs

Objective
9-8

After studying this lesson, you should be able to:
- solve problems by using graphs.

Business men and women, politicians, environmentalists, investors, and a host of other people make many important decisions based on statistics. Since lists of numbers and other raw data are difficult to understand, people often prepare graphs to help them make decisions and to help them convince others of their point of view.

Example

APPLICATION

Sales

> Marcus Taylor is a manager for the High Fashion Department Store. He studies the sales reports for jeans from the last three months. His store sold 310 pairs of Prestige Jeans, 482 pairs of Rugged Jeans, 107 pairs of Best Jeans, 256 pairs of Alpha Jeans, and 44 pairs of Fashionable Jeans. Since the store only has a limited amount of space to display the jeans, Mr. Taylor wishes to show his employees how much space to allot for each brand of jeans based on previous sales. Make a graph to help Mr. Taylor instruct his employees.

Mr. Taylor wants to show his employees what part of the available space should be used for each brand of jeans. A circle graph shows how a part is related to the whole. To make a circle graph, Mr. Taylor must first find the total number of jeans sold in the last three months.

$$310 + 482 + 107 + 256 + 44 = 1199$$

Then he must find the percent represented by each brand of jeans and find that percent of 360°.

Prestige	$\frac{310}{1199} \approx 25.9\%$	25.9% of 360° = 93.2°
Rugged	$\frac{482}{1199} \approx 40.2\%$	40.2% of 360° = 144.7°
Best	$\frac{107}{1199} \approx 8.9\%$	8.9% of 360° = 32.1°
Alpha	$\frac{256}{1199} \approx 21.4\%$	21.4% of 360° = 77.0°
Fashionable	$\frac{44}{1199} \approx 3.7\%$	3.7% of 360° = 13.3°

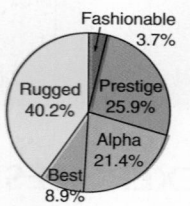

Using these figures, Mr. Taylor can draw a circle graph as shown at the right, or use software to create the circle graph.

ALTERNATE TEACHING STRATEGIES

Using Representation

Discuss the different types of graphs and draw an example of each. Discuss situations where one type of graph would be a better representation of information than another.

Using Applications

All types of professions use statistics: police officers, sportscasters, and people involved in research, marketing, and sales. All of the people in these professions need to display their statistics in some way. Discuss with the students where they see graphs and what graphs represent.

Lesson Resources
- Practice Master 9-8
- Evaluation Master, p. 122
- Activity Master, p. 9

Transparency 9-8 contains the 5-Minute Check and a teaching aid for this lesson.

INTRODUCING THE LESSON

5-Minute Check
(over Lesson 9-7)

Refer to the figure below.

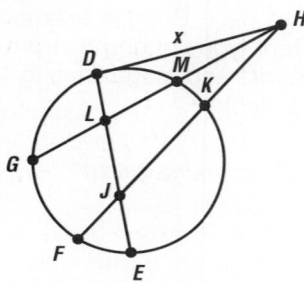

1. If $HK = 4$ and $KF = 10$, find the value of x.   **7.48**
2. If $DJ = 6$, $KJ = 5$, and $JE = 3$, find FJ.   **3.6**
3. If $DL = 3$, $LJ = 4$, $JE = 5$ and $LM = 12$, find GL.   **2.25**
4. If $GM = 9$, $GH = 15$, and $HK = 6$, find FK.   **9**

Motivating the Lesson

Ask students to draw a representation of the inequality $x < 5$ on a number line. Explain that this is a graph, and that there are other types of graphs that they can use to solve problems.

TEACHING THE LESSON

Teaching Tip   In the Example, notice that 93.2 + 144.7 + 32.1 + 77.0 + 13.3 = 360.3, which can be rounded to 360°. The 0.3 is due to round-off error when writing the fractions as percentages.

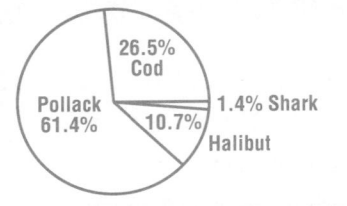
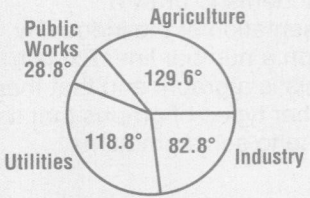
CHECKING FOR UNDERSTANDING

Communicating Mathematics

Read and study the lesson to answer these questions.

1. What brand of jeans should take up the most space? Should this brand take up more or less than half the space? **Rugged; less**

2. If Mr. Taylor decides to discontinue one brand of jeans, what brand would you advise him to discontinue and why? **Fashionable; they sell the least**

3. Do you think that Mr. Taylor could sell more Prestige Jeans than Rugged Jeans if he had a sale on Prestige Jeans? Do you think he could sell more Best Jeans than Rugged Jeans if he had a sale on Best Jeans? Explain your answers. **See margin.**

4. How does the circle graph help you to answer Exercises 1-3? **See margin.**

5. What other types of graphs can be used to display information? **See margin.**

Guided Practice

Use graphs to solve each problem.

6. Mindy invests some of her money in stocks. She keeps track of her stocks by graphing the closing price of each stock on the first day of the month. The graph at the right shows the values of one share of stock in Funky Records and one share of stock in Glamorous Fashions.

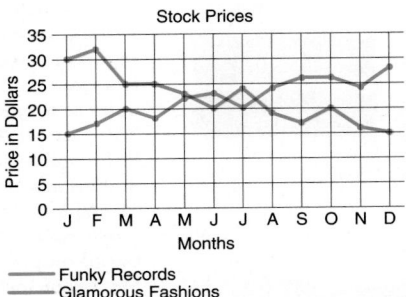

a. Which stock was worth more on the first day of March? **Glamorous Fashions**

b. Which stock is worth more on the first day of June? **Funky Records**

c. In general, is the value of stock in Funky Records going up or down in value? **up**

d. In general, is the value of stock in Glamorous Fashions going up or down in value? **down**   **See margin.**

e. What would you advise Mindy to do with her stocks and why?

7. Lisa is concerned about our natural resources. She has made a study about the use of water in the United States. Use the information in the chart at the right to make a circle graph that would help Lisa illustrate the use of water to her classmates. **See margin.**

Water Use in the U.S.	
Agriculture	36%
Public Water	8%
Utilities	33%
Industry	23%

EXERCISES

Practice   **Solve. Use any strategy.**

8. If you were one billion seconds old, how old would you be in years? **about 32 years old**

Strategies

Look for a pattern.
Solve a simpler problem.
Act it out.
Guess and check.
Draw a diagram.
Make a chart.
Work backward.

10. typed 10^2 as 102:
$101 - 10^2 = 1$; or
omitted minus sign:
$101 - 102 = -1$

9. An electric utility company is interested in buying some coal to fuel their generator. The table at the right gives the location of the coal resources in the United States. **See Solutions Manual.**

U.S. Coal Resources	
Rocky Mountains	45%
Appalachia	30%
Midwest	20%
Other	5%

   a. Use the information at the right to make a circle graph.

   b. What other information might the company need to make a decision about buying their coal?

10. When Sherri typed the equation, "$101 - 102 = 1$," she made just one small error. What did she do wrong? Write the correct equation.

11. Find the next number: 4800, 2400, 800, 200, ___?___. Describe the pattern.
   40; Dividing by 2, 3, 4, 5, . . .

Refer to the graph at the right for Exercises 12-14.

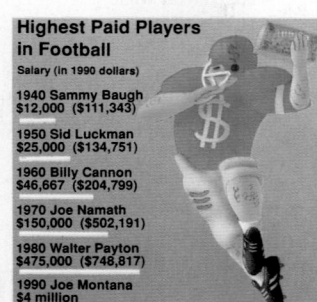

Highest Paid Players in Football

Salary (in 1990 dollars)

1940 Sammy Baugh
$12,000 ($111,343)

1950 Sid Luckman
$25,000 ($134,751)

1960 Billy Cannon
$46,667 ($204,799)

1970 Joe Namath
$150,000 ($502,191)

1980 Walter Payton
$475,000 ($748,817)

1990 Joe Montana
$4 million

12. Using 1990 dollars, what percent of Joe Montana's salary did Joe Namath make? **about 12.6%**

13. Using 1990 dollars, what percent of Walter Payton's salary did Sid Luckman make? **about 18.0%**

14. How many times more is Sammy Baugh's salary in 1990 dollars than it was in 1940? **about 9.3 times more**

COOPERATIVE LEARNING PROJECT

Work in groups. Each person in the group should understand the solution and be able to explain it to any person in the class.

Business people often use statistics and graphs to influence people's decisions. So, you must be able to read a graph and make sure that it accurately represents the data it presents. The graphs below show data in a misleading way. Explain how they are misleading and why someone might draw these graphs this way. **See Solutions Manual.**

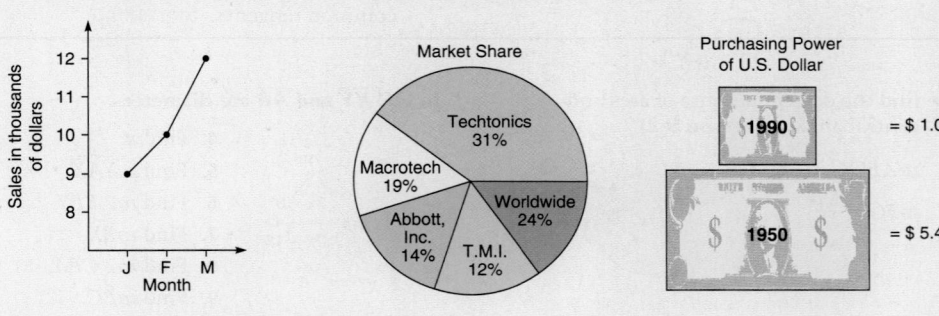

LESSON 9-8   PROBLEM-SOLVING STRATEGY: USING GRAPHS   457

Checking for Understanding

Exercises 1-7 are designed to help you assess students' understanding through reading, writing, speaking, and modeling. You should work through Exercises 1-5 with your students and then monitor their work on Exercises 6-7.

Closing the Lesson

Speaking Activity Have each student state a situation where a circle graph could be used to display information.

Homework Exercises

Assignment Guide

Basic: 8-13
Average: 9-14
Enriched: 9-14

Practice Masters Booklet, p. 65

9-8 NAME _____ DATE _____
Practice Worksheet
Problem-Solving Strategy: Using Graphs

The table at the right shows how Federal funds were spent on education in 1990.

1990 Federal Funds Spent for Education

Elementary/Secondary	$ 7,945,177
Education/handicapped	4,204,099
Post secondary education	12,645,630
Public Library Services	145,367
Other	760,616
Total	$25,700,889

1. **a.** Use the information to make a circle graph.

b. Out of the $12,645,630 spent on post secondary education, $10,801,185 went to post secondary financial assistance. What percent is that of the $12,645,630? **85.4%**

2. Bill is 1,350,000,000 seconds old. How old is he in years? **about 43 years old**

3. Find the next number in the pattern 3, 6, 18, 72, 360, ___?___. Describe the pattern. **2160; Multiply by 2, 3, 4, 5, 6, . . .**

4. Suppose you mark three noncollinear points *inside* a circle. Mark a fourth point so that it is not collinear with any two of the first three. Continue: Mark a fifth point, being careful that it is not collinear with any of the other two already marked. For what number of points will it no longer be possible to do this? **It will always be possible, since otherwise it would be possible to fill the circle and its interior with a finite number of segments.**

5. How many sets of 100 points can you select from a set of 101 points if the order of selection is unimportant. **101**

T65
Glencoe Division, Macmillan/McGraw-Hill

Math Power: Problem Solving

Marcus Taylor needs an estimate of how many jeans will be sold in the next two months to place an order. Use the data given in the Example in the text. **207 pairs of Prestige Jeans, 321 pairs of Rugged Jeans, 71 pairs of Best Jeans, 171 pairs of Alpha Jeans, and 29 pairs of Fashionable Jeans.**

Cooperative Learning Project

This activity provides students an opportunity to learn things together, not just do things together. You may wish to refer to pages T6-T7 and page 408c for the various elements of cooperative groups and specific goals and strategies for using them.

Additional Answer

3.

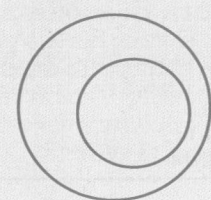

VOCABULARY

Upon completing this chapter, you should be familiar with the following terms:

422 arc of the chord	**418** concentric circles	**416** minor arc
416 central angle	**410** diameter	**434** point of tangency
410 chord	**411** exterior of a circle	**410** radius
410 circle	**448** external secant segment	**412** secant
436 circumscribed polygon	**428** inscribed angle	**448** secant segment
413 common external tangent	**430** inscribed polygon	**416** semicircle
413 common internal tangent	**411** interior of a circle	**412** tangent
413 common tangent	**416** major arc	**436** tangent segment

SKILLS AND CONCEPTS

OBJECTIVES AND EXAMPLES	REVIEW EXERCISES

Upon completing this chapter, you should be able to:

Use these exercises to review and prepare for the chapter test.

▪ name parts of circles. **(Lesson 9-1)**

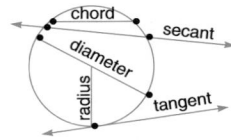

Complete.

1. A radius of a circle is a chord of the circle. Write *yes* or *no*. **no**

2. A diameter of a circle is a chord of the circle. Write *yes* or *no*. **yes**

3. Draw two distinct circles that have no common tangents. **See margin.**

▪ find the degree measure of arcs and central angles. **(Lesson 9-2)**

$m\angle FOG = 38$

$m\widehat{FG} = 38$

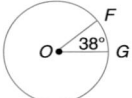

In $\odot P$, $\overline{XY}$ and $\overline{AB}$ are diameters.

4. Find x. **21**
5. Find $m\widehat{YAX}$. **180**
6. Find $m\angle BPY$. **63**
7. Find $m\widehat{BX}$. **117**
8. Find $m\angle CPA$. **57**
9. Find $m\widehat{BC}$. **123**

■ recognize and use relationships between arcs, chords, and diameters. **(Lesson 9-3)**

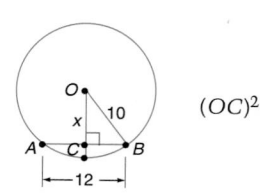

$$CB = \frac{1}{2}AB$$
$$= \frac{1}{2}(12) \text{ or } 6$$

$$(OC)^2 + (CB)^2 = (OB)^2$$
$$x^2 + 6^2 = 10^2$$
$$x^2 + 36 = 100$$
$$x^2 = 64$$
$$x = 8$$

Find each measurement.

10. A chord is 5 centimeters from the center of a circle with radius 13 centimeters. Find the length of the chord. **24 cm**

11. Suppose a 24-centimeter chord of a circle is 32 centimeters from the center of the circle. Find the length of the radius. **about 34.2 cm**

■ recognize and find the measure of inscribed angles. **(Lesson 9-4)**

$$m\angle XYZ = \frac{1}{2}m\widehat{XZ}$$
$$= \frac{1}{2}(78)$$
$$= 39$$

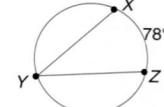

In ⊙P, $\overline{AB} \parallel \overline{CD}$, $m\widehat{BD} = 72$, and $m\angle CPD = 144$. Find each measure.

12. $m\angle DAB$ **36**
13. $m\widehat{CD}$ **144**
14. $m\widehat{CA}$ **72**
15. $m\angle CDA$ **36**
16. $m\widehat{AB}$ **72**

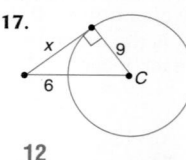

■ use properties of tangents. **(Lesson 9-5)**

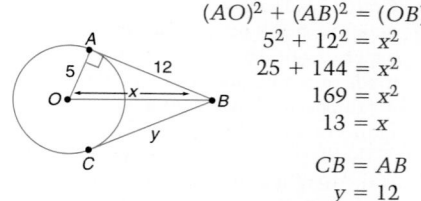

$$(AO)^2 + (AB)^2 = (OB)^2$$
$$5^2 + 12^2 = x^2$$
$$25 + 144 = x^2$$
$$169 = x^2$$
$$13 = x$$

$$CB = AB$$
$$y = 12$$

For each ⊙C, find the value of x. Assume segments that appear to be tangent are tangent.

17.

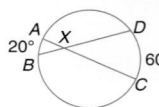

12

18.

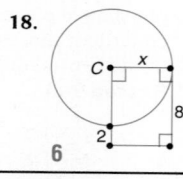

6

■ find the measure of angles formed by the intersection of secants and tangents in relation to intercepted arcs. **(Lesson 9-6)**

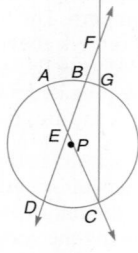

$$m\angle DXC = \frac{1}{2}(m\widehat{DC} + m\widehat{AB})$$
$$= \frac{1}{2}(60 + 20)$$
$$= \frac{1}{2}(80) \text{ or } 40$$

In ⊙P, $m\widehat{AB} = 29$, $m\angle AEB = 42$, $m\widehat{BG} = 18$, and $\overline{AC}$ is a diameter. Find each measure.

19. $m\angle DEC$ **42**
20. $m\widehat{CD}$ **55**
21. $m\angle GFD$ **18.5**
22. $m\widehat{AD}$ **125**
23. $m\angle AED$ **138**
24. $m\widehat{GC}$ **133**

A two-page Cumulative Review from the *Evaluation Masters* is shown below. It can be used to review skills and concepts presented thus far in the text. Standardized Test Practice Questions are also provided in the *Evaluation Masters*.

Evaluation Masters, pp. 123-124

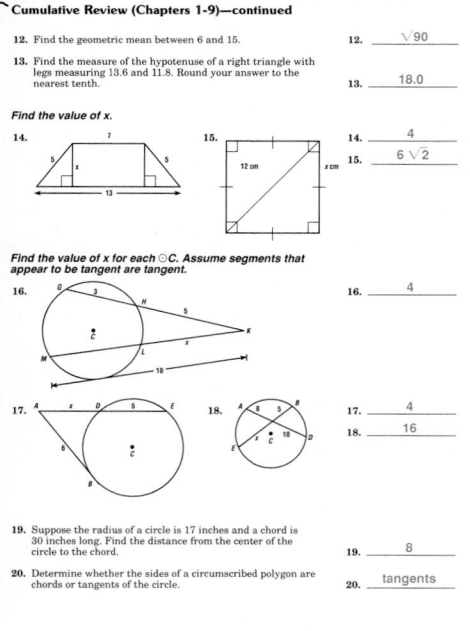

NAME _____ DATE _____

Cumulative Review (Chapters 1-9)

1. The measure of an angle is one-fourth the measure of its supplement. Find the measure of the angle.
   1. ___36___

2. Determine if statement (3) follows from statements (1) and (2) by the law of detachment or the law of syllogism. If it does, state which law you used.
   (1) If an angle measures 28, then it is acute.
   (2) $m\angle A = 28$.
   (3) $\angle A$ is acute.
   2. _yes; detachment_

3. Find the values of x and y that make $\overline{AB}$ parallel to $\overline{DC}$.
   3. __6, 93__

4. Is a right triangle never equilateral?
   4. ___no___

5. Find the value of x if $\overline{AD}$ is an altitude of $\triangle ABC$.
   5. ___34___

6. Is quadrilateral $ABCD$ with vertices $A(-3, 2)$, $B(3, 5)$, $C(3, 7)$, and $D(-3, 4)$ a parallelogram?
   6. ___yes___

7. Find the length of the median $\overline{DE}$ of trapezoid $ABCD$ with vertices $A(0, 0)$, $B(5, 0)$, $C(3, 3)$, and $D(1, 3)$.
   7. ___3.5___

8. Solve the proportion $\frac{22}{x} = \frac{55}{125}$ using cross products.
   8. ___50___

9. Determine whether the pair of triangles is similar. Write yes or no. If they are similar, give a reason.
   9. _yes; SSS Similarity_

10. A 10-foot tree casts a 4.5-foot shadow. How tall is a tree that casts a 27-foot shadow at the same time of day?
    10. __60 ft.__

11. The legs of a right triangle are 8.5 inches and 10 inches long. The shorter leg of a similar triangle is 25.5 inches long. Find the length of the other leg of the second triangle.
    11. __30 in.__

123
Glencoe Division, Macmillan/McGraw-Hill

NAME _____ DATE _____

Cumulative Review (Chapters 1-9)—continued

12. Find the geometric mean between 6 and 15.
    12. __√90__

13. Find the measure of the hypotenuse of a right triangle with legs measuring 13.6 and 11.8. Round your answer to the nearest tenth.
    13. __18.0__

Find the value of x.

14.
    14. ___4___

15.
    15. __6√2__

Find the value of x for each $\odot C$. Assume segments that appear to be tangent are tangent.

16.
    16. ___4___

17.
    17. ___4___

18.
    18. ___16___

19. Suppose the radius of a circle is 17 inches and a chord is 30 inches long. Find the distance from the center of the circle to the chord.
    19. ___8___

20. Determine whether the sides of a circumscribed polygon are chords or tangents of the circle.
    20. __tangents__

124
Glencoe Division, Macmillan/McGraw-Hill

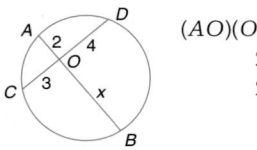

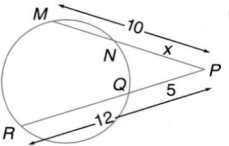

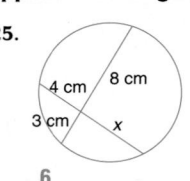

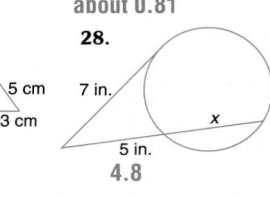

- use properties of chords, secants, and tangents. **(Lesson 9-7)**

$(AO)(OB) = (CO)(OD)$
$2x = 3 \cdot 4$
$2x = 12$
$x = 6$

$(MP)(NP) = (QP)(RP)$
$10x = 5 \cdot 12$
$10x = 60$
$x = 6$

Find the value of x. Assume segments that appear to be tangent are tangent.

25.
   8 cm
   4 cm
   3 cm
   x
   6

26.
   x
   0.8 ft
   0.5 ft
   about 0.81

27.
   6 cm
   x
   5 cm
   3 cm
   $15\frac{1}{3}$

28.
   7 in.
   x
   5 in.
   4.8

Applications and Connections

29. **Food** Carlo made a pizza for his friends. He decides to cut the pizza into pie-shaped pieces. If he cuts it into 10 congruent pieces, what is the measure of the central angle of each piece? **(Lesson 9-2)** **36**

30. **Crafts** Sara makes wooden paper weights to sell at craft shows. For each paperweight, she starts with a sphere made of wood. She cuts off a flat surface for the base. If the original sphere has a radius of 4 centimeters and the diameter of the flat surface is 6 centimeters, what is the height of the paperweight? **(Lesson 9-3)** **about 6.6 cm**

31. **Construction** The support of a bridge is in the shape of an arc. The span of the bridge (the length of the chord connecting the endpoints of the arc) is 28 meters. The highest point of the arc is 5 meters above the imaginary chord connecting the endpoints of the arc. How long is the radius of the circle that forms the arc? **(Lesson 9-3)** **22.1 m**

32. Ms. Schultz is thinking about opening a music store. She gathers information to help her decide what she should sell. Use the information at the right to make a circle graph showing the portion of sales for each type of recording. **(Lesson 9-8)** **See margin.**

Music Sales	
Cassettes	49%
12-inch singles	2%
LPs	4%
45s	6%
Compact discs	39%

Additional Answer

32. Portion of Sales per Recording Type

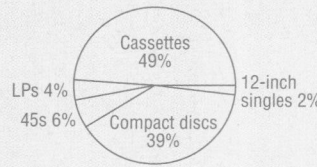

1. Write a definition for the radius of a circle. **See Solutions Manual.**

2. Graph the circle whose equation is $x^2 + y^2 = 49$. Label the center and the measure of the radius on the graph. **See Solutions Manual.**

Find the value of x for each $\odot C$. Assume segments that appear to be tangent are tangent.

3.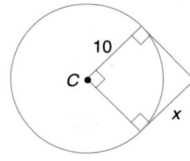

10

4.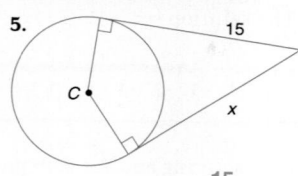

10

5.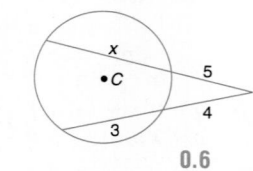

15

6.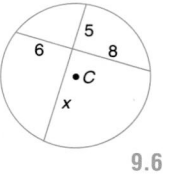

9.6

7.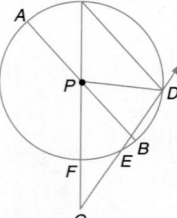

4

8.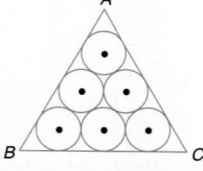

0.6

In $\odot P$, $\overline{AB} \parallel \overline{CD}$, $m\widehat{BD} = 42$, $m\widehat{BE} = 12$, and $\overline{CF}$ and $\overline{AB}$ are diameters. Find each measure.

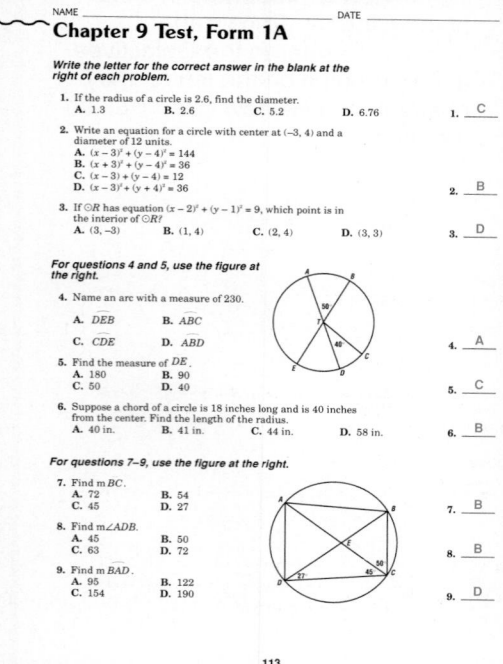

9. $m\angle BPD$ **42**

10. $m\widehat{AC}$ **42**

11. $m\angle APC$ **42**

12. $m\widehat{CD}$ **96**

13. $m\angle BPF$ **42**

14. $m\widehat{FB}$ **42**

15. $m\widehat{AF}$ **138**

16. $m\widehat{FE}$ **30**

17. $m\angle FCD$ **42**

18. $m\angle EDC$ **105**

19. Suppose the diameter of a circle is 10 inches long and a chord is 6 inches long. Find the distance between the chord and the center of the circle. **4 inches**

20. Determine whether the sides of an inscribed polygon are chords or tangents of the circle. **chords**

Bonus

Each circle has a radius of 2 units. $\triangle ABC$ is equilateral. The sides of the triangle are tangent to the circles. Find AC.
$AC = 8 + 4\sqrt{3}$ or about 14.9

Using the Chapter Test

This page may be used as a test or as a review. In addition, two multiple-choice tests (Forms 1A and 1B) and two free-response tests (Forms 2A and 2B) are provided in the *Evaluation Masters*. Chapter 9 Test, Form 1A is shown below.

Evaluation Masters, pp. 113-114

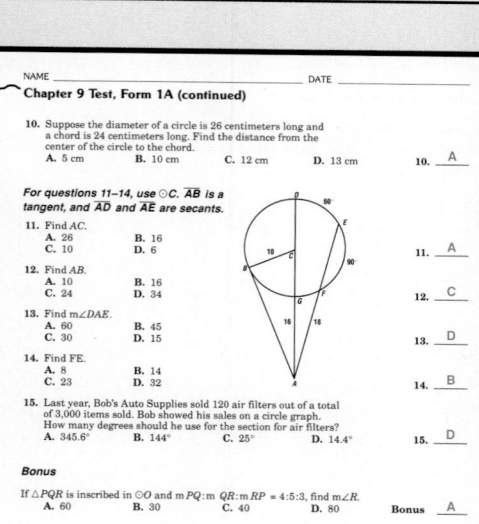

Test and Review Generator software is provided in Apple, IBM, and Macintosh versions. You may use this software to create your own tests or worksheets, based on the needs of your students.

The **Performance Assessment Booklet** provides an alternate assessment for evaluating student progress. An assessment for this chapter can be found on pages 17-18.

Using the Algebra Review

The goals of this two-page review of algebraic skills, concepts, and applications are as follows:

- To provide students a chance to review important concepts from algebra that will be useful as they study geometry.
- To give students an opportunity to reinforce the concepts they learned in previous algebra courses and may need for future mathematics courses.

The review is presented in a side-by-side format. Encourage students to refer to the Objectives and Examples on the left as they complete the Review Exercises on the right.

Additional Answers

1.

2.
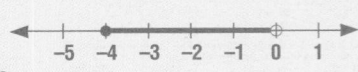

3.
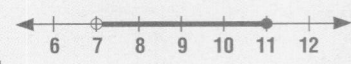

4.

10.
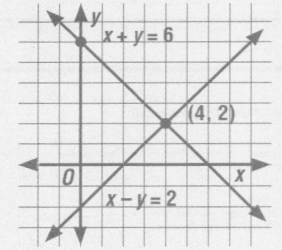

OBJECTIVES AND EXAMPLES	REVIEW EXERCISES

- Solve compound inequalities and graph the solution sets.

$$2a > a - 3 \quad \text{and} \quad 3a < a + 6$$
$$a > -3 \qquad\qquad 2a < 6$$
$$\qquad\qquad\qquad a < 3$$

The solution set is $\{a \mid -3 < a < 3\}$.

Solve each compound inequality. Then graph its solution set. See margin for graphs.

1. $x < -1$ or $x \geq 3$ $\{x \mid x < -1 \text{ or } x \geq 3\}$
2. $y + 1 \geq -3$ and $2y < 0$ $\{y \mid -4 \leq y < 0\}$
3. $4r > 3r + 7$ and $3r + 7 \leq r + 29$ $\{r \mid 7 < r \leq 11\}$
4. $2a + 5 \leq 7$ or $-2a + 4 \geq -3a + 1$
   4. {all real numbers}

- Use factoring and the zero product property to solve equations.

$$n^2 - n = 2$$
$$n^2 - n - 2 = 0$$
$$(n - 2)(n + 1) = 0$$
$$n - 2 = 0 \quad \text{or} \quad n + 1 = 0 \quad \textit{Zero product}$$
$$n = 2 \qquad\qquad n = -1 \quad \textit{property}$$

The solution set is $\{2, -1\}$.

Solve each equation. Check the solution.

5. $a^2 = -17a$ $\{0, -17\}$
6. $y^2 + 13y + 40 = 0$ $\{-5, -8\}$
7. $2x^2 + 13x = 24$ $\{\frac{3}{2}, -8\}$
8. $(x + 6)(x - 1) = 78$ $\{7, -12\}$
9. $25r^3 + 20r^2 + 4r = 0$ $\{0, -\frac{2}{5}\}$

- Solve systems of equations by graphing.

Graph $y = x$ and $y = 2 - x$ to find the solution to the system of equations.

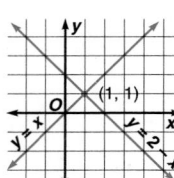

The solution is $(1, 1)$.

Graph each system of equations. Then find the solution to the system of equations. See margin for graphs.

10. $x + y = 6$ $(4, 2)$
    $x - y = 2$
11. $y = 4x - 7$ $(3, 5)$
    $x + y = 8$
12. $5x - 3y = 11$ $(-2, -7)$
    $2x + 3y = -25$

- Simplify square roots.

$$\sqrt{450} = \sqrt{2 \cdot 15^2}$$
$$= \sqrt{2} \cdot \sqrt{15^2}$$
$$= \sqrt{2} \cdot 15$$
$$= 15\sqrt{2}$$

$$\frac{\sqrt{18}}{\sqrt{5}} = \frac{\sqrt{18}}{\sqrt{5}} \cdot \frac{\sqrt{5}}{\sqrt{5}}$$
$$= \frac{\sqrt{2 \cdot 3^2 \cdot 5}}{\sqrt{5 \cdot 5}}$$
$$= \frac{\sqrt{2 \cdot 3^2} \cdot \sqrt{5}}{\sqrt{5^2}}$$
$$= \frac{3\sqrt{10}}{5}$$

Simplify. Use absolute value symbols when necessary to ensure nonnegative results.

13. $\sqrt{108}$ $6\sqrt{3}$
14. $\sqrt{720}$ $12\sqrt{5}$
15. $\frac{\sqrt{5}}{\sqrt{55}}$ $\frac{\sqrt{11}}{11}$
16. $\sqrt{\frac{20}{7}}$ $\frac{2\sqrt{35}}{7}$
17. $\sqrt{96x^4}$ $4x^2\sqrt{6}$
18. $\sqrt{\frac{60}{y^2}}$ $\frac{2\sqrt{15}}{|y|}$

Multiply rational expressions.

$$\frac{x^2 + 5x - 6}{x^2 - x - 12} \cdot \frac{x + 3}{x + 6}$$

$$= \frac{(x + 6)(x - 1)}{(x - 4)(x + 3)} \cdot \frac{x + 3}{x + 6}$$

$$= \frac{x - 1}{x - 4}$$

Find each product. Assume that no denominator is equal to zero.

19. $\dfrac{5x^2y}{8ab} \cdot \dfrac{12a^2b}{25x}$ $\dfrac{3axy}{10}$

20. $\dfrac{r^2 + 3r - 18}{r + 2} \cdot \dfrac{r + 6}{r^2 - r - 6}$ $\dfrac{(r + 6)^2}{(r + 2)^2}$

21. $\dfrac{b^2 + 19b + 84}{b - 3} \cdot \dfrac{b^2 - 9}{b^2 + 15b + 36}$ $b + 7$

Divide rational expressions.

$$\frac{y^2 - 16}{y^2 - 64} \div \frac{y + 4}{y - 8} = \frac{y^2 - 16}{y^2 - 64} \cdot \frac{y - 8}{y + 4}$$

$$= \frac{(y + 4)(y - 4)}{(y + 8)(y - 8)} \cdot \frac{y - 8}{y + 4}$$

$$= \frac{y - 4}{y + 8}$$

Find each quotient. Assume that no denominator is equal to zero.

22. $\dfrac{p^3r}{2q} \div \dfrac{-(p^2)}{4q}$ $-2pr$

23. $\dfrac{7a^2b}{x^2 + x - 30} \div \dfrac{3a}{x^2 + 15x + 54}$ $\dfrac{7ab(x + 9)}{3(x - 5)}$

24. $\dfrac{n^2 + 4n - 21}{n^2 + 8n + 15} \div \dfrac{n^2 - 9}{n^2 + 12n + 35}$ $\dfrac{(n + 7)^2}{(n + 3)^2}$

Calculate functional values for a given function.

If $g(x) = 2x - 1$, find $g(-6)$.

$$g(-6) = 2(-6) - 1$$
$$= -12 - 1 \text{ or } -13$$

If $f(x) = x^2 - x + 1$, find each value.

25. $f(2)$ 3

26. $f(-1)$ 3

27. $f\left(\dfrac{1}{2}\right)$ $\dfrac{3}{4}$

28. $f(a + 2)$ $a^2 + 3a + 3$

Applications and Connections

29. **Chemistry**   How many ounces of a 6% iodine solution need to be added to 12 ounces of a 10% iodine solution to produce a 7% iodine solution? **36 ounces**

30. **Geometry**   The measure of the area of a rectangle is $4m^2 - 3mp + 3p - 4m$. What are its dimensions? **$4m - 3p$ units by $m - 1$ units**

31. **Sales**   Clothes Outlet is having a sale on a certain brand of shirts and ties. Mr. Gill bought 8 shirts and 3 ties for $155. Mr. Ayala bought 5 shirts and 3 ties for $107. What are the sale prices of these shirts and ties? **$16, $9**

32. **Construction**   A rectangular garden is 24 feet by 32 feet. A sidewalk is built along the inside edges of all four sides. If the garden now has an area of 425 ft², how wide is the sidewalk? **3.5 ft**

33. **Physics**   If a ball is thrown upward with an initial velocity of 72 meters per second, its height h, in meters, after t seconds is given by the equation $h = 72t - 4.9t^2$. Make a table of values for this equation to determine how many seconds it takes for the ball to hit the ground, to the nearest second. **about 14.7 seconds**

Additional Answers

11.

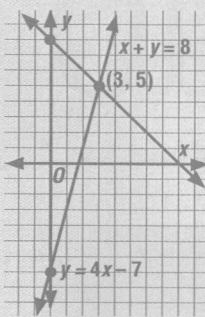

12

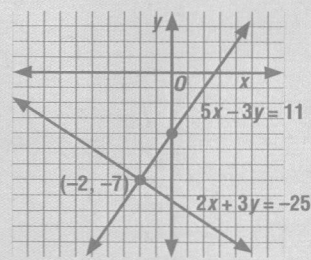

CHAPTER 10

Polygons and Area

PREVIEWING THE CHAPTER

This chapter investigates the characteristics of polygons and develops formulas for finding their areas. Students begin by identifying polygons and the faces, edges, and vertices of polyhedra. Next, they apply the interior angle sum and exterior angle sum theorems finding the areas of parallelograms, triangles, rhombi, and trapezoids. Connections to coordinate geometry are made and subsequently, students find the areas of regular polygons and the circumference and area of circles. Finally, students explore *networks*.

Problem-Solving Strategy Students learn to solve problems by guessing the solution, checking the guess, and using the information from the check to make a better guess.

Lesson Objective Chart

Lesson (Pages)	Lesson Objectives	State/Local Objectives
10-1 (466-472)	**10-1A**: Identify and name polygons.	
	10-1B: Identify faces, edges, and vertices of a polyhedron.	
10-2 (473-479)	**10-2A**: Find the sum of the measures of the interior and exterior angles of a convex polygon.	
	10-2B: Find the measure of each interior and exterior angle of a regular polygon.	
	10-2C: Use angle measures of polygons in problem solving.	
10-3 (480-482)	**10-3**: Solve problems by using guess and check.	
10-4 (483-488)	**10-4**: Find areas of parallelograms.	
10-5 (489-494)	**10-5**: Find the areas of triangles, rhombi, and trapezoids.	
10-6 (495-500)	**10-6**: Find areas of regular polygons.	
10-7 (502-506)	**10-7A**: Find the circumference of a circle.	
	10-7B: Find the area of a circle.	
10-8 (507-511)	**10-8**: Use area to solve problems involving geometric probability.	
10-9 (512-517)	**10-9A**: Recognize nodes and edges as used in graph theory.	
	10-9B: Determine if a network is traceable.	
	10-9C: Determine if a network is complete.	

ORGANIZING THE CHAPTER

You may want to refer to the **Course Planning Calendar** on page T28.

Lesson Planning Guide / Blackline Masters Booklets

Lesson (Pages)	Pacing Chart (days) Course I	II	III	Reteaching	Practice	Enrichment	Evaluation	Technology	Lab Manual	Mixed Problem Solving	Applications	Cooperative Learning Activity	Multicultural	Transparencies
10-1 (466-472)	2	2	1.5	p. 57	p. 66	p. 57			pp.70-73		p. 24			10-1
10-2 (473-479)	2	2	1.5	p. 58	p. 67	p. 58								10-2
10-3 (480-482)	1	1	1		p. 68		Quiz A, p.135							10-3
10-4 (483-488)	2	1.5	1.5	p. 59	p. 69	p. 59	Mid Chapter Test, p. 139	p. 10	pp.74-77					10-4
10-5 (489-494)	2	1.5	1.5	p. 60	p. 70	p. 60	Quiz B, p.135	p. 46						10-5
10-6 (495-500)	2	2	2	p. 61	p. 71	p. 61								10-6
10-7 (502-506)	1.5	1	1	p. 62	p. 72	p. 62	Quiz C, p. 136					p. 38		10-7
10-8 (507-511)	1.5	1	1	p. 63	p. 73	p. 63				p. 10				10-8
10-9 (512-517)	2	2	2	p. 64	p. 74	p. 64	Quiz D, p. 136						p. 10	10-9
Review (518-520)	1	1	1	Multiple Choice Tests, Forms 1A and 2B, pp. 127-130 Free Response Tests, Forms 2A and 2B, pp. 131-134										
Test (521)	1	1	1	Cumulative Review. pp. 137-138 Standardized Tests Practice Questions, p. 140										

Course I: Chapters 1-11; Course II: Chapters 1-12; Course III: Chapters 1-13

Other Chapter Resources

Student Edition

Chapter Opener, pp. 464-465
History Connection, p. 479
Cooperative Learning Project, p. 482
Mid-Chapter Review, p. 488
Journal Entry, pp. 494, 517
Technology, p. 501
Portfolio, p. 511
Developing Reasoning Skills, p. 517
College Entrance Exam Preview, pp. 522-523
More Investigations in Geometry, p. A11-A12
Extended Project 3, pp. B10-B13

Teacher's Classroom Resources

Transparency 10-0
Real World Applications Transparencies, 20, 21
Performance Assessment Booklet, pp. 19-20
Problem-of-the-Week Activity Cards, 27, 28, 29
Tech Prep Applications Booklet, pp. 19-20

Other Supplements

Algebra and Geometry Overhead Manipulative Resources
Glencoe Mathematics Professional Series

Software

Test and Review Generator (Apple, IBM, and Macintosh)
Teacher's Guide for Software Resources

ENHANCING THE CHAPTER

Cooperative Learning

Describing the Student's Responsibilities to the Group

It is important for students to understand that they are expected not merely to work in a group but to work *cooperatively* in a group. Each member must accept responsibility for learning the assigned material and for making sure every other member of the group also learns the material. One way to encourage this attitude is to have the group generate a single product, report, or set of answers that each member must sign to indicate agreement with the responses and the ability to justify or explain why the responses are appropriate. Be alert to other ways to encourage group members to count on each other to look for ways to help one another do better. For example, when you give a quiz or test, you might inform the group that each member will earn his or her own individual score and will also earn bonus points based on how much the group's average score exceeds a preset level of performance.

Technology

The Technology Feature following Lesson 10-6 shows students how to use the features of a spreadsheet program to find the area of a regular polygon. After working through the given example and answering several questions about the example, students are asked to set up a spreadsheet program to find the area of a trapezoid. After students have completed these exercises, you may want to have them set up their own spreadsheet program to find the area of a polygon of their choice.

Critical Thinking

The acquisition of critical-thinking skills related to analysis and synthesis are vital for success in many geometric situations. You can help students improve these skills by taking advantage of the problem-solving activities in Lesson 10-3 that involve the strategy *guess and check*. When working with this strategy, make students aware that you expect them to be able to explain, when their first guess is not the answer, how and why they chose each successive guess. Such analysis of the results of initial guesses to make more intelligent guesses will ensure success with this strategy when applied to real-life problems or to other geometric content.

Cooperative Learning, p. 38

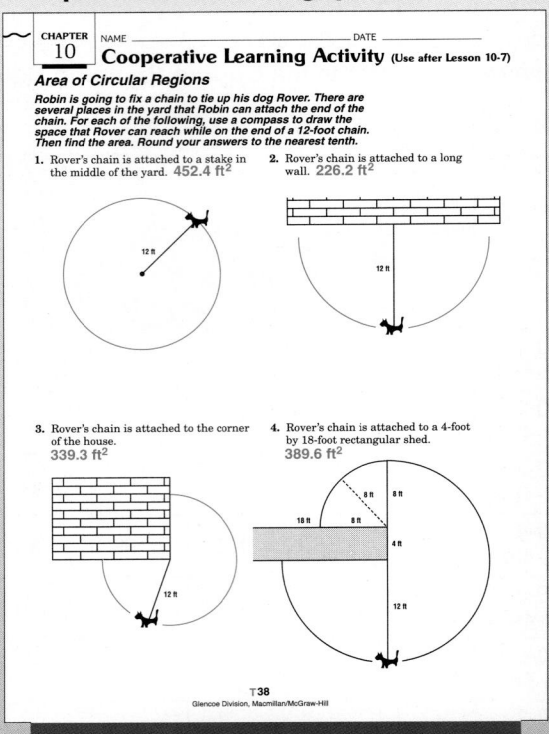

Technology, p. 10

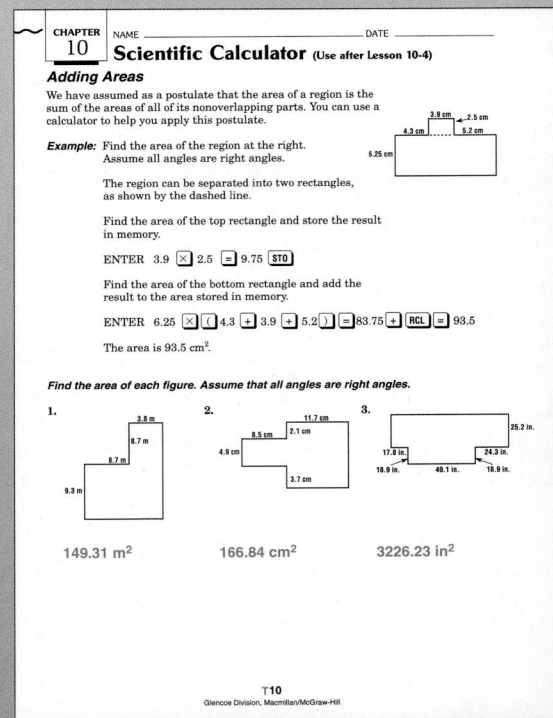

Problem of the Week Activity

The card shown below is one of three available for this chapter. It can be used as a class or small group activity.

Activity Card

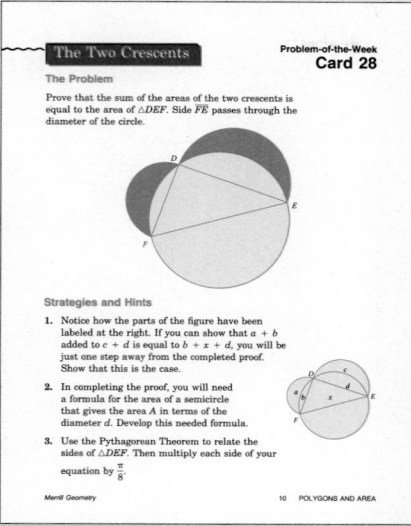

Manipulatives and Models

The following materials may be used as models or manipulatives in Chapter 10.

- polyhedrons (Lesson 10-1)
- scientific calculator (Lesson 10-2)
- tangrams (Lesson 10-3)
- compass, straightedge (Lesson 10-6)
- spreadsheet (Page 501)
- computer (Lesson 10-7)

Outside Resources

Books/Periodicals

Polya, G. *Mathematical Discovery Volume 2.* John Wiley and Sons.

Rucker, R. *The 4th Dimension - Toward a Geometry of a Higher Reality.* Houghton-Mifflin Co.

Steinhaus, H. *Mathematical Snapshots.* Oxford University Press.

Films/Videotapes/Videodiscs

Platonic Solids, Dale Seymour Publications, P.O. Box 10888, Palo Alto, CA 94303

Software

Geometry Inventor, WINGS for Learning/Sunburst, 101 Castleton St., Pleasantville, NY 10570

Cabri Géometre, Brooks/Cole, Wadsworth School Group, 10 Davis Drive, Belmont, CA 94002-3098

Multicultural

Multicultural Activity, p. 10

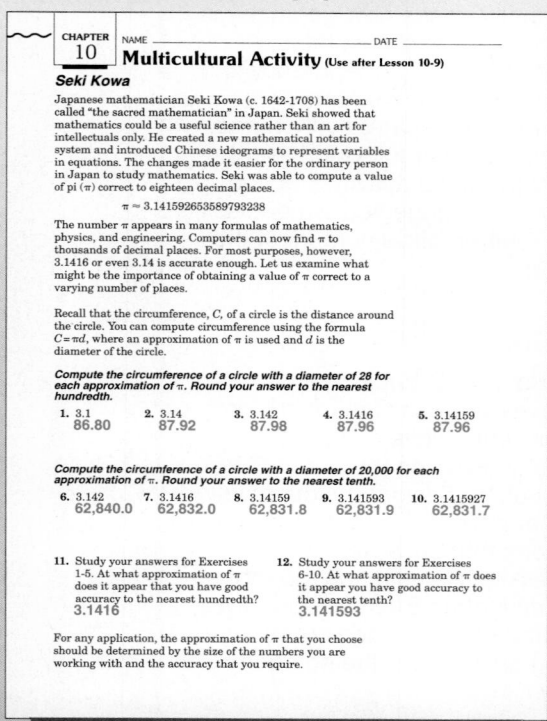

Lab Manual

Lab Activity, pp. 74-77

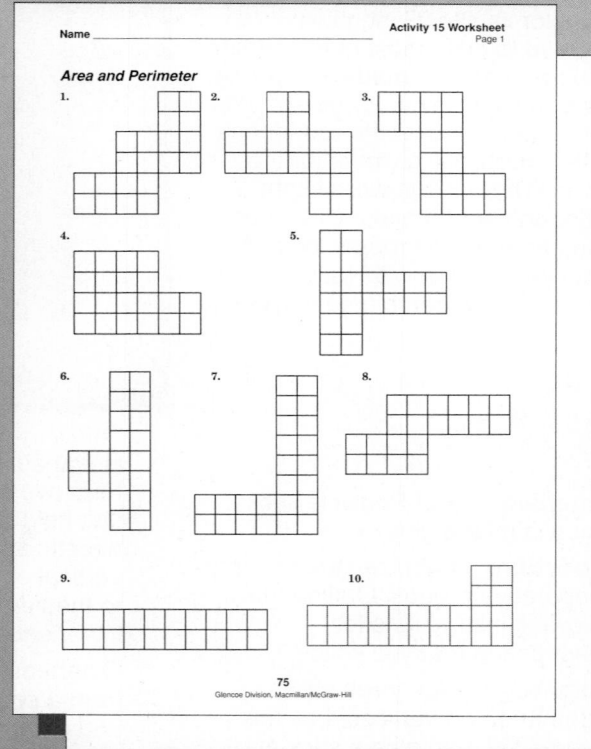

Using the Chapter Opener

This two-page introduction to the chapter provides students with an opportunity to see how geometry is used throughout the world in various cultures. Transparency 10-0, available in the Merrill Geometry Transparency Package, provides another full-color visual and motivational activity that you can use to engage your students in the mathematical content of the chapter.

Multicultural Notes

Canada Arthur Erickson has designed some of Canada's most magnificent buildings. For the Canadian Pavilion for Expo '67 in Montreal, he designed a beautiful wood pavilion; its roof was a pile of octagons that became progressively smaller as the roof became higher. Each octagon was rotated 22.5° with each corner resting on a side of the octagon below.

Japan Itsuko Hasegawa approaches architecture as an interpretation of nature. In 1987, she designed the Shonandai Cultural Center in Fujisawa, a city south of Tokyo. The center is very large for its site. Hasegawa decided to build most of the center underground and made an inviting park above ground. Large spheres in the park suggest the roundness of the world, the cosmos, or the moon. There is a tower of light, wind, and sound and a clock tree. The underground rooms look onto a sunken garden with walls plastered to resemble geological strata.

Chapter Project

Materials box of Popsicle sticks, model airplane glue

Procedure Organize students into cooperative groups. Outline the following instructions for constructing Platonic solids.

Tetrahedron: glue three sticks together at the vertices. Lay this triangle flat, and glue a stick at each vertex to form the three edges of a pyramid.

Hexahedron: glue eight sticks to form two squares. Lay one square flat, hold the second square directly above it, and glue its four vertical edges one stick at a time to the vertices of the upper and lower squares.

Octahedron: glue four sticks to form a square. Lay the square flat and glue four sticks to form the edges of the first pyramid. Have one person hold the pyramid upside down, and glue the last four sticks to form the edges of the opposite pyramid.

Dodecahedron: glue ten sticks to make two pentagons. For the other ten pentagons, use five sticks to shape each pentagon, but glue only three sides. Glue one three-sided pentagon to each vertex of one five-sided pentagon, and before the glue has a chance to set, raise the five pentagons upward and glue one to the other. Finally, glue the halves of the dodecahedron together.

Polygons and Area

GEOMETRY AROUND THE W●RLD
China

China Tower in Hong Kong is probably the only structure on Earth whose design was literally shaped within the architect's hands.

To plan the tower's design, Chinese-born architect I.M. Pei used a square shaft of wood cut diagonally into four equal triangular pieces. He held the four pieces together in one fist and pushed each piece up with the fingers of his other hand. With each thrust of Pei's fingers, each piece rose a bit higher than the preceding piece. The result was an unusual skyscraper design featuring a roof of four triangles rising to different heights.

Pei came to the United States in the 1930s to study at the Massachusetts Institute of Technology and at Harvard. A United States citizen for many years, he has designed buildings all over the world. Among Pei's most famous are the China Tower in Hong Kong, the glass pyramid entrance to the Louvre museum in Paris, and the John F. Kennedy Library in Boston.

GEOMETRY IN ACTION

Pei's design for the Kennedy Library consists of an intersecting square, circle, and triangle. The figure below is a diagram for the library's ground floor. What type of triangle is labeled *A*? What shapes adjoin it on either side?

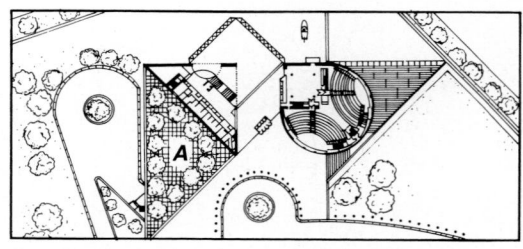

◄ *China Tower in Hong Kong* Inset: *I.M. Pei*

465

CHAPTER OBJECTIVES

In this chapter, you will:
- Identify parts of polygons and polyhedrons.
- Find areas of polygons.
- Find areas and circumferences of circles.
- Solve problems involving geometric probability.
- Determine characteristics of networks.

China Tower's stepped triangular design fits perfectly on the small site I.M. Pei had to work with when he designed the building.

Connections and Applications

Lesson	Connections (C) and Applications (A)	Examples	Exercises
10-1	A: Mineralogy		48
10-2	A: Architecture	1	
	A: Patterns		51
10-4	A: Landscaping	1	
	A: Engineering		25
	A: Interior Design		26
10-5	A: Real Estate	2	
	A: Gardening		28
10-6	A: Home Maintenance	1	
	A: Gardening		35
	A: Construction		36
10-7	A: Bicycling	1	
	A: City Planning		41
	A: Sports		42
	A: Home Economics		43
	A: Sewing		44
10-8	A: Entertainment	1	21
	A: Gardening		20
10-9	A: Travel	1	29
	A: Business		30
	A: Construction		31

Icosahedron: fit 20 equilateral triangles together as in the figure, and then bring them together to form an icosahedron.

As a class, discuss the number of vertices, edges, faces, and the number and measures of angles at each vertex of the models.

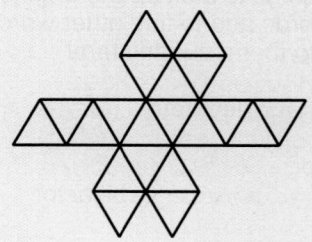

Resources

Wiseman, Carter. I.M. Pei. *A Profile in American Architecture.* Harry N. Abrams, Inc.

Steinhouse, Hugo. *Mathematical Snapshots.* Oxford University Press

Lesson Resources

• Reteaching Master 10-1
• Practice Master 10-1
• Enrichment Master 10-1
• Activity Master, p. 24
• Lab Manual, pp. 70-73

 Transparency 10-1 contains the 5-Minute Check and a teaching aid for this lesson.

INTRODUCING THE LESSON

 5-Minute Check

(over Chapter 9)

1. Draw a circle with center Q, diameter $\overline{AB}$, radius $\overline{QR}$, and tangent $\overleftrightarrow{ST}$.
Sample answer:

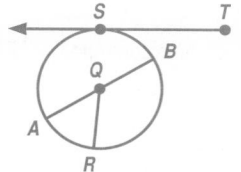

Refer to $\odot O$.

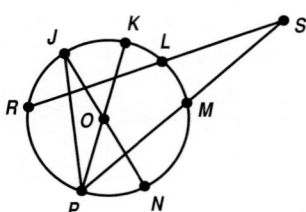

2. If $m\widehat{JK} = 53$, find $m\angle PON$.
53

3. If $m\widehat{LM} = 18$ and $m\widehat{RP} = 69$, find $m\angle RSP$. **25.5**

4. If $SR = 18$, $SL = 4$, and $SM = 6$, find SP. **12**

5. If $m\angle NJP = 25$, find $m\angle NOP$. **50**

Motivating the Lesson

Draw a square, triangle, rectangle, trapezoid, pentagon, and hexagon on the chalkboard. Ask students to describe the characteristics that these shapes have in common.
Sample answer: closed figures, made up of line segments

10-1 Polygons and Polyhedra

Objectives
10-1A
10-1B

After studying this lesson, you should be able to:
▪ identify and name polygons, and
▪ identify faces, edges, and vertices of a polyhedron.

Application

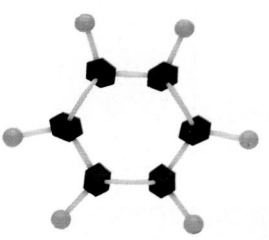

The molecular structure represented at the right is benzene, C_6H_6. The benzene molecule, or ring, consists of six carbon atoms arranged in a flat, six-sided shape with a hydrogen atom attached to each carbon atom. The symbol for benzene is ⬡ . The figure represents the shape in which the atoms are bonded together.

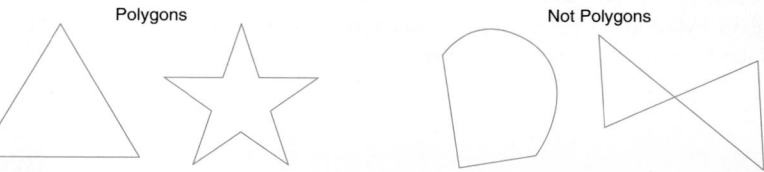

The term **polygon** is derived from the Greek word meaning "many-angled". Look at the figures below on the left. Each polygon is formed by a finite number of coplanar segments (sides) such that:

1. sides that have a common endpoint are noncollinear, and
2. each side intersects exactly two other sides, but only at their endpoints.

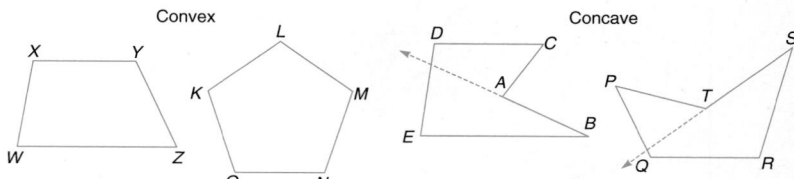

Polygons   Not Polygons

Can you explain why the two nonexamples of polygons shown above at the right fail to satisfy the conditions of the definition of a polygon?

A **convex** polygon is a polygon such that no line containing a side of the polygon contains a point in the interior of the polygon. A polygon that is not convex is called nonconvex or **concave.**

Convex   Concave

Notice that in the nonconvex examples, the extensions of sides $\overline{AB}$ and $\overline{ST}$ fail to satisfy the definition for convex. *Why?*

ALTERNATE TEACHING STRATEGIES

Using Manipulatives

Have students choose a polyhedron to make using cardboard and tape. They may design the piece beforehand or cut out several polygons and fit them together any way they can. Each student should prepare a sheet that tells the name of the polyhedron or describes it and gives the number of faces, edges, and vertices. Display students' work.

Using Connections

Ask students to look up the origins of these words and to find other words related to them: quadrilateral **Latin, four-sided, quadraphonic, quadruped;** geometry **Greek, earth measure, geography, geology;** perimeter **Greek, measure around, periscope, periphery;** bisector **Latin, cut in two, section, bicycle**

Polygons may be classified by the number of sides they have. The chart at the right gives some common names for polygons. In general, a polygon with *n* sides is called an ***n*-gon.** Thus, an octagon can also be called an 8-gon. A polygon with 13 sides is called a 13-gon.

Number of Sides	Polygon
3	triangle
4	quadrilateral
5	pentagon
6	hexagon
7	heptagon
8	octagon
9	nonagon
10	decagon
12	dodecagon
n	*n*-gon

When referring to a polygon, we use its name and list the consecutive vertices in order. Hexagon *ABCDEF* and hexagon *FABCDE* are two possible correct names for the polygon at the right.

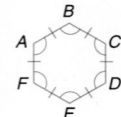

Observe that in hexagon *ABCDEF* all the sides are congruent and all the angles are congruent. When this is true, the polygon is called **regular.** A regular polygon is a convex polygon with all sides congruent and all angles congruent.

Example 1

Classify each polygon by the number of sides, as *convex* or *concave*, and as *regular* or *not regular*.

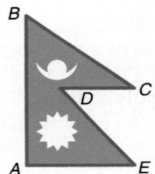

Polygon *ABCDE* has five sides. It is a pentagon.

If $\overline{CD}$ is extended through *D*, it passes through the interior of the pentagon. So, the pentagon is concave.

Since it is concave, pentagon *ABCDE* cannot be regular.

Polygon *PQRSTUVW* has 8 sides, so it is an octagon.

No lines containing sides of the octagon pass through the interior. Therefore, the polygon is convex.

Since all sides and all angles are congruent, octagon *PQRSTUVW* is regular.

LESSON 10-1 POLYGONS AND POLYHEDRA **467**

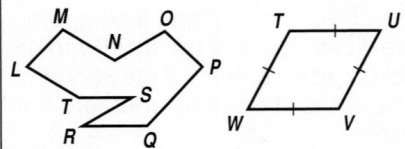

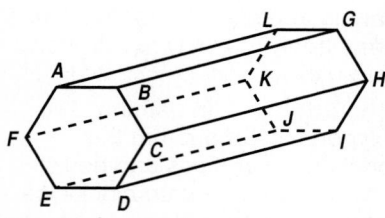

Polyhedra are solids formed by regions shaped like polygons that share a common side. An ice cube and a die are examples of polyhedra. The flat surfaces formed by polygons and their interiors are called **faces.** Pairs of faces intersect at line segments called **edges.** Three or more edges intersect at a point called a **vertex.** *Polyhedra is the plural of polyhedron.*

A polyhedron must have at least three edges intersecting at each vertex. Also, the sum of the measures of the angles formed at each vertex must be less than 360.

The table below lists the faces, edges, and vertices for the polyhedron at the right.

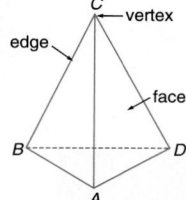

Faces	Edges	Vertices
△*ABC*, △*BCD*, △*ACD*, △*ABD*	$\overline{AB}$, $\overline{AC}$, $\overline{AD}$, $\overline{BD}$, $\overline{BC}$, $\overline{CD}$	*A, B, C, D*

Example 2

Name the faces, edges, and vertices of the polyhedron.

The faces are the regions bounded by the quadrilaterals *AEJF, DEJI, CDIH, BCHG, ABGF,* and pentagons *ABCDE* and *FGHIJ*.

The edges are $\overline{AB}$, $\overline{BC}$, $\overline{CD}$, $\overline{DE}$, $\overline{EA}$, $\overline{FG}$, $\overline{GH}$, $\overline{HI}$, $\overline{IJ}$, $\overline{JF}$, $\overline{FA}$, $\overline{GB}$, $\overline{HC}$, $\overline{ID}$, and $\overline{JE}$.

The vertices are *A, B, C, D, E, F, G, H, I,* and *J*.

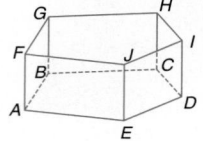

A polyhedron is **regular** if all of its faces are shaped like congruent regular polygons. Since all of the faces of a regular polyhedron are regular and congruent, all of the edges of a regular polyhedron are congruent. There are exactly five types of regular polyhedrons. These are called the *Platonic solids,* because Plato described them so fully in his writings.

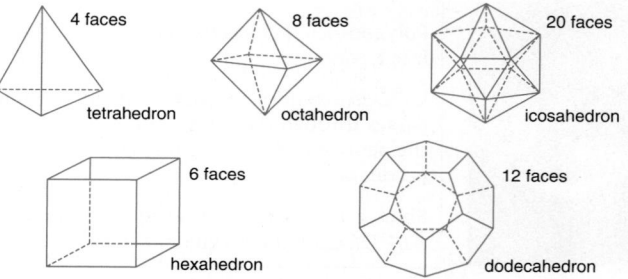

4 faces — tetrahedron

8 faces — octahedron

20 faces — icosahedron

6 faces — hexahedron

12 faces — dodecahedron

CHECKING FOR UNDERSTANDING

Communicating Mathematics

Read and study the lesson to answer these questions.

1. Decide whether each figure below is a polygon. If the figure is not a polygon, explain why not. **a. yes   b. no; sides must be line segments c. no; sides must meet at only one point   d. yes**

   a.   b.   c.   d.

2. Which of the polygons in Exercise 1 are convex? Explain. **The polygon in a. is convex because none of the lines containing the sides pass through the interior.**

3. Name the polygon at the right. Is more than one name possible? Does the polygon appear to be regular? Explain. **decagon *ABCDEFGHIJ*; yes; yes, it is convex and all sides and angles appear congruent.**

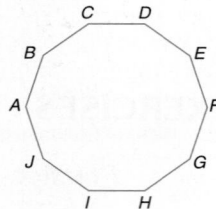

4. In polygon *ABCDE*, all sides are congruent. Is this sufficient for the pentagon to be regular? Draw an example to explain your answer. **no; See margin for drawing.**

5. What is special about the faces of a regular polyhedron? **They are all congruent and are shaped like regular polygons.**

Guided Practice

Classify each figure as a convex polygon, a concave polygon, or not a polygon.

6. 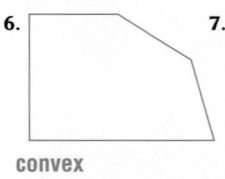   7.    8.    9.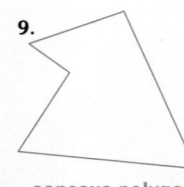

convex polygon   **not a polygon**   **convex polygon**   **concave polygon**

LESSON 10-1   POLYGONS AND POLYHEDRA   469

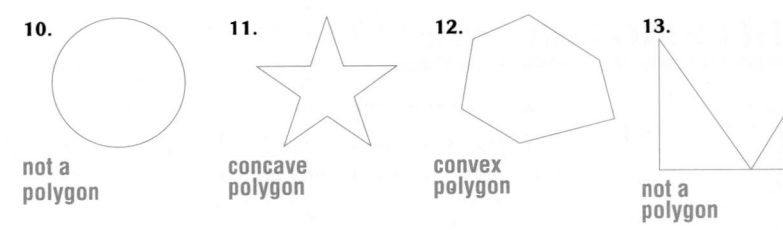

10. not a polygon

11. concave polygon

12. convex polygon

13. not a polygon

Name the faces, edges, and vertices of each polyhedron.
See margin.

14.

15.

16.

APPLYING THE LESSON

Homework Exercises

Assignment Guide

Basic: 17-38, 47-54
Average: 21-42, 47-54
Enriched: 25-54

Additional Answers

14. faces: △*ABD*, △*ADC*, △*DBC*, and △*ABC*; edges: $\overline{DB}$, $\overline{DA}$, $\overline{DC}$, $\overline{BA}$, $\overline{BC}$, and $\overline{AC}$; vertices: *A*, *B*, *C*, and *D*

15. faces: quadrilaterals *ABFE*, *FBCG*, *HGCD*, *EHDA*, *ABCD*, and *EFGH*; edges: $\overline{AE}$, $\overline{EF}$, $\overline{FB}$, $\overline{AB}$, $\overline{FG}$, $\overline{GC}$, CB, $\overline{HG}$, $\overline{CD}$, $\overline{DH}$, $\overline{EH}$, and $\overline{AD}$; vertices: *A*, *B*, *C*, *D*, *E*, *F*, *G*, *H*

16. faces: △*DEF*, △*DAF*, △*DBE*, △*DBA*, △*BAC*, △*EBC*, △*FEC* △*CAF*; edges: $\overline{EC}$, $\overline{CA}$, $\overline{CB}$, $\overline{CF}$, $\overline{AB}$, $\overline{BE}$, $\overline{FA}$, $\overline{EF}$, $\overline{DA}$, $\overline{DF}$, $\overline{DE}$, and $\overline{DB}$; vertices: *A*, *B*, *C*, *D*, *E*, *F*

Reteaching Masters Booklet, p. 57

10-1 NAME ____ DATE ____
Reteaching Worksheet

Polygons and Polyhedra

A **polygon** is a plane figure formed by a finite number of segments such that (1) sides that have a common endpoint are noncollinear and (2) each side intersects exactly two other sides, but only at their endpoints. A **convex polygon** is a polygon such that no line containing a side of the polygon contains a point in the interior of the polygon. Convex polygons with all sides congruent and all angles congruent are called **regular.**

Polygons are two-dimensional, the corresponding three-dimensional figures are **polyhedra.** They are made up of polygon-shaped regions called **faces.** Segments where faces intersect are called **edges.** Points where three or more edges intersect are called **vertices.** A convex polyhedron with congruent, regular faces is a **regular** polyhedron.

Examples: Classify each figure as a convex polygon, a concave polygon, or not a polygon.

concave polygon   not a polygon   convex polygon

Classify each figure as a convex polygon, a concave polygon, or not a polygon. If the figure is a polygon, name it according to the number of sides.

1. not a polygon **2.** concave; hexagon **3.** convex; pentagon **4.** concave; heptagon

Classify each polygon as regular or not regular. Explain.

5. not regular, not all angles are congruent. **6.** regular, it is convex and all sides and angles are congruent. **7.** not regular, not all sides are congruent.

8. State the number of faces, edges, and vertices for the polyhedron. 6, 12, 8

T**57**
Glencoe Division, Macmillan/McGraw-Hill

EXERCISES

Practice

A

Name a polygon with the given number of sides.

17. 3 triangle
18. 10 decagon
19. 20 20-gon
20. 8 octagon
21. 6 hexagon
22. *x* *x*-gon

Classify each figure as a *convex polygon*, a *concave polygon*, or *not a polygon*. If a figure is a polygon, name it according to the number of sides.

23. not a polygon

24. concave heptagon

25. convex pentagon

26. concave quadrilateral

27. not a polygon

28. convex hexagon

RETEACHING THE LESSON

Ask students to draw each of the following: See students' work.
1. five different polygons
2. a figure that is not a polygon
3. a polygon that is concave
4. a polyhedron with six faces
5. a polyhedron with six congruent faces

B Use polygon *MNOPQ* to answer each question. 29. M, N, O, P, Q
30. ∠M, ∠N, ∠O, ∠P, ∠Q 31. MN, NO, OP, PQ, QM 32. convex

29. Name the vertices of the polygon.

30. Name the angles of the polygon.

31. Name the sides of the polygon.

32. Is the polygon convex or concave?

33. Name the polygon according to the number of sides it has. pentagon

34. Is the polygon regular? Explain. no; its sides are not all congruent.

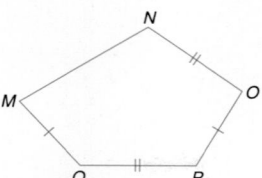

Classify each polygon as either regular or not regular. Explain. See margin.

35.   36.   37.   38.

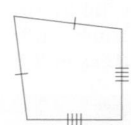         

If possible, draw a polygon that fits each description.
See margin.
39. a regular quadrilateral

40. a quadrilateral with all sides congruent, but not all angles congruent

41. a concave pentagon with all angles congruent

42. a hexagon with all angles congruent

C Answer each question for each of the polyhedrons shown below. See margin.

a.   b.   c.   d.   e.

   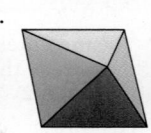   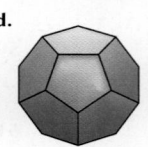   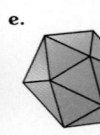

Tetrahedron   Hexahedron   Octahedron   Dodecahedron   Icosahedron

43. Name the type of polygon that forms the faces.

44. What is the number of polygons that intersect at each vertex?

45. List the number of faces, vertices, and edges for each solid.

46. A Swiss mathematician, Leonhard Euler, stated that the number of faces, *F*, the number of vertices, *V*, and the number of edges, *E*, of a polyhedron had the relationship $F + V = E + 2$. Is this true for the regular polyhedra shown above? Justify your answer.

Critical Thinking 47. Describe a counterexample to the statement *Any polygon with all its angles congruent is a regular polygon.* Answers may vary. A sample answer is a rectangle that is not a square.

LESSON 10-1   POLYGONS AND POLYHEDRA   471

Additional Answers

43. a: triangles, b: squares, c: triangles, d: pentagons, e: triangles
44. a: 3, b: 3, c: 4, d: 3, e: 5
45. a: 4, 4, 6; b: 6, 8, 12; c: 8, 6, 12: d: 12, 20, 30, e: 20, 12, 30
46. yes; a: 4 + 4 = 6 + 2; b: 6 + 8 = 12 + 2; c: 8 + 6 = 12 + 2; d: 12 + 20 = 30 + 2; e: 20 + 12 = 30 + 2

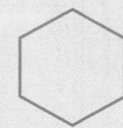
Chapter 10   471

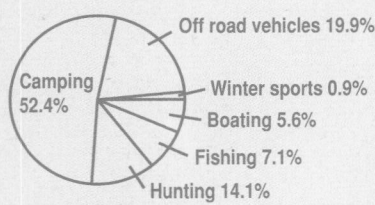
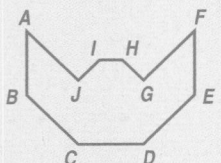
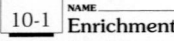

Application

48. **Mineralogy**   Mineral crystals are solids with flat surfaces. The flat surfaces, called faces, are different shapes according to the type of mineral. Each diagram below shows the shape of a single mineral crystal. Name the number of faces and the shapes of the faces. Then identify any faces that appear to be congruent. **See margin.**

   a. borax   **b.** quartz   **c.** calcite

   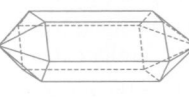   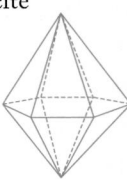

Mixed Review

49. The national parks in the United States are used for many recreational activities. In 1989, they were used for driving off-road vehicles 65,808 times, for camping 173,597 times, for hunting 46,760 times, for fishing 23,392 times, for boating 18,491 times, and for winter sports 3,119 times. Make a circle graph of this data. **(Lesson 9-8) See margin.**

50. The measures of the legs of a right triangle are 4.0 and 5.6. Find the measure of the hypotenuse. Round your answer to the nearest tenth. **(Lesson 8-2) 6.9**

51. Determine whether the pair of triangles is congruent. If so, state the postulate or theorem that you used. **(Lesson 5-2) not enough information**

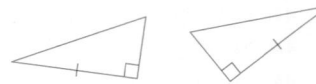

52. Find the slope of the line that passes through (5, 0) and (5, -2). **(Lesson 3-5) undefined**

53. Write the conditional *A regular polygon is convex and has all sides congruent* in if-then form. **(Lesson 2-2) If a polygon is regular, then it is convex and has all sides congruent.**

Wrap-Up

54. Polygons are classified by the number of sides they have and by whether they are concave or convex. Draw and label a concave decagon. **See margin.**

472   CHAPTER 10   POLYGONS AND AREA

EXTENDING THE LESSON

Math Power: Problem Solving

How many diagonals can be drawn in a 20-gon?   **170**

10-2 Angles of Polygons

Objectives
After studying this lesson, you should be able to:
10-2A ▪ find the sum of the measures of the interior and exterior angles of a convex polygon,
10-2B ▪ find the measure of each interior and exterior angle of a regular polygon, and
10-2C ▪ use angle measures of polygons in problem solving.

Application

When an architect designs a window like this one, what should she designate as the measure of each angle of this regular octagon? To answer this question, consider each convex polygon below with all possible diagonals drawn from one vertex. *You will solve this problem in Example 1.*

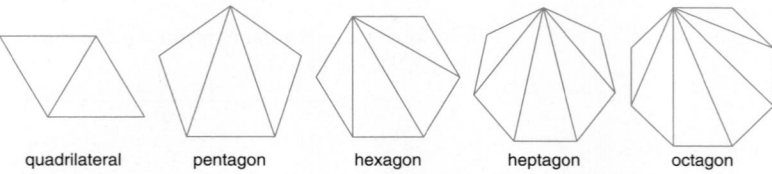

| quadrilateral | pentagon | hexagon | heptagon | octagon |

Notice that in each case, the polygon is separated into triangles. The sum of the measures of the angles of each polygon can be found by adding the measures of the angles of the triangles. Since the sum of the measures of the angles in a triangle is 180, we can easily find this sum. Let's make a chart to find the sum of the angle measures for several convex polygons.

Convex Polygon	Number of Sides	Number of Triangles	Sum of Angle Measures
triangle	3	1	(1 · 180) or 180
quadrilateral	4	2	(2 · 180) or 360
pentagon	5	3	(3 · 180) or 540
hexagon	6	4	(4 · 180) or 720
heptagon	7	5	(5 · 180) or 900
octagon	8	6	(6 · 180) or 1080

Look for a pattern in the angle measures. In each case, the sum of the angle measures is 2 less than the number of sides in the polygon times 180. So in an n-gon, the sum of the angle measures will be $(n - 2)180$ or $180(n - 2)$. Our inductive reasoning has led us to a correct conclusion. This conclusion is stated formally in Theorem 10-1.

10-2 Lesson Notes

Lesson Resources
• Reteaching Master 10-2
• Practice Master 10-2
• Enrichment Master 10-2

 Transparency 10-2 contains the 5-Minute Check and a teaching aid for this lesson.

INTRODUCING THE LESSON

 5-Minute Check
(over Lesson 10-1)

Draw each of the following. See students' work.

1. a convex hexagon
2. a concave octagon
3. a regular quadrilateral
4. a concave heptagon
5. a convex pentagon
6. a regular hexagon

Motivating the Lesson
Ask students to draw three different polygons on a sheet of paper. For each figure, ask them to draw all the diagonals from one vertex. Point out that each figure is now subdivided into triangles. Ask students how many triangles are formed in each figure and compare results among the class.

TEACHING THE LESSON

Teaching Tip In drawing diagonals within polygons, point out that it does not matter which vertex is chosen.

ALTERNATE TEACHING STRATEGIES

Using Calculators
In general, what key sequence should be used on a scientific calculator to find the measure of an interior angle of a regular polygon given the number of its sides, n?

Using Communication
Ask students to make up a problem about interior or exterior angles of a polygon. Have them exchange their problems for solution and work together to check the answers.

Theorem 10-1 Interior Angle Sum Theorem	If a convex polygon has n sides and S is the sum of the measures of its interior angles, then $S = 180(n - 2)$.

We can use the interior angle sum theorem to find the measure of each angle of the octagonal window.

Example 1

Find the measure of each interior angle of the regular octagonal window.

First use the interior angle sum theorem to find the sum of the angle measures in a convex octagon.

$S = 180(n - 2)$ *Interior angle sum theorem*
$S = 180(8 - 2)$ *An octagon has 8 sides, so substitute 8 for n.*
$S = 180(6)$
$S = 1080$

All the angles in a regular octagon are congruent. So the measure of each angle is $\dfrac{1080}{8}$ or 135.

Example 2

Two angles of a convex heptagon are congruent. Each of the other five angles has a measure twice that of the other two angles. Find the measure of each angle.

Let $m\angle A = m\angle B = x$. Then the measures of angles C, D, E, F, and G must be $2x$. The sum of the measures of all interior angles is $S = x + x + 2x + 2x + 2x + 2x + 2x$. The interior angle sum theorem says that the sum of the angle measures is $180(7 - 2)$ or 900. Write an equation.

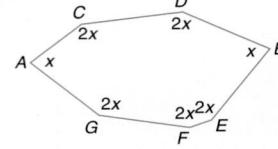

$900 = x + x + 2x + 2x + 2x + 2x + 2x$
$900 = 12x$
$75 = x$

The measures of two angles of the heptagon are 75 each. The measures of the other five angles are $2 \cdot 75$ or 150 each.

The interior angle sum theorem identifies a relationship among the interior angles of a convex polygon. Is there a relationship among the exterior angles of a convex polygon?

1. Draw a convex hexagon.

2. Extend the sides of the hexagon to form one exterior angle at each vertex.

3. Use a protractor to find the measure of each exterior angle.

4. Find the sum of the measures of the exterior angles.

5. Repeat for a triangle, a quadrilateral, and a pentagon. What conjecture can you make?

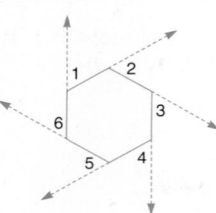

Consider the sum of the measures of the exterior angles for an *n*-gon.

$$
\begin{array}{ccccc}
\text{sum of measures} & = & \text{sum of measures} & - & \text{sum of measures} \\
\text{of exterior angles} & & \text{of linear pairs} & & \text{of interior angles} \\
& = & n \cdot 180 & - & 180(n-2) \\
& = & 180n & - & 180n + 360 \\
& = & 360 &&
\end{array}
$$

So, the sum of the exterior angle measures is 360 for *any* convex polygon.

Theorem 10-2 **Exterior Angle** **Sum Theorem**	**If a polygon is convex, then the sum of the measures of the exterior angles, one at each vertex, is 360.**

Example 3

Use the exterior angle sum theorem to find the measure of an interior angle and an exterior angle of a regular pentagon.

According to the exterior angle sum theorem, the sum of the measures of the five exterior angles is 360.

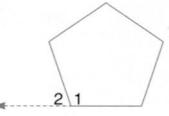

The pentagon is regular, so all of the interior angles are congruent. The interior angles are supplementary to the exterior angles. If two angles are supplementary to congruent angles they are congruent so all of the exterior angles are congruent, and the measure of each exterior angle is $\frac{360}{5}$ or 72.
The measure of each interior angle is 180 − 72 or 108.

Checking for Understanding

Exercises 1-21 are designed to help you assess students' understanding through reading, writing, speaking, and modeling. You should work through Exercises 1-3 with your students and then monitor their work on Exercises 4-21.

Closing the Lesson

Writing Activity Ask students to write a brief paragraph explaining two ways of finding the measure of an interior angle of a regular polygon. Use Theorem 10-1 and divide by the number of sides; use Theorem 10-2 to find the measure of an exterior angle and find its supplement.

APPLYING THE LESSON

Homework Exercises

Assignment Guide

Basic: 22-42, 50-58
Average: 25-45, 50-58
Enriched: 29-58

CHECKING FOR UNDERSTANDING

Communicating Mathematics

Read and study the lesson to answer these questions.

1. Does the sum of the exterior angles of a convex polygon depend on the number of sides in the polygon? Explain your answer. **no; The sum of the measures of the exterior angles of any convex polygon is 360.**

2. Your friend is working on a problem and claims that the sum of the measures of the interior angles of a convex polygon is 2070. Explain why this is not possible. **2070 is not divisible by 180, and a polygon must have an integral number of sides.**

3. The sum of the measures of the interior angles of a regular polygon is 24,840. Write and solve an equation to find the number of sides the polygon has. **Let s represent the number of sides. $180(s - 2) = 24,840$; 140**

Guided Practice

Find the sum of the measures of the interior angles of each convex polygon.

4. pentagon **540**

5. hexagon **720**

6. dodecagon **1800**

7. 25-gon **4140**

8. 36-gon **6120**

9. x-gon **$180(x - 2)$**

The number of sides of a regular polygon is given. Find the measure of each interior angle of the polygon.

10. 5 **108**

11. 7 **$128 \frac{4}{7}$**

12. 15 **156**

13. x **$\frac{180x - 360}{x}$**

The measure of an exterior angle of a regular polygon is given. Find the number of sides of the polygon.

14. 45 **8**

15. 72 **5**

16. 60 **6**

17. n **$\frac{360}{n}$**

The sum of the measures of the interior angles of a convex polygon is given. Find the number of sides in each polygon.

18. 720 **6**

19. 1440 **10**

20. 2880 **18**

21. 3240 **20**

EXERCISES

Practice

Find the sum of the measures of the interior angles of each convex polygon.

22. 17-gon **2700**

23. 20-gon **3240**

24. 13-gon **1980**

25. 15-gon **2340**

26. 59-gon **10,260**

27. $2t$-gon **$360t - 360$**

The measure of an interior angle of a regular polygon is given. Find the number of sides in each polygon.

28. 160 **18** 29. 120 **6** 30. 156 **15**

31. 165 **24** 32. 144 **10** 33. 179 **360**

The number of sides of a regular polygon is given. Find the measure of an interior angle and an exterior angle of the polygon.

34. 4 **90, 90** 35. 8 **135, 45** 36. 10 **144, 36**

37. 20 **162, 18** 38. 18 **160, 20** 39. x $\frac{180(x-2)}{x}, \frac{360}{x}$

B 40. The sum of the measures of eight interior angles of a convex nonagon is 1190. Find the measure of the ninth angle. **70**

41. The sum of the measures of seven exterior angles of a convex octagon is 339. Find the measure of the eighth angle. **21**

42. The measure of the exterior angles of a convex quadrilateral are x, 2x, 3x, and 4x. Find the value of x and the measure of each exterior angle. **36; 36, 72, 108, 144**

43. The measure of each exterior angle of a regular decagon is x + 10. Find the value of x and the measure of each exterior angle. **26; 36**

44. The measure of an exterior angle of a regular polygon is 2x, and the measure of an interior angle is 4x. Find the number of sides in the polygon. **6**

45. If you extend the sides of a regular pentagon as shown, you can form a five-pointed star. Find the measure of the angle at each point. **36**

46. Use a regular hexagon to draw a six-pointed star. Are the angles at the points of the star congruent? If so, what is the measure of each angle? **yes; 60**

C 47. The sum of the measures of the interior angles of a convex polygon is between 7300 and 7500.

   a. How many sides does the polygon have? **43**

   b. What is the exact sum of the measures of the interior angles? **7380**

48. The sum of the measures of five of the interior angles of an octagon is 890. Exactly two of the three remaining angles are complementary, and exactly two are supplementary. Find the measures of these three angles. **80, 10, 100**

49. Study the following pattern.
   $$11 \times 1 = 11$$
   $$11 \times 2 = 22$$
   $$11 \times 3 = 33$$
   $$11 \times 4 = 44$$

   a. If you were to continue the pattern, how would you write 11 × 10? **1010**

   b. What is the actual value of 11 × 10? **110**

   c. What does this tell you about inductive arguments? Can you prove something with only an inductive argument? **They don't always work; no.**

For Exercise 45, there is more than one approach. Students can begin with an exterior angle such as ∠1 that is a base angle of an isosceles triangle such as △ABC or they can begin with an interior angle such as ∠2 that is the vertex angle of an isosceles triangle such as △DEB. There may be other ways.

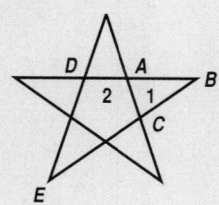

Reteaching Masters Booklet, p. 58

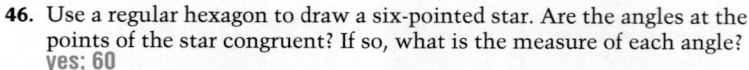

NAME _____ DATE _____

10-2 Reteaching Worksheet

Angles of Polygons

The following two theorems involve the interior and exterior angles of a convex polygon.

Interior Angle Sum Theorem	If a convex polygon has n sides and S is the sum of the measures of its interior angles, then $S = 180(n-2)$.
Exterior Angle Sum Theorem	If a polygon is convex, then the sum of the measures of the exterior angles, one at each vertex, is 360.

Example: Find the sum of the measures of the interior angles of a convex polygon with 13 sides.

$$S = 180(n-2) \quad \text{Interior Angle Sum Theorem}$$
$$S = 180(13-2)$$
$$S = 180(11)$$
$$S = 1980$$

Find the sum of the measures of the interior angles of each convex polygon.

1. 10-gon **1440** 2. 16-gon **2520** 3. 30-gon **5040**

The measure of an exterior angle of a regular polygon is given. Find the number of sides of the polygon.

4. 30 **12** 5. 20 **18** 6. 5 **72**

The sum of the measures of the interior angles of a convex polygon is given. Find the number of sides in each polygon.

7. 2160 **14** 8. 6120 **36** 9. 4140 **25**

10. The measure of the interior angle of a regular polygon is 157.5. Find the number of sides of the polygon. **16**

T58

Glencoe Division, Macmillan/McGraw-Hill

RETEACHING THE LESSON

Use the figure to answer these questions.

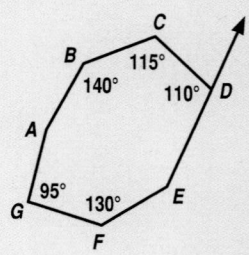

1. Is the figure regular? **no**
2. Is the figure convex? **yes**
3. What is the sum of the angle measures? **900°**
4. If ∠A ≅ ∠E, find m∠E. **155**
5. Find the measure of the exterior angle at D. **70**

Critical Thinking

50. Complete each statement.
  a. As the number of sides of a convex polygon increases, the sum of the measures of the interior angles ___?___. **increases**
  b. The measure of an interior angle of a regular polygon with n sides is ___?___ than the measure of an interior angle of a regular polygon with $n + 1$ sides. **less**
  c. As the number of sides of a convex polygon increases, the sum of the exterior angles ___?___. **stays 360**

Application

51. Patterns that cover a plane with repeated shapes so that there are no empty spaces are called *tessellations*. A *regular tessellation* uses only one type of regular polygon. You can use squares to make a regular tessellation. This tessellation is often used for floor tiles.

  a. Mark a point A on a piece of plain paper. Try to draw several copies of an equilateral triangle, each with point A as a vertex, so that no space is left empty and no two triangles overlap. If you can do it, then a regular triangle can tessellate the plane. Repeat the process with a regular pentagon, a regular hexagon, a regular heptagon, and a regular octagon. Copy the table below. Use your results to complete the table.

Regular Polygon	triangle	square	pentagon	hexagon	heptagon	octagon
Does it tessellate the plane?	_?_ yes	_?_ yes	_?_ no	_?_ yes	_?_ no	_?_ no
Measure, m, of one interior angle	_?_ 60	_?_ 90	_?_ 108	_?_ 120	_?_ $128\frac{4}{7}$	_?_ 135
Is m a factor of 360?	_?_ yes	_?_ yes	_?_ no	_?_ yes	_?_ no	_?_ no

  b. Make a conjecture about the types of regular polygons that will tessellate the plane. **If the measure of an interior angle of a regular polygon is a factor of 360, the polygon will tessellate the plane.**

Mixed Review

52. Classify the figure at the right as a convex polygon, a concave polygon, or neither. If it is a polygon, name it according to the number of sides. **(Lesson 10-1) concave polygon;heptagon**

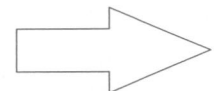

53. A chord of a circle is 10 inches long, and it is 12 inches from the center of the circle. Find the length of the radius of the circle. **(Lesson 9-3) 13 in.**

54. A tree casts a shadow 75 feet long, and at the same time, a 6-foot fence post casts a shadow 10 feet long. How tall is the tree? **(Lesson 7-6) 45 feet**

478   CHAPTER 10   POLYGONS AND AREA

Practice Masters Booklet, p. 67

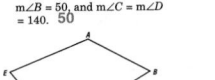 

NAME _____ DATE _____

10-2 **Practice Worksheet**

Angles of Polygons

1. Find m∠E if m∠A = 160, m∠B = 50, and m∠C = m∠D = 140. **50**

2. Find m∠1 if m∠G = 80, m∠F = 110, and m∠H = 74. **84**

3. What is the fewest number of sides a polygon can have? **3**

4. In what convex polygon is the sum of the measures of the exterior angles, one per vertex, equal to the sum of the measures of the interior angles? **quadrilateral**

Find the sum of the measures of the interior angles of each convex polygon.

5. heptagon **900**   **6.** octagon **1080**   **7.** 13-gon **1980**

The number of sides of a regular polygon is given. Find the measure of an interior and an exterior angle of the polygon.

8. 5 **108, 72**   **9.** 9 **140,40**   **10.** 10 **144, 36**

The measure of one exterior angle of a regular polygon is given. Find the number of sides.

11. 30 **12**   **12.** 40 **9**   **13.** 90 **4**

T67
Glencoe Division, Macmillan/McGraw-Hill

478   Chapter 10

55. Graph $A(7, 6)$, $B(3, 7)$, $C(5, 11)$, and $D(9, 10)$, and then draw quadrilateral $ABCD$. Determine if $ABCD$ is a parallelogram. Justify your answer. **(Lesson 6-3)** See Solutions Manual for graph; yes.

56. The vertex angle of isosceles triangle ABC measures 88°. Find the measures of the base angles. **(Lesson 4-7)** 46

57. The supplement of an angle measures 58° more than the angle. Find the measure of the angle. **(Lesson 1-8)** 61

Wrap-Up
58. Draw a convex hexagon with one exterior angle at each vertex. Cut out the exterior angles and arrange them so that they all have a common vertex. What is the sum of the measures of the exterior angles? Do the results agree with the exterior angle sum theorem? 360; yes

HISTORY CONNECTION

Poets often write that no two snowflakes are alike, but did you know that all snowflakes are shaped like hexagons? In 1591, Thomas Hariot, for the first time in European history, recognized that snowflakes are hexagonal. He jotted his findings down in his private manuscripts, but never published them. In 1611, Johannes Kepler made the first European publication about snowflakes. However, the Chinese knew of the hexagonal structure of snowflakes in or before the second century B.C. In his book *Moral Discourses Illustrating the Han Text of the 'Book of Songs,'* Han Ying wrote "Flowers of plants and trees are generally five-pointed, but those of snow, which are called *ying*, are always six-pointed."

Snowflakes have a hexagonal structure because of the arrangement of the hydrogen and oxygen atoms in a water molecule. The crystalline structure of a snowflake is an intricate arrangement of tiny crystal prisms, each one reflecting a rainbow of bright colors to give snow its shimmering beauty.

EXTENDING THE LESSON

Math Power: Reasoning
Three angles of a hexagon are congruent to each other. The remaining three angles are also congruent to each other, but have a measure twice that of the first three. Find the measure of each angle. Three angles measure 80°, and three angles measure 160°.

History Connection
The History Connection features introduce students to persons or cultures involved in the development of mathematics. You may want students to further research Thomas Hariot or snowflake structure.

Enrichment Masters Booklet, p. 58

10-2 **Enrichment Worksheet**
NAME_____ DATE_____

Polygonal Numbers

Certain numbers related to regular polygons are called **polygonal numbers**. The chart shows several triangular, square, and pentagonal numbers. The **rank** of a polygonal number is the number of dots on each "side" of the outer polygon. For example, the pentagonal number 22 has a rank of 4.

	Rank 1	Rank 2	Rank 3	Rank 4
Triangle	· 1	△ 3	△ 6	△ 10
Square	· 1	□ 4	▦ 9	▦ 16
Pentagon	· 1	⬠ 5	⬠ 12	⬠ 22

Polygonal numbers can be described with formulas. For example, a triangular number T of rank r can be described by $T = \frac{r(r+1)}{2}$.

Answer each question.

1. Draw a diagram to find the triangular number of rank 5.
   15

2. Draw a diagram to find the pentagonal number of rank 5.
   35

3. Write a formula for a square number S of rank r.
   $S = r^2$

4. Write a formula for a pentagonal number P of rank r.
   $P = \frac{r(3r-1)}{2}$

5. What is the rank of the pentagonal number 70?
   7

6. List the hexagonal numbers for ranks 1 to 5. (Hint: Draw a diagram.)
   1, 6, 15, 28, 45

T58
Glencoe Division, Macmillan/McGraw-Hill

Problem-Solving Strategy: Guess and Check

Lesson Resources

• Practice Master 10-3
• Evaluation Master p. 135

Transparency 10-3 contains the 5-Minute Check and a teaching aid for this lesson.

INTRODUCING THE LESSON

Objective
10-3

After studying this lesson, you should be able to:
▪ solve problems by using guess and check.

The problem-solving strategy guess and check, or trial and error, is a powerful strategy. To use this strategy, guess the answer to a problem and then use the conditions of the problem to check to see if the answer is correct. If the first guess is not correct, use the information gathered from that guess to continue guessing until you find the correct answer.

5-Minute Check
(over Lesson 10-2)

The number of sides of a regular polygon are given. Find the measure of an interior angle and an exterior angle of the polygon.

1. 6   120, 60
2. 9   140, 40
3. 10   144, 36
4. 24   165, 15

The measure of an interior angle of a regular polygon is given. Find the number of sides of the polygon.

5. 162   20
6. 135   8

Example 1

The license plate on Anna Silver's car has a five-digit number. The plate was installed upside down, but it still shows a five-digit number. The number that shows now exceeds the number that is supposed to appear on the plate by 63,783. What is the original license number?

Since the license plate still shows a five-digit number when it is upside down, the number must consist of digits that are readable when they are upside down. These are 0, 1, 6, 8, and 9.

The units digit in the difference is 3, so they must have subtracted 6 from 9 or 8 from 1. Let's guess that they subtracted 6 from 9. So the last digit in the new number would be 9 and the last digit in the original number is 6. That makes the first digits 6 in the new number and 9 in the original number, since the digits are upside down.

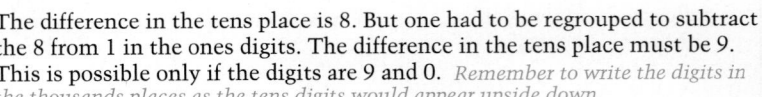

```
  6 ☐☐☐ 9   ← new number
- 9 ☐☐☐ 6   ← original number
  6 3 7 8 3
```

But, if the first digits are 9 and 6, their difference would be -3, not 6. The last digits must be 1 and 8.

```
  8 ☐☐☐ 1
- 1 ☐☐☐ 8
  6 3 7 8 3
```

The difference in the tens place is 8. But one had to be regrouped to subtract the 8 from 1 in the ones digits. The difference in the tens place must be 9. This is possible only if the digits are 9 and 0. *Remember to write the digits in the thousands places as the tens digits would appear upside down.*

Motivating the Lesson

Ask students to name some real-life problems that they have had to solve by guessing and then checking their guesses.   **Sample answers: determining which of three keys opens a door, finding a lost shoe**

TEACHING THE LESSON

ALTERNATE TEACHING STRATEGIES

Chalkboard Example

For Example 1
Find a two-digit number such that the sum of the digits is 10 and three times the tens digit is twice the units digit.   **46**

Teaching Tip   In Example 1, point out that it is important to use the information you received from an incorrect guess.

Using Manipulatives

Give each student a set of tangrams. Ask them to form a parallelogram using all seven pieces.   **Sample answer:**

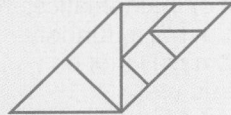

Using Calculators

Several numbers on the calculator look like letters when the calculator is turned upside down. For example, 102 • 9 spells *BIG* on the calculator.
Write a problem that spells *hello* on the calculator.   **Any problem that has the answer 0.7734 will spell *hello* when the calculator is turned upside down.**

$$\begin{array}{r} 8\ 0\ \blacksquare\ 9\ 1 \\ -\ 1\ 6\ \blacksquare\ 0\ 8 \\ \hline 6\ 3\ 7\ 8\ 3 \end{array}$$

The digits in the center have a difference of 7. Notice that one must have been regrouped in the thousands place for the subtraction to be correct. The only possible digits are 6 and 9.

$$\begin{array}{r} 8\ 0\ 6\ 9\ 1 \\ -\ 1\ 6\ 9\ 0\ 8 \\ \hline 6\ 3\ 7\ 8\ 3 \end{array}$$

The license number is 16908.

Be sure to use the information that you can gather from your guesses to help you make better guesses the next time.

Example 2

Place operation symbols in the equation below to make it correct.

$$9\ \underline{\ ?\ }\ 6\ \underline{\ ?\ }\ 2\ \underline{\ ?\ }\ 1\ \underline{\ ?\ }\ 4 = 6$$

Guess at a combination of symbols and evaluate the sentence.

$$9 + 6 \div 2 - 1 + 4 = 15$$

The result was 15, which is 9 greater than 6. So we must change the symbols to make the result lower.

$9 - 6 \div 2 - 1 - 4 = 1$ *Now the result is too low.*

$9 - 6 - 2 - 1 + 4 = 4$ *Getting closer.*

$9 - 6 - 2 + 1 + 4 = 6$ *Correct!*

CHECKING FOR UNDERSTANDING

Communicating Mathematics

Read and study the lesson to answer these questions.

1. Describe a situation in which you might use the strategy guess and check. **Answers may vary. A sample answer is when another, more direct method is not obvious.**
2. How can you use the results of incorrect guesses to speed up the guessing process? **Look at the results and see how close you are. Adjust guesses accordingly.**

LESSON 10-3   PROBLEM-SOLVING STRATEGY: GUESS AND CHECK   481

Homework Exercises

Assignment Guide

Basic: 6-10
Average: 6-10
Enriched: 6-10

Guided Practice

Solve by using guess and check.

3. What is the least three-digit number that is divisible by the first three prime numbers and by the first three composite numbers? **120**

4. One answer is
$35 - 64 + 752 + 6 - 17 = 712$.

4. Place two addition symbols and two subtraction symbols in the equation below to make it a true equation.

$$3\ 5\ 6\ 4\ 7\ 5\ 2\ 6\ 1\ 7 = 712$$

5. Copy the figure at the right and fill in circles with prime numbers so that the sum of all six numbers is 20, and the sum of the numbers on every small triangle is the same. **Answers may vary. A sample answer is shown.**

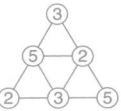

EXERCISES

Strategies

Look for a pattern.
Solve a simpler problem.
Act it out.
Guess and check.
Draw a diagram.
Make a chart.
Work backward.

Solve. Use any strategy. 6. 37, 38   8. $144 - 12 = 132$

6. Which two consecutive whole numbers have squares that differ by 75?

7. Fill in the blank in the following pattern. 25, 30, 20, _?_, 15, 40, 10 **35**

8. In the United States, dates are usually written month / day, so 4/6 would represent April sixth. However, in Canada, dates are written day / month, so 4/6 would represent the fourth of June. How many dates can be written so that they mean one date to an American and another to a Canadian?

9. Find the pairs of consecutive whole numbers less than 50 that have squares that differ by a perfect square. **0, 1; 4, 5; 12, 13; 24, 25; 40, 41**

10. Substitute a different digit for each letter in the equation below to make it true. **Sample answers are 9802 + 9802 = 19604 or 9703 + 9703 = 19406.**

$$\begin{array}{r} HALF \\ + \underline{\ HALF} \\ WHOLE \end{array}$$

COOPERATIVE LEARNING PROJECT

Work in groups. Each person in the group must understand the solution and be able to explain it to any person in class.

A set of dominoes has 28 rectangular pieces with two numbers on each one. Each number 0 through 6, is paired with every other number, including itself, on exactly one domino. The grid at the right was made by arranging the dominoes and then recording the numbers. Four dominoes are shown. Copy the grid and draw in the remaining dominoes.
(Hint: If you come to a point where you can't deduce which numbers are on a domino, guess and check to see if it leads you to a contradiction.)

1	0	2	0	0	5	4	1
1	1	5	3	6	2	4	2
3	3	1	0	3	5	3	4
0	6	6	4	6	5	1	1
0	4	0	2	5	4	2	6
1	2	3	2	6	4	5	2
3	5	5	0	3	4	6	6

Practice Masters Booklet, p. 68

10-3   NAME _____ DATE _____
Practice Worksheet
Problem Solving Strategy: Guess and Check
Solve. Use any strategy.

1. The house numbers on the Browns' house were nailed on a plaque upside down and backwards. The house number is four digits long. If the number that shows is 720 greater than their actual house number, what is the Browns' actual house number? **6089**

2. Which two consecutive whole numbers have cubes that differ by 2107? **26, 27**

3. Use the digits 1-9, once each, to fill in each circle so that the sum of each row, each column, and each diagonal is the same.
Answers may vary. Sample answer:

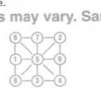

4. Insert operation symbols (+, −, ×, ÷) between the digits to form a true equation.
9 ___ 7 ___ 3 ___ 4 ___ 2 = 10
$9 + 7 - 3 \times 4 \div 2 = 10$

5. How many digits will there be in the product of 10000001 and 9999999? Try to answer *without* multiplying to get the actual product. **14 digits** (If one factor is $10^n + 1$ and the other is $10^n - 1$, the product will be $10^{2n} - 1$, which will have $2n$ digits, for any whole number n that is greater than 0).

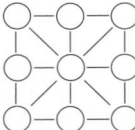

T68
Glencoe Division, Macmillan/McGraw-Hill

Math Power: Connections

The sum of the measures of all but one angle of a convex polygon is 1837. What is the measure of the other angle? **143**

Cooperative Learning Project

This activity provides students an opportunity to *learn* things together, not just do things together. You may wish to refer to pages T6-T7 and page 464c for the various elements of cooperative groups and specific goals and strategies for using them.

10-4 Area of Parallelograms

Objective
10-4

After studying this lesson, you should be able to:
- find areas of parallelograms.

Application

In 1991, Worthington Kilbourne High School was built in Worthington, Ohio. To use the empty lot behind the school for football practice fields, they had to have sod installed. How much sod was needed? If the sod cost 85¢ a square yard, how much did the sod for the fields cost? *You will solve this problem in Example 1.*

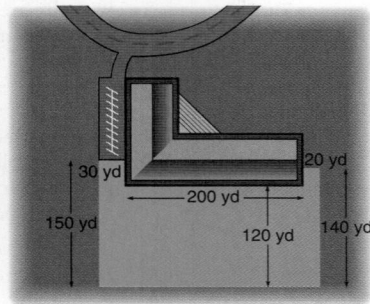

To find the amount of sod that the school needed, we must find the area of the lot. The **area** of a figure is the number of square units contained in the interior of the figure. The area of a rectangle, A square units, can be found using the formula $A = \ell w$, where ℓ units is the length of the rectangle and w units is the width.

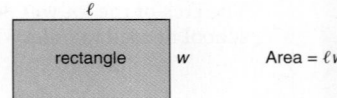

As we learned in Chapter 6, a square is a special rectangle in which the sides are all congruent. So, we can use the formula for the area of a rectangle to find the area of a square. If the length of a side of the square is s units, the area is $A = s \cdot s$ or s^2.

To find the area of a figure that is made up of several figures, you must find the area of each figure. Then add these to find the total area. This is stated in the postulate below.

Postulate 10-1	**The area of a region is the sum of the areas of all of its nonoverlapping parts.**

We can use this property with the formulas for the area of a rectangle and a square to find the amount of sod that was needed for the practice football fields at Worthington.

LESSON 10-4   AREA OF PARALLELOGRAMS   483

ALTERNATE TEACHING STRATEGIES

Using Communication
Have students write a letter to an absent or imaginary classmate explaining how the area of a parallelogram is related to the area of a rectangle.

Using Logical Reasoning
Ask whether the following statement is true or false and why. "If two parallelograms have the same measures for their sides, their areas are equal."   **False. If their angles are not congruent, the parallelograms will have different heights and therefore different areas.**

Lesson Resources
- Reteaching Master 10-4
- Practice Master 10-4
- Enrichment Master 10-4
- Evaluation Master, p. 139
- Technology Master, p. 10
- Lab Manual, p. 74-77

Transparency 10-4 contains the 5-Minute Check and a teaching aid for this lesson.

INTRODUCING THE LESSON

🕐 5-Minute Check
(over Lesson 10-3)

Solve. Use guess and check.

1. If 4 pens cost a bookstore 50¢ and can be sold at 3 for 50¢, how many pens bring a profit of $10?   **240 pens**
2. Fill in the missing operation signs to make a true equation. 5 ? 10 ? 4 ? 3 = 5 $5 \div 10 \cdot 4 + 3 = 5$
3. $2.90 is made up of 22 nickels, dimes, and quarters. The number of quarters is the same as the number of nickels. How many of each type of coin are there?   **7 quarters, 7 nickels, and 8 dimes**

Motivating the Lesson
Ask students to draw and cut out a square from a piece of paper. Have them cut the square into two pieces of any size. Ask students if the area of the whole square is equal to the area of these two parts.   **yes**

TEACHING THE LESSON

Teaching Tip   When reviewing the formulas for the area of a rectangle or square, ask students to explain what is meant by a square unit.

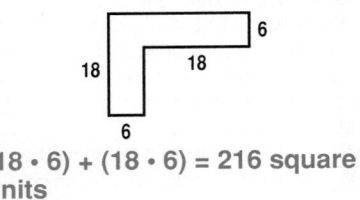
Teaching Tip After Example 1, ask students if they can see other ways of dividing the region into nonoverlapping parts.

Teaching Tip In the paragraph at the bottom of the page, note the distinction between the use of the word *altitude* for the segment and *height* for the measure.

Example 1

APPLICATION
Landscaping

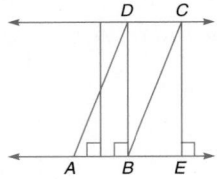

Refer to the opening application.

a. How much sod did the school need to order for the lot?

The field can be separated into a rectangle and two squares. Since these parts of the lot are nonoverlapping, we can find the area of the lot by finding the sum of the areas of the parts.

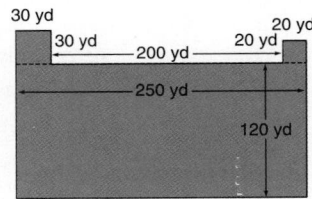

The rectangle is 250 yards long and 120 yards wide. One square is 30 yards long on each side, and the other is 20 yards long on each side. Use the formulas for the area of a rectangle and a square to find the area of each part.

$$\text{Area of rectangle} = \ell w$$
$$= 250 \cdot 120 \quad \textit{Substitute 250 for } \ell \textit{ and 120 for w.}$$
$$= 30{,}000 \text{ sq yd}$$

$$\text{Area of square 1} = s^2 \qquad\qquad \text{Area of square 2} = s^2$$
$$= 30^2 \quad s = 30 \qquad\qquad\qquad = 20^2 \quad s = 20$$
$$= 900 \text{ sq yd} \qquad\qquad\qquad\quad = 400 \text{ sq yd}$$

The area of the lot was $30{,}000 + 900 + 400$ or $31{,}300$ square yards. The school needed to order 31,300 square yards of sod.

b. If the sod cost 85¢ a square yard, how much did the sod cost?

The sod cost $0.85(31{,}300)$ or $\$26{,}605$.

The formula for the area of a parallelogram is closely related to the formula for the area of a rectangle. Before we derive the formula, we must discuss some parts of a parallelogram.

Any side of a parallelogram can be called a **base.** For each base, there is a corresponding **altitude.** In $\square ABCD$, $\overline{AB}$ is considered to be the base. A corresponding altitude is any perpendicular segment between the parallel lines $\overleftrightarrow{AB}$ and $\overleftrightarrow{DC}$. So in $\square ABCD$, $\overline{CE}$ and $\overline{DB}$ are altitudes. The length of the altitude is called the **height.**

Copy ☐*PQRS.*

Use a compass and straightedge to construct an altitude from *S* to $\overline{QR}$. Label the point of intersection *T.* Let $h = ST$ and $b = PS$.

Cut out the parallelogram. Then cut △*STR* from the parallelogram and place it so that $\overline{RS}$ lies on $\overline{PQ}$.

The new figure you have formed is a rectangle. It has the same area as ☐*PQRS.* Since $VP = TS = h$, the area of the rectangle is bh square units. So, the area of ☐*PQRS* is also bh square units.

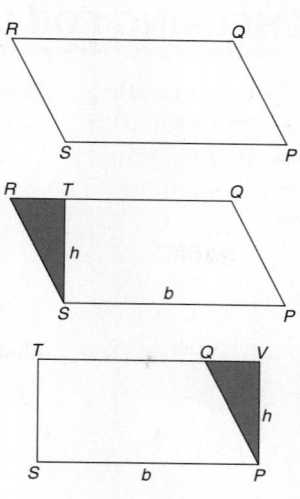

The area of a parallelogram is the same as the area of a rectangle that has the same base and height.

Area of a Parallelogram	If a parallelogram has an area of *A* square units, a base of *b* units, and a height of *h* units, then $A = bh$.

Example 2

Find the area of ☐*MNOP.* Round your answer to the nearest hundredth.

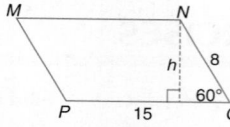

Recall that in a 30°-60°-90° triangle, the length of the hypotenuse is twice the length of the shorter leg and the length of the longer leg is $\sqrt{3}$ times the length of the shorter leg. Therefore, the length of the shorter leg is $\frac{8}{2}$ or 4 units and $h = 4\sqrt{3}$.

$$A = bh \qquad \textit{Formula for the area of a parallelogram}$$
$$A = 15(4\sqrt{3})$$
$$A = 60\sqrt{3}$$

The area of ☐*MNOP* is $60\sqrt{3}$ or about 103.92 square units.

Chalkboard Example

For Example 2
Find the area of ☐*STAR.* Round your answer to the nearest hundredth.

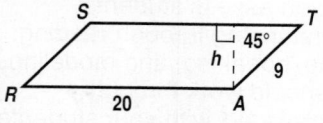

Since $9 = h\sqrt{2}$, $h = \dfrac{9\sqrt{2}}{2} = 4.5\sqrt{2}$.

$A = bh$
$A = 20(4.5\sqrt{2})$
$A = 90\sqrt{2} \approx 127.28$ **square units**

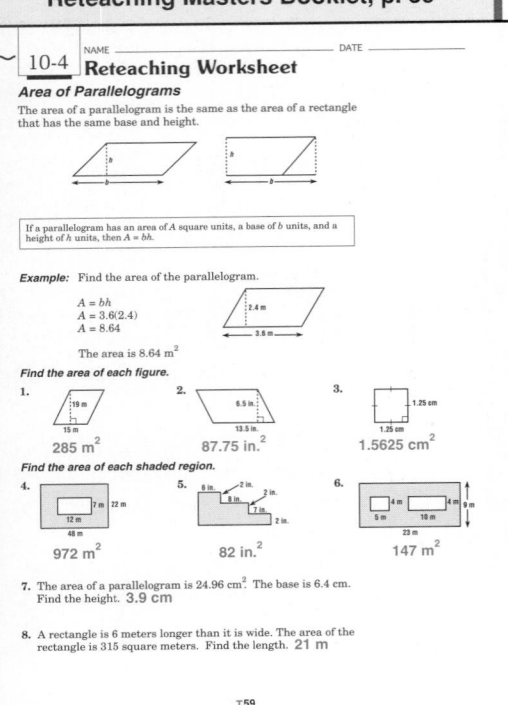
CHECKING FOR UNDERSTANDING

Communicating Mathematics

Read and study the lesson to answer these questions.

1. Why are the formulas for the area of a square and the area of a rectangle related? **A square is a special rectangle.**

2. Region Z is made up of nonoverlapping regions X and Y. If the area of region X is a square units and the area of region Y is b square units, what is the area of region Z? **$(a + b)$ square units**

3. Is the area of the parallelogram at the right 48 square units? Explain. **no; 6 is not the measure of the altitude**

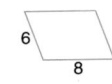

Guided Practice Find the area of each figure.

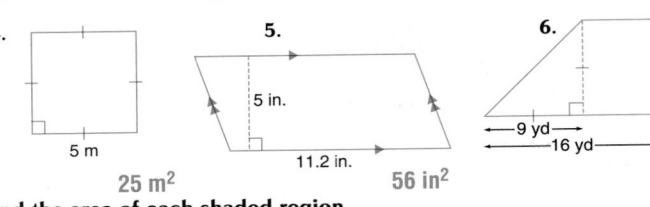

4. **25 m²** 5. 5 in. 11.2 in. **56 in²** 6. 9 yd 16 yd **144 yd²**

Find the area of each shaded region.

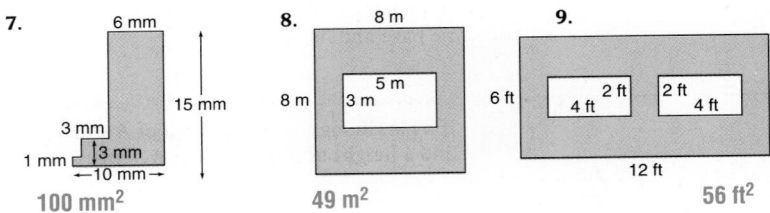

7. 6 mm 15 mm 3 mm 1 mm 3 mm 10 mm **100 mm²** 8. 8 m 8 m 5 m 3 m **49 m²** 9. 6 ft 2 ft 4 ft 2 ft 4 ft 12 ft **56 ft²**

EXERCISES

Practice **Find the missing measure of each quadrilateral.**

A

10. A rectangle is 6 feet long and 2 feet wide. Find its area. **12 ft²**

11. A parallelogram has an area of 36 m² and a base of 9 m. Find its height. **4 m**

12. The area of a rectangle is 20 square yards. If it is 4 yards wide, find the length. **5 yd**

13. The area of parallelogram $ABCD$ is 3810 mm². If the base is 120 mm long, find the height. **31.75 mm**

B

The coordinates of the vertices of a quadrilateral are given. Graph the points and draw the quadrilateral and an altitude. Then identify the quadrilateral as a square, a rectangle, or a parallelogram and find its area. **See margin.**

14. (3, 4), (2, 1), (8, 4), (9, 7)

15. (3, 7), (-3, 3), (1, -3), (7, 1)

16. (6, 2), (1, 7), (-5, 5), (0, 0)

17. (0, -5), (3, -4), (1, 2), (-2, 1)

486   CHAPTER 10   POLYGONS AND AREA

RETEACHING THE LESSON

Show students how to find the area of the figure below by partitioning it into three rectangles: two 2 by 6 rectangles and one 2 by 4 rectangle.

Have them find another way to partition the figure into rectangles. **one 8 by 2 rectangle and two 2 by 4 rectangles** Ask if they both give the same area. **yes, 32 mm²**

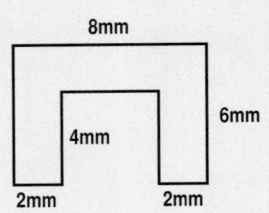

18. The areas of a rectangle and a parallelogram are equal. The rectangle has a length of 8 meters and a width of 6 meters. If the parallelogram has a base of 12 meters, find the height. **4 meters**

19. The area of a parallelogram is $2x^2 + 9x + 4$ cm^2. If the length of the base is $2x + 1$ cm, find the length of the altitude. **$x + 4$ cm**

20. A rectangle is 4 cm longer than it is wide. The area of the rectangle is 117 cm^2. Find the length and the width. **13 cm, 9 cm**

21. If the length of each side of a square is doubled, the area of the resulting square is increased by 363 in^2. Find the length of the original square. **11 in.**

22. When the length of each side of a square is increased by 5 inches, the area of the resulting square is 2.25 times the area of the original square. What is the area of the original square? **100 square inches**

23. The vertices of square *MNOP* are the midpoints of square *ABCD*. Explain why the area of *ABCD* is twice the area of *MNOP*. **See margin.**

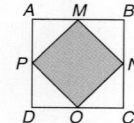

Critical Thinking

24. The figure at the right consists of six congruent squares and has an area of 486 square centimeters. Find the perimeter of the figure. **126 cm**

Applications

25. **Engineering** A metal part is under stress when force is applied to stretch or compress it. When this force is applied perpendicular to the cross sectional area, the stress, S, in pounds per square inch that the part is under is found by the formula $S = \dfrac{F}{A}$, where F is the force in pounds and A is the cross sectional area. Find the stress on a rod whose cross section is a square with length 1.5 inches if a squeezing force of 3550 pounds is applied. **1577.8 pounds per square inch**

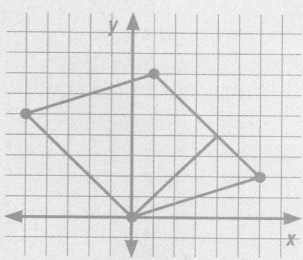
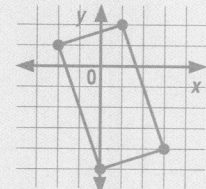
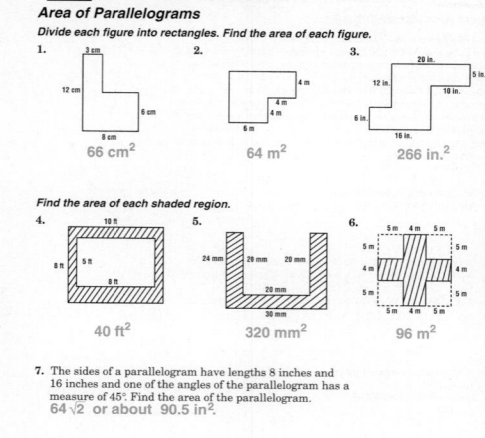
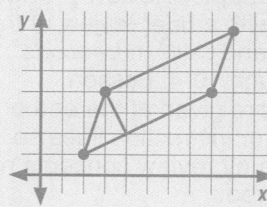
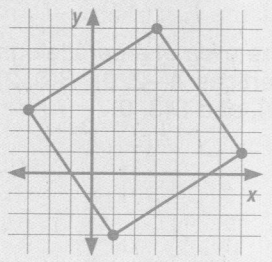

29. Statements (Reasons)
  a. $\overline{AB} \parallel \overline{DC}$ (Given)
  b. $\angle A$ and $\angle D$ are supplementary. (If 2 $\parallel$ lines are cut by a transversal, consecutive int. $\angle$s are supp.)

26. Interior Design Dale and Kathy Husted are having new carpet installed in their living room and dining room. A scale drawing of the rooms is shown at the right. **a. 448 sq ft**

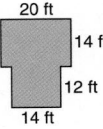

20 ft
14 ft
12 ft
14 ft

  a. Find the total area to be carpeted.
  b. The carpet store will not sell a fraction of a square yard. Also, extra yardage must be allowed for going around corners. If the Husteds add 4 square yards of carpet for waste, how many square yards of carpet will they buy? **54 square yards**
  c. If the carpet Mr. and Mrs. Husted have chosen is $16.99 a square yard, find the cost of the carpeting. **$917.46**

Mixed Review

27. Insert one set of parentheses in the equation $4 \cdot 5 - 2 + 7 = 19$ so that the equation is true. **(Lesson 10-3)** $4 \cdot (5 - 2) + 7 = 19$

28. The measure of an interior angle of a regular polygon is 160. How many sides does the polygon have? **(Lesson 10-2)** **18**

29. Write a two-column proof. **(Lesson 6-6)**
  Given: trapezoid $ABCD$
  $\overline{AB} \parallel \overline{DC}$
  Prove: $\angle A$ and $\angle D$ are supplementary.
  See margin.

A   B
D   C

Wrap-Up

30. Write a word problem that involves finding the area of a figure containing squares, rectangles, or parallelograms. Be sure to provide the answer to your problem. **See students' work.**

MID-CHAPTER REVIEW

Classify each figure as a *convex polygon*, a *concave polygon*, or *not a polygon*. If a figure is a polygon, name it according to the number of sides. **(Lesson 10-1)**

1.
concave; pentagon

2.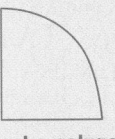
not a polygon

3.
convex; quadrilateral

4.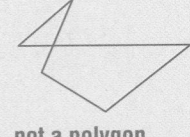
not a polygon

The number of sides of a regular polygon is given. Find the measure of an interior angle and an exterior angle of the polygon. **(Lesson 10-2)**

5. 6 **120, 60**

6. 16 **157.5, 22.5**

7. 30 **168, 12**

8. Use the problem-solving strategy guess and check, to find the least prime number greater than 720. **(Lesson 10-3)** **727**

9. Horticulture Mr. Jackson is going to apply fertilizer to his lawn. If a 20-pound bag of fertilizer covers 500 square yards, will he need more than one bag? **(Lesson 10-4)**
Yes, the area is 650 sq yd.

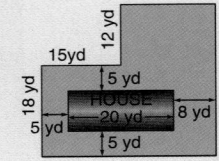

12 yd
15 yd
18 yd
5 yd
HOUSE
20 yd
8 yd
5 yd
5 yd

488   CHAPTER 10   POLYGONS AND AREA

EXTENDING THE LESSON

Math Power: Problem Solving

Find the area of a parallelogram with vertices $A(-2, 0)$, $B(0, 2)$, $C(5, 2)$, and $D(3, 0)$. **10 square units**

Mid-Chapter Review

The Mid-Chapter Review provides students with a brief review of the concepts and skills in Lessons 10-1 through 10-4. Lesson numbers are given at the end of problems or instruction lines so students may review concepts not yet mastered.

10-5 Area of Triangles, Rhombi, and Trapezoids

Objective
10-5

After studying this lesson, you should be able to:
- find the areas of triangles, rhombi, and trapezoids.

Application

When developers lay out the streets and lots in a new development, they often make lots that are not rectangular or square. Since the area of a lot must be listed in the legal description of the property, the developer must use geometry to find the area.

An important property of area is described in Postulate 10-2.

Postulate 10-2

Congruent figures have equal areas.

INVESTIGATION

You can learn more about triangles in Investigation 12 on page A11.

In the previous lesson, we found the area of a parallelogram by multiplying the measure of the base by the height. The formula for the area of a triangle is derived from this formula.

Suppose we are given a parallelogram $ABCD$ with diagonal $\overline{AC}$. The opposite sides of a parallelogram are congruent, so $\overline{AB} \cong \overline{CD}$ and $\overline{BC} \cong \overline{DA}$. Also, $\overline{AC} \cong \overline{AC}$ because congruence of segments is reflexive. Therefore, $\triangle ABC \cong \triangle CDA$ by SSS. Postulate 10-2 says that congruent figures have equal areas, so the area of $\triangle ABC$ is equal to the area of $\triangle CDA$. Since the area of parallelogram $ABCD$ is the sum of the areas of its nonoverlapping parts, we can write the equation below.

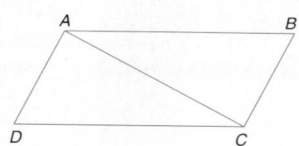

area of $\triangle ABC$ + area of $\triangle CDA$ = area of $\square ABCD$

$2(\text{area of } \triangle ABC) = \text{area of } \square ABCD$

$2(\text{area of } \triangle ABC) = bh$

$\text{area of } \triangle ABC = \frac{1}{2}bh$

area of $\triangle ABC$
= area of $\triangle CDA$

This leads us to the formula for the area of a triangle.

Area of a Triangle

If a triangle has an area of A square units, a base of b units, and a corresponding height of h units, then $A = \frac{1}{2}bh$.

LESSON 10-5   AREA OF TRIANGLES, RHOMBI, AND TRAPEZOIDS   489

ALTERNATE TEACHING STRATEGIES

Using Investigation
You can guide students to discover the formula for the area of a triangle. In Investigation 12 on page A11 of **More Investigations in Geometry,** students use construction and measurement to **explore the area of triangles.**

Using Charts
Have students design a chart that lists all the area formulas covered so far and including a diagram of each figure.

Lesson Resources
- Reteaching Master 10-5
- Practice Master 10-5
- Enrichment Master 10-5
- Evaluation Master, p. 135
- Technology Master, p. 46

   Transparency 10-5 contains the 5-Minute Check and a teaching aid for this lesson.

INTRODUCING THE LESSON

5-Minute Check
(over Lesson 10-4)

Find the area. Refer to the figure below.

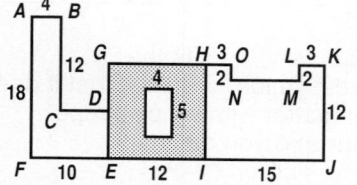

1. *ABCDEF*   108 sq. units
2. shaded part of *GHIE*   124 sq. units
3. *HONMLKJI*   162 sq. units
4. the entire figure including the unshaded part of *GHIE*   414 sq. units

Motivating the Lesson
Have students draw any type of triangle on graph paper and cut out two copies of it. Ask them to fit the two triangles together so that they form a parallelogram. Ask them how the base and height of the triangle relate to the base and height of the parallelogram.   They are the same.

TEACHING THE LESSON

Teaching Tip   In the statement of the area of a triangle, point out the phrase "corresponding height," and be sure students understand what this means.

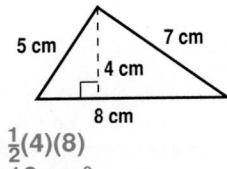
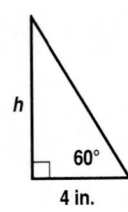
Example 1 | **Find each area.**

a.

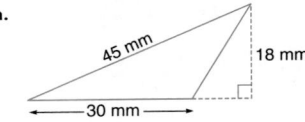

b.

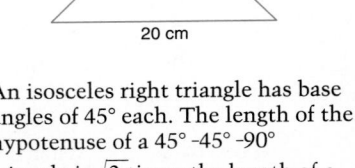

$A = \frac{1}{2}bh$ *Formula for the area of a triangle*

$= \frac{1}{2}(30)(18)$

$= 270 \text{ mm}^2$

An isosceles right triangle has base angles of 45° each. The length of the hypotenuse of a 45°-45°-90° triangle is $\sqrt{2}$ times the length of a leg. So the length of a leg is $\frac{20}{\sqrt{2}}$ cm.

$A = \frac{1}{2}bh$

$= \frac{1}{2}\left(\frac{20}{\sqrt{2}}\right)\left(\frac{20}{\sqrt{2}}\right)$ *The legs of a right triangle are the base and the height.*

$= \frac{1}{2}\left(\frac{400}{2}\right)$

$= 100 \text{ cm}^2$

The formula for the area of a parallelogram can be used to derive the formula for the area of a trapezoid.

INVESTIGATION

Make two copies of the trapezoid below and cut them out.

Position the trapezoids to form a parallelogram. If the lengths of the bases of the original trapezoid are b_1 units and b_2 units and its height is h units, what is the area of the parallelogram? $h(b_1 + b_2)$ units²

Since the two trapezoids are congruent, the area of each trapezoid is half the area of the parallelogram. What is the area of each trapezoid? $\frac{1}{2}h(b_1 + b_2)$ units²

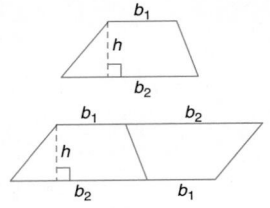

Area of a Trapezoid

If a trapezoid has an area of A square units, bases of b_1 units and b_2 units, and an height of h units, then $A = \frac{1}{2}h(b_1 + b_2)$.

Building lots are often in the shape of a trapezoid. So, the formula for the area of a trapezoid can be very useful to developers.

Example 2

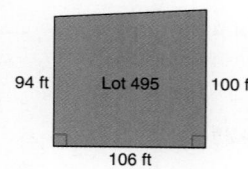
APPLICATION
Real Estate

Charlotte Burrows is an engineer laying out a new housing development. A scale drawing of lot 495 is shown at the right. Find the area of lot 495.

Since the bases are parallel and the 106-foot side is perpendicular to both bases, it is an altitude. So, $h = 106$, $b_1 = 94$, and $b_2 = 100$.

$$A = \tfrac{1}{2}h(b_1 + b_2)$$
$$= \tfrac{1}{2}(106)(94 + 100)$$
$$= 53(194)$$
$$= 10{,}282$$

The area of lot 495 is 10,282 square feet.

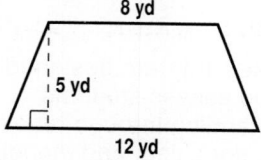
94 ft Lot 495 100 ft
106 ft

The formula for the area of a triangle can be used to derive the formula for the area of a rhombus. You will be asked to do this in Exercise 25.

Area of a Rhombus	**If a rhombus has an area of A square units, and diagonals of d_1 and d_2 units, then $A = \tfrac{1}{2}d_1d_2$.**

Example 3

A rhombus with a 48-inch diagonal has an area of 768 square inches. Find the length of a side of the rhombus.

$A = \tfrac{1}{2}d_1d_2$ *Formula for the area of a rhombus*

$768 = \tfrac{1}{2}(48)d_2$

$768 = 24d_2$

$32 = d_2$

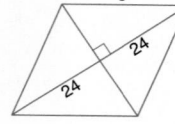

The diagonals are 48 and 32 inches long.

Since the diagonals are perpendicular and bisect each other, we can use the Pythagorean Theorem to find the length of a side.

$s^2 = 24^2 + 16^2$

$s^2 = 576 + 256$

$s^2 = 832$

$s \approx 28.8$

Each side is about 28.8 inches long.

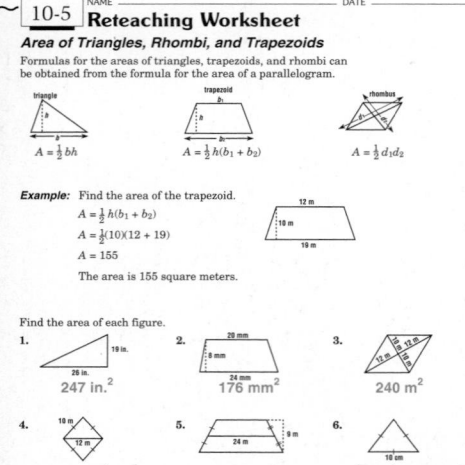

Summary of Area Formulas	
Area of a square	$A = s^2$
Area of a rectangle	$A = \ell w$
Area of a parallelogram	$A = bh$
Area of a triangle	$A = \frac{1}{2}bh$
Area of a trapezoid	$A = \frac{1}{2}h(b_1 + b_2)$
Area of a rhombus	$A = \frac{1}{2}d_1d_2$

CHECKING FOR UNDERSTANDING

Communicating Mathematics

Read and study the lesson to answer these questions.

1. The area of quadrilateral *FGHI* is 76 square units. If quadrilateral *OPQR* is congruent to quadrilateral *FGHI*, what is its area? Why? **76 sq units; Postulate 10-2 says that congruent figures have equal areas**

2. An engineering book gives the formula for the area of a trapezoid as the product of the height and the length of the median. Is this formula valid? Justify your answer. **Yes; the length of a median is $\frac{1}{2}(b_1 + b_2)$ units.**

3. If the side of the trapezoid in Example 2 was not perpendicular to the bases, could Ms. Burrows find the area in the same way? Explain. **She could use the same formula, but the value of *h* would be different.**

Guided Practice

Find the area of each figure.

4. 13 cm, 8 cm **52 cm²**

5. 14 ft, 5 ft, 7 ft **52.5 ft²**

6. 7 in., 4 in., 4 in., 7 in. **56 in.²**

7. 6 ft, 5 ft **24 ft²**

8. 14 m, 10 m **140 m²**

9. 6 m **$9\sqrt{3}$ or about 15.6 m²**

10. A rhombus has a 120° angle and its longer diagonal is 10 inches long. Find the area of the rhombus. **about 28.9 in²**

11. The perimeter of a trapezoid is 29 inches. Its nonparallel sides are 4 inches and 5 inches long. If the height of the trapezoid is 3 inches, find its area. **30 in²**

RETEACHING THE LESSON

Use these three exercises to review how to find the area of a triangle, a trapezoid, and a rhombus. Draw a picture of each figure on the chalkboard, and explain the formulas used.

1. triangle with base measuring 12 inches and height of 5 inches **30 in.²**

2. trapezoid with bases measuring 10 centimeters and 13 centimeters and height of 7 centimeters. **80.5 cm²**

3. rhombus with diagonals measuring 8 meters and 11 meters **44 m²**

EXERCISES

Practice **Find each missing measure.**

12. The area of a triangle is 88 square units. If the height is 16 units, what is the length of the base? **11 units**

13. The diagonals of a rhombus are 19 and 12 centimeters long. Find the area of the rhombus. **114 cm²**

14. The area of a trapezoid is 96 square units. If its altitude is 6 units long, find the length of its median. **16 units**

15. The altitude of a trapezoid is 11 m long. The bases are 16 m and 11 m long. Find the area. **148.5 m²**

16. A trapezoid has an area of 997.5 cm². If the altitude measures 21 cm and one base measures 40 cm, find the length of the other base. **55.0 cm**

17. A rhombus has a perimeter of 52 units and a diagonal 24 units long. Find the area of the rhombus. **120 square units**

18. The bases of a trapezoid are 30 miles and 20 miles. If the area is 850 square miles, find the length of the altitude. **34 mi**

19. One side of a triangle is 7 inches long and its corresponding altitude is 4 inches long. Find the length of the corresponding altitude of another side of the triangle whose length is 8 inches. **3.5 in.**

20. The measures of the consecutive sides of an isosceles trapezoid are in the ratio of 10:5:2:5. The perimeter of the trapezoid is 88 inches. If its height is 12 inches, find the area of the trapezoid. **288 sq in**

21. The area of an isosceles trapezoid is 36 cm². The perimeter is 28 cm. If a leg is 5 cm long, find the height of the trapezoid. **4 cm**

22. Describe what the figure below represents. **How the area of a triangle is related to the area of a rectangle.**

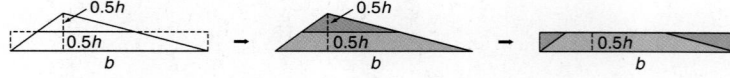

23. A triangle and a parallelogram of the same height have equal areas. How do their bases compare? **The base of the triangle is twice as long as the base of the parallelogram.**

24. Trapezoid *TRAP* has diagonal $\overline{RP}$. Use the formula for the area of a triangle to derive the formula for the area of a trapezoid. **See margin.**

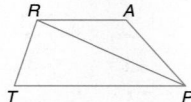

25. Use the formula for the area of a triangle to derive the formula for the area of a rhombus. **See margin.**

LESSON 10-5 AREA OF TRIANGLES, RHOMBI, AND TRAPEZOIDS 493

Additional Answer

24. Let $RA = b_1$ and $TP = b_2$. Let *h* represent the height of *TRAP*.
    area of *TRAP* = area of △*RAP* + area of △*TRP*
    area of *TRAP* = $\frac{1}{2}(b_1)h + \frac{1}{2}(b_2)h$
    area of *TRAP* = $\frac{1}{2}h(b_1 + b_2)$

Additional Answer

25. The diagonals of a rhombus are perpendicular, so $\overline{AE} \perp \overline{BD}$ and $\overline{CE} \perp \overline{DB}$. Therefore, $\overline{AE}$ is an altitude of △*ABD* and $\overline{CE}$ is an altitude of △*BCD*. Since the diagonals of a rhombus bisect each other, $\overline{AE} \cong \overline{EC}$. So $AE = \frac{1}{2}AC$ and $EC = \frac{1}{2}AC$.

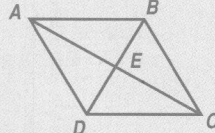

area of *ABCD* = area of △*ABD* + area of △*BCD*
= $\frac{1}{2}(BD)(AE) + \frac{1}{2}(BD)(EC)$
= $\frac{1}{2}(BD)(\frac{1}{2}AC) + \frac{1}{2}(BD)(\frac{1}{2}AC)$
= $\frac{1}{4}(BD)(AC) + \frac{1}{4}(BD)(AC)$
= $\frac{1}{2}(BD)(AC)$

The area is one-half the product of the diagonals.

Additional Answers

26. No; area $MQRP = \frac{1}{2}(\frac{1}{2}h)(MP + QR)$
area $QNOR = \frac{1}{2}(\frac{1}{2}h)(QR + NO)$. Since $MP \neq NO$, the areas are not equal.

27. Works for a rectangle; $a = l$, $b = w$, $c = l$, and $d = w$, so
$$\frac{(a + c)(b + d)}{4} = \frac{(l + l)(w + w)}{4}$$
$$= \frac{(2l)(2w)}{4} = \frac{4lw}{4} = lw$$
Area is equal to the product of the length and the width. Doesn't work for a rhombus; all sides are congruent, so $a = b = c = d$.
$$\frac{(a + c)(b + d)}{4} = \frac{(s + s)(s + s)}{4} =$$
$$\frac{(2s)(2s)}{4} = \frac{4s^2}{4} = s^2$$
Area is not equal to the length of a side squared, unless the rhombus is a square.

Enrichment Masters Booklet, p. 60

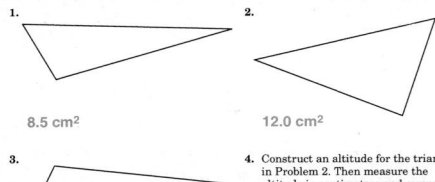

10-5 Enrichment Worksheet

Heron's Formula

If you know the lengths of the sides of a triangle, you can use Heron's formula to find the area.

Heron's Formula:
The area, A, of a triangle with sides measuring a, b, and c is $A = \sqrt{s(s - a)(s - b)(s - c)}$, where $s = \frac{a + b + c}{2}$.

Example: Use Heron's formula to find the area of the triangle.

$s = \frac{2.7 + 3.8 + 5.3}{2} = 5.9$

$A = \sqrt{5.9(5.9 - 2.7)(5.9 - 3.8)(5.9 - 5.3)}$

$= \sqrt{(5.9)(3.2)(2.1)(0.6)}$

$\approx \sqrt{23.8} \approx 4.9$

The area is about 4.9 cm.^{2}

Measure the sides of each triangle in centimeters. Then use Heron's formula to find the area. Round your answers to the nearest tenth.

1.   **2.**

8.5 cm^2 12.0 cm^2

3.   **4.** Construct an altitude for the triangle in Problem 2. Then measure the altitude in centimeters and compute the area using the formula $A = \frac{1}{2}bh$. Did you get the same result as with Heron's formula?
See students' work. Results should be approximately the same.

9.2 cm^2

T60
Glencoe Division, Macmillan/McGraw-Hill

26. $\overline{QR}$ is the median of trapezoid *MNOP*. Are the areas of trapezoids *MQRP* and *QNOR* equal? Explain. **See margin.**

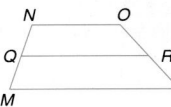

Critical Thinking

27. The ancient Babylonians found the area of a quadrilateral whose sides had lengths of a, b, c, and d units using the formula $A = \frac{(a + c)(b + d)}{4}$. Does the formula work for a rectangle? Does it work for a rhombus? **See margin.**

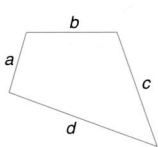

Application

28. Gardening   Hector is applying fertilizer to his lawn. According to the instructions on the package, he is to mix one scoop of fertilizer to one gallon of water for every fifty square feet of grass. Use the diagram at the right to determine how many gallons of fertilizer Hector should mix. **48.75 gallons**

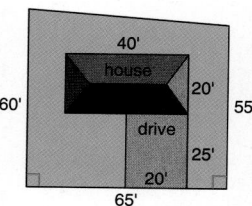

Computer

29. The BASIC program at the right finds the area of a trapezoid given the height and the measures of the bases. Use the program to find the area of each trapezoid.

a. $h = 5$, $b_1 = 8$, $b_2 = 6$ **35 sq units**

b. $h = 3.5$, $b_1 = 7.1$, $b_2 = 8.4$
27.125 sq units

```
10 INPUT "ENTER THE HEIGHT OF THE
   TRAPEZOID."; H
20 INPUT "ENTER THE LENGTH OF ONE
   BASE OF THE TRAPEZOID."; B1
30 INPUT "ENTER THE LENGTH OF THE
   OTHER BASE OF THE TRAPEZOID.";
   B2
40 A = 0.5*H*(B1 + B2)
50 PRINT "THE AREA OF THE
   TRAPEZOID IS "; A; "SQUARE
   UNITS."
60 END
```

Mixed Review

30. The sides of a parallelogram are 32 and 18 inches long. One angle of the parallelogram measures 45°. Find the area of the parallelogram.
(Lesson 10-4) **$288\sqrt{2}$ or about 407.3 square inches**

31. Find the geometric mean between 7 and 14. **(Lesson 8-1)** **$\sqrt{98}$ or about 9.9**

32. Find the next number in the pattern. **(Lesson 6-2)**
$6, -2, \frac{2}{3}, -\frac{2}{9}, \underline{\ ?\ }$ $\frac{2}{27}$

33. Can segments of measure 4, 9, and 21 form a triangle? Explain.
(Lesson 5-6) **No; $4 + 9 < 21$; it fails the triangle inequality.**

 Wrap-Up

34. Journal Entry   Write a few sentences in your journal to describe what you think is the most useful formula you learned in this lesson. Explain.
See students' work.

EXTENDING THE LESSON

Math Power: Problem Solving

David Laing wants to fertilize his lawn. A diagram of his lot, which is in the shape of a trapezoid, is shown. Before he purchases the fertilizer, he needs to know the area of his lawn. Calculate the number of square feet the fertilizer must cover.   **9200 ft²**

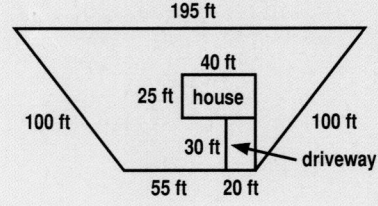

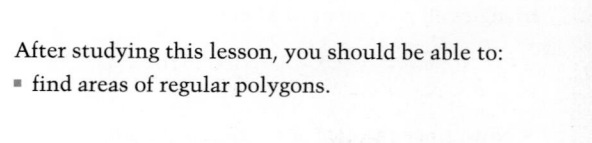

10-6 Area of Regular Polygons

Objective
10-6

After studying this lesson, you should be able to:
- find areas of regular polygons.

Application

Keith Heyen built a deck in the shape of a regular hexagon with sides 12 feet long on the back of his house. He now needs to apply water sealant to the surface of the deck to protect the wood from the weather. Mr. Heyen needs to determine the total area of the deck in order to know how much sealant to buy.

Fortunately for Mr. Heyen, his daughter Lauren is taking geometry. Together they explored the area of a regular hexagon. To begin, Lauren remembered that all regular polygons can be inscribed in a circle. She showed her dad a construction she learned in class.

CONSTRUCTION

Construct a regular hexagon.

1. Use your compass to draw ⊙P. P will also be the **center** of the hexagon. The radius of ⊙P is the **radius** of the hexagon and is congruent to a side of the hexagon.

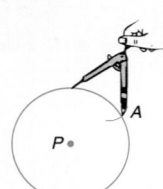

2. Using the same compass setting, place the compass point on the circle and draw an arc, labeling the point of intersection with the circle point A.

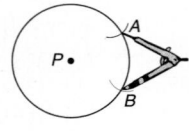

3. Place the compass point on A and draw another arc. Label the point of intersection with the circle B.

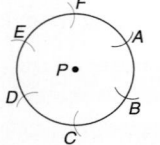

4. Continue this process, labeling points C, D, E, and F on the circle. Point F should be where the point of the compass was placed to locate point A.

5. Use a straightedge to connect A, B, C, D, E, and F consecutively. ABCDEF is a regular hexagon inscribed in ⊙P.

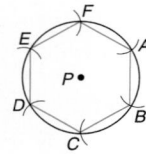

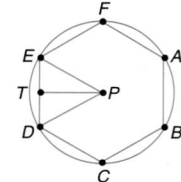

You can draw $\overline{PE}$ and $\overline{PD}$. You can also draw $\overline{PT}$ so that $\overline{PT}$ is perpendicular to $\overline{ED}$. A segment like $\overline{PT}$ that is drawn from the center of a regular polygon perpendicular to a side of the polygon is called an **apothem**.

LESSON 10-6 AREA OF REGULAR POLYGONS 495

Lesson Resources
- Reteaching Master 10-6
- Practice Master 10-6
- Enrichment Master 10-6

Transparency 10-6 contains the 5-Minute Check and a teaching aid for this lesson.

INTRODUCING THE LESSON

5-Minute Check
(over Lesson 10-5)

Find each area.

1. triangle with base measuring 50 millimeters and height of 100 millimeters   2500 mm²
2. trapezoid with bases measuring 15 inches and 21 inches and a height of 10 inches   180 in.²
3. isosceles trapezoid with bases measuring 14 centimeters and 18 centimeters and leg measuring 9 centimeters   140.4 cm²
4. rhombus with diagonals measuring 24 feet and 20 feet   240 ft²
5. right triangle with one leg measuring 5 yards and a hypotenuse measuring 13 yards   30 yd²

Motivating the Lesson
Ask students to name some real objects in the shape of regular polygons.   Sample answer: tiles, faces of geodesic domes, road signs, pieces of leather on a soccer ball

TEACHING THE LESSON

Teaching Tip   After reading about the apothem at the bottom of the page, ask students how many different apothems can be drawn in this figure.   6

ALTERNATE TEACHING STRATEGIES

Using Discussion
What facts that you learned in previous chapters do you use when finding the measure of an apothem of a regular polygon?   Sample answers: facts about isosceles triangles, trigonometry, central angles of circles

Using Logical Thinking
Regular pentagon *ABCDE* and regular pentagon *LMNOP* each have an apothem that measures 2.4 centimeters. Can you determine whether or not they have the same area? Explain your answer.   Yes: If the apothems are the same, the measures of the sides are the same.

496   Chapter 10

Chalkboard Example

For Example 1
The Smiths have built a gazebo in the shape of a regular hexagon. The length of each side of the gazebo is 8 yards. They want to buy outdoor carpeting for it.

a. Find the area of the floor of the gazebo.
The apothem of the hexagon is $4\sqrt{3}$.
$A = \frac{1}{2}Pa$
$A = \frac{1}{2}(48)(4\sqrt{3})$
$A = 166.28$ yard²

b. Find the cost of carpeting the gazebo if carpeting costs $18 per square yard.
$166.28 \cdot \$18 = \$2993.04$

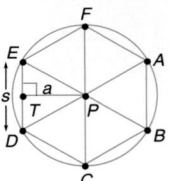

△*PED* is an isosceles triangle, since sides $\overline{PE}$ and $\overline{PD}$ are radii of ⊙*P*. If Lauren were to draw in all of the radii of hexagon *ABCDEF*, they would separate the hexagon into six triangles all congruent to △*PED*.

Now, since the area of a region is the sum of the areas of its nonoverlapping parts, Lauren and her dad can find the area of the hexagon by adding the areas of the triangles. Since $\overline{PT}$ is perpendicular to $\overline{ED}$, it is an altitude of △*PED* as well as an apothem of hexagon *ABCDEF*. Let *a* represent the measure of $\overline{PT}$ and *s* represent the length of a side of the hexagon.

$$\text{Area of } \triangle PED = \frac{1}{2}\,bh \quad \textit{Formula for the area of a triangle}$$
$$= \frac{1}{2}\,sa$$

The area of one of the six triangles is $\frac{1}{2}sa$ units². So the area of the hexagon is $6\left(\frac{1}{2}\right)sa$ units². Notice that the perimeter of hexagon *ABCDEF* is 6*s* units. Therefore, if the perimeter of the hexagon is *P* units, the area will be $\frac{1}{2}Pa$ units². This area formula can be used for any regular polygon.

Area of a Regular Polygon	**If a regular polygon has an area of *A* square units, a perimeter of *P* units, and an apothem of *a* units, then $A = \frac{1}{2}Pa$.**

Example 1

Refer to the opening application.

a. Find the area of Mr. Heyen's deck.

Look at the diagram of △*PED* with apothem $\overline{PT}$ at the top of the page. $\overline{PT}$ separates △*PED* into two 30°-60°-90° triangles. The length of the longer leg in a 30°-60°-90° triangle is $\sqrt{3}$ times the length of the shorter leg. The shorter leg of the triangle is $\frac{1}{2}(12)$ or 6 feet long, so the longer leg is $6\sqrt{3}$ feet long. Therefore, $a = 6\sqrt{3}$.

$$\text{Area of hexagonal deck} = \frac{1}{2}\,Pa \quad \textit{Formula for the area of a regular polygon}$$
$$= \frac{1}{2}\,(6 \cdot 12)(6\sqrt{3}) \quad \textit{The perimeter is six times the length of one side.}$$
$$= 36(6\sqrt{3})$$
$$= 216\sqrt{3}$$

The deck has an area of $216\sqrt{3}$ or about 374 square feet.

b. If one gallon of water sealant covers 200 square feet, how many gallons will Mr. Heyen need? If a one-gallon can of water sealant costs $11.99, how much will the water sealant for the deck cost?

Mr. Heyen will need $\frac{374}{200}$ or 1.87 gallons of water sealant. He should buy 2 one-gallon cans at a total cost of $23.98.

Chalkboard Example

For Example 2
Find the area of a regular pentagon whose perimeter is 60 centimeters.

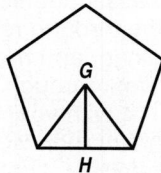

First, find the length of an apothem, $\overline{GH}$.

$\tan 36° = \dfrac{6}{GH}$

$GH = \dfrac{6}{\tan 36°} \approx 8.26$ cm

$A = \frac{1}{2}Pa$

$A = \frac{1}{2}(60)(8.26)$

$A = 247.8 \approx 248$ cm²

The angle formed by two radii drawn to consecutive vertices of a regular polygon is called a **central angle** of the polygon. All of the central angles of a regular polygon are congruent.

Example 2

Find the area of a regular pentagon whose perimeter is 45 inches.

Since the perimeter is 45 inches and the pentagon is regular, the length of each side is $\frac{45}{5}$ or 9 inches.

To use the formula for the area of a regular polygon, we must find the length of the apothem $\overline{OT}$. The central angles of *ABCDE* are all congruent. Therefore, the measure of each one is $\frac{360}{5}$ or 72. Since $\overline{OT}$ is an apothem of pentagon *ABCDE*, it is perpendicular to $\overline{AB}$. It forms right triangle *BOT* with $m\angle BOT = 36$ and *BT* is 4.5 inches long.

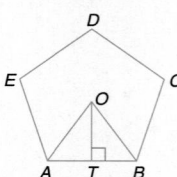

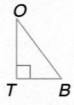

Use the trigonometric ratios that we learned in Chapter 8.

$$\tan O = \frac{BT}{OT} \qquad tan = \frac{opposite}{adjacent}$$

$$\tan 36° = \frac{4.5}{OT}$$

$$\tan 36° \,(OT) = 4.5$$

$$OT = \frac{4.5}{\tan 36°} \qquad \textit{Use your calculator}$$

$$OT \approx 6.19$$

Now use the formula for the area of a regular polygon.

$$A = \frac{1}{2}Pa \qquad \textit{Area of a regular polygon}$$

$$A \approx \frac{1}{2}(45)(6.19) \qquad \textit{P = 45 and a} \approx \textit{6.19.}$$

$$A \approx 139.3$$

The area of a regular pentagon with a perimeter of 45 inches is about 139 square inches.

LESSON 10-6 AREA OF REGULAR POLYGONS 497

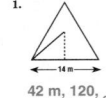
CHECKING FOR UNDERSTANDING

Communicating Mathematics

Read and study the lesson to answer these questions.

1. Describe the difference between a radius and an apothem in a regular polygon. **A radius is a segment between the center and a vertex and an apothem is a segment from the center perpendicular to a side.**
2. What is the measure of a central angle of a regular polygon with 10 sides? a regular polygon with 24 sides? a regular polygon with n sides? **36; 15; $\frac{360}{n}$**
3. How is the formula for the area of a regular polygon related to the formula for the area of a triangle? **The formula for the area of a polygon is based on the sum of the areas of several triangles in a polygon.**
4. Describe how to find the measure of the apothem of a polygon if you know its radius. **Let $x = \frac{180}{\text{number of sides}}$, then $a = r \cos x°$.**

Guided Practice

Use the figure below to answer each question. Triangle ABC is equilateral and inscribed in circle O, and $\overline{AB}$ is 10 cm long.

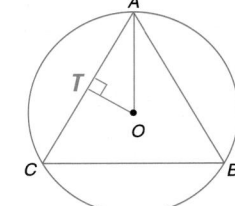

5. Find the perimeter of $\triangle ABC$. **30 cm**

6. Copy the figure. Draw radius $\overline{OA}$ and construct apothem $\overline{OT}$ to side $\overline{AC}$.

7. **30°-60°-90°; central angle COA would measure 120; $\overline{OT}$ bisects $\angle COA$, so $m\angle TOA = 60$.**
   What type of right triangle is $\triangle OTA$? Explain.

8. What is the length of $\overline{AT}$? Why? **5 feet; it is half the length of $\overline{AC}$.**

9. **See Solutions Manual for drawing. OT, $\frac{5}{\sqrt{3}}$ or about 2.89 cm; OA, $\frac{10}{\sqrt{3}}$ or about 5.77 cm**
   Draw right triangle OTA separately and label the measure of the angles. Use the properties of right triangles to find the lengths of $\overline{OT}$ and $\overline{OA}$.

10. Find the area of $\triangle ABC$ using the formula for regular polygons. **about 43.3 cm²**

Find the perimeter, the measure of a central angle, the length of an apothem, and the area for each regular polygon. **See margin.**

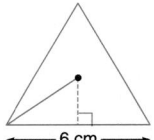 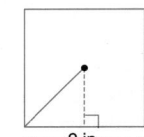 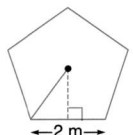

11.   ←— 6 cm —→
12.   ←—9 in.—→
13.   ←2 m→

RETEACHING THE LESSON

Use these exercises to review how to find the area of regular polygons. Draw a picture of each polygon on the chalkboard. Then find the area of each polygon.

1. a pentagon with an apothem 6.9 meters long and a side 10 meters long
   172.5 m²

2. a hexagon with a side that measures 11 inches and an apothem that measures 9.5 inches   **313.5 in²**

3. an octagon that measures 20 millimeters on a side and has an apothem of 24.1 millimeters
   1928 mm²

EXERCISES

Practice Find the area of each regular polygon. Round your answers to the nearest tenth. **17. 289.3 mi² 18. 261 m²**

14. an equilateral triangle with an apothem 5.8 centimeters long and a side 20 centimeters long **174 cm²**

15. a square with a side 16 inches long and an apothem 8 inches long **256 in²**

16. a hexagon with a side 19.1 millimeters long and an apothem 16.5 millimeters long **945.5 mm²**

17. a pentagon with an apothem 8.9 miles long and a side 13.0 miles long

18. a hexagon with an apothem 8.7 meters long and a side 10 meters long

19. an octagon with an apothem 7.5 feet long and a side 6.2 feet long **186 ft²**

APPLYING THE LESSON

Homework Exercises

Assignment Guide
Basic: 14-28, 34-40
Average: 16-30, 34-40
Enriched: 19-40

Additional Answers

26. $30\sqrt{3}$ cm; 5 cm; $75\sqrt{3}$ cm²
27. 60 cm; $5\sqrt{3}$; $150\sqrt{3}$ cm²
28. 61.2 cm; 9.2 cm; 281.5 cm²

Find the area of each orange region. Assume that polygons that appear to be regular are regular.

20.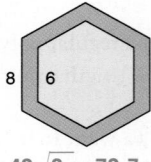

$42\sqrt{3} \approx 72.7$ units²

21.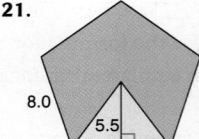

88 units²

22.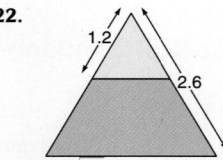

$1.33\sqrt{3} \approx 2.3$ units²

23.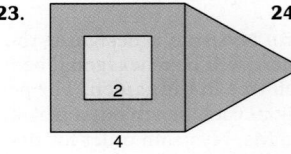

$12 + 4\sqrt{3} \approx 18.9$ units²

24.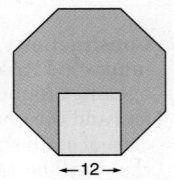

551.3 units²

25.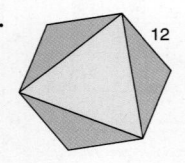

$108\sqrt{3} \approx 187.1$ units²

Find the perimeter, the length of the apothem, and the area of each regular polygon. **See margin.**

26.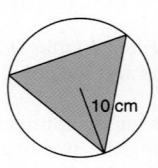

27.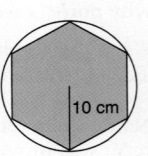

28.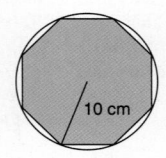

Practice Masters Booklet, p. 71

10-6 Practice Worksheet

NAME _____ DATE _____

Area of Regular Polygons

Find the area of each regular polygon. Round your answers to the nearest tenth.

1. an octagon with an apothem 4.8 centimeters long and a side 4 centimeters long
76.8 cm²

2. a square with a side 24 inches long and an apothem 12 inches long
576 in.²

3. a hexagon with a side 23.1 meters long and an apothem 20.0 meters long
1386 m²

4. a pentagon with an apothem 316.6 millimeters long and a side 460 millimeters long
364,090 mm²

Find the perimeter, the length of the apothem, and the area of each regular polygon. Round your answers to the nearest tenth.

5.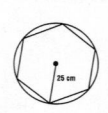

41.6 in., 4 in., 83.1 in.²

6.

117.6 cm, 16.2 cm, 951.1 c...

7.

150 cm, 21.7 cm, 1623.8 cm²

8.

61.2 m, 9.2 m, 282.8 m²

71
Glencoe Division, Macmillan/McGraw-Hill

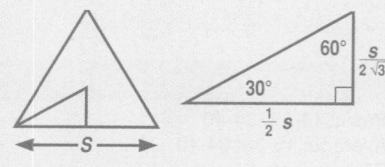
Enrichment Masters Booklet, p. 61

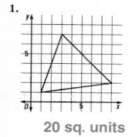

NAME _____ DATE _____

10-6 **Enrichment Worksheet**

Aerial Surveyors and Area

Many land regions have irregular shapes. Aerial surveyors often use coordinates when finding areas of such regions. The coordinate method described in the steps below can be used to find the area of *any* polygonal region. Study how this method is used to find the area of the region at the right.

Step 1 List the ordered pairs for the vertices in counter-clockwise order, repeating the first ordered pair at the bottom of the list.

Step 2 Find *D*, the sum of the downward diagonal products (from left to right).
$D = (5 \cdot 5) + (2 \cdot 1) + (2 \cdot 3) + (6 \cdot 7)$
$= 25 + 2 + 6 + 42$ or 75

(5, 7)

Step 3 Find *U*, the sum of the upward diagonal products (from left to right).
$U = (2 \cdot 7) + (2 \cdot 5) + (6 \cdot 1) + (5 \cdot 3)$
$= 14 + 10 + 6 + 15$ or 45

(2, 5)
(2, 1)
(6, 3)
(5, 7)

Step 4 Use the formula $A = \frac{1}{2}(D - U)$ to find the area.

$A = \frac{1}{2}(D - U)$

$= \frac{1}{2}(75 - 45)$

$= \frac{1}{2}(30)$ or 15

The area is 15 square units. Count the number of square units enclosed by the polygon. Does this result seem reasonable?

Use the coordinate method to find the area of each region in square units.

1.

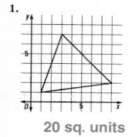

20 sq. units

2.

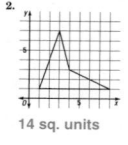

14 sq. units

3.

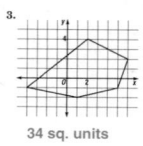

34 sq. units

T61
Glencoe Division, Macmillan/McGraw-Hill

500 **Chapter 10**

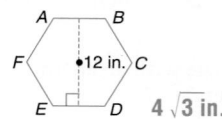

29. *ABCDEF* is a regular hexagon. Find the length of each side.

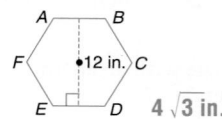

$4\sqrt{3}$ in.

30. Find the ratio of the area of square *ABCD* to the area of square *BFCE*.

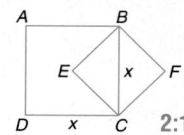

2:1

31. $P = 24.72$ ft, $A = 47.02$ ft^2

31. Find the perimeter and area of a regular decagon with a radius of 4 feet.

32. A circle inscribes a regular hexagon and circumscribes another. If the radius of the circle is 10 units long, find the ratio of the area of the smaller hexagon to the area of the larger hexagon. **3 to 4**

33. Draw a regular octagon with sides 1 inch long.
   a. Draw segments to join the midpoints of four nonadjacent sides of the octagon. What figure is produced? **a square**
   b. Find the area of the figure formed by joining the midpoints of the nonadjacent sides of the octagon. Round your answer to the nearest hundredth. **2.91 in^2**
   c. Find the area of the region that is inside of the octagon but outside of the figure. **1.91 in^2**

Critical Thinking

34. Use the formula for the area of a regular polygon to show that the area of an equilateral triangle with side length *s* units is $\dfrac{\sqrt{3}}{4}\,s^2$ units^2. **See margin.**

Applications

35. **Gardening** Dave and Kelly Rea want to install a fence to keep animals out of their rose garden. Each side of the triangular garden is 18 feet long.
   a. Find the amount of fencing material that they will need to buy. **54 ft**
   b. What is the area of their garden to the nearest tenth of a square foot? **140.3 ft^2**

36. **Construction** Carol Nystrom is designing the garden area of the new Inniswood Park. There will be a hexagonal bench with a hexagonal opening around each tree in the garden. The perimeter of each bench is 36 feet and the opening in each bench has a perimeter of 12 feet. How many cans of stain should Ms. Nystrom order for the seats of the benches if there will be 14 benches in the garden and one can of stain covers 175 square feet? **7 cans**

38. No; $18 + 32 \le 67$, so these lengths fail the triangle inequality.

Mixed Review

39. If two figures are congruent, then they have equal areas. Two figures are congruent. They have equal areas.

37. Find the area of a rhombus whose diagonals are 17 and 24 feet long. **(Lesson 10-5) 204 ft^2**

38. Can a triangle have sides with lengths of 18, 32, and 67 inches? If not, why not? **(Lesson 5-6)**

39. Write the conditional *Congruent figures have equal areas* in if-then form. Then identify the hypothesis and the conclusion. **(Lesson 2-2)**

Wrap-Up

40. Name three terms from this lesson connected to regular polygons. Which term was important in finding the area of a regular polygon? **center, apothem, radius, central angle; apothem**

500 **CHAPTER 10 POLYGONS AND AREA**

EXTENDING THE LESSON

Math Power: Reasoning

Find the area of the shaded region. The figure is a regular hexagon.
110.4 square units

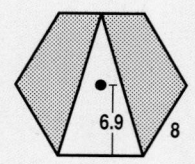

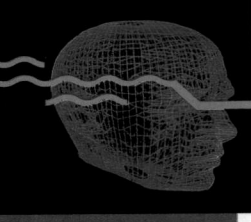

Technology

Area

BASIC
Geometric Supposer
Graphing calculators
LOGO
Spreadsheets

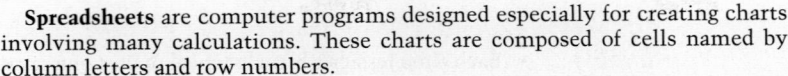

Using Technology

Objective This optional page shows how spreadsheets can be set up to find the area of regular polygons.

Teaching Suggestions

If a computer spreadsheet program is available, have students enter the program for finding the area of regular polygons. Have students enter various values for the number of sides, length of a side, and measure of the apothem and investigate the changes in the area.

Note that the measure of the apothem is not arbitrary. Students cannot make up just any number to insert here. You may want to have students work in groups to determine the apothem for various regular polygons, given the measure of a side.

You may also have students modify the spreadsheet so that it finds the area of any regular hexagon, given the measure of one of its sides.

Spreadsheets are computer programs designed especially for creating charts involving many calculations. These charts are composed of cells named by column letters and row numbers.

The spreadsheet below is set up to find the area of a regular polygon. Cells A1, B1, C1, D1, and E1 hold the labels N, S, P, A, and AREA for the number of sides, the length of a side, the perimeter, the length of the apothem, and the area of the polygon. Cells A3 to A7 hold the values for the number of sides of each polygon, cells B3 to B7 hold the values for the length of a side of each polygon, cells C3 to C7 hold the values for the perimeter of each polygon, cells D3 to D7 hold the length of the apothem of each polygon, and cells E3 to E7 hold the area of the polygon.

```
====A========B========C========D========E=====
1:   N        S        P        A        AREA
2:--------------------------------------------
3:   4        6        24       4.2      50.4
4:   6        6        36       5.2      93.6
5:   3        12       36       3.5      63
6:   7        14       98       14.5     710.5
7:   10       8        80       12.3     492
```

Each cell in column C holds a formula to find the perimeter of the regular polygon described in that row. Since cells A3 and B3 hold the values for the number of sides in the polygon and the measure of each side, the computer will multiply these together to find the perimeter. So, cell C3 holds the formula A3 * B3. The cells in column E hold a formula to compute the area of the regular polygon.

EXERCISES

1. What formula does cell E3 of the spreadsheet hold for finding the area of a regular polygon? **0.5 * C3 * D3**

2. Why does the formula contained in cell C3 of the spreadsheet work for finding the perimeter of the polygon? **The polygon is regular, so to find the perimeter multiply the number of sides by the length of a side.**

3. Set up a spreadsheet program to find the area of a trapezoid. **See students' work.**

TECHNOLOGY   501

INTRODUCING THE LESSON

 5-Minute Check

(over Lesson 10-6)

Find the area of each polygon.

1. square with a side of 4 centimeters and an apothem of 2 centimeters   **16 cm²**
2. regular pentagon with a side of 6 yards and an apothem of 4.13 yards   **61.95 yd²**
3. regular octagon with a side of 10 inches and an apothem of 12.07 inches   **482.8 in.²**
4. regular decagon with a side of 7 feet   **376.95 ft²**

Motivating the Lesson

Ask students to use string and a ruler marked in millimeters to measure the circumference and diameter of circular objects such as coins. Have them divide the circumference by the diameter and compare their results.

TEACHING THE LESSON

Teaching Tip You may want to divide the class into groups to confirm the data in the chart for figures with 3, 4, 5, 6, and 8 sides.

10-7 Area and Circumference of a Circle

Objectives

10-7A
10-7B

After studying this lesson, you should be able to:
- find the circumference of a circle, and
- find the area of a circle.

Application

Each time Jessica's bicycle wheel makes one revolution, the distance it travels is the same as the **circumference** of the wheel. The circumference of a circle is the distance around the circle. If the wheel on Jessica's bike has a radius of 12 inches, how many revolutions will the wheel make while Jessica travels down the block 500 feet? *You will answer this question in Example 1.*

Start   Turning   All the way around

The circumference of a circle can be approximated by considering the perimeter of regular polygons. Notice that as the number of sides of the inscribed polygon increases, the perimeter of the polygon becomes closer to the circumference of the circle.

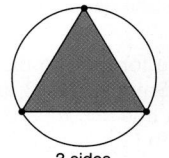 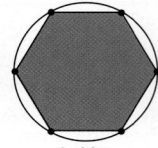 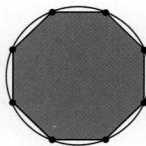 

3 sides   6 sides   8 sides   20 sides

The chart below shows the approximate perimeter and area of each regular polygon inscribed in a circle of radius *r*.

Number of Sides	3	4	5	6	8	10	20	50	100
Measure of a Side	1.73r	1.41r	1.18r	r	0.77r	0.62r	0.31r	0.126r	0.0628r
Perimeter	5.20r	5.64r	5.90r	6.00r	6.16r	6.20r	6.20r	6.30r	6.28r
Measure of Apothem	0.5r	0.71r	0.81r	0.87r	0.92r	0.95r	0.99r	0.998r	0.9995r
Area	1.30r^2	2.00r^2	2.39r^2	2.61r^2	2.83r^2	2.95r^2	3.07r^2	3.14r^2	3.14r^2

502   CHAPTER 10   POLYGONS AND AREA

ALTERNATE TEACHING STRATEGIES

Using Reasoning

A circular field must have an area of 800 square feet. What should the length of its diameter be?   **about 32 feet**

Using Computers

Write a BASIC program that computes the circumference and area of a circle given its diameter.

```
10 INPUT "ENTER THE DIAMETER OF
   THE CIRCLE"; X
20 LET A = (X/2)*(X/2)*3.14
30 LET C = X*3.14
40 PRINT "THE CIRCUMFERENCE
   IS"; C; "AND THE AREA IS"; A
50 END
```

Look at the rows for perimeter and area. Notice that as the number of sides of the inscribed polygon increases, the perimeter and the area both approach a different limiting number. The perimeter approaches the circumference of the circle, and the area approaches the area of the circle. Notice that $6.28 = 2 \cdot 3.14$ and 3.14 is an approximation of the irrational number called π (pi). So, $6.28r \approx 2\pi r$ and $3.14r^2 \approx \pi r^2$.

Teaching Tip When reading the formulas at the top of the page, point out that another formula for the circumference is $C = \pi d$.

Circumference of a Circle	**If a circle has a circumference of C units and a radius of r units, then $C = 2\pi r$.**
Area of a Circle	**If a circle has an area of A square units and a radius of r units, then $A = \pi r^2$.**

Example 1

APPLICATION
Bicycling

The wheel on Jessica's bike has a radius of 12 inches. How many revolutions will the wheel make while Jessica travels 500 feet?

For each revolution that the wheel makes, it travels a distance equal to the circumference of the wheel. So, we must first find the circumference of the wheel.

$$C = 2\pi r \qquad \text{\textit{Formula for the circumference of a circle}}$$
$$C = 2\pi(12)$$

Use a calculator to find the circumference. *If your calculator doesn't have a π key, use 3.14 to approximate π.*

Enter: 2 ⊠ π ⊠ 12 ⊟ 75.398224

The circumference is about 75 inches or 6.25 feet. The wheel will travel about 6.25 feet each time it makes a revolution. Now, find the number of revolutions that the wheel will make in 500 feet.

$$\text{number of revolutions} = \text{total distance} \div \text{distance per revolution}$$
$$\approx 500 \div 6.25$$
$$\approx 80$$

The wheel will make about 80 revolutions as it travels 500 feet.

Example 2

Find the area of the shaded region.

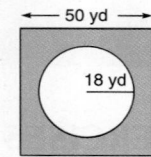

← 50 yd →

18 yd

$$\text{area of shaded region} = \text{area of square} - \text{area of circle}$$
$$= s^2 \qquad - \qquad \pi r^2$$
$$= (50)^2 - \pi(18)^2$$
$$= 2500 - 324\pi$$
$$\approx 1482.12$$

The area of the shaded region is about 1482 square yards.

You can use what you learned about the general equation for a circle to find the area of the circle.

LESSON 10-7   AREA AND CIRCUMFERENCE OF A CIRCLE   503

Chalkboard Examples

For Example 1
The wheel on Steve's bike has a radius of 16 inches. How many revolutions will the wheel make while Steve travels 400 feet?
$C = 2\pi r$
$C = 2\pi(16) \approx 100.53$
100.53 in. $\div 12 = 8.38$ ft
$400 \div 8.38 = 47.73$ revolutions

For Example 2
Find the area of the shaded region.

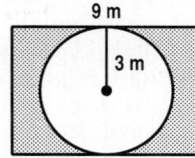

9 m

3 m

Area of shaded region = area of rectangle − area of circle
$a = 9(6) - \pi(3)^2$
$a = 54 - 28.27$
$a = 25.73$

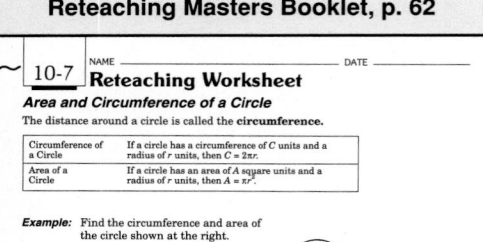

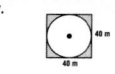 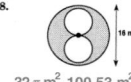

Example 3

Find the area of a circle with equation $(x - 2)^2 + (y + 5)^2 = 81$.

The general form of the equation for a circle with center (h, k) is
$(x - h)^2 + (y - k)^2 = r^2$, where r is the radius of the circle. Therefore, the
radius of the given circle is $\sqrt{81}$ or 9. Now use the formula for the area of a
circle.

$$A = \pi r^2 \qquad \text{\textit{Formula for area of a circle}}$$
$$= \pi(9)^2$$
$$= 81\pi$$

The area of the circle is 81π or about 254.5 square units.

CHECKING FOR UNDERSTANDING

Communicating Mathematics

Read and study the lesson to answer these questions.
1. **Answers may vary.**
1. π is the first letter in a Greek word that means "measure around". Why
   do you think π is used in the formula for the circumference of a circle?

**2. The measure of the
diameter is twice the
measure of the radius.**
2. The circumference of a circle is sometimes expressed as $C = \pi d$, where d
   is the measure of the diameter of the circle. Why is this formula
   equivalent to $C = 2\pi r$?

3. In stating the exact values of the circumference and area for a circle with
   diameter 24 feet, Alan tells Mary that the circumference is 24π feet and
   the area is 576π square feet. Explain why Alan is only partially correct.
   The area is 144π square feet.

Guided Practice

Copy and complete the chart from the information given about different
circles. Give exact answers using π when necessary.

	r	d	C	A	
4.	12 cm	_?_	_?_	_?_	$d = 24$ cm; $C = 24\pi$ cm; $A = 144\pi$ cm²
5.	_?_	4.8 km	_?_	_?_	$r = 2.4$ km; $C = 4.8\pi$ km; $A = 5.76\pi$ km²
6.	_?_	_?_	20π in.	_?_	$r = 10$ in.; $d = 20$ in.; $A = 100\pi$ in²
7.	_?_	_?_	_?_	81π ft²	$r = 9$ ft; $d = 18$ ft; $C = 18\pi$ ft

8. The area of a circular pool is approximately 7,850 ft². The owner has
   decided to place a fence around the pool. If the fence is five feet from the
   edge of the pool, how many feet of fencing will be needed? **about 346 feet**

EXERCISES

Practice

A

**Find the circumference of a circle with a radius of the given length. Round
your answers to the nearest tenth.**

9. 10 m **62.8 m**   10. 4 in. **25.1 in.**   11. 7 yd **44.0 yd**
12. 3.6 km **22.6 km**   13. 1.1 mm **6.9 mm**   14. $\frac{1}{4}$ mi **1.6 mi**

RETEACHING THE LESSON

Use these exercises to review how
to find the area of a circle when
given the radius or diameter. Draw
a picture of each circle on the
chalkboard and explain the formula
used. Review the relationship
between the diameter and the
radius.
1. radius of 3 meters   **28.3 m²**
2. diameter of 14 inches
   153.9 in.²

Find the area of a circle with a radius of the given length. Round your answers to the nearest tenth.

15. 18 in. **1017.9 in²**   16. 5.8 m **105.7 m²**   17. 9.7 km **295.6 km²**

18. 0.4 in. **0.5 in²**   19. $3\frac{1}{3}$ yd **34.9 yd²**   20. $4\sqrt{5}$ cm **251.3 cm²**

 State the measure of the radius of a circle with each equation. Then find the area of each circle. Give exact answers using π.

21. $x^2 + y^2 = 121$ **11; 121π**   22. $(x - 3)^2 + y^2 = 49$ **7; 49π**

23. $(x - 6)^2 + y^2 = 11$ **$\sqrt{11}$; 11π**   24. $(x - 8)^2 + (y - 6)^2 = 15$ **$\sqrt{15}$; 15π**

25. $x^2 + (y + 1)^2 = 625$ **25; 625π**   26. $(x + 1)^2 + (y + 2)^2 = 68$
$\sqrt{68}$; 68π

27. Find the circumference and the area of a circle inscribed in a square whose sides are 6 meters long. **6π m; 9π m²**

28. The diagonal of a square is 8 feet long. Find the circumference and the area of a circle inscribed in the square. **$4\sqrt{2\pi}$ ft; 8π ft²**

Find the area of each shaded region. Assume that all polygons are regular. Express each answer as an exact number involving π and a decimal rounded to the nearest hundredth.

29.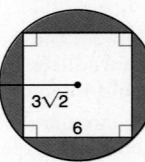

18π − 36 units², 20.55 units²

30.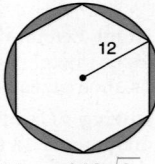

144π − 216$\sqrt{3}$ units²; 78.27 units²

31.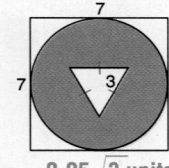

12.25π − 2.25$\sqrt{3}$ units²; 34.59 units²

32.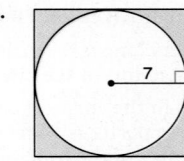

196 − 49π units²; 42.06 units²

33.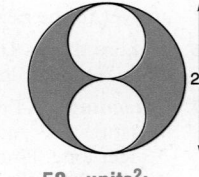

50π units²; 157.08 units²

34.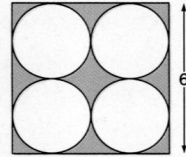

36 − 9π units²; 7.73 units²

 35.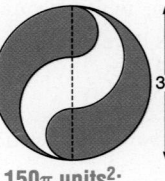

150π units²; 471.24 units²

36.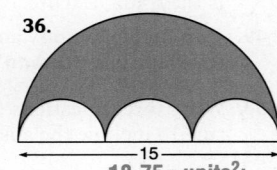

18.75π units²; 58.90 units²

37.

56.25π − 108 units², 68.71 units²

LESSON 10-7   AREA AND CIRCUMFERENCE OF A CIRCLE   505

APPLYING THE LESSON

Homework Exercises

Assignment Guide

Basic: 9-31, 39-50
Average: 12-34, 39-50
Enriched: 16-50

Exercise Notes

For Exercises 8-20, 29-37, and 41-44 an approximation of 3.1415927 for π was used to calculate the answers. Using different approximations may yield slightly different answers.

For Exercise 27, students should note that they are given the diameter of the circle.

For Exercise 28, a diagram will help students see that they must find the measure of the side of the square to find the diameter of the circle.

Practice Masters Booklet, p. 72

 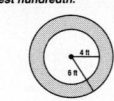
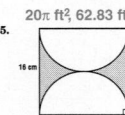 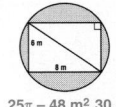
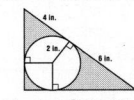

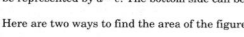
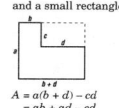
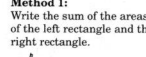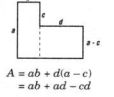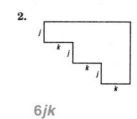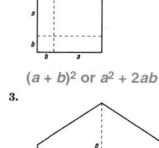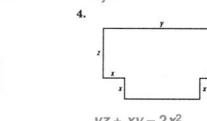
---

38. A circle is inscribed in a rhombus whose diagonals are 24 and 32 feet long.
  a. Find the area of the circle. 92.16π ft^2
  b. What is the area of the region that is inside the rhombus but outside the circle? $384 - 92.16\pi$ ft^2

Critical Thinking
39. The area of the shaded region is one-half of the area of large circle.

39. Find the area of the shaded region if $r = 2, 3, 4, 5, 6$, and 8. What is the relationship between the area of the shaded region and the area of the large circle?

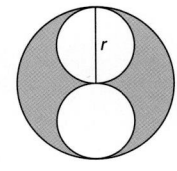

40. The ratio of the circumferences for two circles is 3:5. Is the ratio for the areas the same? Explain. **See margin.**

Applications

41. City Planning   A new system of sirens is being considered for the city of Grandview. The system will be used to alert the city's residents in the event of a tornado or other severe weather. The sound emitted from each siren will travel up to 1.5 miles. Find the area of the city that will benefit from each siren. **about 7 square miles**

42. Sports   A diagram of the new practice track and football field at Edison High School is shown at the right. Find the amount of sod it would take to cover the area inside the track. **about 13,827 sq yd**

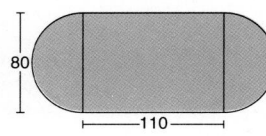

43. Home Economics   A recipe for a 14-inch pizza calls for a 15-ounce can of pizza sauce. How much sauce would be needed for a 10-inch pizza? (A 14-inch pizza has a diameter of 14 inches.) **about 7.7 ounces**

44. Sewing   Carolyn is making a circular tablecloth for a table whose diameter is 48 inches. The top of the table is 28 inches from the floor. If the tablecloth is to reach to the floor, how many yards of lace should Carolyn buy to place around the edge of the tablecloth? **about 9.1 yards**

Mixed Review
45. Find the area of a regular hexagon with sides 10 inches long. Round your answer to the nearest hundredth. **(Lesson 10-6)** 259.81 in^2

46. A chord that is 16 centimeters long is 6 centimeters from the center of a circle. Find the length of the radius of the circle. **(Lesson 9-3)** 10 cm

47. Gardening   A flower bed is in the shape of an obtuse triangle. One angle measures 103°, and the side opposite is 14 feet long. The shortest side is 7.5 feet long. Find the measures of the remaining side and angles. **(Lesson 8-6)** 10.3 feet; 31, 46

48. The measures of the angles in a triangle are $x + 16$, $8x + 7$, and $11x - 3$. Is the triangle acute, obtuse, right, or equiangular? **(Lesson 4-2)** acute

49. Two supplementary angles have measures of $6y + 14$ and $22y - 2$. Find the value of y. **(Lesson 1-8)** 6

Wrap-Up
50. Write three questions that could be used as a quiz over this lesson. Be sure to include the answers to your questions. **See students' work.**

EXTENDING THE LESSON

Math Power: Connections

Suppose a piece of rope is wrapped around earth at its equator. Assume the equator is 25,000 miles long and earth is perfectly round. Suppose the length of the rope is increased by 1 yard. How far above earth will the new rope be at each point along the equator?   **5.8 in.**

10-8 Geometric Probability

Objective
10-8

After studying this lesson, you should be able to:
- use area to solve problems involving geometric probability.

Application

WGEO radio station is having a "Call In To Win" Contest. The song of the day is announced at 7:00 A.M. each day. Then, sometime during each hour of the day, the song of the day is played. The first person to call the station when the song of the day begins to play wins $100. If you turn on your radio at 12:20 P.M., what is the probability that you have not missed the start of the song of the day played sometime between 12:00 P.M. and 1:00 P.M.?

This problem can be solved using **geometric probability.** Geometric probability involves using the principles of length and area to find the probability of an event. One of the principles of geometric probability is stated in Postulate 10-3.

Postulate 10-3
Length Probability
Postulate

If a point on $\overline{AB}$ is chosen at random and C is between A and B, then the probability that the point is on $\overline{AC}$ is $\dfrac{\text{length of } \overline{AC}}{\text{length of } \overline{AB}}$.

To find the probability that you have not missed the start of the song of the day, draw a line segment to represent the time from 12:00 to 1:00. Point C represents the time that you started listening.

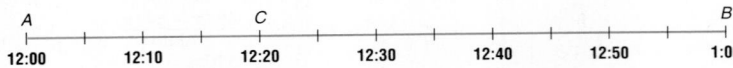

| A | | | C | | | | | | B |

12:00   12:10   12:20   12:30   12:40   12:50   1:00

The length of $\overline{AB}$ represents the entire hour. The length of $\overline{AC}$ represents the time from 12:00 to 12:20, and the length of $\overline{CB}$ represents the time from 12:20 to 1:00.

You have not missed the song of the day if the station plays the song after 12:20. So, the probability of having not missed the song is $\dfrac{\text{length of } \overline{CB}}{\text{length of } \overline{AB}}$.

$$P(\text{not missed the song}) = \dfrac{\text{length of } \overline{CB}}{\text{length of } \overline{AB}}$$
$$= \dfrac{40 \text{ units}}{60 \text{ units}}$$
$$= \dfrac{2}{3}$$

The probability that you have not missed the song of the day is $\dfrac{2}{3}$.

INVESTIGATION

You can learn more about geometric probability in Investigation 13 on page A12.

ALTERNATE TEACHING STRATEGIES

Using Investigation

You can guide students to discover the principles of geometric probability. In Investigation 13 on page A12 of **More Investigations in Geometry,** students use experimentation with a graphing calculator program to explore probability and how it relates to area.

Using Problem Solving

Jenna rode her bike 10 miles along the beach road. At the end of the ride, she realized that she had dropped her water bottle. What is the probability that she dropped it between the boathouse and her stopping point if the boathouse is 7 miles back?   0.7

Lesson Resources

- Reteaching Master 10-8
- Practice Master 10-8
- Enrichment Master 10-8
- Activity Master, p. 10
- Transparency 10-8 contains the 5-Minute Check and a teaching aid for this lesson.

INTRODUCING THE LESSON

5-Minute Check
(over Lesson 10-7)

Find the area of each circle. Round your answers to the nearest tenth.

1. radius of 12 centimeters
   452.4 cm²
2. diameter of 6 inches
   28.3 in.²
3. radius of 40 millimeters
   5026.5 mm²

Find the circumference of each circle. Round answers to the nearest tenth.

4. diameter of 10 meters
   31.4 m
5. radius of 7 inches   44.0 in.
6. diameter of 23 yards
   72.3 yd

Motivating the Lesson

Ask students if they have ever tried to win a radio contest. What strategies did they use to try to be the caller chosen?

TEACHING THE LESSON

Teaching Tip   After reading Postulate 10-3, discuss with students why the line segment is a good model for time in this problem.

Postulate 10-4 Area Probability Postulate	If a point in region A is chosen at random, then the probability that the point is in region B, which is in the interior of region A, is $\dfrac{\text{area of region } B}{\text{area of region } A}$.

Example 1 uses the area probability postulate.

Example 1

APPLICATION Entertainment

The children at Joshua's birthday party are playing a game for prizes. Each child tosses a beanbag at the target on the floor. Depending on where one marked corner of the beanbag lands, prizes are given. Red gets a jumbo squirtgun; blue gets a yo-yo; green gets a candy bar. If the corner of a beanbag lands on the target, find the probability of a child winning each prize. Round your answers to the nearest hundredth.

12 in. 10 in. 8 in.

Use geometric probability to find the probability of the corner of the bag landing in each region.

Red area: probability $= \dfrac{\text{area of red circle}}{\text{area of target}}$ *Area probability postulate*

$= \dfrac{\pi(12)^2}{\pi(30)^2}$ *Formula for area of a circle*

$= \dfrac{144\pi}{900\pi}$

$= \dfrac{4}{25}$ or 0.16

Blue area: probability $= \dfrac{\text{area of blue ring}}{\text{area of target}}$

$= \dfrac{\pi(22)^2 - \pi(12)^2}{\pi(30)^2}$ *Area of blue ring = area of blue and red circle − area of red circle.*

$= \dfrac{484\pi - 144\pi}{900\pi}$

$= \dfrac{340\pi}{900\pi}$

$= \dfrac{17}{45}$ or about 0.38

Green area: probability $= \dfrac{\text{area of green ring}}{\text{area of target}}$

$= \dfrac{\pi(30)^2 - \pi(22)^2}{\pi(30)^2}$ *Area of green ring = area of target − area of blue and red circle.*

$= \dfrac{900\pi - 484\pi}{900\pi}$

$= \dfrac{416\pi}{900\pi}$

$= \dfrac{104}{225}$ or about 0.46

The probability of winning a jumbo squirtgun is 0.16, the probability of winning a yo-yo is about 0.38, and the probability of winning a candy bar is about 0.46.

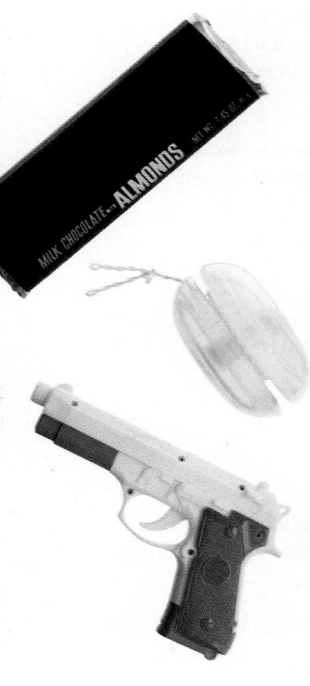

Chalkboard Example

For Example 1

Joanna designed a new darts game. A dart in section A earns 10 points; a dart in section B earns 5 points; a dart in section C earns 2 points. Find the probability of earning each score. Round answers to the nearest hundredth.

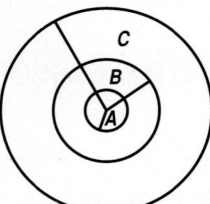

radius $\odot A = 2$ in.
radius $\odot B = 5$ in.
radius $\odot C = 10$ in.

10 points: 0.04; 5 points: 0.21; 2 points: 0.75

Teaching Tip   After Example 1, point out that the three probabilities have a sum of 1.

Chalkboard Example

For Example 2

Jorge is planning a circular flower garden with a radius of 2 meters. He plans to plant tulips in the sectors marked with a T and daffodils in the sectors marked with a D. How many square meters will he plant with tulips?

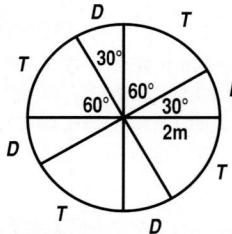

Area of one T sector: $\dfrac{60}{360}\,\pi 2^2$

$\dfrac{1}{6}\pi 4$

$\dfrac{2\pi}{3} \approx 2.1 \text{ m}^2$

Total area: 4(2.1) = 8.4 m²

Sometimes when you are finding a geometric probability, you will need to find the area of a **sector of a circle**. A sector of a circle is a region of a circle bounded by a central angle and its intercepted arc.

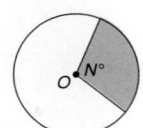

Area of a Sector of a Circle	If a sector of a circle has an area of A square units, a central angle measuring $N°$, and a radius of r units, then $A = \frac{N}{360} \pi r^2$.

Example 2

If Mitzi gets a 3 on her next spin, she will win the game. What is the probability that Mitzi will spin a 3?

Find the area of the sector of the circle and the area of the circle.

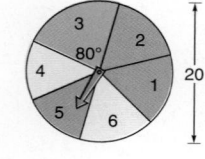

Area of sector

$$A = \frac{N}{360} \pi r^2$$
$$= \frac{80}{360} (\pi)(10)^2$$
$$= \frac{200}{9} \pi \text{ or } 22\frac{2}{9} \pi$$

Area of circle

$$A = \pi r^2$$
$$= \pi (10)^2$$
$$= 100\pi$$

Now find the geometric probability.

$$\text{probability} = \frac{\text{area of sector}}{\text{area of circle}}$$
$$= \frac{22\frac{2}{9}\pi}{100\pi}$$
$$= \frac{2}{9}$$

The probability Mitzi will spin a 3 is $\frac{2}{9}$.

CHECKING FOR UNDERSTANDING

Communicating Mathematics

1. probability = $\frac{\text{area of region } Y}{\text{area of region } X}$

Read and study the lesson to answer these questions.

1. A point is chosen at random from the interior of region X. Explain how to find the probability that the point is in region Y if region Y is in region X.

2. Suppose that the radius of the red circle of the target in Example 1 is increased to 14 inches and the widths of the blue and green rings remain the same. Find the probability of winning each prize. **squirtgun — about 0.19, yo-yo — about 0.37, candy bar — about 0.44**

3. Describe a situation where geometric probability may be used in everyday life. **Answers may vary. A sample answer is carnival games.**

RETEACHING THE LESSON

Find the probability that a point on $\overline{AE}$, chosen at random, will be on the segment.

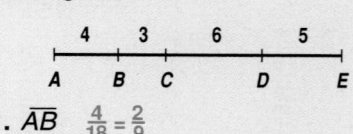

1. $\overline{AB}$ $\frac{4}{18} = \frac{2}{9}$
2. $\overline{BD}$ $\frac{1}{2}$
3. $\overline{DE}$ $\frac{5}{18}$
4. $\overline{AC}$ $\frac{7}{18}$

Find the probability that a point chosen at random in this circle will be in the section.

5. A $\frac{5}{36}$
6. B $\frac{1}{3}$
7. C $\frac{1}{6}$
8. D $\frac{1}{9}$
9. E $\frac{1}{4}$

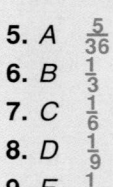

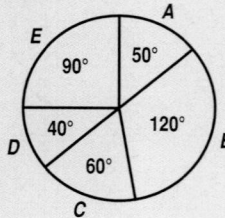

EVALUATING THE LESSON

Checking for Understanding

Exercises 1-12 are designed to help you assess students' understanding through reading, writing, speaking, and modeling. You should work through Exercises 1-3 with your students and then monitor their work on Exercises 4-12.

Closing the Lesson

Speaking Activity Have students describe a situation that can be solved by finding a geometric probability and explain how to find the probability in that case, without actually computing it.

Reteaching Masters Booklet, p. 63

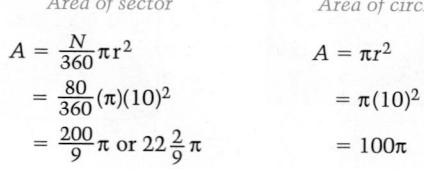

Guided Practice

Find the probability that a point chosen at random on $\overline{AG}$ is on each segment.

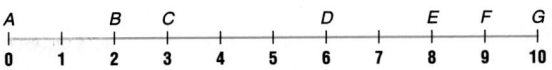

4. $\overline{AC}$ $\frac{3}{10}$

5. $\overline{AE}$ $\frac{8}{10} = \frac{4}{5}$

6. $\overline{CF}$ $\frac{3}{5}$

7. $\overline{DE}$ $\frac{2}{10} = \frac{1}{5}$

8. $\overline{AG}$ 1

9. $\overline{GC}$ $\frac{7}{10}$

Find the probability that a point chosen at random in each figure is in the shaded region. Assume polygons that appear to be regular are regular. Round your answer to the nearest hundredth.

10.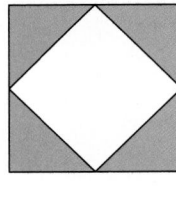

11.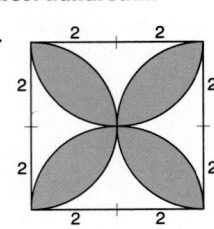

12.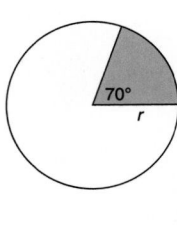

0.50

0.57

0.19

EXERCISES

Practice

13. A point is chosen at random on $\overline{XY}$. If Z is the midpoint of $\overline{XY}$, W is the midpoint of $\overline{XZ}$, and V is the midpoint of $\overline{WY}$, what is the probability that the point is on $\overline{XV}$? **0.625**

14. Points A, B, C, D, and E are collinear. $\overline{CA} \cong \overline{AE}$, $\overline{AD} \cong \overline{DE}$, and $\overline{CA} \cong \overline{EB}$.
    a. Draw a diagram of the figure.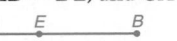
    b. If another point M is on the line above, what is the probability that M is between C and D? $\frac{1}{2}$
    c. If another point N is on the line above, what is the probability that N is between A and B? $\frac{2}{3}$

15. To win at a carnival game, you must throw a dart at a board that is 6 feet by 3 feet and hit one of the 25 playing cards on the board. The playing cards are each $2\frac{1}{2}$ by $3\frac{1}{2}$ inches.
    a. Draw a diagram of the dartboard. **See students' work.**
    b. What is the probability that a randomly thrown dart that hits the board hits a playing card? Round your answer to the nearest hundredth. **0.08**
    c. Does the arrangement of the cards on the board affect the probability? Explain. **No; as long as the dart is randomly thrown and the cards do not overlap, the area of the board and the cards is always the same.**

510   CHAPTER 10   POLYGONS AND AREA

 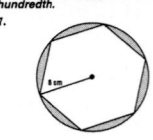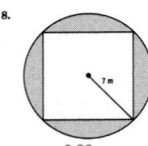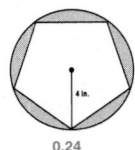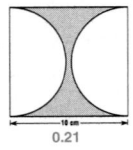

Portfolio

Select some of your work from this chapter that shows how you used a calculator or computer. Place it in your portfolio.

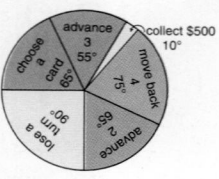

16. Find the probability for each outcome on the game spinner. Round your answers to the nearest hundredth.
 a. lose a turn **0.25**
 b. choose a card **0.18**
 c. advance 2 **0.18**
 d. collect $500 **0.03**

17. You tell a friend that you will arrive at the mall sometime between 12:00 and 12:30. Since she is not sure she will be able to come, your friend says not to wait for her for longer than 10 minutes. If your friend comes at 12:25, what is the probability that she missed you? $\frac{2}{3}$

C

18. The method of using probability to approximate the area of a region is called the *Monte Carlo method*. To use the Monte Carlo method, choose points randomly in a figure. The percentage of the points that fall in a region is the same as the percentage of the total area that is in the region. For example, suppose you throw 100 darts at a square with sides 1 foot long and 22 of those darts land in the red region. The area of the red region is approximately 22% of the total area or 0.22 square feet.

 a. Peg cut out a map of the 48 contiguous United States and placed it on a dartboard. She randomly threw 300 darts at the board and 252 of them landed on the map. Of the 252, 25 darts landed in Texas. If the area of the contiguous United States is approximately 2,962,000 square miles, what is the approximate area of Texas? **293,849 sq mi**

 b. Thirteen of the 252 darts landed in Montana. What is the approximate area of Montana? **152,802 sq mi**

 c. If Peg threw 100 more darts, do you think her approximations would get better? Explain. **Yes; more trials make the approximation more accurate.**

Critical Thinking

19. The bull's eye on Jim's dartboard has one-sixteenth of the area of the dartboard. If Jim hits the dartboard on two out of every three throws, what is the probability that Jim will hit the bull's eye in one throw? *Hint: probability of hitting bull's eye in one throw = $\dfrac{\text{probability of hitting bull's eye}}{\text{probability of hitting dartboard}}$* $\frac{3}{32}$

Applications

20. Gardening A sprinkler with a range of 5 meters waters a portion of the lawn. If the head of the sprinkler can rotate 150°, find the area of the lawn that is watered. Round to the nearest tenth of a square meter. **32.7 m²**

21. Entertainment You can win a large stuffed animal at a game on the State Fair Midway if you can toss a quarter onto a grid board so that it doesn't touch a line. If the sides of the squares of the grid are 32 millimeters long and the radius of a quarter is 12 millimeters, what is the probability that you will win? *Hint: Look at the area in which the center of the coin could land so that the edges will not touch a line.* **0.0625**

Mixed Review

22. Find the circumference and the area of a circle with a diameter of 1.6 in. Round your answers to the nearest tenth. **(Lesson 10-7) 5.0 in., 2.0 in²**

23. Find the geometric mean between 26 and 44. **(Lesson 8-1)** $\sqrt{1144} \approx 33.8$

Wrap-Up

24. Write an application problem that involves geometric probability. Be sure to give the answer to your problem. **See students' work.**

LESSON 10-8   GEOMETRIC PROBABILITY   511

EXTENDING THE LESSON

Math Power:
Critical Thinking

Tell whether the following statement is true or false. Give a reason for your answer. "To find the geometric probability a point chosen at random in a circle, is in a particular sector of the circle, it is not necessary to know the radius of the circle."

True. The probability will be the ratio of the central angle to 360° and is not affected by the radius.

Enrichment Masters Booklet, p. 63

10-8 Enrichment Worksheet

NAME_____ DATE_____

Polygon Probability

Each problem on this page involves one or more regular polygons. To find the probability of a point chosen at random being in the shaded region, you need to find the ratio of the shaded area to the total area. If you wish, you may substitute numbers for the variables.

Find the probability that a point chosen at random in each figure is in the shaded region. Assume polygons that appear to be regular are regular. Round your answer to the nearest hundredth.

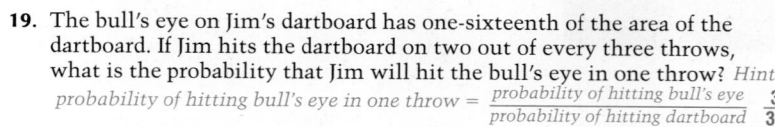

1. $\frac{1}{5}$ or 0.20

2. $\frac{1}{24} \approx 0.04$

3. $\frac{1}{2 + 2\sqrt{2}} \approx 0.21$

4. $\frac{\sqrt{3}}{16 + 4\sqrt{3}} \approx 0.08$

5. $\frac{\sqrt{3}}{2 + \sqrt{3}} \approx 0.46$

6. $\frac{\sqrt{3}}{\sqrt{3} + 1} \approx 0.63$

T63

Glencoe Division, Macmillan/McGraw-Hill

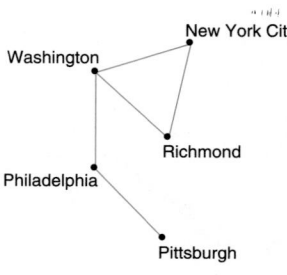

10-9 Polygons As Networks

Lesson Resources

- Reteaching Master 10-9
- Practice Master 10-9
- Enrichment Master 10-9
- Evaluation Master, p. 136
- Multicultural Master, p. 10

 Transparency 10-9 contains the 5-Minute Check and a teaching aid for this lesson.

INTRODUCING THE LESSON

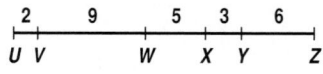 **5-Minute Check**

(over Lesson 10-8)

A point on $\overline{UZ}$ is chosen at random. What is the probability that the point will be on the segment?

$$\begin{array}{cccccc} 2 & 9 & 5 & 3 & 6 \\ \hline U\ V & & W & X\ Y & & Z \end{array}$$

1. $\overline{UV}$ $\frac{2}{25}$
2. $\overline{WX}$ $\frac{1}{5}$
3. $\overline{VW}$ $\frac{9}{25}$
4. $\overline{WZ}$ $\frac{14}{25}$

A point on a circle is chosen at random. What is the probability that it will be in the sector whose central angle is given?

5. $75°$ $\frac{5}{24}$
6. $100°$ $\frac{5}{18}$
7. $125°$ $\frac{25}{72}$
8. $10°$ $\frac{1}{36}$

Motivating the Lesson

Ask students to define *graph* in their own words. Tell them that their definition must be broad enough to include every kind of graph.

TEACHING THE LESSON

Teaching Tip To trace the figure at the bottom of the page, have students copy it on a sheet of paper and use a different color to trace it.

Objectives

10-9A
10-9B
10-9C

After studying this lesson, you should be able to:
- recognize nodes and edges as used in graph theory,
- determine if a network is traceable, and
- determine if a network is complete.

Application

Corporate Air provides daily air service between Richmond and Washington, D.C., Richmond and New York City, New York City and Washington, D.C., Washington, D.C. and Philadelphia, and Philadelphia and Pittsburgh. Their daily routes can be represented using a **network** like the one at the right. Such a diagram illustrates a branch of mathematics called **graph theory.** In a network, the points are called **nodes** and the paths connecting the nodes are called **edges.** Edges may be straight or curved.

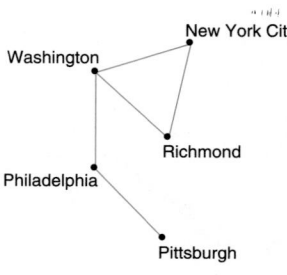

Straight edges can be used to form *open* or *closed* graphs. If an edge of a closed graph intersects exactly two other edges only at their endpoints, then the graph forms a polygon.

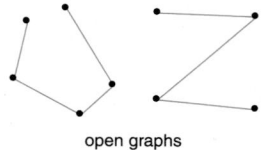 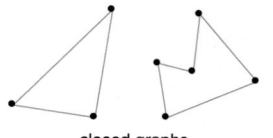

open graphs   closed graphs

The study of networks began with a famous problem about the bridges in the city of Königsberg, which is now Kaliningrad. The city had seven bridges connecting both sides of the Pregel River to two islands in the river. The problem was to find a path that would take you over all seven bridges without crossing the same bridge twice.

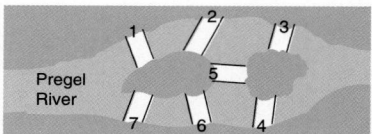

W and E represent the islands, N and S are the sides of the river.

The problem caught the attention of eighteenth century mathematician Leonhard Euler (pronounced OY-lur). He studied the problem by modeling it as a network. The edges of the network on the left represent the bridges and the nodes represent the sides of the river and the two islands. Can you trace this network with your finger without lifting your finger or retracing an edge? If you can, then the network is **traceable.**

512   CHAPTER 10   POLYGONS AND AREA

ALTERNATE TEACHING STRATEGIES

Using Cooperative Groups

Give each small group of students a map. Ask them to draw a network representing a messenger service route. The map should include five nodes, be traceable, and be complete.

Using Models

Have students work together to build a model of a traceable network from cardboard. Chalk can be used to prove its traceability.

The degree of a node is the number of edges that are connected to that node. The traceability of a network is related to the degrees of the nodes in the network.

Example 1

Find the degree of each node in the network of the Königsberg bridges.

Node	Edges at the node	Degree of node
N	B1, B2, B3	3
E	B3, B5, B4	3
S	B4, B6, B7	3
W	B1, B2, B5, B6, B7	5

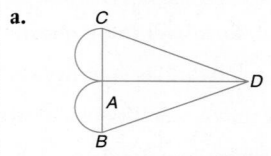

You probably concluded that the network that represents the Königsberg bridges is not traceable. Two tests for traceability are described below.

A network is traceable if and only if one of the following is true:
1. All of the nodes in the network have even degrees.
2. Exactly two nodes in the network have odd degrees.

Look back at Example 1. All of the nodes in the network for the bridge problem have an odd degree. Neither of the conditions for traceability is met. Therefore, there is no path that you could walk to travel over all seven bridges without recrossing at least one of the bridges.

Example 2

Determine if each network is traceable.

a.
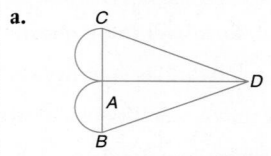

Node	Degree
A	5
B	3
C	3
D	3

No; all of the nodes have odd degrees.

b.

Node	Degree
A	2
B	3
C	2
D	3

Yes; exactly two nodes, *B* and *D*, have odd degrees.

Try to trace the network in Example 2b with your finger. Does it matter where you start to trace? If you start at node *A* it doesn't seem to work. Euler noticed that when a path goes through a node, it uses two edges. When a traceable network has an odd node, it must be a starting or finishing point of the traceability path.

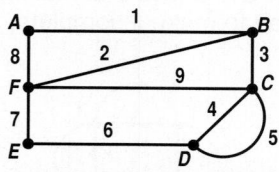
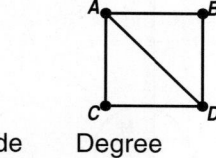
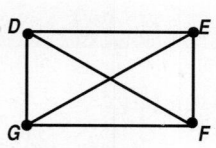

514   Chapter 10

Chalkboard Example

For Example 3
Determine if each network is complete. If it is not complete, name the edges that must be added to make it complete.

a.

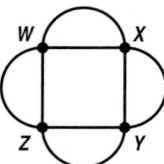

Incomplete. Edges must be drawn between W and Y, and X and Z.

b.

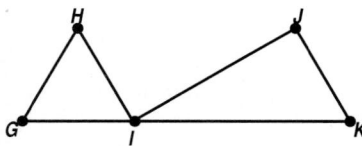

Incomplete. Edges must be drawn between G and J, H and J, and H and K.

c.

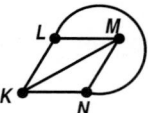

Complete. All the pairs of nodes are connected by an edge.

EVALUATING THE LESSON

Checking for Understanding

Exercises 1-13 are designed to help you assess students' understanding through reading, writing, speaking, and modeling. You should work through Exercises 1-4 with your students and then monitor their work on Exercises 5-13.

Not all the pairs of nodes are connected by an edge in some networks. A network like this is called **incomplete**. A **complete network** has at least one path between each pair of nodes.

Example 3   **Determine if each network is complete. If a network is not complete, name the edges that must be added to make the network complete.**

a.

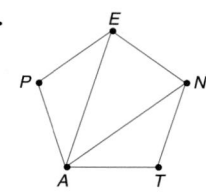

No; edges must be added between nodes *P* and *N*, *P* and *T*, and *E* and *T*.

b.

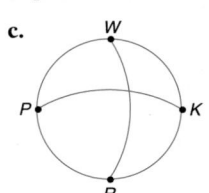

No; edges must be added between nodes *A* and *H* and nodes *M* and *T*.

c.

Yes; all the pairs of nodes are connected by an edge.

CHECKING FOR UNDERSTANDING

Communicating Mathematics

Read and study the lesson to answer these questions. See students' work.

1. Draw an example of a network. Is your network traceable? Is it complete?

2. List the two tests for the traceability of a network. See margin.

3. Is the network at the right complete? Explain. No; nodes *L* and *O* are not connected by an edge.

4. Mark and Judy are discussing where they should start to trace the network at the right. Mark says node *M* and Judy says node *L*. Who is right and why? Judy; node *L* has odd degree and *M* has even degree.

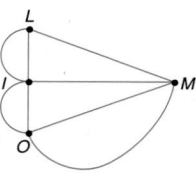

Guided Practice

Find the degree of each node in each network. See margin.

5.

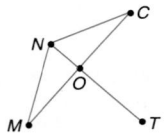

6.

7.

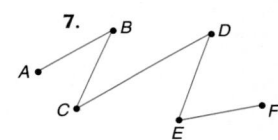

Additional Answers

2. All of the nodes in the network have even degrees, or exactly two nodes in the network have odd degrees.
5. A, 1; M, 1; C, 0
6. N, 3; C, 2; O, 4; M, 2; T, 1
7. A, 1; B, 2; C, 2; D, 2; E, 2; F, 1

Determine if each network is traceable.

8.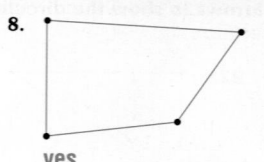

yes

9.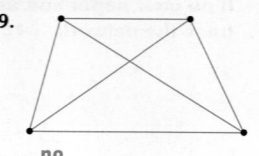

no

10.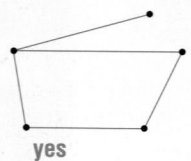

yes

Determine if each network is complete. If a network is not complete, name the edges that must be added to make the network complete.

11.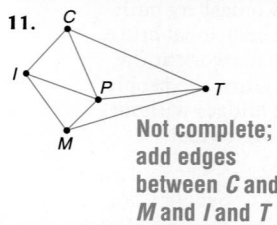

Not complete; add edges between C and M and I and T

12.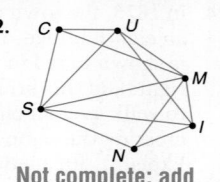

Not complete; add edges between C and I, C and N, and U and N.

13.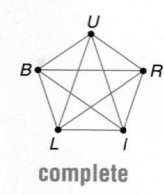

complete

EXERCISES

Practice **Find the degree of each node in the network.** See margin.

14.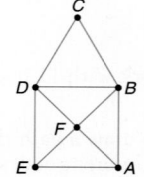

15.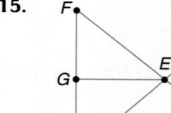

16.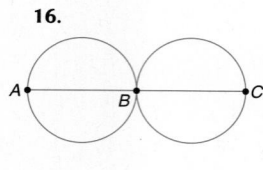

Name the additional edges that must be drawn for each network to be complete. See margin.

17.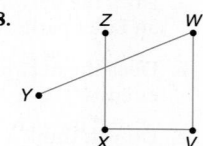

18.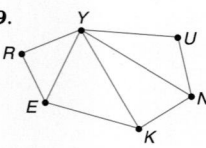

19.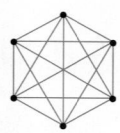

 20. Each of the networks below are complete.

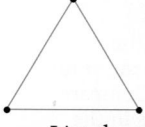 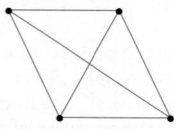 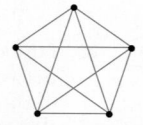

a. List the number of nodes and edges in each network. See margin.
b. Do you notice a pattern in the number of edges in the complete networks? Describe the pattern. add 3, add 4, add 5, ...
c. How many edges would a complete network with 10 nodes have? 45

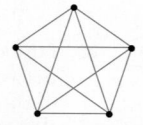

LESSON 10-9 POLYGONS AS NETWORKS 515

Closing the Lesson
Writing Activity Have students write a brief paragraph explaining networks, nodes, and traceability.

APPLYING THE LESSON

Homework Exercises

Assignment Guide
Basic: 14-23, 28-36
Average: 17-26, 28-36
Enriched: 18-36

Additional Answers

14. *A*, 3; *B*, 4; *C*, 2; *D*, 4; *E*, 3; *F*, 4
15. *A*, 3; *B*, 2; *C*, 3; *D*, 2; *E*, 5; *F*, 2; *G*, 3
16. *A*, 3; *B*, 6; *C*, 3
17. edges between *P* and *E*, *E* and *N*, *P* and *N*
18. edges between *Y* and *Z*, *Y* and *V*, *Y* and *X*, *Z* and *V*, *Z* and *W*, *X* and *W*
19. edges between *R* and *U*, *R* and *N*, *R* and *K*, *E* and *U*, *E* and *N*, *K* and *U*
20a. 3 and 3; 4 and 6; 5 and 10; 6 and 15

Reteaching Masters Booklet, p. 64

RETEACHING THE LESSON

Have each student draw a picture of a network. Some might choose to produce traceable networks, some complete networks, and some incomplete networks. Have each student in turn present his or her network to the class. Help the class decide which of the networks are traceable, which are complete, and why.

NAME _____ DATE _____

10-9 **Reteaching Worksheet**

Polygons As Networks

A network is a set of points called **nodes** that are connected by paths called **edges**. Often the nodes represent locations on a map and the edges represent connecting routes. The edges can be straight or curved. A network is **traceable** if you can trace it with your finger without lifting your finger or retracing an edge. A **complete** network is one with at least one edge between each pair of nodes.

The **degree** of a node is the number of edges connected to it. A network is traceable only if one of the following is true:

1. All of the nodes in the network have even degrees.
2. Exactly two nodes in the network have odd degrees.

Example: Determine if the network at the right is traceable.

Node	Degree
A	3
B	4
C	3

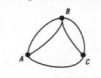

The network is traceable.

Find the degree of each node in the network.

1. 2. 3.

A-3, *B*-3, *C*-2   *D*-3, *E*-1, *F*-2   *R*-2, *S*-3, *V*-2, *T*

Determine if each network is complete. If a network is not complete, name the edges that must be added to make the network complete.

4. 5. 6.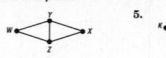

not complete; edge *WX*   complete   not complete; edge *LM*, *MN*, *NP*, *PQ*, *Q*

Determine whether each network is traceable.

7. 8. 9.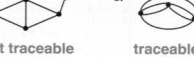

not traceable   traceable   traceable

T64
Glencoe Division, Macmillan/McGraw-Hill

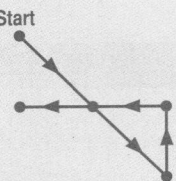
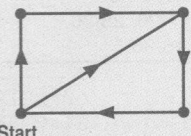
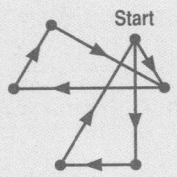
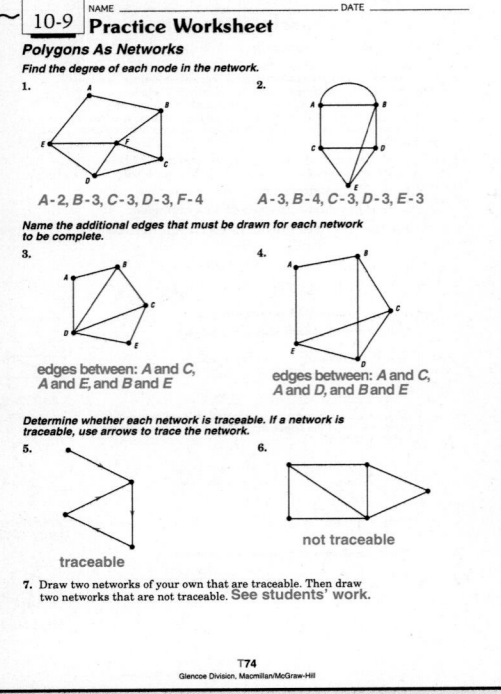
Determine whether each network is traceable. If a network is traceable, copy it on your paper and use arrows to show the direction of the paths taken to trace the network. **See margin.**

21.   22.   23.

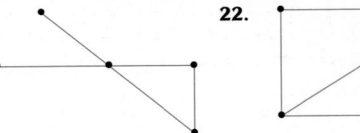

24. In 1875, the town of Königsberg built an eighth bridge. The additional bridge is shown in red in the network at the right. Did this bridge allow the people to walk over all eight bridges without crossing the same bridge twice? Explain. **See margin.**

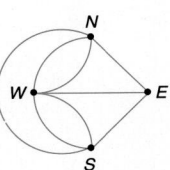

 25. Add one or more edges to the network at the right to make the network traceable. **See margin.**

26. Construct a traceable network with 11 nodes and 18 edges. **See margin.**

27. If you can use your pencil to draw a path through a network so that the path starts and ends at two different nodes and no edge is passed more than once, the path is called an *Euler path*. If the path can be drawn so that the path starts and ends at the same node and no edge is passed more than once, the path is called an *Euler circuit.*

  a. Does the network at the right have an Euler path? **yes**

  b. Does the network contain an Euler circuit? **no**

  c. Do you think a network could contain both an Euler path and an Euler circuit? Explain. **No; if a network has an Euler circuit, each node has an even degree, so any path will return to its starting node.**

Critical Thinking

28. Find the degree of each node in the network at the right. Then find the sum of the degrees of all the nodes. Compare this sum to the number of edges in the network. Is there a relationship between the number of edges and the sum of the degrees of the nodes? Draw several networks to verify your answer. **The sum of the degrees of the nodes is twice the number of edges.**

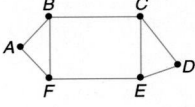

Additional Answers

24. Yes. The network is traceable since exactly two nodes have odd degrees.

25. Sample answer:

26. Sample answer:

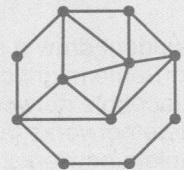

Applications

29. Travel The Budgetminded Bus Company offers service between Chicago and Bloomington, Chicago and Springfield, Springfield and Fort Wayne, Columbus and Fort Wayne, and Columbus and Chicago.
  a. Draw a network to represent the bus routes. **See margin.**
  b. Could you take a bus from Columbus to Springfield by passing through one other city? **yes; through Chicago or Fort Wayne**

30. Business The network to the right represents streets on Tom's newspaper route. To maximize efficiency, he would like to ride his bike down each street exactly once. Is this possible? Why or why not? **no; not traceable**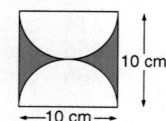

31. Construction The new campus for the Rosepoint Medical Center will have seven buildings built around the edge of a circular courtyard. There will be a sidewalk between each pair of buildings.
  a. What type of network does this represent? **complete**
  b. How many sidewalks will there be? **21**

Mixed Review

32. Find the probability that a randomly thrown dart that lands on the board will land in the red region. Round your answer to the nearest hundredth. **(Lesson 10-8) 0.21**

33. Write the given statement and draw the figure for a proof of the statement *If two lines intersect, then at least one plane contains both lines.* Then write the assumption you would make to write an indirect proof. **(Lesson 5-4) See margin.**

34. What property justifies the statement $m\angle K = m\angle K$? **(Lesson 2-4) reflexive**

35. Draw and label a figure showing planes *M*, *N*, and *L* that do not intersect. **(Lesson 1-2) See margin.**

Wrap-Up

36. Journal Entry Write a sentence or two in your journal to describe what you have learned about networks. **See students' work.**

DEVELOPING REASONING SKILLS

The game of Sprouts begins with any number of dots or nodes. Each player takes a turn by connecting one of the nodes with another node or with itself and then placing another node on the edge connecting the nodes. No edge can intersect itself or another edge, and a maximum of three edges can meet at any node. The last person to be able to move wins.
A three-dot game of Sprouts is shown below.

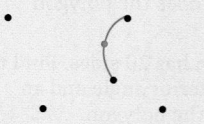   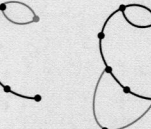   

| Begin | First Move | Second Move | Third Move | Fourth Move | Fifth Move | Sixth Move | Last Move |

EXTENDING THE LESSON

Math Power: Reasoning

If all the possible diagonals of an octagon are drawn, will the figure be a traceable network? Explain your answer. **No. From each node there will be seven edges.**

Developing Reasoning Skills

Sprouts is a good strategy game. Have students work in pairs to play games beginning with three dots. Have them take turns going first. Then have them play the game beginning with four dots. After students have played awhile, discuss strategies as a class.

Additional Answers

29a.

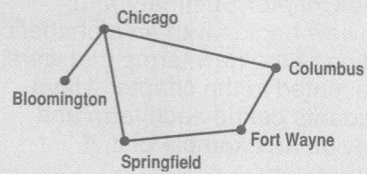

33. Given: Lines *l* and *m* intersect at *P*.
Prove: Plane *R* contains both *l* and *m*.

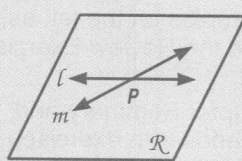

Assumption: Plane *R* does not contain both *l* and *m*.

35.

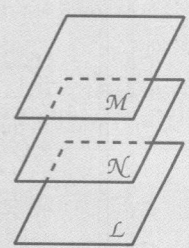

Enrichment Masters Booklet, p. 64

10-9 Enrichment Worksheet
NAME _____ DATE _____

Defining Networks

A network may be defined by a table of its edges and nodes. Each edge connects one or two nodes. If an edge connects only one node, the edge is a **loop**. Study the network and its corresponding table.

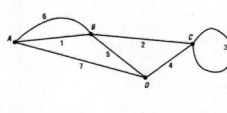

Edge	Nodes
1	{A, B}
2	{B, C}
3	{C}
4	{C, D}
5	{B, D}
6	{A, B}
7	{A, D}

Notice that the network has a loop at node *C*. Also, notice that two edges, 1 and 6, connect *A* and *B*.

Complete the table of edges and nodes for each network.

1.

Edge	Nodes
1	{F, G}
2	{G, H}
3	{H, K}
4	{G, K}
5	{F, J}
6	{F, H}
7	{H, J}
8	{J, K}

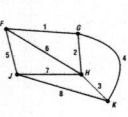

2.

Edge	Nodes
1	{W}
2	{W, X}
3	{X}
4	{X, Z}
5	{X, Y}
6	{W, Y}

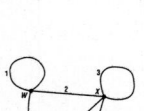

3. Draw a network with five nodes. Make a table of edges and nodes. **See students' work.**

T64
Glencoe Division, Macmillan/McGraw-Hill

VOCABULARY

Upon completing this chapter, you should be familiar with the following terms:

484	altitude	513	degree of a node	512	nodes
495	apothem	468	edge	466	polygon
483	area	468	face	468	polyhedron
484	base	507	geometric probability	467	regular
497	central angle	484	height	509	sector of a circle
502	circumference	514	incomplete network	501	spreadsheet
514	complete network	512	network	512	traceable
466	concave	467	n-gon	468	vertex
466	convex				

SKILLS AND CONCEPTS

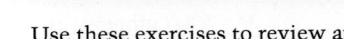

OBJECTIVES AND EXAMPLES	REVIEW EXERCISES

Upon completing this chapter, you should be able to:

Use these exercises to review and prepare for the chapter test.

■ classify and identify parts of polygons and polyhedrons **(Lesson 10-1)**

The vertices of the polygon are A, B, C, D, and E. The edges are $\overline{AB}$, $\overline{BC}$, $\overline{CD}$, $\overline{DE}$, and $\overline{AE}$. It is convex and is not regular.

Refer to the polyhedron at the right. See margin.

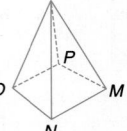

1. Name the vertices and edges.
2. Name the faces.
3. Is the polyhedron regular? Explain.

■ find measure of angles in polygons. **(Lesson 10-2)**

Interior Angle Sum Theorem (Theorem 10-1) If a convex polygon has n sides and S is the sum of the measures of its interior angles, then $S = 180(n - 2)$.

Exterior Angle Sum Theorem (Theorem 10-2) If a polygon is convex, then the sum of the measures of the exterior angles, one at each vertex, is 360.

4. Find the measure of an interior angle of a regular decagon. **144**
5. The sum of the measures of the interior angles of a convex polygon is 1980. How many sides does the polygon have? **13**
6. A regular polygon has 20 sides. Find the measure of an interior angle and an exterior angle of the polygon. **162; 18**

■ find areas of parallelograms. **(Lesson 10-4)**

Find the area of the parallelogram.

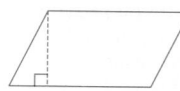

$A = bh$ *Formula for area of a parallelogram*
$A = (65)(36)$ $b = 65, h = 36.$
$A = 2340$ square centimeters

Find the missing measure of each quadrilateral.

7. A rectangle has a base of 7 feet and an altitude of 2.9 feet. Find the area. **20.3 ft²**

8. The area of parallelogram $ABCD$ is 134.19 in². If the base is 18.9 inches long, find the height. **7.1 in.**

9. If the length of each side of a square is tripled, the area of the resulting square is increased by 648 m². Find the length of the original square. **9 m**

■ find areas of triangles, rhombi, and trapezoids. **(Lesson 10-5)**

Area Formulas	
Triangle	$A = \frac{1}{2}bh$
Trapezoid	$A = \frac{1}{2}h(b_1 + b_2)$
Rhombus	$A = \frac{1}{2}d_1d_2$

Find each missing measure.

10. The area of a triangle is 48 mm². If the height is 6 mm, find the length of the base. **16 mm**

11. A rhombus has diagonals 8.6 cm and 6.3 cm long. What is its area? **27.09 cm²**

12. The area of an isosceles trapezoid is 7.2 ft². The perimeter is 6.8 ft. If a leg is 1.9 ft long, find the height. **4.8 ft**

■ find areas of regular polygons. **(Lesson 10-6)**

Find the area of a regular hexagon with an apothem 12 cm long.

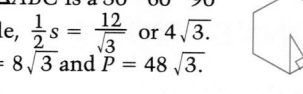

Since $\triangle ABC$ is a 30°-60°-90° triangle, $\frac{1}{2}s = \frac{12}{\sqrt{3}}$ or $4\sqrt{3}$. So, $s = 8\sqrt{3}$ and $P = 48\sqrt{3}$.

$A = \frac{1}{2}Pa$
$A = \frac{1}{2}(48\sqrt{3})(12)$
$A = 288\sqrt{3}$ or about 498.8 cm²

Find the area of each regular polygon. Round your answers to the nearest tenth.

13. an equilateral triangle with an apothem 8.9 inches long **411.6 in²**

14. a pentagon with an apothem 0.4 feet long **0.6 ft²**

15. a hexagon with sides 64 millimeters long **10,641.7 mm²**

16. a square with an apothem n centimeters long **$4n^2$ cm²**

■ find the circumference and area of a circle. **(Lesson 10-7)**

If a circle has a radius of r units,

$$\text{Area} = \pi r^2$$
$$\text{Circumference} = 2\pi r$$

Find the circumference and area of a circle with a radius of the given length. Round your answers to the nearest tenth.

17. 7 mm **44.0 mm; 153.9 mm²**

18. 19 in. **119.4 in.; 1134.1 in²**

19. 0.9 ft **5.7 ft; 2.5 ft²**

Alternate Review Strategy

To provide a brief in-class review, you may wish to read the following questions to the class and have them answer verbally.

1. What is the measure of an interior angle of a regular nonagon?   **140**

2. Find the area of a parallelogram if the length of a base is 24 centimeters and its height is 10 centimeters.   **240 cm²**

3. The area of a triangle is 345 square inches. If its altitude measures 23 inches, what is the length of its base?   **30 in.**

4. Find the area of a regular hexagon with sides that measure 10 meters. Round your answer to the nearest tenth. **259.8 m²**

5. Find the circumference of a circle with a radius of 5 centimeters. Round your answer to the nearest tenth.   **31.4 cm**

6. Find the area of a circle with a radius of 8 inches. Round your answer to the nearest tenth. **201.1 in.²**

7. A radio station gives a 10-minute local news report once every hour. If you turn on the radio at any random time, what is the probability that you will hear some local news?   **$\frac{1}{6}$**

A two-page Cumulative Review from the *Evaluation Masters* is shown below. It can be used to review skills and concepts presented thus far in the text. Standardized Test Practice Questions are also provided in the *Evaluation Masters*.

Evaluation Masters, pp. 137-138

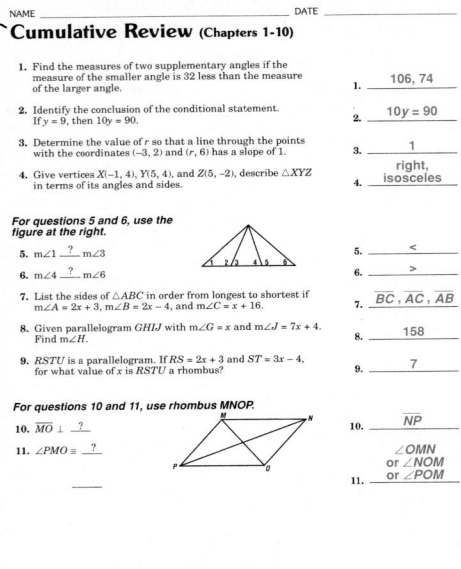

OBJECTIVES AND EXAMPLES

- find geometric probabilities. **(Lesson 10-8)**

Length Probability Postulate (Postulate 10-3)
If a point on $\overline{AB}$ is chosen at random and C is between A and B, then the probability that the point is on $\overline{AC}$ is $\dfrac{\text{length of } \overline{AC}}{\text{length of } \overline{AB}}$.

Area Probability Postulate (Postulate 10-4)
If a point in region A is chosen at random, then the probability that the point is in region B, which is in region A, is
$\dfrac{\text{area of region } B}{\text{area of region } A}$.

- determine if a network is traceable or complete. **(Lesson 10-9)**

The network at the right is traceable, since exactly two nodes have odd degrees. However, it is not complete since there is no edge between M and A.

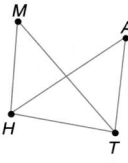

REVIEW EXERCISES

20. During the morning rush hour, a bus arrives at the bus stop at Indianola and Morse Roads every seven minutes. A bus will wait for thirty seconds before departing. If you arrive at a random time, what is the probability that there will be a bus waiting? $\dfrac{1}{14}$

Use the network at the right to answer each question. See margin.

21. Name the nodes and edges in the network.

22. Is the network traceable?

23. Is the network complete? If not, what edges need to be added for the network to be complete?

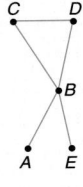

APPLICATIONS AND CONNECTIONS

24. **Number Theory** Using the digits 1, 2, 3, 4, 5, and 6 only once, find two whole numbers whose product is as great as possible. **(Lesson 10-3)** 631 and 542

25. **Interior Design** John and Cynthia are buying paint for the walls of their kitchen. Three of the walls are 8 feet long and one is ten feet long. The ceiling is 8 feet high. If a gallon of paint covers 400 square feet, will one gallon be enough to paint the kitchen? **(Lesson 10-4)** yes; the total area is 272 ft²

26. **Manufacturing** A wooden planter has a square base and sides that are shaped like trapezoids. An edge of the base is 8 inches long and the top edge of each side is 10 inches long. If the height of a side is 12 inches, how much wood does it take to make a planter? **(Lesson 10-5)** 496 in²

Additional Answers

21. A, B, C, D, E; $\overline{AB}, \overline{BC}, \overline{BE}, \overline{CD}, \overline{BD}$

22. yes

23. No: Edges need to be drawn between A and C, A and D, A and E, C and E, and D and E.

Use the polygon at the right for 1-7.

1. Name the vertices of the polygon. **Q, R, S, T, U**
2. Name the sides of the polygon. **$\overline{QR}, \overline{RS}, \overline{ST}, \overline{TU}, \overline{UQ}$**
3. Classify the polygon by the number of sides. **pentagon**
4. Classify the polygon as convex or concave. **convex**
5. Classify the polygon as regular or not regular. Explain. **regular; all sides congruent and convex**
6. Find the sum of the measures of the interior angles of the polygon. **540**
7. Find the measure of one exterior angle of the polygon. **72**

8. Use the strategy of guess and check to find the least prime number greater than 720. **727**
9. Find the area of a parallelogram with a base of 4.95 feet and a height of 0.51 feet. **2.5245 ft²**
10. A square has a perimeter of 258 inches. Find the length of one side and the area of the square. **64.5 in.; 4160.25 in²**
11. A triangle has a base of 16 feet and a height of 30.6 feet. Find its area. **244.8 ft²**
12. The area of triangle ABC is $3x^2 + 6x$. If the height is $3x + 6$ units, find the measure of the base. **2x**
13. The median of a trapezoid is 13 feet 6 inches long. If the height is 10 feet, what is the area of the trapezoid? **135 ft²**
14. A regular hexagon has sides 10 centimeters long. What is the area? **259.8 cm²**

Circle O has a diameter of 4 inches. Find the missing measures. Round your answers to the nearest tenth.

15. What is the area of circle O? **12.6 in²**
16. What is the circumference of circle O? **12.6 in.**
17. A sector of circle O has a central angle measuring 30°. Find the area of the sector. **1.0 in²**

A circular dartboard has a diameter of 18 inches. The bull's eye has a diameter of 3 inches and the blue ring around the bull's eye is 4 inches wide.

18. What is the probability that a randomly thrown dart that hits the dartboard will land in the bull's eye? **0.028**
19. What is the probability that a randomly thrown dart that hits the dartboard will land in the blue ring? **0.346**

20. Draw a complete network with 6 nodes. How many edges does it have? **15**

Bonus Ed dropped 100 ball bearings from a ladder and 92 of them landed on the figure shown at the right. How many of the ball bearings do you think fell in the green region? **10**

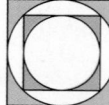

Using the Chapter Test

This page may be used as a test or as a review. In addition, two multiple-choice tests (Forms 1A and 1B) and two free-response tests (Forms 2A and 2B) are provided in the *Evaluation Masters*. Chapter 10 Test, Form 1A is shown below.

Evaluation Masters, pp. 127-128

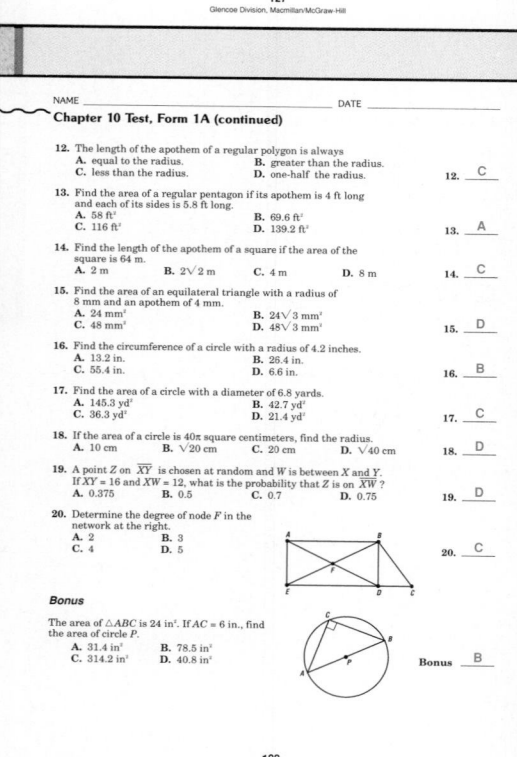

NAME _____ DATE _____
Chapter 10 Test, Form 1A

Write the letter for the correct answer in the blank at the right of each problem.

1. Classify the figure at the right.
   A. regular concave decagon
   B. regular convex decagon
   C. concave decagon
   D. convex decagon   1. **C**

2. Name a polygon with 7 sides.
   A. heptagon   B. hexagon
   C. octagon   D. decagon   2. **A**

3. Find the sum of the measures of the interior angles of a convex 16-gon.
   A. 2880   B. 2520   C. 2700   D. 3240   3. **B**

4. How many sides does a regular polygon have if the measure of one interior angle is 144?
   A. 8   B. 9   C. 10   D. 12   4. **C**

5. What is the sum of the measures of the exterior angles of a convex 11-gon?
   A. 360   B. 540   C. 1620   D. 180   5. **A**

6. Use the strategy guess and check to find two consecutive prime numbers with a sum of 30.
   A. 15 and 15   B. 11 and 19
   C. 7 and 23   D. 13 and 17   6. **D**

7. Find the area of a rectangle that is 9 cm long and 4 cm wide.
   A. 36 cm²   B. 72 cm²   C. 18 cm²   D. 26 cm²   7. **A**

8. A parallelogram has a height that is 2 inches less than the length of the base. The area of the parallelogram is 168 in². Find the height.
   A. 14 in.   B. 10 in.   C. 12 in.   D. 16 in.   8. **C**

9. Find the area of a triangle with a base of 14 m and an altitude of 9 m.
   A. 126 m²   B. 63 m²
   C. 31.5 m²   D. 252 m²   9. **B**

10. If the diagonals of a rhombus are 10 cm and 24 cm long, find the area of the rhombus.
    A. 60 cm²   B. 240 cm²
    C. 120 cm²   D. 480 cm²   10. **C**

11. A trapezoid with a height of 6 ft has bases of 12 ft and 10 ft. Find the area of the trapezoid.
    A. 132 ft²   B. 720 ft²
    C. 33 ft²   D. 66 ft²   11. **D**

127
Glencoe Division, Macmillan/McGraw-Hill

NAME _____ DATE _____
Chapter 10 Test, Form 1A (continued)

12. The length of the apothem of a regular polygon is always
    A. equal to the radius.   B. greater than the radius.
    C. less than the radius.   D. one-half the radius.   12. **C**

13. Find the area of a regular pentagon if its apothem is 4 ft long and each of its sides is 5.8 ft long.
    A. 58 ft²   B. 69.6 ft²
    C. 116 ft²   D. 139.2 ft²   13. **A**

14. Find the length of the apothem of a square if the area of the square is 64 m.
    A. 2 m   B. $2\sqrt{2}$ m   C. 4 m   D. 8 m   14. **C**

15. Find the area of an equilateral triangle with a radius of 8 mm and an apothem of 4 mm.
    A. 24 mm²   B. $24\sqrt{3}$ mm²
    C. 48 mm²   D. $48\sqrt{3}$ mm²   15. **D**

16. Find the circumference of a circle with a radius of 4.2 inches.
    A. 13.2 in.   B. 26.4 in.
    C. 55.4 in.   D. 6.6 in.   16. **B**

17. Find the area of a circle with a diameter of 6.8 yards.
    A. 145.3 yd²   B. 42.7 yd²
    C. 36.3 yd²   D. 21.4 yd²   17. **C**

18. If the area of a circle is 40π square centimeters, find the radius.
    A. 10 cm   B. $\sqrt{20}$ cm   C. 20 cm   D. $\sqrt{40}$ cm   18. **D**

19. A point Z on $\overline{XY}$ is chosen at random and W is between X and Y. If $XY = 16$ and $XW = 12$, what is the probability that Z is on $\overline{XW}$?
    A. 0.375   B. 0.5   C. 0.7   D. 0.75   19. **D**

20. Determine the degree of node F in the network at the right.
    A. 2   B. 3
    C. 4   D. 5   20. **C**

Bonus
The area of $\triangle ABC$ is 24 in². If $AC = 6$ in., find the area of circle P.
A. 31.4 in²   B. 78.5 in²
C. 314.2 in²   D. 40.8 in²   Bonus **B**

128
Glencoe Division, Macmillan/McGraw-Hill

Test and Review Generator
software is provided in Apple, IBM, and Macintosh versions. You may use this software to create your own tests or worksheets, based on the needs of your students.

The Performance Assessment Booklet
provides an alternate assessment for evaluating student progress. An assessment for this chapter can be found on pages 19-20.

College Entrance Exam Preview

The questions on these pages involve comparing two quantities, one in Column A and one in Column B. In certain questions, information related to one or both quantities is centered above them.

Directions:
Write A if the quantity in Column A is greater. Write B if the quantity in Column B is greater. Write C if the quantities are equal. Write D if there is not enough information to determine the relationship.

	Column A	Column B
1. C	$x = 4$	
	$x^2 + 3$	$5x - 1$
2. D	$x > y$	
	x^2	y^2
3. B	$A \# B = 5A - 2B$	
	$\left(\frac{3}{4}\right) \# 6$	$5 \# \left(\frac{3}{4}\right)$
4. D	a given chord in a given circle	the radius of the same circle
5. A	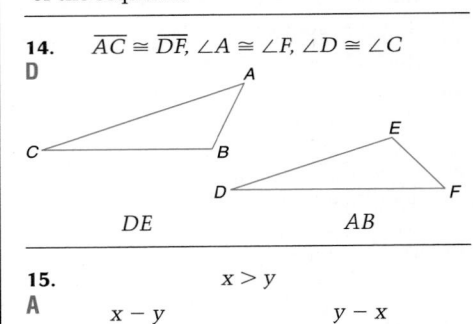 4 cm / 4 cm	
	the area of the shaded region	the area of the unshaded region
6. D	$|-a|$	a
7. C	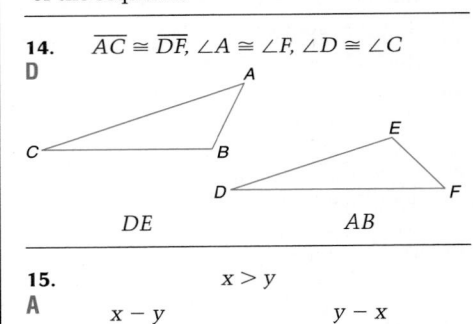 $XY = XZ$	
	$m\angle 1$	$m\angle 2$

	Column A	Column B
8. C	circumference of circle with radius $2x$	perimeter of square with side πx
9. B	$s > 0, t < 0$	
	st	$-\frac{s}{t}$
10. A	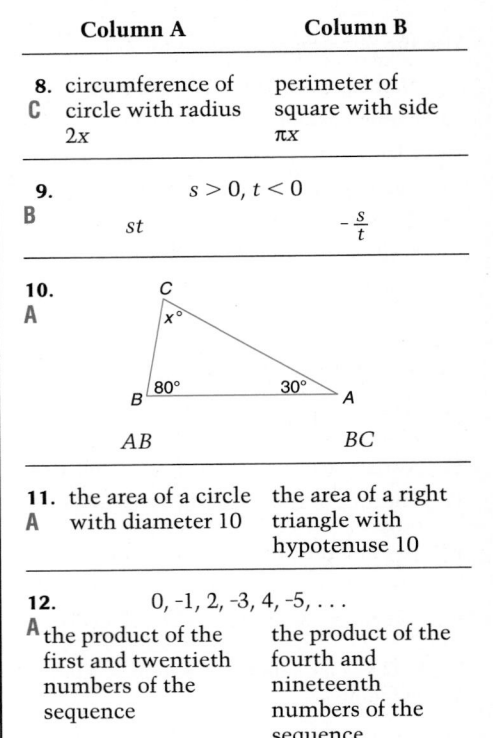	
	AB	BC
11. A	the area of a circle with diameter 10	the area of a right triangle with hypotenuse 10
12. A	$0, -1, 2, -3, 4, -5, \ldots$	
	the product of the first and twentieth numbers of the sequence	the product of the fourth and nineteenth numbers of the sequence
13. B	$0, -1, 2, -3, 4, -5, \ldots$	
	the sum of the first twenty numbers of the sequence	0
14. D	$\overline{AC} \cong \overline{DF}, \angle A \cong \angle F, \angle D \cong \angle C$	
	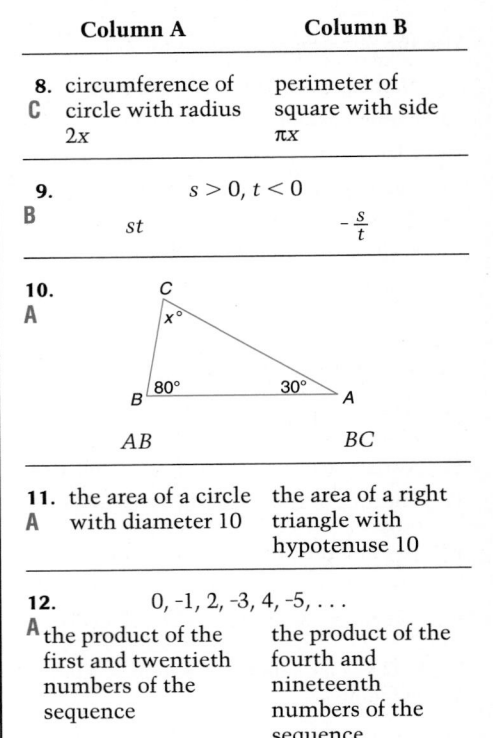	
	DE	AB
15. A	$x > y$	
	$x - y$	$y - x$

Solve. You may use a calculator.

16. The figure below is formed from a semicircle and a rectangle. The diameter of the semicircle is the length of the rectangle. Write a formula for the area of the figure if the length of the rectangle is $3x$ and the width is x.

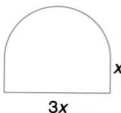

$\frac{9\pi x^2}{8} + 3x^2$

17. An airplane can travel 1716 feet in 3 seconds. Find the speed of the plane in miles per hour.

390 mph

18. In the figure below, P and Q lie on circle O. $\overline{OP}$ is 8 units long, and $\angle POQ$ measures 80°. Find the length of minor arc PQ.

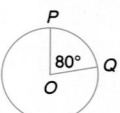

$\frac{32\pi}{9}$ or about **11.2 units**

19. Find the solution set for $\frac{7}{x-3} - \frac{1}{2} > \frac{3}{x-4}$.

$\{x \mid 3 < x < 4 \ \text{or} \ 5 < x < 10\}$

20. A survey of 100 adults showed that 65% of the women were registered to vote and 55% of the men were registered to vote. If 40 men were surveyed, how many people surveyed were not registered to vote?
39 people

TEST-TAKING TIP

Quantitative Comparisons

Substitute values for variables to make a quantitative comparison. Remember that a variable may represent a positive number greater than 1, a negative number less than -1, a number between 0 and 1, or a number between -1 and 0. Numbers from these different groups often behave differently, so it is important to examine a comparison for each case.

Example

Column A	Column B
$x^2 - 1$	$x^3 + 1$

Try the values 2, -2, $\frac{1}{2}$, and $-\frac{1}{2}$.

$(2)^2 - 1 = 3$	$(2)^3 + 1 = 9$

Column B is greater.

$(-2)^2 - 1 = 3$	$(-2)^3 + 1 = -7$

Column A is greater.

$\left(\frac{1}{2}\right)^2 - 1 = -\frac{3}{4}$	$\left(\frac{1}{2}\right)^3 + 1 = 1\frac{1}{8}$

Column B is greater.

$\left(-\frac{1}{2}\right)^2 - 1 = -\frac{3}{4}$	$\left(-\frac{1}{2}\right)^3 + 1 = \frac{7}{8}$

Column B is greater.

Since we don't know which type of number x is, there is not enough information to determine the relationship between the quantities.

11

Surface Area and Volume

PREVIEWING THE CHAPTER

This chapter explores the concepts of surface area and volume as they relate to prisms, cylinders, cones, pyramids, and spheres. Initially, the chapter explores the meaning of surface area and uses dot paper to help students visualize three-dimensional objects on a two-dimensional plane. Students then develop formulas for finding the lateral area of the four non-spherical solids as well as the surface area of right prisms, right cylinders, and right circular cones. Next, students study the concept of volume beginning with looking at the same four non-spherical solids. The chapter concludes by using some of the ideas developed in Chapter 9 to examine the surface area and volume of a sphere.

Problem-Solving Strategy Students learn that they can use the strategy of making a model to simulate a situation to make a problem easier to solve.

Lesson Objective Chart

Lesson (Pages)	Lesson Objectives	State/Local Objectives
11-1 (526-528)	**11-1**: Solve problems by making a model.	
11-2 (529-534)	**11-2A**: Create, draw, and fold three-dimensional figures.	
	11-2B: Make two-dimensional nets for three-dimensional solids.	
11-3 (536-541)	**11-3A**: Identify the parts of prisms and cylinders.	
	11-3B: Find the lateral areas and surface areas of right prisms and right cylinders.	
11-4 (542-547)	**11-4A**: Find the lateral area of a regular pyramid.	
	11-4B: Find the lateral area and surface area of a right circular cone.	
11-5 (548-553)	**11-5**: Find the volume of a right prism and a right cylinder.	
11-6 (554-559)	**11-6**: Find the volume of a pyramid and a circular cone.	
11-7 (560-565)	**11-7A**: Recognize and define basic properties of spheres.	
	11-7B: Find the surface area of a sphere.	
	11-7C: Find the volume of a sphere.	

ORGANIZING THE CHAPTER

You may want to refer to the **Course Planning Calendar** on page T28.

Lesson Planning Guide

Blackline Masters Booklets

Lesson (Pages)	Course I	Course II	Course III	Reteaching	Practice	Enrichment	Evaluation	Technology	Lab Manual	Mixed Problem Solving	Applications	Cooperative Learning Activity	Multicultural	Transparencies
11-1 (526-528)	1	1	1		p. 75									11-1
11-2 (529-534)	1.5	1.5	1.5	p. 65	p. 76	p. 65	Quiz A, p.149	p. 11						11-2
11-3 (536-541)	1.5	1.5	1.5	p. 66	p. 77	p. 66		p. 47						11-3
11-4 (542-547)	2	1.5	1.5	p. 67	p. 78	p. 67	Quiz B, p.149 Mid-Chapter Test, p. 153		pp.78-81			p. 39		11-4
11-5 (548-553)	2	1.5	1.5	p. 68	p. 79	p. 68							p. 11	11-5
11-6 (554-559)	2	2	1.5	p. 69	p. 80	p. 69	Quiz C, p.150				p. 25			11-6
11-7 (560-565)	2	2	1.5	p. 70	p. 81	p. 70	Quiz D, p.150		pp.82-85	p. 11				11-7
Review (566-568)	1	1	1	Multiple Choice Tests, Forms 1A and 1B, pp. 141-144										
Test (569)	1	1	1	Free Response Tests, Forms 2A and 2B, pp. 145-148 Cumulative Review. pp. 151-152 Standardized Tests Practice Questions, p. 154										

Course I: Chapters 1-11; Course II: Chapters 1-12; Course III: Chapters 1-13

Other Chapter Resources

Student Edition

Chapter Opener, pp. 524-525
Cooperative Learning Project, p. 528
Journal Entry, pp. 534, 553
Technology, p. 535
Mid-Chapter Review, p. 547
Portfolio, p. 559
History Connection, p. 565
Algebra Review, pp. 570-571
More Investigations in Geometry, p. A13
Extended Project 4, pp. B14-B16

Teacher's Classroom Resources

Transparency 11-0
Real World Applications Transparencies, 22, 23
Performance Assessment Booklet, pp. 21-22
Problem-of-the-Week Activity Cards, 30, 31, 32
Tech Prep Applications Booklet, pp. 21-22
LOGO Instruction Materials, Technology Masters pp. 19-36

Other Supplements

Algebra and Geometry Overhead Manipulative Resources
Glencoe Mathematics Professional Series

Software

Test and Review Generator (Apple, IBM, and Macintosh)
Teacher's Guide for Software Resources

ENHANCING THE CHAPTER

Cooperative Learning

Establishing Individual Accountability

It is important for the success of a cooperative-learning session that students recognize their individual responsibility to the whole group. Not only is it unfair when only a few members of the group do all the work, it is also contrary to the purpose of a cooperative-learning group; that is, to enhance the learning of each and every member. One way to encourage every-member participation is to make positive and rewarding comments about the members' contributions to the group. Another way is to evaluate the performance of each member of the group. Some tactics that can be used are to ask a reluctant participant to paraphrase what another member has just said, to ask a member if they agree with a statement just made by another member, and to say at the outset that you will randomly select a member from the group to explain the group's answers. Since the members of a group quickly observe who is a participant and who is not, another successful tactic is to assign the role of *encourager* to one of the members of the group. This student's main responsibility is to encourage each and every member of the group to participate.

Technology

The Technology Feature following Lesson 11-2 uses LOGO commands to draw three-dimensional figures. Parallel lines, special pairs of angles, and students' knowledge of supplementary angles are used in the commands given to draw a rectangular solid. Students are asked to experiment with the LOGO commands to draw different parallelograms and to devise a plan for drawing a solid that has parallelograms for its bases. A similar exercise using triangles is also included. As an extension of this feature, you may wish to have students continue experimenting with different polygons, and then use their polygons as bases for solid figures.

Critical Thinking

Frequent use of the term "higher" to describe the levels of analysis, synthesis, and evaluation in Bloom's taxonomy can lead one to make the false assumption that students must master content at the levels of knowledge, comprehension, and application before they can move on to these higher levels. Students who may have difficulty memorizing certain facts often exhibit, in a proper environment, the creative ability to analyze and identify patterns in these facts or find parallel models and new applications. The higher levels of Bloom's taxonomy should provide guideposts for planning interesting and challenging activities in mathematics that engage in the intellect of all students, not just those with special talents.

Cooperative Learning, p. 39

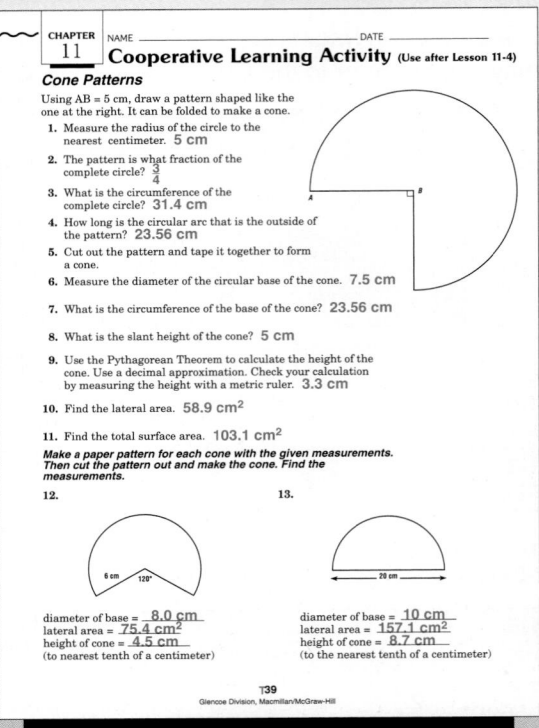

Technology, p. 47

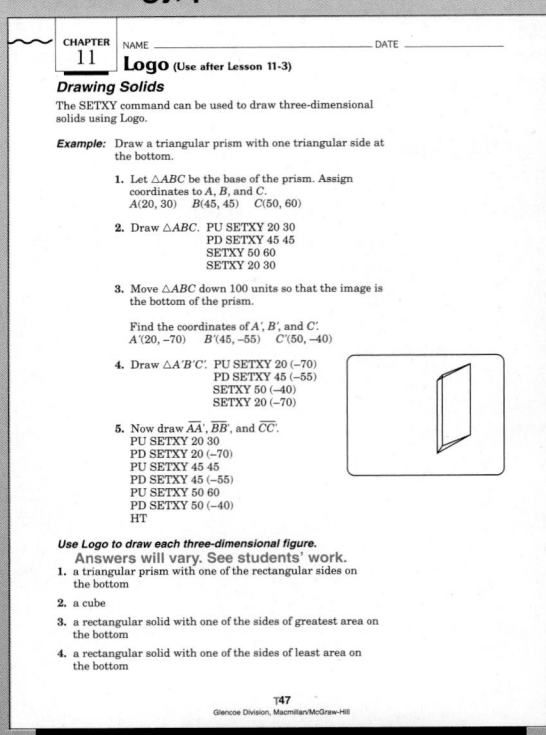

Problem of the Week Activity

The card shown below is one of three available for this chapter. It can be used as a class or small group activity.

Activity Card

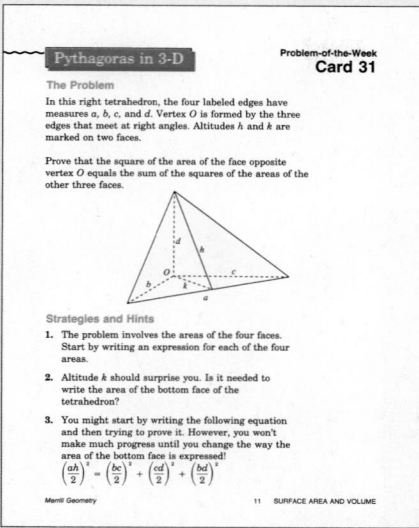

Pythagoras in 3-D

Problem-of-the-Week
Card 31

The Problem

In this right tetrahedron, the four labeled edges have measures a, b, c, and d. Vertex O is formed by the three edges that meet at right angles. Altitudes h and k are marked on two faces.

Prove that the square of the area of the face opposite vertex O equals the sum of the squares of the areas of the other three faces.

Strategies and Hints

1. The problem involves the areas of the four faces. Start by writing an expression for each of the four areas.

2. Altitude k should surprise you. Is it needed to write the area of the bottom face of the tetrahedron?

3. You might start by writing the following equation and then trying to prove it. However, you won't make much progress until you change the way the area of the bottom face is expressed!

$$\left(\frac{ah}{2}\right)^2 = \left(\frac{bc}{2}\right)^2 + \left(\frac{cd}{2}\right)^2 + \left(\frac{bd}{2}\right)^2$$

Merrill Geometry   11   SURFACE AREA AND VOLUME

Manipulatives and Models

The following materials may be used as models or manipulatives in Chapter 11.

- rectangular solid (Lesson 11-2)
- dot paper (Lesson 11-2)
- right cylinder (Lesson 11-3)
- cone-shaped drinking cup (Lesson 11-4)
- cylindrical measuring glass (Lesson 11-6)

Outside Resources

Books/Periodicals

Gray, Jeremy. *Ideas of Space*. Clarendon Press.

Hogben, L. *The Wonderful World of Mathematics*. Garden City Books.

McGervey, John D. *Probabilities in Everyday Life*. Nelson-Hall.

Films/Videotapes/Videodiscs

Cylinders, Prisms, Pyramids, Coronet Instructional Films, 108 Wilmot Dr., Deerfield, IL 60015

Software

Logo, The Logo Foundation, 250 West 57th Street, Suite 2603, New York, NY 10107

3D Images, William K. Bradford Publishing Company, 310 School Street, Acton, MA 01720

Multicultural

Multicultural Activity, p. 11

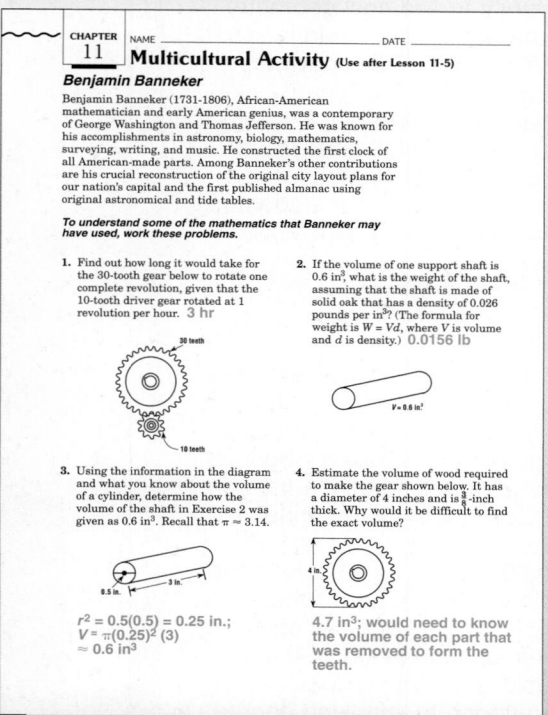

CHAPTER 11   NAME _____ DATE _____

Multicultural Activity (Use after Lesson 11-5)

Benjamin Banneker

Benjamin Banneker (1731-1806), African-American mathematician and early American genius, was a contemporary of George Washington and Thomas Jefferson. He was known for his accomplishments in astronomy, biology, mathematics, surveying, writing, and music. He constructed the first clock of all American-made parts. Among Banneker's other contributions are his crucial reconstruction of the original city layout plans for our nation's capital and the first published almanac using original astronomical and tide tables.

To understand some of the mathematics that Banneker may have used, work these problems.

1. Find out how long it would take for the 30-tooth gear below to rotate one complete revolution, given that the 10-tooth driver gear rotated at 1 revolution per hour. **3 hr**

2. If the volume of one support shaft is 0.6 in³, what is the weight of the shaft, assuming that the shaft is made of solid oak that has a density of 0.026 pounds per in³? (The formula for weight is $W = Vd$, where V is volume and d is density.) **0.0156 lb**

3. Using the information in the diagram and what you know about the volume of a cylinder, determine how the volume of the shaft in Exercise 2 was given 0.6 in³. Recall that $\pi \approx 3.14$.

$r^2 = 0.5(0.5) = 0.25$ in.;
$V = \pi(0.25)^2 (3)$
≈ 0.6 in³

4. Estimate the volume of wood required to make the gear shown below. It has a diameter of 4 inches and is $\frac{3}{8}$-inch thick. Why would it be difficult to find the exact volume?

4.7 in³; would need to know the volume of each part that was removed to form the teeth.

Lab Manual

Lab Activity, pp. 78-81

Name _____   Activity 16 Worksheet
Page 1

Surface Area of Cylinders and Cones

1. Find the lateral area (L) and total surface area (T) of each right cylinder.

   a. L = _____   b. L = _____
   T = _____   T = _____

2. List the formulas for each of the following:

   a. area of a circle _____   b. area of a sector _____

   c. circumference of a circle _____

3. Measure the radius of the sectors on the next page.

   #1 _____   #2 _____   #3 _____   #4 _____

4. Find the area of each sector from question 3. (Use the formula: Area = $\frac{n}{360} \pi r^2$, where n = measure of central angle.)

   #1 _____   #2 _____   #3 _____   #4 _____

5. How do the areas compare for cones 1 and 2? _____

   Cones 3 and 4? _____

Construct four cones from the patterns and instructions on the next page.

6. Measure and record the following:

	Cone 1	Cone 2	Cone 3	Cone 4
slant height (l)				
height (h)				
radius of the base (r)				

7. Check the accuracy of your measurements using the Pythagorean Theorem.

   Example $3^2 + 4^2 = 5^2$

   #1 _____   #2 _____

   #3 _____   #4 _____

79
Glencoe Division, Macmillan/McGraw-Hill

Using the Chapter Opener

This two-page introduction to the chapter provides students with an opportunity to see how geometry is used throughout the world in various cultures. **Transparency 11-0**, available in the *Merrill Geometry Transparency Package*, provides another full-color visual and motivational activity that you can use to engage your students in the mathematical content of the chapter.

Multicultural Notes

Iraq Throughout the ancient cities of Ur, Uruk, and Babylon in the country known today as Iraq, are stepped pyramids called *ziggurats*. Each ziggurat has outside tiers or staircases leading to a shrine at the top. Some ziggurats are as high as 300 feet. As a scale model of earth's northern hemisphere, each Babylonian ziggurat consists of seven continous steps, the dimensions of which are believed to correspond to shrinking degrees of latitude between earth's equator and the north pole. Thus, the ziggurat's wide base represents the equator, while the structure's narrow vertex represents the north pole.

Mexico The ancient Aztec city of Teotihuacan in Mexico includes three stepped pyramids: Quetzalcoatl Pyramid, Sun Pyramid, and Moon Pyramid. As with Babylonian ziggurats, the Pyramids of Teotihuacan each has seven encompassing outside steps that are thought to correspond to earth's degrees of latitude.

Chapter Project

Materials ruler, protractor, compass, posterboard, graph paper, pencil

Procedure Organize students into cooperative groups. Have each group select one of the following pyramid design projects:

- Design an Egyptian pyramid in which the perimeter of the base divided by twice the height equals π.
- Design an Egyptian pyramid in which the area of each lateral face equals the square of its height.
- Design an Egyptian pyramid in which the slant height of each lateral face divided by one-half its base length equals ϕ.
- Design an Egyptian pyramid as a scale model of earth's northern hemishpere.

CHECKING FOR UNDERSTANDING

Communicating Mathematics

Read and study the lesson to answer these questions. See margin.

1. In the example, Selvi only used whole numbers for the measures of the sides. Do you think Selvi could get a larger area if she used fractional measurements? Why or why not?

2. Ron has 16 square tiles. Each side of each tile is 1 inch long. Ron wants to arrange the tiles so that the perimeter is 22 inches. Describe a way to solve this problem using models.

3. An interior decorator is planning a furniture arrangement for a living room. He makes a model for possible arrangements by drawing a scale drawing of the room and cutting out pieces of paper to represent the furniture using the same scale.
   a. What are the advantages of using such a model?
   b. What are the disadvantages of using models to plan furniture arrangements?

Guided Practice

Make a model to solve each problem.

4. A circular fountain has a diameter of 9 feet. A 3-foot wide flower garden surrounds the fountain. A sidewalk circles the garden. If the sidewalk is 2 feet wide, find the total area of the fountain, garden, and sidewalk. **90.25π or about 284 ft²**

5. There are 32 volleyball teams playing in a single-elimination tournament. In other words, any team that loses a game is out of the tournament. How many games will be played in the tournament? **31 games**

6. A train is 1 mile long. It travels through a tunnel 1 mile long at the speed of 60 miles per hour. How much time elapses from the time the engine enters the tunnel until the entire train is out of the tunnel? **2 min**

EXERCISES

Practice

Strategies

Look for a pattern.
Solve a simpler problem.
Act it out.
Guess and check.
Draw a diagram.
Make a chart.
Work backward.

Solve. Use any strategy.

7. Insert two addition signs and two subtraction signs on the left side of the equals sign to make the statement true.
$$1\ 2\ 3\ 4\ 5\ 6\ 7\ 8\ 9 = 116$$
$$12 - 34 + 56 - 7 + 89 = 116$$

8. The escalator between the first and second floors of Cole's Department Store travels at a rate of x steps per second. Kelly walked up the escalator at a rate of one step per second and reached the top in 10 seconds. Dominic walked up the escalator at a rate of three steps per second and reached the top in 6 seconds. If the escalator is turned off, how many steps would you have to climb to reach the second floor? **30 steps**

LESSON 11-1   PROBLEM-SOLVING STRATEGY: MAKE A MODEL   527

TEACHING THE LESSON

Chalkboard Example

For the Example
Julio wants to build a fort that has an area of 24 square feet. The fence materials can be bought in 1-foot pieces. How much fence should Julio buy if he wants to spend the least amount of money? **20 feet**

EVALUATING THE LESSON

Checking for Understanding

Exercises 1-6 are designed to help you assess students' understanding through reading, writing, speaking, and modeling. You should work through Exercises 1-3 with your students and then monitor their work on Exercises 4-6.

Closing the Lesson

Modeling Activity Have each student bring in or make a model and explain what it models and how it is used.

APPLYING THE LESSON

Homework Exercises

Assignment Guide

Basic: 7-13
Average: 8-14
Enriched: 9-15

RETEACHING THE LESSON

Give students the measurements of the classroom and have each of them make a scale model of it. They can do this individually or in groups. In their models, students should include all of the desks and tables in the room in their model, as well as any other objects that take up space. Discuss how you can do this when arranging furniture for a room.

Additional Answers

1. Sample answer: no, because the area seems to get bigger as the figure becomes "closer" to a square.

2. Sample answer: Use 16 small squares made out of paper or other material. Move these squares around until you find a rectangle with a perimeter of 22 units.

3a. Sample answer: Moving paper is easier than moving furniture. If you find out that something is too big or too little for the space, you will know not to buy it.

3b. Sample answer: It is hard to visualize 3-dimensional objects on a 2-dimensional drawing. Colors and designs are not shown on the drawing, so it is hard to tell how everything will look.

For exercise 10, use the strategy of solving a simpler problem.

For Exercises 11 and 12, have students try solving a puzzle with one marker of each color and three spaces, and for two markers of each color and five spaces. Then have them look for a pattern.

For Exercise 15, make a chart or list the possibilities of three coins.

Additional Answers

13.

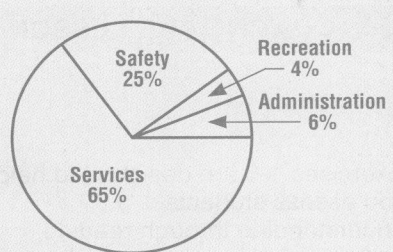

Recreation 4%
Administration 6%
Safety 25%
Services 65%

11-1 **Practice Worksheet**

NAME _____ DATE _____

Problem-Solving Strategy: Make a Model

Solve. Use any strategy.

1. Insert one addition, one subtraction, one multiplication, and one division sign on the left side of the equals sign to make the statement true.
   1 2 3 4 5 6 7 8 9 = 158
   $12 \div 3 \times 45 + 67 - 89 = 158$

2. A certain bacteria doubles its population every 6 hours. At the end of the second full day, there were 800,000 bacteria. How many bacteria were there at the beginning of the first day?
   3125

3. Consider the perfect squares between 5000 and 10,001. What percent of these numbers are even numbers?
   50%

4. Two pennies, two nickels, three dimes, and a quarter are in a change purse. Three coins are removed at random. What are the possible values of the coins?
   7¢, 11¢, 12¢ (2 pennies, 1 dime), 16¢, 20¢, 21¢, 25¢, 27¢, 30¢, 31¢, 35¢, 36¢, 40¢, 45¢

5. Suppose you draw five straight lines across a rectangle and cut along each line. What is the greatest number of sides possible for the polygonal pieces you obtain? What is maximum possible number of such pieces?
   9; 1

T75
Glencoe Division, Macmillan/McGraw-Hill

---

9. Lisa is studying a certain type of bacteria in the laboratory. She knows this bacteria doubles its population every 8 hours. At the end of the second full day, there are 1600 bacteria. How many bacteria did Lisa have at the beginning of the first day? **25 bacteria**

10. Consider the perfect squares between 0 and 5000. What percent of these numbers are odd numbers? **50%**

11. Consider the following game. The red markers must always move to the right. The blue markers must always move to the left. A marker can move into an empty space next to it or jump one marker of the other color if it lands on an empty space. How many moves will it take to switch the positions of the red and blue markers? **15**

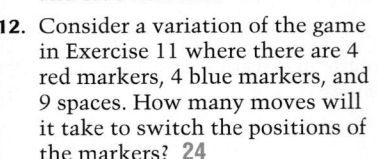

12. Consider a variation of the game in Exercise 11 where there are 4 red markers, 4 blue markers, and 9 spaces. How many moves will it take to switch the positions of the markers? **24**

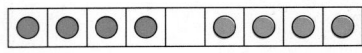

13. During a certain year, the community of Oxford spent 65% of its income on services, 25% on public safety, 4% on recreation, and 6% on administration. Construct a circle graph to show how Oxford spent its income. **See margin.**

14. There are four children in the Monroe family: Andy, Sally, Lisa, and John. Andy is a middle child. Lisa is one of the two older children. John is the "baby" of the family. Sally always looks up to her older sister and her older brother. List the siblings from the youngest to the oldest. **14. John, Sally, Andy, Lisa**

15. Two pennies, a nickel, a dime, and a quarter are in a change purse. Three coins are removed at random. What are the possible values of the coins?
7¢, 12¢, 16¢, 27¢, 31¢, 36¢, 40¢

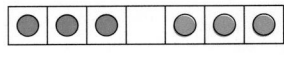

COOPERATIVE LEARNING PROJECT

Work in groups. Each person in the group must understand the solution and be able to explain it to any person in class.

The diagram at the right shows how a 9 × 4 rectangle can be cut into two pieces that can be arranged to form a 6 × 6 square. Draw a 16 × 9 rectangle and a 25 × 16 rectangle and cut each into two pieces to form a 12 × 12 square and a 20 × 20 square respectively. **See Solutions Manual.**

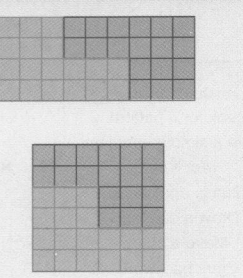

EXTENDING THE LESSON

Math Power: Problem Solving

Would Snickers have more room in a circular pen with a circumference of 24 feet or a square pen with a perimeter of 24 feet?
Circular pen: A ≈ 45.84 ft²
Square pen: A = 36 ft²
Snickers would have more room in a circular pen.

Cooperative Learning Project

This activity provides students an opportunity to *learn* things together, not just do things together. You may wish to refer to pages T6-T7 and page 524c for the various elements of cooperative groups and specific goals and strategies for using them.

Exploring Surface Area

Objectives
11-2A
11-2B

After studying this lesson, you should be able to:
- create, draw, and fold three-dimensional figures, and
- make two-dimensional nets for three-dimensional solids.

Application

FYI...

The average duck weighs 2.5 pounds and has a wing-loading factor of $3.12 \frac{lb}{ft^2}$. The average finch weighs 0.06 pounds and has a wing-loading factor of $0.64 \frac{lb}{ft^2}$.

Aircraft manufacturers take surface area very seriously. The **surface area** of a three-dimensional object or **solid** is the sum of the areas of its faces. It is used to determine the amount of material it takes to cover the outer surface of an airplane and to determine the design of the aircraft.

The surface area of the wing on an aircraft is used to determine a design factor known as wing-loading. Wing-loading is the total weight of the aircraft and its load on take-off divided by the total surface area of its wings. If the wing-loading factor is exceeded, the pilot must either reduce the fuel load or remove passengers or cargo.

Surface area is important in other areas of everyday life. For example, we need to consider it when we resurface a highway, wallpaper a room, wrap a birthday gift, fertilize a field, or paint a house.

In this lesson, we will consider surface areas that are related to geometric solids with flat surfaces or faces. Solids with flat surfaces are called **polyhedrons** or **polyhedra.** The faces or flat surfaces are polygons, and the lines where the faces intersect are called edges.

The polyhedron at the right is called a **pyramid.** Its faces are $\triangle ABC$, $\triangle BCD$, $\triangle ACD$, and $\triangle ABD$. Points A, B, C, and D are vertices of the polyhedron. Its edges are $\overline{AB}$, $\overline{BD}$, $\overline{DA}$, $\overline{CA}$, $\overline{CB}$, and $\overline{CD}$.

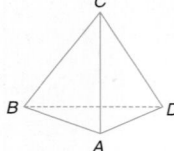

Some other polyhedrons are shown below.

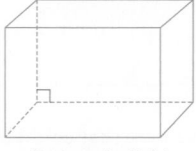
Rectangular Solid

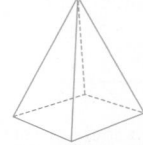
Square Pyramid

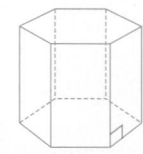
Hexagonal Solid

LESSON 11-2   EXPLORING SURFACE AREA   529

Lesson Resources

- Reteaching Master 11-2
- Practice Master 11-2
- Enrichment Master 11-2
- Evaluation Master, p. 149
- Technology Master, p. 11

 Transparency 11-2 contains the 5-Minute Check and a teaching aid for this lesson.

INTRODUCING THE LESSON

5-Minute Check
(over Lesson 11-1)

1. Name three types of models.
   Sample answer: sketch, drawing, three-dimensional object

Make a model to solve each problem.

2. Joe is making a sandbox in his backyard. The sandbox is 4 feet by 6 feet. It will have a bench that is 2 feet wide all the way around it and a 1-foot wide gravel path around the bench. Find the perimeter of the outer edge of the gravel path and the area of the sandbox, the bench, and the path together.   44 ft; 120 ft²

3. Sixteen teams are playing in a double-elimination softball tournament. In other words, a team must lose two games to be out of the tournament. How many games will be played in the tournament if the winner has not lost a game?   30

ALTERNATE TEACHING STRATEGIES

Using Construction
Have students use stiff paper or cardboard to create a polyhedron such as a cube or pyramid.

Explain that the sum of the areas of each piece is the surface area of the polyhedron.

Using Manipulatives
Have students each bring an empty cardboard box to class. Have them cut open the box along the edges until it lies flat in a single layer. Explain that this is a net of the box. If two students have the same box, have them compare nets. They may not be the same.

Motivating the Lesson
Ask students what they think of when they hear the term *3-D.* Explain that something that is 3-D adds a third dimension of depth.

Chalkboard Example

For the Example
Use rectangular dot paper to draw a net for a rectangular solid 5 units high, 6 units long, and 3 units wide.

Teaching Tip In step 2 of the investigation, point out that the use of broken lines is for perspective.

Teaching Tip When drawing the net in Example 1, emphasize that other nets can be drawn for the same figure and draw an alternative.

A sketch of a rectangular solid is more complex than a sketch of a plane figure because it is three-dimensional. The use of isometric dot paper makes it easier to draw some three-dimensional figures.

INVESTIGATION

Using isometric dot paper, sketch a rectangular solid 4 units high, 6 units long, and 2 units wide.

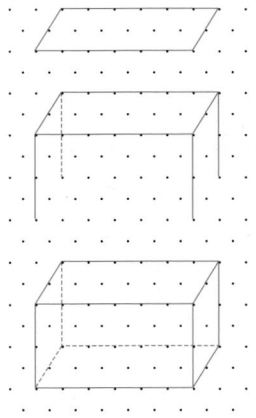

Step 1:
Draw the top of the solid 6 × 2 units.

Step 2:
Draw a segment 4 units down from each vertex. Hidden edges are shown by dashed lines.

Step 3:
Connect the corresponding vertices.

When a polyhedron such as the one at the right is unfolded, the result is a two-dimensional figure known as a **net**. Nets are very useful in helping us see the polygonal shapes whose areas must be computed in finding the total surface area of the polyhedron.

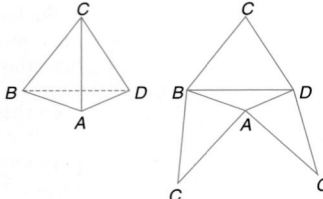

Example 1

Use rectangular dot paper to draw a net for the rectangular solid in the Investigation.

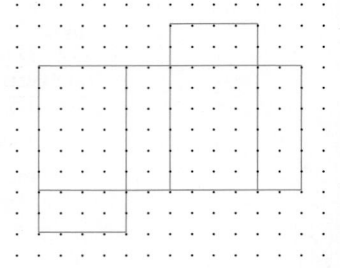

Often there are several different nets that could be used to produce the same solid. Could you design a different one for Example 1?

530 CHAPTER 11 SURFACE AREA AND VOLUME

CHECKING FOR UNDERSTANDING

Communicating Mathematics

Read and study the lesson to answer these questions. See margin.

1. What is the difference between isometric and rectangular dot paper? Why is each type of paper important?

2. Describe a net and explain why nets are important.

3. How is wing-loading in the aircraft industry related to the geometric concept of surface area?

4. Why won't the figure at the right produce a cube when folded?

Guided Practice

Use isometric dot paper to draw each polyhedron. See margin.

5. a rectangular solid 3 units high, 6 units long, and 4 units wide

6. a cube 5 units on each edge

Given each polyhedron, copy its net and label the remaining vertices.

7.
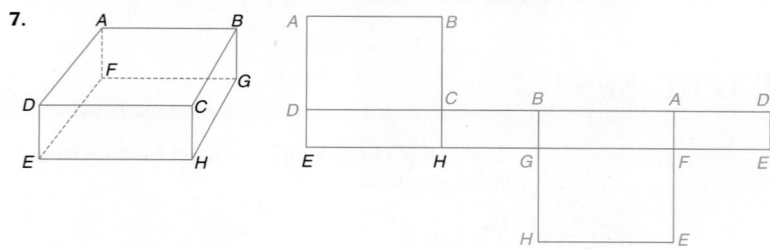

8.
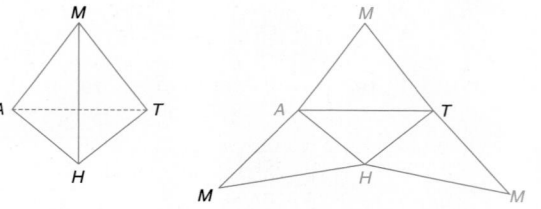

Identify the number and type of polygons that are faces in each polyhedron.

9.
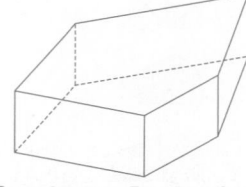

2 pentagons, 5 rectangles

10.
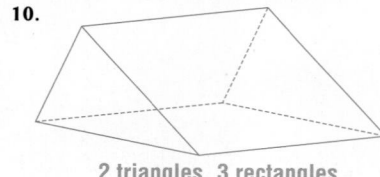

2 triangles, 3 rectangles

LESSON 11-2   EXPLORING SURFACE AREA   531

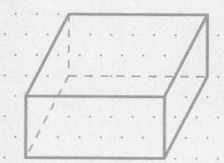
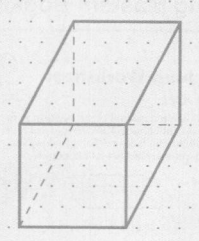
Additional Answers

1. On isometric dot paper, the dots are arranged in triangles, which aid in drawing three-dimensional objects. On rectangular dot paper, the dots are arranged in squares, which aid in drawing two-dimensional objects such as nets.

2. A net is the unfolded two-dimensional pattern of a three-dimensional object. The sum of the areas of the polygonal shapes in the net is the surface area of the polyhedron.

3. Wing-loading is the total weight of the aircraft on take-off divided by the total surface of its wings.

4. The net won't fold into a cube because two of the squares will overlap instead of folding to become the top and bottom.

Match each net to one of the solids at its right.

11. 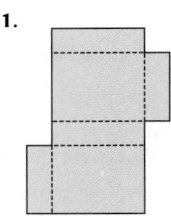   **a.** 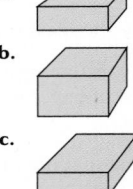   **12.** 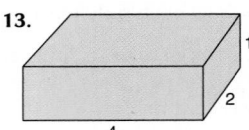   **a.**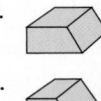

b. 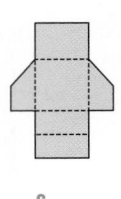   **b.**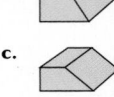

c. 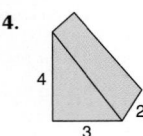   **c.**

c   c

Use rectangular dot paper to draw a net for each solid.   See margin.

13. 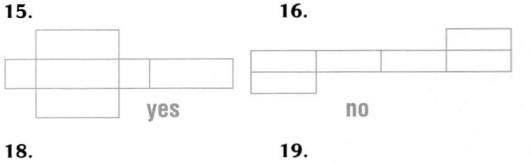 1
2
4

14.
4
3   2

EXERCISES

Practice

A

Determine whether figure is a net for a rectangular solid. Write *yes* or *no*.

15.   **16.**   **17.**

yes   no   no

18. 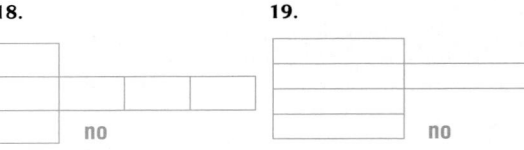   **19.** 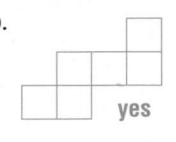   **20.**

no   no   yes

B

Match each net to one of the solids at its right.

21. 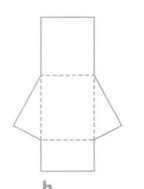   **a.**   **22.** 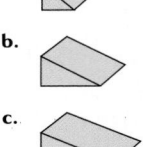   **a.**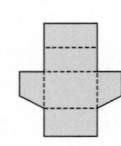

b.   **b.**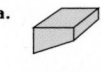

c.   **c.**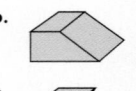

b   c

Closing the Lesson

Modeling Activity Have each student select a three-dimensional object in the classroom and draw a net for the solid.

APPLYING THE LESSON

Homework Exercises

Assignment Guide
Basic: 15-30, 37-44
Average: 17-33, 37-44
Enriched: 19-24, 26-44

Additional Answers

13.

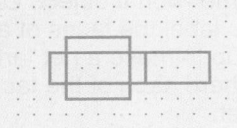

14.

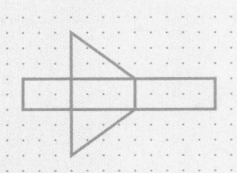

Reteaching Masters Booklet, p. 65

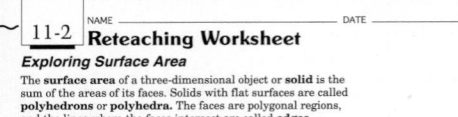

11-2 **Reteaching Worksheet**
NAME _____ DATE _____

Exploring Surface Area

The **surface area** of a three-dimensional object or **solid** is the sum of the areas of its faces. Solids with flat surfaces are called **polyhedrons** or **polyhedra.** The faces are polygonal regions, and the lines where the faces intersect are called **edges.**

 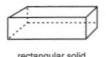 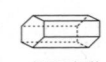

pyramid   rectangular solid   hexagonal solid

When a polyhedron is unfolded, the result is a two-dimensional figure called a **net.**

Example: Match the net at the left with one of the solids at the right.

 a. **b.** **c.**

The net represents solid c.

Identify the number and type of polygons that are faces of each polygon.

1.    **2.**   **3.**

2 pentagons, 5 rectangles   1 rectangle, 4 triangles   6 triangles

For each polyhedron, label the remaining vertices of its net.

4.   **5.**

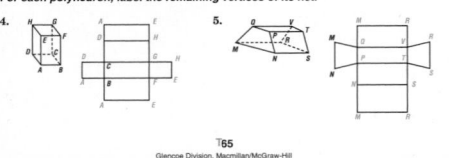

T65
Glencoe Division, Macmillan/McGraw-Hill

RETEACHING THE LESSON

Have students think about the words surface and area. They can also look the terms up in the dictionary. Putting the two words together for "surface area" means putting together the meaning of the two words, or the amount of area on the surface.

Identify the number and types of polygons that are faces in each polyhedron.

23. 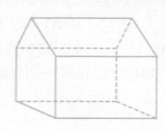 24. 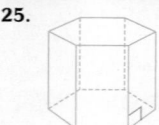 25.

 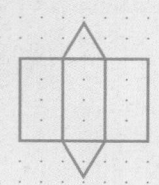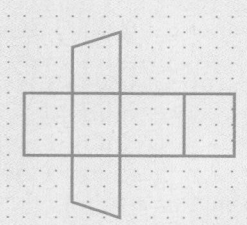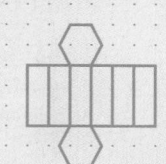
Nets are not drawn to scale.

Given each polyhedron, copy its net and label the remaining vertices.

26.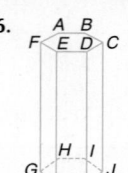

27.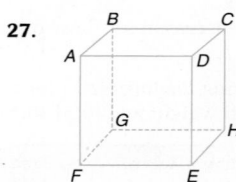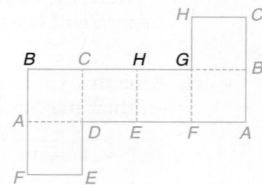

Use rectangular dot paper to draw a net for each solid. See margin.

28. 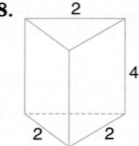 29. 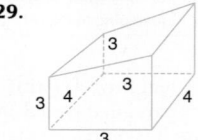 30.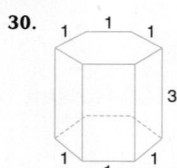

A standard die as used in most board games is shown at the right. The opposite faces are numbered so that their sum is 7. Determine whether each numbered net can be folded to result in a standard die.

6 on the back
5 on the side
4 on the bottom

31. 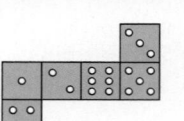 yes 32. 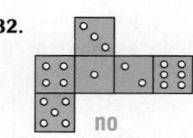 no 33. 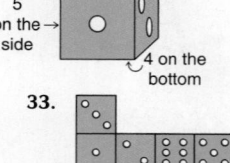 yes

34. 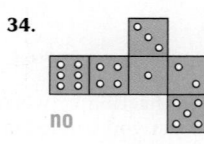 no 35. 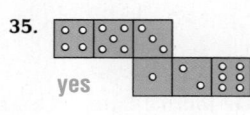 yes 36. 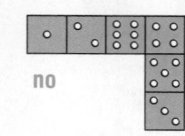 no

LESSON 11-2   EXPLORING SURFACE AREA   533

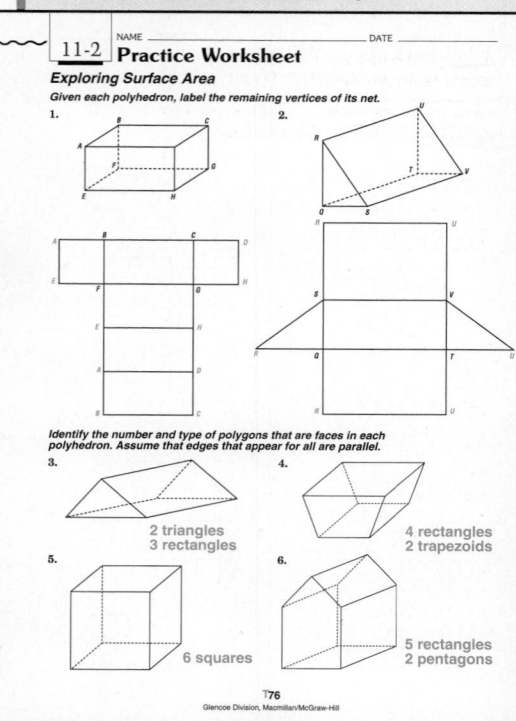

38. Sample answer:

In the net, every polygon is an entire face in the solid. In the cardboard box cutout, some of the polygons are part of a face and parts of faces are covered twice. This gives the cardboard box more stability when it is folded up and allows gluing.

44. The total surface area of a geometric solid is the sum of the areas of the shapes that make up its faces. A net gives a two-dimensional view of these faces, which allows us to use area formulas to compute total surface area. Although there are several ways to arrange the polygons that will fold up into the geometric solid, all of these nets have the same surface area.

Enrichment Masters Booklet, p. 65

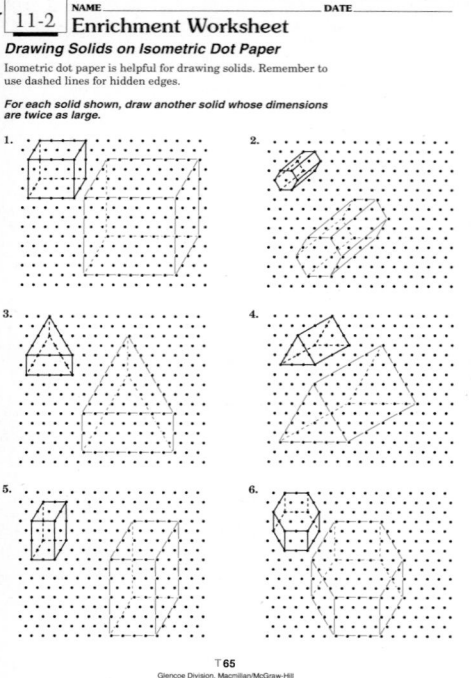

Critical Thinking

37. Design three different nets that could produce a rectangular solid 4 units long, 2 units wide, and 1 unit high. Then lay out a cutting pattern on an 18×30 rectangular grid using the net that will allow you to produce the largest number of complete rectangular solids and at the same time minimize the waste in the grid. **See Solutions Manual.**

Applications

38. Manufacturing When cardboard boxes are manufactured, the flat cutout resembles a net. However there are a few differences. Examine the pattern for a cardboard box. Sketch a net for the same geometric solid. Explain the differences between the cardboard box pattern and your net. Give a reason for these differences. **See margin.**

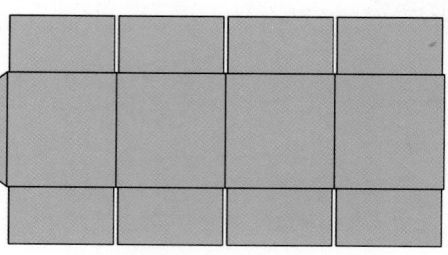

39. Aircraft Compute the wing-loading factor for the following aircraft based on their maximum takeoff weight and total surface area of their wings.

Aircraft	Maximum Takeoff Weight	Surface Area of Wings	Wing-loading Factor in lb/ft²
Wright brothers' plane	750 lb	532 ft²	1.41 __?__
Four-passenger plane	1150 lb	117 ft²	9.83 __?__
Supersonic transport	750,000 lb	7700 ft²	97.40 __?__

Mixed Review

40. A rectangular painting is 30 inches by 20 inches. The painting is surrounded by a 3-inch matting and placed in a frame that adds another 5 inches on each side. What is the total area of the painting, matting, and frame? **(Lesson 11-1)** 1656 in²

41. Brianna's little brother's tricycle tire has a diameter of 12 inches. About how far does the tricycle travel in one turn of the wheel? **(Lesson 10-7)** 12π or 37.7 in.

42. Find the area of a triangle with a base 7 feet long and a height of 2 feet. **(Lesson 10-5)** 7 ft²

43. Complete each statement. Refer to the figure at the right. **(Lesson 5-7)**

a. If $AB = BC$, and $m\angle 1 < m\angle 2$, then AD __?__ CD. $<$

b. If $AD = DC$ and AB __?__ BC, then $m\angle 3 > m\angle 4$. $>$

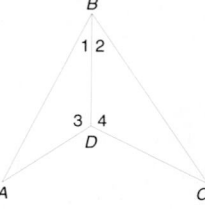

Wrap-Up

44. Journal Entry Describe the connection between finding the total surface area of a geometric solid and what you studied in this lesson. **See margin.**

534　**CHAPTER 11　SURFACE AREA AND VOLUME**

EXTENDING THE LESSON

Math Power: Reasoning

Sketch two closed solid figures that are not polyhedrons. **Sample answers:**

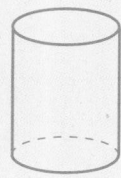

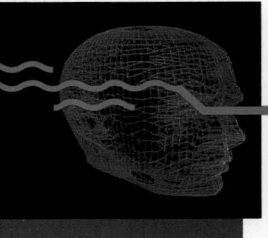

Technology

Drawing Three-Dimensional Figures

LOGO can be used to draw three-dimensional figures. Remember that the drawing of many solid figures involves the use of parallel lines. By using special pairs of angles and what you know about supplementary angles, you can draw the figure below using LOGO commands.

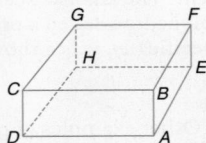

FD 40 LT 90 FD 80 LT 90 FD 40 LT 90 FD 80 LT 90   *Draws ABCD.*
RT 30 FD 70 BK 70   *Rotates the turtle and draws $\overline{AE}$.*

PU LT 30 FD 40 PD   *Rotates the turtle and moves it to B without drawing.*
RT 30 FD 70 BK 70   *Rotates the turtle and draws $\overline{BF}$.*

PU LT 120 FD 80 RT 90 PD   *Rotates turtle ; moves it to C without drawing.*
RT 30 FD 70 BK 70   *Rotates the turtle and draws $\overline{CG}$.*

LT 30 BK 40 RT 30 FD 70 LT 30   *Moves the turtle to D and draws $\overline{DH}$.*

FD 40 RT 90 FD 80 RT 90 FD 40 RT 90 FD 80   *Draws HGFE.*

Study the commands to draw the prism. Do you see any patterns in the groups of steps?

EXERCISES

1-3 See students' work.

1. Draw another rectangular solid using different lengths for the sides and different angle measures to position the parallel lines.

2. Experiment with the LOGO commands to draw different parallelograms. Devise a plan for drawing a solid that has parallelograms for its bases.

3. Use LOGO commands to draw a triangle. Then draw a solid that has triangles for its bases.

TECHNOLOGY 535

- Reteaching Master 11-3
- Practice Master 11-3
- Enrichment Master 11-3
- Technology Master p. 47

 Transparency 11-3 contains the 5-Minute Check and a teaching aid for this lesson.

INTRODUCING THE LESSON

 5-Minute Check

(over Lesson 11-2)

Refer to the figure below.

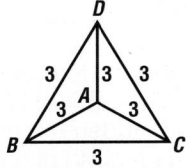

1. Identify the number and type of polygons that are faces.
   4 triangles
2. Draw a net for the solid and label each vertex.

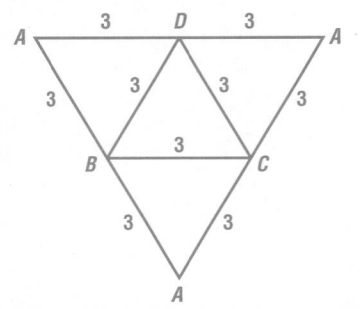

Motivating the Lesson

Ask students to name the parts of a prism before giving them any of the terminology in this lesson. Then explain that the words *face*, *base*, *vertex*, and *lateral edge* can be used to describe different parts.

Surface Area of Prisms and Cylinders

Objectives
11-3A
11-3B

After studying this lesson, you should be able to:
- identify the parts of prisms and cylinders, and
- find the lateral areas and surface areas of right prisms and right cylinders.

Application

A certain inn provides shower caps for its guests. Each shower cap is packaged in a box such as the one shown at the right. The box is a special kind of polyhedron called a **prism.** More specifically, it is a rhombohedron.

Other examples of prisms are cubes and rectangular solids. Prisms have the following characteristics.

- Two faces, called **bases,** are formed by congruent polygons that lie in parallel planes.

- The faces that are not bases, called **lateral faces,** are formed by parallelograms.

- The intersections of two adjacent lateral faces are called **lateral edges** and are parallel segments.

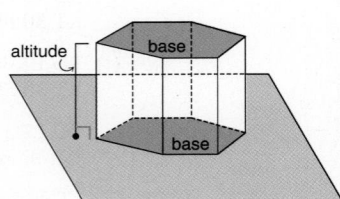

An **altitude** of a prism is a segment perpendicular to the planes containing the two bases, with an endpoint in each plane. The length of an altitude of a prism is called the **height** of the prism. If the lateral edges of a prism are also altitudes, then the prism is a **right prism.** Otherwise, the prism is an **oblique prism.**

A prism can be classified by the shape of its bases.

Lateral faces of right prisms are rectangles.

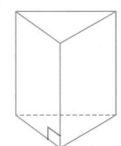
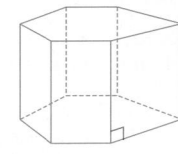
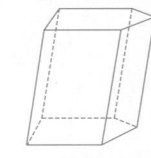

Lateral edges of oblique prisms are not altitudes.

Right triangular prism

Right hexagonal prism

Oblique pentagonal prism

ALTERNATE TEACHING STRATEGIES

Using Modeling

Bring in an empty can from home and remove both lids. Use the lids of the can and the label around the can to make a net for the can. Ask students what the area of the label and the area of the lids are. Relate these measures to the lateral area and the surface area of a right cylinder.

Using Measurement

Bring in or find a right prism and have students measure all of its sides. Write down the measurement for each side and also write the equation for adding up all of the areas. Point out that this would be its surface area. Ask students if they notice any patterns. Use these measures to derive the formula for lateral area.

One way to find the **surface area** (T) of a prism is to add the areas of each of the faces. Another way is to develop and use a formula. We must first find a formula for the area of the lateral faces.

The **lateral area** (L) of a prism is the area of all the lateral faces. As a result of the Distributive Property, the lateral area of a right prism can be found by multiplying the height by the perimeter (P) of the base as shown below. Note that a, b, c, d, e, and f are the measures of the sides of the base.

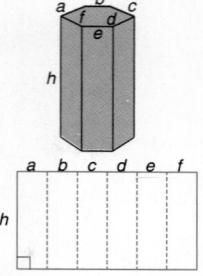

$$L = ah + bh + ch + dh + eh + fh$$
$$= (a + b + c + d + e + f)h$$
$$= Ph$$

The formula for the lateral area of any right prism is generalized as follows.

Lateral Area of a Right Prism	If a right prism has a lateral area of L square units, a height of h units, and each base has a perimeter of P units, then $L = Ph$.

Since the bases are congruent, they have the same area (B). The surface area (T) of a right prism is found by adding the lateral area to the area of both bases ($2B$).

Surface Area of a Right Prism	If the total surface area of a right prism is T square units, its height is h units, and each base has an area of B square units and a perimeter of P units, then $T = Ph + 2B$.

Example 1

Find the lateral area and surface area of a right triangular prism with a height of 15 inches and a right triangular base with legs of 4 and 3 inches.

First, use the Pythagorean Theorem to find c, the measure of the hypotenuse. Then use the value of c to find the measure of the perimeter.

$c^2 = 3^2 + 4^2$	$P = 4 + 3 + c$	$B = \frac{1}{2}bh$
$c^2 = 25$	$= 4 + 3 + 5$	$= \frac{1}{2}(4)(3)$
$c = 5$	$= 12$	$= 6$
$L = Ph$	$T = L + 2B$	Thus, the lateral area is
$= (12)(15)$	$= 180 + 2(6)$	180 in², and the surface
$= 180$	$= 192$	area is 192 in².

LESSON 11-3   SURFACE AREA OF PRISMS AND CYLINDERS   537

Chalkboard Example

For Example 1
Find the lateral area and surface area of the triangular prism.

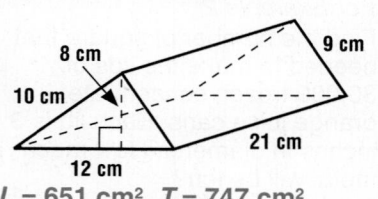

$L = 651$ cm², $T = 747$ cm²

Another type of solid is a **cylinder**. The **bases** of a cylinder are formed by two congruent circles that lie in parallel planes. The segment whose endpoints are centers of these circles is called the **axis** of the cylinder.

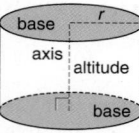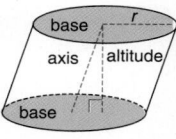

Right cylinder   Oblique cylinder

An altitude of a **cylinder** is a segment perpendicular to the planes containing the bases with an endpoint in each plane. If the axis of a cylinder is also an altitude of the cylinder, then the cylinder is called a **right cylinder**. Otherwise, the cylinder is an **oblique cylinder**.

A net for a right cylinder would resemble the figure at the right.

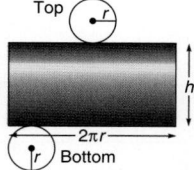

The lateral area of a cylinder is the area of the curved surface. The curved surface is a rectangle whose width is the height of the cylinder, h units, and whose length is the circumference of one of its bases, $2\pi r$ units.

Lateral Area of a Right Cylinder	If a right cylinder has a lateral area of L square units, a height of h units, and the bases have radii of r units, then $L = 2\pi rh$.

The surface area of a cylinder is the sum of the lateral area and the areas of the bases.

Surface Area of a Right Cylinder	If a right cylinder has a total surface area of T square units, a height of h units, and the bases have radii of r units, then $T = 2\pi rh + 2\pi r^2$.

Example 2

APPLICATION

Manufacturing

Find the number of square feet of cardboard needed to make the sides of 30,000 frozen concentrate orange juice cans if each can is 6 inches tall and 3 inches in diameter.

If the diameter of the base of a can is 3 inches long, the radius is 1.5 inches long.

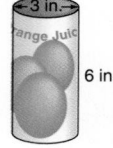

3 in.

6 in.

$L = 2\pi rh$
$\quad = 2\pi(1.5)(6)$ *Substitute 1.5 for r and 6 for h.*
$\quad = 18\pi$
$\quad \approx 56.5$

The lateral area of each can is about 56.5 square inches. So, the lateral area of 30,000 cans is about $30{,}000 \times 56.5$ or about 1,695,000 square inches. Since there are 144 square inches in a square foot, about $1{,}695{,}000 \div 144$ or 11,771 square feet of cardboard are needed.

CHECKING FOR UNDERSTANDING

Communicating Mathematics

Read and study the lesson to answer these questions.

1. Refer to the shower cap box on page 536.

   a. What are the shapes of the polygonal faces that make up the shower cap box? Be specific. **2 rhombi and 4 parallelograms**

   b. Why do you think it is called a rhombohedron? **two faces are rhombi**

   c. Draw a net of the shower cap box on isometric dot paper. **See margin.**

2. Describe the difference between lateral area and surface area. **See Solutions Manual.**

3. If a printer is making labels for canned soup, what dimensions are important for him or her to know? The area of the label is closely related to which concept you studied in this lesson? **See Solutions Manual.**

4. Describe in your own words the difference between a right prism and an oblique prism. **See Solutions Manual.**

5. Where are the endpoints of the axis of a cylinder located in relation to its bases? Illustrate your answer with a diagram. **See Solutions Manual.**

Guided Practice

Find the surface area of each right rectangular prism. Round your answers to the nearest tenth.

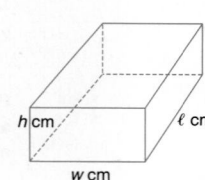

6. $\ell = 20$, $w = 5$, and $h = 3$ **350 cm²**

7. $\ell = 14.5$, $w = 7.5$, and $h = 8$ **569.5 cm²**

Find the surface area of each right triangular prism. The triangular bases are equilateral. Round your answers to the nearest tenth.

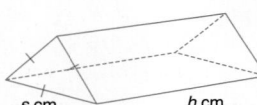

8. $s = 5$ and $h = 12$ **about 201.7 cm²**

9. $s = 6.2$ and $h = 20.4$ **about 412.7 cm²**

Find the surface area of each cylinder. Round your answers to the nearest tenth.

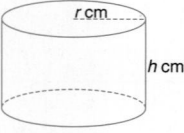

10. $r = 4$ and $h = 8$ **about 301.6 cm²**

11. $r = 6.8$ and $h = 17$ **about 1016.9 cm²**

12. Find the radius of a cylinder that has a height of 35 inches and a lateral area of 630 square inches. **about 2.86 in.**

LESSON 11-3   SURFACE AREA OF PRISMS AND CYLINDERS   539

RETEACHING THE LESSON

Draw a prism and a cylinder on the chalkboard or overhead. Ask students about the parts of the solids and what type of solid they are. For example, ask them to identify the bases, faces, lateral edges, altitudes, and the axis of a cylinder; if the solid is right or oblique and why, etc.

Additional Answer

1c.

EVALUATING THE LESSON

Checking for Understanding

Exercises 1-12 are designed to help you assess students' understanding through reading, writing, speaking, and modeling. You should work through Exercises 1-5 with your students and then monitor their work on Exercises 6-12.

Error Analysis

Finding the bases of prisms may pose difficulty for students. Emphasize that the bases of prisms (and cylinders) are parallel and congruent, and that the bases can sometimes appear to be sides of the solid. Also, the altitude of the prism connects the two bases.

Closing the Lesson

Writing Activity Have students draw a prism and a cylinder and label the parts of each. Have them tell what type of solid it is.

Reteaching Masters Booklet, p. 66

11-3 | NAME _____ DATE _____
Reteaching Worksheet

Surface Area of Prisms and Cylinders

Prisms are polyhedrons with congruent polygonal bases in parallel planes. **Cylinders** have congruent and parallel circular bases. An **altitude** is a perpendicular segment joining the planes of the bases. The length of an altitude is the **height** of the figure. **Right** prisms have lateral edges that are altitudes. A right cylinder is one whose **axis** is an altitude.

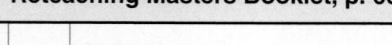

In the following formulas, L is lateral area and T is total area.

Prisms $L = Ph$ **Cylinders** $L = 2\pi rh$
$\qquad\quad T = Ph + 2B$ $\qquad\qquad\quad T = 2\pi rh + 2\pi r^2$

Example: Find the surface area of the cylinder at the right.

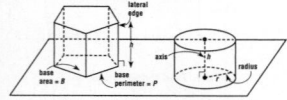

$T = 2\pi rh + 2\pi r^2$
$T = 2\pi(3.5)(6) + 2\pi(3.5)^2$
$T = 66.5\pi$ or about 208.92 cm²

Find the lateral area and surface area of each right prism or right cylinder. Round your answers to the nearest tenth.

1.

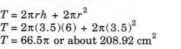

$L = 216$ m²
$S = 264$ m²

2.

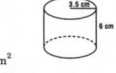

$L = 43.7$ cm²
$S = 92.6$ cm²

3.

$L = 119.4$ cm²
$S = 276.5$ cm²

4.

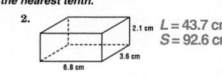

$L = 62.6$ m²
$S = 71.6$ m²

T66
Glencoe Division, Macmillan/McGraw-Hill

Practice Masters Booklet, p. 77

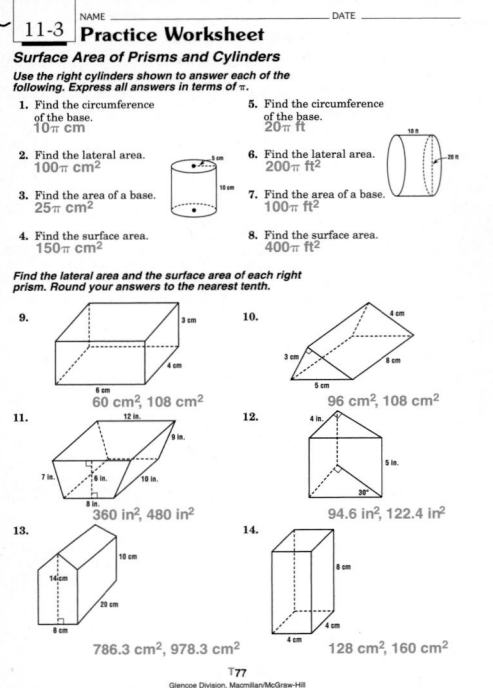

EXERCISES

Practice

Use the prism at the right to answer each of the following.

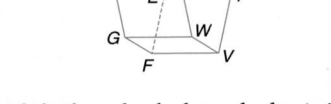
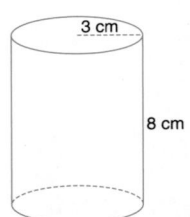

13. Is the prism a right prism or an oblique prism? **right prism**

14. **heptagons, rectangles**

14. What is the polygonal shape of its bases and lateral faces?

15. If the bases are regular polygons with sides 6 units long, find the perimeter of the base. **42 units**

16. If the perimeter of the base is 56 units and the length of a lateral edge is 7 units, find the lateral area of the prism. **392 square units**

Use the right cylinder at the right to answer each of the following. Express all answers in terms of π.

17. Find the circumference of a base. **6π cm**

18. Find the lateral area. **48π cm²**

19. Find the area of the base. **9π cm²**

20. Find the surface area. **66π cm²**

B

Find the lateral area and surface area of each right prism. Round your answers to the nearest tenth. Assume that polygons that appear regular are regular.

21. $L = 432$ in²,
$T = 432 + 108\sqrt{3}$
or about 619.1 in²

22. $L = 252$ m²,
$T = 264$ m²

23. $L = 150 + 50\sqrt{3}$
or about 236.6 ft²,
$T = 150 + 150\sqrt{3}$
or about 409.8 ft²

24. $L = 640$ yd²,
$T = 1248$ yd²

21.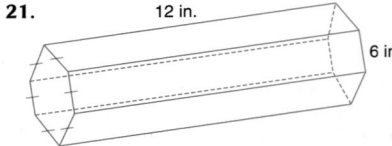

22.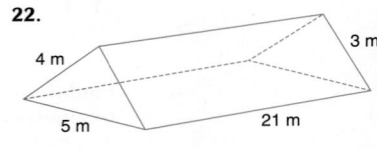

23.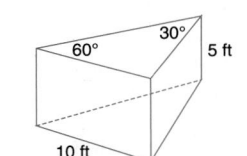

24.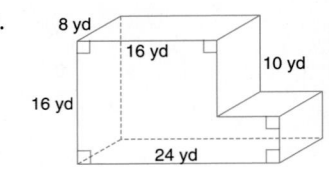

25. Find the surface area of a cube whose lateral edge is 8 units long. **384 units²**

26. If the lateral area of a right rectangular prism is 144 square centimeters, its length is three times its width, and its height is twice its width, find its surface area. **198 cm²**

27. Find the surface area of a cylindrical water tank that is 8 meters tall and has a diameter of 8 meters. **96π or about 301.6 m²**

Find the surface area of each oblique rectangular prism. Round your answers to the nearest tenth.

28.

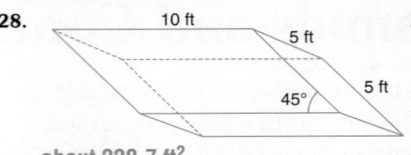

10 ft
5 ft
5 ft
45°

about 220.7 ft²

29.

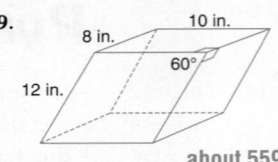

8 in.
10 in.
60°
12 in.

about 559.8 in²

30. Find the total surface area of the solid at the right, including the surface area inside the cylindrical hole.
about 638.8 units²

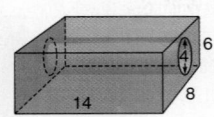

6
4
14
8

Critical Thinking

31. Suppose you are designing a solid figure with two congruent parallel bases. The distance around each base is fixed, and the height is always the same. If you wanted a maximum surface area, what shape would you make the base? Justify your answer. **See margin.**

Applications

32. **Manufacturing** A rectangular cake pan is 9 inches by 13 inches and 2 inches deep. It needs to be coated with a non-stick coating. What is the area of the surface to be coated? **205 in²**

33. **Agriculture** Over the years the acid associated with filling a silo with silage eats away at the cement sides, resulting in spoilage. The acid also weakens the cement walls and may seriously damage its structural integrity. In order to properly maintain a silo, a farmer must have the inside of the silo resurfaced. The cost of the process is directly related to the lateral area of the inside of the silo. Find the lateral area of a silo 40 feet tall with an interior diameter of 16 feet. **about 2010.6 ft²**

34. **Manufacturing** Gum manufacturers always cover sticks of gum with paper.

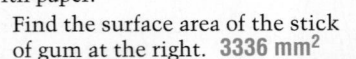

2 mm
74 mm
20 mm

a. Find the surface area of the stick of gum at the right. **3336 mm²**
b. If the foil wrapper for the gum is designed to overlap 2 millimeters and have foldover ends of 6.5 millimeters on each of the shorter ends, what are the dimensions of the foil wrapper and its area? **87 mm × 46 mm; 4002 mm²**

Mixed Review

35. Draw a net for the prism at the right.
(Lesson 11-2) **See margin.**

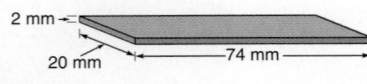

If $\overline{AE} \parallel \overline{BD}$ and $\overline{AE} \perp \overline{ED}$, find each measure.

36. EC (Lesson 7-3) **7.5**
37. BC (Lesson 8-2) **10**
38. AB (Lesson 7-5) **2.5**
39. area of $ABDE$ (Lesson 10-5) **13.5**

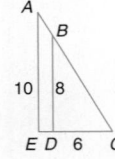

A
B
10 8
E D 6 C

Wrap-Up

40. What are the essential ideas in this lesson that you should know in order to be successful on the next quiz or test? **Answers may vary.**

LESSON 11-3   SURFACE AREA OF PRISMS AND CYLINDERS   541

EXTENDING THE LESSON

**Math Power:
Problem Solving**

Healthy Food Company sells vegetables in cans that are 4 inches high and have a diameter of 3 inches. How many square feet of paper are required to make the labels for 15,000 cans if there is a 1-inch overlap of the label on each can? **4343.7 ft²**

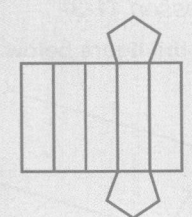
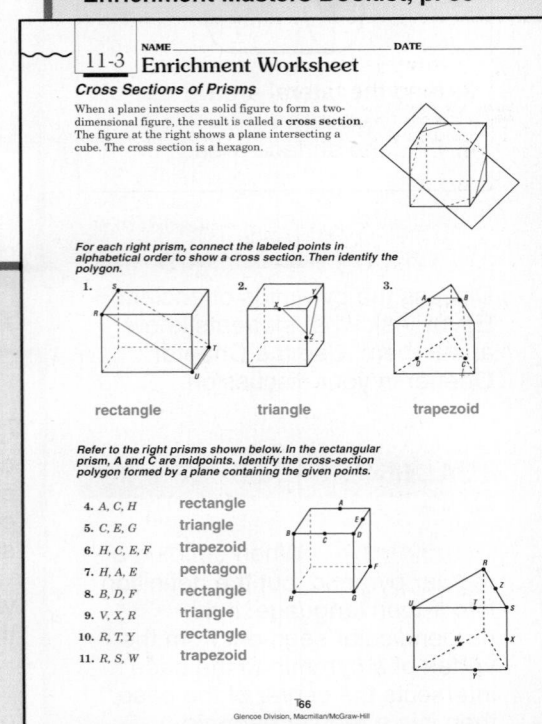

Lesson Resources

- Reteaching Master 11-4
- Practice Master 11-4
- Enrichment Master 11-4
- Evaluation Masters, pp. 149, 153
- Activity Master, p. 38
- Lab Manual, p. 78-81

 Transparency 11-4 contains the 5-Minute Check and a teaching aid for this lesson.

INTRODUCING THE LESSON

5-Minute Check

(over Lesson 11-3)

Refer to the figure below.

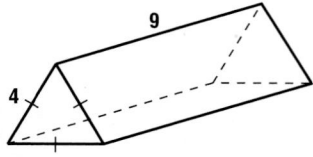

1. Find the lateral area. **108 square units**
2. Find the surface area. **about 121.9 square units**

Refer to the figure below.

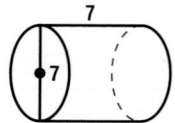

3. Find the lateral area. **about 153.9 square units**
4. Find the surface area. **about 230.9 square units**

Motivating the Lesson

Discuss the pyramids of ancient Egypt. Ask what students know about them. Use the Chapter Opener in your discussion.

TEACHING THE LESSON

Teaching Tip   When defining a regular pyramid, put the definition into if-then language: if the perpendicular segment from the vertex of a pyramid to the base intersects the center of the base, then it is a regular pyramid.

Objectives
11-4A
11-4B

After studying this lesson, you should be able to:
- find the lateral area of a regular pyramid, and
- find the lateral area and surface area of a right circular cone.

Application

In large metropolitan areas that experience severe winter weather, state and local highway departments frequently spread salt to help keep ice from forming on the roads. In some states, buildings like this one are strategically located to provide highway crews with a ready supply of dry salt. This building is designed in this way, because the salt supply stored inside is piled up in the shape of a cone. The shape of the building closely resembles that of a pyramid.

A pyramid has the following characteristics.

- All the faces, except one, intersect at a point called the **vertex.**
- The face that does not intersect the other faces at the vertex is called the **base** and is a polygon.
- The faces intersecting at the vertex are called **lateral faces** and form triangles. The edges of the lateral faces that have the vertex as an endpoint are called **lateral edges.**
- The segment from the vertex perpendicular to the base is called the **altitude.**

A pyramid is a **regular pyramid** if its base is a regular polygon and the segment whose endpoints are the center of the base and the vertex is perpendicular to the base. This segment is called the **altitude.**

All of the lateral faces are congruent isosceles triangles. The height of each lateral face is called the **slant height,** ℓ, of the pyramid.

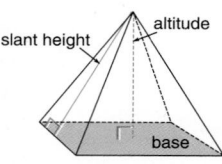

Regular Pyramid

ALTERNATE TEACHING STRATEGIES

Using Construction

Give each student a cone shaped drinking cup. Have the students cut the side from the brim to the apex of the cone and flatten out the cup. What is the shape of the flat surface?   **It is a circle with a sector missing.** Ask how they would use this shape to help them find the surface area of the cone.

Using Comparison

Ask students to draw what they think a pyramid is on a piece of paper. Using the drawings that are correct, ask students what each of the drawings has in common. Compare their definitions to the definitions in the book. Continue until all parts of a pyramid have been defined. Ask students what they think a regular pyramid would be.

The figure at the right is a regular hexagonal pyramid. Its lateral area (L) can be found by adding the areas of all its congruent triangular faces as shown in its net below.

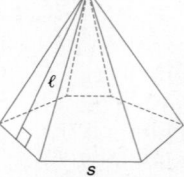

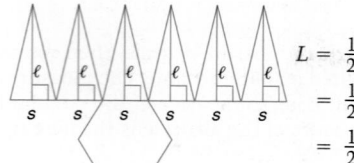

$L = \frac{1}{2} s\ell + \frac{1}{2} s\ell + \frac{1}{2} s\ell + \frac{1}{2} s\ell + \frac{1}{2} s\ell + \frac{1}{2} s\ell$

$= \frac{1}{2} (s + s + s + s + s + s)\ell$

$= \frac{1}{2} P\ell \qquad P = s + s + s + s + s + s$

This suggests the following formula.

Lateral Area of a Regular Pyramid	If a regular pyramid has a lateral area of L square units, a slant height of ℓ units, and its base has a perimeter of P units, then $L = \frac{1}{2} P\ell$.

The **surface area** of a regular pyramid is the sum of its lateral area and the area of its base.

Example 1

A regular square pyramid has a slant height of 15 units and a lateral edge of 17 units. Find its lateral area.

Use the Pythagorean Theorem to find the measure of half of each edge of the base (s).

$\frac{1}{2} s = \sqrt{17^2 - 15^2}$

$\frac{1}{2} s = \sqrt{64}$

$\frac{1}{2} s = 8$

$s = 16$

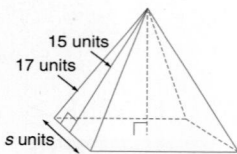

Thus, the length of each edge of its base is 16 units, and the perimeter of its base is 4×16, or 64 units.

$L = \frac{1}{2} P\ell$

$= \frac{1}{2} (64)(15)$

$= 480$

The lateral area of the pyramid is 480 square units.

Teaching Tip   In Example 1, use the triangle that is half of one of the faces of the pyramid. The slant height is the longer leg and the lateral edge is the hypotenuse.

Chalkboard Example

For Example 1
A regular triangular pyramid has a slant height of 12 units and a lateral edge of 13 units. Find its lateral area.

$\frac{1}{2}s = \sqrt{13^2 - 12^2}$

$\frac{1}{2}s = 5$

$s = 10$

$L = \frac{1}{2}(3 \cdot 10)(12)$

$L = 180$ square units

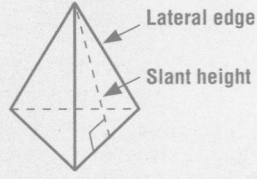
The figure at the right is a **right circular cone.** It has a circular **base** and a **vertex** at T. Its **axis,** $\overline{TC}$, is the segment whose endpoints are the vertex and the center of the base. The **altitude** of a cone is the segment that has the vertex as one endpoint and is perpendicular to the base.

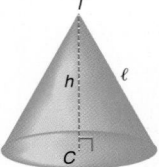

If the axis of a cone is also an altitude, then the cone is called a **right cone.** Otherwise it is called an **oblique cone.** The measure of any segment joining the vertex of a right cone to the edge of the circular base is called its **slant height,** ℓ. The measure of the altitude is the **height,** h, of the cone.

Finding the lateral area and surface area of a right cone is similar to finding those same measures for a regular pyramid. If a cone is cut along its slant height and unfolded, the resulting surface is a sector of a circle whose radius is the slant height ℓ. The area of the sector is proportional to the area of the circle. Notice that the arc length of this sector is equal to the circumference of the base of the original cone, $2\pi r$.

$$\frac{\text{area of sector}}{\text{area of circle}} = \frac{\text{measure of arc}}{\text{circumference of circle}}$$

$$\frac{\text{area of sector}}{\pi \ell^2} = \frac{2\pi r}{2\pi \ell}$$

$$\text{area of sector} = \pi r \ell$$

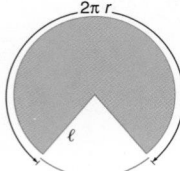

Lateral Area and Surface Area of a Right Cone	If a right circular cone has a lateral area of L square units, a surface area of T square units, a slant height of ℓ units, and the radius of the base is r units, then $L = \pi r \ell$ and $T = \pi r \ell + \pi r^2$.

Example 2

APPLICATION
Manufacturing

The National Paper Products Company makes cone-shaped cups for snow cones. If the diameter of the top of a cup is 8 centimeters long and its slant height is 11 centimeters, what is the lateral area of a cup?

If the diameter is 8 centimeters, the radius is $\frac{1}{2} \times 8$, or 4 centimeters.

$L = \pi r \ell$
  $= \pi(4)(11)$ *Substitute 4 for r and 11 for ℓ.*
  $= 44\pi$
  ≈ 138.2

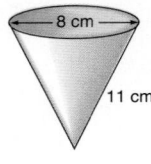

The lateral area is about 138.2 square centimeters.

CHECKING FOR UNDERSTANDING

Communicating Mathematics

Read and study the lesson to answer these questions. 1-3 See margin.

1. Describe the differences between the lateral edges of a pyramid and those of a prism.

2. As the number of sides of the base of a regular pyramid increases, the base begins to resemble a familiar shape. What shape is it? As this transformation takes place, what happens to the shape of the pyramid?

3. For a regular pyramid, which is longer, one of its lateral edges or its slant height? Sketch a pyramid to illustrate your answer.

4. In what case would the axis of a cone not be the altitude of the cone?
   if the cone were oblique and not a right cone

Guided Practice

Determine whether the condition given is characteristic of all pyramids or all prisms, both, or neither.

5. It has only one base. **pyramid**
6. It can have as few as five faces. **both**
7. Its lateral faces are parallelograms. **prism**
8. It has the same number of lateral faces as vertices. **neither**

Find the lateral area of each regular pyramid or right cone. Round your answers to the nearest tenth.

9.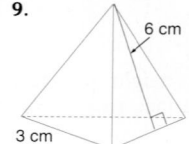
6 cm
3 cm
27 cm²

10.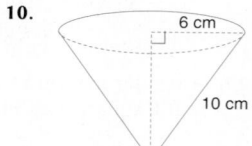
6 cm
10 cm
about 188.5 cm²

11.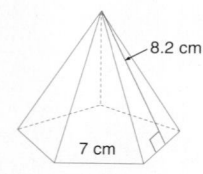
8.2 cm
7 cm
143.5 cm²

Find the surface area of each solid. Round your answers to the nearest tenth.

12.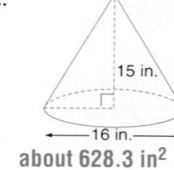
15 in.
16 in.
about 628.3 in²

13.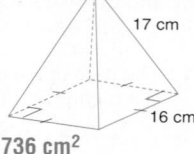
17 cm
16 cm
736 cm²

14.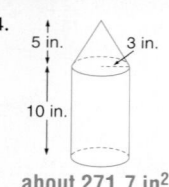
5 in.   3 in.
10 in.
about 271.7 in²

EXERCISES

Practice

Determine whether the condition given is characteristic of all pyramids or all prisms, both, or neither.

15. It has two bases. **prism**
16. Its lateral faces are triangles. **pyramid**
17. It always has an even number of faces. **neither**
18. It can have as few as four faces. **pyramid**
19. It always has an even number of edges. **pyramid**

LESSON 11-4   SURFACE AREA OF PYRAMIDS AND CONES   545

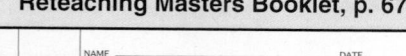
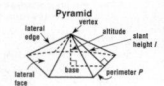
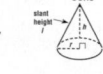
 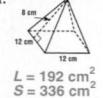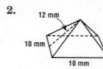

Use the regular pyramid at the right to answer each of the following. See margin.

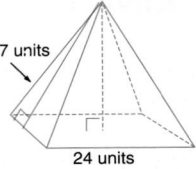

20. Find the slant height of each lateral face.
21. Find the area of each lateral face.
22. Find the pyramid's lateral area.
23. Find the pyramid's surface area.

17 units

24 units

B **Find the lateral area of each regular pyramid or right cone.**

24.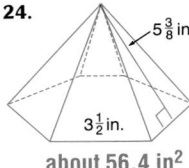

$5\frac{3}{8}$ in.

$3\frac{1}{2}$ in.

about 56.4 in²

25.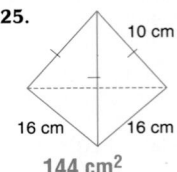

10 cm

16 cm   16 cm

144 cm²

26.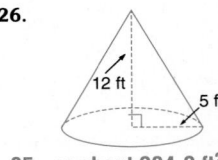

12 ft

5 ft

65π or about 204.2 ft²

Find the surface area of each solid.

27.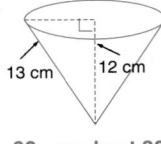

13 cm   12 cm

90π or about 282.7 cm²

28.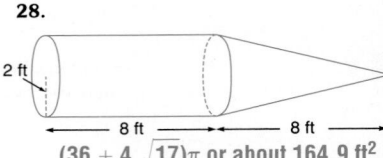

2 ft

8 ft   8 ft

(36 + 4 √17)π or about 164.9 ft²

29. A regular pyramid has a slant height of 16 feet. The area of its square base is 100 square feet. Find its surface area. **420 ft²**

30. Suppose that the vertices T, O, and P on a cube form the base of a pyramid with vertex V. If $TV = 16$, find the lateral area and the surface area of the pyramid. $L = 384$ units², $T \approx 605.7$ units²

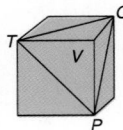

O

T V

P

C 31. The base of a rectangular pyramid is 30 inches by 12 inches. The altitude is 8 inches. All lateral edges are congruent. Find its surface area. **864 in²**

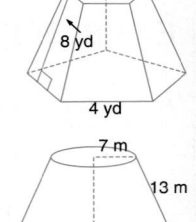

2 yd

8 yd

4 yd

32. A frustum of a pyramid is the part of the pyramid that remains after the top portion of the pyramid has been cut off by a plane parallel to the base. The figure at the right is a frustum of a regular pyramid. Find its lateral area. **120 yd²**

7 m

13 m

12 m

33. Find the surface area of the frustum of a cone shown at the right. **440π or about 1382.3 m²**

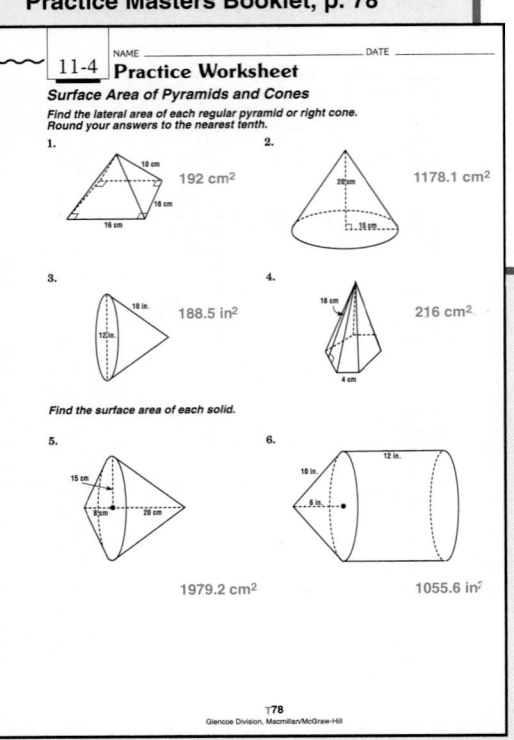

Critical Thinking

34. As the vertex of a right cone moves down the axis toward the center of the base, describe what happens to the lateral area of the cone. Be as specific as possible and demonstrate the validity of your answer with a series of diagrams. **See margin.**

Applications

35. **Buildings** The Transamerica Tower in San Francisco is a pyramid with a square base that is 149 feet on each side and a height of 853 feet. Find its lateral area. **about 255,161.7 ft²**

36. **about 215,401 ft²**

36. **Mining** Open pit mines approximate inverted right cones. If the base of the cone of an open pit mine is to be 420 feet across and the depth of the pit is to be 250 feet, what will the lateral area of the exposed surface be?

37. **Highway Management** A building used to store salt is in the shape of a pyramid. It has a height of 32 feet and a slant height of 56 feet. If the salt is piled up in the shape of a cone, what is the longest possible radius for the base of the pile? **about 46 ft**

Mixed Review

38. Is the statement *The axis is an altitude in an oblique cylinder* true or false? **(Lesson 11-3) false**

39. A circular area rug has a diameter of 4 yards. What is the area of the rug? **(Lesson 10-7) 4π or about 12.6 yd²**

40. The measure of the inscribed angle is half the measure of the central angle.

40. How are the measures of a central angle and an inscribed angle that intercept the same arc related? **(Lesson 9-4)**

41. How are the two diagonals of a rhombus related? **(Lesson 6-1) They are perpendicular.**

Wrap-Up

42. Write a three-question quiz for this lesson. Be sure to include complete solutions to your quiz questions. Trade quizzes with another student and take each other's quizzes. Then grade each other's work. **See students' work.**

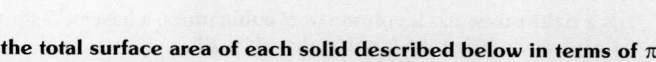
MID-CHAPTER REVIEW
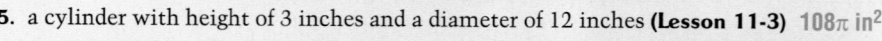

Use the regular pyramid at the right for Exercises 1-4. (Lesson 11-1)

1. Name its vertex. *T*
2. Name its altitude. $\overline{TO}$
3. How many faces does it have? **6**
4. Draw a net for the pyramid. **See margin.**

Find the total surface area of each solid described below in terms of π.

5. a cylinder with height of 3 inches and a diameter of 12 inches **(Lesson 11-3) 108π in²**

6. a cone with slant height of 14 centimeters and radius of 8 centimeters **(Lesson 11-4) 176π cm²**

7. Find the lateral area of a regular square pyramid with a base edge of 24 units and slant height of 15 units. **(Lesson 11-4) 720 units²**

EXTENDING THE LESSON

Math Power: Connections

How can you relate the formulas for the lateral area of a pyramid and for the lateral area of a cone? Both lateral areas are found by multiplying ½(perimeter or circumference) by the slant height, ℓ.

Mid-Chapter Review

The Mid-Chapter Review provides students with a brief review of the concepts and skills in Lessons 11-1 through 11-4. Lesson numbers are given at the end of problems or instruction lines so students may review concepts not yet mastered.

Additional Answer

34. The lateral area approaches the area of the base. This can be seen by showing a series of cones cut on their slant heights and folded out into sectors. As the altitude approaches zero, the slant height approaches the radius of the base, and the sector narrows, approaching a complete circle.

Mid-Chapter Review

4.

Enrichment Masters Booklet, p. 67

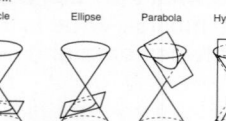

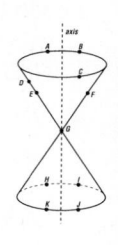

Lesson Resources

- Reteaching Master 11-5
- Practice Master 11-5
- Enrichment Master 11-5
- Multicultural Master, p. 11

 Transparency 11-5 contains the 5-Minute Check and a teaching aid for this lesson.

INTRODUCING THE LESSON

 5-Minute Check

(over Lesson 11-4)

Refer to the figures below.

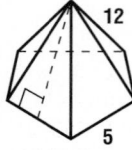 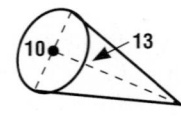

1. Find the slant height of the regular pyramid. **about 11.7 units**
2. Find the lateral area of the regular pyramid. **about 146.7 square units**
3. Find the slant height of the right circular cone. **about 13.9 units**
4. Find the lateral area of the right circular cone. **about 218.8 square units**
5. Find the surface area of the right circular cone. **about 297.3 square units**

Motivating the Lesson

Ask students what they think the word *volume* means. What is the difference between area and volume? **Area is two-dimensional and volume is three-dimensional.** Point out that volume is the amount of space that a solid takes up.

11-5 Volume of Prisms and Cylinders

Objective 11-5

After studying this lesson, you should be able to:
- find the volume of a right prism and a right cylinder.

Application

FYI···

Artificial cement was invented in 1824 in London, England, by Joseph Aspdin. It was called Portland cement.

As you drive by a new housing development and see workers pouring cement sidewalks, garage floors, and driveways, you probably have not given much thought to all the geometry that is involved in their work. Their ability to correctly compute the volume of cement needed for each job is absolutely critical. Being able to determine volume exactly often means the difference between making or losing money on the job. For a small contractor, making mistakes in computing volume may mean the end of the business.

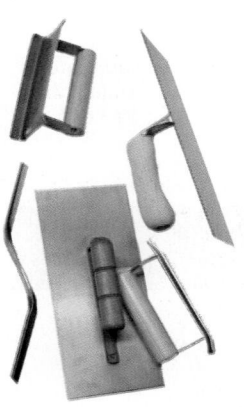 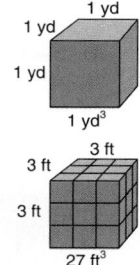

Cement is ordered in cubic yards, usually simply called yards, from ready-mix companies. A cubic unit, such as a cubic yard, is a unit of **volume.** A cubic yard is equivalent to the volume of a cube 1 yard, or 3 feet, on each edge. Thus, a cube 3 feet by 3 feet by 3 feet has a volume of 27 cubic feet and is equivalent to 1 cubic yard. If two solid regions are the same size and the same shape, they have equal volumes.

Observe that in the second cube shown above, each layer of small cubes has 3 by 3 or 9 cubes. Notice that the base has 9 cubes and there are three layers each with the same number of cubes. Therefore, there are 3×9 or 27 cubes in the solid.

Volume of a Right Prism	If a right prism has a volume of V cubic units, a base of B square units, and a height of h units, then $V = Bh$.

Example 1

APPLICATION
Construction

Find the cubic yards of cement that are required for a 60-foot long driveway that is 8 inches thick and 20 feet wide.

Since this driveway can be thought of as a right prism, we can use the formula $V = Bh$.

548   CHAPTER 11   SURFACE AREA AND VOLUME

ALTERNATE TEACHING STRATEGIES

Using Demonstration

Give each student a paper clip and ask how much metal is used to make it. **Unbend the paper clip so that it forms a cylinder and use the formula for volume to find out how much metal is necessary to make one paper clip.**

Using Manipulatives

Bring in a Rubik's Cube and ask students how many small cubes are in the 3-by-3 large cube. Have students use sugar cubes to build other types of prisms, calculate the volume, and check it by counting the number of small cubes used. For cylinders, fill a cup or can to the top with water and ask how much water is inside. Point out that the water represents the volume of the cylinder.

The area of the base is 20 feet times 60 feet or 1200 square feet. The height in feet is $\frac{8}{12}$ or $\frac{2}{3}$.

Thus, the volume is $1200 \times \frac{2}{3}$ or 800 cubic feet. Since a cubic yard equals 27 cubic feet, they will need $\frac{800}{27}$ or about 29.6 cubic yards of cement. The cement contractor will order 30 cubic yards.

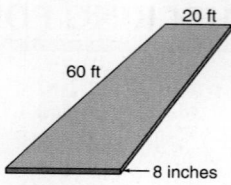

The volume of a right cylinder can be found using the same process we used to find the volume of a right prism.

Consider the stack of coins shown at the right. Each coin represents a circular layer. Taken together, the stack of coins represents the volume of a right cylinder. In a similar way, the volume of a right cylinder is the area of each layer times the height of the stack. Since the base of a cylinder is a circle, the area of the base is πr^2.

Volume = area of base × height
$$V = \pi r^2 \times h$$

Volume of a Right Cylinder	If a right cylinder has a volume of V cubic units, a height of h units, and a radius of r units, then $V = \pi r^2 h$.

Example 2

APPLICATION

Manufacturing

A certain metal pipe is made by boring a cylindrical hole in a metal cylinder. The outer diameter is 2.5 centimeters and the inside diameter is 1.8 centimeters. If the metal pipe is 30 centimeters long, find the volume of metal contained in the pipe to the nearest cubic centimeter.

The volume of the metal pipe equals the volume of the cylinder minus the volume of the cylindrical hole.

Let r_1 represent the radius of the cylinder.
$$r_1 = (0.5)(2.5) \text{ or } 1.25 \text{ cm}$$

Let r_2 represent the radius of the hole.
$$r_2 = (0.5)(1.8) \text{ or } 0.9 \text{ cm}$$

$$V = \pi(r_1)^2 h - \pi(r_2)^2 h$$
$$= \pi(1.25)^2(30) - \pi(0.9)^2(30)$$
$$\approx 70.9$$

The volume of the metal in the pipe is about 70.9 cm³.

LESSON 11-5 VOLUME OF PRISMS AND CYLINDERS 549

Teaching Tip In the coin stack example, point out that you do not multiply the number of coins, just the area represented by one coin multiplied by the height of the stack.

Chalkboard Example

For Example 1
To resurface a football field, it was dug 6 inches deep. How many cubic feet of dirt is necessary to fill the field? A football field is 65 yards wide and 120 yards long.
$$V = Bh$$
$$= (120 \cdot 3)(65 \cdot 3)(\tfrac{1}{2})$$
$$= 35{,}100 \text{ ft}^3$$

For Example 2
There are 150 1-inch washers in a box. When the washers are stacked, they measure 9 inches in height. If the inside hole of the washers has a diameter of 3/4 inches, find the volume of metal in one washer.
$$V = \pi(0.5)^2(9) - \pi(0.375)^2(9)$$
$$\approx 7.1 - 4.0$$
$$\approx 3.1$$
The volume of metal in the washers is about 3.1 in.³.
$$\frac{3.1}{150} = 0.02 \text{ in.}^3$$
Each washer has about 0.02 in³ of metal.

Exercises 1-12 are designed to help you assess students' understanding through reading, writing, speaking, and modeling. You should work through Exercises 1-4 with your students and then monitor their work on Exercises 5-12.

Error Analysis

Students may have difficulty understanding the concept of volume. If this is the case, explain that the surface area of a figure surrounds the volume of the figure.

Closing the Lesson

Modeling Activity Have students make a prism or cylinder. Have them measure the solid and find the volume.

Additional Answers

1. **Sample answers: Topsoil, sand, and gravel are sold in cubic yards. Crude oil is sold in barrels. Grain and apples are sold in bushels and pecks. Milk is sold in pints, quarts, and gallons. Gasoline is sold in gallons.**
3. **Sample answer: A deck of playing cards might be used to develop the volume formula for a prism.**
4. **The volumes of two congruent geometric solids are equal.**

CHECKING FOR UNDERSTANDING

Communicating Mathematics

Read and study the lesson to answer these questions.

1. Besides cement, what other items are purchased by volume? State the units of measure used in their purchase. **See margin.**

2. How many cubic feet are in one cubic yard? **27**

3. Recall how coins were used to develop the volume of the right cylinder. What objects might be used in a similar way to develop the formula for the volume of a right prism? **See margin.**

4. Describe the relationship between the volumes of two geometric solids that are the same size and shape. **See margin.**

Guided Practice

Find the volume of each solid. Round your answers to the nearest tenth.

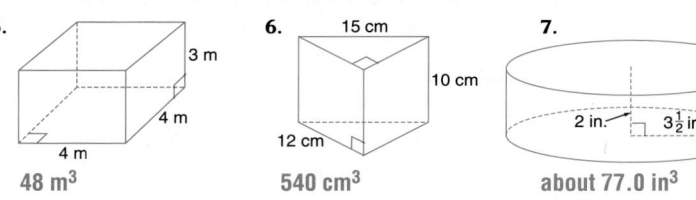

5. **48 m³**   6. **540 cm³**   7. **about 77.0 in³**

8. Find the volume of a right prism whose base has an area of 12 square meters and a height of 3.5 meters. **42 m³**

9. Find the volume of a right cylinder whose radius is 2 meters long and has a height of 8 meters. **32π or about 100.5 m³**

10. Find the volume of a right hexagonal prism that has a height of 20 centimeters and whose base is a regular hexagon with sides of 8 centimeters. Round the answer to the nearest cubic unit.
about 3326 cm³

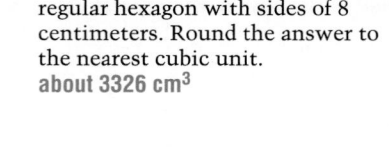

11. Find the volume of the partial right cylinder shown at the right. Round your answer to the nearest tenth.
about 1950.9 ft³

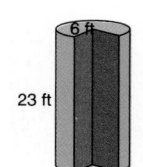

12. A right prism is formed by folding this net. Find its volume. **40 m³**

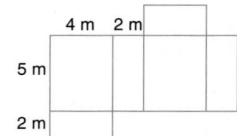

EXERCISES

Practice **Find each of the following.**

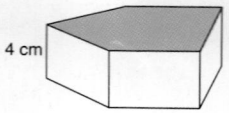

A 13. The area of the shaded base of the right prism is 68 square centimeters. Find the volume of the prism. **272 cm³**

14. Find the volume of a cube that has an edge of 9 inches. **729 in³**

15. Find the length of a lateral edge of a right prism with a volume of 962 cubic centimeters and a base whose area is 52 square centimeters. **18.5 cm**

16. Find the volume of a right prism that has a base with an area of 17.5 square centimeters and a height of 14 centimeters. **245 cm³**

17. Find the volume of a right prism that has a base with an area of 16 square feet and a height of 4.2 feet. **67.2 ft³**

18. Find the volume of a right cylinder whose radius is 3.2 centimeters and height is 10.5 centimeters. **107.52π or about 337.8 cm³**

19. Find the volume of a right cylinder whose diameter is 3 feet and height is 4 feet. **9π or about 28.3 ft³**

B **Find the volume of each solid. Round your answers to the nearest tenth.**

20.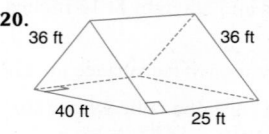

14,966.6 ft³

21.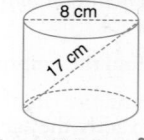

about 754.0 cm³

22.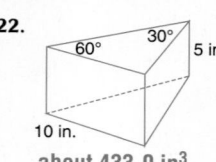

about 433.0 in³

23.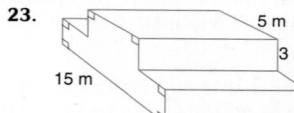

600 m³

24.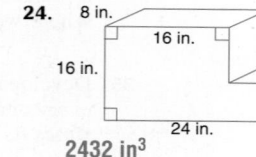

2432 in³

25. Find the volume of the regular hexagonal right prism at the right. Round your answer to the nearest tenth. **about 2598.1 in³**

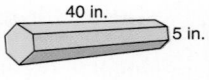

26. Find the volume of a trapezoidal prism that has a height of 20 centimeters. The trapezoidal base has a height of 3 centimeters, and the two bases of the trapezoid measure 5 and 9 centimeters. **420 cm³**

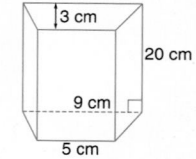

LESSON 11-5   VOLUME OF PRISMS AND CYLINDERS   551

APPLYING THE LESSON

Homework Exercises

Assignment Guide
Basic: 13-28, 35-37, 40-45
Average: 16-31, 35, 37-38, 40-45
Enriched: 19-35, 38-45

Exercise Notes

For Exercises 14-19, it may help to draw a diagram of the solid.

For Exercise 26, use the formula for the area of a trapezoid to find the area of the base of the solid. Then multiply by the height of the solid to find its volume.

Reteaching Masters Booklet, p. 68

RETEACHING THE LESSON

Bring examples of prisms and cylinders to class and have students measure the solids and find their volumes.

27. A hole with a diameter of 4 millimeters is drilled through a block of copper as shown at the right.

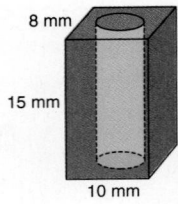

8 mm

15 mm

10 mm

27a. about 1011.5 mm³

  a. Find the volume of the resulting solid.

  b. The *density* of a substance is its mass per unit of volume. At room temperature, the density of copper is 8.9 grams per cubic centimeter. What is the mass of this block? **about 9 grams**

28. Find the volume of a cube for which a diagonal of one of its faces measures 12 centimeters. **about 610.9 cm³**

The nets below form a right prism and a right cylinder. Find the volume of the solid formed by each net.

29. 12 cm

3 cm

10 cm

360 cm³

30. 1.3 in.

4.2 in.

22.3 in²

31. A cylindrical glass pitcher full of water is poured into a rectangular cake pan with dimensions 9 inches by 12 inches by 2 inches. If the pitcher has a diameter of 6 inches and a height of 14 inches, will the pan hold all the water? **no**

32. Find the volume of a cube whose surface area is 54 square inches. **27 in³**

33. Find the length of the edge of a cube whose surface area and volume have exactly the same measure. **6 units**

34. Describe the effect upon the volume of a rectangular solid when one dimension is doubled and the other two remain the same. What happens when two dimensions are doubled? **See margin.**

Critical Thinking

35. Develop an argument that would verify the conjecture *The volume of every oblique prism or oblique cylinder is equal to the area of its base times its height.* **See margin.**

Applications

36. Food A wedge of cheese is cut from a fresh wheel of cheese (cylindrical block) which is 6 inches thick. The vertex of the wedge is at the center of the wheel whose radius is 10 inches. If the central angle of the wedge measures 50°, find the volume of this wedge of cheese. $\frac{250\pi}{3}$ **or about 261.8 in³**

37. Business If the trunk of an oak tree 30 feet long and 4 feet in diameter is split up for firewood, how many cords will it produce? A cord of firewood makes a stack 4 × 4 × 8 feet. **almost 3 cords**

38. Agriculture A farmer stores water in a rectangular tank with dimensions as shown at the right. The tank was filled with water, but developed a leak. If it loses 0.1 cubic feet of water each second, what percent of the water remains in the tank after 1 hour? **6.25%**

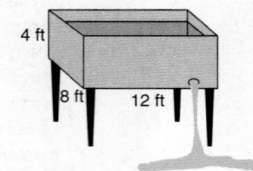

39. Construction A drawing of the cement driveway for a new home is shown at the right.

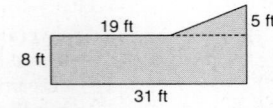

   a. Boards are laid out in the shape of the driveway to contain the cement when it is poured. What is the total length of lumber required? **84 feet**

   b. The driveway is to be 6 inches thick. What is the volume of cement that will be needed? **139 ft³ or about 5.15 yd³**

   c. If cement costs $2.65 per cubic foot, how much will the cement cost? **$368.35**

Mixed Review

40. The diameter of the base of a right circular cone measures 6.4 millimeters, and the slant height measures 5.2 millimeters. Find the lateral area. **(Lesson 11-4)** **52.3 mm²**

41. The diameter of a circle measures 10 centimeters, and the length of a chord is 8 centimeters. Find the distance from the chord to the center of the circle. **(Lesson 9-3)** **3 cm**

Find the value of x.

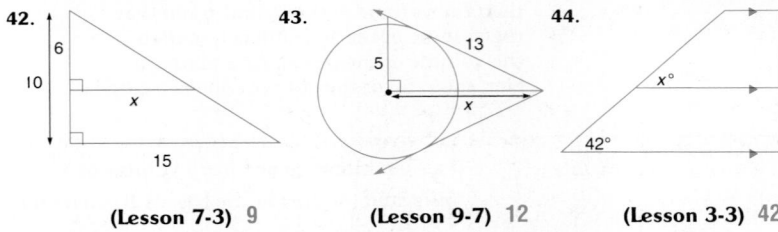

   42. **(Lesson 7-3)** **9**   **43.** **(Lesson 9-7)** **12**   **44.** **(Lesson 3-3)** **42**

Wrap-Up

45. Journal Entry Describe the difference between the concepts of area and volume. Give the formulas for lateral area, surface area, and volume of right prisms and cylinders. **See margin.**

EXTENDING THE LESSON

Math Power: Problem Solving

For a given cylinder, the height is twice the radius, and the total surface area is 54π. Find the volume of the cylinder in terms of π. **54π cubic units**

Additional Answer

45. Area is a two-dimensional measurement, while volume is a three-dimensional measurement. Prisms: $L = Ph$; $T = Ph + 2B$; $V = Bh$; Cylinders: $L = 2\pi rh$; $T = 2\pi rh + 2\pi r^2$; $V = \pi r^2 h$

Enrichment Masters Booklet, p. 68

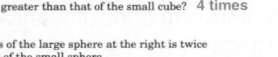

Lesson Resources

- Reteaching Master 11-6
- Practice Master 11-6
- Enrichment Master 11-6
- Evaluation Master, p. 150
- Activity Master, p. 25

 Transparency 11-6 contains the 5-Minute Check and a teaching aid for this lesson.

INTRODUCING THE LESSON

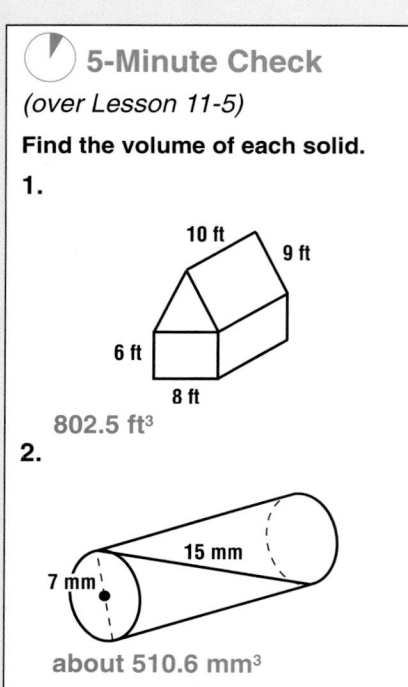

5-Minute Check

(over Lesson 11-5)

Find the volume of each solid.

1.

10 ft
9 ft
6 ft
8 ft

802.5 ft³

2.

15 mm
7 mm

about 510.6 mm³

Motivating the Lesson

Ask how much ice cream an ice cream cone will hold. How can students find out without filling the cone with ice cream?

TEACHING THE LESSON

Teaching Tip When defining the volume of a right circular cone, substitute the area of a circle, πr^2, for *B* in the equation.

11-6 Volume of Pyramids and Cones

Objective
11-6

After studying this lesson, you should be able to:
- find the volume of a pyramid and a circular cone.

Application

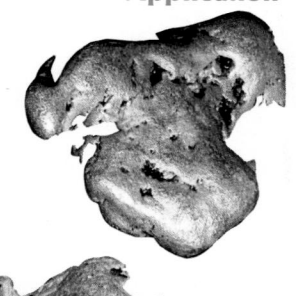

A mining company is trying to decide whether to develop an open pit gold mining operation in the Elk mountain range located in Colorado. Mining companies will usually use open pit mines whenever the ore is relatively close to the surface because they are cheaper to operate than underground mines. An open pit gold mine usually has a shape that is close to an inverted right cone.

In order for the company to decide whether to commit to an investment of several million dollars, it must calculate its return on investment. To do that, it must be able to estimate the amount of gold it's likely to mine. This can be determined from assay reports on core samples taken from the potential mining site. Assay reports will reveal the number of ounces of gold per ton of the material (ore and waste) mined.

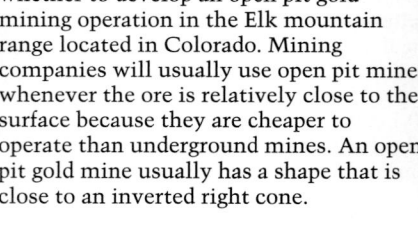

FYI···

The Lost Dutchman's gold mine, somewhere in the mountains of Arizona, is said to have been so rich that, if you were to tap on the walls with a hammer, nuggets of gold would come tumbling down.

A report indicates that each ton of material will have a volume of approximately 10 cubic feet. Now all the company needs to do is compute the volume of the material they expect to remove from this cone-shaped mine. Then they can estimate the possible amount of gold that can be extracted.

A formula to compute the volume of a cone is needed. In the figures at the right, the cone and cylinder have the same base and height, and the pyramid and prism have the same base and height. You can see that the volume of the cone is less than the volume of the cylinder and that the volume of the pyramid is less than the volume of the prism. As a matter of fact, the ratio of the volumes in each case is 1:3.

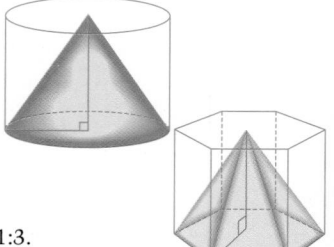

Volume of a Right Circular Cone	If a right circular cone has a volume of *V* cubic units, a height of *h* units, and the area of the base is *B* square units, then $V = \frac{1}{3}Bh$.
Volume of a Right Pyramid	If a right pyramid has a volume of *V* cubic units, a height of *h* units, and the area of the base is *B* square units, then $V = \frac{1}{3}Bh$.

554 CHAPTER 11 SURFACE AREA AND VOLUME

ALTERNATE TEACHING STRATEGIES

Using Experimentation

Have students use water or sand, a cone, and a cylindrical glass to do a volume experiment. Have them make a cone that has the same height and the same circumference as the glass. How many cones of water or sand will it take to fill the glass?   **three**

Using Discovery

Have students make two cones with the same height and base, one oblique and one right. Have them draw a circle around each cone that is halfway between the top and bottom and measure the circumference of the circles. Since the circumferences are the same, the areas must be the same. This demonstrates Cavalieri's Principle.

Example 1

Find the volume of the right circular cone with a radius of 2.7 centimeters and a slant height of 9.5 centimeters. Round your answer to the nearest tenth.

Use the Pythagorean Theorem to find the height.

$$h^2 + r^2 = \ell^2$$
$$h^2 + 2.7^2 = 9.5^2 \quad \textit{Substitute 2.7 for r and 9.5 for } \ell.$$
$$h^2 = 82.96$$
$$h \approx 9.1 \text{ cm}$$

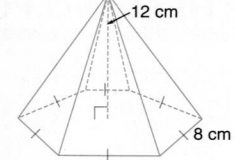

Now find the volume.

$$V = \frac{1}{3} Bh \qquad B = \pi r^2$$
$$\approx \frac{1}{3} \pi (2.7)^2 (9.1)$$
$$\approx 69.5 \text{ cm}^3 \qquad \textit{Use your calculator.}$$

Example 2

Find the volume of a regular hexagonal pyramid if each edge of the base is 8 centimeters long and the height is 12 centimeters.

$$V = \frac{1}{3} Bh$$

The area of a regular polygon is $A = \frac{1}{2} Pa$.

$$V = \frac{1}{3} \left(\frac{1}{2} \cdot 48 \cdot 4\sqrt{3} \right) 12 \qquad \textit{P is the perimeter of}$$
$$= 384\sqrt{3} \qquad \qquad \textit{the regular hexagon.}$$
$$\approx 665.1 \qquad \qquad \textit{a is the apothem.}$$

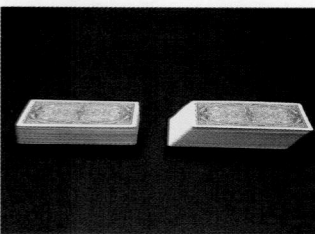

The volume of this pyramid is about 665.1 cubic centimeters.

So far, only the formulas for the volume of right prisms, cylinders, pyramids, and cones have been presented in this chapter. However, an exercise in the last lesson asked you to develop an argument in support of the conjecture that the volumes of some oblique solids are equal to the volumes of corresponding right solids. You may have wondered if the same formulas can be applied to all oblique solids.

The photograph at the right shows two matching decks of cards. One represents a right prism, and the other represents an oblique prism. Since the decks have the same number of cards with all cards the same size and shape, the two prisms represented by the decks have the same volume. This observation was first made by Cavalieri, an Italian mathematician of the seventeenth century. It is known as **Cavalieri's Principle.**

LESSON 11-6   VOLUME OF PYRAMIDS AND CONES   555

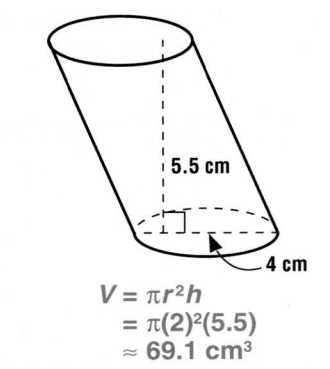
Cavalieri's Principle	If two solids have the same cross-sectional area at every level and the same height, then they have the same volume.

As a result of Cavalieri's Principle, we know that if a prism has a base with an area of B square units and a height of h units, then its volume is Bh cubic units, whether it is right or oblique. Similarly, the volume formulas for cylinders, cones, prisms, and pyramids hold whether they are right or oblique.

Example 3

Using Cavalieri's Principle, find the volume of the cone at the right.

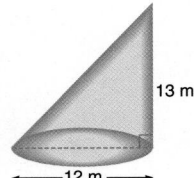

$V = \frac{1}{3} Bh$

$= \frac{1}{3} \pi(6)^2(13)$

$= 156\pi$

≈ 490.1

The volume is about 490.1 cubic meters.

CHECKING FOR UNDERSTANDING

Communicating Mathematics

Read and study the lesson to answer these questions. See margin.

1. How would you find the volume of an ice cream cone?

2. How is the volume of a cone related to that of a cylinder with the same altitude and a base congruent to that of the cone?

3. Devise and describe an experiment that would help convince a friend that the volume of a pyramid is one third the volume of a prism that has the same base and height as the pyramid.

Guided Practice

Find the volume of each solid. Round your answers to the nearest tenth.

4.
8 in.
10 in.
12 in.
320 in³

5.
5 in.
13 in.
about 314.2 in³

6.
11 cm
8 cm
about 609.7 cm³

7. Using the figure at the right, find the volume of the resulting solid if the smaller cone is removed from the larger cone. **about 536.2 in³**

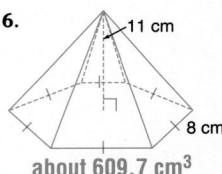
3 in. 8 in.
8 in.

8. If a pyramid has a height of 30 meters and its base is an equilateral triangle with sides of 8 meters, find its volume. **about 277.1 m³**

Additional Answers

1. Sample answer: Measure the radius and the height and use the formula for the volume of a cone.

2. The volume of a cone is one-third the volume of a cylinder of the same height as the cone and with bases congruent to the base of the cone.

3. Sample answer: Use an open pyramid and an open prism with the same base and the same height. Fill the pyramid with sand and pour the sand into the prism. Repeat this procedure until the prism is filled. The pyramid will have to be filled three times in order to fill the prism.

9. Find the volume of a right cone with a slant height of 18 and an angle of 60° at the point of the cone. **about 1322.3 units³**

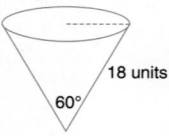
18 units
60°

EXERCISES

Practice

Find the volume of each pyramid. Round your answers to the nearest tenth.

10. The base has an area of 27.9 square millimeters, and the height is 18.5 millimeters. **172.1 mm³**

11. The base has an area of 15 square feet, and the height is 7 feet. **35 ft³**

Find the volume of each cone. Round your answers to the nearest tenth.

12. The base has a radius of 5 feet, and the height is 16 feet. **about 418.9 ft³**

13. about 190.3 m³

13. The base has a diameter of 8.4 meters, and the height is 10.3 meters.

14. The volume of a pyramid is 729 cubic units. If the area of the base is 243 square units, find the height of the pyramid. **9 units**

15. Find the volume of the oblique cone whose height is 21 units and whose base has a radius of 8 units. **about 1407.4 units³**

16. The base of a rectangular pyramid is 30 units by 12 units. If the altitude is 8 units, find its volume. **960 units³**

Find the volume of each solid. Round your answers to the nearest tenth.

17.
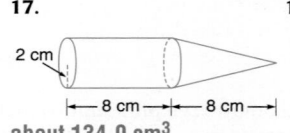
2 cm
|← 8 cm →|← 8 cm →|
about 134.0 cm³

18.
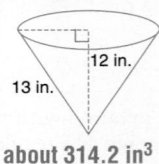
12 in.
13 in.
about 314.2 in³

19.
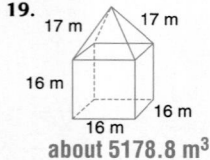
17 m   17 m
16 m
16 m
16 m
about 5178.8 m³

20. A regular square pyramid has a slant height of 15 meters and a lateral edge of 17 meters. What is the volume of this pyramid? **about 1082.8 m³**

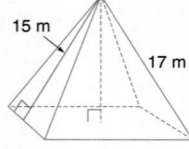
15 m
17 m

21. Find the volume of the regular pyramid at the right if its lateral edges are each 17 units long and its base is 24 units on a side. **192 units³**

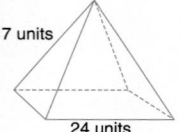
17 units
24 units

LESSON 11-6   VOLUME OF PYRAMIDS AND CONES   557

RETEACHING THE LESSON

Have a student draw a picture of a pyramid or cone. Have another student give a measure for the height, and a third give a measure for either the radius or the length of an edge. Have students continue to add data until one is able to compute the volume of the solid. Continue in this fashion with several problems until all students have participated.

APPLYING THE LESSON

APPLYING THE LESSON

Homework Exercises

Assignment Guide

Basic: 10-24, 31, 33, 35-42
Average: 10-12, 15-27, 31-32, 35-42
Enriched: 11-21 odd, 22-31, 34-42

Reteaching Masters Booklet, p. 69

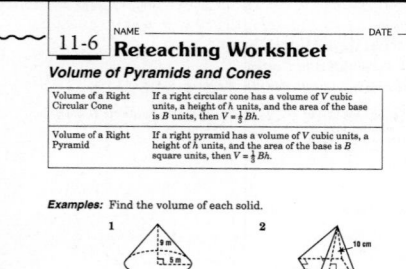

11-6   **Reteaching Worksheet**
Volume of Pyramids and Cones

| Volume of a Right Circular Cone | If a right circular cone has a volume of V cubic units, a height of h units, and the area of the base is B units, then $V = \frac{1}{3}Bh$. |
| Volume of a Right Pyramid | If a right pyramid has a volume of V cubic units, a height of h units, and the area of the base is B square units, then $V = \frac{1}{3}Bh$. |

Examples: Find the volume of each solid.

1
$V = \frac{1}{3}Bh$
$V = \frac{1}{3}\pi(5^2)(9)$
$V = 75\pi$ or about 235.6 m³

2
$V = \frac{1}{3}Bh$
$V = \frac{1}{3}(49) 10$
$V = \frac{490}{3}$ or about 163.3 cm³

Find the volume of each solid. Round your answers to the nearest tenth.

1. 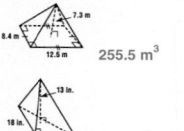 255.5 m³
2. 1187.5 ft³
3. 858 in.³
4.  2513.3 m³
5. 235.6 m³
6. 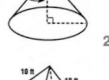 1981.9 ft³

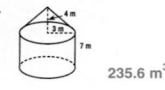
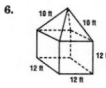

T69
Glencoe Division, Macmillan/McGraw-Hill

Exercise Notes

For Exercise 26, use the tangent function to find the height and the measure of the diagonal. Then use relationships in a 45°- 45° - 90° triangle to find the length of a side.

For Exercise 28, use the Pythagorean Theorem and the relationships in a 30° - 60° - 90° triangle to find the height and the area of the base.

Practice Masters Booklet, p. 80

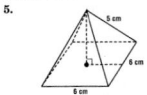
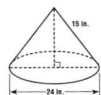

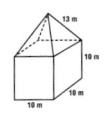
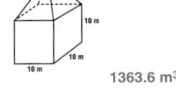
558   Chapter 11

---

22. The eight faces of the regular octahedron at the right are congruent equilateral triangles. If each edge is 12 centimeters, find its volume. **about 814.6 cm³**

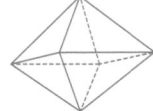

23. Refer to the figure at the right. **108 units³**
    a. Find the volume of the shaded pyramid cut from the rectangular solid shown.
    b. What is the ratio of the volume of the pyramid to the volume of the rectangular solid from which it is cut? **1 to 6**

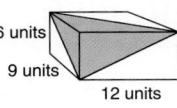

6 units
9 units
12 units

24. A pyramid with a rectangular base has a volume of 80 cubic inches and a height of 5 inches. How many different rectangles are possible for the base if its edge measures are whole numbers? **5 possibilities**

25. Two right circular cones have the same axis, the same vertex, and the same height. The smaller cone lies within the larger one. Find the volume of the space between the two cones if the diameter of one cone is 6 inches, the diameter of the other is 9 inches, and the height of both is 5 inches. **58.9 in³**

26. Find the volume of the regular square pyramid shown at the right. Give your answer to the nearest cubic unit.
    435 units³

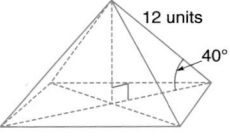

12 units
40°

27. Find the volume of the pyramid shown at the right. **about 48.9 units³**

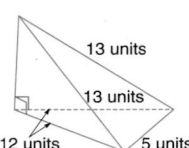

13 units
13 units
12 units
5 units

28. A pyramid with four congruent equilateral triangles as its only faces is known as a regular tetrahedron. If the length of one of its edges is 12 units, find the volume of the tetrahedron. **about 203.6 units³**

29. Find the volume of the frustum of a cone shown below.
    about 5730.3 units³

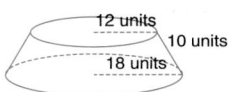

12 units
10 units
18 units

30. Find the volume of the frustum of a pyramid shown below.
    91 in³

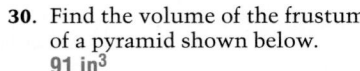
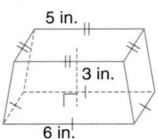

5 in.
3 in.
6 in.

Critical Thinking

31. A cone with a slant height equal to the length of the diameter of the base is inscribed in a sphere with a radius of 8 inches. What is the volume of the cone? *Hint: The definition of sphere appears on page 560.* **about 603.2 in³**

Application

32. Mining A certain open pit mine being dug in the Elk mountain range is to be 420 feet across with a depth of 250 feet. Suppose the assay report projects that the company will be able to retrieve an average of 0.115 ounces of gold per ton of ore and waste mined.

a. What would be the volume of ore and waste material removed during its mining operation? **about 11,545,353 ft³**

32b. about 132,771.6 oz

b. How many ounces of gold should the company expect to retrieve from this mine? (Assume one ton is equivalent to 10 cubic feet.)

c. If the price of gold is $350 per ounce, what is the estimated value of the gold that will be extracted from this mine? **about $46,470,060**

33. History One of the Great Pyramids in Egypt has a square base that is 750 feet on a side. If its original height is estimated to have been 481 feet tall, what was its original volume? **90,187,500 ft³**

34. Landscaping A certain landscaping company has piled a quantity of dry, loose soil against a building. The highest point of the soil is 5 feet above the ground. The base of the pile is semicircular in shape and 12 feet in width along the building. About how many cubic feet of soil are in the pile? **about 94.2 ft³**

Computer

The BASIC computer program below will find the volume of a right circular cone rounded to the nearest cubic unit.

```
10 INPUT "ENTER THE RADIUS OF THE BASE OF THE CONE."; R
20 INPUT "ENTER THE HEIGHT OF THE CONE."; H
30 V = INT ((3.14159 * R^2 * H)/3 + 0.5)
40 PRINT "THE VOLUME OF THE CONE IS ABOUT "; V; " CUBIC
   UNITS."
50 END
```

35. What does line 30 of the program represent? **the formula for the volume of a cone rounded to the nearest unit**

36. How could you change the program to find the volume of a cylinder? **Change line 30 to V = INT (3.14159 * R^2 * H + 0.5)**

37. Use the computer program to check your answers for Exercises 12 and 13.

Mixed Review

38. Find the volume of a rectangular prism that is 3 feet by 5 feet by 8 feet. **(Lesson 11-5) 120 ft³**

39. Find the probability that a point chosen at random in the figure at the right is in the shaded region. Round your answer to the nearest hundredth. **(Lesson 10-8)**
0.82

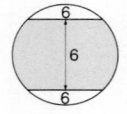

40. What must be true of the two acute angles of a right triangle? **(Lesson 4-1) They are complementary.**

41. Find the distance between the graphs of $A(0, 4)$ and $B(-8, 1)$. **(Lesson 1-4)** $\sqrt{73} \approx 8.5$

Wrap-Up

42. Compare the volumes of cones and cylinders and the volumes of pyramids and prisms. **See margin.**

EXTENDING THE LESSON

Math Power: Problem Solving

Joshua is planning to sell popcorn at the fair. He is either going to use a 2 inches by 6 inches by 8 inches box to put the popcorn in or he is going to use a cone with a radius of 3 inches and a slant height of 10 inches. Which will be more economical for him to use and why?

The cone. Both shapes hold about the same amount of popcorn (box, 96 in.³; cone. 90 in.³), but the box has a much larger surface area (152 in.² vs. 94 in.²), and so is likely to be more expensive.

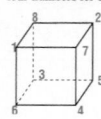
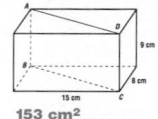
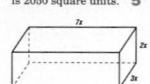
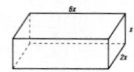
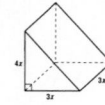
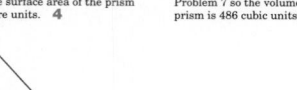

INTRODUCING THE LESSON

 5-Minute Check

(over Lesson 11-6)

1. Using Cavalieri's Principle, find the volume of the cone below.   **about 139.8 cubic units**

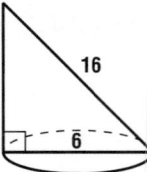

2. A regular square pyramid has a slant height of 16 meters and a lateral edge of 22 meters. Find the volume of the pyramid.   **about 1608.6 m³**

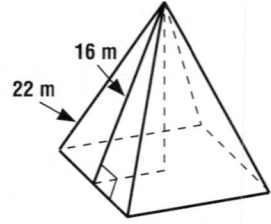

Motivating the Lesson

Go around the room and have each student give an example of something that is a sphere. Point out how common spheres are in our world.

Surface Area and Volume of Spheres

Objectives

After studying this lesson, you should be able to:

- **11-7A** ▪ recognize and define basic properties of spheres,
- **11-7B** ▪ find the surface area of a sphere, and
- **11-7C** ▪ find the volume of a sphere.

Application

Have you ever noticed how small a basketball looks in the hands of someone like Michael Jordan? Great players like Jordan make the ball look like a toy, to do with as they like!

How big is a basketball anyway? That question could be answered by giving its surface area, its volume, its weight, its diameter, or all four.

In this lesson, we will use a basketball as a model of a sphere, and our attention will be focused on finding the surface area and volume of spheres.

For a moment, let's consider infinitely many congruent circles in space, all with the same point for their center. Considered together, all these circles form a **sphere**. In space, a sphere is the set of all points that are a given distance from a given point called its center.

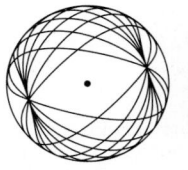 

Several special segments and lines related to spheres are defined and illustrated below.

FYI · · ·

The final score of the first game of basketball was 1 - 0 after 30 minutes of play. The game was stopped so the players could climb up and retrieve the soccer ball from the peach basket.

▪ A **radius** of a sphere is a segment whose endpoints are the center of the sphere and a point on the sphere. In the figure, $\overline{CR}$, $\overline{CP}$, and $\overline{CQ}$ are radii.

▪ A **chord** of a sphere is a segment whose endpoints are points on the sphere. In the figure, $\overline{TS}$ and $\overline{PQ}$ are chords.

▪ A **diameter** of a sphere is a chord that contains the sphere's center. In the figure, $\overline{PQ}$ is a diameter.

▪ A **tangent** to a sphere is a line that intersects the sphere in exactly one point. In the figure, $\overleftrightarrow{AB}$ is tangent to the sphere at X.

ALTERNATE TEACHING STRATEGIES

Using Examples

Bring in and discuss examples of spheres. Ask students what criteria must be met for the solid to be a sphere. You can also use a soft rubber ball to demonstrate a sphere and then squash the ball to form circular solids that are not spheres. This may help students to define the criteria for a sphere.

Using Investigation

You can guide students to discover the formula for the surface area of a sphere. In Investigation 14 on page A13 of **More Investigations in Geometry,** students use manipulatives to explore spheres.

A point

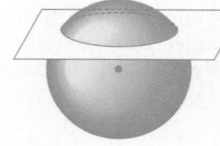

A circle

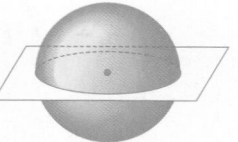

A great circle

A plane can intersect a sphere in a point or in a circle. When a plane intersects a sphere so that it contains the center of the sphere, the intersection is called a **great circle.** A great circle has the same center as the sphere, and its radii are also radii of the sphere. On the surface of a sphere, the shortest distance between any two points is the length of the arc of a great circle passing through those two points. Each great circle separates a sphere into two congruent halves called **hemispheres.**

INVESTIGATION

You can learn more about spheres in Investigation 14 on page A13.

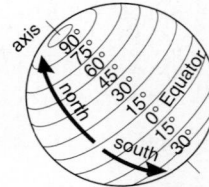

Lines of longitude

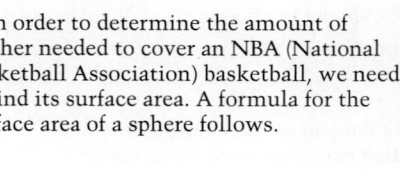

Lines of latitude

The surface of a globe is a good model of a sphere. Each north-south meridian goes halfway around the globe and meets another line at both poles to make a great circle. Of the parallel latitudes, only the equator is a great circle.

In order to determine the amount of leather needed to cover an NBA (National Basketball Association) basketball, we need to find its surface area. A formula for the surface area of a sphere follows.

Surface Area of a Sphere	If a sphere has a surface area of T square units and a radius of r units, then $T = 4\pi r^2$.

Example 1

Sports

The diameter of an NBA basketball is about 9.5 inches. Find its surface area.

The radius of the basketball is about 4.75 inches.

$$T = 4\pi r^2$$
$$= 4\pi(4.75)^2$$
$$\approx 283.5 \text{ in}^2 \quad \textit{Use a calculator.}$$

The surface area of an NBA basketball is about 283.5 square inches.

The development of a formula for the volume of a sphere can be related to the volume of a right pyramid and the surface area of a sphere.

LESSON 11-7   SURFACE AREA AND VOLUME OF SPHERES   561

Chalkboard Example

For Example 2
Find the volume of the empty space in a box containing three golf balls. The diameter of each ball is about 1.5 inches.

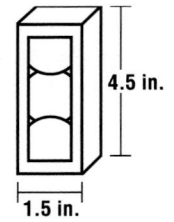

4.5 in.

1.5 in.

$V = Bh - 3\left(\frac{4}{3}\pi r^3\right)$

$= (2.25)(4.5) - 3\left(\frac{4}{3}\right)\pi(0.75)^3$

$\approx 4.8 \text{ in.}^3$

There are about 4.8 in.³ of empty space in the box.

EVALUATING THE LESSON

Checking for Understanding

Exercises 1-13 are designed to help you assess students' understanding through reading, writing, speaking, and modeling. You should work through Exercises 1-4 with your students and then monitor their work on Exercises 5-13.

Closing the Lesson

Speaking Activity Go around the room and have each student state one fact about spheres, their surface area, or their volume.

Imagine separating the space inside a sphere into infinitely many small pyramids, all with their vertices located at the center of the sphere. Collectively, all their bases equal the surface of the sphere shown below. Observe that the height of these very small pyramids is equal to the radius, r, of the sphere.

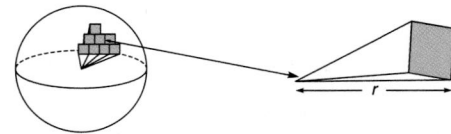

The volume of each pyramid is $\frac{1}{3}Bh$, where B is the area of its base and h is its height. The volume of the sphere is equal to the sum of the volumes of all the infinitely many small pyramids. The volume, V, of the sphere can then be represented as follows.

$$V = \frac{1}{3}B_1h_1 + \frac{1}{3}B_2h_2 + \frac{1}{3}B_3h_3 + \ldots + \frac{1}{3}B_nh_n$$
$$= \frac{1}{3}B_1r + \frac{1}{3}B_2r + \frac{1}{3}B_3r + \ldots + \frac{1}{3}B_nr$$
$$= \frac{1}{3}r(B_1 + B_2 + B_3 + \ldots + B_n)$$
$$= \frac{1}{3}r(4\pi r^2) \qquad B_1 + B_2 + B_3 + \ldots + B_n \text{ is the surface area of the sphere.}$$
$$= \frac{4}{3}\pi r^3$$

Volume of a Sphere
If a sphere has a volume of V cubic units and a radius of r units, then $V = \frac{4}{3}\pi r^3$.

Example 2

Sports

Find the volume of the empty space in a tennis ball can containing three tennis balls. The inside diameter of the can and the diameter of each ball is about 6.5 cm.

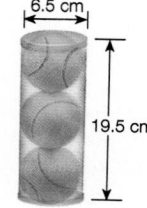
6.5 cm
19.5 cm

$V(\text{empty space}) = V(\text{cylinder}) - V(\text{tennis balls})$

$V = \pi r^2 h - 3\left(\frac{4}{3}\pi r^3\right)$

$= \pi(3.25)^2(19.5) - 3\left(\frac{4}{3}\right)\pi(3.25)^3$

≈ 215.7

There are about 215.7 cubic centimeters of empty space in the can.

CHECKING FOR UNDERSTANDING

Communicating Mathematics

Read and study the lesson to answer these questions. See margin.

1. Transoceanic flights by major airlines always fly a path that is related to a sphere. Describe its relation to a sphere.

2. Describe all the different ways a plane and a sphere can intersect.

Additional Answers

1. A transoceanic flight between two cities follows the great circle that is formed by a plane intersecting the sphere and passing through the two cities and the center of the sphere.
2. A plane and a sphere can either intersect in a point (be tangent) or in a circle.

3. What is a great circle?
4. Describe how the formula for the volume of a sphere was developed in this lesson.

Guided Practice   **Determine whether each statement is *true* or *false*.**

5. A diameter of a sphere is a chord of the sphere. true
6. A radius of a sphere is a chord of the sphere. false
7. All great circles of the same sphere are congruent. true

In the figure, *P* is the center of the sphere, and plane $\mathcal{B}$ intersects the sphere in $\odot R$.

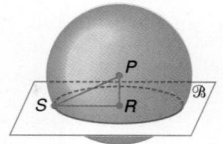

8. Suppose $PS = 25$ and $PR = 7$, find RS. 24
9. Suppose $PS = 13$ and $RS = 12$, find PR. 5

Find the surface area and volume of each sphere described below.

10. The radius is 10 centimeters long. $T \approx 1256.6$ cm^2, $V \approx 4188.8$ cm^3
11. The area of one of its great circles is 50.24 square centimeters.

11. $T = 200.96$ cm^2
$V \approx 267.9$ cm^3

12. Find the volume of a sphere whose surface area is 256π square centimeters. about 2144.7 cm^3
13. Find the volume of air that is contained in the NBA basketball described in Example 1. Ignore the thickness of the ball. about 448.9 in^3

EXERCISES

Practice   **Describe each object as a model of a *circle*, a *sphere*, or *neither*.**

14. ball bearing sphere
15. basketball hoop circle
16. orbit of an electron circle
17. telephone dial circle
18. ping pong ball sphere
19. record circle
20. Jupiter sphere
21. chicken egg neither
22. an orange sphere
23. football neither

Determine whether each statement is *true* or *false*.

24. All radii of a sphere are congruent. true
25. The chord of greatest length in a sphere will always pass through the sphere's center. true
26. A plane and a sphere may intersect in exactly two points. false
27. All diameters of a sphere are congruent. true
28. A diameter of a great circle is a diameter of the sphere. true
29. Two spheres may intersect in exactly one point. true
30. Two different great circles of a sphere intersect in exactly one point. false
31. The intersection of two spheres may be a circle. true
32. The intersection of two spheres with congruent radii may be a great circle. false

LESSON 11-7   SURFACE AREA AND VOLUME OF SPHERES   563

Assignment Guide

Basic: 14-20, 24-37, 42-44, 49-54
Average: 15-23 odd, 24-39, 42, 45-46, 49-54
Enriched: 14-28 even, 29-42, 47-54

Additional Answers

3. The intersection of a plane that contains the center of the sphere and the sphere is called a great circle.
4. The volume of a sphere was generated by summing the volumes of an infinite number of small pyramids. Each pyramid has its base on the surface of the sphere and its height from the base to the center of the sphere.

Reteaching Masters Booklet, p. 70

11-7 NAME _____ DATE _____
Reteaching Worksheet
Reading Mathematics
In the following statements, certain key words or expressions have been left out. Complete each statement with the correct word or expression.

1. The length of the diameter of a circle is twice the length of the **radius**.
2. To find the circumference of a circle, multiply the length of the diameter by **π**.
3. The number of faces in a rectangular solid is **6**.
4. In a prism, there are two faces called **bases** that lie in parallel planes.
5. The two parallel bases of a **cylinder** are circular.
6. In a pentagonal prism, there are two bases and **5** lateral faces.
7. If the lateral edges of a prism are also altitudes, then the prism is a(n) **right** prism. Otherwise, the prism is a(n) **oblique** prism.
8. If a right prism has a lateral area of L square units, a height of h units, and each base has a perimeter of P units then $L =$ **Ph**.
9. If the total surface area of a right prism is T square units, a height of h units, and each base has an area of B square units and a perimeter of P units, then $T =$ **$Ph + 2B$**.
10. In a pyramid all the faces except one intersect at a point called the **vertex**.
11. If a right pyramid has a volume of V cubic units, a height of h units, and the area of the base is B square units, then $V =$ _____. $\frac{1}{3}Bh$
12. If a right cylinder has a volume of V cubic units, a height of h units, and a radius of r units, then $V =$ _____. $\frac{1}{3}\pi r^2 h$
13. If a **sphere** has a surface area of A square units and a radius of r units, then $A = 4\pi r^2$.
14. If a sphere has a volume of V cubic units and a radius of r units, then $V =$ _____. $\frac{4}{3}\pi r^3$
15. The height of each lateral face in a pyramid is called the **slant** height.

T70
Glencoe Division, Macmillan/McGraw-Hill

RETEACHING THE LESSON

Draw a three-dimensional sphere on the chalkboard or overhead. Do not label any of its parts. Then go around the room and ask students to draw and label parts of the sphere. Use the terminology defined in this lesson.

In the figure, *P* is the center of the sphere, and plane $\mathcal{B}$ intersects the sphere in $\odot R$.

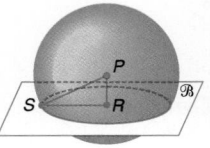

33. Suppose $PS = 15$ and $PR = 9$, find RS. **12**

34. Suppose $PS = 26$ and $RS = 24$, find PR. **10**

Find the surface area and volume of each sphere described below.

35. The diameter is 4000 feet long. $T \approx 50{,}265{,}482 \text{ ft}^2$, $V \approx 33{,}510{,}321{,}640 \text{ ft}^3$

36. $T \approx 113.0 \text{ m}^2$
$V = 112.9 \text{ m}^3$

36. The circumference of one of its great circles is 18.84 meters.

37. If the volume of a sphere is $\frac{32}{3}\pi$ cubic inches, what is the radius? **2 in.**

C

38. What is the ratio of the radii of two spheres if the surface area of one is 4 times the surface area of the other? **2:1**

39. Find the ratio of the volumes of a hemisphere and a cone having congruent bases and equal heights. **2:1**

For Exercises 40 and 41, the volume of the cube is 1728 cubic centimeters.

40. Find the volume of the sphere that can be inscribed inside the cube. **about 905 cm³**

41. Find the volume of the sphere that can be circumscribed about the cube. **about 4701 cm³**

Critical Thinking

42. The edge of a cube, the diameter and height of a cylinder, and the diameter of a sphere all have the same measure. Which has the least surface area? Which has the least volume? **the sphere; the sphere**

Applications

43. Travel Name some cities, countries, or other significant geographic features that a transoceanic great circle route from Chicago, Illinois, to Frankfurt, Germany, would fly over. **See margin.**

44. Sports Find the surface area and volume of a soccer ball that has a circumference of 27 inches. $T \approx 232.05 \text{ in}^2$; $V \approx 332.38 \text{ in}^3$

45. Sports A hemispherical plastic dome is used to cover several indoor tennis courts. If the diameter of the dome measures 400 feet, find the volume enclosed by the dome in cubic yards. **about 620,563 yd³**

46. Food An ice cream cone is 10 centimeters deep and has a diameter of 4 centimeters. A scoop of ice cream with a diameter of 4 centimeters rests on the top of the cone.

a. If all the ice cream melts into the cone, will the cone overflow? **no**

b. If the cone does not overflow, what percentage of the cone will be filled? **80%**

47. Architecture If the hemispherical dome of the Iowa State Capitol is 80 feet in diameter, find the surface area of the dome. **about 10,053.1 ft²**

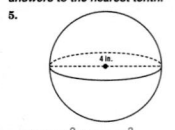
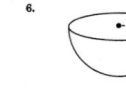

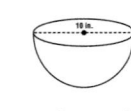

48. Science Consider Earth to be a sphere with a radius of 4000 miles.
a. Find the approximate surface area of Earth. **about 201,061,930 mi²**
b. The area of the land on Earth is about 57,900,000 square miles. What percentage of Earth's surface is land? **28.8%**

Mixed Review

49. Find the volume of a right circular cone if the radius of the base is 5 feet and the height of the cone is 16 feet. **(Lesson 11-6) about 418.9 ft³**

50. Find the area of a trapezoid whose median is 8.5 feet long and whose altitude is 7.1 feet long. **(Lesson 10-5) 60.35 ft²**

51. Can 2.7, 3.0, and 5.3 be the measures of the sides of a right triangle? Explain. **(Lesson 8-2) no; 2.7² + 3.0² ≠ 5.3²**

52. Two isosceles triangles have congruent legs. Must the triangles be congruent? **(Lesson 4-4) no**

53. In the figure, find the value of x. **(Lesson 3-2) 10**

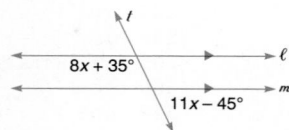

$8x + 35°$

$11x - 45°$

Wrap-Up

54. As the radius of a sphere gets longer, which of the sphere's measurements increases more, the surface area or the volume? Defend your answer. **See margin.**

HISTORY CONNECTION

Why were the European sailors of the fourteenth and fifteenth centuries afraid of plunging off the edge of a flat Earth? At least sixteen centuries earlier, Greek mathematicians not only knew that the Earth was round, but had calculated its circumference!

Eratosthenes of Cyrene (275-194 B.C.) was director of the Alexandrian Library. He knew that on the first day of summer, the Sun was directly over the Egyptian city of Syene, near present-day Aswan. He also knew that Syene was 5000 stades directly south of Alexandria. (An Egyptian stade is roughly 0.1575 kilometers.)

Eratosthenes assumed that the Sun was far enough away that its rays of light arrived at Earth in parallel lines. He measured the angle, α, formed by the top of a pole in Alexandria and the pole's shadow as $7\frac{1}{5}°$. He concluded that ∠AOS was equal to α, where O represented the center of a spherical Earth. He used the following proportion to calculate the circumference of Earth.

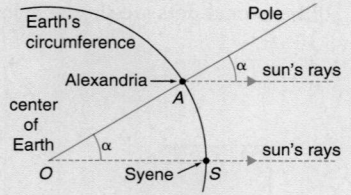

$$\frac{\text{distance from Syene to Alexandria}}{\text{Earth's circumference}} = \frac{\text{measure of angle } \alpha}{360°}$$

$$\frac{5000 \text{ stades}}{\text{Earth's circumference}} = \frac{1}{50}$$

$$\text{Earth's circumference} = 250,000 \text{ stades}$$

Eratosthenes' measurement is 39,375 kilometers. This is remarkably close to the current accepted value of 40,075 kilometers.

LESSON 11-7   SURFACE AREA AND VOLUME OF SPHERES   565

EXTENDING THE LESSON

Math Power: Communication

Suppose a sphere and a cube have equal surface area. Let r represent the measure of the radius of the sphere and s represent the measure of an edge of the cube. Write an equation to show the relationship between r and s.

$$s = \frac{r\sqrt{6\pi}}{3} \text{ or } r = \frac{s\sqrt{6\pi}}{2\pi}$$

History Connection

The History Connection features introduce students to persons or cultures who were involved in the development of mathematics. You may want students to further research the mathematician Eratosthenes of Cyrene.

Additional Answers

54. the volume, since the radius is cubed. In the surface area formula, the radius is only squared.

Enrichment Masters Booklet, p. 70

11-7 Enrichment Worksheet

NAME _____ DATE _____

Spheres and Density

The **density** of a metal is a ratio of its mass to its volume. For example, the mass of aluminum is 2.7 grams per cubic centimeter. Here is a list of several metals and their densities.

Aluminum	2.7 g/cm³	Copper	8.96 g/cm³
Gold	19.32 g/cm³	Iron	7.874 g/cm³
Lead	11.35 g/cm³	Platinum	21.45 g/cm³
Silver	10.50 g/cm³		

To calculate the mass of a piece of metal, multiply volume by density.

Example: Find the mass of a silver ball that is 0.8 cm in diameter.
$M = D \cdot V$
$= 10.5 \cdot \frac{4}{3} \pi (0.4)^3$
$\approx 10.5 (0.27)$
$= 2.83$
The mass is about 2.83 grams.

Find the mass of each metal ball described. Assume the balls are spherical. Round your answers to the nearest tenth.

1. a copper ball 1.2 cm in diameter **8.1 g**

2. a gold ball 0.6 cm in diameter **2.2 g**

3. an aluminum ball with radius 3 cm **305.4 g**

4. a platinum ball with radius 0.7 cm **30.8 g**

Solve. Assume the balls are spherical. Round your answers to the nearest tenth.

5. A lead ball weighs 326 g. Find the radius of the ball to the nearest tenth of a centimeter. **1.9 cm**

6. An iron ball weighs 804 g. Find the diameter of the ball to the nearest tenth of a centimeter. **5.8 cm**

7. A silver ball and a copper ball each have a diameter of 3.5 cm. Which weighs more? How much more? **silver; 34.6 g**

8. An aluminum ball and a lead ball each have a radius of 1.2 cm. Which weighs more? How much more? **lead; 62.6 g**

T70

Glencoe Division, Macmillan/McGraw-Hill

Chapter 11   565

VOCABULARY

Upon completing this chapter, you should be
familiar with the following terms:

536 altitude	**537** lateral area	**544** right circular cone
544 axis	**536** lateral edge	**538** right cylinder
536 base	**536** lateral face	**536** right prism
555 Cavalieri's Principle	**530** net	**542** slant height
560 chord	**544** oblique cone	**529** solid
544 cone	**538** oblique cylinder	**560** sphere
538 cylinder	**536** oblique prism	**529** surface area
560 diameter	**536** prism	**560** tangent
561 great circle	**542** pyramid	**542** vertex
536 height	**560** radius	**548** volume
561 hemisphere	**542** regular pyramid	

SKILLS AND CONCEPTS

OBJECTIVES AND EXAMPLES	REVIEW EXERCISES

Upon completing this chapter, you should
be able to:

- draw two-dimensional nets for three-
  dimensional solids. **(Lesson 11-2)**

A polyhedron and one of its two-
dimensional nets are shown below.

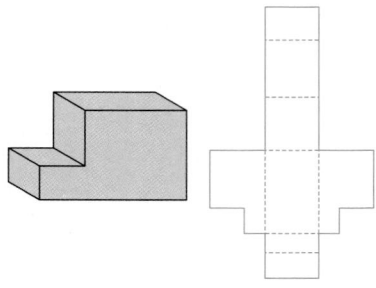

Use these exercises to review and prepare
for the chapter test.

Match each polyhedron with its net.

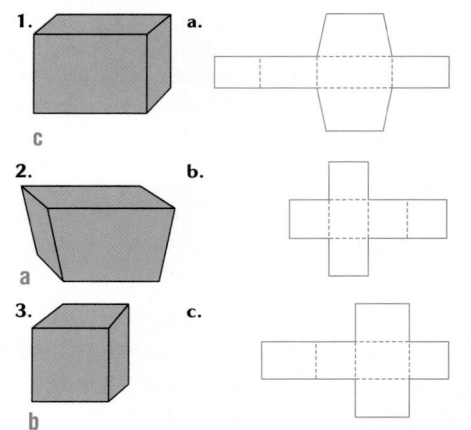

The Chapter Summary and
Review begins with an alphabetical
listing of the new terms that were
presented in the chapter. Have
students define each term and
provide an example of it, if
appropriate.

The Skills and Concepts presented
in the chapter are reviewed using a
side-by-side format. Encourage
students to refer to the Objectives
and Examples on the left as they
complete the Review Exercises on
the right.

The Chapter Summary and
Review ends with exercises that
review Applications and
Connections.

- find the lateral areas and surface areas of right prisms and right cylinders. **(Lesson 11-3)**

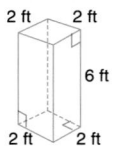 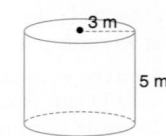

$L = Ph$
$= (8)(6) = 48 \text{ ft}^2$
$T = Ph + 2B$
$= 48 + 2(4)$
$= 56 \text{ ft}^2$

$L = 2\pi rh$
$= 2\pi(3)(5) \approx 94.2 \text{ m}^2$
$T = 2\pi rh + 2\pi r^2$
$\approx 94.2 + 2\pi 3^2$
$\approx 150.7 \text{ m}^2$

Find the lateral area and the surface area of each right prism or right cylinder.
See margin.

4.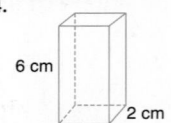

5.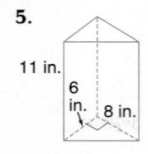

6.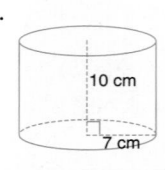

7.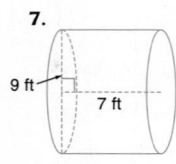

- find the lateral areas and surface areas of regular pyramids and right circular cones. **(Lesson 11-4)**

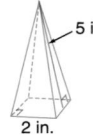 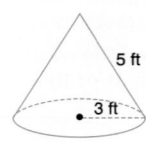

$L = \frac{1}{2}P\ell$
$= \frac{1}{2}(8)(5)$ or 20 in^2
$T = L + B$
$= 20 + 4$
$= 24 \text{ in}^2$

$L = \pi r\ell$
$= \pi(3)(5)$ or 47.1 ft^2
$T = \pi r\ell + \pi r^2$
$\approx 47.1 + \pi 3^2$
$\approx 75.4 \text{ ft}^2$

Find the lateral area and the surface area of each regular pyramid or right circular cone.
See margin.

8.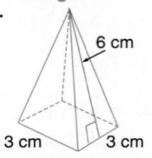

9.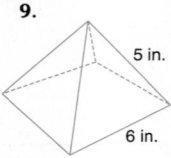

10.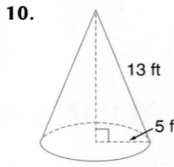

11.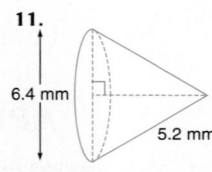

- find the volume of a right prism and a right cylinder. **(Lesson 11-5)**

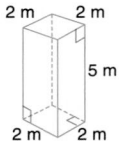 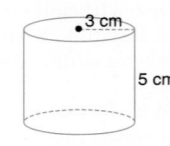

$V = Bh$
$= (4)(5)$
$= 20 \text{ m}^3$

$V = \pi r^2 h$
$= \pi 3^2(5)$
$\approx 141.4 \text{ cm}^3$

Find each of the following. 12. about 5196.2 cm³

12. Find the volume of a regular hexagonal prism if its radius is 10 centimeters and its height is 20 centimeters.

13. Find the volume of a right cylinder if its radius is 10 centimeters and its height is 20 centimeters. about 6283.2 cm³

14. Find the volume of a right cylinder if its diameter is 10 feet and its height is 13 feet. about 1021.0 ft³

CHAPTER 11   567

Alternate Review Strategy

To provide a brief in-class review, you may wish to read the following questions to the class and have them answer verbally.

1. Can a row of six squares be a net for a cube?   no
2. Find the lateral area and surface area of a right prism having a rectangular base of 6 yards by 5 yards and a height of 13 yards. $L = 286$ yd²; $T = 346$ yd²
3. Find the lateral area and surface area of a right cylinder with a radius of 8 units and a height of 45 units. $L \approx 2261.9$ square units; $T \approx 2664.1$ square units
4. Find the lateral area and surface area of a regular pyramid with a slant height of 22 centimeters and a square base with edges measuring 10 centimeters. $L = 440$ cm²; $T = 540$ cm²
5. Find the lateral area and surface area of a right circular cone if its slant height measures 7 inches and its diameter measures 9 inches. $L \approx 99.0$ in.²; $T \approx 162.6$ in.²
6. Find the volume of a regular hexagonal prism if one side of its base is 4 meters and its height is 18 meters.   about 748.2 m³
7. Find the volume of a right cylinder if its radius is 4 meters and its height is 18 meters.   about 904.8 m³
8. Find the volume of a triangular pyramid if its base is an equilateral triangle with sides 7 millimeters long and it has a height of 21 millimeters.   about 148.5 mm³
9. Find the volume of a right circular cone if its height is 14.4 feet and its radius is 4.7 feet.   about 333.1 ft³
10. Find the surface area and volume of a sphere if its diameter is 9.1 miles. $A \approx 260.2$ mi²; $V \approx 394.6$ mi³

A two-page Cumulative Review from the *Evaluation Masters* is shown below. It can be used to review skills and concepts presented thus far in the text. Standardized Test Practice Questions are also provided in the *Evaluation Masters*.

Evaluation Masters, pp. 151-152

NAME _____ DATE _____

Cumulative Review (Chapters 1-11)

For questions 1-4, refer to the net at the right.

15 cm / 8 cm

1. Identify the solid. 1. _triangular prism_
2. Find the lateral area. 2. _360 cm²_
3. Find the total surface area. 3. _408 cm²_
4. Find the volume. 4. _360 cm³_

For questions 5 and 6, use a regular polygon with an exterior angle measuring 45°.

5. Identify the kind of polygon. 5. _octagon_
6. Find the measure of each interior angle. 6. _135_

7. Cindy bought $5.00 worth of postage stamps to mail letters and postcards. If she used all of the stamps, how many letters at 29¢ each and how many postcards at 19¢ each did she mail? 7. _12 letters, 8 postcards_

8. The perimeter of a trapezoid is 37 inches. Its nonparallel sides are 6 inches and 9 inches long. If the height of the trapezoid is 4 inches, find its area. 8. _44 in²_

For questions 9 and 10, use ⊙T in a coordinate plane. The equation of ⊙T is (x − 3)² + y² = 36.

9. Find the radius. 9. _6_
10. Find the coordinates of the center. 10. _(3, 0)_

11. m∠AOB = 90 and AB = 12√2. Find the area of the shaded region. Use 3.14 for π. 11. _41.04 square units_

For questions 12-14, use the circle at the right. BF is a tangent segment.

12. If DCB = 126, find m∠DBF. 12. _63_
13. If CE = x + 5, AE = 3, DE = 8, and EB = 9, find CE. 13. _24_
14. If AB = 38, and DC = 110, find m∠DEC. 14. _74_

151
Glencoe Division, Macmillan/McGraw-Hill

NAME _____ DATE _____

Cumulative Review (Chapters 1-11)—continued

For questions 15 – 17, refer to the figure on the right.

15. If m∠DAB = 37 and m∠ADB = 28, find m∠DBC. 15. _65_
16. If m∠DAB = m∠ADB = 30, and AB = 14, find BC. 16. _7_
17. If DB = 6, and AD = 8, and m∠ADB = 60, find AB. Leave the answer in radical form. 17. _√52_

18. A map is scaled so that one-half inch represents 25 miles. Two towns are 3½ inches apart on the map. What is the actual distance between the towns? 18. _175 miles_

19. In △DEF, G is the midpoint of DE and H is the midpoint of DE. If GH = 2x + 5 and DF = 5x − 6, find GH. 19. _37_

20. △ABC ∼ △DEF. If AB = 16, AC = 24, and DE = 6, find DF. 20. _9_

For questions 21 – 23, use ▱JKLM. Suppose KM bisects JL at O.

21. If m∠JKL = 9x + 10 and m∠KLM = 5x −12, find m∠MJK. 21. _175 miles_
22. If JO = 2x + 1 and JL = 5x − 8, find OL. 22. _21_
23. If JK = KL, m∠KLO = x + 3 and m∠KJM = 3x − 5, find m∠JKL. 23. _152_

24. Joe spent ⅓ of his money on a ticket for the movies. He spent ¼ of what was left on snacks during the movie. After the movies, he spent ½ of what was left for a hamburger and yogurt. He took a bus home for $1 and had $2 left. How much money did he have before he went to the movies? 24. _$12_

25. In △RST, m∠R = 72, and m∠T = 55. Which side is the shortest side in △RST? 25. _RT_

152
Glencoe Division, Macmillan/McGraw-Hill

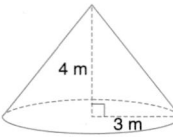
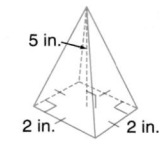
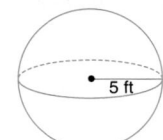

OBJECTIVES AND EXAMPLES	REVIEW EXERCISES

■ find the volume of a circular cone and a pyramid. **(Lesson 11-6)**

4 m / 3 m

5 in. / 2 in. / 2 in.

$$V = \frac{1}{3} Bh$$
$$= \frac{1}{3} \pi(3^2)(4)$$
$$\approx \frac{1}{3} (28.3)(4)$$
$$\approx 37.7 \text{ m}^3$$

$$V = \frac{1}{3} Bh$$
$$= \frac{1}{3} (4)(5)$$
$$= 6.7 \text{ in}^3$$

Find each of the following.

15. Find the volume of a triangular pyramid if its base is an equilateral triangle with sides 9 centimeters long and its height is 15 centimeters. **about 175.4 cm³**

16. Find the volume of a right circular cone if its height is 22 centimeters and its radius is 11 centimeters. **about 2787.6 cm³**

17. Find the volume of a right circular cone if the circumference of its base is 62.8 millimeters and its height is 15 millimeters. **about 1570.8 mm³**

■ find the surface area and volume of a sphere. **(Lesson 11-7)**

5 ft

$$T = 4\pi r^2$$
$$= 4\pi 5^2 \text{ or } 314.2 \text{ ft}^2$$

$$V = \frac{4}{3} \pi r^3$$
$$= \frac{4}{3} \pi 5^3 \text{ or } 523.6 \text{ ft}^3$$

Answer each of the following.

18. All great circles of a sphere are congruent. Write *yes* or *no*. **yes**

19. Find the surface area of the moon if its diameter is approximately 2160 miles.

20. Find the volume of a sphere with a radius of 20 feet. **about 33,510.3 ft³**

19. **about 14,657,415 mi²**

APPLICATIONS AND CONNECTIONS

21. Make a model to solve this problem. Brett has a number of cubic blocks. He makes a square by putting them all together on a flat surface. Then he takes the same blocks and makes a cube. What is the least number of blocks greater than one that Brett can have? **(Lesson 11-1) 64 blocks**

22. **Science** Suppose two different crystals occur in the shape of right prisms. One crystal has a rectangular base of 2 units by 3 units and a height of 2.5 units. The other crystal has a regular hexagonal base with sides of 2.1 units and a height of 2.3 units. Which crystal has the greater surface area? **(Lesson 11-3) crystal with hexagonal base**

23. A waterbed is 6.5 feet long, 5.5 feet wide, and 1 foot thick. If water weighs about 60 pounds per cubic foot, what is the total weight of the water in the waterbed? **(Lesson 11-5) 2145 lb**

24. **Manufacturing** A ball is formed by molding rubber in a form that gives it an inside diameter of 8 centimeters and an outside diameter of 85 millimeters. What volume of rubber is used to produce this ball? **(Lesson 11-7) about 53.5 cm³**

1-2. See Solutions Manual.

1. Draw a rectangular prism with a square base that is 5 units on each side and a height that is 10 units.

2. Sketch a net of a right circular cylinder.

Find the surface area of each solid figure. Round answers to the nearest tenth. Assume that the bases of each pyramid or prism are regular.

3.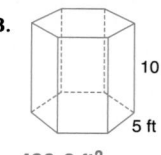

10 ft

5 ft

429.9 ft²

4.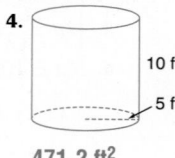

10 ft

5 ft

471.2 ft²

5.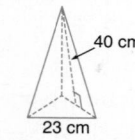

40 cm

23 cm

1609.1 cm²

6. a right circular cone with a radius of 27 millimeters and a height of 30 millimeters **5713.8 mm²**

7. a sphere with diameter of 6 inches **113.1 in²**

Find the volume of each solid figure. Round answers to the nearest tenth. Assume that the bases of each pyramid or prism are regular.

8.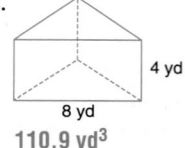

4 yd

8 yd

110.9 yd³

9.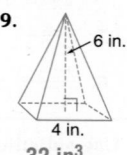

6 in.

4 in.

32 in³

10.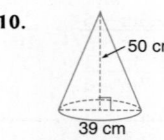

50 cm

39 cm

19,909.8 cm³

11. a right cylinder with diameter of 39 centimeters and a height of 50 centimeters **59,729.5 cm³**

12. a sphere with radius of 18 millimeters **24,429.0 mm³**

Answer each of the following.

13. A rectangular swimming pool is 4 meters wide and 10 meters long. A concrete walkway is poured around the pool. The walkway is 1 meter wide and 0.1 meter deep. What is the volume of the concrete? **3.2 m³**

14. The base of a right prism is a right triangle with legs 6 inches and 8 inches. If the height of the prism is 16 inches, find the lateral area of the prism. **384 in²**

15. Find the volume of the figure at the right. Round your answer to the nearest tenth. **1492.3 cm³**

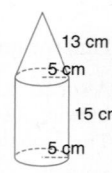

13 cm

5 cm

15 cm

5 cm

Bonus

The base of a right prism is a rectangle. The length of the rectangular base is twice its width. The height of the prism is twice the longest side of its base. If the volume of the prism is 216 cubic feet, find its surface area. **252 ft²**

Using the Chapter Test

This page may be used as a test or as a review. In addition, two multiple-choice tests (Forms 1A and 1B) and two free-response tests (Forms 2A and 2B) are provided in the *Evaluation Masters*. Chapter 11 Test, Form 1A is shown below.

Evaluation Masters, pp. 141-142

NAME _____ DATE _____
Chapter 11 Test, Form 1A

Write the letter for the correct answer in the blank at the right of each problem.

1. Which solid corresponds to the net shown at the right?
A.   B.
C.   D.
1. __A__

2. The base of a right rectangular prism is 12 cm by 8 cm. The height is 5 cm. Find its surface area.
A. 196 cm² B. 480 cm² C. 392 cm² D. 200 cm²
2. __C__

3. The slant height of a regular pentagonal pyramid is 8 cm, and the length of each side of the base is 4 cm. Find the lateral area.
A. 160 cm² B. 32 cm² C. 60 cm² D. 80 cm²
3. __D__

4. The radius of the base of a right circular cone is 9 in., and its slant height is 13 in. Find the total surface area to the nearest tenth. Use 3.14 for π.
A. 367.4 in² B. 254.3 in² C. 621.7 in² D. 898 in²
4. __C__

For questions 5-7, refer to the figure at the right.

5. Find the lateral area.
A. 21 π m² B. 42 π m² C. 63 π m² D. 147 π m²
5. __B__

6. Find the surface area.
A. 51 π m² B. 63 π m² C. 21 π m² D. 60 π m²
6. __D__

7. Find the volume.
A. 63 π m³ B. 42 π m³ C. 21 π m³ D. 126 π m³
7. __A__

8. The volume of a cube is 125 in³. Find the surface area.
A. 25 in² B. 150 in² C. 100 in² D. 625 in²
8. __B__

141
Glencoe Division, Macmillan/McGraw-Hill

NAME _____ DATE _____
Chapter 11 Test, Form 1A (continued)

9. In which way can a plane intersect a sphere?
A. a circle only B. a line only C. a point only D. a point or a circle
9. __D__

10. Find the surface area of a sphere with a radius of 5 in.
A. 100 π in² B. 166 ⅔ π in² C. 50 π in² D. 83 ⅓ π in²
10. __A__

11. Find the volume of the figure on the right
A. 120 π cm³ B. 162 π cm³ C. 68 π cm³ D. 102 π cm³
11. __D__

12. Jon placed a cubical stone block with 12 inch edges in a water-filled cube with edges 15 inches long. How much water is displaced?
A. 1728 in³ B. 1647 in³ C. 27 in³ D. 180 in³
12. __A__

13. The length of the base of a rectangular prism is twice the width. The perimeter of the base is 42 cm. Find the height of the prism if the volume is 980 cm³.
A. 14 cm B. 23.3 cm C. 10 cm D. 18 cm
13. __C__

14. The area of a rectangle is to be 24 square units. The length and width are to be whole numbers. What dimensions give the greatest perimeter?
A. 8 units by 3 units B. 12 units by 2 units C. 6 units by 4 units D. 24 units by 1 unit
14. __D__

15. If the lateral edges of a prism are not altitudes, then the prism is a(n) __?__ prism.
A. right B. oblique C. regular D. lateral
15. __B__

Bonus

A right circular cone has its vertex on the surface of a sphere, and its base is a section of the sphere made by a plane passing through the center. Find the ratio of the volume of the cone to the volume of the sphere.
A. 4:1 B. 3:4 C. 1:4 D. 1:3
Bonus __C__

142
Glencoe Division, Macmillan/McGraw-Hill

Test and Review Generator software is provided in Apple, IBM, and Macintosh versions. You may use this software to create your own tests or worksheets, based on the needs of your students.

The **Performance Assessment Booklet** provides an alternate assessment for evaluating student progress. An assessment for this chapter can be found on pages 21-22.

Using the Algebra Review

The goals of this two-page review of algebraic skills, concepts, and applications are as follows:

- It provides students a chance to review important concepts from algebra that will be useful as they study geometry.
- It gives students an opportunity to retain the concepts they learned in previous algebra courses and may need for future mathematics courses.

The review is presented in a side-by-side format. Encourage students to refer to the Objectives and Examples on the left as they complete the Review Exercises on the right.

Algebra Review

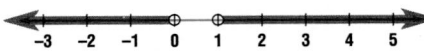

OBJECTIVES AND EXAMPLES	REVIEW EXERCISES

■ Solve open sentences involving absolute value and graph the solution sets.

$$|2x - 1| > 1$$

$$2x - 1 > 1 \quad \text{or} \quad 2x - 1 < -1$$
$$2x > 2 \qquad\qquad 2x < 0$$
$$x > 1 \qquad\qquad x < 0$$

The solution set is $\{x | x > 1 \text{ or } x < 0\}$.

number line from -3 to 5

Solve each open sentence. Then graph its solution set. See Solutions Manual for graphs.

1. $|y - 1| \le 5$ $\{y | -4 \le y \le 6\}$
2. $|2 - n| = 5$ $\{n | n = -3 \text{ or } n = 7\}$
3. $\left|2p - \frac{1}{2}\right| > \frac{9}{2}$ $\{p | p < -2 \text{ or } p > \frac{5}{2}\}$
4. $|7a - 10| < 0$ ∅

■ Add and subtract rational expressions.

$$\frac{m-1}{m+1} + \frac{4}{2m+5}$$

$$= \frac{2m+5}{2m+5} \cdot \frac{m-1}{m+1} + \frac{m+1}{m+1} \cdot \frac{4}{2m+5}$$

$$= \frac{2m^2 + 3m - 5}{2m^2 + 7m + 5} + \frac{4m + 4}{2m^2 + 7m + 5}$$

$$= \frac{2m^2 + 7m - 1}{2m^2 + 7m + 5}$$

Find each sum or difference.

5. $\frac{x}{x^2 + 3x + 2} + \frac{1}{x^2 + 3x + 2}$ $\frac{1}{x+2}$
6. $\frac{2x}{4x^2 - 9} - \frac{3}{9 - 4x^2}$ $\frac{1}{2x-3}$
7. $\frac{x}{x+3} - \frac{5}{x-2}$ $\frac{x^2 - 7x - 15}{x^2 + x - 6}$
8. $\frac{2x+3}{x^2 - 4} + \frac{6}{x+2}$ $\frac{8x-9}{x^2-4}$

■ Solve systems of equations by the substitution method.

Use substitution to solve the system of equations $y = x - 1$ and $4x - y = 19$.

$$4x - y = 19 \qquad\qquad y = x - 1$$
$$4x - (x - 1) = 19 \qquad y = 6 - 1$$
$$3x + 1 = 19 \qquad\qquad y = 5$$
$$3x = 18$$
$$x = 6$$

The solution is $(6, 5)$.

Use substitution to solve each system of equations.

9. $x = 2y$ $(4, 2)$
   $x + y = 6$
10. $2m + n = 1$ $(3, -5)$
    $m - n = 8$
11. $3a - 2b = -4$ $(0, 2)$
    $3a + b = 2$
12. $3x - y = 1$ $\left(\frac{1}{2}, \frac{1}{2}\right)$
    $2x + 4y = 3$

$\frac{11}{20}$ or 0.55

■ Find the probability of a simple event.

A soccer team consists of 8 seniors, 7 juniors, 3 sophomores, and 2 freshmen. The probability that a player chosen at random is a senior is $\frac{8}{20}$ or 0.4.

13. For the soccer team listed at the left, find the probability that a player chosen at random is not a junior or a freshman.

14. What is the probability that a number chosen at random from the first 100 positive integers is prime? $\frac{25}{100}$ or 0.25

OBJECTIVES AND EXAMPLES	REVIEW EXERCISES

Graph inequalities in the coordinate plane.

Graph
$2x + 7y < 9$.

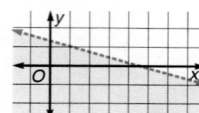

Graph each inequality. See margin.

15. $x + 2y > 5$

16. $4x - y \leq 8$

17. $3x - 2y < 6$

18. $\frac{1}{2} y \geq x + 4$

Simplify radical expressions involving addition and subtraction.

$\sqrt{48} + \sqrt{54} - 2\sqrt{3}$
$= \sqrt{4^2 \cdot 3} + \sqrt{3^2 \cdot 6} - 2\sqrt{3}$
$= 4\sqrt{3} + 3\sqrt{6} - 2\sqrt{3}$
$= 2\sqrt{3} + 3\sqrt{6}$

Simplify.

19. $2\sqrt{13} + 8\sqrt{15} - 3\sqrt{15} + 3\sqrt{13}$ $\mathbf{5\sqrt{13} + 5\sqrt{15}}$

20. $4\sqrt{27} + 6\sqrt{48}$ $\mathbf{36\sqrt{3}}$

21. $5\sqrt{18} - 3\sqrt{112} - 3\sqrt{98}$ $\mathbf{-6\sqrt{2} - 12\sqrt{7}}$

22. $\sqrt{8} + \sqrt{\frac{1}{8}}$ $\mathbf{\frac{9\sqrt{2}}{4}}$

Solve quadratic equations by using the quadratic formula.

Solve $2x^2 + 7x - 16 = 0$.

$x = \dfrac{-b \pm \sqrt{b^2 - 4ac}}{2a}$ $a = 2, b = 7, c = -16$

$= \dfrac{-7 \pm \sqrt{7^2 - 4(2)(-16)}}{2(2)}$ or $\dfrac{-7 \pm \sqrt{177}}{4}$

The roots are $\dfrac{-7 + \sqrt{177}}{4}$ and $\dfrac{-7 - \sqrt{177}}{4}$.

Solve each quadratic equation by using the quadratic formula.

23. $x^2 - 8x = 20$ **10, -2**

24. $5b^2 + 3 = -9b$

25. $9k^2 = 12k + 1$ $\mathbf{\frac{2 \pm \sqrt{5}}{3}; 1.41, -0.08}$

26. $2m^2 - \frac{17m}{6} + 1 = 0$ $\mathbf{\frac{3}{4}, \frac{2}{3}}$

24. $\mathbf{\frac{-9 \pm \sqrt{21}}{10}}$; **-0.44, -1.36**

Applications and Connections

27. Finance   Last year, Jodi invested $10,000, part at 8% annual interest and the rest at 6% annual interest. If she received $760 in interest at the end of the year, how much did she invest at each rate? **$2000 at 6%, $8000 at 8%**

28. Physics   The height h, in feet, of a rocket t seconds after blast-off is given by the formula $h = 1440t - 16t^2$. After how many seconds will this rocket reach a height of 25,000 feet? 35,000 feet? **≈ 23.5 sec., ≈ 66.5 sec; never**

29. Sales   When you use Ray's Taxi Service, a two-mile trip costs $6.30, a five-mile trip costs $11.25, and a ten-mile trip costs $19.50. Write an equation to describe this relationship and use it to find the cost of a one-mile trip. $\mathbf{y = 1.65x + 3; \$4.65}$

30. Geometry   Find the measure of the area of the shaded region below.
$\mathbf{x^2 + 4x}$

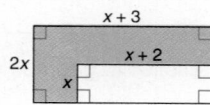

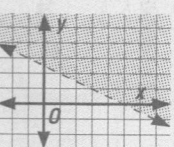
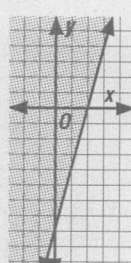
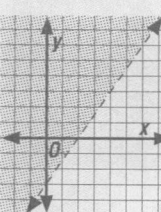
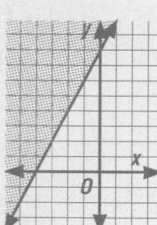

12

More Coordinate Geometry

PREVIEWING THE CHAPTER

This chapter demonstrates several uses of coordinate geometry. Students begin by graphing linear equations, using intercepts and the slope-intercept method. Then, they write equations for lines based on information given about their graphs. Students then learn to use coordinate geometry to prove theorems. In the ensuing introduction to vectors, students find the magnitude and direction of a vector, determine if two vectors are equal, and perform operations with vectors. Finally, students learn to use coordinates to locate points in space, to apply distance and midpoint formulas in space, and to determine the center and radius of a sphere.

Problem-Solving Strategy Students learn to solve problems by writing and solving an equation.

Lesson Objective Chart

Lesson (Pages)	Lesson Objectives	State/Local Objectives
12-1 (574-579)	**12-1A**: Graph linear equations using the intercepts method.	
	12-1B: Graph linear equations using the slope-intercept method.	
12-2 (580-585)	**12-2**: Write an equation of a line given information about its graph.	
12-3 (586-591)	**12-3**: Relate equations of lines and statistics to geometric concepts.	
12-4 (592-594)	**12-4**: Solve problems by using equations.	
12-5 (595-600)	**12-5**: Prove theorems using coordinate proofs.	
12-6 (601-606)	**12-6A**: Find the magnitude and direction of a vector.	
	12-6B: Determine if two vectors are equal.	
	12-6C: Perform operations with vectors.	
12-7 (607-612)	**12-7A**: Locate a point in space.	
	12-7B: Use the distance and midpoint formulas for points in space.	
	12-7C: Determine the center and radius of a sphere.	

ORGANIZING THE CHAPTER

You may want to refer to the **Course Planning Calendar** on page T28.

Lesson Planning Guide / Blackline Masters Booklets

Lesson (Pages)	Pacing Chart (days) Course I	II	III	Reteaching	Practice	Enrichment	Evaluation	Technology	Lab Manual	Mixed Problem Solving	Applications	Cooperative Learning Activity	Multicultural	Transparencies
12-1 (574-579)		1.5	1.5	p. 71	p. 82	p. 71		p. 12						12-1
12-2 (580-585)		1.5	1.5	p. 72	p. 83	p. 72	Quiz A, p.163		pp.86-89					12-2
12-3 (586-591)		2	2	p. 73	p. 84	p. 73		p. 48			p. 26			12-3
12-4 (592-594)		1	1		p. 85		Quiz B, p.163 Mid-Chapter Test, p. 167							12-4
12-5 (595-600)		2	1.5	p. 74	p. 86	p. 74						p. 40		12-5
12-6 (601-606)		2	1.5	p. 75	p. 87	p. 75	Quiz C, p.164			p. 12				12-6
12-7 (607-612)		1	1	p. 76	p. 88	p. 76	Quiz D, p.164						p. 12	12-7
Review (614-616)		1	1	Multiple Choice Tests, Forms 1A and 1B, pp. 155-158 Free Response Tests, Forms 2A and 2B, pp. 159-162										
Test (617)		1	1	Cumulative Review. pp. 165-166 Standardized Tests Practice Questions, p. 168										

Course I: Chapters 1-11; Course II: Chapters 1-12; Course III: Chapters 1-13

Other Chapter Resources

Student Edition

Chapter Opener, pp. 572-573
History Connection, p. 579
History Connection, p. 591
Cooperative Learning Project, p. 594
Mid-Chapter Review, p. 600
Journal Entry, pp. 600, 612
Portfolio, p. 606
Technology, p. 613
College Entrance Exam Preview, pp. 618-619
More Investigations in Geometry, p. A14
Extended Project 4, pp. B14-B16

Teacher's Classroom Resources

Transparency 12-0
Real World Applications Transparencies, 24, 25, 26
Performance Assessment Booklet, pp. 23-24
Problem-of-the-Week Activity Cards, 33, 34
Tech Prep Applications Booklet, pp. 23-24
LOGO Instruction Materials, Technology Masters pp. 19-36

Other Supplements

Glencoe Mathematics Professional Series

Software

Test and Review Generator (Apple, IBM, and Macintosh)
Teacher's Guide for Software Resources

ENHANCING THE CHAPTER

Cooperative Learning

Providing Closure to the Lesson

After each session, ample time should be provided for students to summarize what they have learned. To reinforce their understanding of the academic content acquired during the session, groups should review the major points covered and discuss any additional questions that they may have about the content. Class discussions can be a proper forum for this review. For example, select a member of one group to discuss with the class what his or her group concluded and how they reached these conclusions. Encourage the reporter to be thorough by asking for specific examples or additional details about various points. Do not immediately accept or reject the report, but involve the rest of the class by asking members of other groups if they agree or disagree with the conclusions reached by the reporter's group and if any group used different procedures to arrive at the same conclusions. You can also ask groups to relate this content to content learned earlier and to provide examples of different settings or applications where the content could be utilized. Such sharing of ideas and methods will ensure a greater retention of the academic content learned during the group activities.

Technology

The Technology Feature following Lesson 12-7 uses graphing calculators to make perspective drawings. Formulas for converting three-dimensional coordinates to projection coordinates are given. Students are asked to use these formulas to find the projection coordinates and graph the perspective drawings. After students have completed the exercises given in this feature, you may want to have them experiment by choosing their own three-dimensional coordinates to use to make perspective drawings.

Critical Thinking

To encourage students to develop their critical-thinking skills, use questioning techniques that stimulate thought and investigation, such as, "What do you think will happen if...?", "What patterns do you see?", "How can you tell?", "Can you think of an example when...?", and so on. For example, ask students what they think will happen when $|x|$ gets extremely large in the standard equation for a hyperbola. (The hyperbola is virtually indistinguishable from its asymptotes.) Get students to suggest ways to explore the question, make conjectures, and demonstrate their conclusions. Begin a collection of similar questions that can be used to stimulate students' thinking as you read professional books or journals such as *The Mathematics Teacher*.

Cooperative Learning, p. 40

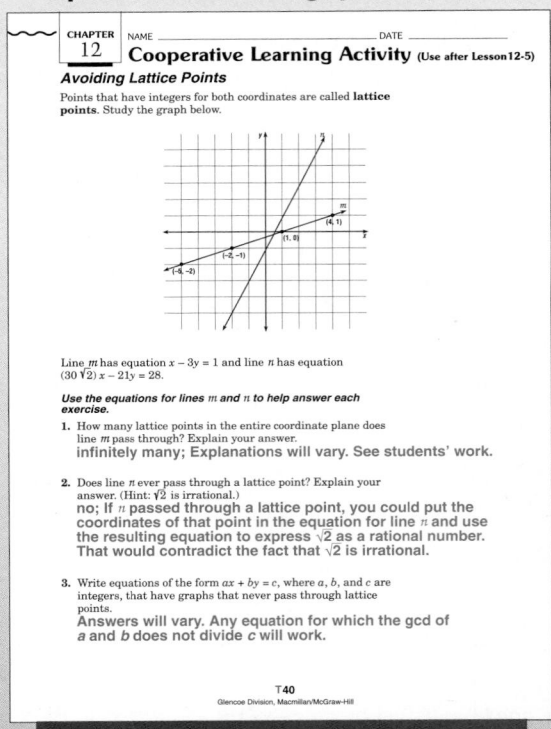

Technology, p. 12

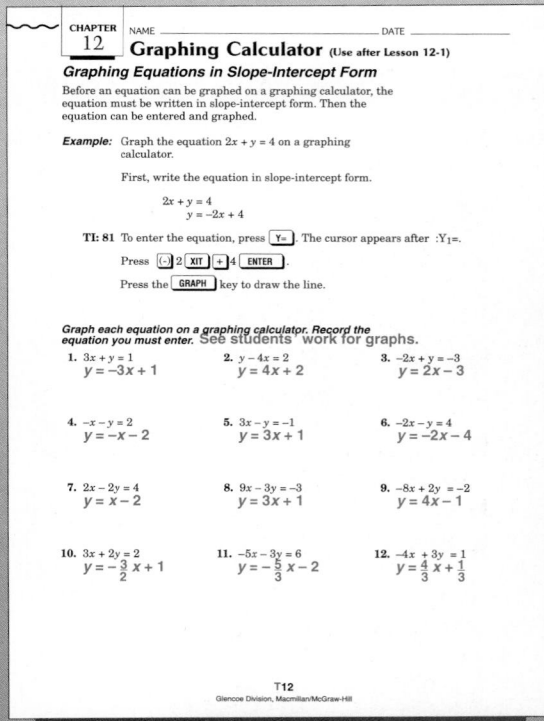

Problem of the Week Activity

The card shown below is one of two available for this chapter. It can be used as a class or small group activity.

Activity Card

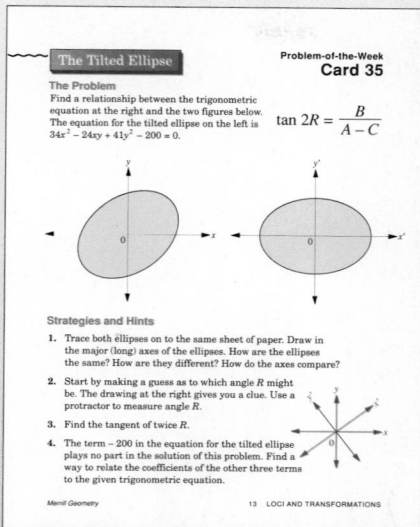

The Tilted Ellipse

Problem-of-the-Week
Card 35

The Problem

Find a relationship between the trigonometric equation at the right and the two figures below. The equation for the tilted ellipse on the left is $34x^2 - 24xy + 41y^2 - 200 = 0$.

$$\tan 2R = \frac{B}{A - C}$$

Strategies and Hints

1. Trace both ellipses on to the same sheet of paper. Draw in the major (long) axes of the ellipses. How are the ellipses the same? How are they different? How do the axes compare?

2. Start by making a guess as to which angle R might be. The drawing at the right gives you a clue. Use a protractor to measure angle R.

3. Find the tangent of twice R.

4. The term -200 in the equation for the tilted ellipse plays no part in the solution of this problem. Find a way to relate the coefficients of the other three terms to the given trigonometric equation.

Merrill Geometry   13   LOCI AND TRANSFORMATIONS

Manipulatives and Models

The following materials may be used as models or manipulatives in Chapter 12.

- grid paper, stopwatch, ball, toy car (Lesson 12-6)
- scientific calculator (Lesson 12-6)
- grid paper, ruler, protractor (Lesson 12-6)
- rectangular solid (Page 613)
- graphing calculator (Page 613)

Outside Resources

Books/Periodicals

Cole, R.J. *Vector Methods.* Van Nostrand Reinhold Company.

Davis, P. and R. Hersh. *Descartes' Dream.* Harcourt Brace Jovanovich.

Posamentier, Alfred and William Wernick. *Advanced Geometric Constructions.* Dale Seymour Publications.

Films/Videotapes/Videodiscs

Modeling the Universe, Pyramid Film and Video, Box 1048, Santa Monica, CA 90406

Adventures in Perceptions, Phoenix/BFA Films and Video, Inc., 468 Park Ave. South, New York, NY 10018

Software

Geometric Connectors: Coordinates, WINGS for Learning/Sunburst, 101 Castleton Street, Pleasantville, NY 10570

Data Insights, WINGS for Learning/Sunburst, 101 Castleton Street, Pleasantville, NY 10570

Multicultural

Multicultural Activity, p. 12

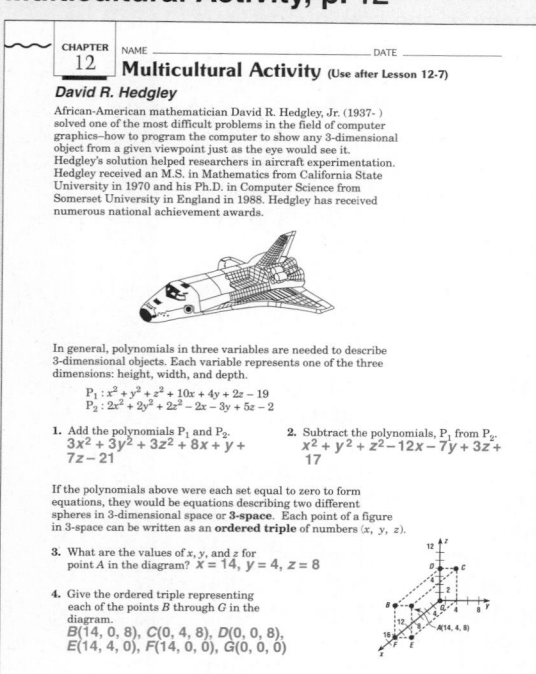

CHAPTER 12   NAME _____ DATE _____

Multicultural Activity (Use after Lesson 12-7)

David R. Hedgley

African-American mathematician David R. Hedgley, Jr. (1937-) solved one of the most difficult problems in the field of computer graphics–how to program the computer to show any 3-dimensional object from a given viewpoint just as the eye would see it. Hedgley's solution helped researchers in aircraft experimentation. Hedgley received an M.S. in Mathematics from California State University in 1970 and his Ph.D. in Computer Science from Somerset University in England in 1988. Hedgley has received numerous national achievement awards.

In general, polynomials in three variables are needed to describe 3-dimensional objects. Each variable represents one of the three dimensions: height, width, and depth.

$P_1 : x^2 + y^2 + z^2 + 10x + 4y + 2z - 19$
$P_2 : 2x^2 + 2y^2 + 2z^2 - 2x - 3y + 5z - 2$

1. Add the polynomials P_1 and P_2.
   $3x^2 + 3y^2 + 3z^2 + 8x + y + 7z - 21$

2. Subtract the polynomials, P_1 from P_2.
   $x^2 + y^2 + z^2 - 12x - 7y + 3z + 17$

If the polynomials above were each set equal to zero to form equations, they would be equations describing two different spheres in 3-dimensional space or **3-space**. Each point of a figure in 3-space can be written as an **ordered triple** of numbers (x, y, z).

3. What are the values of x, y, and z for point A in the diagram? $x = 14$, $y = 4$, $z = 8$

4. Give the ordered triple representing each of the points B through G in the diagram.
   $B(14, 0, 8)$, $C(0, 4, 8)$, $D(0, 0, 8)$, $E(14, 4, 0)$, $F(14, 0, 0)$, $G(0, 0, 0)$

Lab Manual

Lab Activity, pp. 86-89

Name _____   Activity 18 Worksheet
Page 1

Graphing Lines in the Coordinate Plane

$Y \cup X$ Graph Game

A game of graphing lines on the Cartesian Coordinate System

Players: 2 to 4

Getting Ready to Play:

1. Before beginning the game, each group must construct a spinner. See the instructions on the next page.

2. Each player chooses 4 or 5 Pick-Up Sticks® to use for graphing his/her lines. Each player should choose a different color, when possible.

3. Each player spins the $Y \cup X$ spinner. The player who spins a slope closer to zero plays first.

Rules:

1. Player # 1 will spin the $Y \cup X$ spinner and determine the slope of the spin arrow. Next, the player will roll the number cube for a y-intercept.

   Example:

   $m = 1$ $b = 2$

2. The player then graphs the line by placing a Pick-Up Stick® on the game board.

3. Players # 2, 3, and 4 each take their turns.

4. The winner is determined by the first player to graph a line perpendicular or parallel to an axis or another line already graphed on the board.

Variations:

1. Players may wish to record the linear equations to verify the winning line algebraically.

2. Points may be awarded for parallel and perpendicular lines until all the sticks have been placed on the board. The player with the most points wins.

87

Glencoe Division, Macmillan/McGraw-Hill

Using the Chapter Opener

This two-page introduction to the chapter provides students with an opportunity to see how geometry is used throughout the world in various cultures. **Transparency 12-0**, available in the *Merrill Geometry Transparency Package*, provides another full-color visual and motivational activity that you can use to engage students in the mathematical content of the chapter.

Multicultural Notes

Australia Jøern Utzon's original design for the glittering white Sydney Opera House on Bennelong Point, extending into Australia's Sydney Harbor, was submitted in 1956, but the structure was not completed until 1973. The three shell clusters, the largest of which is 67 meters tall, house the concert hall, opera theater, and restaurant. The huge granite-clad platform, or podium, on which the opera house rests was inspired by Mayan temple platforms.

Italy Italian architects and engineers have concentrated on the development of concrete; its tremendous flexibility allows great variety in design. Many Italian building designs include sweeping curves, self-supporting roofs, vaults, and shell coverings. The great engineer and builder Pier Luigi Nervi was a consultant for the hyperbolic paraboloid design of St. Mary's Cathedral in San Francisco and the double-shell design of Collegiate Church in St. Louis.

Chapter Project

Materials posterboard, string (2 colors), fishing weights, hole punch, ruler, pencil, scissors

Procedure Organize students into cooperative groups. Each group will construct a model of a hyperbolic paraboloid.

Give the following instructions to each group.

1. Cut a large square *ABCD* out of posterboard.
2. Mark each side into six equal divisions. Punch a hole about 1 centimeter from the edge in each of the divisions along the sides.
3. Score the posterboard lightly along diagonal $\overline{AC}$ so that it will bend without tearing.
4. Run strings up through each hole along $\overline{AB}$ and down through the hole directly across the square along $\overline{CD}$.
5. Attach a fishing weight to each end of each string running from $\overline{AB}$ to $\overline{CD}$ so that the strings are pulled tight.
6. Run strings of a second color up

More Coordinate Geometry

CHAPTER OBJECTIVES

In this chapter, you will:
- Write and graph linear equations.
- Prove theorems using coordinate proofs.
- Perform operations with vectors.
- Locate points in space.

GEOMETRY AROUND THE WORLD
Mexico

If you like unusual architecture, perhaps some day you can take a trip to Mexico to feast your eyes on the graceful concrete churches, office buildings, restaurants, and warehouses designed by Felix Candela. Candela, an architect and engineer born in 1910, based his designs on the geometry of the *hyperbolic paraboloid*.

This design, featuring curves similar to those in a horse saddle, combines two geometric shapes. A *hyperbola* is a plane curve having two branches formed by a plane intersecting both halves of a pair of right circular cones. A *paraboloid* is a surface having cross-sections that are *parabolas*—a plane curve formed by a plane intersecting a right circular cone.

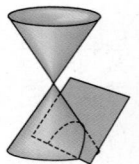 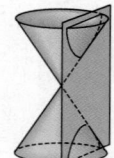

parabola   hyperbola

A hyperbolic paraboloid building is pleasing to the eye. Its open-air design, thin walls, and light roof are well suited to the hot Mexican climate. And because it requires less construction material than more traditional designs, it's less expensive to build.

GEOMETRY IN ACTION

With your finger, trace the lines that form the parabolas in the figure at the right.

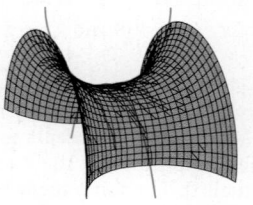

◀ *Mexican Church*

The arches inside this Mexican church designed by Felix Candela make the building beautiful and structurally sound.

Connections and Applications

Lesson	Connections (C) and Applications (A)	Examples	Exercises
12-1	A: Road Grade		52
	A: Business		53
	C: Algebra	3	58
12-2	C: Algebra	1	
	A: Sports		38
	A: Business		39
12-3	C: Algebra	2	
	A: Investments		24
	A: Health		25
12-4	A: Sports	1	
12-5	A: Theater		29
	A: Interior Decorating		30
	A: Air Traffic Control		31
12-6	A: Physics	3	
	A: Navigation		43
	A: Recreation		44
	A: Sports		45
12-7	C: Algebra	4	
	A: Aviation	1	
	A: Air Traffic Control		45
	A: Recreation		46

573

through the holes along $\overline{BC}$, across the square, and down through the holes along $\overline{AD}$.
7. Attach a fishing weight to each end of each string running from $\overline{BC}$ to $\overline{AD}$ so that the strings are pulled tight.
8. With your fingers on both sides of diagonal $\overline{AC}$ from underneath, fold the posterboard upward along $\overline{AC}$. Allow the weights to hang and form a hyperbolic paraboloid. Have each group present its model to the class for discussion.

Resources

Mansbridge, John. *Graphic History of Architecture*. Viking Press

Damaz, Paul F. *Art in Latin American Architecture*. Reinhold Publishing Corporation

Pappas, Theoni. *The Joy of Mathematics: Discovering Mathematics All Around You*. Wide World Publishing / Tetra

Lorenz, Clare. *Women in Architecture*. Rizzoli International Publications, Inc.

Lesson Resources

• Reteaching Master 12-1
• Practice Master 12-1
• Enrichment Master 12-1
• Technology Master, p. 12

Transparency 12-1 contains the 5-Minute Check and a teaching aid for this lesson.

INTRODUCING THE LESSON

🕐 5-Minute Check

(over Chapter 11)

1. Find the volume of a right circular cone with radius 4 meters and height 7 meters. **about 117.3 m³**

2. Find the surface area of a right cylinder with a height of 3 feet and a radius of 5 feet. **about 251.3 ft²**

3. Find the surface area of a regular square pyramid with a slant height of 18 inches and a base with sides measuring 20 inches. **1120 in²**

4. Find the volume of a right rectangular prism with a length of 19 units, a height of 3 units, and a width of 6 units. **342 cubic units**

5. Find the volume of a sphere with diameter 15 centimeters. **about 1767.1 cm³**

Motivating the Lesson

Ask students to think of a steep road they know. Ask them how they know that a road is steep. **Sample answers: It is harder to walk up, car must work harder, ball rolls down faster.**

TEACHING THE LESSON

Teaching Tip In the definition of a linear equation in standard form, point out that "*A* and *B* are not both zero" means that one or the other but not both may be zero.

12-1 Graphing Linear Equations

Objectives

After studying this lesson, you should be able to:

12-1A ▪ graph linear equations using the intercepts method, and

12-1B ▪ graph linear equations using the slope-intercept method.

Application

The maximum road grade recommended by the Federal Highway Commission is 12%. This means that the slope of a road should be no more than $\frac{12}{100}$ or 0.12. At the maximum grade, a road would change 12 feet vertically for every 100 feet horizontally.

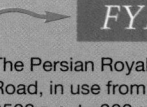

FYI···

The Persian Royal Road, in use from 3500 B.C. to 300 B.C. was the first highway. It took about 93 days to travel the 1775 miles from Shushan on the Persian Gulf to Smyrna on the Aegean Sea.

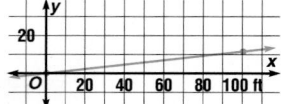

A line that represents this road grade could be drawn on a coordinate grid using the points with coordinates (0, 0) and (100, 12).

Every line drawn on a coordinate plane has a corresponding **linear equation** that describes the line algebraically. A linear equation can be written in the form $Ax + By = C$, where A, B, and C are any real numbers, and A and B are not both zero. A linear equation written in the form $Ax + By = C$ is said to be in **standard form.**

The equations $x + 3y = 12$, $4x = 11y + 8$, $7x - y = \frac{1}{2}$, and $y = 4$ are all linear equations. Each can be written in the form $Ax + By = C$. The equations $2x + 3y^2 = 8$ and $\frac{1}{y} + x = 4$ are not linear equations. *Why not?* **The variables are not all to the first power.**

The graph of a linear equation is the set of all points with coordinates (x, y) that satisfy the equation $Ax + By = C$. One technique for graphing a linear equation is called the **intercepts method.** This method uses two special values, the *x-intercept* and the *y-intercept*. The *x*-intercept is the value of *x* when *y* equals 0. The *y*-intercept is the value of *y* when *x* equals 0. These values can be used as long as the line is not parallel to either axis.

574   CHAPTER 12   MORE COORDINATE GEOMETRY

ALTERNATE TEACHING STRATEGIES

Using Investigation

You can guide students to discover the characteristics of a family of lines. In Investigation 15 on page A14 of **More Investigations in Geometry,** students use graphing calculators to explore graphs of lines.

Using Discussion

Ask students whether or not every line can be written in slope-intercept form. Have students give reasons for their answers. **Equations for vertical lines cannot be written in slope-intercept form since their slopes are undefined.**

Example 1

The Family Treasures Furniture Company makes chairs and tables. The equation $15x + 30y = 30,000$ represents the cost of making x chairs and y tables. Graph the equation by finding the intercepts.

Let $x = 0$ to find the y-intercept.

$$15(0) + 30y = 30,000$$
$$30y = 30,000$$
$$y = 1000$$

Let $y = 0$ to find the x-intercept.

$$15x + 30(0) = 30,000$$
$$15x = 30,000$$
$$x = 2000$$

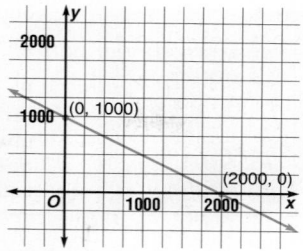

The x-intercept is 2000, and the y-intercept is 1000. To graph $15x + 30y = 30,000$, plot $(0, 1000)$ and $(2000, 0)$ and draw a line through the points.

Another method for graphing is more convenient to use if the equation is rewritten so one side has y by itself. Use a graphing calculator, graphing software, or graph paper to graph the family of equations that appear below.

$$y = 2x + 8$$
$$y = 2x + 0$$
$$y = 2x - 4$$

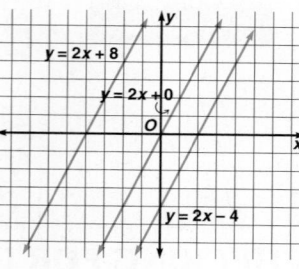

Recall from algebra that the coefficient is the numerical part of a term and a constant term contains no variables.

Notice that the graphs are parallel lines and that the slope of each line is 2. Compare the slope of each line to its equation. Did you notice that the slope of each line is equal to the coefficient of x in its equation? Also the y-intercept of each line is equal to the constant term of the equation. A linear equation written in the form $y = mx + b$ is called the **slope-intercept form** of the equation.

Theorem 12-1 Slope-Intercept Form	If the equation of a line is written in the form $y = mx + b$, m is the slope of the line and b is the y-intercept.

Proof of Theorem 12-1

The slope, m, of a line passing through points with coordinates (x_1, y_1) and (x_2, y_2) is given by
$$m = \frac{y_2 - y_1}{x_2 - x_1}.$$

Notice that if $x = 0$, $y = b$. Therefore, b is the y-intercept. If $x = 1$, $y = m + b$. Since the ordered pairs for two points on the line have coordinates $(0, b)$ and $(1, m + b)$, the slope is $\frac{(m + b) - b}{1 - 0}$ or m.

Horizontal and vertical lines are special cases. The graph of an equation of the form $x = a$ is a vertical line and has an undefined slope. The graph of an equation of the form $y = b$ is a horizontal line and has a slope of 0.

LESSON 12-1   GRAPHING LINEAR EQUATIONS   575

Chalkboard Example

For Example 1

Golden Sporting Goods makes tennis and squash racquets. The equation $3x + 4y = 36,000$ represents the cost of making x tennis racquets and y squash racquets. Graph the equation by finding the intercepts.

Let $x = 0$ to find the y-intercept.

$3(0) + 4y = 36,000$

$y = 9,000$

Let $y = 0$ to find the x-intercept.

$3x + 4(0) = 36,000$

$x = 12,000$

To graph the equation, plot the points $(0, 9000)$ and $(12,000, 0)$ and draw a line through them.

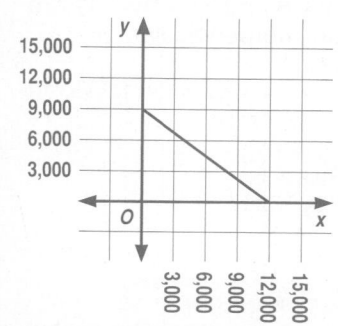

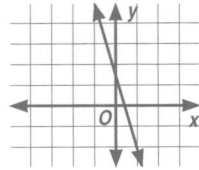
You can graph a line if you know its slope and *y*-intercept.

Example 2

Graph $y = \frac{1}{4}x + 5$ using the slope and the *y*-intercept.

Since the equation is in slope-intercept form, the slope is $\frac{1}{4}$ and the *y*-intercept is 5.

Plot the point with coordinates (0, 5) and from this point move up 1 unit and to the right 4 units. This point, which has coordinates (4, 6), must also lie on the line. Draw the line containing the two points.

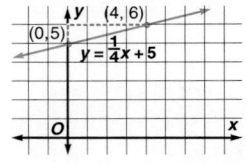

The slope-intercept form of a linear equation can also be used to determine if two lines are parallel or perpendicular without graphing the equations. Remember that if two nonvertical lines are parallel, they have the same slope. If two lines are perpendicular and neither is vertical, the product of their slopes is -1.

Example 3

Determine if the graphs of $2x + y = 3$ and $4x + 2y = 5$ are parallel, perpendicular, or neither.

Write each equation in slope-intercept form.

$$2x + y = 3 \qquad\qquad 4x + 2y = 5$$
$$y = -2x + 3 \qquad\qquad 2y = -4x + 5$$
$$\qquad\qquad\qquad\qquad y = -2x + \frac{5}{2}$$

Since for each equation $m = -2$ and the *y*-intercepts are not equal, the graphs are parallel lines.

CHECKING FOR UNDERSTANDING

Communicating Mathematics

1. $x = 4$; A vertical line means *x* always equals one value, in this case 4, and *y* can equal anything.

Read and study the lesson to answer these questions.

1. A vertical line contains the point with coordinates (4, -7). What is an equation of the line? Explain your answer.

2. *True* or *false:* Horizontal lines are perpendicular to the *x*-axis. Explain your reasoning. **False; horizontal lines are parallel to the *x*-axis.**

3. The graph at the right displays a "family" of parallel lines. What must be true about the equations of these lines? **They have the same value for *m* when expressed in slope-intercept form.**

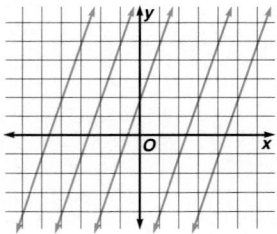

4. Describe two methods of graphing a linear equation. Which method is more convenient for graphing $2x - 3y = 10$? Explain. **intercepts, slope-intercept; Answers may vary.**

5. One way to graph the equation $y = \frac{1}{2}x + 3$ is to start at the point with coordinates $(0, 3)$ and move up 1 and to the right 2 to determine the coordinates of a second point on the line. What other ways can you use to locate other points on the line? **Sample answer: Move down 1 and to the left 2; move up 2 and to the right 4**

Guided Practice

7. no; y is squared
8. no; x is cubed
10. no; x and y are both squared

Determine whether each equation is a linear equation. Explain your reasoning.

6. $y = 2x - 1$ **yes**   **7.** $3x + 4y^2 = 9$ **8.** $y = x^3$
9. $x = 8$ **yes**   **10.** $x^2 + y^2 = 10$ **11.** $4x = 9 - y$ **yes**

Find the x- and y-intercepts of the graph of each equation.

12. $y = x$ **0; 0**   **13.** $4x - y = 4$ **1; -4**   **14.** $x + 2y = 6$ **6; 3**
15. $x = 4$ **4; no y-intercept**   **16.** $y + 3 = x$ **3; -3**   **17.** $3x - 6y = 6$ **2; -1**

Graph each equation. Determine if this line and the line already drawn on the coordinate axes are parallel, perpendicular, or neither. Verify by finding the slope of each line.

18. $3x + y = 6$ **19.** $x - y = 4$ **20.** $y = \frac{1}{2}x + 3$

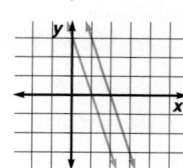   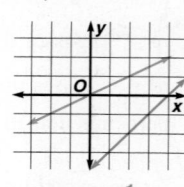   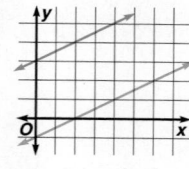

parallel; -3, -3   neither; 1, $\frac{1}{2}$ parallel; $\frac{1}{2}$, $\frac{1}{2}$

21. $y = 3$ **22.** $3x = 4y + 6$ **23.** $y = 8 - x$

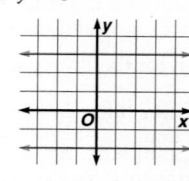   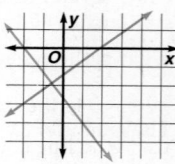   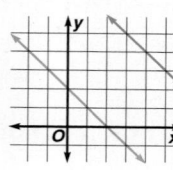

parallel; 0, 0   perpendicular; $\frac{3}{4}$, $-\frac{4}{3}$ **23.** parallel; -1, -1

EXERCISES

Practice

A

Graph each equation. Explain the method you used to draw the graph. **See Solutions Manual.**

24. $y = 4x - 2$ **25.** $y = 3x$ **26.** $5x + 2y = 0$
27. $y = 2x - 10$ **28.** $x + 4y = 16$ **29.** $3x - 4y = 6$

LESSON 12-1   GRAPHING LINEAR EQUATIONS   577

RETEACHING THE LESSON

Work with students to help them graph Exercises 1-2 which are already in slope-intercept form. Ask them which number gives the slope and which number gives the y-intercept. Then show them how to rewrite Exercises 3-4 in slope-intercept form in order to simplify the graphing process.

1. $y = -2x + 1$ **2.** $y = \frac{3}{4}x - 3$
3. $3x + y = -2$ **4.** $x - 2y = 4$

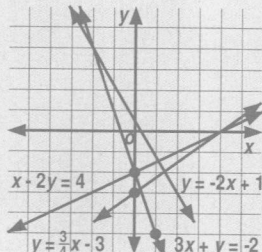

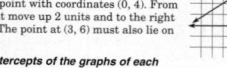
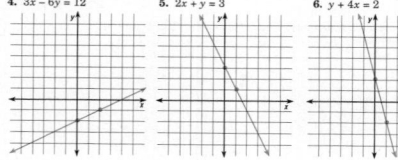
Chapter 12   577

Additional Answers

48. See students' graphs. All are of the form $y = 2x + b$, but all have a different value for b.

49. See students' graphs. All are of the form $y = mx + 3$, but all have a different value for m.

33. $m = 1$, $b = 0$
34. $m = -3$, $b = 5$
35. $m = -\frac{3}{4}$, $b = 2$
36. $m = 0$, $b = 6$

Graph each pair of linear equations on the same coordinate plane. Determine if the lines are parallel, perpendicular, or neither by finding the slope of each line. See Solutions Manual for graphs.

30. $y = 6 - x$
$x + y = 2$
parallel

31. $5x - y = 0$
$y = 5x - 3$
parallel

32. $2y + x = 4$
$y = 2x - 5$
perpendicular

If they exist, find the slope and y-intercept of the graph of each equation.

33. $y = x$

34. $3x + y = 5$

35. $3x + 4y = 8$

36. $y = 6$

37. $x = 9$

38. $2x + y = 6$

37. m is undefined, no y-intercept

38. $m = -2$, $b = 6$

Draw each line described on a separate coordinate plane. Then write the equation of each line in slope-intercept form. See Solutions Manual for graphs.

39. $m = -\frac{1}{3}$, y-intercept $= 2$ $y = -\frac{1}{3}x + 2$

40. $m = 4$, passes through $(0, 5)$ $y = 4x + 5$

41. $m = 4$, y-intercept $= -3$ $y = 4x - 3$

42. parallel to y-axis through $(2, 0)$ $x = 2$

43. $m = 2$, passes through $(0, 3)$ $y = 2x + 3$

44. parallel to x-axis through $(0, -6)$ $y = -6$

45. $m = \frac{1}{3}$, passes through $(0, 4)$ $y = \frac{1}{3}x + 4$

46. $m = 4$, passes through $(0, 7)$ $y = 4x + 7$

47. perpendicular to the x-axis, passes through $(2, 0)$ $x = 2$

48. Draw several lines having a slope of -2. Describe the similarities and the differences between the equations of these lines. **See margin.**

49. See margin.

49. Draw several lines passing through the point $(0, 3)$. Describe the similarities and the differences between the equations of these lines.

50. What is the general equation for the lines parallel to the y-axis? $x = a$

Critical Thinking

51. The graphs of $3x + 2y = 10$ and $3x + 2y = 4$ are parallel lines. Find the equation of the line that is parallel to both lines and lies midway between them.
$3x + 2y = 7$

Applications

52. Road Grade   A certain road has an 8% grade. The Hendersons' mailbox and the Pauls' mailbox are located along this road and are 650 feet apart. What is the vertical change in distance between these mailboxes?   about 51.8 feet

578   CHAPTER 12   MORE COORDINATE GEOMETRY

Practice Masters Booklet, p. 82

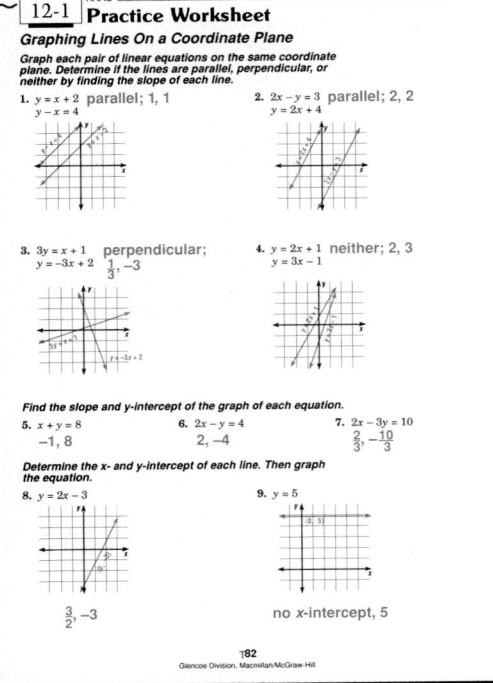

12-1   NAME _____ DATE _____
Practice Worksheet

Graphing Lines On a Coordinate Plane

Graph each pair of linear equations on the same coordinate plane. Determine if the lines are parallel, perpendicular, or neither by finding the slope of each line.

1. $y = x + 2$ parallel; 1, 1
$y - x = 4$

2. $2x - y = 3$ parallel; 2, 2
$y = 2x + 4$

3. $3y = x + 1$ perpendicular;
$y = -3x + 2$ $\frac{1}{3}$, -3

4. $y = 2x + 1$ neither; 2, 3
$y = 3x - 1$

Find the slope and y-intercept of the graph of each equation.

5. $x + y = 8$
-1, 8

6. $2x - y = 4$
2, -4

7. $2x - 3y = 10$
$\frac{2}{3}$, $-\frac{10}{3}$

Determine the x- and y-intercept of each line. Then graph the equation.

8. $y = 2x - 3$
$\frac{3}{2}$, -3

9. $y = 5$
no x-intercept, 5

T82
Glencoe Division, Macmillan/McGraw-Hill

578   Chapter 12

53. Business Just Like Grandma's Bake Shop spends $1400 a month for rent and utilities. For each day of operation, they spend $200 for employees' wages, benefits, and baking supplies. If x represents the number of days of operation in a month, $y = 200x + 1400$ represents the cost of operation for the month.

   a. What is the slope of the line that represents the bake shop's cost of operation for the month? **200**

   b. What is the y-intercept? **1400**

   c. Graph the equation. **See margin.**

Mixed Review

54. about 523.6 in³
55. about 113.1 ft²

54. Find the volume of a sphere with a radius of 5 inches. **(Lesson 11-7)**

55. Find the surface area of a sphere with radius of 3 feet. **(Lesson 11-7)**

56. Find the slope of the line that passes through the points with coordinates $(3, 0)$ and $(8, -2)$. **(Lesson 3-4)** $-\frac{2}{5}$

57. Draw a figure to illustrate two lines that are perpendicular to a third line, but are not parallel to each other. **(Lesson 3-1)** **See margin.**

58. Algebra Find the measures of $\angle 1$ and $\angle 2$, if $m\angle 1 = 2x + 15$ and $m\angle 2 = 8x - 5$. **(Lesson 2-7)** $m\angle 1 = 49,$ $m\angle 2 = 131$

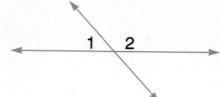

59. Determine if a valid conclusion can be made from the statements *If it snows Saturday, then we will go skiing,* and *If we go skiing, then we will need to rent skis.* State the law of logic that you used. **(Lesson 2-3)** **If it snows Saturday, then we will have to rent skis; law of syllogism**

Wrap-Up

60. Write an example of a linear equation in standard form and another linear equation in slope-intercept form. Describe the graph of each equation. **See students' work.**

HISTORY CONNECTION

Did you know that sound travels at a different speed in water than it does in air? Berthel Carmichael, the first African-American woman to go to sea on a military sealift oceanographic research ship, is a research mathematician who studied the properties of sound waves under water.

Ms. Carmichael is a native of Richmond, Virginia, and a graduate of Virginia Union University. She taught in the public school system before joining the Naval Research Laboratory in Washington, D.C. While working in the Acoustics Division Propagation Branch, Ms. Carmichael spent time aboard the U.S.S. Hayes and the U.S.S. Mizar in the Arctic Ocean.

EXTENDING THE LESSON

Math Power: Problem Solving

Write the equation in slope-intercept form of a line that has a y-intercept of -3 and passes through the point $(2, 2)$.
$y = \frac{5}{2}x - 3$

History Connection

The History Connection features introduce students to persons or cultures who were involved in the development of mathematics. You may want students to further research oceanography, sound waves, or sonar.

Additional Answers
53c.

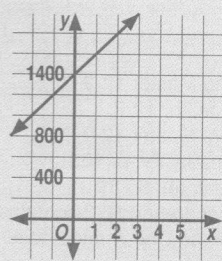

57.

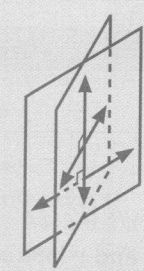

Enrichment Masters Booklet, p. 71

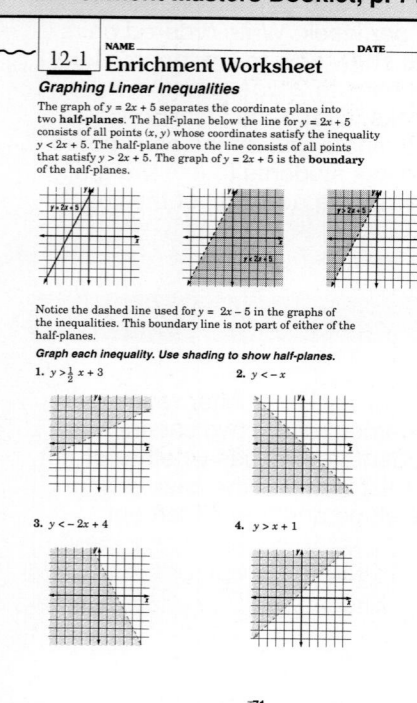

Lesson Resources

Lesson Resources

• Reteaching Master 12-2
• Practice Master 12-2
• Enrichment Master 12-2
• Evaluation Master, p. 163
• Lab Manual, pp. 86-89

 Transparency 12-2 contains the 5-Minute Check and a teaching aid for this lesson.

INTRODUCING THE LESSON

 5-Minute Check

(over Lesson 12-1)

Find the *x*- and *y*-intercepts of the graph of each equation.

1. $2x + 3y = -12$ $(0, -4),$ $(-6, 0)$
2. $x - 5y = 15$ $(0, -3), (15, 0)$
3. $4x - 3y = -6$ $(0, 2), (-\frac{3}{2}, 0)$

Find the slope and *y*-intercept of the graph of each equation.

4. $4x - 2y = 5$ $2, -\frac{5}{2}$
5. $x + 3y = 9$ $-\frac{1}{3}, 3$
6. $5x + y = -7$ $-5, -7$

Motivating the Lesson

Tell students that Jerry has $10 in savings and gets an allowance of $4 per week. Write ordered pairs that show how much money Jerry will have in 2 weeks and in 4 weeks. Graph the points on a coordinate grid on the chalkboard and ask students to use the graph to write the equation of the line. (2, 18), (4, 26); $y = 4x + 10$

TEACHING THE LESSON

Teaching Tip   After reading the statement of the two cases, ask students to discuss whether or not this list includes the case giving the slope and the *y*-intercept. **It is similar to case 1 since they are given the slope and a point.**

12-2 Writing Equations of Lines

Objective
12-2

After studying this lesson, you should be able to:
▪ write an equation of a line given information about its graph.

Application

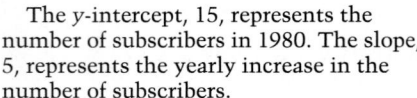 *FYI ···*

There are about 90,100,000 televisions in the United States. 98% of American households own at least one T.V.

In 1980, there were 15 million cable television subscribers. If the number of subscribers increases by 5 million each year, the equation $y = 5x + 15$ can be used to find *y*, the number of cable subscribers (in millions) for any number of years, *x*, after 1980.

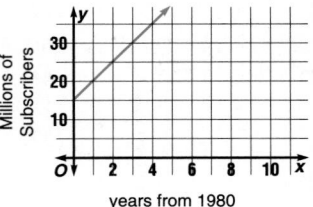

years from 1980

The *y*-intercept, 15, represents the number of subscribers in 1980. The slope, 5, represents the yearly increase in the number of subscribers.

In this problem, the slope and *y*-intercept were used to write the equation in slope-intercept form. This equation can be useful for making predictions regarding the number of cable subscribers in the years after 1980. For example, to find the number of subscribers in the year 2000, we would substitute 20 for *x* and solve for *y*. *Why 20?*

$$y = 5x + 15$$
$$y = 5(20) + 15 \quad \textit{Substitute 20 for x.}$$
$$y = 115$$

If the yearly increase in subscribers remains constant, there will be 115 million cable subscribers in the year 2000. *Do you think this is a reasonable answer? Explain.*

In general you can write an equation of a line if you are given:
▪ **Case 1:** the slope and the coordinates of a point on the line, or
▪ **Case 2:** the coordinate of two points on the line.

Consider Case 1. To write an equation of a line given the slope and the coordinates of a point on the line, substitute the slope in the equation $y = mx + b$. Then substitute the coordinates of the point for *x* and *y* and solve for *b*. Finally, write an equation of the line by substituting the values for *m* and *b* into $y = mx + b$.

580   CHAPTER 12   MORE COORDINATE GEOMETRY

ALTERNATE TEACHING STRATEGIES

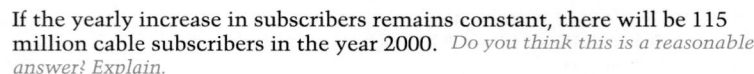

Using Applications

A word-processing service charges $65 for typing a 15-page report and $133 for typing a 32-page report. How much would it cost to have them type a 50-page report?   **$205**

Using Problem Solving

Write the equation of a line that is parallel to a line with an undefined slope and that goes through the point (4, 5). *x = 4*

Example 1

CONNECTION
Algebra

Write an equation of the line whose slope is 3 and *x*-intercept is -10.

Since we know that the slope is 3, we can substitute 3 for m in $y = mx + b$.
$$y = 3x + b$$

Now, since the *x*-intercept is -10, the point (-10, 0) is on the line. Substitute the coordinates of this point into the equation to find the value of b.

$$y = 3x + b$$
$$0 = 3(-10) + b \qquad \textit{y = 0 and x = -10}$$
$$0 = -30 + b$$
$$30 = b \qquad \textit{Solve for b.}$$

The slope-intercept form of the equation of the line is $y = 3x + 30$.

The following example illustrates Case 2. You can find an equation of a line given the coordinates of two points on the line using the **point-slope form** of a linear equation. The point-slope form is $y - y_1 = m(x - x_1)$, where (x_1, y_1) are the coordinates of a point on the line and m is the slope of the line.

Example 2

With a certain long-distance carrier, the price of a 4-minute long-distance telephone call is $1.90. A 13-minute call with the same carrier costs $5.05.
a. Write a linear equation that describes the cost of telephone calls.

The line passes through the points (4, 1.9) and (13, 5.05). Find the slope of the line.

$$m = \frac{y_2 - y_1}{x_2 - x_1}$$
$$= \frac{5.05 - 1.9}{13 - 4}$$
$$= \frac{3.15}{9} \text{ or } 0.35$$

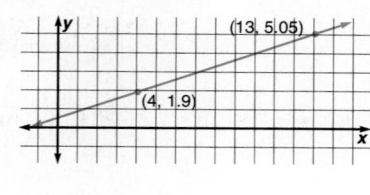

Now use the point-slope form to write the linear equation.

$$y - y_1 = m(x - x_1) \qquad \textit{Use point-slope form.}$$
$$y - 1.9 = 0.35(x - 4) \qquad \textit{Use the coordinates of either point for } (x_1, y_1).$$
$$y - 1.9 = 0.35x - 1.4 \qquad \textit{We chose (4, 1.9).}$$
$$y = 0.35x + 0.5$$

The slope-intercept form of the equation of the line is $y = 0.35x + 0.5$.
What do 0.35 and 0.5 represent? **the rate per minute and the flat fee**

b. How much would a 30-minute telephone call cost?

Use the equation to find the cost of a 30-minute telephone call.

$$y = 0.35x + 0.5$$
$$y = 0.35(30) + 0.5 \qquad \textit{Substitute 30 for x.}$$
$$y = 10.5 + 0.5$$
$$y = 11$$

A 30-minute call costs $11.

LESSON 12-2   WRITING EQUATIONS OF LINES   581

582   Chapter 12

Chalkboard Example

For Example 3
Write an equation of the line that is the perpendicular bisector of $\overline{XY}$ with endpoints of $X(3, 2)$ and $Y(7, -4)$.
Find the slope of $\overline{XY}$.

$$m = \frac{-4 - 2}{7 - 3}$$

$$m = \frac{-3}{2}$$

The slope of a line perpendicular to $\overline{XY}$ must be $\frac{2}{3}$.

Find the midpoint of $\overline{XY}$.

$$M = \left(\frac{3 + 7}{2}, \frac{2 + (-4)}{2}\right)$$

$$M = (5, -1)$$

$$y - y_1 = m(x - x_1)$$

$$y - (-1) = \frac{2}{3}(x - 5)$$

$$y = \frac{2}{3}x - \frac{10}{3} - 1$$

An equation of the perpendicular bisector of $\overline{XY}$ is $y = \frac{2}{3}x - \frac{13}{3}$.

EVALUATING THE LESSON

Checking for Understanding

Exercises 1-12 are designed to help you assess students' understanding through reading, writing, speaking, and modeling. You should work through Exercises 1-4 with your students and then monitor their work on Exercises 5-12.

Closing the Lesson

Speaking Activity Ask students to explain how the equation of a line can be found given two points on the line or given the slope and one point on the line. Encourage them to state a specific example and work it out on the chalkboard or overhead.

Example 3

Write an equation of the line that is the perpendicular bisector of $\overline{AB}$ with endpoints at $A(8, 1)$ and $B(-10, -1)$.

Find the slope of $\overline{AB}$ by using the coordinates of A and B.

$$m = \frac{y_2 - y_1}{x_2 - x_1}$$

$$= \frac{1 - (-1)}{8 - (-10)}$$

$$= \frac{2}{18} \text{ or } \frac{1}{9}$$

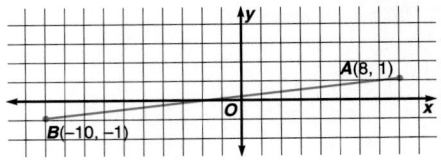

Since the slope of $\overline{AB}$ is $\frac{1}{9}$, the slope of the perpendicular bisector is -9. *Why?*

To find a point on the perpendicular bisector, recall that the perpendicular bisector must pass through the midpoint of the segment. Use the midpoint formula to find the midpoint of $\overline{AB}$.

$$M = \left(\frac{x_1 + x_2}{2}, \frac{y_1 + y_2}{2}\right)$$

$$= \left(\frac{8 + (-10)}{2}, \frac{1 + (-1)}{2}\right) \quad \textit{Substitute (8, 1) for } (x_1, y_1) \textit{ and (-10, -1) for } (x_2, y_2).$$

$$= (-1, 0)$$

Now write an equation.

$$y - y_1 = m(x - x_1) \quad \textit{Use the point-slope form of the equation.}$$

$$y - 0 = -9(x - (-1)) \quad \textit{The slope is -9 and the point with coordinates (-1, 0) is on the line.}$$

$$y = -9x - 9$$

An equation of the perpendicular bisector of $\overline{AB}$ is $y = -9x - 9$.

CHECKING FOR UNDERSTANDING

Communicating Mathematics

Read and study the lesson to answer these questions.

1. Determine if each of the following is sufficient information to write an equation of exactly one line. Explain your answer. **See margin.**

   a. a point on the line

   b. the slope of the line

   c. two points on the line

   d. the slope and a point on the line

2. There are currently 5.3 million cellular telephone users. Each year the number of cellular phone users increases by 1.2 million.

   2a. $y = 1.2x + 5.3$

   a. Write a linear equation that represents y, the total number of cellular telephone users x years from now if the rate of increase stays the same.

   b. Approximately how many cellular telephone users will there be in 10 years if the rate of increase stays the same? **17.3 million**

Additional Answers

1a. No, because infinitely many lines pass through a point.

1b. No, because infinitely many lines have the same slope.

1c. Yes: Use the two points to determine the slope. Then substitute the slope and the coordinates of one point in $y = mx + b$ and solve for b.

1d. Yes: Substitute the slope and coordinates of the point in $y = mx + b$ and solve for b.

3. Find the slope of $\overleftrightarrow{AB}$. **1**

4. Write an equation for $\overleftrightarrow{CD}$.

$y = -\frac{1}{3}x - 1$

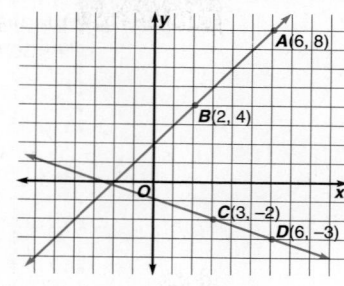

APPLYING THE LESSON

Homework Exercises

Assignment Guide

Basic: 13-30, 37-46
Average: 16-33, 37-46
Enriched: 19-46

Guided Practice

Write the equation in slope-intercept form of the line that satisfies the given conditions.

5. $m = 4$, y-intercept $= 2$ $y = 4x + 2$

6. $m = -\frac{1}{2}$, y-intercept $= 1$ $y = -\frac{1}{2}x + 1$

7. $m = 5$, passes through $(-1, 3)$ $y = 5x + 8$

8. $m = -3$, x-intercept $= 6$ $y = -3x + 18$

9. passes through $(-7, 4)$ and $(-5, -6)$ $y = -5x - 31$

10. passes through $(6, -1)$ and $(-3, -7)$ $y = \frac{2}{3}x - 5$

11. parallel to $y = 3x + 4$, passes through $(3, 7)$ $y = 3x - 2$

12. perpendicular to $y = -\frac{1}{3}x - 2$, passes through $(1, 2)$ $y = 3x - 1$

EXERCISES

Practice

State the slope and y-intercept for each line. Then write the equation of the line in slope-intercept form.

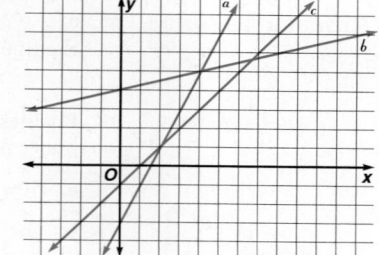

13. a $2, -3$; $y = 2x - 3$

14. b $\frac{1}{4}, 4$; $y = \frac{1}{4}x + 4$

15. c $1, -1$; $y = x - 1$

Write the equation in slope-intercept form of the line having the given slope and passing through the given point.

17. $y = \frac{1}{6}x - 5$

16. $3, (1, -4)$ $y = 3x - 7$ 17. $\frac{1}{6}, (12, -3)$ 18. $-\frac{2}{3}, (-3, 2)$ $y = -\frac{2}{3}x$

19. $-4, (-3, -2)$ 20. $-1, (5, 0)$ $y = -x + 5$ 21. $0, (6, 7)$ $y = 7$
$y = -4x - 14$

LESSON 12-2   WRITING EQUATIONS OF LINES   583

RETEACHING THE LESSON

Show students how they can use graphing to determine the equation of a line, given its slope and a point on the graph. For example, given a slope of 4 and a point (1, -3), have them plot the point, and from that point draw a line with a slope of 4. By extending the line to where it crosses the y-axis, they can obtain the y-intercept and write the equation in slope-intercept form. $y = 4x - 7$

Reteaching Masters Booklet, p. 72

12-2 NAME _____ DATE _____
Reteaching Worksheet

Writing Equations of Lines

You can write an equation of a line if you are given
1. the slope and a point on the line, or
2. two points on the line.

Example: Write the equation in slope-intercept form of the line that has slope 5 and an x-intercept of 3.

Since the slope is 5, you can substitute 5 for m in
$y = mx + b$.
$y = 5x + b$

Since the x-intercept is 3, the point $(3, 0)$ is on the line.
$y = 5x + b$
$0 = 5(3) + b$ $y = 0$ and $x = 3$
$0 = 15 + b$
$b = -15$ Solve for b.
So the equation is $y = 5x - 15$.

If you know two points on a line, you will need to use the point-slope form of the equation, that is, $y - y_1 = m(x - x_1)$.

Write the equation in slope-intercept form of the line that satisfies the given conditions.

1. $m = 3$, y-intercept $= -4$ 2. $m = -\frac{2}{5}$, x-intercept $= 6$
   $y = 3x - 4$ $y = -\frac{2}{5}x + \frac{12}{5}$

3. passes through $(-5, 10)$ and $(2, 4)$ 4. passes through $(8, 6)$ and $(-3, -3)$
   $y = -\frac{6}{7}x + \frac{40}{7}$ $y = \frac{9}{11}x - \frac{6}{11}$

5. perpendicular to the y-axis,   6. parallel to the y-axis,
   passes through $(-6, 4)$ passes through $(-7, 3)$
   $y = 4$ $x = -7$

7. $m = 3$ and passes through $(-4, 6)$ 8. perpendicular to the graph of
   $y = 3x + 18$ $y = 4x - 1$ and passes through $(6, -3)$
                                            $y = -\frac{1}{4}x - \frac{3}{2}$

T72
Glencoe Division, Macmillan/McGraw-Hill

Exercise Notes

For Exercise 36, students must recall that a tangent is perpendicular to a radius at the point at which the tangent meets the circle.

B Write the equation in slope-intercept form of the line satisfying the given conditions.

22. $m = 0$, y-intercept = 7 $y = 7$

23. $m = -2$, y-intercept = 1 $y = -2x + 1$

24. $m = \frac{3}{4}$, y-intercept = 8 $y = \frac{3}{4}x + 8$

25. $m = -\frac{1}{2}$, passes through (5, 3) $y = -\frac{1}{2}x + \frac{11}{2}$

26. $m = 6$, passes through (-3, 1) $y = 6x + 19$

27. parallel to $y = -4x + 1$, passes through (-3, 1) $y = -4x - 11$

28. parallel to the y-axis, passes through (3, 9) $x = 3$

29. perpendicular to the y-axis, passes through (-8, 2) $y = 2$

30. passes through points (0, 3) and (4, -3) $y = -\frac{3}{2}x + 3$

31. passes through (9, -4) and (-2, 7) $y = -x + 5$

32. the perpendicular bisector of the segment whose endpoints have coordinates (2, 5) and (-2, -1) $y = -\frac{2}{3}x + 2$

C
33. Write the equation in slope-intercept form of the line that has a slope of -5 and bisects a segment whose endpoints have coordinates (-4, 10) and (5, -7). $y = -5x + 4$

34. Write the equation in slope-intercept form of the line that is the perpendicular bisector of a segment whose endpoints have coordinates (-3, -7) and (5, 1). $y = -x - 2$

35. $y = \frac{3}{4}x + 8$

35. A line is parallel to the line whose equation is $3x - 4y = 11$ and passes through (-4, 5). Write the equation of the line in slope-intercept form.

36. Write the equation in slope-intercept form of the line tangent to the circle with equation $x^2 + (y - 3)^2 = 25$ at the point with coordinates (4, 0). $y = \frac{4}{3}x - \frac{16}{3}$

Critical Thinking
37. The x-intercept of a line is s and the y-intercept is t. Write the equation of the line in slope-intercept form in terms of s and t. $y = -\frac{tx}{s} + t$

Applications
38. Business Handy Helper Hardware sells about 360 gallons of interior house paint in a week.

a. How many gallons of paint will they sell in x weeks? **360x**

b. The store has 2880 gallons of paint on hand. Write an equation that describes how many gallons they will have in stock in x weeks if no new stock is added. $y = 2880 - 360x$

c. Draw a graph that represents the number of gallons of paint the store will have at any given time. **See margin.**

d. If it takes three weeks to receive a shipment of paint from the warehouse after it is ordered, when should the manager order more paint so that the store will not run out? **in 5 weeks**

584 CHAPTER 12 MORE COORDINATE GEOMETRY

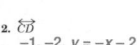
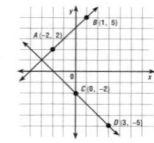
584 Chapter 12

39. Sports It costs about $900 to equip an Olympic skier with skis, poles, and boots. The costs are expected to increase $12 per year. Write the linear equation in slope-intercept form that represents the approximate cost of equipping a skier x years from now. Assume that the rate of increase remains constant.
$y = 12x + 900$

Computer

40. The BASIC program given below will write an equation for the line passing through two points. Use the program to check your answers to Exercises 22-36.

```
10   PRINT "ENTER THE COORDINATES OF THE FIRST POINT."
20   INPUT X1, Y1
30   PRINT "ENTER THE COORDINATES OF THE SECOND POINT."
40   INPUT X2, Y2
50   IF (X2 - X1) = 0 THEN PRINT "AN EQUATION OF THE LINE
     IS  X = "; X1; ".": GOTO 130
60   M = (Y2 - Y1)/(X2 - X1)
70   IF M = 0 THEN PRINT "AN EQUATION OF THE LINE IS Y =
     "; Y1; ".": GOTO 130
80   B = Y1 - M*X1
90   A$ = "+"
100  IF B < 0 THEN B = ABS(B): A$ = "-"
120  PRINT "AN EQUATION OF THE LINE IS Y = "; M; "X"; A$;
     " "; B; "."
130  END
```

Mixed Review

41. Graph the line $6x - 4y = 3$ and state its slope and y-intercept. **(Lesson 12-1)** See margin.

42. Find the missing measures in $\triangle ABC$. **(Lesson 8-6)** $m\angle C \approx 23.9$, $m\angle A \approx 40.4$ $AC \approx 11.1$

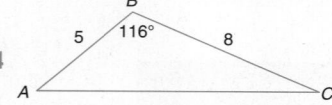

43. Prove that if one pair of alternate interior angles formed by two lines cut by a transversal is congruent, then the other pair of alternate interior angles is congruent also. **(Lesson 3-1)** See margin.

44. Given $A(5, -1)$ and $B(-2, -6)$, find the measure of $\overline{AB}$. **(Lesson 1-4)** $\sqrt{74} \approx 8.6$

45. Given $M(2, 3)$ and $N(-5, -1)$, find the coordinates of the midpoint of $\overline{MN}$. **(Lesson 1-5)** $(-1.5, 1)$

Wrap-Up

46. Write a few sentences to explain how to write an equation of a line given the coordinates of two points on the line. **See students' work.**

LESSON 12-2   WRITING EQUATIONS OF LINES   585

EXTENDING THE LESSON

Math Power: Reasoning

Is it possible for a line to have a negative slope, a positive y-intercept, and a negative x-intercept? Explain your answer.

No; sample answer: Look at the signs in the equation.

$$y = mx + b$$
$$0 = mx + b$$
$$-b = mx$$

Since *b* is positive, −*b* is negative; *m* is negative; therefore, *x* must be positive.

Additional Answer

38c.

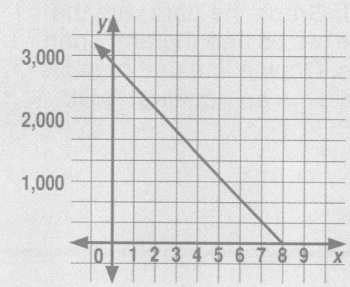

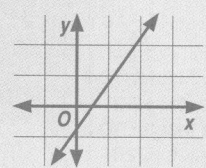
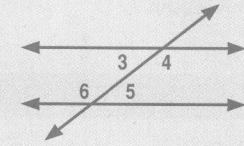
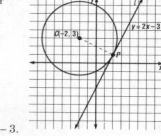
Chapter 12   585

Lesson Resources

- Reteaching Master 12-3
- Practice Master 12-3
- Enrichment Master 12-3
- Activity Master, p. 26
- Technology Master p. 48

 Transparency 12-3 contains the 5-Minute Check and a teaching aid for this lesson.

INTRODUCING THE LESSON

 5-Minute Check

(over Lesson 12-2)

Find the equation of the line with the given slope and passing through the given point.

1. 3, (2, −1) $y = 3x − 7$
2. $−\frac{3}{4}$, (4, −2) $y = −\frac{3}{4}x + 1$
3. −4, (2, −5) $y = −4x + 3$

Find the equation of the line passing through points with the given coordinates.

4. (3, 2) and (4, 1) $y = −x + 5$
5. (4, −2) and (7, −4)
   $y = −\frac{2}{3}x + \frac{2}{3}$
6. (−2, 5) and (6, 5) $y = 5$

Motivating the Lesson

Ask students to give examples of kinds of predictions that are based on gathered data. **Sample answers: winning teams in sports, accident frequency on a road**

TEACHING THE LESSON

Teaching Tip   The line on the graph of the scatter plot is sometimes called the *line of best fit*.

12-3 Connections to Algebra and Statistics

Objective
12-3

After studying this lesson, you should be able to:
- relate equations of lines and statistics to geometric concepts.

Application

Can you predict the temperature by how much noise crickets make? Crickets make their sounds by moving one wing over the other. Scientists have noticed that crickets move their wings faster in warm weather than in cold weather. The table gives the number of chirps per minute at different temperatures.

Chirps per minute	20	16	20	18	18	16	15	17	15	16	15	17	16	17	14
Temperature (°F)	88	72	93	84	82	75	70	82	69	83	73	83	81	84	76

A **scatter plot**, like the one at the right, shows the relationship between the variables by plotting a set of data as points. In the graph at the right, we can fit a line as a way to summarize the data, and find an equation that will express the approximate temperature in terms of the number of chirps. Notice that the points do not lie in a straight line, but they do suggest a linear pattern. Using the points with coordinates (20, 88) and (15, 73), you can determine an equation for this line using techniques from algebra.

You can use a graphing calculator to find the equation of the line that summarizes this data best. This line is called a least squares line of regression.

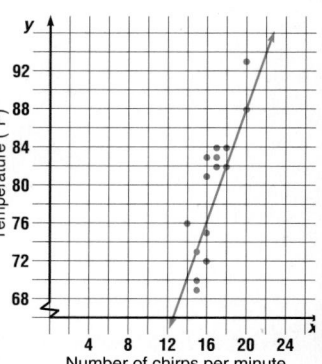

First, find the slope of the line.

$$m = \frac{y_2 − y_1}{x_2 − x_1}$$
$$= \frac{88 − 73}{20 − 15} \quad (x_1, y_1) = (15, 73), (x_2, y_2) = (20, 88)$$
$$= \frac{15}{5} \text{ or } 3$$

Substitute the slope and the coordinates of one point into the point-slope form to find an equation.

$$y − y_1 = m(x − x_1)$$
$$y − 88 = 3(x − 20) \quad \text{The slope is 3 and one point has coordinates (20, 88).}$$
$$y − 88 = 3x − 60$$
$$y = 3x + 28$$

Therefore, an equation that relates the temperature and number of chirps per minute is $y = 3x + 28$.

586   CHAPTER 12   MORE COORDINATE GEOMETRY

ALTERNATE TEACHING STRATEGIES

Using Models

Find 10 people and record their heights and the span of their arms when outstretched. Graph the data with the height on the *x*-axis and the arm span on the *y*-axis. Draw a line that best fits the data and write an equation for it. **Answers will vary.**

Using Logical Reasoning

If you are given the coordinates of the vertices of the vertex angle and one base angle of an isosceles triangle, for which of the following can you find a unique solution?
1. the length of a leg   **yes**
2. the equation of the line containing the altitude   **no**
3. the equation of a line containing one leg   **yes**

You can use the equation to predict the temperature if a cricket chirps a certain number of times or predict the number of chirps that would occur given the temperature. Find the approximate temperature if a cricket chirps 19 times per minute by substituting 19 for x.

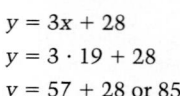

$y = 3x + 28$

$y = 3 \cdot 19 + 28$

$y = 57 + 28$ or 85

The temperature will be approximately 85° F.

Whenever you work with coordinates, it is a good idea to begin by graphing the information you are given.

Example 1

Determine whether $A(4, 3)$, $B(-2, -9)$, and $C(7, 9)$ are collinear.

One way to approach the problem is to find the equation of $\overleftrightarrow{AB}$ and see if the coordinates of C satisfy the equation. First find the slope of $\overleftrightarrow{AB}$.

$$m = \frac{y_2 - y_1}{x_2 - x_1}$$

$$= \frac{3 - (-9)}{4 - (-2)} \qquad \begin{array}{l} A(4, 3) = (x_2, y_2), \\ B(-2, -9) = (x_1, y_1) \end{array}$$

$$= \frac{12}{6} \text{ or } 2$$

$y - y_1 = m(x - x_1)$ *Use point-slope form.*

$y - 3 = 2(x - 4)$ *The slope is 2 and (4, 3) are the*

$y - 3 = 2x - 8$ *coordinates of a point on the line.*

$y = 2x - 5$

The equation of $\overleftrightarrow{AB}$ is $y = 2x - 5$. Since $9 = 2(7) - 5$, $C(7, 9)$ satisfies the equation, the points are collinear.

Example 2

CONNECTION

Algebra

Given $\triangle ABC$ with $A(-6, -8)$, $B(6, 4)$, and $C(-6, 10)$, write the equation of the line containing the altitude from A.

The altitude from A is perpendicular to $\overline{BC}$. So the slopes of the altitude and of $\overline{BC}$ are opposite reciprocals. To find the equation of the line containing the altitude from A, first find the slope of $\overline{BC}$.

LESSON 12-3 CONNECTIONS TO ALGEBRA AND STATISTICS 587

Chalkboard Examples

For Example 1
Determine whether $P(2, 5)$, $Q(4, 6)$, and $R(1, 3)$ are collinear. Find the equation of $\overleftrightarrow{PQ}$.
$m = \frac{1}{2}$
$y - 5 = \frac{1}{2}(x - 2)$
$y = \frac{1}{2}x + 4$
Check the coordinates of R.
$3 \overset{?}{=} \frac{1}{2}(1) + 4$
$3 \neq 4\frac{1}{2}$
The points are not collinear.

For Example 2
Given $\triangle PQR$ with $P(-3, 2)$, $Q(1, 6)$, and $R(5, -3)$, write the equation of the line containing the altitude from P.
First, find the slope of $\overleftrightarrow{QR}$.
$m = -\frac{9}{4}$
The line containing the altitude must have a slope of $\frac{4}{9}$ and must pass through $P(-3, 2)$.
$y - 2 = \frac{4}{9}(x + 3)$
$y = \frac{4}{9}x + \frac{10}{3}$

Teaching Tip After Example 1, ask students what figure would be formed if the points were not collinear.   a triangle

Checking for Understanding

Exercises 1-6 are designed to help you assess students' understanding through reading, writing, speaking, and modeling. You should work through Exercises 1-3 with your students and then monitor their work on Exercises 4-6.

Error Analysis

When writing equations of lines that are perpendicular to a given line, students may forget that the slope must be the *opposite* reciprocal. Tell students to be sure to check that the signs of the two slopes are opposites.

Closing the Lesson

Writing Activity Write a brief paragraph explaining how to find an equation that relates two variables, given data points for the variables that form a linear pattern when graphed.

Additional Answers

1. Sample answer:

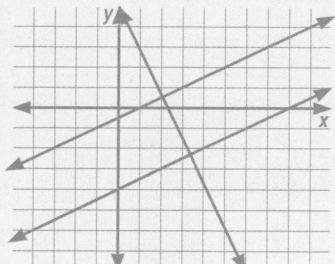

The slopes of the parallel lines are equal. The product of the slopes of the perpendicular lines equals –1.
2. Sample answer:
   a. Make $x = 0$, and solve $5y = 10$.
   b. Change this equation to the slope-intercept form and state the y-intercept.
4. $y = -\frac{5}{3}x - \frac{5}{3}$, $y = \frac{7}{3}x + \frac{19}{3}$, $y = \frac{1}{3}x + \frac{7}{3}$
5. $y = -x - 1$, $y = 3x + 7$, $y = 1$

$$m = \frac{y_2 - y_1}{x_2 - x_1}$$
$$= \frac{10 - 4}{-6 - 6}$$
$$= \frac{6}{-12} \text{ or } -\frac{1}{2}$$

The slope of $\overline{BC}$ is $-\frac{1}{2}$. So the slope of the line containing the altitude drawn to $\overline{BC}$ is 2. Find the equation of the line that has a slope of 2 and passes through the point with coordinates (-6, -8).

$y - y_1 = m(x - x_1)$	*Use point-slope form.*
$y - (-8) = 2(x - (-6))$	*The slope is 2 and the point with coordinates (-6, -8) is*
$y + 8 = 2x + 12$	*on the line.*
$y = 2x + 4$	

The equation of the line containing the altitude is $y = 2x + 4$.

CHECKING FOR UNDERSTANDING

Communicating Mathematics

Read and study the lesson to answer these questions. 1-2. See margin.

1. On a coordinate plane, draw examples of two lines that are parallel and two lines that are perpendicular. How are their slopes related?

2. Describe two ways to find the y-intercept of the graph of $2x + 5y = 10$.

3. What do you call the graphs of paired data points? scatter plots

Guided Practice

The vertices of $\triangle RST$ are $R(-4, -3)$, $S(2, 3)$, and $T(-4, 5)$. See margin.

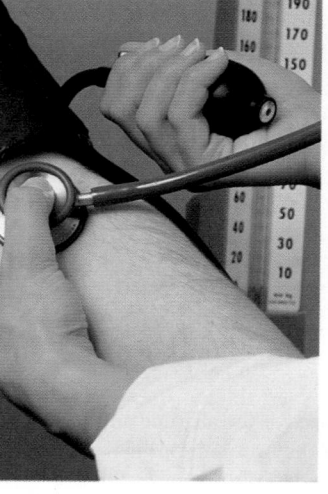

4. Find the equations of the lines containing the medians to each of the sides of $\triangle RST$.

5. Find the equations of the lines containing perpendicular bisectors of the sides of $\triangle RST$.

6. The table below shows the age and systolic blood pressure for a group of people who recently donated blood.

Age	35	24	48	50	34	55	30	26	41	37
Blood Pressure	128	108	140	135	119	146	132	104	132	121

a. Draw a scatter plot to show how age, x, and systolic blood pressure, y, are related. See Solutions Manual.

b. Write an equation that relates a person's age to their approximate systolic blood pressure. Sample answer: $y = \frac{4}{3}x + 76$

c. Find the approximate blood pressure of a person 54 years old.

d. List a few factors that may affect a person's actual systolic blood pressure. Sample answers are exercise, diet, and heredity.

6c. Answers may vary; based on the equation for 6b, 148

EXERCISES

Practice

A

Determine whether the three points listed are collinear.

7. $A(9, 0)$, $B(4, 2)$, $C(2, -1)$ no

8. $X(6, 9)$, $Y(3, -1)$, $Z(4, 0)$ no

9. $L(0, 4)$, $M(2, 3)$, $N(-4, 6)$ yes

10. $D(9, -3)$, $E(4, 8)$, $F(0, 0)$ no

11. The table below lists the Federal Income Tax due from a single person with the given taxable income for 1991.

Taxable Income	11,905	7,412	22,898	19,054	10,995	3,268	18,753
Tax due	1,789	1,114	3,760	2,861	1,646	491	2,816

b. Answers may vary. A typical answer is $y = 0.15x + 3$.

a. Draw a scatter plot to show how taxable income, x, and Federal Income Tax due, y, are related. **See Solutions Manual.**

b. Write an equation that relates a single person's taxable income and their approximate Federal Income Tax due.

c. Angela's taxable income for 1991 was $12,982. Approximately how much did she owe in Federal Income Tax? **Answers may vary. based on the equation for 11b, $1950.30**

B

12. Find the equation of the line containing the perpendicular bisector of the segment whose endpoints have coordinates $(2, 5)$ and $(-2, -1)$. $y = -\frac{2}{3}x + 2$

13. Find the equations of the lines containing the sides of an isosceles triangle if the vertex is at the y-intercept of the line whose equation is $y = -2x + 6$ and a vertex of a base angle is at $(4, -2)$. **See margin.**

The vertices of $\triangle ABC$ are $A(0, 14)$, $B(2, -4)$, and $C(6, 2)$. **14.** $y = -\frac{2}{3}x + 14$

14. Write the equation of the line containing the altitude to $\overline{BC}$.

15. Write the equation of the line containing the perpendicular bisector of $\overline{AB}$. $y = \frac{1}{9}x + \frac{44}{9}$

16. Find the equation of the line containing $\overline{BE}$ if $\overline{BE}$ is a median of $\triangle ABC$. $y = 12x - 28$

The vertices of $\triangle RST$ are $R(-6, -8)$, $S(6, 4)$, and $T(-6, 10)$. **See margin.**

17. Write the equations of the lines containing the sides of $\triangle RST$.

18. Write the equations of the lines containing the medians of $\triangle RST$.

19. Write the equations of the lines containing the altitudes of $\triangle RST$.

LESSON 12-3   CONNECTIONS TO ALGEBRA AND STATISTICS   589

RETEACHING THE LESSON

Explain how to use a graphing calculator to find an equation of a line when given the coordinates of two points on the line. Then give them the coordinates of three points and ask how they can use the calculator to decide if the three points are collinear. **Find the**

equation of the line between two of the points. Then substitute the coordinates of the third point in the equation to see if the coordinates satisfy the equation. Then have them use that method to test these points: $D(3, 5)$, $E(5, 9)$, $F(4, 8)$. **no**

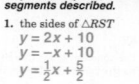

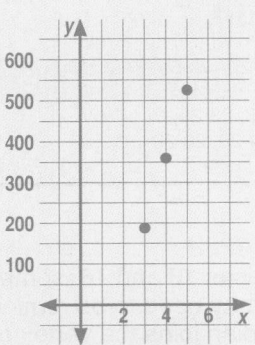
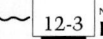
20. The sum of the measures of the angles of a triangle is 180°. This can be represented by the ordered pair (3, 180). The relationship between the number of sides and the sum of the measures of the angles of a rectangle is represented by (4, 360). This relationship for pentagons is represented by (5, 540).

    a. Plot the points and prove they are collinear. **See margin.**

    b. Write the equation of the line determined by the points. $y = 180x - 360$

    c. Use the equation of the line to predict the sum of the measures of the angles in a 10-sided polygon. **1440**

 The equation of a circle is $(x + 1)^2 + (y - 2)^2 = 25$.

21. Show that the point with coordinates (3, 5) is on the circle. **See margin.**

22. Find the equation of the tangent to the circle at (3, 5). $y = -\frac{4}{3}x + 9$

Critical Thinking

23. The equations of two parallel lines are $y = 2x + 10$ and $y = 2x + 3$. Jason says that the two lines are 7 units apart. Do you agree? Why or why not? **no; The distance between parallel lines is the length of a perpendicular line segment between the parallel lines.**

Applications

24. **Investments**   Terry can invest his money in an investment that pays 7% interest or in a higher risk investment that pays 10% interest. He has decided to place some of his money in each investment so that he can earn fairly high interest and still have a relatively safe investment.

    a. If he would like to make $210 in interest after one year, write an equation that would describe his investment. $0.07x + 0.10y = 210$

    b. Graph the equation. **See margin.**

    c. Find the intercepts and explain what they mean.

    d. If Terry would like to make at least $210 in interest in one year, how would this change the graph? **See margin.**

    24c. 3000 and 2100, amounts at 7% and 10% for $210 in interest

25. **Health**   The ages and optimum exercise heart rates for several people are listed in the table below.

Age	31	42	18	24	55	61	44	15
Heart Rate	117	107	127	122	104	99	109	127

    a. Draw a scatter plot to show how age, x, and optimum exercise heart rate, y, are related. **See Solutions Manual.**

    b. Write an equation that relates a person's age to their optimum exercise heart rate. **Answers may vary. A typical answer is $y = -\frac{5}{6}x + 142$.**

    c. Miguel is 19 years old. What is his optimum exercise heart rate? **Answers may vary; based on the equation for 25b, about 126**

Mixed Review

26. Belinda Jackson bought a microwave oven for $60 more than half its original price. She paid $274 for the oven. What was the original price of the oven? **(Lesson 12-2)** $428

27. Find the total surface area of the solid shown at the right. **(Lesson 11-3)** 248 cm²

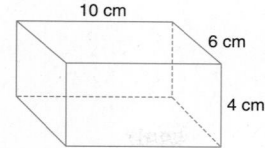

10 cm
6 cm
4 cm

28. What can you conclude about RS and QR from the figure below? State whether the SAS or the SSS Inequality can be used to justify your answer. **(Lesson 5-7)** *RS* > *QR*; SAS Inequality

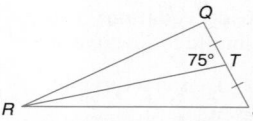

Q
75° T
R
S

Wrap-Up

29. Write a three-question quiz that covers the material in this lesson. Exchange quizzes with a partner and take each other's quiz. **See students' work.**

HISTORY CONNECTION

Emilie du Chatelet (1706-1749) was a well-published mathematician, scientist, classicist, and translator because when she was six or seven years old, her father thought that she would be a homely woman and would never marry. So, he provided the best tutors for her studies and riding and fencing instructors as well. By the age of fifteen, Emilie had grown to be a beautiful woman. And because of her exceptional intelligence and education, she had both beauty and brains.

Emilie du Chatelet's greatest work was a translation and analysis of Isaac Newton's *Principia*. This translation brought modern science and mathematics to Europe. To this day, her work is the only French translation of this important scientific document.

LESSON 12-3   CONNECTIONS TO ALGEBRA AND STATISTICS   591

EXTENDING THE LESSON

Math Power: Connections

Write the slope-intercept form of the equation of a line that is perpendicular to a line with slope r and that passes through the point $T(a, b)$.

$$y = \frac{-x}{r} + \frac{a + br}{r}$$

History Connection

The History Connection features introduce students to persons or cultures who were involved in the development of mathematics. You may want students to further research Emilie du Châtelet or Isaac Newton's *Principia*.

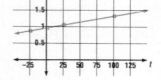

Lesson Resources

- Practice Master 12-4
- Evaluation Master, p. 163
- Activity Master, p. 12

Transparency 12-4 contains the 5-Minute Check and a teaching aid for this lesson.

INTRODUCING THE LESSON

🕐 5-Minute Check

(over Lesson 12-3)

Determine whether the three points are collinear.

1. $A(2, -3)$, $B(4, -7)$, $C(-1, 3)$
   yes
2. $D(-4, -2)$, $E(5, 7)$, $F(0, 2)$
   yes
3. $G(-1, -2)$, $H(3, 6)$, $I(2, -6)$
   no

△QRS has vertices with coordinates $Q(-1, 4)$, $R(3, 1)$, and $S(-5, 1)$.
4. Find the slope of $\overline{QS}$. $\frac{3}{4}$
5. Find the slope of a line perpendicular to $\overline{QS}$ $-\frac{4}{3}$
6. Find the equation of the line containing the altitude from R to $\overline{QS}$. $y = -\frac{4}{3}x + 5$

Motivating the Lesson

Write the equation $a = 23b + 6$ on the chalkboard. Ask students to volunteer several possibilities for what a and b might represent.

TEACHING THE LESSON

Teaching Tip In reading the list of steps, point out that it is important to state the unit of the defined variable.

12-4 Problem-Solving Strategy: Write an Equation

Objective
12-4

After studying this lesson, you should be able to:
- solve problems by using equations.

Application

Neva is lining a soccer field. The length should be 75 yards shorter than 3 times its width. The perimeter of the field is 370 yards. What are the length and the width of the field? An equation can help you solve Neva's problem.

FYI...
A game similar to soccer called tsu-chu was played in China as early as the fourth century B.C.

To solve problems using equations, you should follow five steps.

1. Define a variable.
2. Write an equation.
3. Solve the equation.
4. Check the solution.
5. Answer the problem.

Example 1

APPLICATION
Sports

Find the length and width of the soccer field that Neva is lining.

1. Define a variable.

   Let x represent the width in yards.
   Then the length will be $3x - 75$ yards.

2. Write an equation.

   The perimeter of a rectangle equals 2 times the length plus 2 times the width.

   $$370 = 2(3x - 75) + 2x$$

3. Solve the equation.

   $$370 = 2(3x - 75) + 2x$$
   $$370 = 6x - 150 + 2x$$
   $$520 = 8x$$
   $$65 = x$$

   If $x = 65$, $3x - 75 = 120$.

ALTERNATE TEACHING STRATEGIES

Using Communication

Have students make up three problems that can be solved by writing an equation. Explain that a solution manual not only gives the answers to problems but also shows how the answers were obtained. Ask the students to prepare solution manuals for their problems.

Using Critical Thinking

Ask students what kind of solution they can find if they are given two unknowns and one relationship between them. **a set of ordered pairs**

4. Check your solution.

If the length is 120 yards and the width is 65 yards, will the perimeter equal 370?

$$2(120) + 2(65) = 370$$
$$240 + 130 = 370$$
$$370 = 370 ✔$$

5. Answer the problem.

The length of the soccer field is 120 yards and the width is 65 yards.

CHECKING FOR UNDERSTANDING

Communicating Mathematics

Read and study the lesson to answer these questions. 1-2. See margin.

1. Why should you define the variable before you write an equation?

2. Explain the steps used to solve the equation in Example 1.

3. Define a variable and write an equation for the following problem.

Felipe's bowling handicap is 7 less than half his average. His handicap is 53. What is Felipe's bowling average?

x = average; $\frac{1}{2}x - 7 = 53$

Guided Practice

Solve. Use an equation.

4. To estimate when to harvest her early pea crop, Dorothy counts heat units. As of June 1 she has counted 835 heat units. There are usually 30 heat units per day in June. Early peas require 1165 heat units to mature. On what day can Dorothy plan to harvest her crop? **June 12**

5. Ron is on his way to San Diego, 300 miles away. He drives 45 miles per hour for 3 hours. He drives 55 miles per hour for the rest of the trip. How long does Ron drive at 55 miles per hour? **3 hours**

6. The length of a rectangular garden is 40 meters less than 2 times its width. Its perimeter is 220 meters. Find its length and width. **60 m, 50 m**

7. Jenny sold tickets for the annual spring concert at Middletown High School. The concert tickets cost $3.50 for adults and $2.50 for students. If Jenny sold 4 more student tickets than adult tickets and she has a total of $58.00 in sales, how many of each type of ticket did she sell? **8 adult tickets and 12 student tickets**

LESSON 12-4   PROBLEM-SOLVING STRATEGY: WRITE AN EQUATION   593

RETEACHING THE LESSON

Help students set up an equation or devise an arithmetic strategy to solve each problem. Then have them solve the problems individually or in small groups. Discuss the answers with them. Have students critique their solutions.

1. A 150-foot fence encloses a field that is 20 feet wide. How long is the field? **55 ft**

2. Nancy sold twice as many children's tickets, at $5 each, as adult tickets, at $12 each, for the town's skating party. If she collected $572, how many of each kind of ticket did she sell? **52 children's, 26 adult**

3. Leon plans to drive 270 miles today. By noon, he had driven 160 miles. If he can drive the rest of the way at 55 miles per hour, how long will it take him to complete the trip? **2 hours**

APPLYING THE LESSON

Homework Exercises

Assignment Guide

Basic: 8-14
Average: 8-14
Enriched: 8-14

Exercise Notes

For Exercise 8, the strategy of acting it out would be appropriate.

For Exercises 9-11 and 14, drawing a diagram would be helpful. An equation would also be helpful for Exercise 11.

For Exercises 10 and 13, guess and check would be a good strategy. An equation could be written for Exercise 13.

For Exercise 12, students must work backward.

Additional Answer

8.

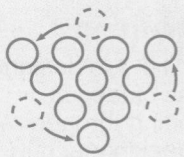

Practice Masters Booklet, p. 85

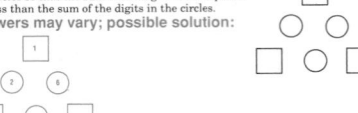
EXERCISES

Practice — Solve. Use any strategy.

Strategies

Look for a pattern.
Solve a simpler problem.
Act it out.
Guess and check.
Draw a diagram.
Make a chart.
Work backward.

8. Turn this triangle upside down by moving just 3 coins.
See margin.

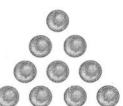

9. Suppose a student who is 5 feet tall could walk around the equator. How much farther would his head travel than his feet? $10\pi \approx$ **31.4 feet**

10. Assign each of the numbers from 1 to 8 to one of the vertices of a cube so that the sum of the numbers assigned to the vertices of each face is 18.
See Solutions Manual.

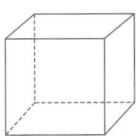

11. San Francisco and Los Angeles are 470 miles apart by train. An express train leaves Los Angeles at the same time a passenger train leaves San Francisco. The express train travels 10 miles per hour faster than the passenger train. The 2 trains pass each other in 2.5 hours. How fast is each train traveling? **89 mph and 99 mph**

12. A certain bacteria doubles its population every 8 hours. After 3 days there are 12,800 bacteria. How many bacteria were there at the beginning of the first day? **25 bacteria**

13. The sum of the digits of a two-digit number is 10 and three times its tens digit is twice its ones digit. What is the number? **46**

14. Six equilateral triangles are placed together to form a hexagon. The length of a side of one triangle is 2 inches. What is the diameter of the smallest circle that includes all six vertices of the hexagon? **4 inches**

COOPERATIVE LEARNING PROJECT

Work in groups. Each person in the group must understand the solution and be able to explain it to any person in class.

A helium tank fills a balloon at a steady rate. It takes 3 seconds for the radius of a balloon to become 5 centimeters long. How many seconds would it take for the radius of an empty balloon to become 10 centimeters long? (Assume that a balloon is approximately spherical.) **24 seconds**

594   CHAPTER 12   MORE COORDINATE GEOMETRY

EXTENDING THE LESSON

Math Power: Problem Solving

Eleanor gets paid at an hourly rate for the first 40 hours she works in a week and $1\frac{1}{2}$ times that rate for any time over 40 hours. Last week, she worked 45 hours and earned $403.75. How much does she earn per hour? **$8.50**

Cooperative Learning Project

This activity provides students an opportunity to *learn* things together, not just do things together. You may wish to refer to pages T6-T7 and page 572c for the various elements of cooperative groups and specific goals and strategies for using them.

12-5 Coordinate Proof

Objective
12-5

After studying this lesson, you should be able to:
- prove theorems using coordinate proofs.

Application

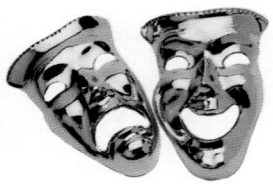

FYI···

Teatro Olimpico in Italy which was completed in 1582 is the oldest indoor theatre.

The stage of the Palace Theater is formed by a semicircle and a rectangle. When the theater was renovated, the architect made a scale drawing of the stage and assigned coordinates to the drawing. Then the architect used algebra to find the best locations for the microphones and lights.

The diameter of the semicircle that forms part of the stage of the Palace Theater is 30 feet long. The width of the rectangle is 10 feet. Using the placement of the stage as shown, you can name the coordinates of the front center point of the stage.

Start by naming the vertices of the rectangle as shown. The *x*-coordinate of the front center is 15, and the *y*-coordinate is 10 + 15 or 25. So the coordinates of the front center point are (15, 25).

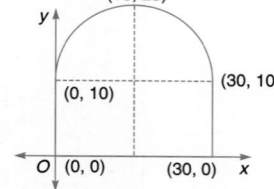

In geometry, we can assign coordinates to figures and use the coordinates to prove theorems. An important part of planning a **coordinate proof** is the placement of the figure on the coordinate plane.

Guidelines for Placing Figures on a Coordinate Plane

1. Use the origin as a vertex or center.
2. Place at least one side of a polygon on an axis.
3. Keep the figure within the first quadrant if possible.
4. Use coordinates that make computations simple.

Example 1

Position and label a right triangle with legs of *a* units and *b* units on the coordinate plane.

Use the origin as the vertex of the right angle. Place the legs of the triangle on the positive *x*- and *y*-axes. Label the vertices *P*, *Q*, and *R*. Since *Q* is on the *y*-axis, its *x*-coordinate is 0. Its *y*-coordinate is *b*, because the leg is *b* units long. Since *R* is on the *x*-axis, its *y*-coordinate is 0 and its *x*-coordinate is *a* because it is *a* units long. *P* is at the origin, so both coordinates are 0.

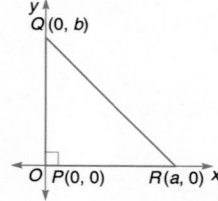

LESSON 12-5   COORDINATE PROOF   595

ALTERNATE TEACHING STRATEGIES

Using Discussion

Ask students to explain in their own words what to consider when placing a figure for a coordinate proof.

Using Technology

You may want to have students draw the figures for coordinate proofs of the computer screen. Refer to the LOGO instructional materials in the *Merrill Geometry Technology Masters* booklet.

Chalkboard Examples

For Example 1

Position and label an isosceles right triangle with legs of *a* units on the coordinate plane.

Use the origin as the vertex of the right angle. Place the triangle's legs on the positive axes.
Label the vertices $A(0, 0)$, $B(0, a)$, and $C(a, 0)$.

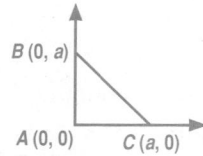

For Example 2

Use a coordinate proof to prove that, if a segment from a vertex in a triangle is the perpendicular bisector of the opposite side, the triangle is isosceles.

Given: $\triangle MIT$, $\overline{MC}$ is the perpendicular bisector of $\overline{IT}$.
Prove: $\triangle MIT$ is isosceles.

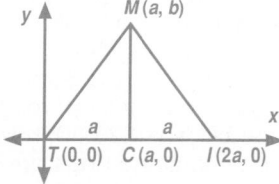

Because $\overline{MC} \perp \overline{TI}$, $\overline{MC}$ is a vertical segment and $\overline{TI}$ is a horizontal segment. Since C is on the perpendicular bisector and on $\overline{TI}$, it has the same x-coordinate as M, and its y-coordinate is halfway between that of T and I. The Distance Formula can be used to show that $\overline{MT} \cong \overline{MI}$.

$MI = \sqrt{(2a - a)^2 + (0 - b)^2}$
$\quad = \sqrt{a^2 + b^2}$
$MT = \sqrt{(a - 0)^2 + (b - 0)^2}$
$\quad = \sqrt{a^2 + b^2}$

Since $MI = MT$, $\overline{MI} \cong \overline{MT}$ and $\triangle MIT$ is isosceles.

Some examples of figures placed on the coordinate plane are given below.

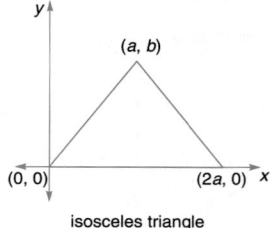

isosceles triangle

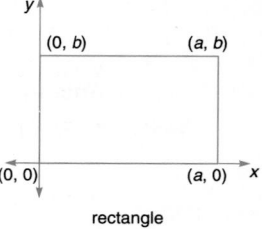

rectangle

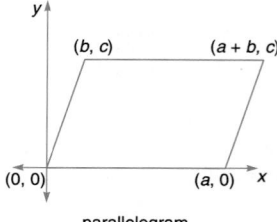

parallelogram

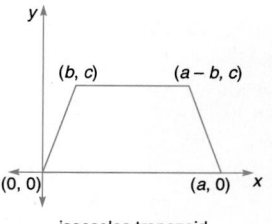

isosceles trapezoid

Example 2

Use a coordinate proof to prove that the midpoint of the hypotenuse of a right triangle is equidistant from the vertices.

Given: $\triangle QPR$ is a right triangle.
M is the midpoint of $\overline{QR}$.

Prove: M is equidistant from Q, P, and R.

Proof:

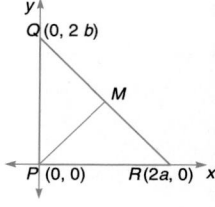

Place right $\triangle QPR$ on the coordinate plane and label coordinates as shown. (Using coordinates that are multiples of 2 for Q and R will make the computation easier.) By the Midpoint Formula, the coordinates of M are $\left(\frac{2a}{2}, \frac{2b}{2}\right) = (a, b)$.

Use the Distance Formula to find MR and PM.

$MR = \sqrt{(a - 2a)^2 + (b - 0)^2}$ $\qquad PM = \sqrt{(a - 0)^2 + (b - 0)^2}$
$\quad = \sqrt{(-a)^2 + (b)^2}$ $\qquad\qquad\quad = \sqrt{(a)^2 + (b)^2}$
$\quad = \sqrt{a^2 + b^2}$ $\qquad\qquad\qquad\quad = \sqrt{a^2 + b^2}$

Thus, $MR = PM$. Also, by the definition of midpoint, $QM = MR$. By the transitive property, $QM = MR = PM$, and M is equidistant from Q, P, and R.

CHECKING FOR UNDERSTANDING

Communicating Mathematics

Read and study the lesson to answer these questions. See margin.

1. When planning a coordinate proof, why is it helpful to place at least one of the sides of a polygon on an axis?

2. Show how to place an isosceles triangle on a coordinate plane in two ways.

3. Two ways of positioning a rectangle on coordinate planes are shown below. Which drawing would be a better way to start a coordinate proof? Explain your answer.

a.
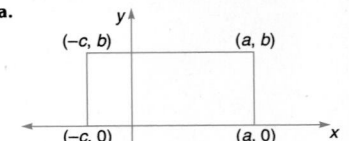

b.
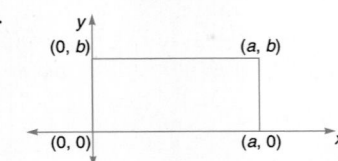

Guided Practice

Name the missing coordinates in terms of the given variables.

4. $\triangle BAT$ is isosceles. $B(-a, 0)$

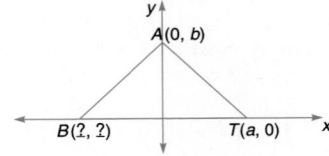

5. $ABCE$ is a parallelogram. $E(d - f, r)$

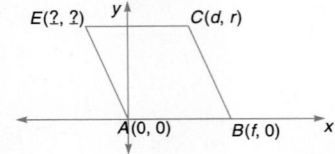

6. Use $\triangle LPT$ with coordinates as indicated in the figure to answer each of the following.

   a. What kind of triangle is $\triangle LPT$? Explain your answer. **right isosceles**
   b. If $\overline{TM}$ is a median, find the coordinates of M. (b, b)
   c. Find the slope of $\overline{TM}$. **1**
   d. Find the slope of $\overline{LP}$. **-1**
   e. What conclusion can you make about $\overline{TM}$ and $\overline{LP}$? See margin.

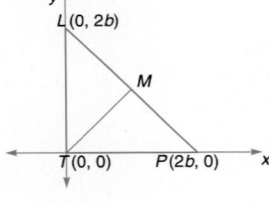

Use the quadrilateral at the right to prove each of the following. See Solutions Manual.

7. The segments joining the midpoints of the sides of a quadrilateral form a parallelogram.

8. The segments joining the midpoints of opposite sides of a quadrilateral bisect each other.

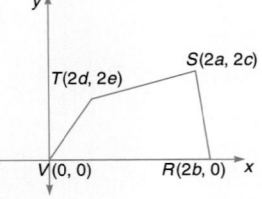

LESSON 12-5   COORDINATE PROOF   597

Checking for Understanding

Exercises 1-10 are designed to help you assess students' understanding through reading, writing, speaking, and modeling. You should work through Exercises 1-3 with your students and then monitor their work on Exercises 4-10.

Error Analysis

Some students may use coordinates that imply more than the given information. For example, they may draw and label an isosceles or right triangle when the proof calls for a statement about any triangle. Remind them that their selection of points must include all possible cases.

Closing the Lesson

Speaking Activity Have students come to the chalkboard and draw a figure on a coordinate plane. Ask students to explain their choice of position and labels.

Additional Answers

1. Because some of the coordinates will be 0, which will make the computations easier

2. Sample answers:

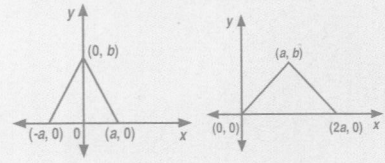

3. Sample answer: *b* is better because there are fewer variables.

6e. The median $\overline{TM}$ is perpendicular to the hypotenuse $\overline{LP}$.

Homework Exercises

Assignment Guide

Basic: 11-23, 28-40
Average: 13-25, 28-40
Enriched: 16-40
All: Mid-Chapter Review, 1-11

Exercise Notes

For Exercises 19-27, encourage students to take their time positioning figures on the coordinate plane. Have students work together on these exercises.

Reteaching Masters Booklet, p. 74

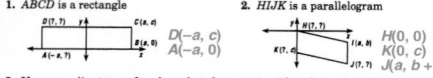

Position and label each figure on the coordinate plane. Then write a coordinate proof for each of the following. See Solutions Manual.

9. The diagonals of an isosceles trapezoid are congruent.

10. The medians to the legs of an isosceles triangle are congruent.

EXERCISES

Practice **Name the missing coordinates in terms of the given variables.**

11. $\triangle DAY$ is isosceles and right.
$A(0, 0), Y(b, 0)$

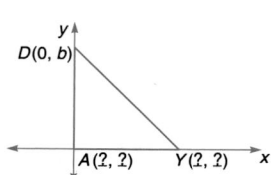

12. $TUES$ is a square.
$E(a, a), S(0, a)$

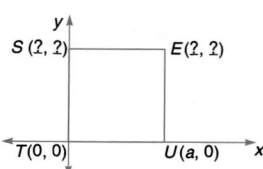

13. $\triangle RUN$ is isosceles and right.
$R(-b, 2b)$

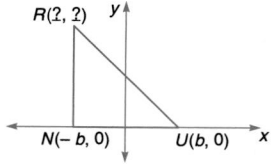

14. $RIDE$ is an isosceles trapezoid.
$D(a - b, c), E(0, 0)$

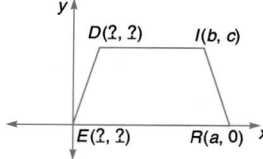

Prove using a coordinate proof. See Solutions Manual.

15. $\triangle ABC$ is isosceles.

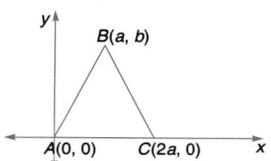

16. $HIJK$ is a parallelogram.

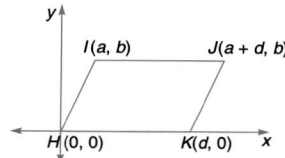

17. $\triangle DEF$ is equilateral.

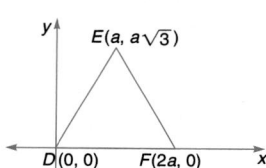

18. $\triangle PQR$ is a right triangle.

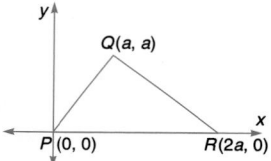

RETEACHING THE LESSON

Have groups of students draw and label figures on the coordinate plane for each of the following: square, rectangle, parallelogram, right triangle, triangle. Remind them to use as few variables as possible. Have groups compare their work and then go back and alter it if they choose.

19. The diagonals of a square are perpendicular.

20. The three segments joining the midpoints of the sides of an isosceles triangle form another isosceles triangle.

21. The diagonals of a parallelogram bisect each other.

22. The segments joining the midpoints of the sides of an isosceles trapezoid form a rhombus.

23. If a line segment joins the midpoints of two sides of a triangle, then it is parallel to the third side.

24. If a line segment joins the midpoints of two sides of a triangle, then its length is equal to one-half the length of the third side.

25. The line segments joining the midpoints of the sides of a rectangle form a rhombus.

26. If the diagonals of a parallelogram are congruent, then it is a rectangle.

27. If the diagonals of a parallelogram are perpendicular, then the parallelogram is a rhombus.

Critical Thinking

28. Position a regular hexagon on a coordinate plane and label the vertices using as few variables as possible. **See margin.**

Applications

29. Theater A stage is in the shape of a semicircle with a 40-foot diameter. If a scale drawing of the stage is assigned coordinates as shown at the right, find the equation of the line that bisects the stage into two congruent parts. $x = 20$

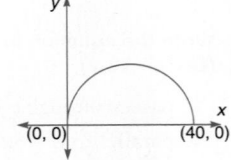

30. Interior Decorating When planning the design of a room, a decorator makes a scale drawing of the room on the coordinate plane. The vertices are given as points $A(4, 8)$, $B(0, 8)$, $C(4, 0)$, and $D(0, 0)$. What are the coordinates of the center of the room? **(2, 4)**

31. Air Traffic Control An airplane is 5 kilometers east and 3 kilometers north of the airport, while a second airplane is 2 kilometers west and 6 kilometers north. Use your knowledge of coordinate geometry to find the distance between the airplanes. $\sqrt{58} \approx 7.6$ km

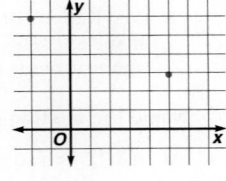

Mixed Review

Determine whether each statement is *true* or *false*.

32. To find an equation for the line that passes through (-1, 4) and (5, 0), first find the *y*-intercept and then find the slope. **(Lesson 12-2)** false

33. An obtuse triangle cannot be isosceles. **(Lesson 4-1)** false

34. The altitude of a triangle can sometimes be located outside the triangle. **(Lesson 5-1)** true

35. AAS is a test for congruent triangles. **(Lesson 4-5)** true

36. The measures of the three sides of a triangle can be 5, 4, and 6. **(Lesson 5-6)** true

37. The opposite angles of a parallelogram are supplementary. **(Lesson 6-1)** false

LESSON 12-5   COORDINATE PROOF   599

Exercise Notes

For Exercises 26 and 27, students must remember that opposite sides of a parallelogram are congruent and parallel. Those properties determine the kind of figure to be used in the proof.

Additional Answer

28.

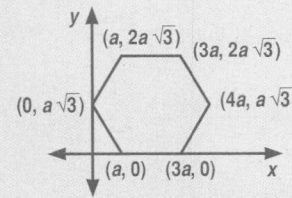

Practice Masters Booklet, p. 86

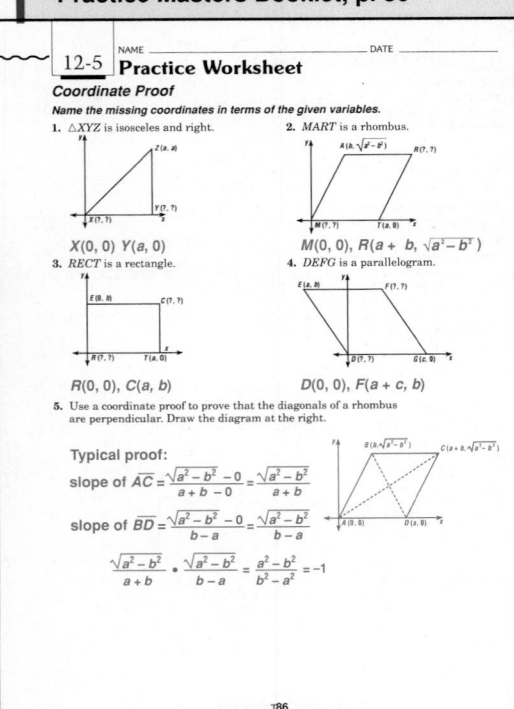

Additional Answers

40a. Sample answer:

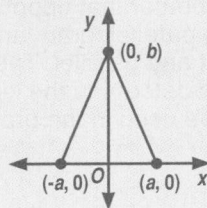

40b. Sample answer:

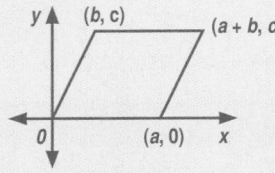

40c. Sample answer:

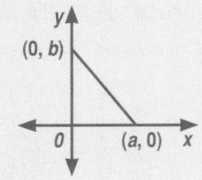

Enrichment Masters Booklet, p. 74

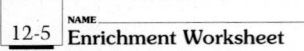
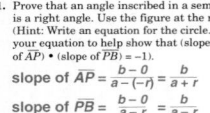
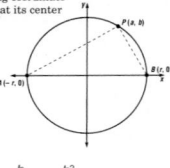
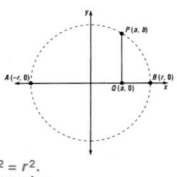

Determine whether each statement is *true* or *false*.

38. The diagonals of an isosceles trapezoid bisect each other. **(Lesson 6-6)** false

39. An equilateral polygon must also be an equiangular polygon. **(Lesson 10-1)** false

Wrap-Up

40. **Journal Entry**   Show how you would position each of the following on a coordinate plane to start a proof. Label the vertices with as few variables as possible. **See margin.**

a. an isosceles triangle
b. a parallelogram
c. a right triangle

～～～～～ MID-CHAPTER REVIEW ～～～～～

Find the x-intercept and y-intercept of the graph of each equation if they exist. (Lesson 12-1)

1. $4x - 3y = 12$ **3; −4**

2. $y = 15$ **no x-intercept; 15**

Write the equation in slope-intercept form of the line that satisfies the given conditions. (Lesson 12-2)

3. passes through (−1, 4) and (2, 2) $y = -\frac{2}{3}x + \frac{10}{3}$

4. parallel to $y = 3x - 4$, passes through (0, 0) $y = 3x$

5. $m = -\frac{1}{2}$, x-intercept = 6 $y = -\frac{1}{2}x + 3$

Determine whether the three points listed are collinear. (Lesson 12-3)

6. $A(8, 0)$, $B(9, -2)$, $C(0, 16)$ **yes**

7. $X(-2, 2)$, $Y(8, -1)$, $Z(4, 3)$ **no**

8. Ms. Kelly is driving the 88 miles from her office to an appointment at her client's office. If she averages 40 miles per hour on the trip and is fifteen minutes early for her 1:00 appointment, what time did she leave her office? **(Lesson 12-4)** **10:33**

Name the missing coordinates in terms of the given variables. (Lesson 12-5)

9. $ABCD$ is a square.
$A(-b, 0)$, $C(b, 2b)$, $D(-b, 2b)$

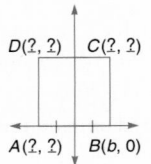

10. $EFGH$ is a parallelogram.
$E(0, 0)$, $G(a, b + c)$

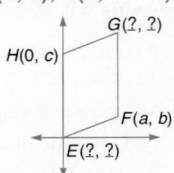

11. Use a coordinate proof to show that the medians drawn to the congruent sides of an isosceles triangle are congruent. **See Solutions Manual.**

EXTENDING THE LESSON

Math Power: Connections

A circle with radius r is placed on a coordinate plane with its center at the origin. Segment $\overline{AB}$ is drawn from the origin to a point (x, y) on the circle and in the first quadrant. What are the sine, cosine, and tangent of the angle, C, formed by $\overline{AB}$ and the x-axis?

$\sin C = \frac{y}{r}$, $\cos C = \frac{x}{r}$, $\tan C = \frac{y}{x}$

Mid-Chapter Review

The Mid-Chapter Review provides students with a brief review of the concepts and skills in Lessons 12-1 through 12-5. Lesson numbers are given at the end of problems or instruction lines so students may review concepts not yet mastered.

12-6 Vectors

Objectives

12-6A
- find the magnitude and direction of a vector,

12-6B
- determine if two vectors are equal, and

12-6C
- perform operations with vectors.

After studying this lesson, you should be able to:

Application

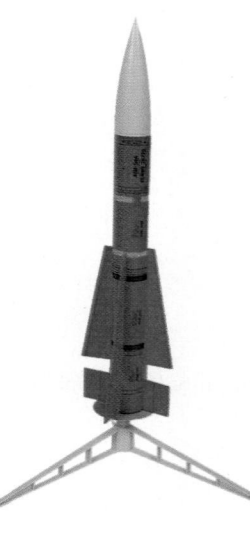

The speed and direction of a rocket can be represented by a directed segment called a **vector.** A vector is any quantity that has both **magnitude** (length) and **direction.** In this case, the length of the segment represents the speed of the rocket. The direction of the rocket is indicated by the direction of the segment.

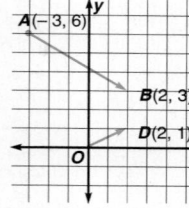

In symbols, a vector is written as $\vec{v}$ or $\overrightarrow{AB}$. A vector can be represented by an ordered pair (change in x, change in y). In the diagram above, vector OD ($\overrightarrow{OD}$) is in standard position: that is, its initial point is at the origin. $\overrightarrow{OD}$ can be represented by the ordered pair (2, 1). To represent $\overrightarrow{AB}$ as an ordered pair, find the change in x and the corresponding change in y and write as an ordered pair.

$$\overrightarrow{AB} = (x_2 - x_1, y_2 - y_1)$$
$$= (2 - (-3), 3 - 6) \qquad (x_1, y_1) = A(-3, 6), (x_2, y_2) = B(2, 3)$$
$$= (5, -3)$$

Because the magnitude and direction are not changed by moving, or translating, a vector, (5, -3) represents the same vector as $\overrightarrow{AB}$.

You can use the distance formula to find the magnitude, or length, of a vector. The symbol for the magnitude of $\overrightarrow{AB}$ is $|\overrightarrow{AB}|$. The direction of a vector is the measure of the angle that the vector forms with the positive x-axis or another horizontal line. You can use the trigonometric ratios to find the direction of a vector.

Example 1

Given A(1, 2) and B(3, 5), find the magnitude and direction of $\overrightarrow{AB}$.

magnitude
$$|\overrightarrow{AB}| = \sqrt{(3-1)^2 + (5-2)^2}$$
$$= \sqrt{13} \text{ or about 3.6 units}$$

direction
$$\tan A = \frac{3}{2} \qquad \tan A = \frac{opposite}{adjacent}$$
$$m\angle A \approx 56.3$$

$\overrightarrow{AB}$ has a magnitude of about 3.6 units and a direction of about 56.3°.

INTRODUCING THE LESSON

5-Minute Check
(over Lesson 12-5)

Find the coordinates of each.

1. A of square SQAR with vertices S(0, 0), Q(0, a), and R(a, 0)   (a, a)
2. E of parallelogram TILE with vertices T(0, 0), I(a, b), and L(c + a, b)   (c, 0)
3. Z of equilateral triangle XYZ with vertices X(0, 0) and Y(2w, 0)   (w, w√3)
4. Prove that $\overline{PQ} \cong \overline{QR}$ if P(0, 0), Q(p, q), and R(2p, 0).
   $PQ = \sqrt{p^2 + q^2}$
   $QR = \sqrt{p^2 + q^2}$
   Since $PQ = QR$, $\overline{PQ} \cong \overline{QR}$.

Motivating the Lesson

Have students sketch a diagram of their route to school on grid paper. Ask how they could show the difference between going to school and returning home. Sample answer: Use directed line segments.

ALTERNATE TEACHING STRATEGIES

Using Models

Each small group will need grid paper, a stop watch, and something that rolls (small ball or toy car). Have students practice rolling the object in a straight line down one side of the grid paper. Then, one member blows on the object in a direction perpendicular to its path. After 2 seconds of rolling and blowing, stop the ball. That point will be the end of resultant vector.

Using Communication

Have your students write a brief paragraph explaining how graph paper, a calculator, and a protractor can be used to find the magnitude and direction of a vector. Graph the points, draw the vector, and use a protractor to measure the angle formed with a horizontal. To find the magnitude, simplify $\sqrt{(x_1 - x_2)^2 + (y_1 - y_2)^2}$.

For Example 1
Given $P(2, 4)$ and $Q(5, 1)$, find the magnitude and direction of $\overrightarrow{PQ}$.

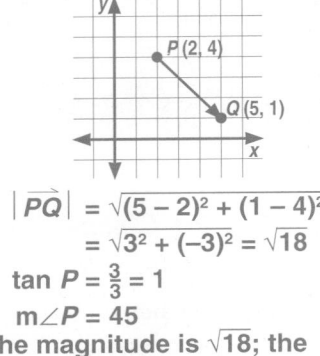

$|\overrightarrow{PQ}| = \sqrt{(5-2)^2 + (1-4)^2}$
$\qquad = \sqrt{3^2 + (-3)^2} = \sqrt{18}$
$\tan P = \frac{3}{3} = 1$
$\quad m\angle P = 45$
The magnitude is $\sqrt{18}$; the direction is 45°.

Teaching Tip After reading the first two lines of the page, point out that $\overrightarrow{AB}$ is not the same as $\overrightarrow{BA}$.

Teaching Tip The procedure shown at the bottom of the page is called the *parallelogram method of adding vectors*.

Two vectors are equal if they have the same magnitude and direction. They are parallel if they have the same direction or slope.

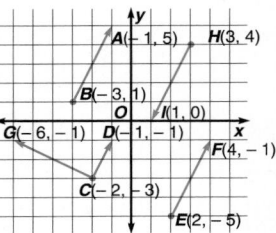

$\overrightarrow{BA} \parallel \overrightarrow{CD}$ Both have a slope of 2, but have different lengths.

$\overrightarrow{BA} = \overrightarrow{EF}$ Both have a length of $2\sqrt{5}$ units and a slope of 2.

$\overrightarrow{BA} \neq \overrightarrow{CG}$ Both have a length of $2\sqrt{5}$ units, but have different directions.

$\overrightarrow{BA}$ is *not* considered to be parallel to $\overrightarrow{HI}$ because they have opposite directions.

A vector can be multiplied by a constant that will change the magnitude of the vector but not affect the direction. If $\overrightarrow{v} = (2, 6)$, then $2\overrightarrow{v} = (2 \times 2, 2 \times 6)$ or $(4, 12)$. Now compare the magnitudes of $\overrightarrow{v}$ and $2\overrightarrow{v}$.

$$|\overrightarrow{v}| = \sqrt{2^2 + 6^2} \qquad\qquad |2\overrightarrow{v}| = \sqrt{4^2 + 12^2}$$
$$\phantom{|\overrightarrow{v}|} = \sqrt{4 + 36} \qquad\qquad \phantom{|2\overrightarrow{v}|} = \sqrt{16 + 144}$$
$$\phantom{|\overrightarrow{v}|} = \sqrt{40} \qquad\qquad\quad \phantom{|2\overrightarrow{v}|} = \sqrt{160}$$
$$\phantom{|\overrightarrow{v}|} = 2\sqrt{10} \qquad\qquad \phantom{|2\overrightarrow{v}|} = 4\sqrt{10}$$

Notice that multiplying the vector by 2 doubled its magnitude. Multiplying a vector by a constant is called **scalar multiplication.**

It is also possible to add vectors. Suppose a plane flew from Chicago to Nashville and then from Nashville to Washington, D.C. This has the same result as flying directly from Chicago to Washington, D.C. In terms of vectors, $\overrightarrow{CN} + \overrightarrow{NW} = \overrightarrow{CW}$.

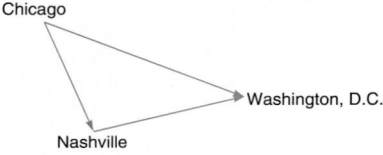

To add vectors, you can use the **parallelogram law.** The **resultant** or sum of two vectors is the diagonal of the parallelogram made by using the given vectors as sides. To add $\overrightarrow{AB}$ and $\overrightarrow{AD}$, draw parallelogram $ADCB$ using the magnitude and direction of $\overrightarrow{AB}$ for side DC and that of $\overrightarrow{AD}$ for side BC. The sum of the vectors is the diagonal of the parallelogram.

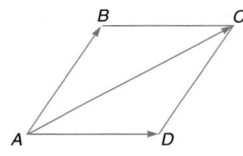

602   CHAPTER 12   MORE COORDINATE GEOMETRY

Vectors can also be added by adding their coordinates.

$$(a, b) + (c, d) = (a + c, b + d)$$
$$\overrightarrow{RS} + \overrightarrow{ST} = \overrightarrow{RT}$$
$$(5, 2) + (1, 3) = (5 + 1, 2 + 3)$$
$$= (6, 5)$$

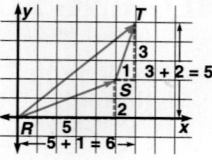

Example 2

If $\vec{v} = (5, 1)$ and $\vec{w} = (1, 3)$, find the coordinates of $2\vec{v} + \vec{w}$.

$$2\vec{v} + \vec{w} = (2 \times 5, 2 \times 1) + (1, 3)$$
$$= (10, 2) + (1, 3)$$
$$= (10 + 1, 2 + 3)$$
$$= (11, 5)$$

Example 3

APPLICATION

Physics

A rocket is traveling straight up at the speed of 600 miles per hour. A 50-mile per hour wind is blowing at a right angle on the path of the rocket. How does the wind affect the speed and direction of the rocket?

Use coordinates to make a model. Let each unit represent 50 miles. $\overrightarrow{OR}$ is the vector that represents the speed and direction of the rocket. $\overrightarrow{OW}$ is the vector that represents the speed and direction of the wind.

$$\overrightarrow{OR} = (0, 600)$$
$$\overrightarrow{OW} = (50, 0)$$

$\overrightarrow{OT}$ is the resultant of $\overrightarrow{OR} + \overrightarrow{OW}$.

$$\overrightarrow{OT} = \overrightarrow{OR} + \overrightarrow{OW}$$
$$= (0 + 50, 600 + 0) \text{ or } (50, 600)$$

Find the magnitude of $\overrightarrow{OT}$.

$$|\overrightarrow{OT}| = \sqrt{50^2 + 600^2}$$
$$= \sqrt{2500 + 360,000}$$
$$= \sqrt{362,500} \approx 602.1$$

Find the direction of $\overrightarrow{OT}$.

$$\tan x = \frac{50}{600} \qquad \tan x = \frac{OW}{OR}$$
$$\tan x \approx 0.0833$$
$$x \approx 4.8$$

The wind blows the rocket off course by about 4.8° and increases its speed to about 602.1 miles per hour.

Teaching Tip Note that the method of adding vectors by adding their coordinates is somewhat like finding a translation of a point.

Chalkboard Examples

For Example 2
If $\vec{X} = (2, 5)$ and $\vec{Y} = (1, 6)$, find the coordinates of $\vec{X} + 3\vec{Y}$.
$$\vec{X} + 3\vec{Y} = (2, 5) + (1 \cdot 3, 6 \cdot 3)$$
$$= (2, 5) + (3, 18)$$
$$= (2 + 3, 5 + 18)$$
$$= (5, 23)$$

For Example 3
A boat is traveling due north at a speed of 8 miles per hour across a river that is flowing east at 3 miles per hour. How does the current of the river affect the speed and direction of the boat? Use coordinates to make a model.

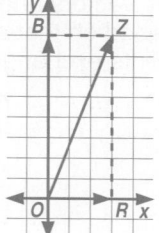

$\overrightarrow{OB} = (0, 8)$, $\overrightarrow{OR} = (3, 0)$
$\overrightarrow{OZ}$ is the resultant of $\overrightarrow{OB} + \overrightarrow{OR}$.
$$\overrightarrow{OZ} = \overrightarrow{OB} + \overrightarrow{OR}$$
$$= (0, 8) + (3, 0)$$
$$= (3, 8)$$
Find the magnitude of $\overrightarrow{OZ}$.
$$|\overrightarrow{OZ}| = \sqrt{3^2 + 8^2}$$
$$= \sqrt{73} \approx 8.5$$
Find the direction of $\overrightarrow{OZ}$.
$$\tan z = \frac{8}{3}$$
$$z = 69.4°$$
The river moves the boat off course by 69.4° and increases its speed to 8.5 miles per hour.

CHECKING FOR UNDERSTANDING

Communicating Mathematics

Read and study the lesson to answer these questions. 1-4. See Solutions Manual.

1. What is the difference between a vector and a line segment?

2. Is $\overrightarrow{AB}$ the same as $\overrightarrow{BA}$? Explain your answer.

3. What is the difference between two parallel vectors and two equal vectors?

4. Describe the effect of scalar multiplication on a vector.

5-7. See margin.

5. Draw two different diagrams showing addition of vectors.

6. Draw two vectors with the same magnitude but different directions.

7. Draw two vectors with the same direction but different magnitudes.

Guided Practice

Sketch each vector. Then find the magnitude and direction to the nearest degree.

8. $\overrightarrow{SL} = (5, 1)$ $\sqrt{26} \approx 5.1, 11°$

9. $\overrightarrow{AB} = (3, 8)$ $\sqrt{73} \approx 8.5, 69°$

10. $\overrightarrow{RT}$ if R(-2, -5) and T(1, 7) $\sqrt{153} \approx 12.4, 76°$

Given **A(0, 0), B(2, 4), C(7, 4)**, and **D(5, 0)**, draw vectors $\overrightarrow{AB}$, $\overrightarrow{BC}$, $\overrightarrow{DC}$, $\overrightarrow{DA}$, $\overrightarrow{AC}$, and $\overrightarrow{BD}$. Use your diagram to answer each question. Explain your answers.

11. Which vectors are parallel? $\overrightarrow{AB}$ and $\overrightarrow{DC}$

12. Which vectors are equal? $\overrightarrow{AB}$ and $\overrightarrow{DC}$

13. Name a pair of vectors that are not equal. sample answer $\overrightarrow{AB}$ and $\overrightarrow{BC}$

14. Name a pair of vectors that are the same magnitude, but different directions. sample answer $\overrightarrow{DA}$ and $\overrightarrow{BC}$

Copy each pair of vectors and draw a resultant vector.

15. 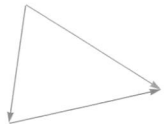   16.    17.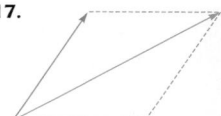

Given $\overrightarrow{v} = (3, 2)$, $\overrightarrow{s} = (2, 7)$, $\overrightarrow{t} = (-5, 6)$, and $\overrightarrow{w} = (2, -4)$, find the coordinates of each of the following.

18. $\overrightarrow{w} + \overrightarrow{s}$ (4, 3)

19. $2\overrightarrow{v} + \overrightarrow{t}$ (1, 10)

20. $3\overrightarrow{v} + \overrightarrow{s}$ (11, 13)

21. $\overrightarrow{w} + \overrightarrow{s} + \overrightarrow{t}$ (-1, 9)

604   CHAPTER 12   MORE COORDINATE GEOMETRY

RETEACHING THE LESSON

Find the magnitude to the nearest tenth and the direction to the nearest degree for each vector.

1. $\overrightarrow{AB} = (2, 6)$ 6.3, 72°
2. $\overrightarrow{CD} = (3, 4)$ 5, 53°
3. $\overrightarrow{EF} = (7, 2)$ 7.3, 16°
4. $\overrightarrow{GH} = (10, 5)$ 11.2, 27°

Have students draw each of these vectors on grid paper and make a

ruler from a strip of the grid paper. Have them use the grid-paper ruler to check their calculation of the magnitude of the vector. Have them use a protractor to check their calculation of the direction. Measurements will be approximate but should provide reasonable estimates for each exercise.

EXERCISES

Practice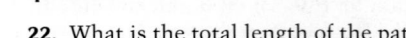

Given a path from *C* north 6 units to *A*, then west 6 units to *B*, answer each question.

22. What is the total length of the path? **12 units**

23. What is the magnitude of $\overrightarrow{CB}$? **$6\sqrt{2} \approx 8.5$ units**

24. Describe the direction of *C* to *B*. **45° north of west**

Sketch each vector. Then find the magnitude of $\overrightarrow{AB}$ to the nearest tenth and the direction to the nearest degree.

25. *A*(4, 2), *B*(8, 6)
$4\sqrt{2} \approx 5.7$ units, 45°

26. *A*(-2, 4), *B*(5, 10)
$\sqrt{85} \approx 9.2$ units, 41°

Given *A*(-6, -4), *B*(4, 2), *C*(6, 8), and *D*(-4, 2), draw the vectors, $\overrightarrow{AB}$, $\overrightarrow{BC}$, $\overrightarrow{CD}$, and $\overrightarrow{AD}$. Use your diagram to answer each question. Explain your answers.

27. Which vectors are parallel? $\overrightarrow{BC}$ and $\overrightarrow{AD}$

28. Which vectors are equal? $\overrightarrow{BC}$ and $\overrightarrow{AD}$

Given the quadrilateral *RPTQ*, complete each statement.

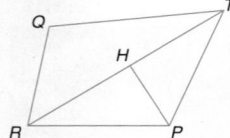

29. $\overrightarrow{RP} + \overrightarrow{PT} = \underline{\ ?\ }$ $\overrightarrow{RT}$

30. $\overrightarrow{TQ} + \overrightarrow{QR} = \underline{\ ?\ }$ $\overrightarrow{TR}$

31. $\overrightarrow{PH} + \overrightarrow{HR} = \underline{\ ?\ }$ $\overrightarrow{PR}$

32. $\overrightarrow{RT} + \overrightarrow{TQ} = \underline{\ ?\ }$ $\overrightarrow{RQ}$

Given $\vec{v} = (2, 5)$ and $\vec{u} = (7, 1)$, find the coordinates of each of the following.

33. $\vec{v} + \vec{u}$
(9, 6)

34. $\vec{v} + 2\vec{u}$
(16, 7)

35. $2\vec{u} + 3\vec{v}$
(20, 17)

B

36. a. Supply the reasons for the following proof.

Given: $\overrightarrow{AB} = \overrightarrow{BC}$ and $\overrightarrow{CD} = \overrightarrow{DE}$

Prove: $\overrightarrow{BD} = \frac{1}{2} \overrightarrow{AE}$ **See margin.**

Proof:

Statements	Reasons
1. $\overrightarrow{BC} + \overrightarrow{CD} = \overrightarrow{BD}$	1. _?_
2. $\overrightarrow{AC} + \overrightarrow{CE} = \overrightarrow{AE}$	2. _?_
3. $\overrightarrow{AB} = \overrightarrow{BC}, \overrightarrow{CD} = \overrightarrow{DE}$	3. _?_
4. $2\overrightarrow{BC} + 2\overrightarrow{CD} = \overrightarrow{AE}$	4. _?_
5. $2(\overrightarrow{BC} + \overrightarrow{CD}) = \overrightarrow{AE}$	5. _?_
6. $2\overrightarrow{BD} = \overrightarrow{AE}$	6. _?_
7. $\overrightarrow{BD} = \frac{1}{2} \overrightarrow{AE}$	7. _?_

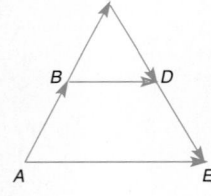

b. What theorem does this prove?

LESSON 12-6 VECTORS 605

Additional Answers

5. Sample answers:

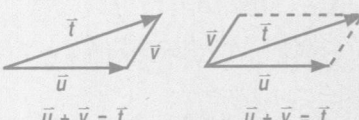

$\vec{u} + \vec{v} = \vec{t}$ $\vec{u} + \vec{v} = \vec{t}$

6. Sample answer:

7. Sample answer:

APPLYING THE LESSON

Homework Exercises

Assignment Guide

Basic: 22-37, 42-50
Average: 24-39, 42-50
Enriched: 26-50

Additional Answers

36a. 1. Definition of vector addition
2. Definition of vector addition
3. Given
4. Substitution prop.
5. Distributive prop.
6. Substitution prop.
7. Multiplication prop. of equality

36b. If a segment has as its endpoints the midpoints of two sides of a triangle, its length is one-half the length of the third side.

Practice Masters Booklet, p. 87

NAME _____ DATE _____

12-6 Practice Worksheet

Vectors

Given $\vec{a} = (8, 6)$, $\vec{b} = (4, 3)$, $\vec{c} = (1, 2)$, and $\vec{d} = (-3, -6)$, answer each of the following.

1. Find the magnitude of $\vec{a}$.
10

2. Find the magnitude $\vec{c}$.
√5

3. Determine if $\vec{b}$ and $\vec{d}$ are equal.
no

4. Determine if $\vec{c}$ and $\vec{d}$ are equal.
no

5. Find the coordinates of $\vec{a} + \vec{b}$.
(12, 9)

6. Find the coordinates of $(\vec{b} + \vec{c}) + \vec{d}$.
(2, −1)

7. Given *A*(2, 5) and *B*(7, 10), find the magnitude and direction of $\overrightarrow{AB}$.
≈ 7.1, 45°

8. Given *C*(0, 1) and *D*(8, 12), find the magnitude and direction of $\overrightarrow{CD}$.
≈ 13.6, ≈ 54°

Given path from *A* south 5 units to B, then east 12 units to C, answer each question.

9. What is the total length of the path?
17

10. What is the magnitude of $\overrightarrow{AC}$?
13

T87
Glencoe Division, Macmillan/McGraw-Hill

38. The magnitudes are the same, but they are in opposite directions.

42. Sample answer:

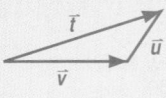

$\vec{t} - \vec{v} = \vec{u}$

If $\vec{t} = (x_1, y_1)$ and $\vec{v} = (x_2, y_2)$,
$\vec{t} - \vec{v} = (x_1 - x_2, y_1 - y_2)$

46.

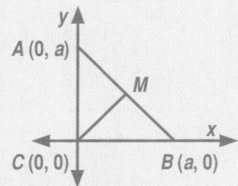

Midpoint M is
$\left(\dfrac{0+a}{2}, \dfrac{a+0}{2}\right) = \left(\dfrac{a}{2}, \dfrac{a}{2}\right)$.

Slope of $\overline{AB}$ is $\dfrac{0-a}{a-0} = \dfrac{-a}{a} = -1$.

Slope of $\overline{CM}$ is $\dfrac{\frac{a}{2}-0}{\frac{a}{2}-0} = \dfrac{\frac{a}{2}}{\frac{a}{2}} = 1$.

Since $-1 \cdot 1 = -1$, $\overline{CM}$ is perpendicular to $\overline{AB}$.

Portfolio

Select one of the graphs from this chapter that you found especially challenging. Place it in your portfolio.

37. Given $A(2, 5)$, $B(x, -4)$, $C(6, 1)$, and $D(4, 3)$, find x if $\overrightarrow{AB} \parallel \overrightarrow{CD}$.   11

38. How do the magnitude and direction of $\overrightarrow{BO}$ compare with $\overrightarrow{OB}$?   **See margin.**

Given $A(0, 0)$, $B(2, 5)$, $R(0, -3)$, $S(-8, -6)$, and $L(8, 3)$, draw $\overrightarrow{AB}$, $2\overrightarrow{AB}$, $\overrightarrow{AB} + \overrightarrow{BL}$, $\overrightarrow{SR}$, and $\overrightarrow{BL}$. Use your diagram to answer each question.
See Solutions Manual for diagram.

39. Which vectors are parallel? $\overrightarrow{AB}$ and $2\overrightarrow{AB}$, $\overrightarrow{AB} + \overrightarrow{BL}$ and $\overrightarrow{SR}$

40. Which vectors are equal? $\overrightarrow{AB} + \overrightarrow{BL}$ and $\overrightarrow{SR}$

41. If two vectors are represented by a single ordered pair, it is possible to determine whether they are perpendicular by using the dot product test. If $\vec{a} = (x_1, y_1)$ and $\vec{b} = (x_2, y_2)$, their dot product $\vec{a} \cdot \vec{b}$ is $x_1 \cdot x_2 + y_1 \cdot y_2$. If the dot product is 0, the vectors are perpendicular. Determine which of the following vectors are perpendicular.
$\vec{v} = (7, -2)$ $\vec{w} = (4, 14)$ $\vec{u} = (-2, 7)$ $\vec{t} = (2, 7)$
$\vec{v}$ and $\vec{w}$, $\vec{v}$ and $\vec{t}$

Critical Thinking

42. In this lesson, you studied vector addition. Find an algebraic way to perform vector subtraction and show how this would look geometrically.
See margin.

43. The resulting speed is 250 km/h and the direction is about 16° south of west.

Applications

43. Navigation   An airplane flies due west at 240 kilometers per hour. At the same time, the wind is blowing due south at 70 kilometers per hour. How does the wind affect the speed and direction of the plane?

44. Recreation   A hiker leaves camp and walks 15 kilometers due north. The hiker then walks 15 kilometers due east. What is the hiker's direction and distance from the starting point?   45° east of north, $15\sqrt{2} \approx 21.2$ km

45. Sports   Two soccer players kick the ball at the same time. One player's foot exerts a force of 70 newtons west. The other's foot exerts a force of 50 newtons north. What is the magnitude and direction of the resultant force on the ball?   about 86 newtons, about 54° west of north

Mixed Review

46. $\triangle ABC$ is a right isosceles triangle. M is the midpoint of $\overline{AB}$. Use a coordinate proof to show that $\overline{CM}$ is perpendicular to $\overline{AB}$. **(Lesson 12-3)**
See margin.

47. Find the volume of a cylinder with a radius of 5 m and a height of 2 m. **(Lesson 11-5)**   about 157.1 m²

48. A car tire has a radius of 8 inches. How far does the car travel in one revolution of the tire? **(Lesson 10-7)**   about 50.3 in.

49. The measures of the sides of a triangle are 6, 9, and 11. If the shortest side of a similar triangle measures 12, what are the measures of its other two sides? **(Lesson 7-4)**   18, 22

Wrap-Up

50. Write a few sentences about vectors. Include a definition of a vector, the meaning of equal vectors, and a description of how to add vectors. **See students' work.**

EXTENDING THE LESSON

Math Power: Connections

Use the parallelogram method of adding vectors to show that vector addition is commutative and associative.
$\overrightarrow{AB} + \overrightarrow{AC} = \overrightarrow{AC} + \overrightarrow{AB}$

$(\overrightarrow{AB} + \overrightarrow{AC}) + \overrightarrow{AD} = \overrightarrow{AB} + (\overrightarrow{AC} + \overrightarrow{AD})$

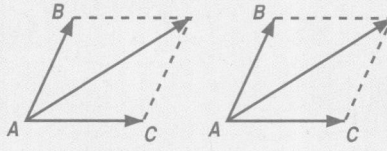

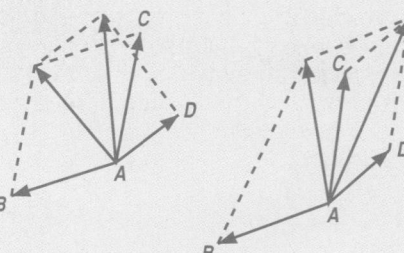

Coordinates in Space

Objectives

12-7A
12-7B
12-7C

After studying this lesson, you should be able to:
- locate a point in space,
- use the distance and midpoint formulas for points in space, and
- determine the center and radius of a sphere.

Application

FYI···

Egyptian engineers were experimenting with airplanes 2300 years ago. An airplane model similar to the American Hercules transport aircraft was found in Sakkara in 1898.

Wanda Burgess is an air traffic controller. She needs to keep accurate information about the location of the aircraft around the airport. Suppose an aircraft is 3 miles east and 2 miles south of the airport. If you think of the airport as being at the origin of a coordinate plane, the coordinates of the aircraft could be (3, –2). However, the aircraft is actually above this point. If the aircraft is 1 mile above ground, the coordinates of the aircraft would be (3, -2, 1).

In a coordinate plane, the ordered pair for each point has two numbers, or coordinates, to describe its location because a plane has two dimensions. In space, each point requires three numbers, or coordinates, to describe its location because space has three dimensions. In space, the *x*-, *y*-, and *z*-axes are perpendicular to each other.

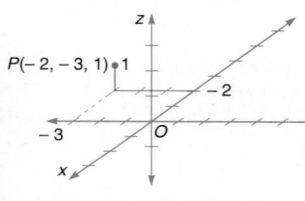

A point in space is represented by an **ordered triple** of real numbers (x, y, z). In the figure at the left, the ordered triple $(-2, -3, 1)$ locates point *P*. Notice that a parallelogram is used to help convey the idea of the third dimension.

Just as the Pythagorean Theorem can be used to find the formula for the distance between two points in a plane, it can also be used to find the formula for the distance between two points in space.

The distance between points *A* and *B* on $\triangle ABD$ can be found as follows.

$(AD)^2 = (AC)^2 + (CD)^2$ and
$(AB)^2 = (AD)^2 + (BD)^2$ *Pythagorean Theorem*
$(AB)^2 = (AC)^2 + (CD)^2 + (BD)^2$ *Substitute $(AC)^2 + (CD)^2$ for $(AD)^2$.*
$AB = \sqrt{(AC)^2 + (CD)^2 + (BD)^2}$ *Take the square root of each side.*
$AC = |x_2 - x_1|$, $CD = |y_2 - y_1|$, and $BD = |z_2 - z_1|$.

Therefore, $AB = \sqrt{(x_2 - x_1)^2 + (y_2 - y_1)^2 + (z_2 - z_1)^2}$ by substitution.

LESSON 12-7 COORDINATES IN SPACE 607

Lesson Resources

- Reteaching Master 12-7
- Practice Master 12-7
- Enrichment Master 12-7
- Evaluation Master, p. 164
- Multicultural Master, p. 12

Transparency 12-7 contains the 5-Minute Check and a teaching aid for this lesson.

INTRODUCING THE LESSON

5-Minute Check
(over Lesson 12-6)

Find the magnitude to the nearest tenth and the direction to the nearest degree for each vector.

1. $\vec{AB} = (1, 4)$ 4.1, 76°
2. $\vec{CD} = (2, 2)$ 2.8, 45°

Use the vectors above to solve.

3. $3\vec{AB}$ (3, 12)
4. $\vec{AB} + \vec{CD}$ (3, 6)

Motivating the Lesson

Hold a pencil point in the air. Ask students how they would describe its position. Ask them if they could describe the position using coordinates.

TEACHING THE LESSON

Teaching Tip It may be difficult for some students to follow the steps given at the bottom of the page for finding *AB*. It may help to have students copy the diagram and use colored pencils to outline the two different right triangles being used.

ALTERNATE TEACHING STRATEGIES

Using Manipulatives

Have students make a model of three-dimensional space by fitting together two pieces of cardboard that have been covered with grid paper. They can use their model to locate points or to measure the length, width, and height of a small box. Have them compute the volume of the box in cubic units.

Using Discussion

Discuss why it is necessary to use three variables to name a point in space. Suggest a situation in which three people decide to meet inside the southwest corner of a particular building. But, they miss their appointment because one person is on the first floor, another is on the fourth floor, and the third is in the basement.

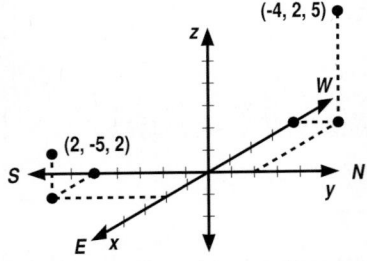
Theorem 12-2	Given two points $A(x_1, y_1, z_1)$ and $B(x_2, y_2, z_2)$ in space, the distance between A and B is given by the following equation. $$AB = \sqrt{(x_2 - x_1)^2 + (y_2 - y_1)^2 + (z_2 - z_1)^2}$$

This formula is an extension of the distance formula in the two-dimensional coordinate system.

Example 1

APPLICATION

Aviation

With reference to an airport, an airplane is 3 miles east, 2 miles south, and 1 mile up. Another airplane is 5 miles west, 7 miles south, and 2 miles up. Find the distance between the two airplanes.

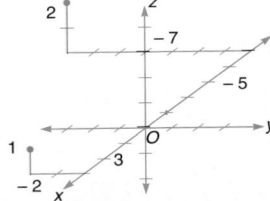

Relative to the airport, the coordinates of the first airplane are (3, -2, 1), and the coordinates of the other airplane are (-5, -7, 2). Use Theorem 12-2 to find the distance between the two airplanes.

$$\sqrt{(3 - (-5))^2 + (-2 - (-7))^2 + (1 - 2)^2} = \sqrt{(3 + 5)^2 + (-2 + 7)^2 + (1 - 2)^2}$$
$$= \sqrt{(8)^2 + (5)^2 + (-1)^2}$$
$$= \sqrt{64 + 25 + 1}$$
$$= \sqrt{90} \approx 9.5$$

The airplanes are about 9.5 miles apart.

Suppose M is the midpoint of $\overline{PQ}$, a segment in space. The midpoint has the following coordinates.

$$\left(\frac{x_1 + x_2}{2}, \frac{y_1 + y_2}{2}, \frac{z_1 + z_2}{2}\right)$$

This formula is an extension of the midpoint formula in the two-dimensional coordinate system.

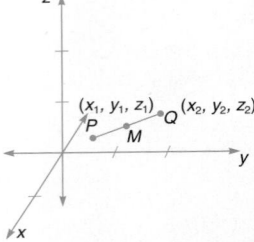

Example 2

Find the coordinates of the midpoint of a segment in space whose endpoints P and Q have coordinates (3, -7, 0) and (5, 1, 7).

Let (3, -7, 0) be (x_1, y_1, z_1) and (5, 1, 7) be (x_2, y_2, z_2).

Then, $\left(\dfrac{3 + 5}{2}, \dfrac{-7 + 1}{2}, \dfrac{0 + 7}{2}\right) = \left(\dfrac{8}{2}, -\dfrac{6}{2}, \dfrac{7}{2}\right)$
$= (4, -3, 3.5)$

The coordinates of the midpoint of $\overline{PQ}$ are (4, -3, 3.5).

Example 3

Find the volume of the rectangular solid with vertices $A(0, 0, 0)$, $B(0, 6, 0)$, $C(4, 6, 0)$, $D(4, 0, 0)$, $E(4, 0, 7)$, and $F(4, 6, 7)$.

First, find the measures of the length, ℓ, width, w, and height, h.

$w = EF$

$\quad = \sqrt{(4-4)^2 + (0-6)^2 + (7-7)^2}$

$\quad = \sqrt{36}$ or 6

$h = FC$

$\quad = \sqrt{(4-4)^2 + (6-6)^2 + (0-7)^2}$

$\quad = \sqrt{49}$ or 7

$\ell = CB$

$\quad = \sqrt{(4-0)^2 + (6-6)^2 + (0-0)^2}$

$\quad = \sqrt{16}$ or 4

$V = \ell \cdot w \cdot h$

$\quad = 4 \cdot 6 \cdot 7$

$\quad = 168$

The volume is 168 cubic units.

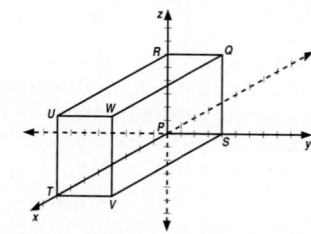

The formula for the equation of a sphere is an extension of the formula for the equation of a circle.

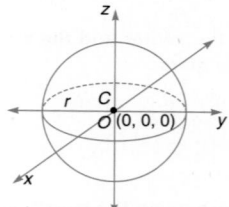

The equation of a sphere whose center is at $(0, 0, 0)$ and whose radius is r units long is as follows.

$$x^2 + y^2 + z^2 = r^2$$

The equation of a sphere whose center is at (i, j, k) and whose radius is r units long is as follows.

$$(x - i)^2 + (y - j)^2 + (z - k)^2 = r^2$$

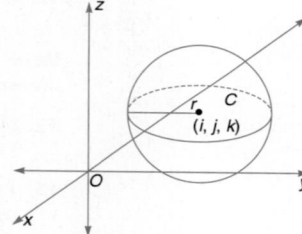

Example 4

Write the equation of a sphere whose center is at $(3, -2, 4)$ and that has a radius of 6 units.

Let $i = 3$, $j = -2$, $k = 4$, and $r = 6$.

$(x - i)^2 + (y - j)^2 + (z - k)^2 = r^2$

$(x - 3)^2 + (y - (-2))^2 + (z - 4)^2 = 6^2$ *Substitute 3 for i, -2 for j, 4 for k,*

$(x - 3)^2 + (y + 2)^2 + (z - 4)^2 = 36$ *and 6 for r.*

The equation of the sphere is $(x - 3)^2 + (y + 2)^2 + (z - 4)^2 = 36$.

Teaching Tip When discussing Example 3, remind students that other vertices could have been used to determine the width, height, and length. For example, $w = HG$, $h = ED$, and $l = DA$.

Chalkboard Examples

For Example 3

Find the volume of the rectangular solid with vertices $P(0, 0, 0)$, $Q(0, 4, 6)$, $R(0, 0, 6)$, $S(0, 4, 0)$, $T(8, 0, 0)$, $U(8, 0, 6)$, $V(8, 4, 0)$, and $W(8, 4, 6)$.

length = PS = 4, width = PT = 8, and height = PR = 6

$V = (4)(8)(6)$

$\quad = 192$ cubic units

For Example 4

Write the equation of a sphere whose center is at $(1, 3, -4)$ and that has a radius of 7 units.

$(x - 1)^2 + (y - 3)^2 + (z - (-4))^2 = 7^2$

$(x - 1)^2 + (y - 3)^2 + (z + 4)^2 = 49$

Checking for Understanding

Exercises 1-16 are designed to help you assess students' understanding through reading, writing, speaking, and modeling. You should work through Exercises 1-4 with your students and then monitor their work on Exercises 5-16.

Closing the Lesson

Speaking Activity

~~find the equation of a sphere,~~ given the coordinates of its center and its radius, and why that procedure works. **Every point on a sphere is the same distance, *r*, from the center. Therefore, use the distance formula for three dimensions to find the equation of the sphere.**

Reteaching Masters Booklet, p. 76

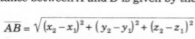

CHECKING FOR UNDERSTANDING

Communicating Mathematics

Read and study the lesson to answer these questions. See margin.

1. Describe the position of the three axes in space.
2. What is the difference between the distance formula for two points in a plane and the distance formula for two points in space?
3. Describe how to find the midpoint of a line segment in space.
4. What is the difference between a circle and a sphere? How does the equation of a circle differ from the equation of a sphere?

Guided Practice

Plot each point in a three-dimensional coordinate system. See Solutions Manual.
5. (1, 5, 7)   6. (-2, 3, 5)

Determine the distance between each pair of points.
7. $A(0, 0, 0)$ and $B(0, 5, 0)$ **5**
8. $P(0, 2, 3)$ and $Q(1, 0, -3)$ $\sqrt{41} \approx 6.4$

Determine the coordinates of the midpoint of the line segment whose endpoints are given.
9. $A(0, -4, 2)$ and $B(3, 0, 2)$ **(1.5, -2, 2)**
10. $S(-6, 3, -1)$ and $T(6, 3, 1)$ **(0, 3, 0)**

Determine the coordinates of the center and the measure of the radius for each sphere whose equation is given.
11. $x^2 + (y-3)^2 + (z-4)^2 = 81$ **(0, 3, 4), 9**
12. $(x+2)^2 + (y+4)^2 + (z-4)^2 = 25$ **(-2, -4, 4), 5**

Write the equation of the sphere given the coordinates of the center and the measure of the radius.
13. (4, 1, -2), 6 **$(x-4)^2 + (y-1)^2 + (z+2)^2 = 36$**
14. (0, 0, 4), 16 **$x^2 + y^2 + (z-4)^2 = 256$**
15. Find the perimeter of the triangle whose vertices are $P(0, 0, 0)$, $Q(3, 4, \sqrt{11})$ and $R(0, 5, 0)$. **$11 + \sqrt{21} \approx 15.6$ units**
16. Find the radius of a sphere whose diameter has endpoints $A(4, 7, -3)$ and $B(0, -2, 9)$. **about 7.8 units**

EXERCISES

Practice

Plot each point in a three-dimensional coordinate system. See Solutions Manual.
17. (0, 0, 5)   18. (2, -1, 4)   19. (3, 1, -4)

Review the formulas developed for finding the distance between two points in the coordinate plane, the midpoint of a segment in the coordinate plane, and the equation for a circle in the coordinate plane. Then present the formulas developed for the same general concepts in this lesson for 3-space. Compare the formulas. Discuss how they are similar and how they differ.

Determine the distance between each pair of points.

20. $A(2, 4, 5)$ and $B(2, 4, 7)$ 2 units

21. $A(0, -2, 5)$ and $B(-3, 4, -2)$ $\sqrt{94} \approx 9.7$ units

22. $A(9, 1, 0)$ and $B(5, -7, 4)$ $\sqrt{96} \approx 9.8$ units

23. $A(8, 10, -3)$ and $B(1, 12, 6)$ $\sqrt{134} \approx 11.6$ units

Determine the coordinates of the midpoint of each line segment whose endpoints are given.

24. $A(1, 3, -2)$, $B(7, -3, 2)$ $(4, 0, 0)$

25. $C(-5, 4, -2)$, $D(5, -4, 2)$ $(0, 0, 0)$

26. $E(5, -6, 3)$, $F(11, -2, 7)$ $(8, -4, 5)$

27. $G(22, 5, -1)$, $H(0, -3, 6)$ $(11, 1, 2.5)$

Determine the coordinates of the center and the measure of the radius for each sphere whose equation is given.

28. $(x - 6)^2 + (y + 5)^2 + (z - 1)^2 = 81$ $(6, -5, 1)$, 9

29. $(x + 2)^2 + (y + 3)^2 + (z - 2)^2 = 100$ $(-2, -3, 2)$, 10

30. $x^2 + (y - 2)^2 + (z - 4)^2 = 4$ $(0, 2, 4)$, 2

31. $(x + 8)^2 + y^2 + (z + 4)^2 = 18$ $(-8, 0, -4)$, $\sqrt{18} \approx 4.2$

Write the equation of the sphere given the coordinates of the center and the measure of the radius.   See margin.

32. $(-1, 2, 4)$, 3

33. $(6, -1, 3)$, 12

34. $(0, 3, -2)$, 11

35. $(-2, 4, 1)$, $\sqrt{13}$

36. Find the perimeter of a triangle whose vertices are $A(6, 4, 1)$, $B(4, 6, 0)$ and $C(3, -2, 3)$. $10 + \sqrt{74} \approx 18.6$ units

37. The diameter of a sphere has endpoints $A(-3, 5, 7)$ and $B(5, -1, 5)$.

 a. Determine the coordinates of the center of the sphere. $(1, 2, 6)$

 b. Determine the radius of the sphere. $\sqrt{26} \approx 5.1$ units

 c. Write an equation of the sphere. $(x - 1)^2 + (y - 2)^2 + (z - 6)^2 = 26$

 d. Sketch a graph of the sphere.   See margin.

 e. Find the surface area of the sphere.   about 326.7 units^2

 f. Find the volume of the sphere.
    about 555.3 units^3

38. Find the surface area and volume of the figure at the right.   96 units^2; 64 units^3

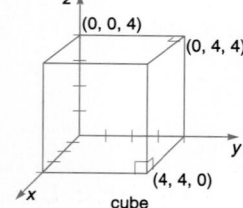

cube

39. Find t if the distance between $A(3t, 5, -t)$ and $B(5, -3, t)$ is 9 units.   2 or $\frac{4}{13}$

40. Find the measures of the medians of the triangle whose vertices are $R(9, 4, 11)$, $S(-3, 8, 1)$ and $T(7, 2, -3)$. $\sqrt{194} \approx 13.9$, $\sqrt{113} \approx 10.6$, $\sqrt{155} \approx 12.4$

Additional Answers

1. The three axes intersect at the same point and are perpendicular to each other.
2. The distance formula in a plane is the square root of the sum of the squares of the differences of the x and y values. The distance formula in space is the square root of the sum of the squares of the differences of the x, y, and z values.
3. The x value of the midpoint is the sum of the x values divided by 2. The y value of the midpoint is the sum of the y values divided by 2. The z value of the midpoint is the sum of the z values divided by 2.
4. A circle is two-dimensional and a sphere is three-dimensional. The equation of a sphere has a z term as well as x and y terms in the equation of a circle.

Additional Answers

32. $(x + 1)^2 + (y - 2)^2 + (z - 4) = 9$

33. $(x - 6)^2 + (y + 1)^2 + (z - 3)^2 = 144$

34. $x^2 + (y - 3)^2 + (z + 2)^2 = 121$

35. $(x + 2)^2 + (y - 4)^2 + (z - 1)^2 = 13$

37d.

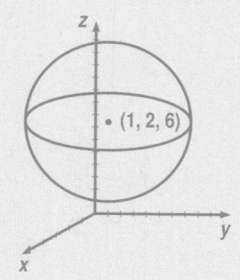

Practice Masters Booklet, p. 88

12-7   NAME _____ DATE _____
Practice Worksheet

Determine the distance between each pair of points.

1. $A(0, 0, 0)$ and $B(1, 2, 3)$
   $\sqrt{14} \approx 3.7$

2. $C(4, -2, 3)$ and $D(0, 2, 0)$
   $\sqrt{41} \approx 6.4$

3. $E(1, -2, 5)$ and $F(1, 2, 5)$
   4

4. $P(0, 1, 0)$ and $Q(-1, 0, 1)$
   $\sqrt{3} \approx 1.7$

Determine the coordinates of the midpoint of each line segment whose endpoints are given.

5. $A(0, 0, 4)$, $B(4, -6, 6)$
   $(2, -3, 5)$

6. $C(-1, 2, 4)$, $D(3, -6, 8)$
   $(1, -2, 6)$

7. $E(-2, -3, 6)$, $F(0, -6, 8)$
   $(-1, -4.5, 7)$

8. $G(-1, 5, \frac{3}{2})$, $H(1, -5, \frac{1}{2})$
   $(0, 0, 1)$

Write an equation of the sphere given the coordinates of the center and the measure of the radius.

9. $C(0, -3, 1)$, $r = 3$
   $x^2 + (y + 3)^2 + (z - 1)^2 = 9$

10. $C(-2, 1, 3)$, $r = 1\frac{1}{2}$
    $(x + 2)^2 + (y - 1)^2 + (z - 3)^2 = \frac{9}{4}$

11. $C(3, 0, -1)$, $r = \sqrt{2}$
    $(x - 3)^2 + y^2 + (z + 1)^2 = \frac{1}{2}$

12. $C(5, 5, 5)$, $r = 7$
    $(x - 5)^2 + (y - 5)^2 + (z - 5)^2 = 49$

13. Find the perimeter of a triangle whose vertices are $A(0, 2, 1)$, $B(-2, 2, 6)$, and $C(4, 2, -2)$.
    $15 + \sqrt{29}$ units

The diameter of a sphere has endpoints $A(-3, 2, 4)$ and $B(1, -6, 5)$.

14. Determine the center of the sphere.
    $(-1, -2, 4.5)$

15. Determine the radius of the sphere.
    4.5 units

16. Write the equation of the sphere.
    $(x + 1)^2 + (y + 2)^2 + (z - 4.5)^2 = 20.25$

17. Find the surface area of the sphere.
    81π square units
    or above 254.5 square units

88

Glencoe Division, Macmillan/McGraw-Hill

One sphere has the equation $x^2 + y^2 + z^2 = 36$, and another has the equation $x^2 + y^2 + z^2 = 100$.

41. What is the ratio of the radii of the two spheres? 3 to 5

42. What is the ratio of the areas of the two spheres? 9 to 25

43. What is the ratio of the volumes of the two spheres? 27 to 125

Critical Thinking

44. Find the other endpoint of a diameter of the sphere if one endpoint is at (4, -6, 10) and the center of the sphere is at (0, 1, -4). (-4, 8, -18)

Applications

45. **Air Traffic Control** One airplane is 7 miles east and 9 miles south of the airport and 2 miles above the ground. Another airplane is 4 miles west and 4 miles south from the airport and 1 mile above the ground. Find the distance between the airplanes. $\sqrt{147} \approx 12.1$ miles

46. **Recreation** Two children are playing a three-dimensional tick-tack-toe game. Three Xs or three Os in any row wins the game. The positions of the Xs are (1, 1, 1) and (1, 3, 3) and the position of the O is (2, 2, 2). Where should the next O be placed? Explain your answer. (1, 2, 2) to block a row of Xs.

Mixed Review

47. Given $\vec{t} = (1, -5)$ and $\vec{u} = (-4, 2)$, find the ordered pair for $2\vec{t} + \vec{u}$. **(Lesson 12-6)** (-2, -8)

Find the area of each region to the nearest tenth. (Lessons 10-5, 10-6, and 10-7)

48.
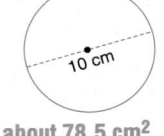
10 cm

about 78.5 cm²

49.
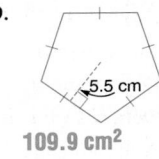
5.5 cm

109.9 cm²

50.
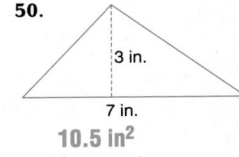
3 in.

7 in.

10.5 in²

51. Two lines intersect and more than one plane contains them.

51. Write the assumption you would make to start an indirect proof of the statement *If two lines intersect, then no more than one plane contains them.* **(Lesson 5-4)**

52. Find the value of x. **(Lesson 3-3)** 100

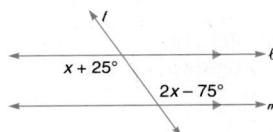
$x + 25°$
$2x - 75°$

Wrap-Up

Journal Entry

53. **Journal Entry** Explain in your own words the relationship between the formulas involving distance and midpoints in two-dimensions and in three-dimensions. See students' work.

EXTENDING THE LESSON

Math Power: Problem Solving

Find the center and the radius of the sphere whose equation is $x^2 + y^2 - 4y + z^2 + 2z = 11$. (0, 2, -1), $r = 4$

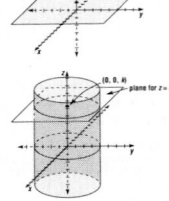

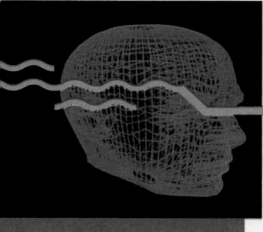

Technology
Perspective Drawing

BASIC
Geometric Supposer
► **Graphing Calculators**
LOGO
Spreadsheets

Perspective drawing, drawing three-dimensional objects on a two-dimensional surface, was highly refined in the Renaissance by artists like Leonardo da Vinci and Albrecht Dürer. Today, computers can make perspective drawings. This technique is used extensively for drawing graphics for television and movies.

Computers make perspective drawings by finding the three-dimensional coordinates of the object being drawn. Then they use algebra to transform these into two-dimensional coordinates. The graph of these two-dimensional coordinates is called a *projection*.

The formulas below will draw one type of projection in which the y-axis is drawn horizontally, the z-axis is drawn vertically, and the x-axis is at an angle of $a°$ with the y-axis. In this system if the three-dimensional coordinates of a point are (x, y, z), then the projection coordinates (X, Y) are

$$X = x(\text{-}\cos a°) + y$$
$$Y = x(\text{-}\sin a°) + z.$$

This projection will give a good perspective drawing, but some lengths may be slightly distorted.

EXERCISES

1. The cube at the right has vertices $A(5, 0, 5)$, $B(5, 5, 5)$, $C(5, 5, 0)$, $D(5, 0, 0)$, $E(0, 0, 5)$, $F(0, 5, 5)$, and $G(0, 5, 0)$ and $H(0, 0, 0)$.

   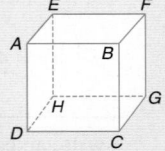

   a. Use the formulas above to find the projection coordinates of each vertex using $a = 45$. Round each coordinate to the nearest whole number. **See margin.**

   b. Use the projection coordinates you found for the vertices of the cube to graph the perspective drawing on your graphing calculator. Sketch the display. **See students' work.**

2. $A(10, 2, 0)$, $B(10, 10, 0)$, $C(2, 10, 0)$, and $D(3, 3, 4)$ are the vertices of a pyramid.

   a. Find the projection coordinates of each vertex using $a = 30$. Round each coordinate to the nearest whole number. **See margin.**

   b. Make a perspective of the pyramid on your graphing calculator by graphing the segments $\overline{AB}$, $\overline{BC}$, $\overline{CD}$, $\overline{DA}$, and $\overline{DB}$. Sketch the display. **See students' work.**

TECHNOLOGY   613

Using Technology
Objective This optional page shows how a graphing calculator can be used to perform mathematical computations and to enhance and extend mathematical concepts.

Teaching Suggestions
Begin by asking students to draw a rectangular solid on a sheet of paper. Ask them to name some things that helped to make a two-dimensional drawing look three-dimensional. Discuss the use of parallel lines and angles.

The DRAW function of a graphing calculator can be used to enter endpoints of line segments. To graph a perspective drawing on the graphing calculator is a painstaking process. However, the finished product will be very impressive and will illustrate how computers can be used to produce perspective drawings.

Additional Answers
1a. $A(-4, 1)$, $B(1, 1)$, $C(1, -4)$, $D(-4, -4)$, $E(0, 5)$, $F(5, 5)$, $G(5, 0)$, $H(0, 0)$
2a. $A(-7, -5)$, $B(1, -5)$, $C(8, -1)$, $D(0, 3)$

Using the Chapter Summary and Review

The Chapter Summary and Review begins with an alphabetical listing of the new terms that were presented in the chapter. Have students define each term and provide an example of it, if appropriate.

The Skills and Concepts presented in the chapter are reviewed using a side-by-side format. Encourage students to refer to the Objectives and Examples on the left as they complete the Review Exercises on the right.

The Chapter Summary and Review ends with exercises that review Applications and Connections.

Additional Answers

1.

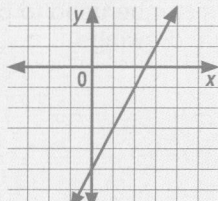

2.

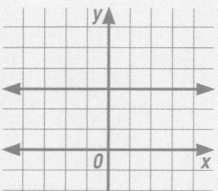

3.

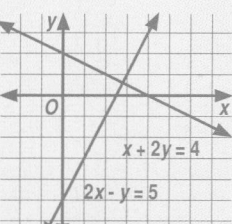

4.

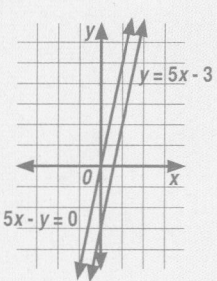

VOCABULARY

Upon completing this chapter, you should be familiar with the following terms:

coordinate proof	**595**	**581**	point-slope form
direction of a vector	**601**	**602**	resultant
intercepts method	**574**	**602**	scalar multiplication
linear equation	**574**	**586**	scatter plot
magnitude of a vector	**601**	**575**	slope-intercept form
ordered triple	**607**	**574**	standard form
parallelogram law	**602**	**601**	vector

SKILLS AND CONCEPTS

OBJECTIVES AND EXAMPLES	REVIEW EXERCISES

Upon completing this chapter, you should be able to:

Use these exercises to review and prepare for the chapter test.

- graph linear equations. **(Lesson 12-1)**

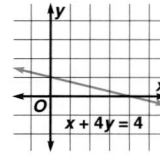

Intercepts Method
x-intercept = 4
y-intercept = 1

Slope-Intercept Form
$y = -\frac{1}{4}x + 1$

$x + 4y = 4$ $m = -\frac{1}{4}$

y-intercept = 1

Graph each equation. See margin.

1. $2x - y = 5$ **2.** $y = 3$

Graph each pair of linear equations on the same coordinate plane. Determine if the lines are parallel, perpendicular, or neither by finding the slope of each line.

3. $2x - y = 5$ **4.** $y = 5x - 3$
   $x + 2y = 4$ $5x - y = 0$
   perpendicular   **parallel**

3-4. See margin for graphs.

- write an equation of a line given information about its graph. **(Lesson 12-2)**

The slope of the line that passes through $(4, -3)$ and $(2, 1)$ is $\frac{1 - (-3)}{2 - 4}$ or $\frac{4}{-2}$ or -2. To find an equation of the line, use the point-slope form.

$y - y_1 = m(x - x_1)$ *Point-Slope Form*
$y - 1 = -2(x - 2)$ $m = -2, (x_1, y_1) = (2, 1)$
$y - 1 = -2x + 4$
$y = -2x + 5$

Write an equation of the line satisfying the given conditions. See margin.

5. parallel to the graph of $y = x - 5$, passes through $(0, 8)$

6. perpendicular to the graph of $y = 3x - 1$, passes through $(6, 0)$

7. parallel to x-axis, passes through $(5, 2)$

8. perpendicular to the x-axis, passes through $(5, 2)$

Additional Answers

5. $y = x + 8$

6. $y = -\frac{1}{3}x + 2$

7. $y = 2$

8. $x = 5$

OBJECTIVES AND EXAMPLES

■ relate equations of lines to geometric concepts. **(Lesson 12-3)**

To find the equation of the perpendicular bisector of a segment whose endpoints have coordinates (5, -3) and (-1, 1), first find the coordinates of the midpoint.

$$\left(\frac{5-1}{2}, \frac{-3+1}{2}\right) = \left(\frac{4}{2}, \frac{-2}{2}\right) \text{ or } (2, -1)$$

Then find the slope of the segment.

$$\frac{-3-1}{5-(-1)} = \frac{-4}{6} \text{ or } -\frac{2}{3}$$

The perpendicular bisector will pass through (2, -1) and have a slope of $\frac{3}{2}$.

$$y - y_1 = m(x - x_1)$$
$$y - (-1) = \frac{3}{2}(x - 2)$$
$$y = \frac{3}{2}x - 4$$

The equation is $y = \frac{3}{2}x - 4$.

■ prove theorems using coordinate proofs. **(Lesson 12-5)**

When planning a coordinate proof, use the following guidelines to position the figure on a coordinate plane.
■ Use the origin as a vertex or center.
■ Position at least one side of a polygon on a coordinate axis.
■ Keep the figure in the first quadrant if possible.
■ Use coordinates which make computations simple.

■ find the magnitude and direction angle of a vector. **(Lesson 12-6)**

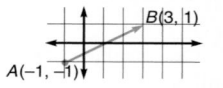

$\tan A = \frac{2}{4}$ or 0.5
$m\angle A \approx 26.6$

$$|\overrightarrow{AB}| = \sqrt{(3-(-1))^2 + (1-(-1))^2}$$
$$= \sqrt{4^2 + 2^2}$$
$$= \sqrt{20} \approx 4.5$$

$\overrightarrow{AB}$ has a magnitude of about 4.5 units and a direction of about 26.6°.

REVIEW EXERCISES

The vertices of △XYZ are X(2, -1), Y(6, 1), and Z(0, -3). See margin.

9. Find the equations of the lines containing the sides of △XYZ.

10. Find the equations of the lines containing the medians of △XYZ.

11. Find the equations of the lines containing the altitudes of △XYZ.

12. Find the equations of the lines containing the perpendicular bisectors of the sides of △XYZ.

Prove using a coordinate proof.
See Solutions Manual.
13. The segment through the midpoints of the nonparallel sides of a trapezoid is parallel to the bases.

14. The length of the segment through the midpoints of the nonparallel sides of a trapezoid is one-half the sum of the lengths of the bases.

Find the magnitude and direction angle of each vector.

15. $\overrightarrow{v} = (7, 1)$ $\sqrt{50} \approx$ 7.1 units; about 8.1°
16. $\overrightarrow{AB}$ with A(1, 0) and B(7, 5) $\sqrt{61} \approx$ 7.8 units; about 39.8°

Find the resultant of each pair of vectors.

17. $\overrightarrow{a} = (2, 4), \overrightarrow{b} = (5, -3)$ (7, 1)
18. $\overrightarrow{r} = (0, 8), \overrightarrow{s} = (4, 0)$ (4, 8)

Additional Answers

9. $y = \frac{1}{2}x - 2$, $y = \frac{2}{3}x - 3$,
   $y = x - 3$
10. $y = \frac{3}{4}x - 3$, $y = -1$, $y = \frac{3}{5}x - \frac{13}{5}$
11. $y = -2x - 3$, $y = -\frac{3}{2}x + 2$,
    $y = -x + 7$
12. $y = -2x + 8$, $y = -\frac{3}{2}x + \frac{7}{2}$,
    $y = -x - 1$

A two-page Cumulative Review from the *Evaluation Masters* is shown below. It can be used to review skills and concepts presented thus far in the text. Standardized Test Practice Questions are also provided in the *Evaluation Masters*.

Evaluation Masters, pp. 165-166

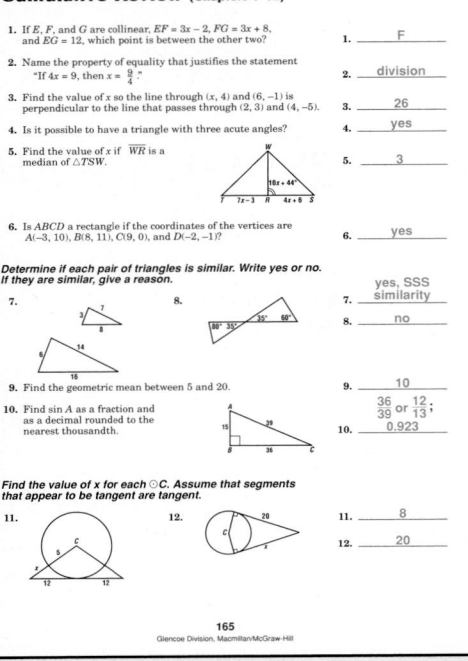

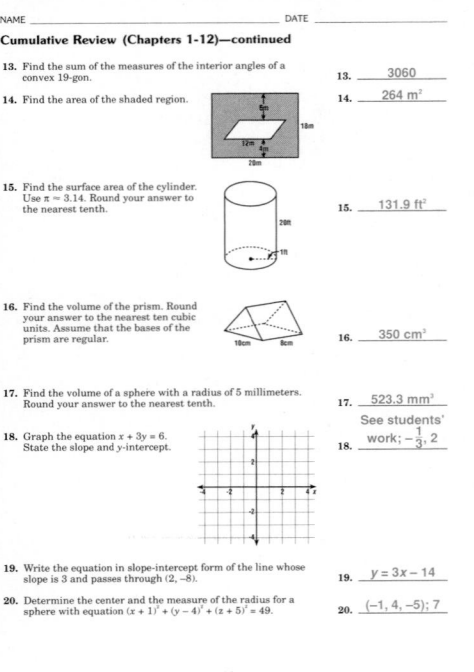

- use the distance and midpoint formulas for points in space. **(Lesson 12-7)**

The distance between (2, 2, 2) and (-6, 0, 5) is $\sqrt{(-6-2)^2 + (0-2)^2 + (5-2)^2}$ or $\sqrt{77}$ units.

The coordinates of the midpoint of a line segment whose endpoints are (2, 2, 2) and (-6, 0, 5) are

$\left(\dfrac{2-6}{2}, \dfrac{2+0}{2}, \dfrac{2+5}{2}\right)$ or (-2, 1, 3.5).

Determine the distance between each pair of points and the coordinates of the midpoint of the segment whose endpoints are given.

19. (3, -3, 1), (7, -3, 5) $4\sqrt{2} \approx 5.7$ units; (5, -3, 3)
20. (2, 4, 6), (0, 2, 4) $2\sqrt{3} \approx 3.5$ units; (1, 3, 5)

Write the equation of the sphere given the coordinates of the center and measure of the radius. 22. $(x+1)^2 + (y-2)^2 + (z+3)^2 = 16$

21. (0, 0, 0), 5   22. (-1, 2, -3), 4

21. $x^2 + y^2 + z^2 = 25$

APPLICATIONS AND CONNECTIONS

23. **Manufacturing** A factory makes dresses and suits. If x represents the number of dresses made in one week and y represents the number of suits made that same week, then $10x + 20y$ represents the number of worker-hours needed to make the items. If $10x + 20y = 500$, draw a graph that represents the production for that week. What do the intercepts represent? **(Lesson 12-1)** See margin.

25. **Theater** An architect is planning the lighting for a stage that is in the shape of an isosceles trapezoid. The front of the stage is 30 feet long and the back of the stage is 40 feet long. The stage is 20 feet deep. If a scale drawing of the stage is assigned coordinates as shown below, what are the coordinates of the front center of the stage? **(Lesson 12-5)** (20, 20)

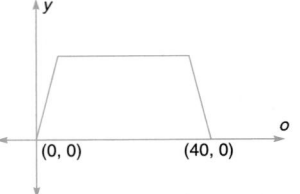

(0, 0)   (40, 0)

24. **Meteorology** Sound travels in air at about 0.21 miles per second. Kara counted 6 seconds between when she saw some lightning strike to when she heard the thunder. How far away did the lightning strike? **(Lesson 12-4)**
about 1.26 miles

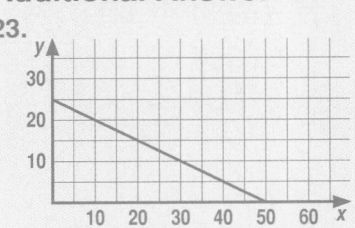

26. **Air Traffic Control** One airplane is 8 miles west and 10 miles south of the airport and 2 miles above the ground. Another airplane is 4 miles east and 8 miles south of the airport and 1 mile above the ground. Find the distance between the airplanes. **(Lesson 12-6)**

$\sqrt{149} \approx 12.2$ miles

Additional Answer

23.

The x-intercept represents the situation that no suits were made that week. The y-intercept represents the situation that no dresses were made that week.

Graph each equation. State the slope and y-intercept. See Solutions Manual for graphs.

1. $x + 2y = 6$ $-\frac{1}{2}; 3$

2. $x = 3$ none; none

3. $y = -3x$ -3; 0

Write the equation in slope-intercept form of the line satisfying the given conditions.

4. $m = -4$, passes through (3, -2) $y = -4x + 10$

5. passes through (-4, 11) and (-6, 3) $y = 4x + 27$

6. parallel to the graph of $y = 2x - 5$, passes through (-1, -4) $y = 2x - 2$

7. parallel to the y-axis, passes through (-4, -2) $x = -4$

Copy each pair of vectors and draw a resultant vector.

8.

9.

10. What is the resultant of $\vec{a} + \vec{b}$ if $\vec{a} = (-3, 5)$, and $\vec{b} = (0, 7)$?   (-3, 12)

Determine the coordinates of the center and the measure of the radius for each sphere whose equation is given.

11. $(x - 4)^2 + (y - 5)^2 + (z + 2)^2 = 81$ (4, 5, -2); 9

12. $x^2 + y^2 + z^2 = 7$ (0, 0, 0); $\sqrt{7} \approx 2.6$

13. Given $\vec{v} = (-5, -3)$, find the magnitude of $\vec{v}$. $\sqrt{34} \approx 5.8$ units

14. Given $A(3, 7)$ and $B(-2, 5)$, find the magnitude of $\overrightarrow{AB}$. $\sqrt{29} \approx 5.4$ units

15. Determine the distance between points at (2, 4, 5) and (2, 4, 7).   2 units

16. Determine the midpoint of the segment whose endpoints are $X(0, -4, 2)$ and $Y(3, 0, 2)$. $\left(\frac{3}{2}, -2, 2\right)$

17. Write the equation of the sphere whose diameter has endpoints at $P(-3, 5, 7)$ and $Q(5, -1, 5)$.

18. Write an equation of the perpendicular bisector whose endpoints are at (5, 2) and (1, -4).

17. $(x - 1)^2 + (y - 2)^2 + (z - 6)^2 = 26$

18. $y = -\frac{2}{3}x + 1$

19. Name the missing coordinates for the parallelogram in terms of the given variables.   (a + b, c)

20. Use a coordinate proof to show that $\overleftrightarrow{NK}$ is a perpendicular bisector of a side of $\triangle LOM$.   See Solutions Manual.

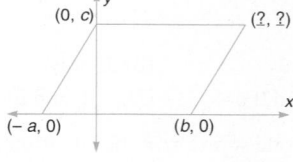

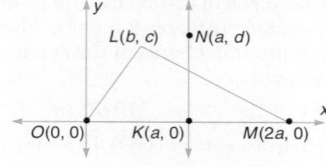

Bonus $\sqrt{75} \approx 8.7$ units

A secant segment $\overline{MN}$ intersects sphere S at R and M. Given the points $N(7, 5, -1)$, $R(3, 2, -1)$, and $M(-5, -4, -1)$, find the length of a tangent segment $\overline{NT}$.

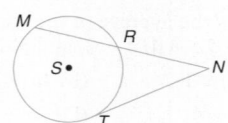

Test and Review Generator

software is provided in Apple, IBM and Macintosh versions. You may use this software to create your own tests or worksheets, based on the needs of your students.

The Performance Assessment

Booklet provides an alternate assessment for evaluating student progress. An assessment for this chapter can be found on pages 23-24.

Using the Chapter Test

This page may be used as a test or as a review. In addition, two multiple-choice tests (Forms 1A and 1B) and two free-response tests (Forms 2A and 2B) are provided in the *Evaluation Masters*. Chapter 12 Test, Form 1A is shown below.

Evaluation Masters, pp. 155-156

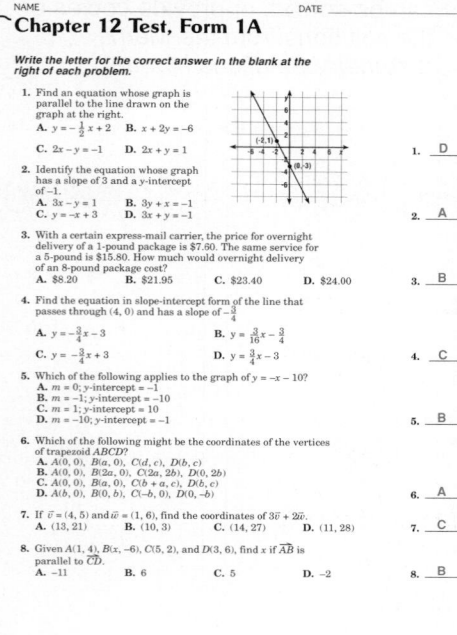

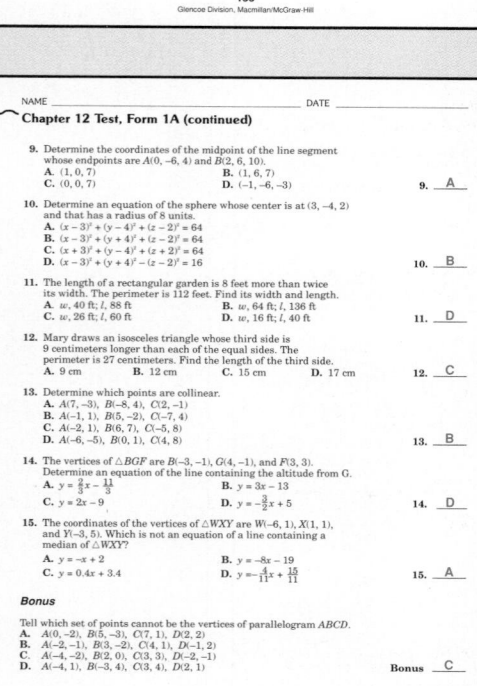

Using the College Entrance Exam Preview

The questions on these pages may be used to help students prepare for college entrance exams such as the SAT test. These questions require careful analysis and a thorough understanding of the concepts.

These pages can be used as an overnight assignment.

After students have completed the pages, discuss how each problem can be solved, or provide copies of the solutions from the *Merrill Geometry Solutions Manual*.

Directions: Choose the one best answer. Write A, B, C, or D. You may use a calculator.

1. A box with a closed top has a square base with sides x cm long and a height of h cm. Write an expression for the surface area of the box.
   D
   (A) $8x + 4x$ (B) hx^2
   (C) $4h + x$ (D) $2x^2 + 4xh$

2. The graph of the equation $y = 4x + 8$ is
   C
   (A) a horizontal line.
   (B) a vertical line.
   (C) a line that rises to the right.
   (D) a line that falls to the right.

3. Suppose the lengths of each of the four sides of a rectangle are tripled. By what factor will the area of the rectangle increase?
   D
   (A) 3   (B) 6
   (C) 8   (D) 9

4. Solve $\frac{s}{3s+6} - \frac{s}{5s+10} = \frac{2}{5}$ for s.
   A
   (A) -3   (B) -2
   (C) -3 or -2   (D) 3 or 2

5. The largest possible circle is cut from a square piece of cardboard. If one side of the square measures 5 inches, what is the approximate area of the scrap cardboard?
   C
   (A) 47.1 in^2 (B) 6.2 in^2
   (C) 5.4 in^2 (D) 53.5 in^2

6. What is the average of the expressions $8a + 7$, $2a + 4$, $a - 3$, and $5a$?
   B
   (A) $16a + 8$ (B) $4a + 2$
   (C) $8a + 4$ (D) $2a - 4$

7. What are the coordinates of point B if the coordinates of point A are $(5, 8)$ and $x = -1$ is the equation of the perpendicular bisector of $\overline{AB}$?
   B
   (A) $(5, -10)$ (B) $(-7, 8)$
   (C) $(-5, -8)$ (D) $(4, 8)$

8. Which of the following represents the solution set of the inequality $-3 - x < 2x < 3 + x$?
   A
   (A) $\{x \mid -1 < x < 3\}$
   (B) $\{x \mid 1 < x < 3\}$
   (C) $\{x \mid -3 < x < 1\}$
   (D) $\{x \mid -3 < x < -1\}$

9. A pulley having a 4-inch diameter is belted to a pulley having a 6-inch diameter as shown below. If the smaller pulley is running at 180 rpm, how fast is the larger pulley running?
   D

   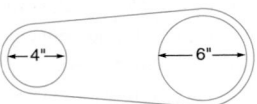

   (A) 270 rpm   (B) 160 rpm
   (C) 240 rpm   (D) 120 rpm

10. If x is between 0 and 1, which of the following increases as x increases?
    A
    I. $x + 1$
    II. $1 - x^2$
    III. $\frac{1}{x}$
    (A) I only   (B) III only
    (C) I and II only   (D) I, II, and III

11. If -3 is one solution of the equation $x^2 + kx - 51 = 0$, what is the value of k?
    D
    (A) 14   (B) 17
    (C) -20   (D) -14

Solve. You may use a calculator.

12. One angle of a triangle measures 68°. The measures of the other two angles are in a ratio of 1 to 3. Find the degree measures of the other two angles.
28°, 84°

13. The average of six numbers is 10, the average of ten other numbers is 6. Find the average of all sixteen numbers. 7.5

14. A swimming pool measures 80 feet by 45 feet. The water level needs to be raised 3 inches. If it takes about 7.5 gallons of water to fill one cubic foot of space, about how much water must be added to the pool?
6750 gallons

15. The charge for shipping a package is 75 cents for the first 4 ounces and 9 cents for each additional ounce. Find the weight of a package that costs $1.83 to ship. 16 ounces

16. In the figure below, $ABCD$ is a square with sides 2 inches long. M and N are the midpoints of sides $\overline{AB}$ and $\overline{BC}$ respectively. What is the ratio of the area of triangle MND to the area of square $ABCD$?
$\frac{3}{8}$

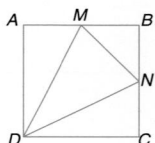

17. Simplify $\dfrac{8x^5y^{-2}z}{16x^{-2}yz^2} \cdot \dfrac{x^7}{2y^3z}$

TEST-TAKING TIP

Time Management

If you finish a college entrance exam before the allotted time is up, use the remaining time wisely.

Check to be sure that you have marked all of your answers in the correct place on the answer sheet.

Be certain that you have answered all of the questions. If guessing is not penalized, answer the questions you can't complete by eliminating as many answers as you can and then guessing.

Make sure that you have marked only one answer for each question. If two answers are marked, the question will be marked wrong even if one of the answers was the correct choice.

18. A cylindrical can has a diameter of 12 inches and a height of 8 inches. If one gallon of liquid occupies 231 cubic inches, what is the approximate capacity of the can in gallons?
3.9 gallons

19. Carrie can paint a room alone in 50 minutes. If she works with Ty, they can paint it in 30 minutes. How long would it take Ty to paint the room alone?
75 minutes or 1 hour 15 minutes

20. When the Downtown Metro travels at 45 miles per hour, it arrives at the first stop on time. When it travels at 50 miles per hour, the Metro arrives 2 minutes early. How far is it from the station to the first metro stop?
15 miles

Loci and Transformations

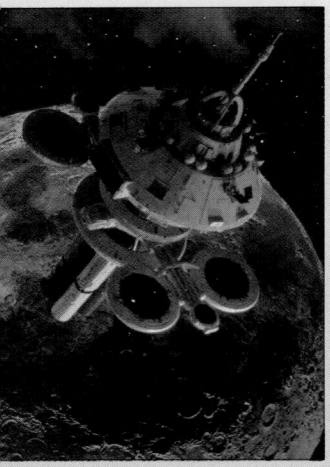

PREVIEWING THE CHAPTER

This chapter examines sets of points and different ways to move those points in a coordinate plane. First, *locus* and *loci* are defined, and an explanation of how to draw a locus both in a plane and in space is presented. The concept of loci is then extended to systems of equations. The chapter then investigates mappings, namely reflections, translations, and rotations. Points and lines of symmetry are defined, and similarities and differences between the three isometries are discussed. The chapter then concludes with the study of a fourth mapping, *dilation*.

Problem-Solving Strategy Students learn to use the strategy *make a table* to organize data, identify missing data, or look for patterns.

Lesson Objective Chart

Lesson (Pages)	Lesson Objectives	State/Local Objectives
13-1 (622-627)	**13-1**: Locate, draw, and describe a locus in a plane or in space.	
13-2 (628-633)	**13-2**: Find the locus of points that solve a system of equations by graphing, substitution, or by elimination.	
13-3 (634-639)	**13-3**: Solve locus problems that satisfy more than one condition.	
13-4 (640-643)	**13-4A**: Name the image and preimage of a mapping.	
	13-4B: Recognize an isometry or congruence transformation.	
13-5 (644-651)	**13-5A**: Name a reflection image with respect to a line.	
	13-5B: Recognize line symmetry and point symmetry.	
	13-5C: Draw reflection images, lines of symmetry, and points of symmetry.	
13-6 (653-658)	**13-6**: Name and draw translation images of figures with respect to parallel lines.	
13-7 (659-664)	**13-7**: Name and draw rotation images of figures with respect to intersecting lines.	
13-8 (665-670)	**13-8A**: Use scale factors to determine if a dilation is an enlargement, a reduction, or a congruence transformation.	
	13-8B: Find the center and scale factor for a given dilation.	
	13-8C: Find the dilation image for a given center and scale factor.	
13-9 (671-673)	**13-9**: Solve problems by making tables.	

ORGANIZING THE CHAPTER

You may want to refer to the **Course Planning Calendar** on page T28.

Lesson Planning Guide

Lesson (Pages)	Pacing Chart (days) Course I	II	III	Reteaching	Practice	Enrichment	Evaluation	Technology	Lab Manual	Mixed Problem Solving	Applications	Cooperative Learning Activity	Multicultural	Transparencies
13-1 (622-627)			1.5	p. 77	p. 89	p.77								13-1
13-2 (628-633)			1.5	p. 78	p. 90	p. 78		p. 13						13-2
13-3 (634-639)			2	p. 79	p. 91	p. 79	Quiz A, p.177							13-3
13-4 (640-643)			1	p. 80	p. 92	p. 80								13-4
13-5 (644-651)			2	p. 81	p. 93	p. 81	Quiz B, p.177 Mid Chapter Test, p.181	p. 49	pp.90-93		p. 27			13-5
13-6 (653-658)			1	p. 82	p. 94	p. 82			pp.94-97			p. 41		13-6
13-7 (659-664)			1.5	p. 83	p. 95	p. 83	Quiz C, p. 178							13-7
13-8 (665-670)			1.5	p. 84	p. 96	p. 84							p. 13	13-8
13-9 (671-673)			1		p. 97		Quiz D, p. 178			p. 13				13-9
Review (674-676)			1	Multiple Choice Tests, Forms 1A and 2B, pp. 169-172 Free Response Tests, Forms 2A and 2B, pp. 173-176										
Test (677)			1	Cumulative Review. pp. 179-180 Standardized Tests Practice Questions, p. 182										

Blackline Masters Booklets — Activities

Course I: Chapters 1-11; Course II: Chapters 1-12; Course III: Chapters 1-13

Other Chapter Resources

Student Edition

Chapter Opener, pp. 620-621
Technology Connection, p. 627
Journal Entry, pp. 639, 658
Mid-Chapter Review, p. 651
Technology, p. 652
Developing Reasoning Skills, p. 658
Portfolio, p. 670
Cooperative Learning Project, p. 673
Algebra Review, pp. 678-679
More Investigations in Geometry, pp. A15-A16
Extended Project 4, pp. B14-B16

Teacher's Classroom Resources

Transparency 13-0
Real World Applications Transparencies, 27, 28
Performance Assessment Booklet, pp. 25-26
Problem-of-the-Week Activity Cards, 35, 36
Tech Prep Applications Booklet, pp. 25-26
LOGO Instruction Materials, Technology Masters pp. 19-36

Other Supplements

Algebra and Geometry Overhead Manipulative Resources
Glencoe Mathematics Professional Series

Software

Test and Review Generator (Apple, IBM, and Macintosh)
Teacher's Guide for Software Resources

ENHANCING THE CHAPTER

Cooperative Learning

Assessing How Well the Group Functioned

To ensure improved performance in cooperative-learning sessions, it is important to process what students have learned about group skills after each session. Whole-class discussions can be a valuable way to do this since groups can learn from the experiences of other groups. Such discussions should concentrate on how well the groups functioned during the session, what things were done well, and what things could be improved. To begin the processing, select one member from a group to discuss with the class one or two things that they did well during the session. Encourage the reporter to provide details and examples. Ask about specific actions taken by group members that helped, such as encouraging each other to participate, keeping one another focused on the task, paraphrasing or expanding on contributions, and so on. If you wish, you can also ask a reporter to discuss something that the group could have done better or on which it would like to work harder. The reporter need not use names but should be as specific as possible. The emphasis should be on improving the effectiveness of students in cooperating with other members of their group. This sharing of ideas and experiences will promote improved group behavior in future sessions.

Technology

The Technology Feature following Lesson 13-5 uses a LOGO procedure to draw figures and their reflections. First, a procedure to draw the coordinate axes is given. Then, procedures to draw a triangle and its reflection on the coordinate axes are given. Students are asked to modify this procedure in the exercises to draw a quadrilateral and its reflection. After students have completed the exercises, you may want to ask them to use LOGO to draw their own polygons and their reflections on the coordinate axes.

Critical Thinking

Students who correctly answer the practice exercises, for the most part, are demonstrating only their knowledge and comprehension of the content presented in the lesson. They are not necessarily exhibiting any ability to utilize the higher-level thinking skills that would be required in real life in which conditions do not always remain stable. One way to help accustom students to sudden or unexpected changes in the rules that often occur in real life is to ask what-if questions. For example, after students demonstrate their ability to simplify an expression by rationalizing the denominator, say, "What if we want to rationalize the numerator? Now what is the solution?"

Cooperative Learning, p. 41

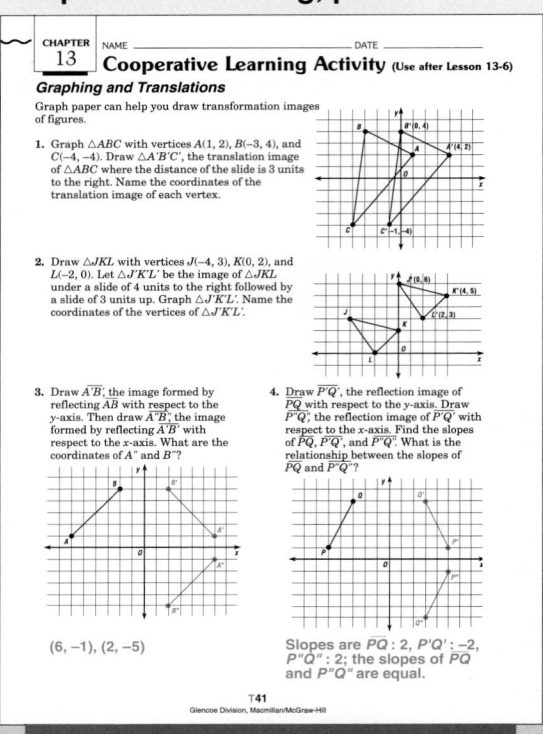

Technology, p. 49

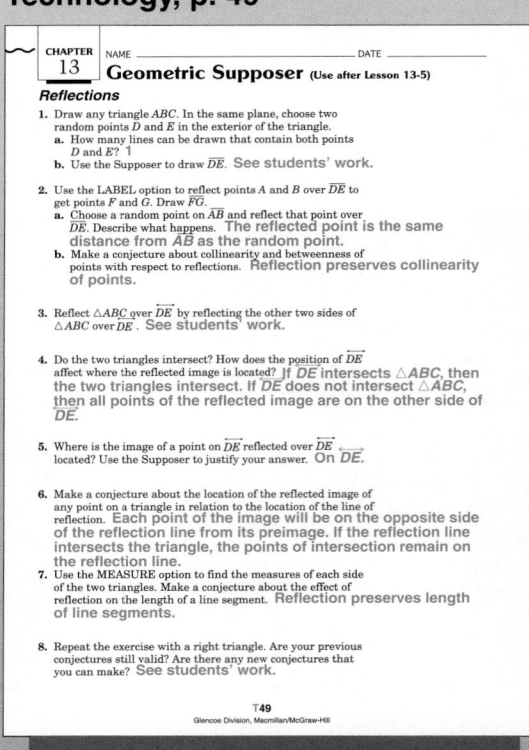

Problem of the Week Activity

The card shown below is one of two available for this chapter. It can be used as a class or small group activity.

Activity Card

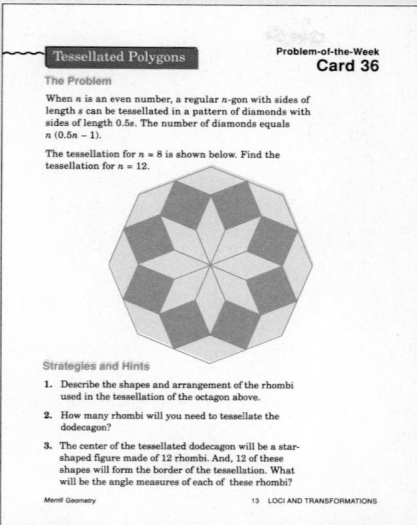

Tessellated Polygons

Problem-of-the-Week
Card 36

The Problem

When n is an even number, a regular n-gon with sides of length s can be tessellated in a pattern of diamonds with sides of length $0.5s$. The number of diamonds equals $n (0.5n - 1)$.

The tessellation for $n = 8$ is shown below. Find the tessellation for $n = 12$.

Strategies and Hints

1. Describe the shapes and arrangement of the rhombi used in the tessellation of the octagon above.

2. How many rhombi will you need to tessellate the dodecagon?

3. The center of the tessellated dodecagon will be a star-shaped figure made of 12 rhombi. And, 12 of these shapes will form the border of the tessellation. What will be the angle measures of each of these rhombi?

Merrill Geometry   13 LOCI AND TRANSFORMATIONS

Manipulatives and Models

The following materials may be used as models or manipulatives in Chapter 13.

- tennis ball (Lesson 13-1)
- tin can (Lesson 13-3)
- map (Lesson 13-3)
- toothpicks (Lesson 13-3)
- ceramic tiles (Lesson 13-4)
- mirror (Lesson 13-5)
- Möbius strip, glue, tape (Lesson 13-6)
- magnifying glass (Lesson 13-8)

Outside Resources

Books/Periodicals

ApSimon, Hugh. *More Mathematical Byways*. Oxford University Press.

Burn, R.P. Groups, *A Path to Geometry*. Cambridge University Press.

Emmett, E.R. *Brain Puzzler's Delight*. Emerson Book, Inc.

Films/Videotapes/Videodiscs

Mathematical Curves, Churchill Films, 12210 Nebraska Ave., Los Angeles, CA 90025

Software

The Geometer's Sketchpad, Key Curriculum Press, 2512 Martin Luther King Jr. Way, Berkeley, CA 94702

Geometric Connectors: Transformations, WINGS for Learning/ Sunburst, 101 Castleton Street, Pleasantville, NY 10570

Multicultural

Multicultural Activity, p. 13

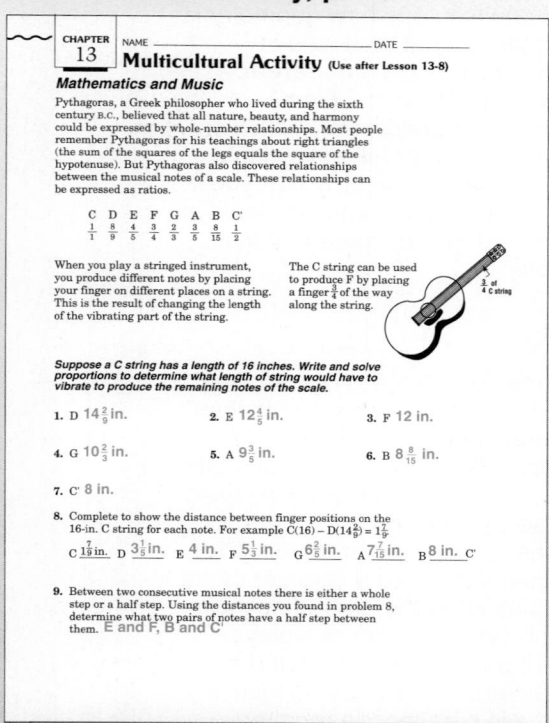

CHAPTER 13 NAME _____ DATE _____

Multicultural Activity (Use after Lesson 13-8)

Mathematics and Music

Pythagoras, a Greek philosopher who lived during the sixth century B.C., believed that all nature, beauty, and harmony could be expressed by whole-number relationships. Most people remember Pythagoras for his teachings about right triangles (the sum of the squares of the legs equals the square of the hypotenuse). But Pythagoras also discovered relationships between the musical notes of a scale. These relationships can be expressed as ratios.

C	D	E	F	G	A	B	C'
$\frac{1}{1}$	$\frac{8}{9}$	$\frac{4}{5}$	$\frac{2}{3}$	$\frac{2}{3}$	$\frac{8}{15}$	$\frac{8}{15}$	$\frac{1}{2}$

When you play a stringed instrument, you produce different notes by placing your finger on different places on a string. This is the result of changing the length of the vibrating part of the string.

The C string can be used to produce F by placing a finger $\frac{3}{4}$ of the way along the string.

Suppose a C string has a length of 16 inches. Write and solve proportions to determine what length of string would have to vibrate to produce the remaining notes of the scale.

1. D $14\frac{2}{9}$ in.   2. E $12\frac{4}{5}$ in.   3. F 12 in.

4. G $10\frac{2}{3}$ in.   5. A $9\frac{3}{5}$ in.   6. B $8\frac{8}{15}$ in.

7. C' 8 in.

8. Complete to show the distance between finger positions on the 16-in. C string for each note. For example C(16) − D($14\frac{2}{9}$) = $1\frac{7}{9}$

C $1\frac{7}{9}$ in. D $3\frac{1}{5}$ in. E $\frac{4}{5}$ in. F $5\frac{1}{3}$ in. G $6\frac{2}{5}$ in. A $7\frac{7}{15}$ in. B 8 in. C'

9. Between two consecutive musical notes there is either a whole step or a half step. Using the distances you found in problem 8, determine what two pairs of notes have a half step between them. E and F, B and C'

Lab Manual

Lab Activity, pp. 90-93

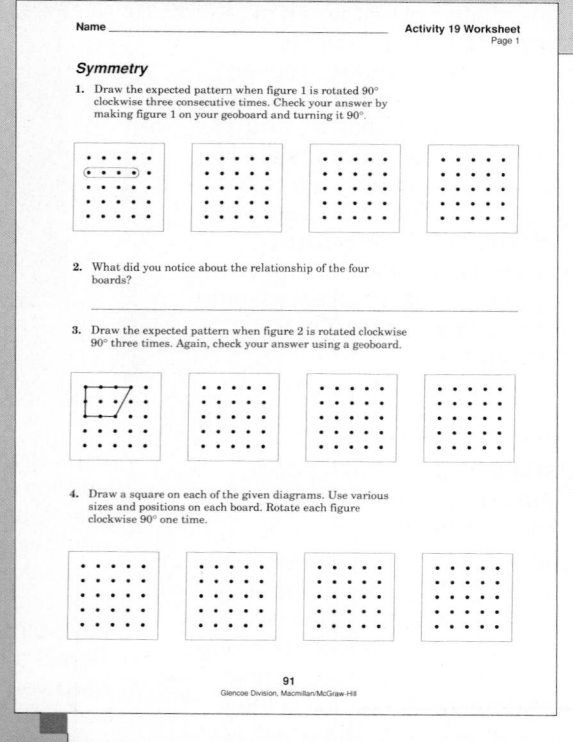

Name _____   Activity 19 Worksheet
Page 1

Symmetry

1. Draw the expected pattern when figure 1 is rotated 90° clockwise three consecutive times. Check your answer by making figure 1 on your geoboard and turning it 90°.

2. What did you notice about the relationship of the four boards?

3. Draw the expected pattern when figure 2 is rotated clockwise 90° three times. Again, check your answer using a geoboard.

4. Draw a square on each of the given diagrams. Use various sizes and positions on each board. Rotate each figure clockwise 90° one time.

91
Glencoe Division, Macmillan/McGraw-Hill

Using the Chapter Opener

This two-page introduction to the chapter provides students with an opportunity to see how geometry is used throughout the world in various cultures. **Transparency 13-0**, available in the *Merrill Geometry Transparency Package*, provides another full-color visual and motivational activity that you can use to engage your students in the mathematical content of the chapter.

Multicultural Notes

France The process of encoding a design for exact duplication was created in the early 1800s by a French silk weaver named Joseph Marie Jacquard. Manually weaving silk designs often led to pattern inconsistency. To correct this error, Jacquard invented a chain of cards that simulated the protruding jacks on the cylinder drum of a player piano. Each card controlled one movement of the weaving loom's shuttle in creating the required design. Jacquard cards replicated so flawlessly that they were used to develop the first computers.

Africa Geometric analyses of repeated pattern symmetries show that there are only 24 types of patterns that can be used to decorate a plane surface: seven *strip patterns*, which translate or move in a single direction; and 17 *plane patterns*, which translate in two or more directions and rotate 360, 180, 120, 90, or 60 degrees. The Bakuba of Zaire create Africa's most striking decorative cloth patterns, using all seven strip patterns and at least 12 of the 17 plane patterns.

Chapter Project

Materials pencil, graph paper, posterboard, meter stick, colored markers, calculator

Procedure Organize students into small groups to create competing ad agencies. Each agency will use *motion* or *transformation geometry* to persuade television's Channel Nine *Noontime News* to be their newest ad account. The agencies must use the geometric transformation techniques of *translation*, *dilation*, and *rotation* to create their graphic design ad campaigns. Instructions: Help your agency select a logo composed of one figure (letter, shape, or number) per agency member. Scale your figure by calculating new coordinates (x', y') for each key point (x , y) on your figure. Select a reference point (x_R, y_R) near your figure that will scale and translate it in the direction you want it to move. Select a scaling factor (SF) between 1.0 and 1.5 to gradually increase the size of your figure. Calculate each new set of coordinates (x', y') for each key point (x, y) using $x' = x_R + [(x - x_R) (SF)]$ and $y' = y_R + [(y - y_R) (SF)]$. Use your reference point as your point of rotation. Select an angle of rotation such that your figure will rotate $360°$ in 12 sequential steps. ($30°$) Use coordinates x', y' in the following rotation equations to find x'', y'' : $x'' = x_R + [(x' - x_R) \cos ø] + [(y' - y_R) \sin ø]$; $y'' = y_R + [(y' - y_R) \cos ø] - [(x' - x_R) \sin ø]$. Using a meterstick, draw the horizontal and vertical lines needed to create a large graph on your posterboard.

Loci and Transformations

CHAPTER OBJECTIVES

In this chapter, you will:
- Draw, locate, or describe a locus in a plane or in space.
- Draw reflection images, lines of symmetry, and points of symmetry.
- Draw translation, rotation, or dilation images.

GEOMETRY AROUND THE WORLD
United States

Do you have access to a computer at school or in your home? If so, you have probably used it to write reports, play games, or enter data. But did you know that computers have long been used to create the stunning graphics that introduce some of your favorite music videos and TV programs?

For years, computer graphics have also played an important role in films. In 1982, computer graphics created the exploding planets and other special effects in "Star Trek: The Wrath of Kahn," directed by Nicholas Meyer. Since then, computer graphics have been used in many other movies produced in the United States and abroad.

In the past, creating computer-generated images was a tedious task. First, a programmer entered the mathematical equations for basic two- and three-dimensional forms into the computer's memory. The computer stored the equations, which were then manipulated to create a variety of moving shapes.

Now, sophisticated computer software automatically performs these functions, and more—including showing objects from different angles, or points of view via **geometric transformations**, operations that move and position objects in either two- or three-dimensional space.

GEOMETRY IN ACTION

One type of geometric transformation is called a **rotation**, which specifies a pivoting or angular displacement about an axis. Use your protractor to measure how many degrees the object in the figure at the right has been rotated on its axis. rotated about 210°

◀ *Graphic images from "Star Trek: The Wrath of Kahn"*

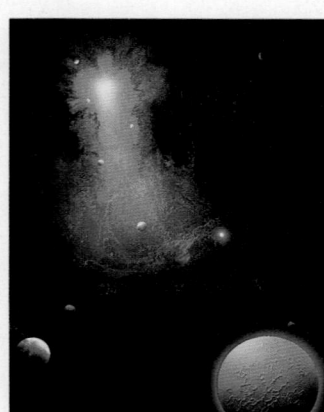

Computer-generated objects in space are manipulated by applying geometric transformations.

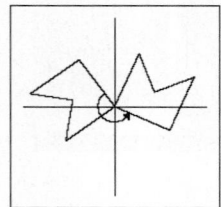

621

Starting at an outside corner, graph your series of geometric transformations, and rotate your figure to its place at the posterboard's center, aligning your figure with the rest of your agency's figures. Color your figure and vote for the best ad!

Resources

Friedhoff, Richard Mark, and William Benzon. *The Second Computer Revolution Visualization.* Harry N. Abrams, Inc.

Kerlow, Isaac Victor, and Judson Rosebush. *Computer Graphics for Designers and Artists.* Van Nostrand Reinhold Company

Goodman, Cynthia. *Digital Visions Computers and Art.* Harry N. Abrams, Inc.

Connections and Applications

Lesson	Connections and Applications (A)	Examples	Exercises
13-1	A: Agriculture	2	
	A: Sports		48
	A: Geography		49
	A: Communications		50
	A: Teaching		51
13-2	A: Demographics	2	
	C: Algebra	3, 4	
	A: Social Studies	1	41
	A: Consumerism		42
	A: Communications		43
13-3	A: City Management	1	45
	C: Algebra	2	
	A: Communications		46
	A: Water Management		47
	A: Food		48
13-4	A: Art	1	40-41
	A: Recreation		42
	A: Cartoons		43
13-5	A: Recreation	1	56
	A: Grooming		57
13-6	A: Art		49-50
	A: Environment		51-52
13-7	A: Manufacturing	3	
	A: Computers		41
	A: Recreation		42-43
13-8	A: Photography	4	60
	A: Art		59
	A: Publishing		61

Lesson Resources

Lesson Resources

- Reteaching Master 13-1
- Practice Master 13-1
- Enrichment Master 13-1

 Transparency 13-1 contains the 5-Minute Check and a teaching aid for this lesson.

INTRODUCING THE LESSON

 5-Minute Check

(over Chapter 12)

1. Write an equation of the line parallel to the graph of $y = -3x + 5$ and passing through (4, 1). $y = -3x + 13$
2. Determine whether the points $A(2, 5)$, $B(-2, 3)$, $C(0, 9)$ are collinear.   **no**
3. Find the magnitude and direction of $\vec{AB}$, with $A(2, 1)$ and $B(6, 4)$.   **5, 37°**
4. Determine the distance between (0, -1, 4) and (-2, 6, 3). $\sqrt{54} \approx 7.3$
5. Determine the coordinates of the midpoint of the segment whose endpoints have coordinates (0, 4, 3) and (-6, 2, 1)   **(-3, 3, 2)**

Motivating the Lesson

Have students look up the word *locus* in a dictionary and explain how they think it may apply to geometry.

TEACHING THE LESSON

Teaching Tip   When defining *locus*, point out that a locus in a plane is limited to points in that plane, while a locus in space is not limited in that way.

Objective 13-1

After studying this lesson, you should be able to:
- locate, draw, and describe a locus in a plane or in space.

Application

FYI...

The first artificial satellite was called *Sputnik I.* It was launched by the Soviet Union on October 4, 1957.

The path of a communications satellite orbiting Earth is controlled by a very strict set of conditions that define its position above Earth at all times. This path can be thought of as a **locus** of points. The word *locus* comes from a Latin word meaning "location" or "place." The plural of locus is loci. Loci is pronounced *low-sigh.*

In geometry, a figure is a locus if it is the set of all the points that satisfy a given condition or set of given conditions. A locus may also be defined as the path of a moving point satisfying a set of given conditions. A locus may be one or more points, lines, planes, surfaces, or any combination of these. A locus in a plane may be different than a locus with the same description that is in space.

Circle P is the locus of points in a plane that are 4 centimeters from P. Sphere P is the locus of points in space that are 4 centimeters from P.

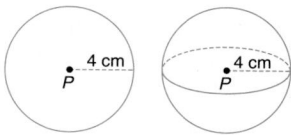

In order to describe a certain locus, you should follow these steps.

- Read the problem carefully.

  Find the locus of all points in a plane that are 15 millimeters from a given line ℓ.

- Draw the given figure.

  The given figure is line ℓ.

- Locate points that satisfy the given conditions.

  Draw points that are 15 mm from line ℓ. Locate enough points to suggest the shape of the locus.

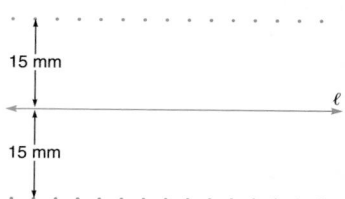

ALTERNATE TEACHING STRATEGIES

Using Demonstration

Cut a circle out of paper and draw a thick line around its edge. Also, bring in a tennis ball or other type of hollow ball, an empty can of food with both the bottom and top removed, or other types of objects that can be used to demonstrate loci.

Using Cooperative Groups

Divide the class into small groups and give each group a few problems that involve finding the locus of a figure. They may use any method to help them find each locus. When each group is finished, have students explain what the locus of each problem is and how they found it. Every student in each group should understand all of the solutions.

- As soon as the shape of a geometric figure begins to appear, draw a smooth geometric figure that contains the points.

  The points suggest parallel lines.

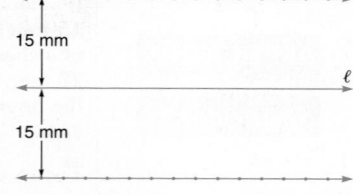

- Describe the locus in words.

  The locus of all points in a plane that are 15 millimeters from a given line ℓ is a pair of parallel lines, one on each side of ℓ, and each 15 millimeters from ℓ.

The steps below summarize the procedure for determining a locus.

Procedure for Determining Locus

1. **Read the problem carefully.**
2. **Draw the given figure.**
3. **Locate the points that satisfy the given conditions.**
4. **Draw a smooth geometric figure.**
5. **Describe the locus.**

Example 1

Determine the locus of all points in space that are 6 millimeters from a given line ℓ.

Draw the given figure.

The given figure is line ℓ.

Locate points that satisfy the given conditions.

Draw enough points to determine the shape. Be sure to consider all possibilities.

Draw a smooth curve or line.

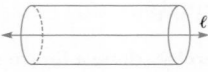

Describe the locus.

The locus of points in space that are 6 millimeters from given line ℓ is a cylindrical surface with line ℓ as the axis and a radius of 6 millimeters.

LESSON 13-1 LOCUS 623

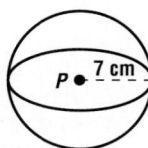

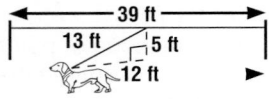

Example 2

APPLICATION

Agriculture

If a horse is tied with a 15-foot rope to the corner of a shed that is 12 feet by 20 feet, find the locus of the boundary of its grazing area.

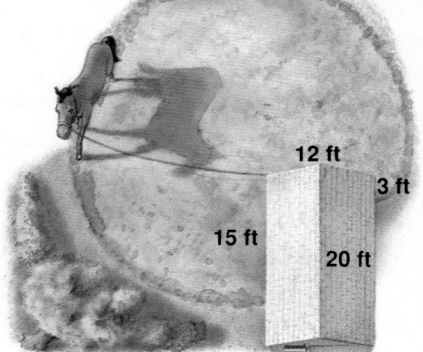

The locus is a path composed of $\frac{3}{4}$ of a circle with radius of 15 feet and center at the corner of the building, $\frac{1}{4}$ of a circle with radius of 3 feet and center at the adjacent corner of the building on the 12-foot side, 15 feet of line segments along one side, 12 feet along the end, and 3 feet along the other side of the shed.

CHECKING FOR UNDERSTANDING

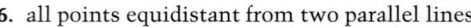

Communicating Mathematics

Read and study the lesson to answer these questions. See margin.

1. In your own words, describe the meaning of a locus of points.
2. Describe the locus of points in a plane 3 inches from a given point *C*.
3. How will the locus in Exercise 2 differ if the words *in a plane* are replaced by *in space?*
4. Describe the locus of points in space 5 centimeters from a given line *AB*.
5. How will the locus in Exercise 4 differ if the words *in space* are replaced by *in a plane?*

Guided Practice

For each exercise, draw a figure showing the locus of points in a plane. Then describe the locus. 6-7. See margin. 8-9. See Solutions Manual.

6. all points equidistant from two parallel lines
7. all points equidistant from the endpoints of a given line segment
8. all points on or in the interior of an acute angle and equidistant from the rays that form the angle
9. all points that are the third vertices of triangles having a given base and a given altitude

For each exercise, draw a figure showing the locus of points in space. Then describe the locus. See Solutions Manual.

10. all points equidistant from two parallel lines
11. all points equidistant from the endpoints of a given line segment
12. all points equidistant from three noncollinear points
13. all points that are the centers of spheres with radii *r* units long and tangent to a given plane

624   **CHAPTER 13   LOCI AND TRANSFORMATIONS**

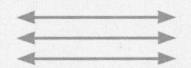

Describe the locus of points in the classroom that meet the following conditions.

14. all points equidistant from the floor and the ceiling

15. all points equidistant from all four corners of the floor

EXERCISES

Practice

Answer each of the following. See Solutions Manual.

16. Describe the locus of points in a plane that are 4 meters from a given line *m*.

17. Describe the locus of points on a football field that are equidistant from the two goal lines.

18. Describe the locus of points in space that are 1 meter from a given point *C*.

19. Describe the locus of points in space that are 4 inches from a given line ℓ.

20. Describe the locus of points on a road that are equidistant from the edges of the road.

For each exercise, draw a figure showing the locus of points in a plane. Then describe the locus. See Solutions Manual.

21. all midpoints of the radii of a circle

22. all points that are the midpoints of parallel chords of a given circle

23. all points that are 3 inches from a circle with radius of 6 inches

24. all points that are less than 6 centimeters from a given point

25. all points of the path of the center of a gear as it rotates around the circumference of a larger gear

26. all points that are equidistant from the points of intersection of two given circles

27. all midpoints of all chords of a given measure that is less than the measure of the diameter in a given circle

28. all points that are equidistant from two intersecting lines

29. all centers of all circles passing through two distinct points

30. all centers of all circles tangent to two intersecting lines

31. all midpoints of all chords formed by secants drawn to a circle from a point outside the circle

32. all midpoints of all chords that have one given endpoint on a circle

RETEACHING THE LESSON

As a group project, have the class as a group find the loci of several problems. Have students give examples of representations of each locus. For example have them use a thumb tack and a string with a piece of chalk attached, to draw loci that are circles. They can vary the length of the string to produce different size circles.

Error Analysis

The concept of locus can be difficult to grasp. Emphasize that a locus is a set of points. Even a locus that is a path can be thought of as a set of points, because the locus would contain all points on the path.

Closing the Lesson

Modeling Activity Have students make a locus for a particular problem. Have them tell why it represents the locus of that problem.

APPLYING THE LESSON

Homework Exercises

Assignment Guide

Basic: 17–45 odd, 47, 50–58
Average: 16–46 even, 47–48, 51–58
Enriched: 16–46 even, 47–49, 52–58

Exercise Notes

For these exercises, almost all of the loci in a plane will be lines or circles; almost all of the loci in space will be planes or spheres.

Have all students do Exercise 47, since it is a good demonstration of an ellipse.

Reteaching Masters Booklet, p. 77

13-1 | NAME _____ DATE _____
Reteaching Worksheet

Locus

A **locus** is the set of all points that satisfy a given condition or set of conditions. In determining a locus, it is often helpful to draw a figure showing several points that meet the given conditions. Remember that the locus is the set of *all* points meeting the conditions. Be sure that your final figure includes all possibilities. Also be careful to note whether you are considering all points in space or only points in a plane.

Example: Describe the locus of points in a plane that are 1 inch from a circle with a radius of 5 inches.

The locus consists of two circles having the same center as the 5-inch circle. One has a radius of 4 inches and the other has a radius of 6 inches.

Draw a figure showing each locus. Then describe the locus.

1. all points in a plane equidistant from two parallel lines that are 3 cm apart

2. all points in a plane that are 18 mm from a given point

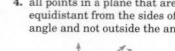

a line parallel to the two parallel lines and halfway between them | a circle with an 18 mm radius and the given point as center

3. all points in a plane that are less than 5 centimeters from a given point *P*

4. all points in a plane that are equidistant from the sides of the angle and not outside the angle

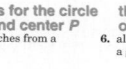

all interior points for the circle of radius 5 cm and center *P* | the angle bisector of the right angle

5. all points in space 2 inches from a given point

6. all points in space 2 inches from a given plane

a sphere with a radius of 2 inches and having the given point as center | two parallel planes on either side of the given plane

177

Glencoe Division, Macmillan/McGraw-Hill

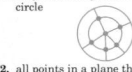
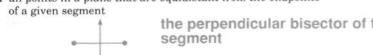

For each exercise, draw a figure showing the locus of points in space. Then describe the locus. See Solutions Manual.

33. all points that are a given distance greater than 0 units from a plane

34. all points that are equidistant from two intersecting planes

35. all centers of spheres that are tangent to a plane at a given point in the plane

36. all points equidistant from the vertices of a rectangular prism

37. all points equidistant from all points on a circle

Use square *ABCD* in plane $\mathcal{R}$ to describe each locus of points. See margin.

38. all points in $\mathcal{R}$ equidistant from the midpoints of the sides of the square

39. all points in space equidistant from the midpoints of the sides of the square

40. all points in $\mathcal{R}$ equidistant from the diagonals of the square

41. all points in space equidistant from the diagonals of the square

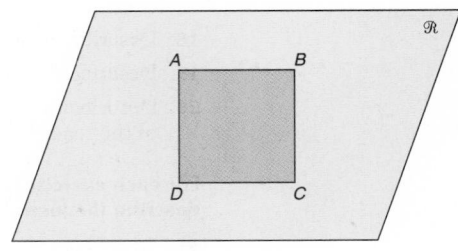

42. Describe the locus of points in $\mathcal{R}$ equidistant from $\overline{AB}$ and $\overline{DC}$.

 Complete each of the following. See margin.

43. Describe the locus of points in a plane formed by the midpoints of all hypotenuses of a given length given the line containing one of the legs and the vertex of one acute angle of a right triangle on that line.

44. Describe the locus of points a ship will travel when it leaves New York and sails a straight course to London, England.

45. Describe the locus of points made by a point on the outermost part of the wheel of a bicycle as it travels down the road.

46. A weight is attached to the end A of a string represented by $\overline{OA}$ that is 100 centimeters long and hangs vertically from O. The weight is pulled to one side and then allowed to swing back and forth. If an obstacle is placed in the path of the string at B which is 50 centimeters below O, describe the locus of points traveled by point A.

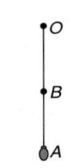

Critical Thinking

47. See margin.

47. What is the locus of points in a plane such that the sum of the distances from two given points A and B is always 6? *(Hint: Place thumbtacks through points A and B on your paper. Then tie the ends of a piece of string 6 units long to each tack. Draw the locus with your pencil inside of the loop of the string.)*

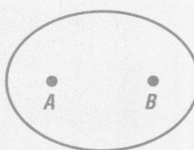

Applications

48. **Sports** A 3-point shot can be made in high school basketball if the shot is made from a distance greater than 19 feet 9 inches from the basket. Describe the locus of points on a basketball court that are more than 19 feet 9 inches from the basket.

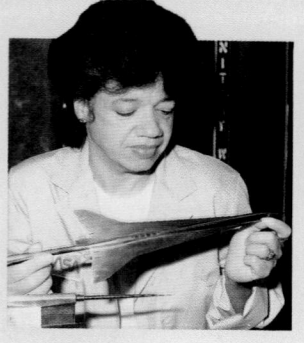

FYI...

In 1989, Dale Ellis of the Dallas Mavericks made 162 three-point shots for an NBA season record.

49. **Geography** If Earth is assumed to be a sphere, what is the locus of points on Earth's surface equidistant from Chicago and London?

50. **Communications** A radio station has a broadcast range of 80 miles. What is the locus of points that can receive that station?

51. **Teaching** A physical education teacher places two students 60 feet apart. The students are supposed to race to a pylon. Describe all the possible placements of the pylon that will make the race fair.

Mixed Review

Complete.

52. In the linear equation $y = mx + b$, m represents the __?__ of the line. **(Lesson 12-1) slope**

53. The surface area of a sphere whose radius measures 10 centimeters is __?__. **(Lesson 11-7) about 1256.6 cm²**

54. The measure of an inscribed angle which intercepts a semicircle is __?__. **(Lesson 9-4) 90**

55. The longest chords of a circle are __?__. **(Lesson 9-1) diameters**

56. If the measures of the sides of a triangle satisfy the Pythagorean Theorem, then the triangle is a __?__. **(Lesson 8-3) right triangle**

57. If two lines do not intersect, then they are parallel or __?__. **(Lesson 3-1) skew**

Wrap-Up

58. Write three locus problems for which the solutions are a plane, a line, a sphere. **See students' work.**

TECHNOLOGY CONNECTION

Can you imagine traveling at two or three thousand miles per hour? Christine Darden, an aerospace engineer in the Advanced Vehicles Division of NASA, is working on designing *supersonic aircraft* that will do just that! She expects that by the year 2000 we will be able to fly from the United States to Europe in about two hours and to Australia in about 4 hours.

Before we can begin to travel at these speeds, however, the United States Congress insists that the sonic boom that occurs on the ground beneath a plane traveling faster than the speed of sound must be reduced or eliminated. Ms. Darden is currently researching changes in the design of the nose and wings of airplanes that may reduce or eliminate the sonic boom.

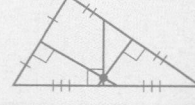

LESSON 13-1 LOCUS 627

EXTENDING THE LESSON

Math Power: Problem Solving

Describe the locus of points in a plane that are equidistant from the three vertices of a triangle. **the point where the perpendicular bisectors of the sides meet**

Technology Connection

The Technology Connection feature introduces students to persons or developments in the field of technology as they relate to mathematics. You may want students to further research NASA or supersonic aircraft.

Enrichment Masters Booklet, p. 77

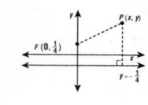
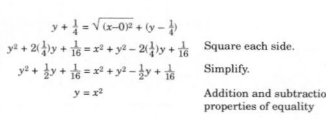

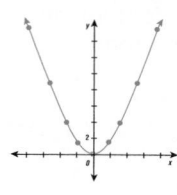
Chapter 13   627

13-2

Locus and Systems of Equations

13-2

Lesson Resources

- Reteaching Master 13-2
- Practice Master 13-2
- Enrichment Master 13-2
- Technology Master, p. 13

 Transparency 13-2 contains the 5-Minute Check and a teaching aid for this lesson.

INTRODUCING THE LESSON

 5-Minute Check

(over Lesson 13-1)

Draw a figure showing the locus of points. Describe the locus.

1. all points in a plane that are equidistant from the endpoints of a semicircular arc

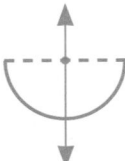

the perpendicular bisector of the segment joining the two endpoints of the arc

2. all points in space that are equidistant from two opposite corners of a cube

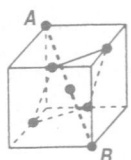

the plane that is the perpendicular bisector of the segment connecting the two opposite corners

Motivating the Lesson

Ask students to describe geographic or architectural features in which straight lines are used.

Objective 13-2

After studying this lesson, you should be able to:

- find the locus of points that solve a system of equations by graphing, substitution, or by elimination.

Application

Parts of straight lines are seen everywhere. Fields are plowed in straight rows. Straight lines are used in designing buildings both for support and appearance. In mathematics, graphs of lines are representations of relationships between two variables. These graphs also represent a locus of points that satisfy a certain set of conditions that are often expressed as equations.

Example 1

APPLICATION

Social Studies

In 1990, the population of Wichita, Kansas, was approximately 304,000 and was growing at the rate of 2400 people per year. If the growth continued at the same rate, draw a graph of the locus of points that represent the population of Wichita in x number of years.

INVESTIGATION

You can learn more about systems of equations in Investigation 16 on page A15.

Let y equal the population of Wichita and x equal the number of years of growth. The locus of points representing the population can be described by an equation of the line that has a slope of 2400 and contains the point (0, 304000). Remember that the equation of a line can be written in the form $y = mx + b$, where m is the slope and b is the y-intercept.

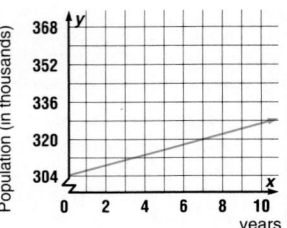

$$y = mx + b$$ *Substitute 2400 for m and 304,000 for b.*

$$y = 2400x + 304,000$$

The locus of points representing the population of Wichita is the line determined by the equation $y = 2400x + 304,000$.

ALTERNATE TEACHING STRATEGIES

Using Investigation

You can guide students to discover when and how to use a graphing calculator to solve a system of equations. In Investigation 16 on page A15 of **More Investigations in Geometry,** students use graphing calculators to explore systems of equations.

Using Comparison

After discussing the three ways to solve a system of equations, solve Example 3 by graphing and by elimination to show that all three ways will produce the same solution. Emphasize that choosing the right method can make solving the system easier.

Example 2

APPLICATION

Demographics

In 1990, St. Louis, Missouri, had a population of about 368,000, which was decreasing at the rate of 5600 people per year.

a. **If the rate of decrease continued, write an equation representing the population of St. Louis.**

Write an equation that represents the population of St. Louis using the point (0, 368,000) and the slope -5600.

$$y = mx + b$$

$$y = -5600x + 368,000$$

b. **Graph this equation on the same coordinate plane as the equation for the population of Wichita found in Example 1.**

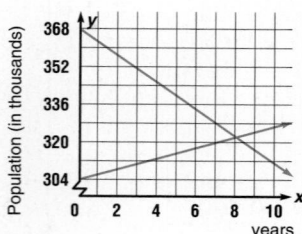

c. **Describe the locus of points that represent the time at which the populations of Wichita and St. Louis will be equal.**

Study the table of values at the right. The graphs intersect at $P(8, 323200)$. Therefore, P is the locus of points that satisfy both equations $y = 2400x + 304,000$ and $y = -5600x + 368,000$.

In eight years, the populations of both cities will be approximately 323,200.

x	Wichita $2400x + 304,000$	St. Louis $-5600x + 368,000$
1	306,400	362,400
2	308,800	356,800
3	311,200	351,200
4	313,600	345,600
5	316,000	340,000
6	318,400	334,400
7	320,800	328,800
8	323,200	323,200

Notice that the graphs in Example 2 intersect at the point with coordinates (8, 323200). Since this point lies on both graphs, its coordinates satisfy both $y = 2400x + 304,000$ and $y = -5600x + 368,000$. The equations $y = 2400x + 304,000$ and $y = -5600x + 368,000$ together are called a **system of equations.** The solution of this system is (8, 323200). You can check this algebraically by substituting 8 for x and 323,200 for y in both equations.

LESSON 13-2   LOCUS AND SYSTEMS OF EQUATIONS   629

TEACHING THE LESSON

Chalkboard Examples

For Example 1

In 1990, the population of Springfield, Illinois was approximately 105,000 and was growing at the rate of 500 people per year. If the growth continues at the same rate, draw a graph of the locus of points that represent the population of Springfield in x number of years.

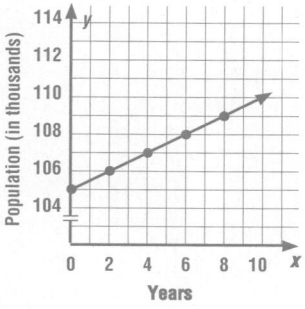

The locus of points representing the population of Springfield is the line determined by the equation $y = 500x + 105,000$.

For Example 2

In 1990, Peoria, Illinois had a population of about 113,000 which was decreasing at the rate of 1000 people per year.

a. If the rate of decrease continues, write an equation representing the population of Peoria. $y = -1000x + 113,000$

b. Graph this equation on the same coordinate plane as the equation for the population of Springfield found in Chalkboard Example 1.

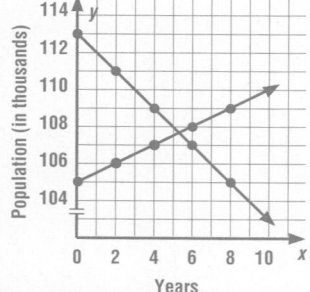

(continued on next page)

You may remember from algebra that a system of equations can be solved by algebraic methods as well as by graphing. Two algebraic methods are the substitution method and the elimination method.

Example 3

CONNECTION
Algebra

Use substitution to find the locus of points that satisfy both equations $y = x - 3$ and $3x + 5y = 9$.

By the first equation, y is equal to $x - 3$. Therefore, $x - 3$ can be substituted for y in the second equation.

$$3x + 5y = 9$$
$$3x + 5(x - 3) = 9 \quad \textit{Substitute } x - 3 \textit{ for } y.$$

The resulting equation has only one variable, x. Solve that equation.

$$3x + 5(x - 3) = 9$$
$$3x + 5x - 15 = 9$$
$$8x - 15 = 9$$
$$8x = 24$$
$$x = 3 \quad \textit{The x-coordinate is 3.}$$

Find y by substituting 3 for x in the first equation.

$$y = x - 3$$
$$y = 3 - 3 \quad \textit{Substitute 3 for } x.$$
$$y = 0 \quad \textit{The y-coordinate is 0.}$$

The point with coordinates (3, 0) is the locus of points that satisfy both equations $y = x - 3$ and $3x + 5y = 9$.

Example 4

CONNECTION
Algebra

Use elimination to find the locus of points that satisfy both equations $3x + 4y = 17$ and $2x + 3y = 11$.

Sometimes adding or subtracting two equations will eliminate a variable. In this case, adding or subtracting the two equations will not eliminate a variable. If both sides of the first equation are multiplied by 2 and both sides of the second equation are multiplied by -3, the system can be solved by adding the equations.

$3x + 4y = 17$ *Multiply by 2.* $6x + 8y = 34$

$2x + 3y = 11$ *Multiply by -3.* $\underline{-6x - 9y = -33}$

$$-y = 1 \quad \textit{Add to eliminate x.}$$
$$y = -1 \quad \textit{The y-coordinate is -1.}$$

Finally, substitute -1 for y in the first equation. Then solve for x.
-1 could also be substituted for y in the second equation.

$$3x + 4y = 17$$
$$3x + 4(-1) = 17$$
$$3x - 4 = 17$$
$$3x = 21$$
$$x = 7 \qquad \textit{The x-coordinate is 7.}$$

The point with coordinates (7, -1) is the locus of points that satisfy both equations $3x + 4y = 17$ and $2x + 3y = 11$.

CHECKING FOR UNDERSTANDING

Communicating Mathematics

Read and study the lesson to answer these questions. **See margin.**

1. Describe the possibilities for the locus of points that belong to the intersection of two lines.

2. Explain how you know that the graph of (-2, 3) is the locus of points that satisfies both of the equations $3x + 4y = 6$ and $2x + 3y = 5$.

3. Determine which method – graphing, substitution, or elimination – you would use to solve each system of equations. Explain your choice.
   a. $y = x + 5$
      $y = 3x - 5$
   b. $3x - 5y = 11$
      $4x + 7y = -2$
   c. $x = 2y - 3$
      $3x - 5y = 11$

Guided Practice

Graph each pair of equations to find the locus of points that satisfy both equations. **See Solutions Manual for graphs.**

4. $x + y = 6$
   $x - y = 2$ **(4, 2)**

5. $y = x - 1$
   $x + y = 11$ **(6, 5)**

6. $y = 4x$
   $x + y = 5$ **(1,4)**

Use an algebraic method to find the locus of points that satisfy both equations.

7. $y = 3x$
   $x + 2y = -21$ **(-3, -9)**

8. $x - y = 5$
   $x + y = 25$ **(15, 10)**

9. $12 - 3y = -4x$
   $40 + 4x = 10y$
   (0, 4)

EXERCISES

Practice

State the locus of points that satisfy the intersection of each pair of lines.

10. c and d **(-2, -2)**

11. a and c **(-2, 2)**

12. a and d **(2, 0)**

13. b and d **(6, 2)**

14. b and c **(-2, 4)**

15. d and the y-axis **(0, -1)**

16. c and the x-axis **(-2, 0)**

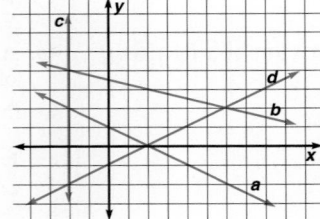

LESSON 13-2   LOCUS AND SYSTEMS OF EQUATIONS   631

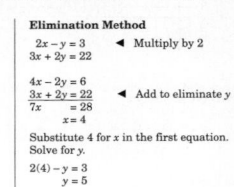

Exercise Notes

For Exercise 39, draw a graph of the two lines, then draw a line perpendicular to both lines through the point (0, 1). Find the two intersection points and use the Distance Formula.

Determine which ordered pairs satisfy each equation or locus of points.

17. $x + 3y = 6$ **a.** $(0, 2)$ **b.** $(-1, 4)$ **c.** $(6, 0)$ **d.** $(-3, 3)$ a,c,d

18. $2x - 5y = -1$ **a.** $(0, 5)$ **b.** $(2, 1)$ **c.** $(-0.5, 0)$ **d.** $(-2, -1)$ b,c

19. $3x = 15$ **a.** $(5, 1)$ **b.** $(5, 0)$ **c.** $(0, 5)$ **d.** $(5, 8)$ a,b,d

Graph each pair of equations to find the locus of points that satisfy both equations. See Solutions Manual for graphs.

20. $3x - 2y = 10$
    $x + y = 0$ (2, -2)

21. $x + 2y = 7$
    $y = 2x + 1$ (1, 3)

22. $y = x + 3$
    $3y + x = 5$ (-1, 2)

Use an algebraic method to find the locus of points that satisfy both equations.

23. $x - y = 6$
    $x + y = 5$ $\left(5\frac{1}{2}, -\frac{1}{2}\right)$

24. $x + 2y = 5$
    $2x + y = 7$ (3, 1)

25. $3x + 4y = -7$
    $2x + y = -3$ (-1, -1)

26. $y = x - 1$
    $4x - y = 19$ (6, 5)

27. $x = y + 10$
    $2y = x - 6$ (14, 4)

28. $9x + y = 20$
    $3x + 3y = 12$ (2, 2)

29. $x - 2y = 5$
    $3x - 5y = 8$ (-9, -7)

30. $3x + 7y = 16$
    $x - 6y = 11$ $\left(\frac{173}{25}, -\frac{17}{25}\right)$

31. $6x + 5 = y$
    $x - y = 0$ (-1, -1)

32. $9x + 7y = 4$
    $6x - 3y = 18$ (2, -2)

33. $2x - 5y = -6$
    $6x - 6y = 18$ (7, 4)

34. $6x + 7y = -9$
    $-9x + 11y = 78$
    (-5, 3)

35. The graphs of $y = 2$, $x - y = 0$, and $3y = -2x + 30$ intersect to form a triangle.
   a. Find the coordinates of the vertices of the triangle. (2, 2), (12, 2), (6, 6)
   b. Find the area of the triangle. 20 units^2

36. In $\triangle IBM$, $I(-8, 6)$, $B(5, 6)$, and $M(-1, -6)$ are coordinates of the vertices. Find the coordinates of the intersection of the altitude from I to $\overline{MB}$ and $\overline{MB}$. $\left(\frac{12}{5}, \frac{4}{5}\right)$

37. Find the locus of points that satisfy both $x - y = 0$ and $(x + 1)^2 + (y - 4)^2 = 25$. (-1, -1) and (4, 4)

38. Find the locus of points that satisfy both $4y - 3x = 26$ and $(x - 1)^2 + (y - 1)^2 = 25$. (-2, 5)

39. Find the distance between the parallel lines whose equations are $y = 3x + 1$ and $y = 3x - 8$.

39. $\frac{9\sqrt{10}}{10} \approx 2.8$

Critical Thinking

40. A line is determined by the equation $y = 2x - 3$. Find equations for each of the following. Answers may vary. See students' work.
   a. a line such that the locus of points that satisfy both equations is the point $(1, -1)$
   b. a line such that there are no points that satisfy both equations
   c. a line such that the locus of points that satisfy both equations is an infinite number of points

---

Practice Masters Booklet, p. 90

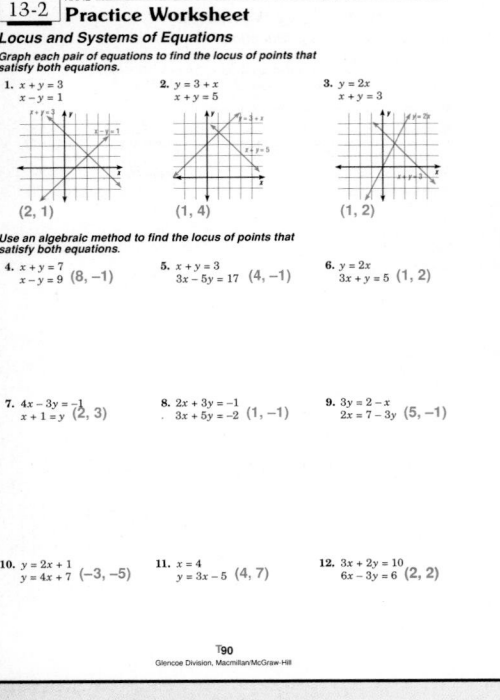

Applications

41. Social Studies The population of Manchester, United Kingdom, is about 4,050,000 and is decreasing at a rate of 22,300 people per year. The population of Guadalajara, Mexico, is about 3,262,000 and is increasing at a rate of 118,900 people per year. Find the locus of points that describes the number of years before the populations of these two cities will be equal. **about 5.58 years or 5 years 7 months**

42. Consumerism The rate for renting a car from Rockwell Cars is $20 plus a fee of $0.25 per mile. Speedy Car rents cars for $25 plus a fee of $0.20 per mile. Find the locus of points that describes the number of miles traveled for which it is less expensive to rent from Speedy Car. **more than 100 miles**

43. Communications On a coordinate grid of a region of the state, radio station WRAY is located at (-18, 0) and station WARC at (20, 10). If WRAY has a range of 22 units and WARC has a range of 20 units, will they ever reach the same audience? Explain your reasoning. **yes; their areas of coverage overlap**

Computer

44. The BASIC computer program given below will determine whether an ordered pair satisfies a linear equation or locus of points. Use the program to check your answers for Exercises 17-19. **See students' work.**

```
10 PRINT "WRITE YOUR EQUATION IN THE FORM Y = MX + B.
   ENTER THE VALUES FOR M AND B."
20 INPUT M, B
30 PRINT "ENTER THE ORDERED PAIR YOU WISH TO TEST."
40 INPUT X, Y
50 IF Y = M * X + B THEN PRINT "THE ORDERED PAIR
   SATISFIES THE EQUATION.": GOTO 70
60 PRINT " THE ORDERED PAIR DOES NOT SATISFY THE
   EQUATION."
70 END
```

Mixed Review

45. Describe the locus of all points in a plane that are 3 inches from a circle with radius measuring 5 inches. **(Lesson 13-1)** **See margin.**

46. Using the information in the figure at the right, find the values of x, y, and z. **(Lesson 8-1)**
$x = \sqrt{76}$ or 8.7, $y = \sqrt{92}$ or 9.6, $z = \sqrt{437}$ or 20.9

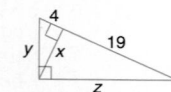

47. Give a counterexample to *All rhombi are squares.* **(Lesson 2-2)** **See margin.**

48. Write the converse of the statement *If three points are coplanar, then they lie in the same plane.* **(Lesson 2-2)** **See margin.**

49. If the supplement of an angle measures 4 times that of the angle itself, find the measure of the angle. **(Lesson 1-8)** **36**

Wrap-Up

50. Describe three different methods you could use to find the locus of points that satisfy both equations $x = y + 10$ and $2y = x - 6$. **See margin.**

LESSON 13-2   LOCUS AND SYSTEMS OF EQUATIONS   633

EXTENDING THE LESSON

Math Power: Connections

The world population grows exponentially. Ask students what this means, and draw a graph of an exponential equation, such as $y = x^2$ or $y = x^4$ to demonstrate. Look at the portion of the graph in the first quadrant. Emphasize that y-values in exponential equations increase much more rapidly when $x > 1$ than in linear equations, where the increase is at a constant rate.

Additional Answers

45. two circles concentric to the given circle, one with a radius of 2 in. and the other with a radius of 8 in.

47.

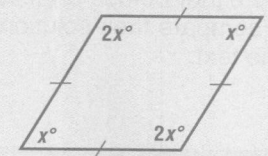

Exercise Notes

For Exercise 40, the locus of points for two equations will be no points, one point, or an infinite number of points. Draw a graph to demonstrate each possibility.

Additional Answers

48. If three points lie in the same plane, then they are coplanar.

50. Sample answer: To solve the system by graphing, graph each equation on the same coordinate plane and find the intersection of the two graphs. To solve the system by substitution, replace x with $y + 10$ in the second equation. Solve for y and then for x. To solve the system by elimination, change the equations so that the x and y values are on the right side of the equations and the constants are on the left. Add the two equations to eliminate x. Solve for y and then for x.

Enrichment Masters Booklet, p. 78

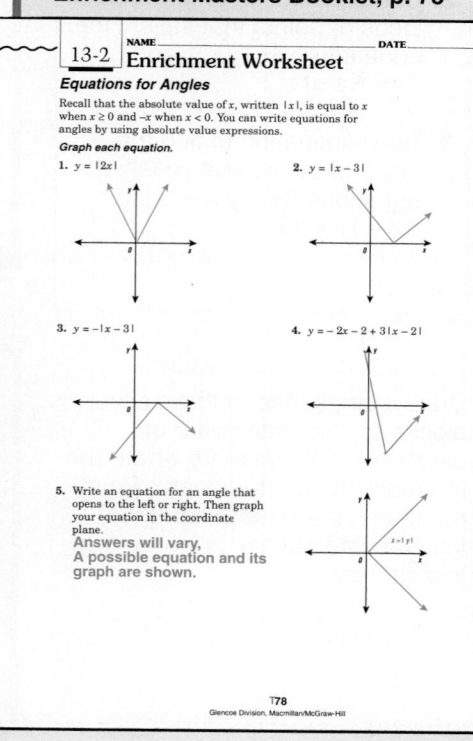

Lesson Resources

- Reteaching Master 13-3
- Practice Master 13-3
- Enrichment Master 13-3
- Evaluation Master p. 177

 Transparency 13-3 contains the 5-Minute Check and a teaching aid for this lesson.

INTRODUCING THE LESSON

 5-Minute Check

(over Lesson 13-2)

1. Graph the system of equations to find the locus of points that satisfy both equations: $y = -\frac{3}{2}x - 2$ and $y = \frac{3}{2}x + 10$.

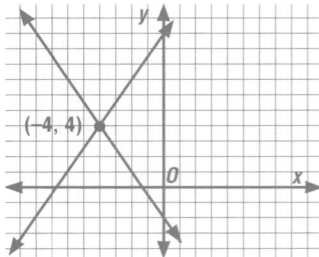

The locus is the point $(-4, 4)$.

2. Use substitution to find the locus of points that satisfy the equations $x = 2y - 1$ and $5x - 6y = 3$.
The locus is the point $(3, 2)$.

3. Use elimination to find the locus of points that satisfy the equations $3x + y = -3$ and $6x - 4y = 12$.
The locus is the point $(0, -3)$.

Motivating the Lesson

Draw a small map of three city blocks on the chalkboard or overhead. Ask students where the intersections of streets are. Point out that, if the streets represent loci, the intersection is where the loci intersect.

13-3 Intersection of Loci

Objective
13-3

After studying this lesson, you should be able to:
- solve locus problems that satisfy more than one condition.

Application

 FYI...

Chicago's O'Hare International Airport and Atlanta's Hartsfield Airport are the busiest airports in the world with a takeoff or landing about every 40 seconds.

Air traffic controllers track the position of airplanes using radar. The flight path of an airplane can be thought of as a locus of points. It is important that the controller realize that the loci of several airplanes might intersect.

Often loci satisfy several conditions. Such loci can usually be determined by finding the intersection of the loci that meet each separate condition.

Example 1

 **APPLICATION**
City Management

A city manager wishes to locate a fire station equidistant from two schools and equidistant from two parallel streets. Determine the locus of points that could be locations for the fire station.

Divide the problem into two separate locus problems.

The locus of all points in a plane equidistant from the two schools is the perpendicular bisector of the segment joining the two schools.

The locus of all points in a plane that are equidistant from the two parallel streets is a line parallel to the given streets and midway between them.

Consider the intersection of the loci of the separate problems.

If A and B are the given schools, and ℓ and m are the given streets, then C is the only point that is equidistant from A and B and equidistant from ℓ and m.

The fire station should be located at point C.

634   CHAPTER 13   LOCI AND TRANSFORMATIONS

ALTERNATE TEACHING STRATEGIES

Using Modeling

Have students cut toothpicks to the size of the segments in the construction on page 635. Instruct students to make a triangle that satisfies the conditions of the construction. Tell the class that the triangles can be either obtuse or acute. Have students compare their solutions with those in the text.

Using Manipulatives

Bring in or make examples of loci and use them to demonstrate how they car intersect. For example, you may use a pencil or pen as an example of a line, and a tennis ball as a sphere. Have students experiment with the intersection of these objects.

Some construction problems involve finding a point that satisfies several conditions.

CONSTRUCTION

Given *AB*, *AC*, and *CD*, such that *AB* > *AC* > *CD*, construct △*ABC* so that *CD* is an altitude of the triangle.

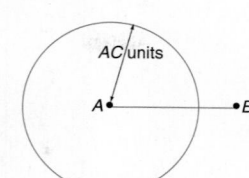

1. Note that vertex *C* of the triangle will lie *AC* units from *A*. The locus of all points *AC* units from *A* is a circle with center *A* and a radius of *AC* units. Vertex *C* will be somewhere on ⊙*A*.

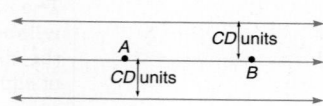

2. Endpoint *D* of altitude $\overline{CD}$ will lie on side $\overline{AB}$ or on the line containing $\overline{AB}$. Since $\overline{CD}$ is an altitude, then $\overline{CD} \perp \overleftrightarrow{AB}$. This means endpoint *C* will lie on a line parallel to $\overleftrightarrow{AB}$, *CD* units from $\overleftrightarrow{AB}$. The locus of all points meeting these conditions are two lines on either side of $\overleftrightarrow{AB}$, parallel to $\overleftrightarrow{AB}$ at a distance of *CD* units.

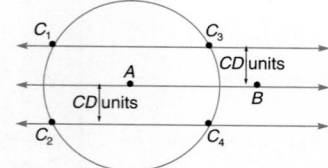

3. Point *C* must satisfy the conditions for being a vertex, Step 1, and the conditions for being an endpoint of an altitude, Step 2. Only four points satisfy these conditions.

There are four possible ways to draw △*ABC*.

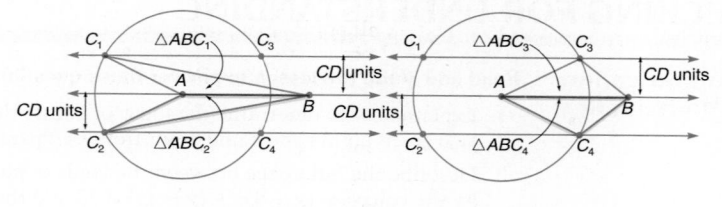

Algebraic equations can be used to represent a locus of points that must satisfy one or more conditions.

LESSON 13-3   INTERSECTION OF LOCI   635

TEACHING THE LESSON

Chalkboard Example

For Example 1
Jessie is looking out the north window of a house, and Terri is looking out the west window. Both windows are the same distance from the northwest corner of the room. If both Jessie and Terri have an angle of sight of 160°, determine the locus of the area outside the house that both girls can see.

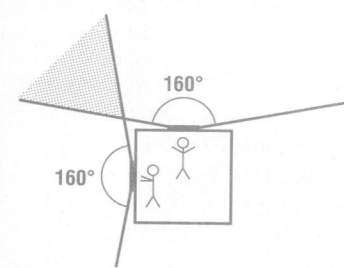

The locus is the area where the angles of sight intersect.

Teaching Tip   Before beginning the construction, point out that $\overline{CD}$ must be perpendicular to $\overleftrightarrow{AB}$ to be an altitude.

636   Chapter 13

explain that the only way for an
equation to equal zero is if one of
the factors is zero. The last line of
the solution is obtained by setting
both factors equal to zero.

Chalkboard Example

For Example 2
Find the locus of points that are
5 units from the point (2, −3)
and that satisfy the equation
$y = 3x − 14$.

$$(x−2)^2 + (y+3)^2 = 25$$
$$(x−2)^2 + (3x−11)^2 = 25$$
$$x^2 − 4x + 4 + 9x^2 − 66x + 121 − 25 = 0$$
$$10x^2 − 70x + 100 = 0$$
$$x^2 − 7x + 10 = 0$$
$$(x−5)(x−2) = 0$$
$$x = 2 \text{ or } x = 5$$

$$y = 3x − 14$$
$$y = 3(2) − 14$$
$$y = −8 \text{ or}$$
$$y = 3(5) − 14$$
$$y = 1$$

The locus of points that
satisfy both conditions are
(2, −8) and (5, 1).

Checking for Understanding

Exercises 1-16 are designed to
help you assess students'
understanding through reading,
writing, speaking, and modeling.
You should work through
Exercises 1-4 with your students
and then monitor their work on
Exercises 5-16.

Error Analysis

Since some loci can intersect in
several ways, students may not
see all possible intersections. To
help, have them use or make
examples of the loci so they can
visualize the solutions.

Example 2

CONNECTION
Algebra

Find the locus of points that are 10 units from the origin in the coordinate plane and that satisfy the equation $y = -x + 10$.

The locus of points 10 units from the origin in
the coordinate plane is a circle with its center
at (0,0) and radius of 10 units.

$$(x − h)^2 + (y − k)^2 = r^2 \qquad \textit{Equation for a circle}$$
$$(x − 0)^2 + (y − 0)^2 = 10^2 \qquad \textit{(h, k) = (0, 0), r = 10}$$
$$x^2 + y^2 = 100$$

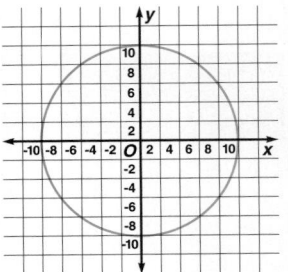

The locus of points that satisfy the equation
$y = -x + 10$ is the set of points on the line with
slope -1 and y-intercept 10.

The locus of points that satisfy both conditions
will be the points of intersection of the line and
the circle. To find this locus, solve the system
of equations $x^2 + y^2 = 100$ and $y = -x + 10$.

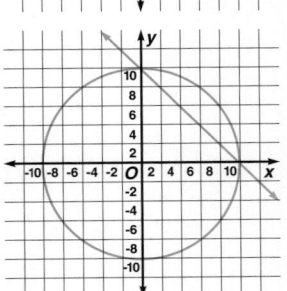

$$x^2 + y^2 = 100$$
$$x^2 + (-x + 10)^2 = 100 \qquad \textit{Substitute -x + 10}$$
$$x^2 + x^2 − 20x + 100 = 100 \qquad \textit{for y.}$$
$$2x^2 − 20x = 0$$
$$2x(x − 10) = 0$$
$$x = 0 \text{ or } x = 10$$

When $x = 0$, $y = 10$ and when $x = 10$, $y = 0$.

The locus of points that satisfy both conditions are (0, 10) and (10, 0).
Check your answer by graphing both equations.

CHECKING FOR UNDERSTANDING

Communicating Mathematics

Read and study the lesson to answer these questions. See margin.

1. Explain how to determine the locus of points that are equidistant from
   two given points and equidistant from two parallel lines.

2. Describe the difference between the locus of points in a plane determined
   by the equation $(x − 4)^2 + (y − 1)^2 = 25$ and the locus of points
   determined by the equation $(x − 4)^2 + (y − 1)^2 = 0$.

3. Describe the difference between the locus of points determined by the
   equation $(x − 4)^2 + (y − 1)^2 = 25$ and the locus of points determined by
   the equation $(x − 4)^2 + (y − 1)^2 + (z + 2)^2 = 25$.

4. Describe the possible ways two parallel lines and a circle can intersect.

Additional Answers

1. **Sample answer: Draw the
   perpendicular bisector of the
   line segment between the two
   points. This represents all the
   points equidistant from the
   two points. Then draw a line
   parallel to the two given lines
   and halfway between them.
   The intersection of the lines
   drawn is the locus of points
   requested.**

2. **$(x − 4)^2 + (y − 1)^2 = 25$ is a
   circle with radius 5 and center**

   **(4, 1); $(x − 4)^2 + (y − 1)^2 = 0$ is
   the point (4, 1).**

3. **$(x − 4)^2 + (y − 1)^2 = 25$ is a
   circle with radius 5 and center
   (4, 1); $(x − 4)^2 + (y − 1)^2 +
   (z + 2)^2 = 25$ is a sphere with
   radius 5 and center (4, 1, −2).**

4. **They may have no points of
   intersection; one or both lines
   may be tangents of the circle;
   one or both lines may be
   secants of the circle; number
   of possible intersections: 0, 1,
   2, 3, or 4.**

Describe the geometric figure whose locus in space satisfies each condition. Be specific. See margin.

5. $(x - 2)^2 + (y + 6)^2 + (z - 5)^2 = 49$ 6. $x = 2$

7. $(x - 5)^2 + (y + 1)^2 = 9$ 8. $y + x = 0$

Describe all possible ways the given figures can intersect. See Solutions Manual.

9. a sphere and a plane

10. two circles

11. two concentric circles and two parallel lines

Draw a diagram to find the locus of points that satisfy the conditions. Then describe the locus. See Solutions Manual.

12. all points in a coordinate plane that are 5 units from the graph of $x = 6$ and equidistant from the graphs of $y = 1$ and $y = 7$

13. all the points in a plane that are 1.5 centimeters from a given line and 3 centimeters from a given point on the line

14. all the points in space that are 2 inches from a given line and 3 inches from a given point on the line

15. all points in a plane that are equidistant from the rays of an angle and equidistant from two points on one of the sides of the angle

CONSTRUCTION

Complete the following construction. See Solutions Manual.

16. Draw two parallel lines, ℓ and m. Choose a point between ℓ and m and label it B. Construct a circle tangent to the 2 lines and containing B.

EXERCISES

Practice

A

Describe the geometric figure whose locus in space satisfies each condition. Be specific. See margin.

17. $(x - 2)^2 + (y + 4)^2 = 36$ 18. $y = 2x - 10$

19. $(x - 3)^2 + (y - 4)^2 + (z - 5)^2 = 16$ 20. $y = 6$

Complete each of the following. See margin.

21. Write the equation for the locus of all points in the coordinate plane 4 units from the graph of $(-1, -6)$.

22. Write the equation of the locus of all points in space 6 units from the graph of $(-2, 5, 1)$.

B

Describe all possible ways the given figures can intersect. See Solutions Manual.

23. two concentric circles and a line

24. two spheres

25. a sphere and two parallel lines

26. a circle and a sphere

27. a sphere and two parallel planes

28. a circle and a plane

LESSON 13-3   INTERSECTION OF LOCI   637

RETEACHING THE LESSON

Use examples to help students find the intersection of two loci. For example, have students find the locus of all points in a plane equidistant from two given intersecting lines and also equidistant from two given parallel lines.   The intersections can be one point or two points.

Additional Answers

5. a sphere with radius 7 and center (2, –6, 5)

6. a plane that is perpendicular to the xy-plane intersecting the xy-plane in $x = 2$

7. a cylinder with radius 3 and an axis passing through points (5, 7, z)

8. a plane perpendicular to the xy-plane intersecting the xy-plane in the line $y + x = 0$

Closing the Lesson

Writing Activity Have each student write two examples of loci on a piece of paper. Have students exchange papers and write the intersection of the two loci.

APPLYING THE LESSON

Homework Exercises

Assignment Guide
Basic: 17-22, 23-37 odd, 44, 47-57
Average: 18-38 even, 39-40, 44, 46-47, 49-57
Enriched: 18, 22, 26-38 even, 39-46, 49-57

Additional Answers

17. a cylinder with radius 6 whose axis is perpendicular to the xy-plane through the point (2, –4, 0)

18. a plane perpendicular to the xy-plane whose intersection with the xy-plane is the line $y = 2x - 10$

19. a sphere with radius 4 and center (3, 4, 5)

20. a plane parallel to the xz-plane which intersects the y-axis at 6

21. $(x + 1)^2 + (y + 6)^2 = 16$

22. $(x + 2)^2 + (y - 5)^2 + (z - 1)^2 = 36$

Reteaching Masters Booklet, p. 79

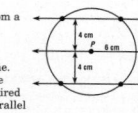

13-3 NAME _____ DATE _____

Reteaching Worksheet

Intersection of Loci

Sometimes locus problems involve sets of points that satisfy more than one set of conditions. In these cases, it is helpful to draw a figure for each set of conditions and then find the point or points where the figures intersect.

Example: Describe the locus of points in a plane 4 cm from a line and 6 cm from a point P on the line.

The locus of points 4 cm from the line is two parallel lines, each one 4 cm from the given line. The locus of points 6 cm from point P is a circle with a radius 6 cm, with P its center. The required locus consists of the 4 points where the two parallel lines intersect the circle.

Draw a diagram to find the locus of points that satisfy the conditions. Then describe the locus.

1. all points in the coordinate plane that are 3 units from the graph of $x = 2$ and equidistant from the graphs of $y = 1$ and $y = 5$

points (5, 3) and (–1, 3)

2. all the points in a plane that are 10 cm from a given line and 12 units from a given point P on the line

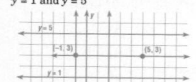

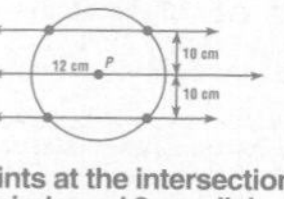

4 points at the intersection of a circle and 2 parallel lines

3. all interior points of an angle that are equidistant from the sides of the angle and 2 cm from the vertex of the angle

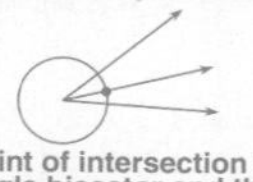

the point of intersection of the angle bisector and the circle of radius 2 cm with center at the vertex

4. all points in space that are 5 inches from a given line and 4 inches from a given point on the line

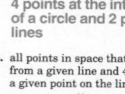

empty set

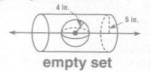

T79

Glencoe Division, Macmillan/McGraw-Hill

36.

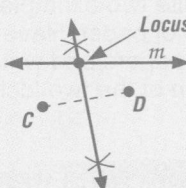

37.

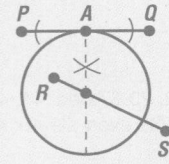

38.

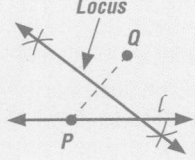

NAME _____ DATE _____

13-3 Practice Worksheet

Intersection of Loci

Describe the locus of points in a plane that satisfy each condition.

1. $x + y = 4$
a line with slope –1 that passes through (0, 4)

2. $x = y$
a line with slope 1 that passes through (0, 0)

3. $y = 5$
a line with slope 0 that passes through (0, 5)

4. $x^2 + (y - 2)^2 = 25$
a circle with center (0, 2) and radius 5

Describe the locus of points in space that satisfy each condition.

5. $(x + 2)^2 + (y - 3)^2 + z^2 = 64$
a sphere with center (–2, 3, 0) and radius 8

6. $(x - 2)^2 + (y + 3)^2 + (z - 1)^2 = 81$
a sphere with center (2, –3, 1) and radius 9

Draw a diagram to find the locus of points that satisfy the conditions. Then describe the locus.

7. all points in a plane that are 3 inches from a given segment and equidistant from the two endpoints
two points on the perpendicular bisector of the segment, one on each side, whose perpendicular distance to the segment is 3 in.

8. all points in a plane that are 3 inches from a given line and 3 inches from a given point on the line
two points, one on each side of the line, whose perpendicular distance from the point on the line is 3 in.

9. all points in a plane that are equidistant from the vertices of a given square
the center of the square; the point of intersection of the diagonals of the square

10. all points in a plane that are 5 centimeters from a given point A and equidistant from points A and B that are 8 centimeters apart
two points, the intersection of the perpendicular bisector of AB and the circle with center A and radius 5

T91
Glencoe Division, Macmillan/McGraw-Hill

Draw a diagram to find the locus of points that satisfy the conditions. Then describe the locus. See Solutions Manual.

29. all the points in a plane that are 2 centimeters from a given line and 5 centimeters from a given point on the line

30. all the points in space that are 2 inches from a given line and 5 inches from a given point on the line

31. all the points in a plane on or inside of a given angle that are equidistant from the sides of the angle and 4 inches from the vertex of the angle

32. all the points in a plane equidistant from two given parallel lines and a given distance from an intersecting line

33. all points in a coordinate plane that are 3 units from the graph of $y = 4$ and equidistant from the graph of $x = 6$ and $x = -2$

34. all the points in space that are 4 centimeters from point A and 2 centimeters from point B if A and B are 5 centimeters apart

35. all points in space that are equidistant from two intersecting lines and 3 units from the point of intersection

Complete each construction. See margin.

CONSTRUCTION

36. Draw a line m and two points, D and C, on one side of the line. Then construct the locus of points in the plane that are equidistant from C and D and on line m.

37. Draw two segments $\overline{PQ}$ and $\overline{RS}$. Choose a point between P and Q and label it A. Then construct a circle tangent to $\overline{PQ}$ at A and whose center lies on $\overline{RS}$.

38. Draw a line ℓ and a point P on the line. Draw point Q not on line ℓ. Then construct the locus of the centers of all circles in the plane that contain P and Q.

Find the locus of points in the coordinate plane that satisfy both equations.

39. $x + y = 4$ and $x^2 + (y + 1)^2 = 4$ ø

40. $(x - 1)^2 + y^2 = 1$ and $(x - 2)^2 + (y - 2)^2 = 4$ (2, 0) and (0.4, 0.8)

In the figure below, $\ell \parallel m$, and the distance between ℓ and m is less than $\frac{1}{2}(AB)$.

41. How many points are there in the locus of all points P on line m such that $\triangle PAB$ is an isosceles triangle? **5 points**

42. How many points are there in the locus of all points P on line m such that $\triangle PAB$ is a right triangle? **4 points**

43. How many points are there in the locus of all points P on line m such that $\triangle PAB$ is an equilateral triangle? **0 points**

Critical Thinking   **44.** Draw and describe the locus of all points in space equidistant from two parallel planes $\mathcal{A}$ and $\mathcal{B}$ and 5 units from a fixed point R. See margin.

Additional Answer

44. no points   one point   a great circle

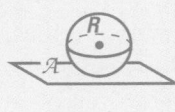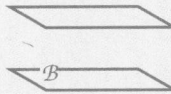
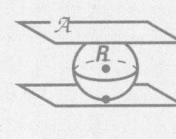
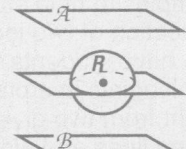

Applications

See margin for 45-47.

45. City Management Hales Corners is a triangular shaped piece of land approximately 3 miles by 3 miles by 3 miles. The community wants to place a fire station equidistant from all three corners of Hales Corners. Draw a diagram to find the locus of points that satisfy the requirements.

3 mi   3 mi

3 mi

46. Communications Two cities, Attica and Rochester, are 70 miles apart. A television station is building a transmitter and, because of the terrain, would like to locate the transmitter 50 miles from Attica and 60 miles from Rochester. Draw a diagram to find the locus of points that could be used as a site for the transmitter.

47. Water Management A house faces east toward a north-south street. One hundred feet from the southeast corner of the house, under the center of the street, is the city water connection. Draw diagrams of the various possibilities for representing the location of the water connection.

48. Food What is the locus of the intersection of the blade of a delicatessen's slicing machine and a cylinder of lunch meat? **a circle and its interior**

Mixed Review

Classify each statement as *always*, *sometimes*, or *never* true.

49. A radius of a circle is perpendicular to a line tangent to the circle. **(Lesson 9-5)** sometimes

50. An angle inscribed in a semicircle is obtuse. **(Lesson 9-4)** never

51. Chords that are equidistant from the center of a circle are congruent. **(Lesson 9-3)** always

52. A chord of a circle is a radius of the circle. **(Lesson 9-1)** never

53. The cosine of an acute angle is less than 1. **(Lesson 8-4)** always

54. If the measures of the sides of a triangle are *a*, *b*, and *c*, then $a^2 + b^2 = c^2$. **(Lesson 8-2)** sometimes

55. The diagonals of a rhombus are congruent. **(Lesson 6-5)** sometimes

56. The diagonals of a rectangle are congruent. **(Lesson 6-4)** always

Wrap-Up

57. Journal Entry Describe the steps you should use to find the locus of points that satisfy two conditions. Give an example. **See Solutions Manual.**

LESSON 13-3 INTERSECTION OF LOCI 639

EXTENDING THE LESSON

Math Power: Problem Solving

Describe the locus of points *P* in a plane such that the sum of the distances from *P* to two given points is a constant C > 0. Hint: look at specific cases. **an ellipse or oval**

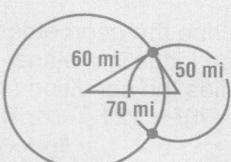
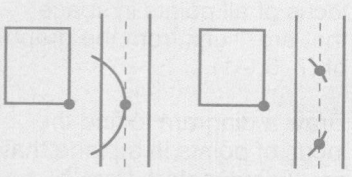

 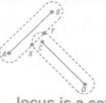 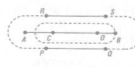

Lesson Resources

- Reteaching Master 13-4
- Practice Master 13-4
- Enrichment Master 13-4

 Transparency 13-4 contains the 5-Minute Check and a teaching aid for this lesson.

INTRODUCING THE LESSON

 5-Minute Check

(over Lesson 13-3)

1. Describe the geometric figure whose locus in a plane satisfies the condition $(x-3)^2 + (y+4)^2 = 121$. **a circle with radius 11 and center at (3, –4)**

2. Write the equation for the locus of all points in space that are 1 unit from the graph of (7, 5, –1). **$(x-7)^2 + (y-5)^2 + (z+1)^2 = 1$**

3. Draw a diagram to find the locus of points in a plane that are 3 centimeters from a given line and 3 centimeters from a given point on the line. Describe the locus.

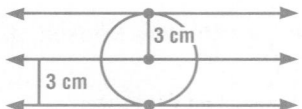

The locus is two points that lie on the circle and on the segment perpendicular to the line at the given point.

Motivating the Lesson

Bring in a book that contains some of Escher's work. Have students use art to look for patterns and mappings.

13-4 Mappings

Objectives

After studying this lesson, you should be able to:

13-4A
- name the image and preimage of a mapping, and

13-4B
- recognize an isometry or congruence transformation.

Application

FYI...

Each tiny piece of an Escher tesselation drawing conveys as much information as the whole drawing.

A Dutch artist Mauritz Escher (1898-1972) created art by using patterns. Study the example of his work at the right. What patterns do you see?

Escher moved figures according to certain rules. Some of the rules are illustrated below.

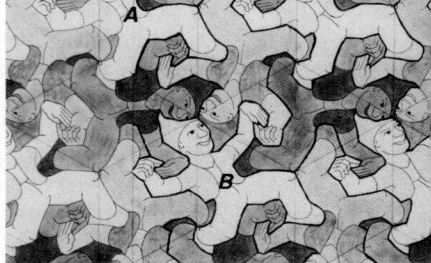

©1938 M.C. Escher/Cordon Art-Baarn, Holland

A figure can be reflected.

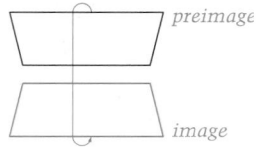

A figure can be rotated.

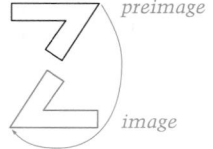

A figure can be slid.

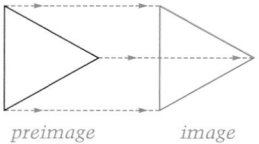

A figure can be enlarged or reduced.

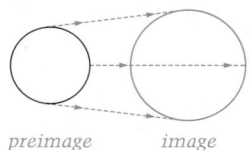

Notice that each point of one figure is paired with exactly one point of the corresponding figure. These are called mappings or **transformations.** A transformation maps a **preimage** onto an **image.**

Definition of Transformation	**In a plane, a mapping is a transformation if each preimage point has exactly one image point, and each image point has exactly one preimage point.**

A transformation is a one-to-one mapping. That is, each point is mapped to a unique point.

ALTERNATE TEACHING STRATEGIES

Using Manipulatives

Use tiles to help students understand the concept of mappings. Explain that if you flip them over, turn them, and slide them you are actually performing a geometric transformation. Have students use tiles to make a design and explain how one tile is mapped to another tile that is the same or similar.

Using Models

Use a piece of paper or other two-dimensional figure to show students what is meant by the three isometries defined in this lesson. For example, flip the paper over to demonstrate reflection, turn the paper to demonstrate rotation, and slide the paper left, right, up, and down to demonstrate translation.

Example 1

APPLICATION

Art

Describe the transformation that moves person A to person B in the Escher art on page 640.

Person A can be moved to person B by sliding person A diagonally down and to the right.

The symbol → is used to indicate a mapping. For example, $\triangle ABC \to \triangle PQR$ means $\triangle ABC$ is mapped onto $\triangle PQR$. $\triangle ABC$ is the preimage and $\triangle PQR$ is the image. The order of the letters indicates the correspondence of the preimage to the image. The first vertices, A and P, are corresponding vertices. Similarly, B and Q are corresponding vertices and C and R are corresponding vertices.

In the figure, $\overline{AC} \to \overline{DF}$, and A and D are corresponding points. C and F are corresponding points. B and E are corresponding points. Every point on $\overline{AC}$ corresponds to a point on $\overline{DF}$, and every point on $\overline{DF}$ corresponds to a point on $\overline{AC}$. Thus, the mapping is a transformation.

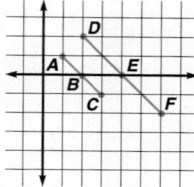

When a geometric figure and its transformation image are congruent, the mapping is called an **isometry** or a **congruence transformation.** When a figure and its transformation image are similar, the mapping is called a **similarity transformation.**

Example 2

Suppose $\triangle ABC \to \triangle PQR$. Show that this mapping is an isometry.

Each side of $\triangle ABC$ is mapped to the corresponding side of $\triangle PQR$. If these corresponding sides are congruent, then the mapping is an isometry. Since their lengths are the same, $\overline{AB} \cong \overline{PQ}$, $\overline{BC} \cong \overline{QR}$, and $\overline{AC} \cong \overline{PR}$. Therefore, $\triangle ABC \cong \triangle PQR$ by SSS. $\triangle ABC$ is the preimage of the isometry, and $\triangle PQR$ is the image.

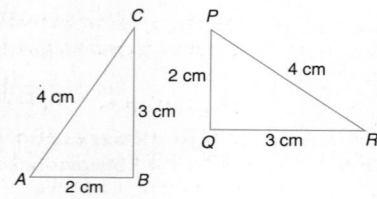

CHECKING FOR UNDERSTANDING

Communicating
Mathematics

Read and study the lesson to answer these questions. See Solutions Manual.

1. What is a transformation?

2. Describe how a preimage is related to an image.

3. Name four ways of creating a transformation. Draw an example of each.

4. Explain the difference between an isometry and a similarity transformation.

LESSON 13-4   MAPPINGS   641

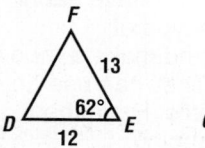 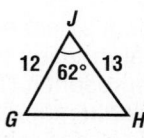
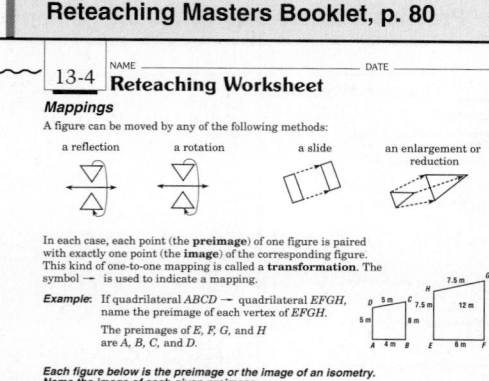
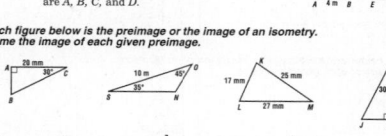

RETEACHING THE LESSON

Have each student draw and cut out a two-dimensional figure. Have them use that figure to draw examples of the four transformations discussed in this lesson: a reflection, a rotation, a slide, and an enlargement or reduction.

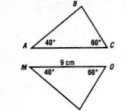 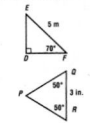 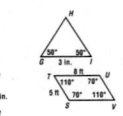 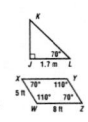

Guided Practice   **Answer the following, if quadrilateral *RSTU* → quadrilateral *ABCD*.**

5. Name the image of $\overline{UT}$. $\overline{DC}$
6. Name the preimage of D. U
7. Name the preimage of ∠B. ∠S
8. Name the image of ∠T. ∠C
9. Name the preimage of $\overline{AB}$. $\overline{RS}$

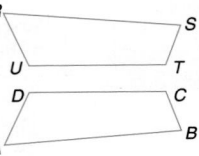

For Exercises 10–21, *△ABC* → *△EBD*. Name the image of each of the following.

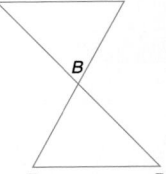

10. A E   11. B B   12. C D
13. ∠CAB ∠DEB 14. ∠BCA ∠BDE 15. $\overline{AC}$ $\overline{ED}$

Name the preimage of each of the following.

16. E A   17. B B   18. D C
19. $\overline{BE}$ $\overline{BA}$ 20. $\overline{DE}$ $\overline{CA}$ 21. ∠DBE ∠CBA

EXERCISES

Practice   **Answer each of the following, if pentagon *ABCDE* → pentagon *PQRST*.**

22. Name the image of $\overline{CD}$. $\overline{RS}$
23. Name the image of ∠E. ∠T
24. Name the preimage of $\overline{PT}$. $\overline{AE}$
25. Name the preimage of ∠Q. ∠B
26. Name the image of $\overline{BC}$. $\overline{QR}$

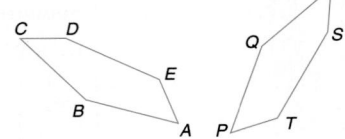

Each figure below is the preimage or the image for an isometry. Write the image of each given preimage.

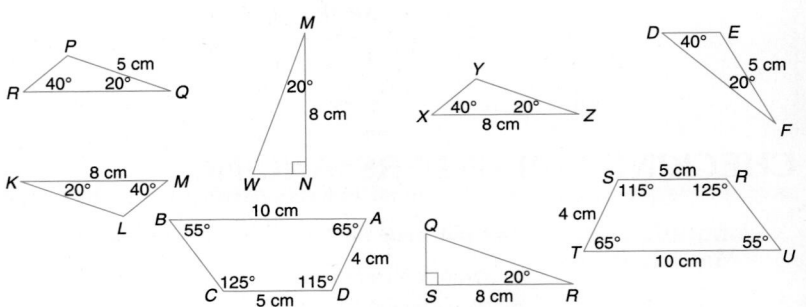

27. △MWN △RQS   28. △PQR △EFD   29. △SRQ △NMW
30. △LMK △YXZ   31. △MKL △XZY   32. △ZYX △KLM
33. quadrilateral RSTU CDAB   34. quadrilateral BADC UTSR

In the figure at the right, $\triangle XYW \cong \triangle ZYW$.

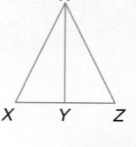

35. Name a segment that is its own preimage. $\overline{WY}$

36. Name two points that are their own preimages. **W and Y**

37. Name a mapping that describes the congruence.
    $\triangle XYW \rightarrow \triangle ZYW$

38. The L-shaped tile at the right is gray on top and
    blue underneath. Suppose two of these L-shaped
    tiles are used to form each of the following figures.
    Name the colors for Section A and Section B.

a.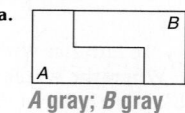
A gray; *B* gray

b.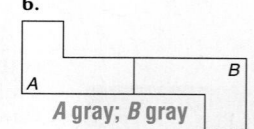
A gray; *B* gray

c.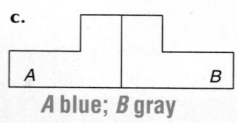
A blue; *B* gray

Critical Thinking

39. A transformation maps each point (x, y) to $(x + 3, y - 1)$. Is this
    transformation an isometry? *(Hint: Choose three points that form a triangle
    and find their images. Do the images form a congruent triangle?)* **yes**

Applications

40. **Art** Study the Escher drawing at
    the right. Describe the
    transformation that moves
    angel *A* to angel *B*. **See margin.**

41. **Art** Describe the transformation
    that moves angel *D* to angel *C*.
    See margin.

42. **Recreation** Sam is walking down
    the beach in his bare feet. He looks
    back at his footprints in the sand.
    Describe what he sees in terms of
    transformations. **See margin.**

©1941 M.C. Escher/Cordon Art-Baarn, Holland

43. **Cartoons** The movement you see when you watch a cartoon is created
    by a series of pictures, each one slightly different than the last one.
    Suppose you are making a cartoon of a bouncing ball, how would you use
    transformations to create the illusion of a moving ball? **See margin.**

Mixed Review

44. Describe the locus of all points in space that are a given distance from a
    line segment and equidistant from the endpoints of the line segment.
    (Lesson 13-3) **a circle**

45. A trapezoid has a median 17.5 cm long. If the height is 18 cm, find the
    area of the trapezoid. **(Lesson 10-5)** **315 cm²**

46. Solve the proportion $\frac{x + 1}{8} = \frac{3}{4}$. **(Lesson 9-1)** **5**

47. Find the geometric mean between 18 and 31. **(Lesson 8-1)** $\sqrt{558} \approx 23.6$

48. Write the converse of the conditional *If a mapping is one-to-one, then it
    is a transformation.* **(Lesson 2-2)** **If a mapping is a transformation, then it
    is one-to-one.**

Wrap-Up

49. Draw a simple figure. Draw four images of the figure showing different
    transformations. **See students' work.**

LESSON 13-4   MAPPINGS   643

EXTENDING THE LESSON

Math Power: Reasoning

Graph the equations $y = x^2$ and
$y = (x - 2)^2 + 4$ on the same graph.
What can you say about the two
graphs? **They are the same
shape but in different places.**
What did the numbers 2 and 4 do
to the graph of x^2? **The graph
moved 2 units right and 4 units
up.** Have students make a
generalization about all equations
of this type.

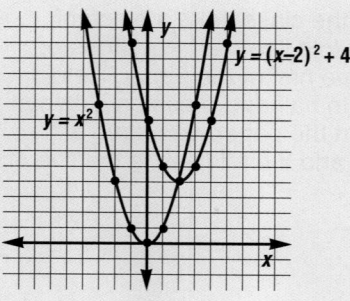

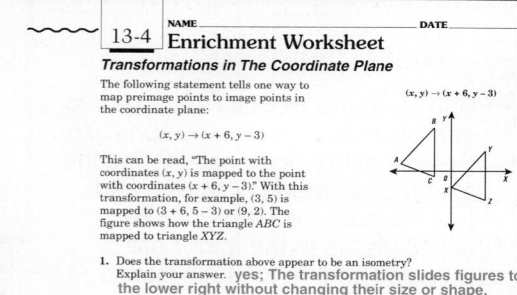
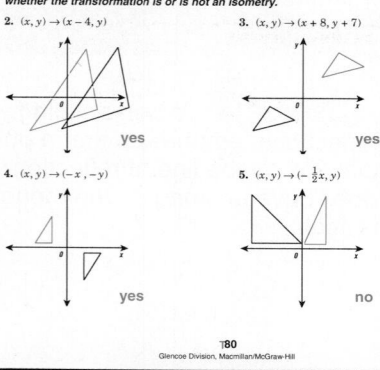

Lesson Resources

- Reteaching Master 13-5
- Practice Master 13-5
- Enrichment Master 13-5
- Evaluation Masters, pp. 177, 181
- Activities Master, p. 27
- Technology Master, p. 49
- Lab Manual, pp. 90-93

 Transparency 13-5 contains the 5-Minute Check and a teaching aid for this lesson.

INTRODUCING THE LESSON

 5-Minute Check

(over Lesson 13-4)

**Quadrilateral ABCD →
quadrilateral MLKN. Write the
name of the image that
corresponds to each given
preimage.**

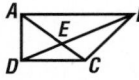 

1. ∠ABC   ∠MLK
2. $\overline{DC}$ $\overline{NK}$
3. $\overline{BE}$ $\overline{LO}$
4. △BDC   △LNK
5. ∠AEB   ∠MOL

Motivating the Lesson

Bring a mirror to class and use it to demonstrate reflection. Emphasize that the mirror does not change the shape of a person or object, and that the parts of the person or object visible to the mirror are reflected so that the reflection is identical to the original.

TEACHING THE LESSON

Teaching Tip   When defining reflections, emphasize that a point that lies on the line of reflection *does* have an image even though it is itself.

13-5 Reflections

Objectives
After studying this lesson, you should be able to:
- **13-5A** ▪ name a reflection image with respect to a line,
- **13-5B** ▪ recognize line symmetry and point symmetry, and
- **13-5C** ▪ draw reflection images, lines of symmetry, and points of symmetry.

Application

All of us are familiar with scenes like the one shown at the left. When the water is perfectly calm, you can see a mirror-like reflection of the things on shore in the water.

A **reflection** is a type of transformation. For example, in the figure below, A is the reflection image of X with respect to ℓ. The line of reflection, ℓ, is a perpendicular bisector of the segment drawn from X to A. Since P is on the line of reflection, its image is P itself.

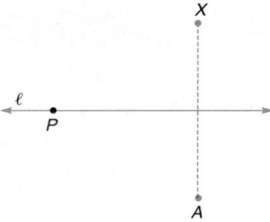

It is also possible to have a reflection image with respect to a point.

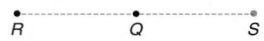

S is the reflection of R with respect to Q. The point of reflection, Q, is the midpoint of the segment drawn from R to S.

The reflection images of collinear points are collinear. The images of collinear points A, B, and C are collinear points P, Q, and R, respectively. Therefore, it is said that reflections preserve collinearity.

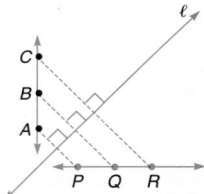

644   CHAPTER 13   LOCI AND TRANSFORMATIONS

ALTERNATE TEACHING STRATEGIES

Using Modeling

In front of the class, take a piece of paper and fold it in half. Put drops of paint on one half of the paper. Refold the paper in half and press on it. When you reopen the paper, you have a reflection, and the fold line is the line of symmetry.

Using Critical Thinking

Have students think of ways to show the types of reflections discussed in this lesson. For example, take a piece of paper and draw a line and a point to the left of the line. Fold the paper along the line and copy the point. Open the paper up and copy the reflection point on the right side. Now you have the reflection of the point.

The reflection image of Y is between the image of X and Z if and only if Y is between X and Z. Thus, reflections preserve betweenness of points.

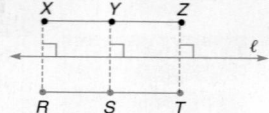

Teaching Tip   Emphasize that reflections preserve collinearity, betweenness of points, angle measure, and distance measure.

Reflections also preserve angle and distance measure. In the figure below, $\triangle XYZ$ is the reflection image of $\triangle ABC$ and $\triangle ABC$ is the reflection image of $\triangle XYZ$. By measuring the corresponding parts of $\triangle ABC$ and $\triangle XYZ$, it appears that $\triangle ABC$ is congruent to $\triangle XYZ$.

Points A, B, and C can be read in a clockwise order. $\triangle ABC$ is said to have a clockwise orientation.

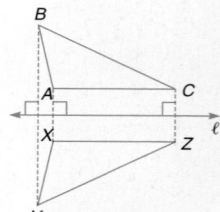

Corresponding points X, Y, and Z are then in a counterclockwise orientation. $\triangle XYZ$ is said to have a counterclockwise orientation.

Suppose $\triangle CBA$ has a counterclockwise orientation, then what is the orientation of the reflection image? **clockwise**

Because only the orientation of a geometric figure is changed, a reflection is an isometry.

CONSTRUCTION

Construct the reflection image of $\triangle ABC$ with respect to line ℓ.

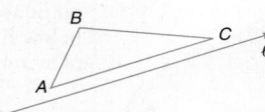

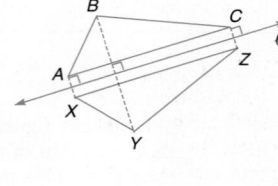

Construct perpendiculars from A, B, and C through line ℓ. Locate X, Y, and Z so that line ℓ is the perpendicular bisector of $\overline{AX}$, $\overline{BY}$, and $\overline{CZ}$. X, Y, and Z are the corresponding vertices of A, B, and C. The reflection image of $\triangle ABC$ is found by connecting the vertices X, Y, and Z.

$$\triangle ABC \rightarrow \triangle XYZ$$

LESSON 13-5   REFLECTIONS   645

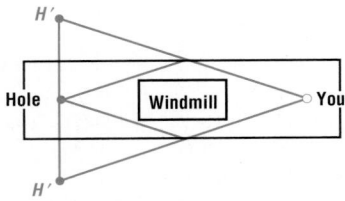
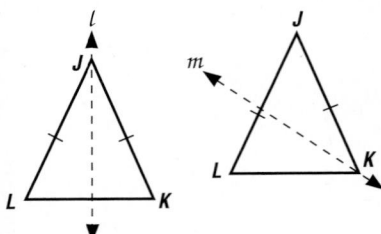
Example 1

APPLICATION
Recreation

Tess is playing miniature golf. If the tee is at point *B*, how can she make a hole-in-one for the situation shown at the right?

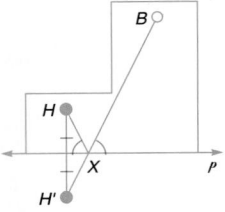

Tess must visualize the reflection image *H′* of hole *H* with respect to line *p*. She then aims for *H′*. The ball hits the side at *X* and rebounds along the preimage of $\overline{XH'}$ making a hole-in-one.

A line can be drawn through many plane figures so that the figure on one side is a reflection image of the figure on the opposite side. In such a case, the line of reflection is called a **line of symmetry.**

Example 2

Test the given lines to see if they are lines of symmetry for rectangle *ABCD*.

By measuring, it appears that line *ℓ* is the perpendicular bisector of both $\overline{AB}$ and $\overline{CD}$. Any point to the left of line *ℓ* has its reflection image to the right of line *ℓ*. Likewise, by measuring, it can be seen that line *m* is the perpendicular bisector of $\overline{AD}$ and $\overline{BC}$. Also any point above line *m* has its reflection image below line *m*. Therefore, lines *ℓ* and *m* are lines of symmetry for rectangle *ABCD*.
You could also test these lines by copying the figures, cutting them out, and folding them along the lines. If the vertices correspond, then the lines are lines of symmetry.

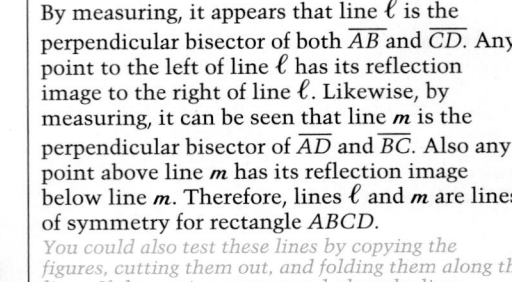
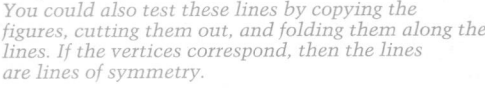

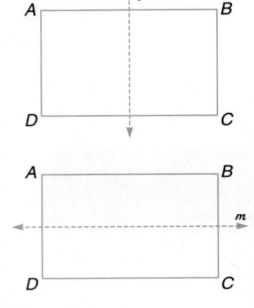

For many figures, a point can be found that is a point of reflection for all points on the figure. This point of reflection is called a **point of symmetry.**

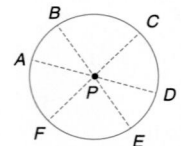 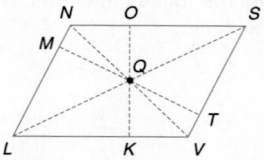 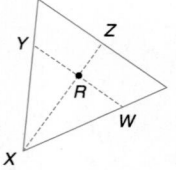

P and Q are points of symmetry.   R is not a point
                                          of symmetry.

A point of symmetry must be a midpoint for all segments with endpoints on the figure. In the two figures above at the left, P and Q are midpoints of the segments drawn. In the figure above at the right, R is not a point of symmetry because R is not the midpoint of $\overline{XZ}$.

CHECKING FOR UNDERSTANDING

Communicating Mathematics

Read and study the lesson to answer these questions. See margin.

1. Describe the relationship between a line of reflection and the line segment joining an image point and its preimage point.

2. What does it mean for a point to have a reflection image with respect to a point?

3. Why is a reflection an isometry?

4. Name some objects that have lines of symmetry.

5. Name some objects that have points of symmetry.

Guided Practice

For the figure at the right, name the reflection image with respect to line ℓ.

6. A   A   7. B   C   8. $\overline{AB}$ $\overline{AC}$

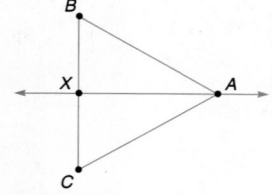

Copy each figure below. Then draw the reflection image of each figure with respect to line m.

9. 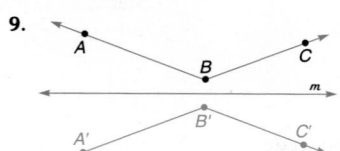   10.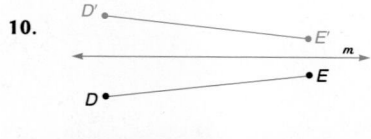

LESSON 13-5   REFLECTIONS   647

Homework Exercises

Assignment Guide

Basic: 18-28, 32-48, 55-66
Average: 19-31 odd, 32-51, 55-66
Enriched: 18-30 even, 33-66
All: Mid-Chapter Review, 1-10

Exercise Notes

For all the exercises, it may help students to copy the figures on a piece of paper and experiment with folds to find lines of symmetry.

Copy the following letters. Draw all possible lines of symmetry. If none exist, write *none*.

11.    12.    13.   14.

Copy each figure below. Then draw the reflection image if *R* is the point of reflection.

15.   16. 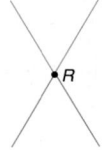   17.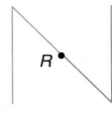

EXERCISES

Practice
A

For each of the figures at the right, name the reflection image with respect to line ℓ.

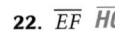

18. *M* L   19. *K* J

20. $\overline{KM}$ JL   21. $\angle DEF$ ∠IHG

22. $\overline{EF}$ HG   23. $\triangle BXA$ △CXA

24. *N* N   25. $\overline{DE}$ IH

For each of the following figures, determine whether ℓ is a line of symmetry. Write *yes* or *no*. Then explain your answer. See margin for explanations.

26. 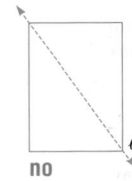   27. 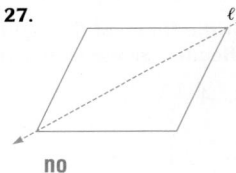   28.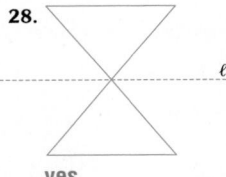
no   no   yes

29. 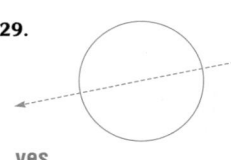   30. 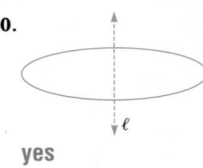   31.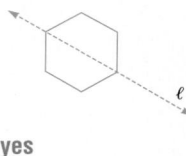
yes   yes   yes

648   CHAPTER 13   LOCI AND TRANSFORMATIONS

Additional Answers

26-27. Not all points are the same distance from *ℓ*.

28-31. For any point on each figure, it is possible to find another point *B* on the figure so that *ℓ* is the perpendicular bisector of $\overline{AB}$.

For each of the following figures, indicate if the figure has line symmetry, point symmetry, or both.

32.

both

33.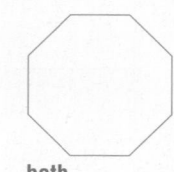

both

34.

point

Copy each figure below. Then draw the reflection image of each figure with respect to line *m*.

35.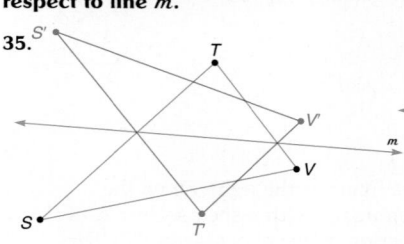

36.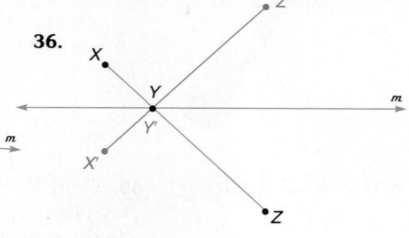

37.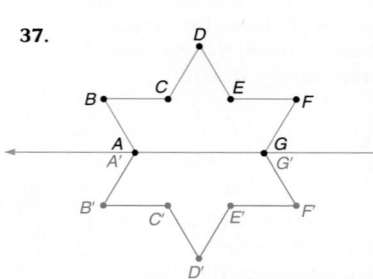

38.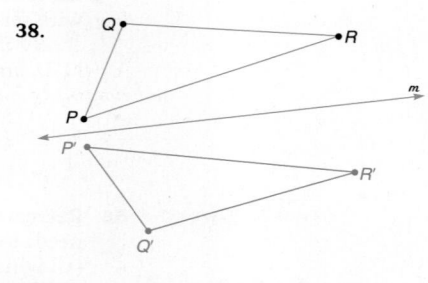

Copy the following letters. Draw all possible lines of symmetry. If none exist, write *none*.

39.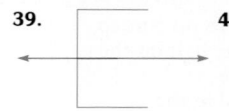

40.

41.

42.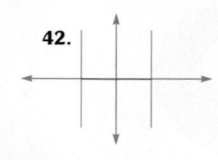

Copy each figure below. Then draw the reflection image if *R* is the point of reflection.

43. 44. 45.

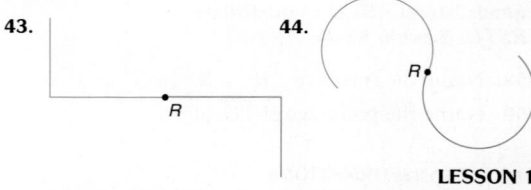

LESSON 13-5   REFLECTIONS   649

RETEACHING THE LESSON

Have each student draw a triangle and a line on a piece of paper. Work through the construction on page 645 with students, using the triangles and lines that they just drew.

 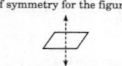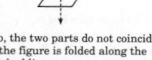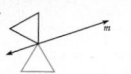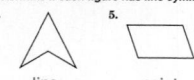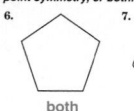

Additional Answers

55.

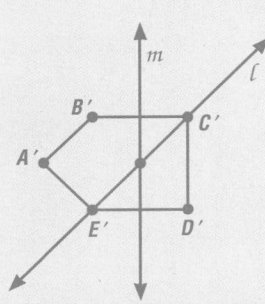

56. Sample answer: Find the reflection image of the 3 ball with respect to the line of one of the long sides of the pool table. Aim the cue ball for the reflection image of the 3 ball.

Practice Masters Booklet, p. 93

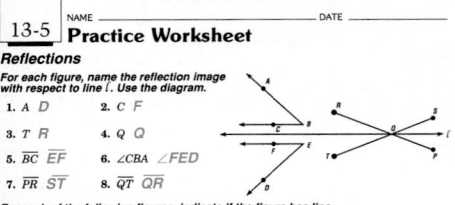

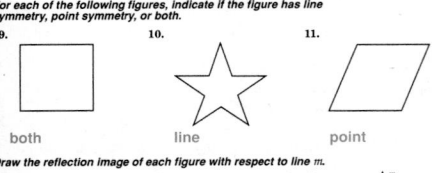

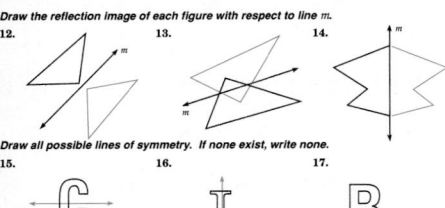

C Copy each figure below. Indicate any points of symmetry. If none exist, write *none*.

46.

47.

none

48.
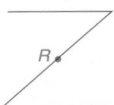

49.
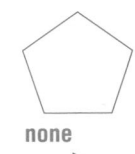
none

50.
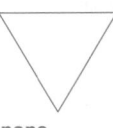
none

51.

none

52.
none

53.

54.

none

Critical Thinking

55. Copy the figure at the right. Draw the reflection image with respect to line *m* of the reflection image of pentagon *ABCDE* with respect to line ℓ. Label the vertices *A'*, *B'*, *C'*, *D'*, and *E'* to correspond to *A*, *B*, *C*, *D*, and *E* respectively. **See margin.**

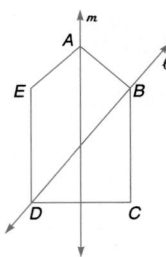

Applications

56. Recreation Amos is playing pool. He needs to hit the 3 ball with the cue ball (all white) without hitting the 8 ball. How can Amos plan his shot?
See margin.

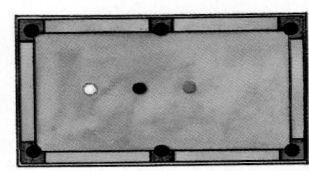

57. Grooming Alison uses two mirrors to check the appearance of the hair on the back of her head. Using the measurements as indicated in the figure, how far away does the image of the back of her head appear to Alison?
168 cm

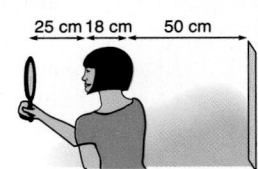

Mixed Review

Answer each of the following, if quadrilateral *ABCD* → quadrilateral *RSTU*. **(Lesson 13-4)**

58. Name the image of ∠*B*. ∠*S*

59. Name the preimage of $\overline{TU}$. $\overline{CD}$

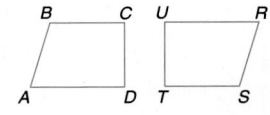

650 CHAPTER 13 LOCI AND TRANSFORMATIONS

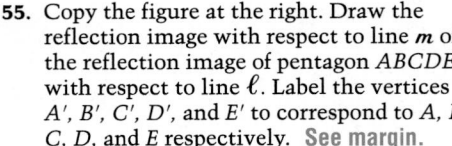

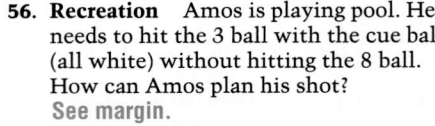

Determine whether each pair of triangles is congruent. If so, state the postulate or theorem used. If there is not enough information, write *not enough information*. (Lessons 4-5, 4-6, and 5-3)

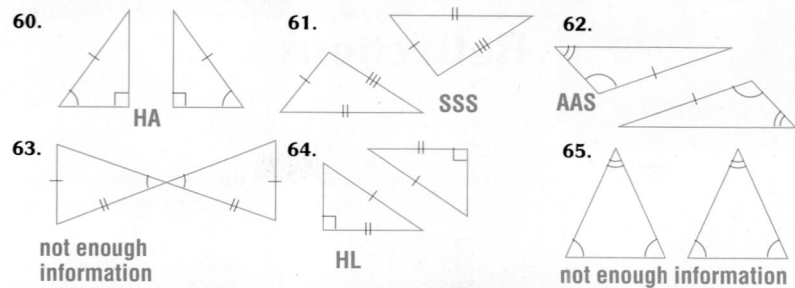

60. **HA**

61. **SSS**

62. **AAS**

63. **not enough information**

64. **HL**

65. **not enough information**

Wrap-Up 66. Find a picture in a magazine that has a line of symmetry and a picture that has a point of symmetry. Show the line of symmetry and the point of symmetry. **See students' work.**

MID-CHAPTER REVIEW

1. What are the five steps in the procedure for determining a locus of points? **(Lesson 13-1)**

2. Describe the locus of points in a plane that are equidistant from two given points. **(Lesson 13-1)**   1-3. See margin.

3. Describe the locus of points in space that are equidistant from two given points. **(Lesson 13-1)**

4. Select the coordinates of the locus of points that satisfy both equations. **(Lesson 13-2)**
   $y = x + 4$
   $y = 2x - 5$ **a.** $(9, 13)$ **b.** $(13, 18)$ **c.** $(13, 9)$ **d.** $(9, 5)$ **a**

5. Select the coordinates of the locus of points that satisfy both equations. **(Lesson 13-2)**
   $x = y - 6$
   $x = 30 - y$ **a.** $(18, 12)$ **b.** $(12, 18)$ **c.** $(30, 36)$ **d.** $(6, 12)$ **b**

6. Describe the locus of points in space that are 3 centimeters from a circle of radius 7 centimeters. **(Lesson 13-3)** See margin.

7. Describe the possible locus of points in space that are 5 units from a given point and 3 units from another given point. **(Lesson 13-3)** See margin.

8. Copy the figure at the right. Then draw the reflection image with respect to line ℓ. Label the reflection image so that $\triangle ABC \rightarrow \triangle LMN$. **(Lesson 13-4)**

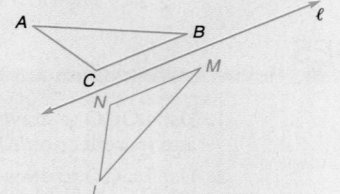

9. Use your drawing for Exercise 8 to name the preimage of $\overline{MN}$. **(Lesson 13-4)** $\overline{BC}$

10. Use your drawing for Exercise 8 to name the preimage of $\angle M$. **(Lesson 13-4)** $\angle B$

LESSON 13-5 REFLECTIONS 651

EXTENDING THE LESSON

Math Power: Connections
Draw segments, points, or lines on the coordinate plane. Have students reflect each segment, point, or line through the y-axis, the y-axis, the origin, and the line $y = x$.

Mid-Chapter Review
The Mid-Chapter Review provides students with a brief review of the concepts and skills in Lessons 13-1 through 13-5. Lesson numbers are given at the end of problems or instruction lines so students may review concepts not yet mastered.

Enrichment Masters Booklet, p. 81

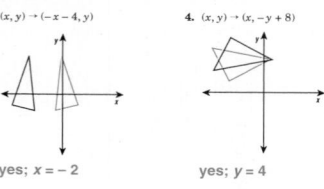

Chapter 13 651

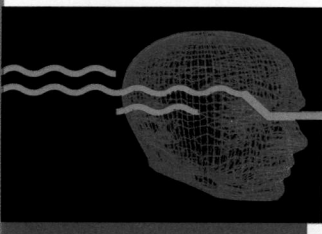

Technology

Reflections

You can draw figures and their reflections of figures using LOGO. The procedure XYAXES given below will draw the coordinate axes.

```
TO XYAXES
  SETY 119        Draws from HOME to the top of the screen.
  HOME
  SETY -119       Draws from HOME to the bottom of the screen.
  HOME
  SETX 139        Draws from HOME to the right edge of the screen.
  HOME
  SETX -139       Draws from HOME to the left edge of the screen.
  HOME
  FULLSCREEN HT   Hides the turtle.
END
```

The procedure TRIANGLE will draw the triangle *ABC*. The triangle *A'B'C'* is the reflection of $\triangle ABC$ with respect to the *y*-axis. $\triangle A'B'C'$ can be drawn with the procedure REFLECTION.

```
TO TRIANGLE
  SETXY 0 40
  SETXY 50 0
  SETXY 0 0
END

TO REFLECTION
  XYAXES
  TRIANGLE
  SETXY 0 40
  SETXY -50 0
  SETXY 0 0
END
```

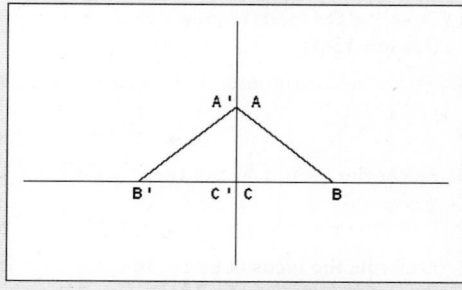

Enter all three procedures. Then type REFLECTION to draw the triangle and its reflection.

EXERCISES

See margin.

1. Use LOGO to draw $\triangle FGH$ with vertices $F(0, 0)$, $G(0, -60)$, and $H(50, -60)$ and its reflection $\triangle F'G'H'$ with respect to the *y*-axis.

2. Use LOGO to draw quadrilateral *MNPQ* with vertices $M(-20, -20)$, $N(-20, -65)$, $P(-55, -65)$, and $Q(-55, -20)$ and its reflection $M'N'P'Q'$ with respect to the *x*-axis.

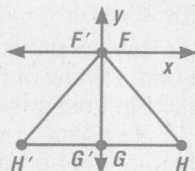
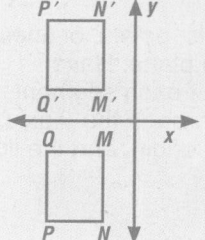

13-6 Translations

Objective 13-6	After studying this lesson, you should be able to: ■ name and draw translation images of figures with respect to parallel lines.

FYI···

The first auto race was a 201-mile race from Green Bay to Madison, Wisconsin. It was won by an Oshkosh steamer.

Application

INVESTIGATION

You can learn more about reflections and translations in Investigation 17 on page A16.

A race car speeds along a track to the finish line. The result of a movement in one direction is a transformation called a **translation.** A transformation moves all points the same distance in the same direction.

To find a translation image, perform two reflections in a row with respect to two parallel lines. For example, the translation image of the blue figure with respect to the parallel lines, *n* and *l*, is the red figure. First the blue figure is reflected onto the green figure with respect to line *n*. Then the green figure is reflected onto the red figure with respect to line *l*. Two successive reflections, such as this one, are called a **composite of reflections.**

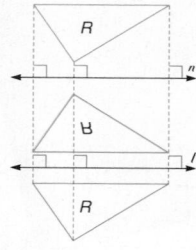

Example 1

Draw the translation image of △*ABC* with respect to the parallel lines *n* and *l*.

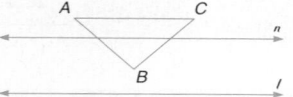

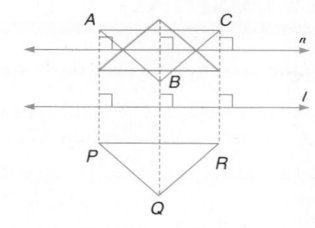

First draw the reflection image of △*ABC* with respect to line *n*. Then draw the reflection image of that figure with respect to line *l*. Thus, △*PQR* is the translation image of △*ABC*.

LESSON 13-6   TRANSLATIONS   653

Lesson Resources

• Reteaching Master 13-6
• Practice Master 13-6
• Enrichment Master 13-6
• Activities Master, p. 41
• Lab Manual, pp. 94-97

Transparency 13-6 contains the 5-Minute Check and a teaching aid for this lesson.

INTRODUCING THE LESSON

⏱ 5-Minute Check

(over Lesson 13-5)

Refer to the figure below. Name the reflection image with respect to line *l*.

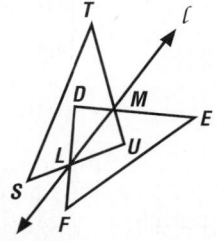

1. $\overline{ST}$ *FE*
2. *U*   *D*
3. $\overline{DM}$ $\overline{UM}$
4. $\overline{LM}$ $\overline{LM}$
5. △*MDL*   △*MUL*

Motivating the Lesson

Discuss with students what a translator does. Emphasize that a translator helps two other people communicate without changing their message. Relate this to geometric translations.

ALTERNATE TEACHING STRATEGIES

Using Models

Take a flat object that has a right side and a wrong side, such as a piece of paper or cloth. Reflect it twice to demonstrate that two reflections equal a translation.

Using Investigation

You can guide students to discover that a reflection over two parallel lines is a translation. In Investigation 17 on page A16 of **More Investigations in Geometry,** students use a mira™ and measurement to explore reflections and translations.

Chalkboard Example

For Example 1
Draw the translation image of
△*DEF* with respect to the
parallel lines *s* and *t*.

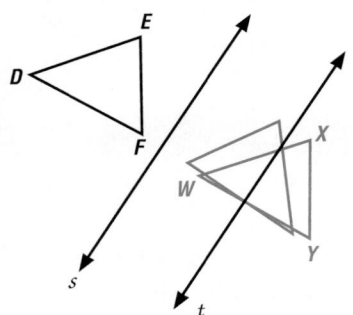

First draw the reflection
image of △*DEF* with respect
to *s*. Then draw the reflection
image of that figure with
respect to *t*. Thus, △*WXY* is
the translation image of
△*DEF*.

Teaching Tip Emphasize that for
a translation, the lines of reflection
must be parallel.

Teaching Tip When discussing
translations, emphasize that the
same properties preserved by
reflections are preserved by
translations.

EVALUATING THE LESSON

Checking for Understanding

Exercises 1-11 are designed to
help you assess students'
understanding through reading,
writing, speaking, and modeling.
You should work through
Exercises 1-3 with your students
and then monitor their work on
Exercises 4-11.

Closing the Lesson

Writing Activity Have students
write the steps needed to draw a
translation.

Since translations are composites of two reflections, all translations are
isometries, and all properties preserved by reflections are preserved by
translations. These properties include collinearity, angle and distance
measure, and betweenness of points.

Use a translation to draw a prism with triangles as bases.

1. Cut a triangle out of a piece of thin
   cardboard. Label its angles 1, 2, and 3.

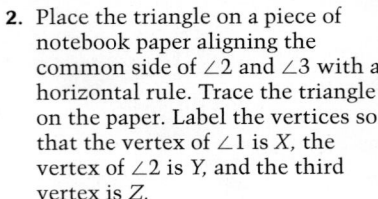

2. Place the triangle on a piece of
   notebook paper aligning the
   common side of ∠2 and ∠3 with a
   horizontal rule. Trace the triangle
   on the paper. Label the vertices so
   that the vertex of ∠1 is *X*, the
   vertex of ∠2 is *Y*, and the third
   vertex is *Z*.

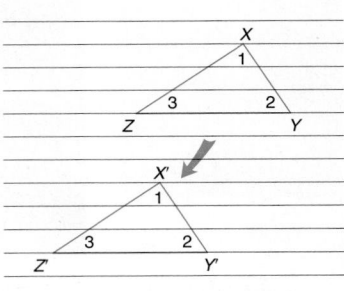

3. Now slide the cutout triangle to
   another place on the paper, making
   sure that the common side of ∠2
   and ∠3 is still aligned with a
   horizontal rule. Trace the cutout
   triangle again. Label the vertices of
   this triangle *X'*, *Y'*, and *Z'* so that
   they correspond to the vertices of
   the first triangle you drew.

   $$\triangle XYZ \rightarrow \triangle X'Y'Z'$$

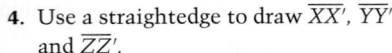
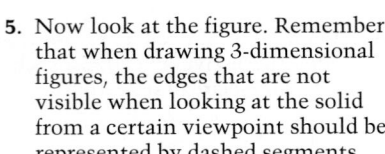

4. Use a straightedge to draw $\overline{XX'}$, $\overline{YY'}$,
   and $\overline{ZZ'}$.

5. Now look at the figure. Remember
   that when drawing 3-dimensional
   figures, the edges that are not
   visible when looking at the solid
   from a certain viewpoint should be
   represented by dashed segments.

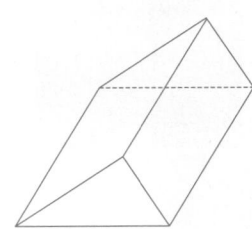

CHECKING FOR UNDERSTANDING

Communicating Mathematics

Read and study the lesson to answer these questions. See margin.

1. Emma says that the designs of wallpaper are usually examples of
   translations. Do you agree with her? Why or why not?

2. Explain why a translation is really the composite of two reflections over
   parallel lines.

3. List the properties that are preserved by translations.

654 CHAPTER 13 LOCI AND TRANSFORMATIONS

Additional Answers

1. Sample answer: Yes, the
   designs on wallpaper keep
   repeating the same pictures.
   The pictures are usually
   translations of each other.
2. In the first reflection, the
   picture is flipped. In the
   second reflection, the picture
   is flipped again, putting the
   image in the same orientation
   as the original picture. The
   second image is a translation
   image of the original picture.
3. collinearity, angle and
   distance measure, and
   betweenness of points

Guided Practice

For each of the following, lines ℓ and m are parallel. Determine whether each red figure is a translation image of the blue figure. Write *yes* or *no*. Then explain your answer.

4.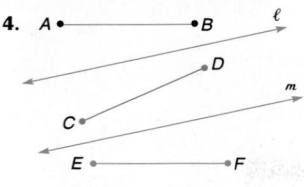

yes

5.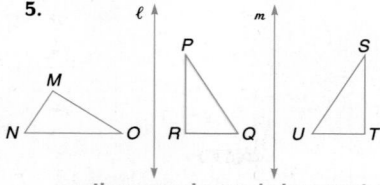

no, the green image is incorrect

6. Name the reflection of $\overline{AB}$ with respect to line ℓ. If there is none, write *none*. $\overline{CD}$

7. Name the reflection of $\triangle MNO$ with respect to line ℓ. If there is none, write *none*. none

8. Name the reflection of $\overline{AB}$ with respect to line m. If there is none, write *none*. none

9. Name the reflection of $\triangle MNO$ with respect to line m. If there is none, write *none*. none

Copy each figure. Then find the translation image of each geometric figure with respect to the parallel lines m and ℓ. See margin.

10.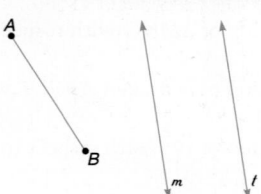

11.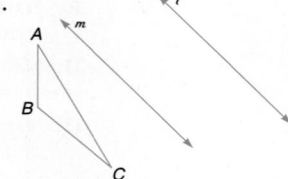

EXERCISES

Practice

A

In the figure below, lines m and n are parallel. For each of the following, name the reflection image with respect to the given line.

12. A, m B 13. F, m F 14. E, m G

15. B, n C 16. H, n H 17. G, n P

18. A, n D 19. F, n Q 20. E, n R

For each of the following, name the translation image with respect to line m, then line n.

21. A C   22. F Q   23. E P

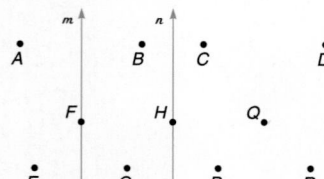

LESSON 13-6 TRANSLATIONS 655

APPLYING THE LESSON

Homework Exercises

Assignment Guide

Basic: 12-39, 48-49, 52-59
Average: 12, 13-19 odd, 21-43, 48, 50-51, 53-59
Enriched: 12-22 even, 23, 25-27, 29-31, 33-48, 51-59

Additional Answers

10.

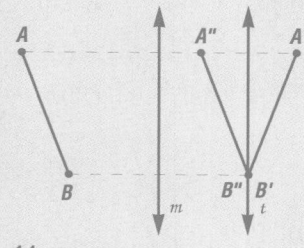

11.

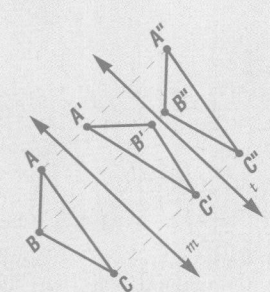

Chapter 13 655

36.

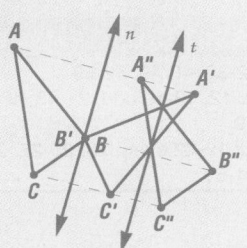

37.

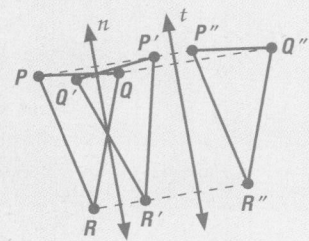

38.

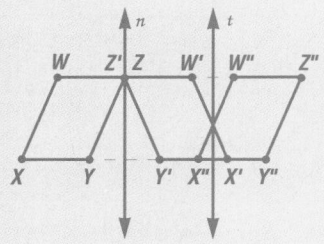

Reteaching Masters Booklet, p. 82

 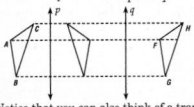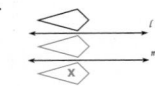
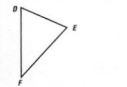 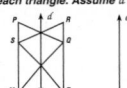

B For each of the following, lines ℓ and *m* are parallel. Determine whether each red figure is a translation image of the blue figure. Write *yes* or *no.* Then explain your answer.

24. 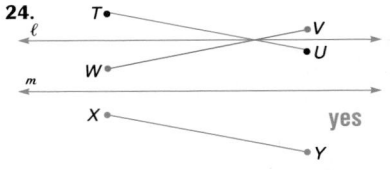 yes

25. 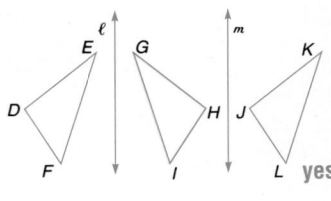 yes

26. 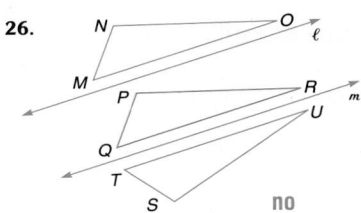 no

27. 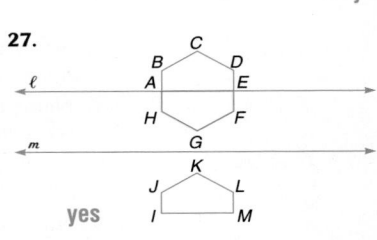 yes

28. Name the reflection of $\overline{TU}$ with respect to line ℓ. If none is drawn, write *none.* **WV**

29. Name the reflection of △DEF with respect to line ℓ. If none is drawn, write *none.* **△HGI**

30. Name the reflection of △MNO with respect to line ℓ. If none is drawn, write *none.* **none**

31. Name the reflection of pentagon ABCDE with respect to line ℓ. If none is drawn, write *none.* **pentagon AHGFE**

32. Name the reflection of $\overline{WV}$ with respect to line *m.* If none is drawn, write *none.* **XY**

33. Name the reflection of △HGI with respect to line *m.* If none is drawn, write *none.* **△JKL**

34. Name the reflection of △PQR with respect to line *m.* If none is drawn, write *none.* **△STU**

35. Name the reflection of pentagon AHGFE with respect to line *m.* If none is drawn, write *none.* **pentagon IJKLM**

Copy each figure. Then find the translation image of each geometric figure with respect to the parallel lines *n* and *ℓ.* **See margin.**

36.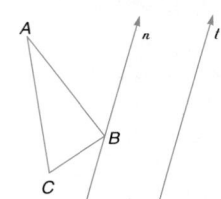

37.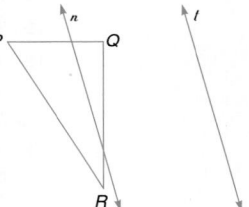

RETEACHING THE LESSON

Draw two parallel lines on the chalkboard or overhead and use a tile or a picture of a geometric object to demonstrate translations. Move the tile or object around and have students translate the figure at each location.

Additional Answer

39.

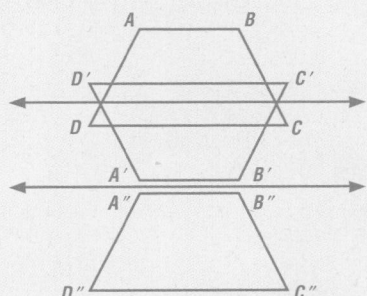

38.

39.

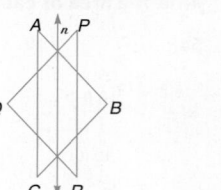

Use the figures below to name each triangle. Assume $n \parallel \ell$.

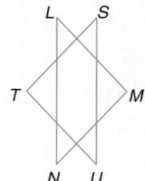

40. reflection image of $\triangle ABC$ with respect to n $\triangle PQR$

41. reflection image of $\triangle XYZ$ with respect to n $\triangle STU$

42. reflection image of $\triangle PQR$ with respect to ℓ $\triangle LMN$

43. translation image of $\triangle ABC$ with respect to n and ℓ $\triangle LMN$

44. translation image of $\triangle PQR$ with respect to n and ℓ $\triangle STU$

45. Plan a proof to show that the translation image of $\triangle ABC$ with respect to parallel lines ℓ and m preserves collinearity. **See margin.**

46. Plan a proof to show that the translation image of $\triangle ABC$ with respect to parallel lines ℓ and m preserves betweenness of points. **See margin.**

47. Plan a proof to show that the translation image of $\triangle ABC$ with respect to parallel lines ℓ and m preserves angle and distance measure. **See margin.**

Critical Thinking

48. Draw $\triangle ABC$ with coordinates $A(3, 3)$, $B(7, 6)$, and $C(9, 2)$ and $\triangle RST$ with coordinates $R(3, -7)$, $S(7, -4)$, and $T(9, -8)$. If $\triangle RST$ is the translation image of $\triangle ABC$ with respect to two parallel lines, give the equations of two possible lines. $y = 1$ and $y = -4$

See margin.

Applications

49. Art Use a translation to draw a prism with pentagons as bases.

50. Art Use a translation to draw a prism with hexagons as bases. **See margin.**

51. Environment A cloud of smoke blows 40 miles north and then 30 miles east. Make a sketch to show the translation of the smoke particles. Indicate the shortest path that would take the particles to the same position. **See margin.**

47. A translation is composed of two successive reflections over parallel lines. The first reflection with respect to line ℓ preserves angle and distance measure. The second reflection with respect to line m preserves angle and distance measure. Therefore, by transitivity, angle and distance measure is preserved from preimage to image.

49.

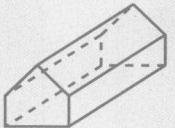

50.

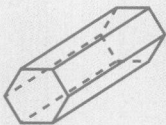

51.

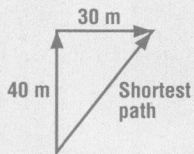

Practice Masters Booklet, p. 94

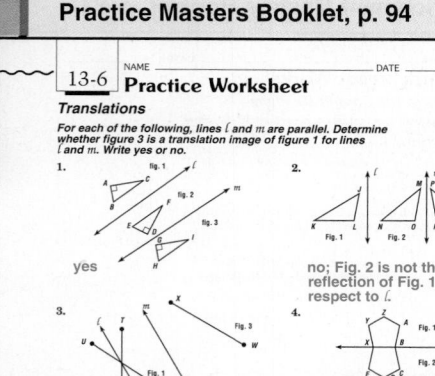

13-6 **Practice Worksheet**

Translations

For each of the following, lines ℓ and m are parallel. Determine whether figure 3 is a translation image of figure 1 for lines ℓ and m. Write yes or no.

1. yes

2. no; Fig. 2 is not the reflection of Fig. 1 with respect to ℓ.

3. yes

4. yes

For exercises 5-8, refer to the figures above.

5. Name the reflection of $\overline{ST}$ with respect to line ℓ. If none is drawn, write none. $\overline{VU}$

6. Name the reflection of $\triangle JKL$ with respect to line ℓ. In none is drawn, write none. none

7. Name the reflection of pentagon $XYZAB$ with respect to line ℓ. In none is drawn, write none. pentagon $XEDCB$

8. Name the reflection of $\overline{UV}$ with respect to line m. If none is drawn, write none. none

Find the translation image of each geometric figure with respect to the parallel lines ℓ and m.

9.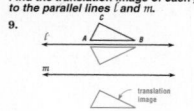

10.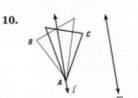

T94

Glencoe Division, Macmillan/McGraw-Hill

Additional Answers

45. A translation is composed of two successive reflections over parallel lines. The first reflection with respect to line ℓ preserves collinearity. The second reflection with respect to line m preserves collinearity. Therefore, by transitivity, collinearity is preserved from preimage to image.

46. A translation is composed of two successive reflections over parallel lines. The first reflection with respect to line ℓ preserves betweenness of points. The second reflection with respect to line m preserves betweenness of points. Therefore, by transitivity, betweenness of points is preserved from preimage to image.

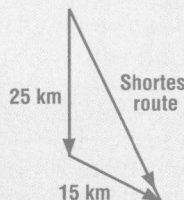
52. Environment A tidal flow of water moves 25 kilometers south and then 15 kilometers southeast. Make a sketch to show the translation of the water particles. Indicate the shortest route that would take the water particles to the same position. **See margin.**

Mixed Review

53. Copy the letters at the right. Draw all possible lines of symmetry. If none exist, write *none*. **(Lesson 13-5)**

Find the area of each figure. (Lessons 10-4, 10-5, and 10-6)

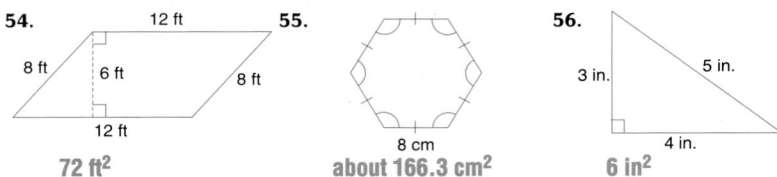

54.   12 ft

8 ft   6 ft

12 ft

72 ft²

55.

8 ft

8 cm

about 166.3 cm²

56.

5 in.

3 in.

4 in.

6 in²

57. The vertices of △PQR have coordinates P(6, 4), Q(8, -2), and R(0, -1). Which angle of the triangle has the greatest measure? **(Lesson 5-5)** ∠P

58. An isosceles triangle has a vertex angle measuring 67°. What are the measures of the base angles? **(Lesson 4-7)** **56.5**

Wrap-Up

59. Journal Entry Draw a simple figure and two parallel lines. Draw the translation image of your drawing with respect to the two lines. **See students' work.**

DEVELOPING REASONING SKILLS

One of the curiosities of geometry is the *Möbius Strip*. To construct one, cut a long strip of paper as shown at the right. Your strip of paper has two surfaces. If it is laying flat on your desk, one is facing you and the other is facing the desk. Now, give the strip of paper a half-twist and glue or tape the ends together. Corner *C* should match to corner *B*, and corner *D* should match to corner *A*. Your Möbius Strip should look like the one at the right.

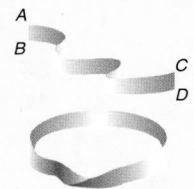

A Möbius Strip has only one surface. Prove it to yourself by drawing a straight line down the center of the strip. If your pencil returns to the same point, you have only one surface. Now cut along the pencil line. What happens? **You get two intertwining strips each with two surfaces.**

EXTENDING THE LESSON

Math Power: Problem Solving

Translate an object twice, once through one pair of parallel lines and then through a different pair of parallel lines intersecting the first pair. What do you notice about the object?   It is slid and rotated.

Developing Reasoning Skills

The Developing Reasoning Skills feature offers students a chance to enhance their understanding of geometry and its applications. You may want students to further research the Möbius Strip.

Objective
13-7

After studying this lesson, you should be able to:
- name and draw rotation images of figures with respect to intersecting lines.

So far you have studied two types of geometric transformations: reflections and translations. A third transformation is illustrated by the triangles at the right. The blue triangle is reflected onto the green triangle with respect to line *n*. Then the green triangle is reflected onto the red triangle with respect to line *l*.

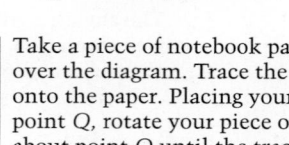

INVESTIGATION

Take a piece of notebook paper and place it over the diagram. Trace the blue triangle onto the paper. Placing your pencil point at point *Q*, rotate your piece of notebook paper about point *Q* until the tracing of the blue triangle coincides with the red triangle.

Since rotations are composites of two reflections, all properties preserved by reflections are preserved by rotations. A rotation is an isometry.

The composite of two reflections with respect to two intersecting lines is a transformation called a **rotation.** In the illustration, the red figure is the rotation image of the blue figure with respect to lines *n* and *l*. *Q*, the intersection of the two lines, is called the **center of rotation.**

Example 1

Suppose lines *n* and *l* intersect and $\triangle ABC$ is on one side of *n* and *l*. Draw the rotation image of $\triangle ABC$ with respect to *n* and then *l*.

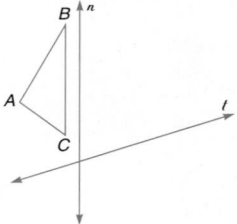

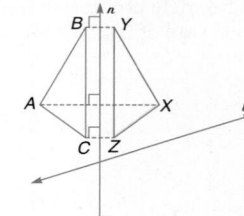

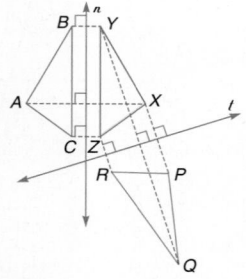

$\triangle ABC$ is on one side of *l* and *n*.

First reflect $\triangle ABC$ with respect to *n*. The image is $\triangle XYZ$.

Then reflect $\triangle XYZ$ with respect to *l*. The image is $\triangle PQR$.

Thus $\triangle PQR$ is the rotation image of $\triangle ABC$ with respect to *n* and *l*.

ALTERNATE TEACHING STRATEGIES

Using Investigation

Complete the investigation on page 659. Emphasize that there is no other center of rotation for this example. After the initial investigation, reflect the green triangle with respect to *t* and then *n*. Is the rotation image the same?   **no**

Using Experimentation

Have students trace the diagram for the investigation on page 659, then fold the paper along line *n* and along line *t*. What do they notice about the figure?   **All three triangles overlap.** Explain that this demonstrates that a rotation is actually two reflections.

13-7 Lesson Notes

Lesson Resources
- Reteaching Master 13-7
- Practice Master 13-7
- Enrichment Master 13-7
- Evaluation Master, p. 178

Transparency 13-7 contains the 5-Minute Check and a teaching aid for this lesson.

INTRODUCING THE LESSON

5-Minute Check
(over Lesson 13-6)

Refer to the figure below to name each segment. $x \parallel y$.

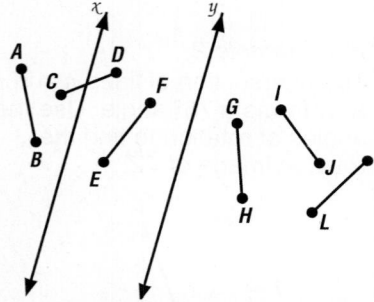

1. reflection of $\overline{FE}$ with respect to y $\overline{GH}$
2. reflection of $\overline{CD}$ with respect to y $\overline{IJ}$
3. reflection of $\overline{AB}$ with respect to x $\overline{FE}$
4. reflection of $\overline{AB}$ with respect to y $\overline{KL}$
5. reflection of $\overline{AB}$ with respect to x and y $\overline{GH}$

Motivating the Lesson

Draw a two-dimensional figure on a stiff piece of paper. Poke the tip of a pencil through the paper. Spin the paper while holding the pencil. Explain that you are rotating the figure.

Chalkboard Examples

For Example 1
Suppose *t* and *s* intersect and △*ABC* is on one side of *t* and *s*. Draw the rotation image of △*ABC* with respect to *t* and then *s*.

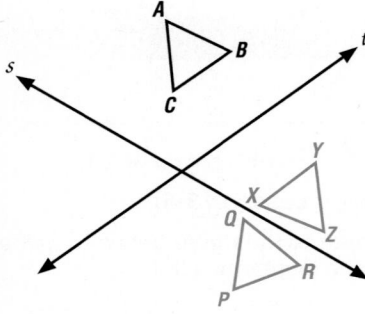

For Example 2
The intersection of lines *a* and *b* at *Q* forms a 75° angle. Use the angles of rotation to find the rotation image of $\overline{TZ}$.

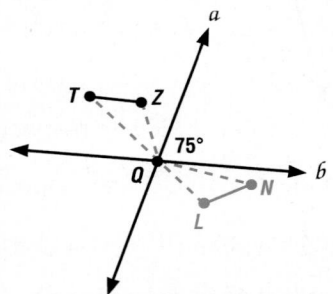

The angle of rotation has a measure of 2(75) or 150. Construct ∠*TQN* such that its measure is 150 and $\overline{TQ} \cong \overline{QN}$. Then construct ∠*ZQL* so that its measure is 150 and $\overline{ZQ} \cong \overline{QL}$. The rotation image of $\overline{TZ}$ is $\overline{NL}$.

Teaching Tip When defining rotation, rotating with respect to *t* and then *s* is not the same as rotating with respect to *s* and then *t*.

Teaching Tip Emphasize that for a rotation the two lines must intersect.

The figure at the right shows how two reflections can be used to find the rotation image of $\overline{AB}$ with respect to lines *ℓ* and *m*. The image is $\overline{PQ}$.

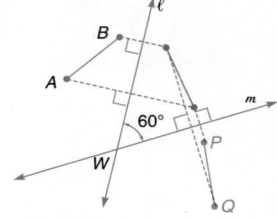

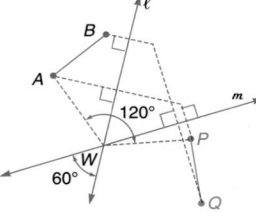

The same rotation image can be determined by using angles. Notice that lines *ℓ* and *m* form a 60° angle. It can be shown that m∠*AWP* = 2(60) or 120. Also, $\overline{AW} \cong \overline{WP}$. Likewise, it can be shown that if segments are drawn from *B* to *W* and from *Q* to *W*, then m∠*BWQ* = 120 and $\overline{BW} \cong \overline{WQ}$.

The angles, ∠*AWP* and ∠*BWQ*, are called **angles of rotation.** In both cases, the measure of the angles is 2(60) or 120.

Postulate 13-1	**In a given rotation, if *A* is the preimage, *P* is the image, and *W* is the center of rotation, then the measure of the angle of rotation, ∠*AWP*, equals twice the measure of the angle formed by intersecting lines of reflection.**

Example 2

The intersection of lines *ℓ* and *m* at *P* forms a 40° angle. Use the angles of rotation to find the rotation image of $\overline{XY}$.

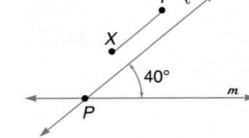

The angle of rotation has a measure of 2(40) or 80.

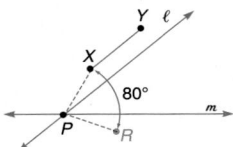

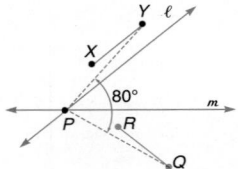

Construct ∠*XPR* so that its measure is 80 and $\overline{XP} \cong \overline{PR}$. Then construct ∠*YPQ* so that its measure is 80 and $\overline{YP} \cong \overline{PQ}$. The rotation image of $\overline{XY}$ is $\overline{RQ}$.

660 CHAPTER 13 LOCI AND TRANSFORMATIONS

Example 3

APPLICATION

Manufacturing

Rex designs paddle fans for Functional Fans Inc. He designs one fan with 5 paddles. What is the measure of the angle of rotation if paddle *A* moves to the position of paddle *B*?

The fan has 5 paddles evenly spaced around the center. Since there are 360° in a complete rotation, the measure of the angle of rotation is 360 ÷ 5 or 72.

CHECKING FOR UNDERSTANDING

Communicating Mathematics

Read and study the lesson to answer these questions. See margin.

1. When is the composite of two line reflections a translation?
2. When is the composite of two line reflections a rotation?
3. Describe the relationship between the measure of the angle between the intersecting lines of reflection and the measure of the angle of rotation.
4. Describe two techniques you can use to locate a rotation image with respect to two intersecting lines.

Guided Practice

5. quadrilateral *EFCD*
6. quadrilateral *JKHG*
7. quadrilateral *HGJK*
8. quadrilateral *CDEF*
9. quadrilateral *CDAB*

Use the figure to answer each problem.

5. Find the reflection image of quadrilateral *ABCD* with respect to line *m*.
6. Find the reflection image of quadrilateral *CDEF* with respect to line *ℓ*.
7. Find the rotation image of quadrilateral *ABCD* with respect to lines *m* and *ℓ*.
8. Find the reflection image of quadrilateral *JKHG* with respect to line *ℓ*.
9. Find the rotation image of quadrilateral *JKHG* with respect to lines *ℓ* and *m*.
10. Find the measure of ∠*APH*. **140**
11. Find the measure of ∠*BPG*. **140**
12. Find the measure of ∠*CPJ*. **140**
13. Find the measure of ∠*DPK*. **140**
14. Find the reflection image of *C* with respect to line *m*. **C**
15. Find the rotation image of $\overline{BD}$ with respect to lines *m* and *ℓ*. $\overline{GK}$

LESSON 13-7 ROTATIONS 661

Additional Answers

1. when the lines are parallel
2. when the lines are intersecting
3. The measure of the angle of rotation is twice the measure of the angle between the intersecting lines.

4. You can find the reflection image with respect to the first line and then the reflection image of that image with respect to the second line. You could also draw angles of rotation to find the rotation image.

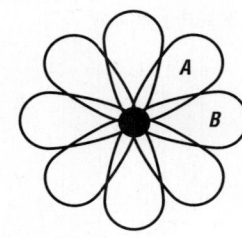

16.

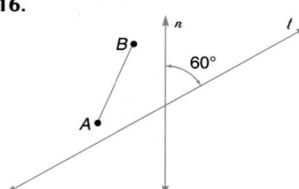

17.

APPLYING THE LESSON

Homework Exercises

Assignment Guide

Basic: 18-33, 40, 42, 44-49
Average: 19-23 odd, 24-36, 40, 43-49
Enriched: 18-28 even, 30-41, 44-49

Additional Answers

16.

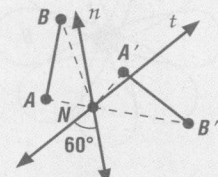

17.

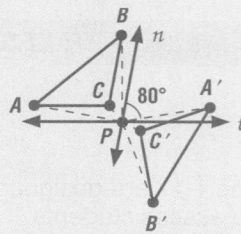

18-19. In both cases, there are proper successive reflections with respect to two intersecting lines.

Reteaching Masters Booklet, p. 83

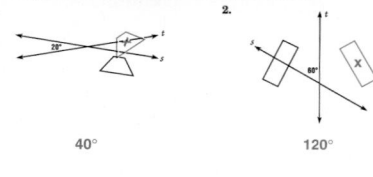

EXERCISES

Practice

For each of the following, determine whether the indicated composition of reflections is a rotation. Explain your answer. **See margin for explanations.**

18.

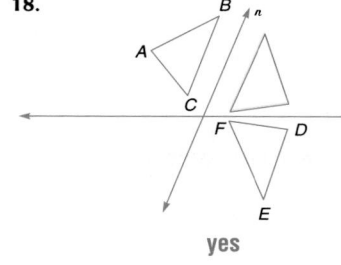

yes

19.

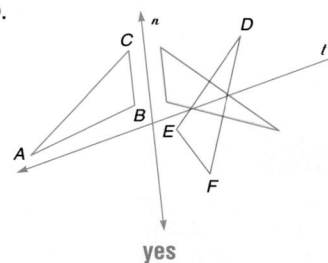

yes

Two lines intersect to form an angle with the following measure. Find the measure of each angle of rotation.

20. 30° 60°   **21.** 45° 90°   **22.** 60° 120°   **23.** 37° 74°

Determine whether each of the following is preserved by a rotation. Write *yes* or *no.*

24. collinearity **yes**

25. betweenness of points **yes**

26. angle measure **yes**

27. distance measure **yes**

B

28. Draw a segment and two intersecting lines. Find the rotation image of the segment with respect to the two intersecting lines. **See margin.**

29. Draw a triangle and two intersecting lines. Find the rotation image of the triangle with respect to the two intersecting lines. **See margin.**

662   CHAPTER 13   LOCI AND TRANSFORMATIONS

RETEACHING THE LESSON

Draw two intersecting lines on the chalkboard or overhead, and draw a geometric figure in the area where the angle formed by the intersecting lines is greater than 90°. Have students tell you how to rotate the figure and follow their instructions as you complete the exercise.

Additional Answer
28. Sample answer:

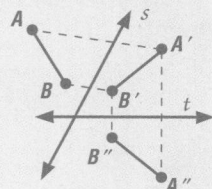

Copy each figure. Then use the angles of rotation to find the rotation image of each geometric figure with respect to lines ℓ and t. See margin.

30.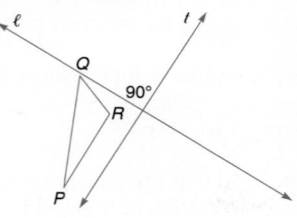

31.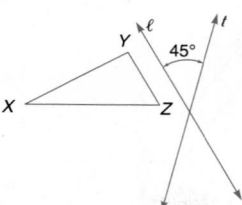

32.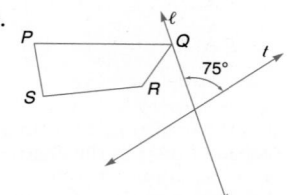

33.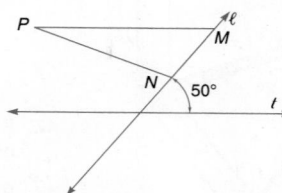

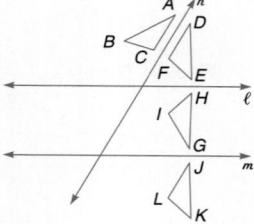

In the figure at the right, ℓ ∥ m. Name the type of transformation for each mapping.

34. △GHI → △DEF   reflection

35. △ABC → △GHI   rotation

36. △DEF → △JKL   translation

 37. Does a rotation preserve or reverse orientation? Explain.   See margin.

Hexagon ABCDEF is a regular hexagon with diagonals as drawn. Point C is the rotation image of Point A.   See margin.

38. List three sets of possible intersecting lines of reflection for this rotation.

39. What is the measure of the angle of each set of intersecting lines of reflection? Explain your answer.

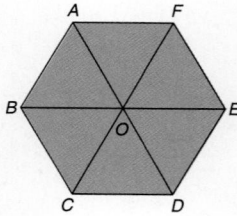

Critical Thinking   **40.** In △ABC, m∠BAC = 40. Triangle AB'C is the reflection image of △ABC and △AB'C' is the reflection image of △AB'C. How many such reflections would be necessary to map △ABC onto itself?   9

Additional Answers

29. Sample answer:

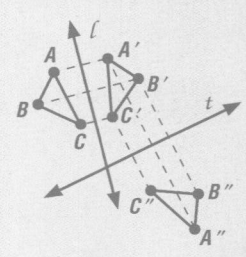

30.

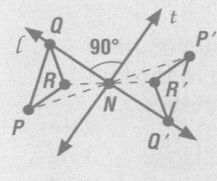

31.

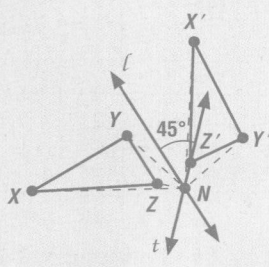

32.

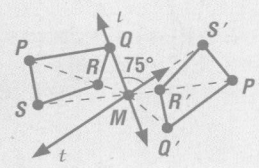

33.

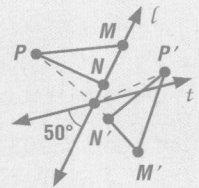

37. It preserves orientation, because if vertices are in clockwise order, the vertices of the image will be in clockwise order.

38. $\overleftrightarrow{AD}$ and $\overleftrightarrow{BE}$; $\overleftrightarrow{BE}$ and $\overleftrightarrow{CF}$; $\overleftrightarrow{CF}$ and $\overleftrightarrow{AD}$

39. m∠AOC is 120, so the measure of the angle of intersecting lines will be 60.

Practice Masters Booklet, p. 95

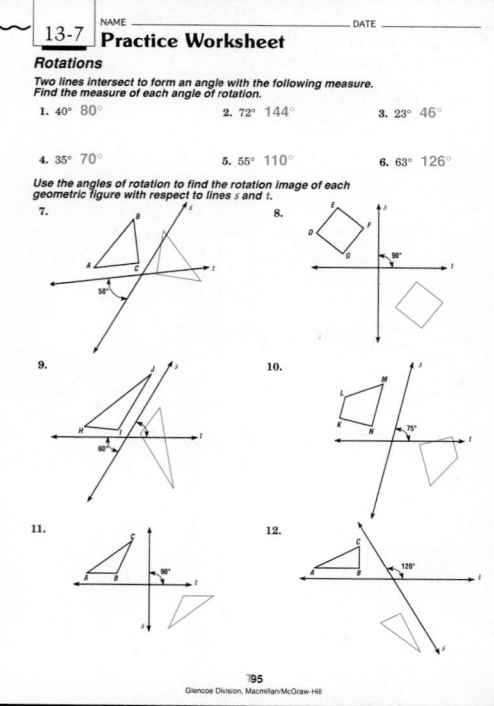

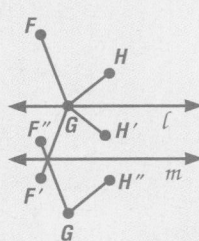
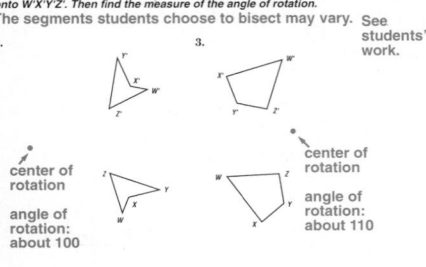
Applications

41. **Computers**   Computer design specialist Wendell Schwartz forms various solids for large machine production by rotating a 2-dimensional geometric figure about a line.

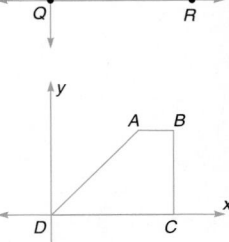

a. Describe the solid that would be formed by a rotation of △PQR about the y-axis. **right circular cone**

b. Describe the solid that Mr. Schwartz would form by a rotation of trapezoid ABCD about the y-axis. **right cylinder with hollowed out right cone**

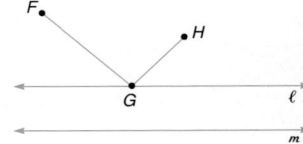

42. **Recreation**   What is the measure of the angle of rotation if seat number 1 of a 10-seat Ferris wheel moves to the position of seat number 3? **72°**

43. **Recreation**   What is the measure of the angle of rotation if seat number 1 of a 10-seat Ferris wheel moves to the position of seat number 4? **108°**

Mixed Review

44. Copy the figure at the right. Then find the translation image of the geometric figure with respect to parallel lines ℓ and m. **(Lesson 13-6) See margin.**

Find the value of x. (Lessons 9-2, 9-4, 9-6)

45.
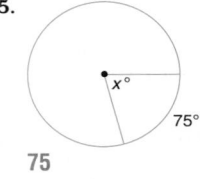
75

46.
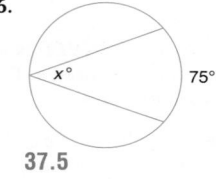
37.5

47.
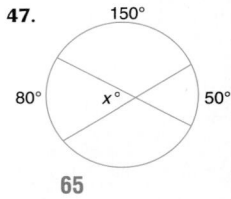
65

48. Can two angles be both complementary and supplementary? Explain. **(Lesson 1-8) no; the sum of their measures would have to be both 90 and 180**

Wrap-Up

49. Explain the difference between successive reflections with respect to two intersecting lines versus two parallel lines. **See margin.**

EXTENDING THE LESSON

Math Power: Connections

Describe the similarities and differences among reflections, translations, and rotations.
Sample answer: They are all isometries; reflections involve one line, translations involve two parallel lines, and rotations involve two intersecting lines.

13-8 Dilations

Objectives

After studying this lesson, you should be able to:

13-8A ▪ use scale factors to determine if a dilation is an enlargement, a reduction, or a congruence transformation,

13-8B ▪ find the center and scale factor for a given dilation, and

13-8C ▪ find the dilation image for a given center and scale factor.

We have already studied how translations, reflections, and rotations of geometric shapes produce figures congruent to each other. Such transformations are called isometries.

Application

A geometric figure can also be altered in size. For example the magnifying glass at the right enlarges the figure. Enlarging or reducing a figure will not change its shape. This type of transformation is called a **dilation** or a **similarity transformation**.

> **FYI···**
>
> In 1250, Roger Bacon of Oxford, England, invented the magnifying glass.

In the figure, $\triangle XYZ$ is the dilation image of $\triangle PQR$. The measure of the distance from C to a point on $\triangle XYZ$ is twice the measure of the distance from C to a point on $\triangle PQR$. For example, the following equations hold.

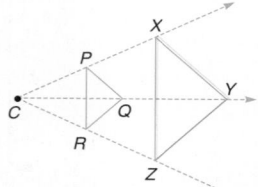

$$CX = 2(CP)$$
$$CY = 2(CQ)$$
$$CZ = 2(CR)$$

In this transformation, $\triangle PQR$ with **center** C and a **scale factor** of 2 is enlarged to $\triangle XYZ$.

This figure shows a dilation where the preimage $\overline{AB}$ is reduced to $\overline{ED}$ by a scale factor of $\frac{1}{3}$. Thus, $CE = \frac{1}{3}(CA)$. Therefore, $\frac{CE}{CA} = \frac{1}{3}$ and $\frac{CD}{CB} = \frac{1}{3}$. By proving $\triangle CAB \sim \triangle CED$, it can be shown that $ED = \frac{1}{3}(AB)$.

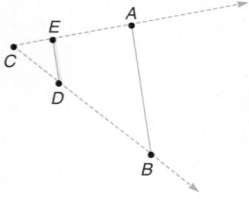

Theorem 13-1

If a dilation with center C and a scale factor k maps A onto E and B onto D, then $ED = k(AB)$. *You will be asked to prove this theorem in Exercise 57.*

LESSON 13-8 DILATIONS 665

Lesson Resources

• Reteaching Master 13-8
• Practice Master 13-8
• Enrichment Master 13-8
• Multicultural Master, p. 13

Transparency 13-8 contains the 5-Minute Check and a teaching aid for this lesson.

INTRODUCING THE LESSON

5-Minute Check
(over Lesson 13-7)

Refer to the figure below.

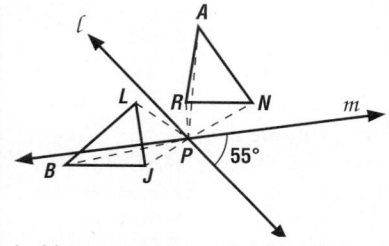

1. Name the lines of reflection. **line ℓ and line m**
2. Name the rotation image of $\triangle ARN$. $\triangle BJL$
3. Give the measure of the angle of rotation. **110**
4. Name two angles of rotation. $\angle APB, \angle NPL, \angle RPJ$

Motivating the Lesson

Bring a magnifying glass to class and ask what it does. Have students relate the image that the glass produces to a dilation.

ALTERNATE TEACHING STRATEGIES

Using Review

Review the relationships between similar triangles and relate them to similarity transformations such as dilations. Point out that the shape of the figure stays the same, the angle measures remain the same, and the lengths of corresponding segments are proportional.

Using Critical Thinking

Help students derive the statements at the top of page 666. Have them put the words together and then translate the words to symbols. Using examples will help.

Chalkboard Examples

For Example 1
Given center *C* and a scale factor of $\frac{3}{2}$, find the dilation image of $\triangle PQR$.

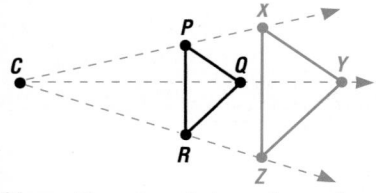

Since the absolute value of the scale factor is greater than 1, the dilation is an enlargement.
Draw $\overrightarrow{CX}$, $\overrightarrow{CY}$, and $\overrightarrow{CZ}$ so that $CX = \frac{3}{2}(CP)$, $CY = \frac{3}{2}(CQ)$, and $CZ = \frac{3}{2}(CR)$. $\triangle XYZ$ is the dilation image of $\triangle PQR$.

For Example 2
Given center *C*, $\triangle ABD$, and its dilation image $\triangle EFG$, examine $\overline{BD}$ and $\overline{FG}$. Then examine $m\angle ABD$ and $m\angle EFG$. Determine whether the measures are greater, lesser, or equal.

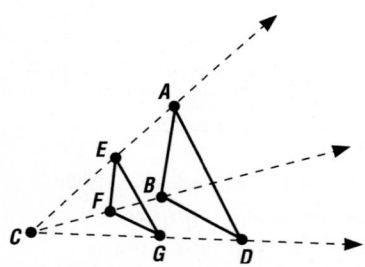

$\overline{BD}$ is reduced to $\overline{FG}$, so $FG < BD$. $m\angle ABD = m\angle EFG$. The reduction preserves angle measures but not segment measure.

Teaching Tip Point out that all aspects of similar triangles also hold true for dilation triangles.

Notice that when the scale factor is 2, the figure is enlarged. When the scale factor is $\frac{1}{3}$, the figure is reduced. In general, if *k* is the scale factor for a dilation with center *C*, then the following is true.

If k = 1, the dilation is the identity transformation. That is, each point is mapped to itself.

If $k > 0$, P', the image of point P, lies on $\overrightarrow{CP}$, and $CP' = k \cdot CP$.

If $k < 0$, P', the image of point P, lies on the ray opposite $\overrightarrow{CP}$, and $CP' = |k| \cdot CP$.   *The center of a dilation is always its own image.*

If $|k| > 1$, the dilation is an enlargement.   *The dilation is not an isometry.*

If $0 < |k| < 1$, the dilation is a reduction.   *The dilation is not an isometry.*

If $|k| = 1$, the dilation is a congruence transformation.   *The dilation is an isometry.*

Example 1

Given center *C* and a scale factor of $\frac{3}{4}$, find the dilation image of $\triangle PQR$.

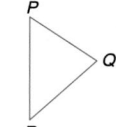

Since the absolute value of the scale factor is less than 1, the dilation is a reduction.

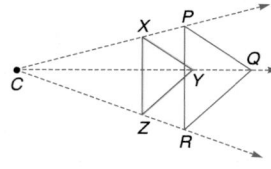

Draw $\overrightarrow{CP}$, $\overrightarrow{CQ}$, and $\overrightarrow{CR}$. Find X, Y, and Z so that $CX = \frac{3}{4}(CP)$, $CZ = \frac{3}{4}(CR)$, and $CY = \frac{3}{4}(CQ)$. $\triangle XYZ$ is the dilation image of $\triangle PQR$.

The following examples illustrate some of the basic properties of dilations.

Example 2

Given center *C*, $\angle EFG$, and its dilation image $\angle QRS$, examine *EF* and *QR*. Then examine $m\angle EFG$ and $m\angle QRS$. Determine whether the measures are greater, lesser, or equal.

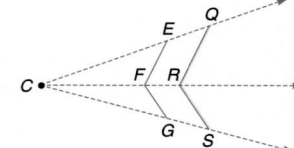

$\overline{EF}$ is enlarged to $\overline{QR}$. So, $EF < QR$.

$m\angle EFG = m\angle QRS$

The dilation preserves angle measure, but not the measure of a segment unless the scale factor is 1.

Example 3 | For each figure, a dilation with center *C* produced the figure in red. What is the scale factor for each transformation?

Count the grids to compare relative sizes.

a.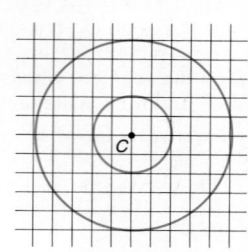

b.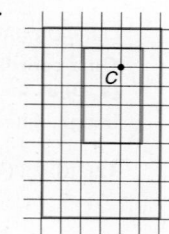

enlargement
The scale factor is $\frac{5}{2}$ or $-\frac{5}{2}$.

reduction
The scale factor is $\frac{3}{6}$ or $\frac{1}{2}$.

Since the image in Example 3a would be the same if $k = \frac{5}{2}$ or $-\frac{5}{2}$, k could be either one.

Example 4

APPLICATION
Photography

A 4-inch by 5-inch photograph is enlarged to make an 8-inch by 10-inch photograph. Find the scale factor of this enlargement.

The 4-inch side of the original photograph corresponds to the 8-inch side of the enlargement. The scale factor is $\frac{8}{4}$ or 2.
How do you know that the scale factor is 2 and not $\frac{1}{2}$?

The photograph is enlarged.

CHECKING FOR UNDERSTANDING

Communicating Mathematics

Read and study the lesson to answer these questions. **See margin.**

1. How is a dilation different from the other transformations?
2. How can you determine if a dilation is a reduction or an enlargement?
3. Is it possible to have a scale factor of 0? Explain your answer.

Guided Practice

In the figure, $\triangle XYZ$ is the dilation image of $\triangle ABC$ with a scale factor of 8. Complete.

4. If $QB = 6$, then $QY = \underline{\ ?\ }$. **48**
5. $\triangle ABC$ is $\underline{\ ?\ }$ to $\triangle XYZ$. **similar**
6. $BC \underline{\ ?\ } YZ$. **<**
7. If $YZ = 32$, then $BC = \underline{\ ?\ }$. **4**
8. If $m\angle BCA = 62$, then $m\angle YZX = \underline{\ ?\ }$. **62**

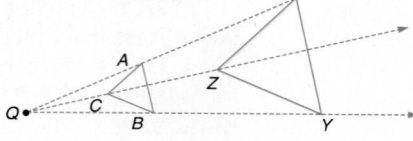

Chalkboard Examples

For Example 3
For each figure, a dilation with center *C* produced the figure in the dotted line. What is the scale factor for each transformation?

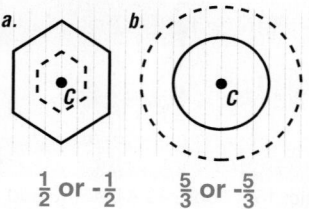

a.   b.

$\frac{1}{2}$ or $-\frac{1}{2}$ $\frac{5}{3}$ or $-\frac{5}{3}$

For Example 4
The back wheels of a tricycle have a diameter of 6 inches. The front wheel has a diameter of 10 inches. Find the scale factor used to reduce the size of the large wheel to the size of the small wheels. **The scale factor is $\frac{6}{10}$ or $\frac{3}{5}$.**

Teaching Tip   The scale factor in Example 4 is 2 and not $\frac{1}{2}$, because the picture is being enlarged.

EVALUATING THE LESSON

Checking for Understanding
Exercises 1-14 are designed to help you assess students' understanding through reading, writing, speaking, and modeling. You should work through Exercises 1-3 with your students and then monitor their work on Exercises 4-14.

Error Analysis
Figuring out whether the dilation is a reduction or an enlargement when no picture is involved may be difficult. Emphasize the importance of knowing which figure is the preimage and which the image. Review Theorem 13-1 and point out that the scale factor, *k*, is multiplied by the measures of the preimage to find the measures of the image.

Additional Answers
1. Sample answer: A dilation does not preserve distance measure, and the other transformations do.
2. If the absolute value of the scale factor is greater than 1, the dilation is an enlargement. If the absolute value of the scale factor is between 0 and 1, the dilation is a reduction.
3. Sample answer: No, all figures would have a single point, namely the center of the dilation, as dilation images.

Speaking Activity Have students state 10 scale factors that will produce an enlargement and 10 scale factors that will produce a reduction. Draw an example using each scale factor.

APPLYING THE LESSON

Homework Exercises

Assignment Guide

Basic: 15-41 odd, 43-44, 45-55 odd, 56, 58-59, 62-69
Average: 16-42 even, 43-44, 46-60 even, 62-69
Enriched: 16-42 even, 43-44, 46-56 even, 57-58, 61-69

Reteaching Masters Booklet, p. 84

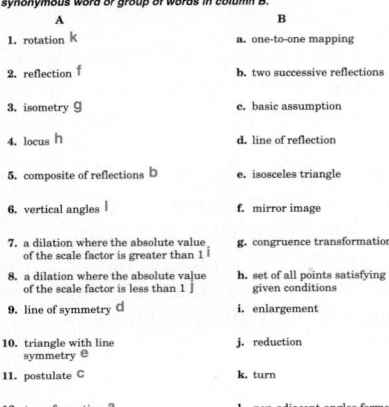

13-8 Reteaching Worksheet

Reading Geometry

A synonym is one of two or more words or expressions that have the same or nearly the same meaning. Synonyms are helpful in reading geometry because they can be used interchangeably. Sometimes a mathematical word has a synonym that is more common or easier to understand. For example, the mathematical term *translation* can be replaced by *slide*. Be careful, however, that you use a word that is truly interchangeable with it. For example, it would be wrong to use rectangle as a synonym for quadrilateral. All rectangles are quadrilaterals, but not all quadrilaterals are rectangles.

For each word or group of words in column A, find a synonymous word or group of words in column B.

A	B
1. rotation k	a. one-to-one mapping
2. reflection f	b. two successive reflections
3. isometry g	c. basic assumption
4. locus h	d. line of reflection
5. composite of reflections b	e. isosceles triangle
6. vertical angles l	f. mirror image
7. a dilation where the absolute value of the scale factor is greater than 1 i	g. congruence transformation
8. a dilation where the absolute value of the scale factor is less than 1 j	h. set of all points satisfying given conditions
9. line of symmetry d	i. enlargement
10. triangle with line symmetry e	j. reduction
11. postulate c	k. turn
12. transformation a	l. non-adjacent angles formed by two intersecting lines

T 84
Glencoe Division, Macmillan/McGraw-Hill

A dilation with center C and a scale factor k maps A onto D and B onto E. Find $|k|$ for each dilation. Then determine whether each dilation is an enlargement, a reduction, or a congruence transformation.

9. $CD = 10, CA = 5$ **10.** $CD = 6, CA = 4$ **11.** $AB = 16, DE = 4$

2; enlargement $\frac{3}{2}$; enlargement $\frac{1}{4}$; reduction

On a coordinate plane, graph the segment whose endpoints are given. Using (0, 0) as the center of dilation and for a scale factor of 2, draw the dilation image. Then repeat this using a scale factor of $-\frac{1}{2}$. **See Solutions Manual.**

12. (0, 2), (4, 0)   **13.** (3, –3), (–2, –2)   **14.** (–2, –1), (–2, –2)

EXERCISES

Practice   For each of the following scale factors, determine whether the dilation is an enlargement, reduction, or a congruence transformation.

A

15. enlargement
16. reduction
17. reduction
18. enlargement
19. reduction
20. enlargement
21. congruence
22. enlargement

15. $4\frac{2}{5}$ **16.** $\frac{3}{8}$ **17.** $\frac{1}{6}$ **18.** $-\frac{3}{2}$

19. -0.61 **20.** -7 **21.** 1 **22.** 2.5

Find the measure of the image of $\overline{AB}$ with respect to a dilation with the given scale factor.

23. $AB = 5, k = -6$ **30**   **24.** $AB = \frac{2}{3}, k = \frac{1}{2}$ **$\frac{1}{3}$**   **25.** $AB = 16, k = 1\frac{1}{2}$ **24**

26. $AB = 3.1, k = -5$ **27.** $AB = 12, k = \frac{1}{4}$ **28.** $AB = 3\frac{1}{3}, k = -9$
     15.5   **3**   **30**

For each scale factor, find the image of A with respect to a dilation with center P.

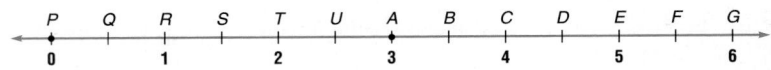

P   Q   R   S   T   U   A   B   C   D   E   F   G
0   1   2   3   4   5   6

29. 1 *A*   **30.** 2 *G*   **31.** $\frac{2}{3}$ *T*   **32.** $1\frac{1}{3}$ *C*

33. $\frac{1}{2}$ *S*   **34.** $1\frac{1}{6}$ *B*   **35.** $1\frac{5}{6}$ *F*   **36.** $1\frac{1}{2}$ *D*

37. 2; enlargement   **38.** 5; enlargement   **39.** $\frac{1}{3}$; reduction

B   A dilation with center C and a scale factor k maps A onto D and B onto E. Find $|k|$ for each dilation. Then determine whether each dilation is an enlargement, a reduction, or a congruence transformation.

37. $CE = 18, CB = 9$ **38.** $CA = 2, CD = 10$ **39.** $AB = 3, DE = 1$

40. $AB = 3, DE = 4$ **41.** $CB = 28, CE = 7$ **42.** $DE = 12, AB = 4$
   $\frac{4}{3}$; enlargement $\frac{1}{4}$; reduction   3; enlargement

668   CHAPTER 13   LOCI AND TRANSFORMATIONS

RETEACHING THE LESSON

Review the four properties that are preserved by isometries; namely, collinearity, betweenness of points, angle measure, and distance measure. Ask if any of these are not preserved by dilations. **Distance measure is not preserved except in the case where |k| = 1.** Then discuss the other methods of finding the distance measure of the dilation, using such things as scale factor.

For each figure, a dilation with center C produced the figure in red. What is the scale factor for each transformation?

43.

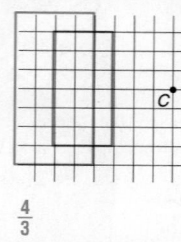

$\frac{4}{3}$

44.

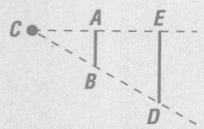

2

Draw and label a figure like the one shown at the right. Then draw the dilation image of △ABC for the given scale factor and center. **See margin.**

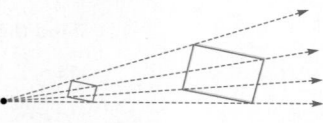

45. 3, center E   **46.** $\frac{1}{3}$, center E

47. -2, center P   **48.** $\frac{1}{2}$, center P

Graph each of the following ordered pairs. Then connect the points in order. Using (0, 0) as the center of dilation and a scale factor of 2, draw the dilation image. Then repeat this using a scale factor of $\frac{1}{2}$. **See Solutions Manual.**

49. (3, 4), (6, 10), (-3, 5)   **50.** (6, 5), (4, 5), (3, 7)
51. (-1, 4), (0, 1), (2, 3)   **52.** (1, -2), (4, -3), (6, -1)
53. (1, 2), (3, 3), (3, 5), (1, 4)   **54.** (4, 2), (-4, 6), (-6, -8), (6, -10)

 ▶

55. A dilation on a rectangle has a scale factor of 4.
   a. What is the effect of the dilation on the perimeter of the rectangle?
   b. What is the effect of the dilation on the area of the rectangle?

56. A dilation on a cube has a scale factor of 4.

   a. What is the effect of the dilation on the surface area of the cube?
   b. What is the effect of the dilation on the volume of the cube?

57. Write a paragraph proof for Theorem 13-1. **See margin.**

Critical Thinking

58. Draw △ABC with coordinates A(3, 4), B(4, 3), and C(2, 1) and △RST with coordinates R(7.5, 2.5), S(10, 0), and T(5, -5). If △RST is the dilation image of △ABC, find the coordinates of the center and the scale factor.
(0,5); $\frac{5}{2}$

55a. The perimeter of the image will be 4 times that of the preimage.

55b. The area of the image will be 16 times that of the preimage.

56a. The surface area of the image will be 16 times that of the preimage.

56b. The volume of the image will be 64 times that of the preimage.

Additional Answers

45.

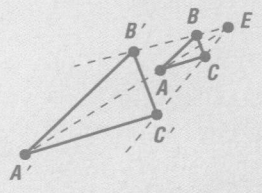

47.

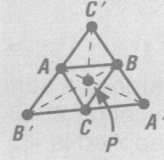

46.

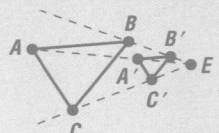

48.

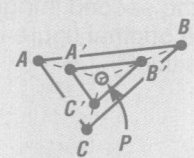

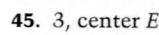

CE = k(CA) and CD = k(CB) by the definition of a dilation. $\frac{CE}{CA} = k$ and $\frac{CD}{CB} = k$.

So, $\frac{CE}{CA} = \frac{CD}{CB}$ by substitution.

∠ACB ≅ ∠ECD, since congruence of angles is reflexive. Therefore, by SAS Similarity, △ACB ~ △ECD. The corresponding sides of similar triangles are proportional, so $\frac{ED}{AB} = \frac{CE}{CA}$.

We know that $\frac{CE}{CA} = k$,

so $\frac{ED}{AB} = k$ by substitution.

Therefore, ED = k(AB) by the multiplication property of equality.

Practice Masters Booklet, p. 96

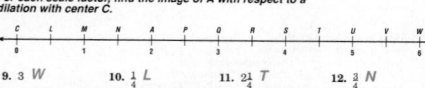

NAME _____ DATE _____

13-8 Practice Worksheet

Dilations

A dilation with center C and a scale factor k maps X onto Y. Find k for each dilation. Then determine whether each dilation is an enlargement, a reduction, or a congruence transformation.

1. CY = 15, CX = 10   **2.** CY = 2, CX = 2
   $\frac{3}{2}$; enlargement   1; congruence
3. CX = 5, CY = 2   **4.** CY = 20, CX = $\frac{1}{2}$
   $\frac{2}{5}$; reduction   40; enlargement

Find the measure of the image of $\overline{AB}$ with respect to a dilation with the given scale factor.

5. AB = 6 in., k = $-\frac{2}{3}$ 4 in.   **6.** AB = 4 in., k = 1 4 in.

7. AB = $1\frac{1}{2}$ in., k = $\frac{1}{2}$ $\frac{3}{4}$ in.   **8.** AB = 20 in., k = $-2\frac{1}{2}$ 50 in.

For each scale factor, find the image of A with respect to a dilation with center C.

9. 3 W   **10.** $\frac{1}{4}$ L   **11.** $2\frac{1}{4}$ T   **12.** $\frac{3}{4}$ N

Graph each of the following ordered pairs. Then connect the points in order. Using (0, 0) as the center of dilation and a scale factor of 2, draw the dilation image of the triangle. Then draw the dilation image using a scale factor of $\frac{1}{2}$.

13. (2, 2), (4, 6), (6, -2)   **14.** (0, 2), (-4, 2), (-4, -2)

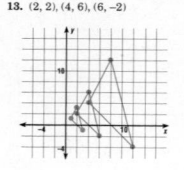

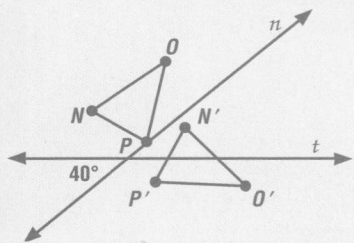
69. A dilation with a scale factor greater than 1 will be an enlargement. In other words, the image will be larger than its preimage. A dilation with scale factor between 0 and 1 will be a reduction. In other words, the image will be smaller than its preimage.

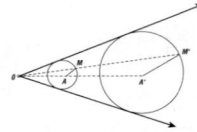
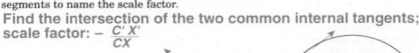
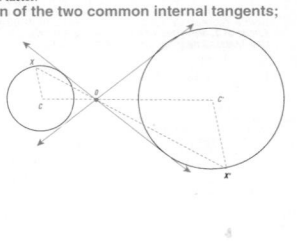
Applications

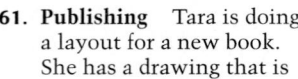
59. **Art** The picture at the right is Mauritz C. Escher's *Fish and Scales*. Explain how this piece of art relates to dilations. **Sample answer: The fish are dilations of each other.**

©1959 M.C. Escher/Cordon Art-Baarn, Holland

60. **Photography** An 8-inch by 10-inch photograph is being reduced by the scale factor of $\frac{3}{4}$. What are the dimensions of the new photograph?
    6 in. by $7\frac{1}{2}$ in.

61. **Publishing** Tara is doing a layout for a new book. She has a drawing that is 12 centimeters by 10 centimeters, but the maximum space available for the drawing is 8 centimeters by 6 centimeters. If she wants the drawing to be as large as possible in the book, what scale factor should she use to reduce the original drawing? $\frac{3}{5}$

Mixed Review

62. Copy the figure at the right. Then use the angles of rotation to find the rotation image of each geometric figure with respect to *n* and *l*. **(Lesson 13-7)**
    See margin.

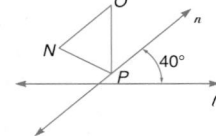

Find the value of x. (Lessons 8-1, 8-2, and 8-5)

63.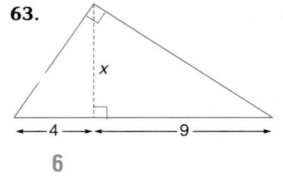
    6

64.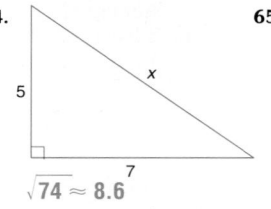
    $\sqrt{74} \approx 8.6$

65.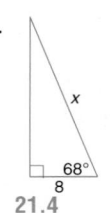
    21.4

66. Construct a rectangle with sides of 2 inches and 4 inches. **(Lesson 6-4)**
    See Solutions Manual.

67. Describe an obtuse triangle. Can a triangle with a 90° angle be an obtuse triangle? **(Lesson 4-1)** **a triangle with one obtuse angle; no**

68. Two supplementary angles have the measures $20 + 5x°$ and $x + 10°$. Find the value of x. **(Lesson 1-8)** **25**

Wrap-Up

69. Explain the difference between a dilation with a scale factor greater than 1 and a dilation with a scale factor between 0 and 1. **See margin.**

EXTENDING THE LESSON

Math Power: Reasoning

A figure undergoes a series of dilations with center at C. The first scale factor applied is -1. Then a scale factor of 2 is applied to the image. What scale factor must be applied to the second image to produce the original figure in its original position? $-\frac{1}{2}$

Problem-Solving Strategy: Make a Table

Objective
13-9

After studying this lesson, you should be able to:
- solve problems by making tables.

Application

Priscilla Adams manages The Clothes Closet. She needs to make decisions about what to order, what merchandise to display in front of the store, and who to schedule for work. Ms. Adams uses tables to help her solve some of these problems.

Example 1

Ms. Adams has five sales associates to cover the daytime hours. Rita and Tony are full-time employees and must work 5 days each week and have 2 consecutive days off. Beth, Cam, and Joshua each work 3 days a week, but Cam never works on Mondays. Ms. Adams knows that she needs 3 associates on Fridays, 4 associates on Saturdays and Sundays, and 2 associates the other days of the week. Make a work schedule for the 5 associates.

Ms. Adams starts by making a table with the days of the week across the top and the names of the associates down the right. Her job is to assign days for the associates to work and still meet all the criteria listed above. One possible solution is shown below.

Name	Sun.	Mon.	Tues.	Wed.	Thurs.	Fri.	Sat.
Rita			X	X	X	X	X
Tony	X	X			X	X	X
Beth	X			X			X
Cam	X		X			X	
Joshua	X	X					X

Ms. Adams checks her final schedule to make sure that all the criteria are met. Has Ms. Adams met all the criteria? **yes**

Sometimes tables are used to relay information to others.

Example 2

Make a table to summarize the properties preserved by the four transformations studied in this chapter.

Transformation	Collinearity	Betweenness	Angle Measure	Distance Measure	Orientation
Reflections	X	X	X	X	
Translations	X	X	X	X	X
Rotations	X	X	X	X	X
Dilations	X	X	X		X

ALTERNATE TEACHING STRATEGIES

Using Discussion

Bring in examples of tables from books, magazines, and newspapers. Use them to discuss with students the different ways that tables can be used to solve problems.

Using Cooperative Groups

Divide the class into small groups and have them use a table to organize some information about the group or the class. For example, they can make a table indicating at what time in the evening each student does homework, and perhaps compare that with a chart indicating at what time each student eats dinner.

Lesson Resources

- Practice Master 13-9
- Evaluation Master, p. 178
- Activity Master, p. 13

 Transparency 13-9 contains the 5-Minute Check and a teaching aid for this lesson.

INTRODUCING THE LESSON

 5-Minute Check

(over Lesson 13-8)

1. What type of dilation has a scale factor of $\frac{1}{3}$? **a reduction**
2. If L, M, and S are collinear with M between L and S, $LM = 4$, and $LS = 20$, find the measure of $\overline{MS}$. **16**
3. Assuming that L is the center and that $\overline{LM}$ maps to $\overline{LS}$, what is the scale factor of the dilation in Exercise 2? **5**

Motivating the Lesson

Ask students if any of them work. If they do, ask them if they have a work schedule. Have them draw a chart of a typical schedule.

TEACHING THE LESSON

Chalkboard Example

For Example 1
If Rita works Monday through Friday, how can you adjust the work schedule in Example 1 so that all the criteria are still met? **Cam must work Saturday, and Joshua must have Monday off. You can then give Cam Tuesday off and have Joshua work then instead.**

Chalkboard Example

For Example 2
Make a table to summarize the areas and perimeters of two-dimensional figures listed.

Figure	Area	Perimeter
Circle	πr^2	$2\pi r$
Square	s^2	$4s$
Rectangle	$l \cdot w$	$2l + 2w$
Triangle	$\frac{1}{2}bh$	$a + b + c$

Teaching Tip   You can also fill tables with data and use them to organize information.

EVALUATING THE LESSON

Checking for Understanding

Exercises 1-5 are designed to help you assess students' understanding through reading, writing, speaking, and modeling. You should work through Exercises 1-2 with your students and then monitor their work on Exercises 3-5.

Closing the Lesson

Writing Activity   Have each student write three situations in which tables could be used as a problem-solving strategy.

APPLYING THE LESSON

Homework Exercises

Assignment Guide
Basic: 6-14
Average: 7-15
Enriched: 8-16

Additional Answer

1. Sample answer: Making a table is a good strategy, because it helps to organize the information so you can see if all the criteria are met.

CHECKING FOR UNDERSTANDING

Communicating Mathematics

Read and study the lesson to answer these questions. See margin.

1. Is making a table a good strategy for solving Example 1? Explain your answer.

2. In this lesson, the purpose for the table in Example 1 is different than the purpose for the table in Example 2. Explain the difference.

Guided Practice

Make a table to solve each problem. See Solutions Manual.

3. Suppose that Rita in Example 1 needs a certain weekend off so she can go to her nephew's wedding. Make a possible work schedule for that week.

4. Tyron is studying for his geometry final exam. Help him to summarize the values for the sine, cosine, and tangent of a 30° angle, a 45° angle, and a 60° angle.

5. To determine a grade point average, 4 points are given for an A, 3 points for a B, 2 for a C, 1 for a D, and 0 for an F. The points for each course are multiplied by the credit value of the course to determine the total points. If each of Greg's five courses is worth one credit and he has a total of 13 points, what combinations of grades could he have?

EXERCISES

Practice

Solve. Use any strategy.

6. Nine dots are arranged as shown at the right. How many isosceles triangles can be drawn by using any three dots as the vertices of the triangle? 32

7. Find three positive integers x, y, and z such that $\frac{1}{x} + \frac{1}{y} + \frac{1}{z} = 1$. 2, 3, 6

8. To determine total bases in softball, 4 bases are given for a home run, 3 for a triple, 2 for a double, and 1 for a single. If Cathy has 15 total bases on 8 hits, what combinations of hits could she have? See margin.

9. At a recent student council meeting, 8 members were present. If each member shook hands with everyone else exactly once, how many handshakes occurred? 28

10. Bell, Thornton, Arnold, and Terri formed a band. The band has a lead guitar player, a rhythm guitar player, a keyboard player, and a drummer. Bell does not play a guitar. Arnold and the keyboard player are neighbors. Terri, the drummer, and the keyboard player like rap music. Thornton wants to learn to play the keyboard. Arnold, the drummer, and the lead guitar player are seniors. What instrument does each person play in the band? See margin.

RETEACHING THE LESSON

Bring in information on various apartment complexes in the area, and have students prepare charts of the features provided by different complexes.

Additional Answer

2. Sample answer: In the first example, the information is put into a table to help solve the problem. In the second example, the information is organized in a table for others to gain information.

The same fractal self-similarity feature we saw in the fractal bush and its natural counterpart can be seen in this cast of the veins and arteries of a child's kidney.

Child's Kidney Venous and Arterial System

The fractal structure seen in the kidney can also be seen in this majestic oak.

Oak Tree, Arastradero Preserve, Palo Alto, California

A self-similar fractal branching or tree-like structure can be seen in these photos that were taken from the Gemini IV spaceprobe that was launched on June 3, 1965.

Wadi Hadramaut, Gemini IV Image

Dawn over the Himalayas, Gemini IV Image

Heinz-Otto Peitgen, Hartmut Jurgens, and Dietmar Saupe, in their new book *Fractals for the Classroom*, describe self-similarity in the following way.

Before we open our gallery of classical fractals and discuss in some detail several of these early masterpieces, let us introduce the concept of self-similarity. It will be an underlying theme in all fractals, more pronounced in some of them and in variations in others. In a way the word self-similarity needs no explanation, and at this point we merely give an example of a natural structure with that property, a cauliflower. It is not a classical mathematical fractal, but here the meaning of self-similarity is readily revealed without any math.

Each cauliflower head contains branches or buds off a main stem. Each main stem has other stems that branch off it. The heads or flowers on these stems all look similar to each other. So they are self-similar.

Cauliflower

The Mandelbrot set is one of the most complex and beautiful mathematical pictures. Let's take a tour of its incredible boundary and its beautiful embedded self-similarity. Study the series of sequential zoom-ins of the Mandelbrot set. The rectangular window in each figure shows the region for the next zoom-in.

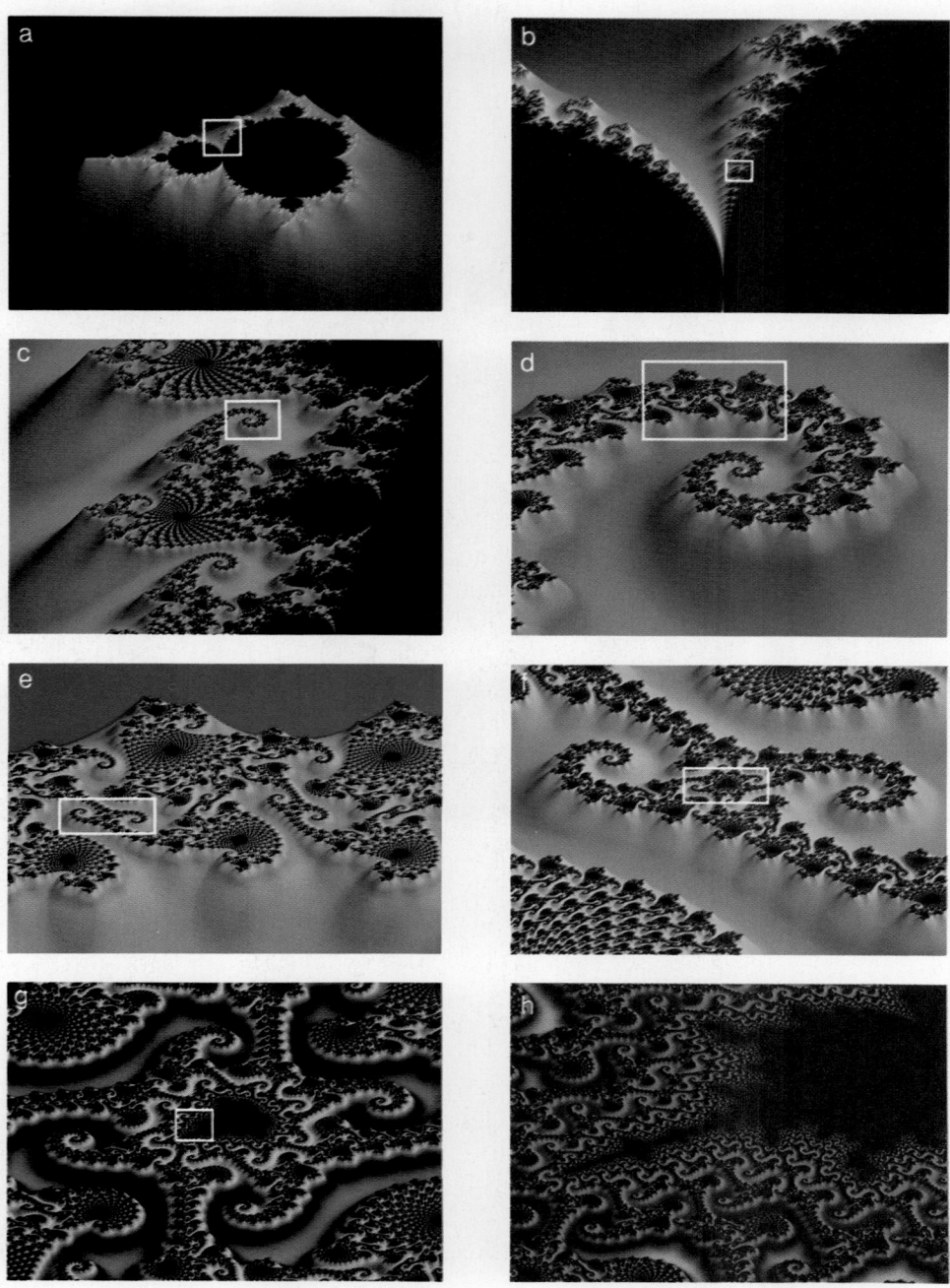

Blowups at the Boundary of the Mandelbrot Set

Study this close-up of the three-dimensional rendering of the Mandelbrot set. It is a high-resolution still picture that simulates a flight over the boundary of the Mandelbrot set.

Escalante 3D

The coloring of the rendering of the Mandelbrot set was inspired by winter scenes at Yellowstone Lake. The clouds in the background are created by a random fractal algorithm.

Yellowstone Lake

The beauty of nature may be random, but it is not without order. The field of fractal geometry is still young and there are many questions still unanswered. But, our understanding of the world around us is growing every day.

APPENDIX:
USING TABLES

A table of squares and approximate square roots and a table of values of trigonometric functions are provided for use in case a scientific calculator is not available. This guide will show you how to use the tables to find squares, square roots, and values of trigonometric functions.

Example 1

Find the square and square root of 51.

Read across the row labeled 51.

SQUARES AND APPROXIMATE SQUARE ROOTS

n	n^2	$\sqrt{n}$	n	n^2	$\sqrt{n}$
1	1	1.000	51	2601	7.141
2	4	1.414	52	2704	7.211
3	9	1.732	53	2809	7.280
4	16	2.000	54	2916	7.348
5	25	2.236	55	3025	7.416

The n^2 column shows that the square of 51 is 2601.
The $\sqrt{n}$ column shows that the square root of 51 to the nearest thousandth is 7.141.

Example 2

Find the sine, cosine, and tangent of 37° to the nearest ten thousandth.

Read across the row labeled 37°.

TRIGONOMETRIC RATIOS

Angle	sin	cos	tan	Angle	sin	cos	tan
36°	0.5878	0.8090	0.7265	81°	0.9877	0.1564	6.3138
37°	0.6018	0.7986	0.7536	82°	0.9903	0.1392	7.1154
38°	0.6157	0.7880	0.7813	83°	0.9925	0.1219	8.1443
39°	0.6293	0.7771	0.8098	84°	0.9945	0.1045	9.5144
40°	0.6428	0.7660	0.8391	85°	0.9962	0.0872	11.4301

The sin column shows that the sine of 37° is 0.6018.
The cos column shows that the cosine of 37° is 0.7986.
The tan column shows that the tangent of 37° is 0.7536.

SQUARES AND APPROXIMATE SQUARE ROOTS

n	n^2	$\sqrt{n}$	n	n^2	$\sqrt{n}$
1	1	1.000	51	2601	7.141
2	4	1.414	52	2704	7.211
3	9	1.732	53	2809	7.280
4	16	2.000	54	2916	7.348
5	25	2.236	55	3025	7.416
6	36	2.449	56	3136	7.483
7	49	2.646	57	3249	7.550
8	64	2.828	58	3364	7.616
9	81	3.000	59	3481	7.681
10	100	3.162	60	3600	7.746
11	121	3.317	61	3721	7.810
12	144	3.464	62	3844	7.874
13	169	3.606	63	3969	7.937
14	196	3.742	64	4096	8.000
15	225	3.873	65	4225	8.062
16	256	4.000	66	4356	8.124
17	289	4.123	67	4489	8.185
18	324	4.243	68	4624	8.246
19	361	4.359	69	4761	8.307
20	400	4.472	70	4900	8.367
21	441	4.583	71	5041	8.426
22	484	4.690	72	5184	8.485
23	529	4.796	73	5329	8.544
24	576	4.899	74	5476	8.602
25	625	5.000	75	5625	8.660
26	676	5.099	76	5776	8.718
27	729	5.196	77	5929	8.775
28	784	5.292	78	6084	8.832
29	841	5.385	79	6241	8.888
30	900	5.477	80	6400	8.944
31	961	5.568	81	6561	9.000
32	1024	5.657	82	6724	9.055
33	1089	5.745	83	6889	9.110
34	1156	5.831	84	7056	9.165
35	1225	5.916	85	7225	9.220
36	1296	6.000	86	7396	9.274
37	1369	6.083	87	7569	9.327
38	1444	6.164	88	7744	9.381
39	1521	6.245	89	7921	9.434
40	1600	6.325	90	8100	9.487
41	1681	6.403	91	8281	9.539
42	1764	6.481	92	8464	9.592
43	1849	6.557	93	8649	9.644
44	1936	6.633	94	8836	9.695
45	2025	6.708	95	9025	9.747
46	2116	6.782	96	9216	9.798
47	2209	6.856	97	9409	9.849
48	2304	6.928	98	9604	9.899
49	2401	7.000	99	9801	9.950
50	2500	7.071	100	10000	10.000

TRIGONOMETRIC RATIOS

Angle	sin	cos	tan	Angle	sin	cos	tan
0°	0.0000	1.0000	0.0000	45°	0.7071	0.7071	1.0000
1°	0.0175	0.9998	0.0175	46°	0.7193	0.6947	1.0355
2°	0.0349	0.9994	0.0349	47°	0.7314	0.6820	1.0724
3°	0.0523	0.9986	0.0524	48°	0.7431	0.6691	1.1106
4°	0.0698	0.9976	0.0699	49°	0.7547	0.6561	1.1504
5°	0.0872	0.9962	0.0875	50°	0.7660	0.6428	1.1918
6°	0.1045	0.9945	0.1051	51°	0.7771	0.6293	1.2349
7°	0.1219	0.9925	0.1228	52°	0.7880	0.6157	1.2799
8°	0.1392	0.9903	0.1405	53°	0.7986	0.6018	1.3270
9°	0.1564	0.9877	0.1584	54°	0.8090	0.5878	1.3764
10°	0.1736	0.9848	0.1763	55°	0.8192	0.5736	1.4281
11°	0.1908	0.9816	0.1944	56°	0.8290	0.5592	1.4826
12°	0.2079	0.9781	0.2126	57°	0.8387	0.5446	1.5399
13°	0.2250	0.9744	0.2309	58°	0.8480	0.5299	1.6003
14°	0.2419	0.9703	0.2493	59°	0.8572	0.5150	1.6643
15°	0.2588	0.9659	0.2679	60°	0.8660	0.5000	1.7321
16°	0.2756	0.9613	0.2867	61°	0.8746	0.4848	1.8040
17°	0.2924	0.9563	0.3057	62°	0.8829	0.4695	1.8807
18°	0.3090	0.9511	0.3249	63°	0.8910	0.4540	1.9626
19°	0.3256	0.9455	0.3443	64°	0.8988	0.4384	2.0503
20°	0.3420	0.9397	0.3640	65°	0.9063	0.4226	2.1445
21°	0.3584	0.9336	0.3839	66°	0.9135	0.4067	2.2460
22°	0.3746	0.9272	0.4040	67°	0.9205	0.3907	2.3559
23°	0.3907	0.9205	0.4245	68°	0.9272	0.3746	2.4751
24°	0.4067	0.9135	0.4452	69°	0.9336	0.3584	2.6051
25°	0.4226	0.9063	0.4663	70°	0.9397	0.3420	2.7475
26°	0.4384	0.8988	0.4877	71°	0.9455	0.3256	2.9042
27°	0.4540	0.8910	0.5095	72°	0.9511	0.3090	3.0777
28°	0.4695	0.8829	0.5317	73°	0.9563	0.2924	3.2709
29°	0.4848	0.8746	0.5543	74°	0.9613	0.2756	3.4874
30°	0.5000	0.8660	0.5774	75°	0.9659	0.2588	3.7321
31°	0.5150	0.8572	0.6009	76°	0.9703	0.2419	4.0108
32°	0.5299	0.8480	0.6249	77°	0.9744	0.2250	4.3315
33°	0.5446	0.8387	0.6494	78°	0.9781	0.2079	4.7046
34°	0.5592	0.8290	0.6745	79°	0.9816	0.1908	5.1446
35°	0.5736	0.8192	0.7002	80°	0.9848	0.1736	5.6713
36°	0.5878	0.8090	0.7265	81°	0.9877	0.1564	6.3138
37°	0.6018	0.7986	0.7536	82°	0.9903	0.1392	7.1154
38°	0.6157	0.7880	0.7813	83°	0.9925	0.1219	8.1443
39°	0.6293	0.7771	0.8098	84°	0.9945	0.1045	9.5144
40°	0.6428	0.7660	0.8391	85°	0.9962	0.0872	11.4301
41°	0.6561	0.7547	0.8693	86°	0.9976	0.0698	14.3007
42°	0.6691	0.7431	0.9004	87°	0.9986	0.0523	19.0811
43°	0.6820	0.7314	0.9325	88°	0.9994	0.0349	28.6363
44°	0.6947	0.7193	0.9657	89°	0.9998	0.0175	57.2900
45°	0.7071	0.7071	1.0000	90°	1.0000	0.0000	∞

POSTULATES, THEOREMS, AND COROLLARIES

If an abbreviation of a postulate, theorem, or corollary is used, it is listed after the number of the page on which the postulate, theorem, or corollary is given.

Chapter 1 The Language of Geometry

Postulate 1-1
Ruler Postulate

The points on any line can be paired with the real numbers so that, given any two points P and Q on the line, P corresponds to zero, and Q corresponds to a positive number. (24)

Postulate 1-2
Segment Addition Postulate

If Q is between P and R, then $PQ + QR = PR$.
If $PQ + QR = PR$, then Q is between P and R. (25)

Postulate 1-3
Protractor Postulate

Given $\overrightarrow{AB}$ and a number r between 0 and 180, there is exactly one ray with endpoint A, extending on each side of $\overrightarrow{AB}$, such that the measure of the angle formed is r. (38)

Postulate 1-4
Angle Addition Postulate

If R is in the interior of $\angle PQS$, then $m\angle PQR + m\angle RQS = m\angle PQS$. If $m\angle PQR + m\angle RQS = m\angle PQS$, then R is in the interior of $\angle PQS$. (39)

Chapter 2 Reasoning and Introduction to Proof

Postulate 2-1

Through any two points there is exactly one line. (77)
(Through any 2 pts. there is 1 line.)

Postulate 2-2

Through any three points not on the same line there is exactly one plane. (77) *(Through any 3 noncollinear pts. there is 1 plane.)*

Postulate 2-3

A line contains at least two points. (78) *(A line contains at least 2 pts.)*

Postulate 2-4

A plane contains at least three points not on the same line. (78) *(A plane contains at least 3 noncollinear pts.)*

Postulate 2-5

If two points lie in a plane, then the entire line containing those two points lies in that plane. (78) *(If 2 pts. are in a plane, then the line that contains them is in the plane.)*

Postulate 2-6

If two planes intersect, then their intersection is a line. (78) *(The intersection of 2 planes is a line.)*

Theorem 2-1

Congruence of segments is reflexive, symmetric, and transitive. (98) *(Congruence of segments is (reflexive/symmetric/transitive).)*

Theorem 2-2 *Supplement Theorem*	If two angles form a linear pair, then they are supplementary angles. (105) *(If 2 ⵥ form a linear pair, they are supp.)*
Theorem 2-3	Congruence of angles is reflexive, symmetric, and transitive. (106) *(Congruence of angles is (reflexive/symmetric/ transitive).)*
Theorem 2-4	Angles supplementary to the same angle or to congruent angles are congruent. (106) *(ⵥ supp. (to the same ∠/ to ≅ ⵥ) are ≅.)*
Theorem 2-5	Angles complementary to the same angle or to congruent angles are congruent. (106) *(ⵥ comp. (to the same ∠/ to congruent ⵥ) are ≅.)*
Theorem 2-6	All right angles are congruent. (107) *(All rt. ⵥ are ≅.)*
Theorem 2-7	Vertical angles are congruent. (107) *(Vertical ⵥ are ≅.)*
Theorem 2-8	Perpendicular lines intersect to form four right angles. (107) *(⊥ lines form four rt. ⵥ.)*

Chapter 3 Parallels

Postulate 3-1 *Corresponding Angles* *Postulate*	If two parallel lines are cut by a transversal, then each pair of corresponding angles are congruent. (128) *(If 2 ∥ lines are cut by a transversal, corr. ⵥ are ≅.)*
Theorem 3-1 *Alternate Interior* *Angle Theorem*	If two parallel lines are cut by a transversal, then each pair of alternate interior angles are congruent. (129) *(If 2 ∥ lines are cut by a transversal, alt. int. ⵥ are ≅.)*
Theorem 3-2 *Consecutive Interior* *Angle Theorem*	If two parallel lines are cut by a transversal, then each pair of consecutive interior angles are supplementary. (129) *(If 2 ∥ lines are cut by a transversal, consec. int. ⵥ are supp.)*
Theorem 3-3 *Alternate Exterior* *Angle Theorem*	If two parallel lines are cut by a transversal, then each pair of alternate exterior angles are congruent. (129) *(If 2 ∥ lines are cut by a transversal, alt. ext. ⵥ are ≅.)*
Theorem 3-4 *Perpendicular* *Transversal Theorem*	In a plane, if a line is perpendicular to one of two parallel lines, then it is perpendicular to the other. (130) *(In a plane, if a line is ⊥ to one of 2 ∥ lines, then it is ⊥ to the other.)*
Postulate 3-2	If two lines are cut by a transversal so that corresponding angles are congruent, then the lines are parallel. (135) *(If 2 lines are cut by a transversal and corr. ⵥ are ≅, then the lines are ∥.)*
Postulate 3-3 *Parallel Postulate*	If there is a line and a point not on the line, then there exists exactly one line through the point that is parallel to the given line. (136)
Theorem 3-5	If two lines in a plane are cut by a transversal so that a pair of alternate interior angles are congruent, then the two lines are parallel. (136) *(If 2 lines are cut by a transversal and alt. int. ⵥ are ≅, then the lines are ∥.)*

Theorem 3-6	If two lines in a plane are cut by a transversal so that a pair of consecutive interior angles is supplementary, then the lines are parallel. (136) *(If 2 lines are cut by a transversal and consec. int. ⦞ are supp., then the lines are ‖.)*
Theorem 3-7	If two lines in a plane are cut by a transversal so that a pair of alternate exterior angles is congruent, then the lines are parallel. (136) *(If 2 lines are cut by a transversal and alt. ext. ⦞ are ≅, then the lines are ‖.)*
Theorem 3-8	In a plane, if two lines are perpendicular to the same line, then they are parallel. (136) *(In a plane, if 2 lines are ⊥ to the same line, they are ‖.)*
Postulate 3-4	Two lines have the same slope if and only if they are parallel and nonvertical. (143)
Postulate 3-5	Two nonvertical lines are perpendicular if and only if the product of their slopes is -1. (143)

Chapter 4 Congruent Triangles

Theorem 4-1 *Angle Sum Theorem*	The sum of the measures of the angles of a triangle is 180. (170) *(The sum of the ⦞ in a Δ is 180.)*
Theorem 4-2 *Third Angle Theorem*	If two angles of one triangle are congruent to two angles of a second triangle, then the third angles of the triangles are congruent. (172) *(If 2 ⦞ in a Δ are ≅ to 2 ⦞ in another Δ, the third ⦞ of the Δs are ≅.)*
Theorem 4-3 *Exterior Angle Theorem*	The measure of an exterior angle of a triangle is equal to the sum of the measures of the two remote interior angles. (172) *(The measure of an ext. ∠ of a Δ = the sum of the measures of the remote int. ⦞.)*
Corollary 4-1	The acute angles of a right triangle are complementary. (173) *(The acute ⦞ of a rt. Δ are comp.)*
Corollary 4-2	There can be at most one right or obtuse angle in a triangle. (173) *(There can be at most 1 rt. or obtuse ∠ in a Δ.)*
Theorem 4-4	Congruence of triangles is reflexive, symmetric, and transitive. (178) *(Congruence of triangles is (reflexive/symmetric/transitive).)*
Postulate 4-1 *SSS Postulate*	If the sides of one triangle are congruent to the sides of a second triangle, then the triangles are congruent. (184)
Postulate 4-2 *SAS Postulate*	If two sides and the included angle of one triangle are congruent to two sides and an included angle of another triangle, then the triangles are congruent. (186)
Postulate 4-3 *ASA Postulate*	If two angles and the included side of one triangle are congruent to two angles and the included side of another triangle, the triangles are congruent. (186)

Theorem 4-5 AAS	If two angles and a non-included side of one triangle are congruent to the corresponding two angles and side of a second triangle, the two triangles are congruent. (192)
Theorem 4-6 *Isosceles Triangle* *Theorem*	If two sides of a triangle are congruent, then the angles opposite those sides are congruent. (202) *(If 2 sides of a Δ are ≅ the ∡ opp. the sides are ≅.)*
Corollary 4-3	A triangle is equilateral if and only if it is equiangular. (203) *(An (equilateral/equiangular) Δ is (equiangular/equilateral).)*
Corollary 4-4	Each angle of an equilateral triangle measures 60°. (203) *(Each ∠ of an equilateral Δ measures 60°.)*
Theorem 4-7	If two angles of a triangle are congruent, then the sides opposite those angles are congruent. (204) *(If 2 ∡ of a Δ are ≅, the sides opp. the ∡ are ≅.)*

Chapter 5 Applying Congruent Triangles

Theorem 5-1	A point on the perpendicular bisector of a segment is equidistant from the endpoints of the segment. (219) *(A pt. on the ⊥ bisector of a segment is equidistant from the endpts. of the segment.)*
Theorem 5-2	A point equidistant from the endpoints of a segment lies on the perpendicular bisector of the segment. (219) *(A pt. equidistant from the endpts. of a segment lies on the ⊥ bisector of the segment.)*
Theorem 5-3	A point on the bisector of an angle is equidistant from the sides of the angle. (219) *(A pt. on the bisector of an ∠ is equidistant from the sides of the ∠.)*
Theorem 5-4	A point in the interior of or on an angle and equidistant from the sides of an angle lies on the bisector of the angle. (219) *(A pt. in the int. of or on an ∠ and equidistant from the sides of an ∠ lies on the bisector of the ∠.)*
Theorem 5-5 LL	If the legs of one right triangle are congruent to the corresponding legs of another right triangle, then the triangles are congruent. (223)
Theorem 5-6 HA	If the hypotenuse and an acute angle of one right triangle are congruent to the hypotenuse and corresponding acute angle of another right triangle, then the two triangles are congruent. (224)
Theorem 5-7 LA	If one leg and an acute angle of one right triangle are congruent to the corresponding leg and acute angle of another right triangle, then the triangles are congruent. (225)
Postulate 5-1 HL	If the hypotenuse and a leg of one right triangle are congruent to the hypotenuse and corresponding leg of another right triangle, then the triangles are congruent. (226)

Theorem 5-8 Exterior Angle Inequality Theorem	If an angle is an exterior angle of a triangle, then its measure is greater than the measure of either of its corresponding remote interior angles. (234) *(If an ∠ is an ext. ∠ of a Δ, then its measure is greater than the measure of either of its corr. remote int. ∡.)*
Theorem 5-9	If one side of a triangle is longer than another side, then the angle opposite the longer side is greater than the angle opposite the shorter side. (240) *(If one side of a Δ is longer than another side, then the ∠ opp. the longer side is greater than the ∠ opp. the shorter side.)*
Theorem 5-10	If one angle of a triangle is greater than another angle, then the side opposite the greater angle is longer than the side opposite the lesser angle. (240) *(If one ∠ of a Δ is greater than another ∠, then the side opp. the greater ∠ is longer than the side opp. the lesser ∠.)*
Theorem 5-11	The perpendicular segment from a point to a line is the shortest segment from the point to the line. (242)
Corollary 5-1	The perpendicular segment from a point to a plane is the shortest segment from the point to the plane. (242)
Theorem 5-12 Triangle Inequality Theorem	The sum of the lengths of any two sides of a triangle is greater than the length of the third side. (246)
Theorem 5-13 SAS Inequality (Hinge Theorem)	If two sides of one triangle are congruent to two sides of another triangle, and the included angle in one triangle is greater than the included angle in the other, then the third side of the first triangle is longer than the third side in the second triangle. (252)
Theorem 5-14 SSS Inequality	If two sides of one triangle are congruent to two sides of another triangle and the third side in one triangle is longer than the third side in the other, then the angle between the pair of congruent sides in the first triangle is greater than the corresponding included angle in the second triangle. (252)

Chapter 6 Quadrilaterals

Theorem 6-1	Opposite sides of a parallelogram are congruent. (267) *(Opp. sides of a ▱ are ≅.)*
Theorem 6-2	Opposite angles of a parallelogram are congruent. (267) *(Opp. ∡ of a ▱ are ≅.)*
Theorem 6-3	Consecutive angles in a parallelogram are supplementary. (267) *(Consec. ∡ in a ▱ are supp.)*
Theorem 6-4	The diagonals of a parallelogram bisect each other. (267) *(Diagonals of a ▱ bisect each other.)*

Theorem 6-5	If both pairs of opposite sides of a quadrilateral are congruent, then the quadrilateral is a parallelogram. (275) *(If opp. sides of a quad. are ≅, it is a ▱.)*
Theorem 6-6	If one pair of opposite sides of a quadrilateral are both parallel and congruent, then the quadrilateral is a parallelogram. (276) *(If a pair of opp. sides of a quad. are ≅ and ‖, it is a ▱.)*
Theorem 6-7	If the diagonals of a quadrilateral bisect each other, then the quadrilateral is a parallelogram. (276) *(If the diagonals of a quad. bisect, it is a ▱.)*
Theorem 6-8	If both pairs of opposite angles in a quadrilateral are congruent, then the quadrilateral is a parallelogram. (276) *(If both pairs of opp. ∡ of a quad. are ≅, it is a ▱.)*
Theorem 6-9	If a parallelogram is a rectangle, then its diagonals are congruent. (282) *(If a ▱ is a rect. then its diagonals are ≅.)*
Theorem 6-10	The diagonals of a rhombus are perpendicular. (288) *(Diagonals of a rhom. are ⊥.)*
Theorem 6-11	Each diagonal of a rhombus bisects a pair of opposite angles. (288) *(Each diagonal of a rhom. bisects opp. ∡.)*
Theorem 6-12	Both pairs of base angles of an isosceles trapezoid are congruent. (294) *(Base ∡ of an iso. trap. are ≅.)*
Theorem 6-13	The diagonals of an isosceles trapezoid are congruent. (295) *(The diagonals of an isos. trap. are ≅.)*
Theorem 6-14	The median of a trapezoid is parallel to the bases and its measure is one half the sum of the measures of the bases. (295) *(Median of a trap. is ‖ to the bases. Length of median of a trap. = $\frac{1}{2}$ (sum of the lengths of bases))*

Chapter 7 Similarity

Postulate 7-1 *AA Similarity*	If two angles of one triangle are congruent to two angles of another triangle, then the triangles are similar. (329)
Theorem 7-1 *SSS Similarity*	If the measures of the corresponding sides of two triangles are proportional, then the triangles are similar. (329)
Theorem 7-2 *SAS Similarity*	If the measures of two sides of a triangle are proportional to the measures of two corresponding sides of another triangle, and the included angles are congruent, then the triangles are similar. (330)
Theorem 7-3	Similarity of triangles is reflexive, symmetric, and transitive. (331) *(Similarity of triangles is (reflexive/symmetric/ transitive).)*
Theorem 7-4 *Triangle Proportionality*	If a line is parallel to one side of a triangle and intersects the other two sides in two distinct points, then it separates these sides into segments of proportional lengths. (336)

Theorem 7-5	If a line intersects two sides of a triangle and separates the sides into corresponding segments of proportional lengths, then the line is parallel to the third side. (337)
Theorem 7-6	A segment whose endpoints are the midpoints of two sides of a triangle is parallel to the third side of the triangle and its length is one-half the length of the third side. (338)
Corollary 7-1	If three or more parallel lines intersect two transversals, then they cut off the transversals proportionally. (338)
Corollary 7-2	If three or more parallel lines cut off congruent segments on one transversal, then they cut off congruent segments on every transversal. (338)
Theorem 7-7 *Proportional* *Perimeters*	If two triangles are similar, then the perimeters are proportional to the measures of corresponding sides. (342)
Theorem 7-8	If two triangles are similar, then the measures of the corresponding altitudes are proportional to the measures of the corresponding sides. (343)
Theorem 7-9	If two triangles are similar, then the measures of the corresponding angle bisectors of the triangles are proportional to the measures of the corresponding sides. (344)
Theorem 7-10	If two triangles are similar, then the measures of corresponding medians are proportional to the measures of the corresponding sides. (344)
Theorem 7-11 *Angle Bisector* *Theorem*	An angle bisector in a triangle separates the opposite side into segments that have the same ratio as the other two sides. (345)

Chapter 8 Right Angles and Trigonometry

Theorem 8-1	If the altitude is drawn from the vertex of the right angle of a right triangle to its hypotenuse, then the two triangles formed are similar to the given triangle and to each other. (360)
Theorem 8-2	The measure of the altitude drawn from the vertex of the right angle of a right triangle to its hypotenuse is the geometric mean between the measures of the two segments of the hypotenuse. (361)
Theorem 8-3	If the altitude is drawn to the hypotenuse of a right triangle, then the measure of a leg of the triangle is the geometric mean between the measures of the hypotenuse and the segment of the hypotenuse adjacent to that leg. (362)
Theorem 8-4 *Pythagorean Theorem*	In a right triangle, the sum of the squares of the measures of the legs equals the square of the measure of the hypotenuse. (365)

Theorem 8-5 *Converse of the* *Pythagorean Theorem*	If the sum of the squares of the measures of two sides of a triangle equals the square of the measure of the longest side, then the triangle is a right triangle. (366)
Theorem 8-6	In a 45°-45°-90° triangle, the hypotenuse is $\sqrt{2}$ times as long as a leg. (371)
Theorem 8-7	In a 30°-60°-90° triangle, the hypotenuse is twice as long as the shorter leg and the longer leg is $\sqrt{3}$ times as long as the shorter leg. (372)

Chapter 9 Circles

Postulate 9-1 *Arc Addition Postulate*	The measure of an arc formed by two adjacent arcs is the sum of the measures of the two arcs. That is, if Q is a point on $\overarc{PR}$, then $m\overarc{PQ} + m\overarc{QR} = m\overarc{PR}$. (417)
Theorem 9-1	In a circle, if a diameter is perpendicular to a chord, then it bisects the chord and its arc. (422) *(In a ⊙, if a diameter is ⊥ to a chord, then it bisects the chord and its arc.)*
Theorem 9-2	In a circle or in congruent circles, two minor arcs are congruent if and only if their corresponding chords are congruent. (423) *(In a ⊙ or in ≅ ⊙s, 2 minor arcs are ≅ if and only if their corr. chords are ≅.)*
Theorem 9-3	In a circle or in congruent circles, two chords are congruent if and only if they are equidistant from the center. (424) *(In a ⊙ or in ≅ ⊙s, 2 chords are congruent if and only if they are equidistant from the center.)*
Theorem 9-4	If an angle is inscribed in a circle, then the measure of the angle equals one-half the measure of the intercepted arc. (428) *(If an ∠ is inscribed in a ⊙, then the measure of the ∠ = $\frac{1}{2}$ the measure of the intercepted arc.)*
Theorem 9-5	If two inscribed angles of a circle or congruent circles intercept congruent arcs or the same arc, then the angles are congruent. (429) *(If 2 inscribed ⧖ of a ⊙ or ≅ ⊙s intercept ≅ arcs or the same arc, then the ⧖ are ≅.)*
Theorem 9-6	If an angle is inscribed in a semicircle, then the angle is a right angle. (429) *(If an ∠ is inscribed in a semicircle, then the ∠ is a rt. ∠.)*
Theorem 9-7	If a quadrilateral is inscribed in a circle, then its opposite angles are supplementary. (430) *(If a quad. is inscribed in a ⊙, then its opp. ⧖ are supp.)*
Theorem 9-8	If a line is tangent to a circle, then it is perpendicular to the radius drawn to the point of tangency. (434)
Theorem 9-9	In a plane, if a line is perpendicular to a radius of a circle at the endpoint on the circle, then the line is a tangent of the circle. (435)

| Theorem 9-10 | If two segments from the same exterior point are tangent to a circle, then they are congruent.   (436) |
| | |

Theorem 9-10   If two segments from the same exterior point are tangent to a circle, then they are congruent.   (436)

Theorem 9-11   If a secant and a tangent intersect at the point of tangency, then the measure of each angle formed is one-half the measure of its intercepted arc.   (440)

Theorem 9-12   If two secants intersect in the interior of a circle, then the measure of an angle formed is one-half the sum of the measures of the arcs intercepted by the angle and its vertical angle.   (441)

Theorem 9-13   If two secants, a secant and a tangent, or two tangents intersect in the exterior of a circle, then the measure of the angle formed is one-half the positive difference of the measures of the intercepted arcs.   (441)

Theorem 9-14   If two chords intersect in a circle, then the products of the measures of the segments of the chords are equal.   (447)

Theorem 9-15   If two secant segments are drawn to a circle from an exterior point, then the product of the measures of one secant segment and its external secant segment is equal to the product of the measures of the other secant segment and its external secant segment.   (448)

Theorem 9-16   If a tangent segment and a secant segment are drawn to a circle from an exterior point, then the square of the measure of the tangent segment is equal to the product of the measures of the secant segment and its external secant segment.   (449)

Chapter 10 Polygons and Area

Theorem 10-1
Interior Angle
Sum Theorem

If a convex polygon has n sides and S is the sum of the measures of its angles, then $S = 180(n - 2)$.   (474)

Theorem 10-2
Exterior Angle
Sum Theorem

If a polygon is convex, then the sum of the measures of the exterior angles, one at each vertex, is 360.   (475)

Postulate 10-1   The area of a region is the sum of the areas of all of its nonoverlapping parts.   (483)

Postulate 10-2   Congruent figures have equal areas.   (489)

Postulate 10-3
Length Probability
Postulate

If a point on $\overline{AB}$ is chosen at random and C is between A and B, then the probability that the point is on $\overline{AC}$ is $\dfrac{\text{length of } \overline{AC}}{\text{length of } \overline{AB}}$.
(507)

Postulate 10-4
Area Probability
Postulate

If a point in region A is chosen at random, then the probability that the point is in region B, which is in the interior of region A, is $\dfrac{\text{area of region } B}{\text{area of region } A}$.   (508)

Chapter 12 More on Coordinate Geometry

Theorem 12-1
Slope-Intercept Form

If the equation of a line is written in the form $y = mx + b$, m is the slope of the line and b is the y-intercept.   (575)

Theorem 12-2

Given two points $A(x_1, y_1, z_1)$ and $B(x_2, y_2, z_2)$ in space, the distance between A and B is given by the following equation.
(608) $AB = \sqrt{(x_2 - x_1)^2 + (y_2 - y_1)^2 + (z_2 - z_1)^2}$

Chapter 13 Loci and Transformations

Postulate 13-1

In a given rotation, if A is the preimage, P is the image, and W is the center of rotation, then the measure of the angle of rotation, $\angle AWP$, equals twice the measure of the angle formed by intersecting lines of reflection.   (660)

Theorem 13-1

If a dilation with center C and a scale factor k maps A onto E and B onto D, then $ED = k(AB)$.   (665)

GLOSSARY

A

absolute value The absolute value of a number is the number of units that it is from zero on a number line. (24)

acute angle An acute angle is one whose degree measure is less than 90. (44)

acute triangle An acute triangle is a triangle with all acute angles. (164)

adjacent angles Two angles in the same plane are adjacent if they have a common side and a common vertex, but no interior points in common. (50)

adjacent arcs Adjacent arcs are arcs of a circle that have exactly one point in common. (417)

alternate exterior angles In the figure, transversal *t* intersects lines ℓ and *m*. ∠5 and ∠3, and ∠6 and ∠4 are alternate exterior angles. (124)

alternate interior angles In the figure, transversal *t* intersects lines ℓ and *m*. ∠1 and ∠7, and ∠2 and ∠8 are alternate interior angles. (124)

altitude of a cone The altitude of a cone is the segment from the vertex perpendicular to the base. (544)

altitude of a parallelogram An altitude of a parallelogram is any perpendicular segment between parallel sides. (484)

altitude of a prism An altitude of a prism is a segment perpendicular to the base planes with an endpoint in each plane. The length of an altitude is called the height of the prism. (536)

altitude of a pyramid The altitude of a pyramid is the segment from the vertex perpendicular to the base. (542)

altitude of a triangle A segment is an altitude of a triangle if the following conditions hold.

1. Its endpoints are a vertex of a triangle and a point on the line containing the opposite side.
2. It is perpendicular to the line containing the opposite side. (216)

angle A figure is an angle if and only if it consists of two noncollinear rays with a common endpoint. The rays are the sides of the angle. The endpoint is the vertex of the angle. An angle separates a plane into three parts, the interior of the angle, the exterior of the angle, and the angle itself. (36)

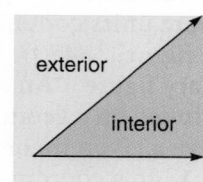

angle bisector A ray, *QS*, is the bisector of ∠PQR if S is in the interior of the angle and ∠PQS ≅ ∠RQS. (45)

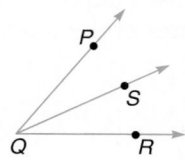

angle of depression An angle of depression is formed when a person must look down from a tower or cliff to see an object below. The angle of depression is the angle the person's line of sight forms with a horizontal line. (385)

angle of elevation When a person must look up to see an object, an angle of elevation is formed. The angle of elevation is the angle the person's line of sight forms with a horizontal line. (384)

angle of rotation The angle of rotation, ∠ABC, is determined by A, the preimage; B, the center of rotation; and C, the rotation image. (660)

apothem A segment that is drawn from the center of a regular polygon perpendicular to a side of the polygon is called an apothem. (495)

arc An arc is an unbroken part of a circle. (416)

arc measure   The degree measure of a minor arc is the degree measure of its central angle. The degree measure of a major arc is 360 minus the degree measure of its central angle. The degree measure of a semicircle is 180.   (417)

arc of a chord   A minor arc that has the same endpoints as a chord is called an arc of the chord.   (422)

area   The area of a figure is the number of square units contained in the interior of the figure.   (483)

auxiliary figure   An auxiliary figure is included on a geometric figure in order to prove a given theorem.   (170)

axis   **1.** In a coordinate plane, the *x*-axis is the horizontal number line and the *y*-axis is the vertical number line.   (8)
2. The axis of a cylinder is the segment whose endpoints are the centers of the bases.   (538)
3. The axis of a cone is the segment whose endpoints are the vertex and the center of the base.   (544)

base   **1.** In an isosceles triangle, the side opposite the vertex angle is called the base.   (165)
2. The parallel sides of a trapezoid are called bases.   (294)
3. Any side of a parallelogram can be called a base.   (484)
4. In a prism, the bases are the two faces formed by congruent polygons that lie in parallel planes.   (536)
5. In a cylinder, the bases are the two congruent circles that lie in parallel planes.   (538)
6. In a pyramid, the base is the face that does not intersect the other faces at the vertex. The base is a polygon.   (542)
7. In a cone, the base is the flat circular side.   (544)

base angle   **1.** In an isosceles triangle, either angle formed by the base and one of the legs is called a base angle.   (165)

2. In the trapezoid at the right, ∠A and ∠D, and ∠B and ∠C are pairs of base angles.   (294)

between   In the figure, point B is between A and C.   (23)

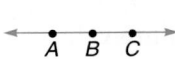

Cavalieri's Principle   If two solids have the same cross-sectional area at every level and the same height, then they have the same volume.   (555)

center of a regular polygon   A point is a center of a regular polygon if it is the common center of its inscribed and circumscribed circles.   (495)

central angle   **1.** A central angle of a circle is an angle formed by two rays coplanar with the circle. The vertex of the angle is the center of the circle.   (416)
2. An angle formed by two radii drawn to consecutive vertices of a regular polygon is called a central angle of the polygon.   (497)

chord   **1.** A chord of a circle is a segment whose endpoints are points on the circle.   (410)
2. A chord of a sphere is a segment whose endpoints are on the sphere.   (560)

circle   A figure is a circle if it is the set of all points in a plane that are a given distance from a given point in the plane, called the center. A circle separates a plane into three parts, the interior, the exterior, and the circle itself.   (410)

circumference   The circumference of a circle is the limit of the perimeter of the inscribed regular polygons as the number of sides increases.   (502)

circumscribed polygon   A polygon is circumscribed about a circle if each side of the polygon is tangent to the circle.   (436)

collinear points   Points are collinear if they lie on the same line.   (9)

common tangent   A line that is tangent to two circles that are in the same plane is called a common tangent of the two circles. A common tangent that does not intersect the segment whose endpoints are the centers of the circles is a common external tangent. A common tangent that intersects the segment whose endpoints are the centers of the circles is a common internal tangent.   (413)

compass   A compass is an instrument used to draw circles and arcs of circles.   (25)

complementary angles   Two angles are complementary if the sum of their degree measure is 90.   (52)

complete network   In graph theory, a complete network has at least one path between each pair of nodes.   (514)

composite of reflections   Two successive reflections are called a composite of reflections.   (653)

concave polygon   A polygon is concave if a line containing a side of the polygon contains a point in the interior of the polygon.   (466)

concentric circles   Concentric circles are circles that lie in the same plane and have the same center.   (418)

conclusion   In a conditional statement, the part immediately following *then* is called the conclusion.   (76)

conditional statement   A conditional statement is a statement that can be written in if-then form. The part following *if* is called the hypothesis. The part following *then* is called the conclusion. Conditional statements may be true or false.   (76)

cone   A cone may be thought of as a pyramid with a circular base. The figure at the right is a cone. It has a circular base and a vertex at *V*. (544)

congruence transformation   When a geometric figure and its transformation image are congruent, the mapping is called a congruence transformation or isometry.   (641)

congruent angles   Two angles are congruent if they have the same measurement.   (44)

congruent segments   Two segments are congruent if they have exactly the same length.   (32)

congruent triangles   Two triangles are congruent if their corresponding parts are congruent.   (177)

conjecture   A conjecture is an educated guess.   (70)

consecutive interior angles   In the figure, transversal *t* intersects lines ℓ and *m*. ∠8 and ∠1, and ∠7 and ∠2 are consecutive interior angles.   (124)

converse   The converse of a conditional statement is formed by interchanging the hypothesis and conclusion.   (77)

convex polygon   A polygon is convex if any line containing a side of the polygon does not contain a point in the interior of the polygon.   (466)

coordinate   In an ordered pair, the first component is called the *x*-coordinate and the second component is called the *y*-coordinate.   (8)

coordinate plane   A coordinate plane is a number plane formed by two perpendicular number lines that intersect at their zero points.   (8)

coordinate proof   A coordinate proof is a format used for proof. The figure is placed on a coordinate plane as an algebraic argument is used. Justification of statements is provided as needed. (595)

coplanar points   Points are coplanar if they lie in the same plane.   (14)

corollary   A statement that can be easily proven using a theorem is called a corollary of that theorem.   (173)

corresponding angles   In the figure, transversal *t* intersects lines ℓ and *m*. ∠5 and ∠1, ∠8 and ∠4, ∠6 and ∠2, and ∠7 and ∠3 are corresponding angles.   (124)

cosine   A ratio is the cosine of an acute angle of a right triangle if it is the ratio of the measure of the leg adjacent to the acute angle to the measure of the hypotenuse.   (376)

counterexample   A counterexample is an example used to show that a statement does not agree with or confirm a given idea.   (71)

cross products   Every proportion has two cross products. In the proportion $\frac{a}{b} = \frac{c}{d}$, where $b \neq 0$ and $d \neq 0$, the cross products are ad and bc. The cross products of a proportion are equal. (309)

cylinder   A cylinder is a figure whose bases are formed by congruent circles in parallel planes. The segment whose endpoints are the centers of the circles is called the axis of the cylinder. The altitude is a segment perpendicular to the base planes with an endpoint in each plane.   (538)

D

deductive reasoning   Deductive reasoning is a system of reasoning used to reach logical conclusions.   (82)

degree   A degree is one of the units of measure used in measuring angles.   (37)

degree of a node   In a network, the number of edges meeting at each node is called the degree of the node.   (513)

diagonal   A segment joining two nonconsecutive vertices of a polygon is called a diagonal of the polygon.   (266)

diameter   **1.** A diameter of a circle is a chord that contains the center of the circle.   (410)
2. A diameter of a sphere is a segment that contains the center, and whose endpoints are points on the sphere. (560)

dilation   A dilation is a transformation in which size is altered based on a center, C, and a scale factor, k. If $k > 1$, the dilation is an enlargement. If $0 < k < 1$, the dilation is a reduction. If $k = 1$, the dilation is a congruence transformation. (665)

distance   The absolute value of the difference of the coordinates of two points on a number line represents the measure of the distance between the two points.   (24)

distance between a point and a line   The distance between a point and a line is the length of the segment perpendicular to the line from the point. The measure of the distance between a line and a point on the line is zero.   (148)

distance between two parallel lines   The distance between two parallel lines is the distance between one of the lines and any point on the other line.   (149)

dot product   If $a = (x_1, y_1)$ and $b = (x_2, y_2)$, then $a \cdot b = x_1 x_2 + y_1 y_2$ is the product of a and b.   (606)

E

edge   **1.** In a polyhedra, pairs of faces intersect at line segments called edges. (468)
2. In graph theory, the path connecting two nodes is called an edge.   (512)

equiangular triangle   An equiangular triangle is a triangle with all angles congruent.   (164)

equilateral triangle   An equilateral triangle is a triangle with all sides congruent. (165)

exterior   **1.** Any point that is not on the angle or in the interior of the angle is in the exterior of the angle.   (37)
2. A point is in the exterior of a circle if the measure of the segment joining the point to the center of the circle is greater than the measure of the radius.   (411)

exterior angle   An angle is an exterior angle of a polygon if it forms a linear pair with one of the angles of the polygon. In the figure, $\angle 2$ is an exterior angle. (172)

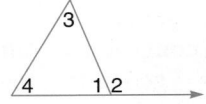

exterior angles In the figure, transversal t intersects lines ℓ and m. $\angle 5$ and $\angle 6$ are exterior angles. (124)

external secant segment An external secant segment is the part of the secant segment that is exterior to the circle. *See secant segment.* (448)

extremes In the proportion $\frac{a}{b} = \frac{c}{d}$, a and d are called the extremes. (309)

face In a polyhedra, flat surfaces formed by polygons and their interiors are called faces. (468)

fractals A fractal is a shape that is irregular or broken. (7)

geometric mean For any positive numbers a and b, x is the geometric mean between a and b if $\frac{a}{x} = \frac{x}{b}$ and x is positive. (360)

geometric probability Geometric probability involves using the principles of length and area to find the probability of an event. (507)

graph theory A representation of a real-world situation involving points that are connected. (512)

great circle If a plane intersects a sphere in more than one point and contains the center of the sphere, the intersection of the plane and the sphere is called a great circle. (561)

height The length of an altitude is called the height. (484)

hemisphere Each great circle separates a plane into two congruent parts called hemispheres. (561)

hypotenuse In a right triangle, the side opposite the right angle is called the hypotenuse. (165)

hypothesis In a conditional statement, the part immediately following *if* is called the hypothesis. (76)

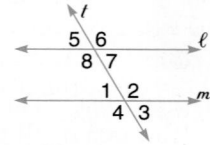

if-then statement An if-then statement is a sentence that states if something is true then something else is true. (76)

image The result of a transformation is called the image. If A is mapped onto A', then A' is called the image of A. The preimage of A' is A. (640)

incenter The center of the circle inscribed in a given triangle is called the incenter. The incenter of a triangle is the point of intersection of the angle bisectors. (436)

included angle In a triangle, the angle formed by two given sides is called the included angle. (185)

incomplete network In a graph theory, an incomplete network has at least one pair of nodes that are not connected by an edge. (514)

indirect proof The steps for writing an indirect proof are listed below.
1. Assume that the hypothesis is true and the conclusion is false.
2. Show that the assumption leads to a contradiction of the hypothesis or some other fact, such as a postulate, theorem, or corollary.
3. Point out that the assumption must be false, and therefore, the conclusion must be true. (233)

indirect reasoning In indirect reasoning, you assume the opposite of what you want to prove. Then, show that this assumption leads to a contradiction. (233)

inductive reasoning Looking at several specific situations to arrive at a conjecture is called inductive reasoning. (70)

inscribed angle   An angle is an inscribed angle if its vertex lies on a circle and its sides contain chords of the circle.   (428)

inscribed polygon   A polygon is inscribed in a circle if each of its vertices lie on the circle.   (430)

intercepted arc   An angle intercepts an arc if and only if each of the following conditions holds.
   1. The endpoints of the arc lie on the angle.
   2. All points of the arc, except the endpoints, are in the interior of the circle.
   3. Each side of the angle contains an endpoint of the arc.   (428)

intercepts method   The intercepts method is a technique for graphing a linear equation that locates the *x*- and *y*-intercepts.   (574)

interior   **1.** A point is in the interior of an angle if it does not lie on the angle itself and it lies on a segment whose endpoints are on each side of the angle.   (37)
   2. A point is in the interior of a circle if the measure of the segment joining the point to the center of the circle is less than the measure of the radius.   (411)

interior angles   In the figure, transversal *l* intersects lines ℓ and *m*. $\angle 1$, $\angle 2$, $\angle 7$, and $\angle 8$ are interior angles.   (124)

intersection   The intersection of two figures is the set of points that are in both figures.   (14)

isometry   When a geometric figure and its transformation image are congruent, the mapping is called an isometry or congruence transformation.   (641)

isosceles trapezoid   An isosceles trapezoid is a trapezoid in which the legs are congruent.   (294)

isosceles triangle   An isosceles triangle is a triangle with at least two sides congruent. The congruent sides are called legs. The angles opposite the legs are base angles. The angle formed by two legs is the vertex angle. The third side is the base.   (165)

lateral area   The lateral area of a prism is the area of all the lateral faces.   (537)

lateral edge   **1.** In a prism, lateral edges are the intersection of two adjacent lateral faces. Lateral edges are parallel segments. (536)
   2. In a pyramid, lateral edges are the edges of the lateral faces and have the vertex as an endpoint.   (542)

lateral faces   **1.** In a prism, the lateral faces are the faces that are not bases. The lateral faces are formed by parallelograms.   (536)
   2. In a pyramid lateral faces are faces that intersect at the vertex.   (542)

law of cosines   Let $\triangle ABC$ be any triangle with *a*, *b*, and *c* representing the measures of sides opposite angles with measures *A*, *B*, and *C* respectively. Then, the following equations hold true.
$$a^2 = b^2 + c^2 - 2bc \cos A$$
$$b^2 = a^2 + c^2 - 2bc \cos B$$
$$c^2 = a^2 + b^2 - 2bc \cos C \quad (394)$$

law of detachment   If $p \rightarrow q$ is a true conditional and *p* is true, then *q* is true. (82)

law of sines   Let $\triangle ABC$ be any triangle with *a*, *b*, and *c* representing the measures of sides opposite angles with measures *A*, *B*, and *C* respectively. Then, $\frac{\sin A}{a} = \frac{\sin B}{b} = \frac{\sin C}{c}$.   (389)

law of syllogism   If $p \rightarrow q$ and $q \rightarrow r$ are true conditionals then $p \rightarrow r$ is also true. (83)

leg   **1.** In a right triangle, the sides opposite the acute angles are legs.   (165)
   2. In an isosceles triangle, the congruent sides are called legs.   (165)
   3. In a trapezoid, the nonparallel sides are called legs.   (294)

line   Line is one of the basic undefined terms of geometry. Lines extend indefinitely and have no thickness or width. Lines are represented by double arrows and named by lower case script letters. A line also can be named using double arrows over capital letters representing two points on the line. (13)

linear equation   An equation is linear if it can be written in the form $Ax + By = C$, where A, B, and C are any real numbers, and A and B are not both 0.   (574)

linear pair   Two angles form a linear pair if they are adjacent and their noncommon sides are opposite rays.   (50)

line of reflection   Line ℓ is a line of reflection if it is the perpendicular bisector of the segment drawn from point X to its reflection image point A.   (644)

line of symmetry   A line of symmetry is a line that can be drawn through a plane figure so that the figure on one side is the reflection image of the figure on the opposite side.   (646)

line symmetry   A figure has line symmetry if it can be folded along the lines of symmetry and the two halves match exactly.   (202)

locus   In geometry, a figure is a locus if it is the set of all points and only those points that satisfy a given condition.   (622)

M

major arc   If $\angle APB$ is a central angle of circle P, and C is any point on the circle and in the exterior of the angle, then points A and B and all points of the circle exterior to $\angle APB$ form a major arc called ACB. Three letters are needed to name a major arc.   (416)

means   In the proportion $\frac{a}{b} = \frac{c}{d}$, b and c are called the means.   (309)

measure   **1.** The measure of $\overline{AB}$, written AB, is the distance between A and B. (23)
2. A protractor can be used to find the measure of an angle.   (37)

median   **1.** A median of a triangle is a segment that joins a vertex of the triangle and the midpoint of the side opposite the vertex.   (216)
2. The median of a trapezoid is the segment that joins the midpoints of the legs.   (295)

midpoint   A point M is the midpoint of a segment, $\overline{PQ}$, if M is between P and Q, and $PM = MQ$.   (30)

minor arc   If $\angle APB$ is a central angle of circle P, then points A and B and all points of the circle interior to the angle form a minor arc called $\overarc{AB}$.   (416)

N

net   A two-dimensional figure that when folded forms the surfaces of a three-dimensional object.   (530)

network   A network is a figure consisting of nodes and edges.   (512)

n-gon   A polygon with n sides is called an n-gon.   (467)

node   The points in graph theory are called nodes.   (512)

noncollinear points   Points are noncollinear if they do not lie on the same line.   (9)

O

oblique cone   A cone that is not a right cone is called an oblique cone.   (544)

oblique cylinder   A cylinder that is not a right cylinder is called an oblique cylinder.   (538)

oblique prism   A prism that is not a right prism is called an oblique prism.   (536)

obtuse angle   An obtuse angle is one whose degree measure is greater than 90.   (44)

obtuse triangle   An obtuse triangle is a triangle with one obtuse angle.   (164)

opposite angles of a parallelogram   In a parallelogram, any pair of nonconsecutive angles are opposite angles. Opposite angles of a parallelogram are congruent.   (267)

opposite rays $\overrightarrow{PQ}$ and $\overrightarrow{PR}$ are opposite rays if P is between Q and R.   (36)

ordered pair   An ordered pair is a pair of numbers in which the order is specified. Ordered pairs are used to locate points in a plane.   (8)

ordered triple   An ordered triple is three numbers in which the order is specific. Ordered triples are used to locate points in space.   (607)

origin   The point of intersection of the *x*-axis and *y*-axis in a coordinate plane is called the origin and named *O*.   (8)

paragraph proof   In a paragraph proof, the statements and reasons are written informally in a paragraph.   (129)

parallel lines   Two lines are parallel if they lie in the same plane and do not intersect.   (122)

parallelogram   A quadrilateral is a parallelogram if both pairs of opposite sides are parallel. Any side of a parallelogram may be called a base. For each base there is a corresponding segment called the altitude that is perpendicular to the base and has its endpoints on the lines containing the base and the opposite side.   (117)

parallelogram law   The parallelogram law is a method for adding two vectors. The two vectors with the same initial point form part of a parallelogram. The resultant or sum of the two vectors is the diagonal of the parallelogram.   (602)

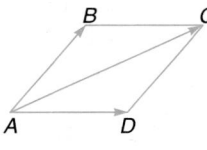

parallelpiped   A parallelpiped is a three-dimensional figure whose six faces are parallelograms.   (117)

parallel planes   Two planes are parallel if they do not intersect.   (122)

perpendicular bisector   A segment bisector is a perpendicular bisector if the bisector is perpendicular to the segment.   (218)

perpendicular lines   Two lines are perpendicular if they intersect to form a right angle.   (56)

plane   Plane is one of the basic undefined terms of geometry. Planes extend indefinitely in all directions and have no thickness. A plane is represented by a four-sided figure and is named by a capital script letter or by three points of the plane not on the same line.   (13)

Platonic solid   A Platonic solid is any one of the five regular polyhedrons: tetrahedron, hexahedron, octahedron, dodecahedron, or icosohedron.   (468)

point   Point is one of the basic undefined terms of geometry. Points have no dimension, are represented by dots, and are named by capital letters.   (13)

point of reflection   Point *S* is the reflection of point *R* with respect to point *Q*, the point of reflection, if *Q* is the midpoint of the segment drawn from *R* to *S*.   (644)

point of symmetry   A point of symmetry is the point of reflection for all points on a figure.   (646)

point of tangency   The point of the intersection of a circle and a tangent to the circle is the point of tangency.   (434)

point-slope form   The equation of a line passing through a point whose coordinates are (x_1, y_1) and that has a slope *m* is $y - y_1 = m(x - x_1)$.   (581)

polygon   A figure is a polygon if it meets each of the following conditions.
1. It is formed by three or more coplanar segments called sides.
2. Sides that have a common endpoint are noncollinear.
3. Each side intersects exactly two other sides, but only at their endpoints called vertices.   (266)

polyhedron   A solid with flat surfaces that form polygons is called a polyhedron. The flat surfaces formed by the polygons and their interiors are called faces. Pairs of faces intersect at edges. Three or more edges intersect at a vertex.   (468)

postulate   A postulate in geometry is a statement that describes a fundamental property of the basic terms. Postulates are accepted as being true.   (77)

preimage In a transformation if A is mapped onto A', then A is the preimage of A'. (640)

prism A solid with the following characteristics is a prism.
1. Two faces, called bases, are formed by congruent polygons that lie in parallel planes.
2. The faces that are not bases, called lateral faces, are formed by parallelograms.
3. The intersections of two adjacent lateral faces are called lateral edges and are parallel segments. (536)

probability Probability is a ratio or fraction that compares the chances of an event happening (or not happening) to all possible outcomes in a given situation. (507)

proof A proof is a method of constructing a valid argument. (89)

proportion A proportion is an equation of the form $\frac{a}{b} = \frac{c}{d}$ that states that two ratios are equivalent. (308)

protractor A protractor is a tool used to find the degree measure of a given angle. (37)

pyramid A solid with the following characteristics is a pyramid.
1. All the faces, except one face, intersect at a point called the vertex.
2. The face that does not intersect at the vertex is called the base and forms a polygon.
3. The faces meeting at the vertex are called lateral faces and form triangles. (542)

Pythagorean Theorem In a right triangle, the sum of the squares of the measures of the legs equals the square of the measure of the hypotenuse. (365)

Pythagorean triple This is a set of numbers that satisfy the equation $a^2 + b^2 = c^2$. (369)

quadrant One of the four regions into which two perpendicular number lines separate the plane is a quadrant. (8)

quadrilateral A four-sided polygon is called a quadrilateral. (266)

radius **1.** A radius of a circle is a segment whose endpoints are the center of the circle and a point on the circle. (410)
2. A segment is a radius of a regular polygon if it is a radius of a circle circumscribed about the polygon. (495)
3. A radius of a sphere is a segment whose endpoints are the center and a point on the sphere. (560)

rate A rate is the ratio of two measurements that may have different types of units. (315)

ratio A ratio is a comparison of two numbers using division. (308)

ray PQ is a ray if it is the set of points PQ and all points S for which Q is between P and S. (36)

rectangle A rectangle is a quadrilateral with four right angles. (282)

reflection A reflection is a transformation that flips a figure over a line called the line of reflection. *Also see lines of reflection and points of reflection.* (644)

regular polygon A polygon is regular if it is a convex polygon with all sides congruent and all angles congruent. (467)

regular polyhedron A regular polyhedron is a polyhedron in which all faces are congruent regular polygons. (468)

regular pyramid A pyramid is a regular pyramid if its base is regular, and the segment is the center of the base, and the vertex is perpendicular to the base. This segment is called the altitude. (542)

regular tessellation A tessellation is a regular tessellation if it is formed by regular polygons. (478)

remote interior angles The angles in a triangle that are not adjacent to a given exterior angle are called remote interior angles. (172)

resultant The sum of two or more vectors is called the resultant of the vectors. (602)

rhombus A quadrilateral is a rhombus if all four sides are congruent. (288)

right angle A right angle is an angle whose degree measure is 90. (44)

right circular cone A solid figure that has a circular base and an axis from the vertex that is perpendicular to the base is a right circular cone. The axis is also the altitude of the cone. (544)

right cylinder A cylinder whose axis is also an altitude of the figure is a right cylinder. (538)

right prism If the lateral edges of a prism are also altitudes, then the prism is a right prism. (536)

right triangle A right triangle is a triangle with one right angle. The side opposite the right angle is called the hypotenuse. The other two sides are called legs. (164)

rotation The composite of two reflections with respect to two intersecting lines is a transformation called a rotation. The intersection of the two lines is called the center of rotation. (621)

ruler postulate The point on any line can be paired with real numbers so that, given any two points P and Q on the line, P corresponds to zero, and Q corresponds to a positive number. (24)

scalar multiplication Multiplying a vector by a constant is called scalar multiplication. (602)

scale factor The ratio of the lengths of two corresponding sides of two similar polygons is called the scale factor. (321)

scalene triangle A scalene triangle is a triangle with no two sides congruent. (165)

scatter plot In a scatter plot, two sets of data are plotted as ordered pairs in a coordinate plane. (586)

secant A secant is a line that intersects a circle in exactly two points. (412)

secant segment A secant segment is a segment that contains a chord of a circle. The part or parts of a secant segment that are exterior to the circle are called external secant segments. (448)

sector A sector of a circle is a region bounded by a central angle and the intercepted arc. (509)

segment A segment is a part of a line that consists of two points, called endpoints, and all the points between them. (23)

segment bisector A segment bisector is a segment, line, or plane that intersects a segment at its midpoint. (31)

self-similarity If any parts of a fractal image are replicas of the entire image, the image is self-similar. (7)

semicircle A line containing the diameter of a circle separates the circle into two semicircles. (416)

side 1. The sides of an angle are the two rays that form the angle. (36)
2. Any segment that forms part of a polygon is a side of the polygon. (164)

similar figures Figures that have the same shape but that may differ in size are called similar figures. (7)

similarity transformation When a geometric figure and its transformation image are similar, the mapping is called a similarity transformation. (641)

similar polygons Two polygons are similar if there is a correspondence such that their corresponding angles are congruent and the measures of their corresponding sides are proportional. (321)

sine A ratio is the sine of an acute angle of a right triangle if it is the ratio of the measure of the leg opposite the acute angle to the measure of the hypotenuse. (376)

skew lines Two lines are skew if they do not intersect and are not in the same plane. (123)

slant height 1. In a regular pyramid, the slant height is the height of a lateral face. (542)
2. In a right circular cone, the slant height is the measure of any segment joining the vertex to the edge of the circular base. (544)

slope The slope of a line containing two points with coordinates (x_1, y_1) and (x_2, y_2) is given by the following formula.

$$m = \frac{y_2 - y_1}{x_2 - x_1} \text{ where } x_2 \neq x_1. \quad (142)$$

slope-intercept form The equation of the line having a slope m and y-intercept b is $y = mx + b$. (575)

solid A solid is a three-dimensional figure consisting of all of its surface points and all of its interior points. (529)

solving the triangle Finding the measures of all the angles and sides of a triangle is called solving the triangle. (389)

space Space is the set of all points. (14)

sphere In space, a figure is a sphere if it is the set of all points that are a given distance from a given point, called the center. (560)

spreadsheets Spreadsheets are computer programs designed especially for creating charts involving many calculations. (501)

square A square is a quadrilateral with four right angles and four congruent sides. (289)

standard form The standard form of a linear equation is $Ax + By = C$. (574)

straight angle A straight angle is one whose degree measure is 180. (37)

straightedge Any instrument used as a guide to draw a line is a straightedge. (25)

supplementary angles Two angles are supplementary if the sum of their degree measures is 180. (51)

surface area The sum of the areas of the faces of a solid figure is the surface area. (529)

system of equations A set of equations with the same variables is a system of equations. (629)

tangent **1.** A ratio is the tangent of an acute angle of a right triangle if it is the ratio of the measure of the leg opposite the acute angle to the measure of the leg adjacent to the acute angle. (376)

2. A tangent is a line in a plane that intersects a circle in the plane in exactly one point. The point of intersection is the point of tangency. (412)

3. A tangent to a sphere is a line that intersects the sphere in exactly one point. (560)

tangent segment A tangent segment is a segment that intersects a circle in exactly one point and lies on a tangent. (436)

tessellation Tiled patterns formed by repeating shapes to fill a plane without gaps or overlaps are tessellations. (478)

theorem A theorem is a statement that must be proven before it is accepted as true. (98)

traceability A network is traceable if it can be traced in one continuous path without retracting any edge. This can be done if the graph has modes with even degrees or the graph has exactly two nodes with odd degrees. (512)

transformation In a plane, a mapping is a transformation if each point has exactly one image point and each image point has exactly one preimage point. (621)

translation A composite of two reflections over two parallel lines is a translation. A translation is also the result of sliding a given figure a given distance. (653)

transversal A line that intersects two or more lines in a plane at different points is a transversal. (124)

trapezoid A quadrilateral is a trapezoid if it has exactly one pair of parallel sides. The parallel sides of a trapezoid are called bases. The nonparallel sides are called legs. The angles formed by bases and the legs are called base angles. The line segment joining the midpoints of the legs of a trapezoid is called the median. The altitude is a segment perpendicular to both bases with its endpoints on the bases. (294)

triangle A triangle is a figure formed by three noncollinear segments called sides. Each endpoint of a side is an endpoint of exactly one other side. The endpoints are the vertices of the triangle. A triangle separates a plane into three parts, the triangle, its interior, and its exterior. (164)

trigonometric ratio   A ratio of the measures of two sides of a regular triangle is called a trigonometric ratio. Trigonometry means triangle measurement.   (376)

two-column proof   A two-column proof is a formal proof in which statements are listed in one column and the reasons for each statement are listed in a second column.   (89)

undefined term   An undefined term is a word that has a meaning that is readily understood. The basic undefined terms of geometry are point, line, and plane.   (14)

vector   A vector is a directed segment. It is a quantity which possesses both magnitude (length) and direction.   (601)

vertex   **1.** The vertex of an angle is the common endpoint of the two rays that form the angle.   (37)
2. In a polygon, each endpoint of a side is called a vertex.   (164)
3. In a polyhedron, three or more edges intersect at a point called a vertex. (468)

4. In a pyramid, the vertex is the point where all but one of the faces intersect. (542)
5. In the figure, the vertex of the cone is point *V*. (544)

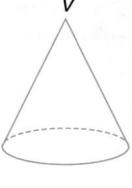

vertex angle   In an isosceles triangle, the angle formed by the congruent sides (legs) is called the vertex angle.   (165)

vertical angles   Two angles are vertical if they are two nonadjacent angles formed by two intersecting lines.   (50)

volume   The measure of the amount of space a figure encloses is the volume of the figure.   (548)

x-axis   The x-axis is the horizontal number line in a coordinate plane.   (8)

x-coordinate   The x-coordinate is the first component in an ordered pair.   (8)

y-axis   The y-axis is the vertical number line in a coordinate plane.   (8)

y-coordinate   The y-coordinate is the second component in an ordered pair. (8)

SELECTED ANSWERS

CHAPTER 1 THE LANGUAGE OF GEOMETRY

Pages 10–12 Lesson 1-1
5. III **7.** *y*-axis **9.** R; (-3, 4) **11.** Find the lengths of each side using the distance formula and then add the sides together. **13.** (3, -1) **15.** (-2, 4)
17, 19, 21.

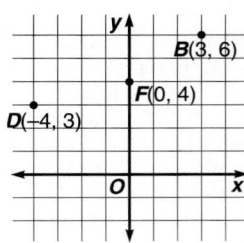

35a. Magic Kingdom **b.** (E, 3)
c. (D, 5), (D, 6)
d. Epcot Center Dr.
e. (C, 1), (D, 1), (D, 2), (E, 3), (E, 4), (F, 4), (F, 5), (F, 6)

23. (0, -11) **25.** (15, 0)
27. (15, -11) **29.** no
31. yes
33a, b.   **c.** (-3, -4)

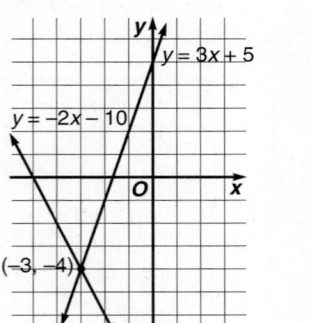

Pages 15–18 Lesson 1-2
7.

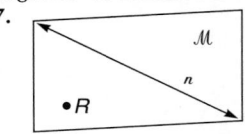

9.

11. true **13.** true **15.** *E* **17.** no; yes **19.** line *TU*
21. *R, U* **23.** no; infinitely many **25.** plane **27.** line
29. plane
31.

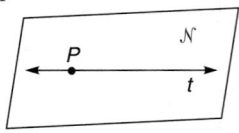

35.

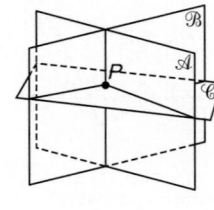

39.

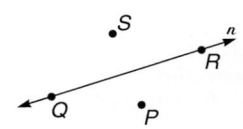

41. no

43. planes *PDC* and *PDA* **45.** parts of the figure that are hidden from view **47.** This figure is not possible unless *P*, *Q*, and *R* are collinear. If points *P*, *Q*, and *R* determine a unique plane, it is not possible for *P*, *Q*, and *R* to be in a plane that does not contain *S* and a different plane that does contain *S*.

49.

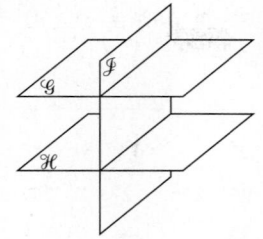

55. Since three points determine a plane, he should use three legs.

57–59.

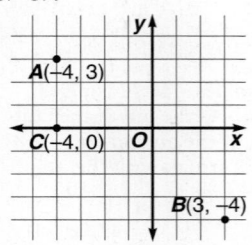

60. (0, 3) **61.** (-1, -2) **62.** 5
63. -2 **65.** 31 **66.** 55
67. 27.84 **68.** 80.22

Pages 21–22 Lesson 1-3
5. 10 combinations **7.** 9 **9.** 22 pieces **11.** Sample answer: $3 \times (3 + 3 \div 3) - 3 \div 3 = 11$ **13.** about $265

Pages 26–29 Lesson 1-4
5. 4 **7.** 6 **9.** 10 **11.** 10 **13.** 10 **15.** 6.32 **17.** 7; 15
19. 1 **21.** 10 **23.** 4 **25.** 17 **27.** 23 **29.** 11.5 **31.** 5
33. 13 **35.** 5 **37.** 1.41 **39.** 9.49 **41.** 1; 5 **43.** 7; 21
45.

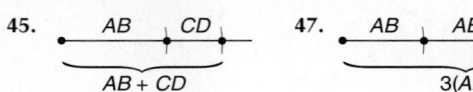

47.

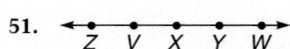

49. 29.31 units

51.

Z V X Y W

55a. the distance formula
b. 10 **c.** ≈ 3.07 **d.** ≈ 16.55

56. (-1, 3) **57.** *E* **58.** *A*

59. *D, A, E, O*

61. 18 area codes

60.

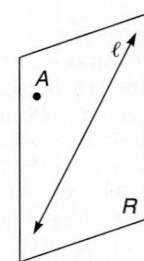

Pages 32–35 Lesson 1-5
5. 3 **7.** 1 **9.** $4\frac{1}{2}$ **11.** (-1, -1) **13.** (2, $-4\frac{1}{2}$) **15.** ($5\frac{1}{2}$, -2)
17. *x* = 4; 34 **19.** true **21.** true **23.** false **25.** true
27. false **29.** *B*(5, 5) **31.** *A*(2, 8) **33.** 8; 54 **35.** 5; 52
37. 8; 18 **39.** no **43.** *P*(4, -1), *Q*(6, -5) **45.** *x* = 2; yes
49. (-1, 5) or (-1, -1) **50a.** *P, Q, R, S* **b.** yes, since any three points are coplanar **51.** 12 ways **52.** 25 **53.** *F* is between *D* and *E*.

1. (1, 3)   **2.** (-1, 1)   **3.** (4, -2)   **4.** true   **5.** -2   **6.** U, V, W, or X **7.** $\overrightarrow{RS}$, $\overrightarrow{TS}$, $\overrightarrow{VS}$ **8.** $\overleftrightarrow{XY}$ **9.** true   **10.** 3 unicycles, 4 bicycles, and 23 tricycles   **11.** T is between R and S.
12. $x = 5$; 13   **13.** 10; (3, 4)   **14.** $x = 8$

Pages 39–42 Lesson 1-6

5. 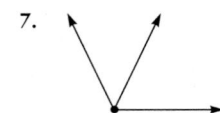   **7.**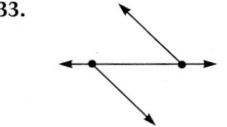

9. $\overrightarrow{QR}$, $\overrightarrow{QT}$ **11.** false   **13.** Y, R, S, or T **15.** N, S, or T
17. 10   **19.** 105   **21.** 80   **23.** 95   **25.** J **27.** V **29.** no

31. 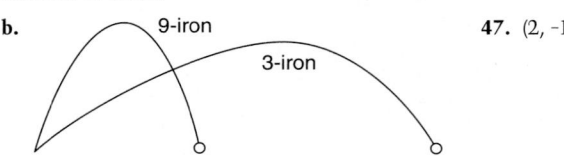   **33.**

35. 29; 122   **37.** 12; 118   **39.** 12 angles   **41.** 24 angles
43. 1; 2 if $PQ \geq 2$, 1 if $PQ < 2$ **45a.** As the loft of the club increases, the ball will travel higher in the air and for a shorter distance, as long as the ball is struck with the same amount of force.

b. 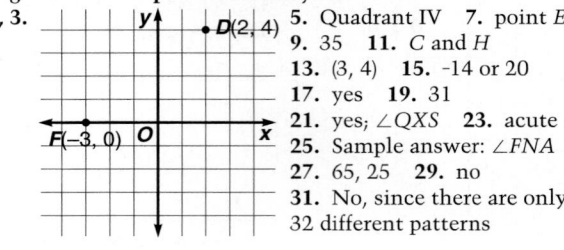   **47.** (2, -1)

48.   **49.** greater than 0
50. 5
51. (-1, 2)
52. $x = 7$

Pages 46–48 Lesson 1-7
11. acute   **13.** straight   **15.** right   **17.** $0 < 3x + 12 < 90$ or $-4 < x < 26$ **19.** acute   **21.** obtuse   **23.** straight
25. acute   **27.** $\angle MHA$ and $\angle HMT$, $\angle MAH$ and $\angle TAH$, $\angle ATM$ and $\angle HTM$ **29.** 29   **31.** 56   **33.** 94; 63   **35.** -7; 19
37. 18   **39.** yes   **41.** $x = 6$, $y = 8$ **45.** $m\angle IMP = 40$, $m\angle IMN = 50$ **46.** point   **47.** 3   **48.** 12   **49.** False, since R is not in the interior of $\angle TPM$.   **50.** 58

Pages 52–55 Lesson 1-8
5. 52, 142   **7.** no complement, 70   **9.** $\angle NML$ and $\angle PMK$
11. $\angle JMP$ and $\angle JML$ **13.** Sample answers: $\angle NMP$ and $\angle PMJ$, $\angle PMJ$ and $\angle JMK$, $\angle JMK$ and $\angle KML$ **15.** 7; 53; 37
17. 33   **19.** 20   **21.** adjacent, complementary
23. adjacent, supplementary, linear pair   **25.** supplementary
27. 13; 89   **29.** 112, 68   **31.** 45   **33.** 28, 62

35. 72, 108, 18   **37.** 12, 36, 144   **41.** 170°   **42.** 4   **43.** 1
44. 21   **45.** yes; $m\angle 1 = m\angle 2$ **46.** 6

Pages 59–61 Lesson 1-9
5. $\overline{CQ}$ **7.** yes; $\angle BQD$ and $\angle CQE$ are right angles, so $m\angle BQD = 90$ and $m\angle CQE = 90$. Therefore $m\angle BQD = m\angle CQE$. $m\angle BQD = m\angle BQC + m\angle CQD$ and $m\angle CQE = m\angle CQD + m\angle DQE$ by the angle addition postulate. By substitution $m\angle BQC + m\angle CQD = m\angle CQD + m\angle DQE$. $m\angle BQC = m\angle DQE$ **9.** yes   **11.** no   **13.** no   **15.** yes
17. no   **19.** no   **21.** yes   **23.** no   **25.** 25; no   **27.** no
29. yes   **31.** no   **33.** yes   **35.** a square   **37.** $x = 60$, $y = 30$ **39.** $x = 15$, $y = 10$ **41.** 45   **42.** 4   **43.** $\overline{CF}$, $\overline{AD}$, $\overline{AF}$, $\overline{FD}$, F **44.** $\angle ACE$, $\angle FCE$, $\angle CEB$ **45.** $x = 6$ **46.** 23

Pages 62–64 Chapter 1 Summary and Review
1, 3. 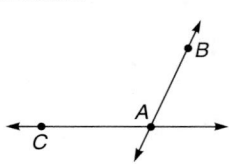   **5.** Quadrant IV   **7.** point E
9. 35   **11.** C and H
13. (3, 4)   **15.** -14 or 20
17. yes   **19.** 31
21. yes; $\angle QXS$ **23.** acute
25. Sample answer: $\angle FNA$
27. 65, 25   **29.** no
31. No, since there are only 32 different patterns

Pages 66–67 Algebra Review
1. 8   **3.** -1.3   **5.** $\frac{3}{8}$ **7.** 11   **9.** -9   **11.** 135   **13.** $9r - 5s$
15. $\frac{5ab}{3} - \frac{a^2}{4}$ **17.** $\frac{18}{7}$ **19.** $4a + 7$ **21.** 3
23. $12 - a^2 = b$ **25.** $xy^2 = t$ **27.** -24   **29.** 22   **31.** -9
33. 4.5   **35.** 35   **37.** $\frac{9}{10}$ **39.** 10.2375 miles   **41.** 1.25 liters

CHAPTER 2 REASONING AND INTRODUCTION TO PROOF

Pages 71–74 Lesson 2-1   **7.** $\angle A \cong \angle B$
5. False; A, B, and C could be as shown. They are not collinear.

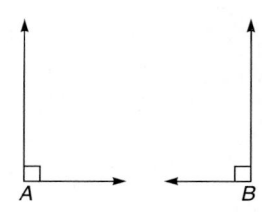

9. Sample answer: **11.** True; any three noncollinear points can be the vertices of a triangle.

$\overline{PQ} \cong \overline{RQ}$

13. false; counterexample:

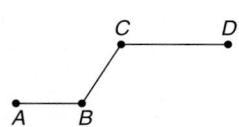

17. Points Q, P, and R are collinear.

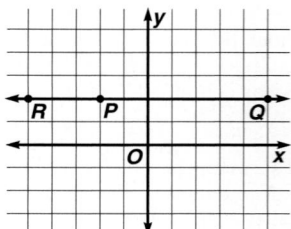

27. $ABCDE$ is a pentagon.

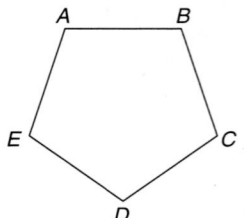

19. $1111^2 = 1,234,321$
21. $\overline{DE}$ is parallel to $\overline{BC}$.

23. false; counterexample:

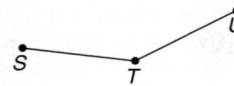

33b. Yes, the fungus is killing the plants.
c. Introduce the fungus to some healthy plants and see if they droop.

34. yes   **36.** 6   **37.** plane

Pages 78–81 Lesson 2-2

7. Hypothesis: two lines are perpendicular; Conclusion: they intersect.   **9.** Hypothesis: $x = 4$; Conclusion: $x^2 = 16$ **11.** If an angle is acute, then it is 37°. False; an angle that measures 58° is acute.   **13.** If he or she may serve as President, then he or she is a native born United States citizen who is at least thirty-five years old. true   **15.** If two planes intersect, then the intersection is a line.   **17.** If an aluminum can is recycled, then it is remelted and back in the store within six weeks.   **19.** false   **21.** false   **23.** Hypothesis: a candy bar is a Milky Way™; Conclusion: it contains caramel.   **25.** true   **27.** false   **29.** true   **31.** If a vehicle is a car, then it has four wheels.   **33.** If an angle is acute, then it has a measure less than 90°.   **35.** If two lines are parallel, then they do not intersect.   **37.** If the distance of a race is about 6.2 miles, then it is 10 kilometers. true   **39.** 2-1   **41.** 2-5   **43.** 2-6   **45.** one   **47.** six   **49.** fifteen   **51.** one   **53.** ten

55.

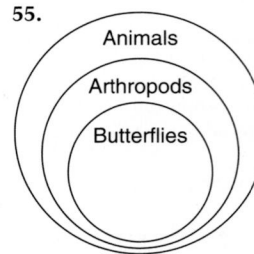

64.

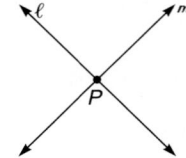

57a. 92   **b.** 1023
59. false; A, B, and P are not necessarily collinear.
60. 72, 108   **61.** 15
62. (1, 4)
63. 51

65. no

Pages 84–87 Lesson 2-3

5. yes; detachment   **7.** no   **9.** no   **11.** $\overline{CD} \cong \overline{CD}$; detachment   **13.** Planes M and N intersect in a line; detachment   **15.** Bobby Rahal is a professional race car driver; detachment   **17.** yes; syllogism   **19.** yes; detachment   **21.** no   **23.** A, B, and C are collinear; detachment   **25.** p and q have a point in common; detachment   **27.** If an ordered pair for a point has 0 as its x-coordinate, then it is not contained in any of the four quadrants; syllogism   **29.** no conclusion   **31.** no conclusion   **33.** Basalt was formed by volcanos; syllogism   **35a.** Sample answer: (2) Angles X and Y are adjacent and supplementary. (3) Angles X and Y are right angles.   **b.** Sample answer: (2) Right angles measure 90°. (3) Angles that are adjacent and supplementary measure 90°.   **37a.** Sample answer: (2) Dr. Garcia is a physician. (3) Dr. Garcia has graduated from medical school.   **b.** Sample answer: (2) All medical school graduates have studied chemistry. (3) All physicians have studied chemistry.   **39.** If a mineral sample is quartz, then it can scratch glass; syllogism   **42.** If a geometry test score is 89, then it is above average.   **43.** acute   **44.** $(\frac{1}{2}, 4)$ **45.** $\sqrt{29}$

46.

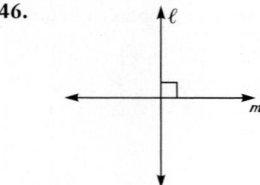

Pages 90–94 Lesson 2-4

5. Subtraction   **7.** Division   **9.** Substitution   **11a.** Given   **b.** Reflexive property of equality   **c.** Addition property of equality   **d.** Angle addition postulate   **e.** Substitution property of equality   **13.** Substitution   **15.** Substitution   **17.** Reflexive   **19.** Subtraction   **21.** Addition   **23a.** Given   **b.** Symmetric property of equality   **c.** Multiplication property of equality   **d.** Distribution property   **e.** Subtraction property of equality   **f.** Multiplication property of equality   **25a.** Given   **b.** Angle addition postulate   **c.** Substitution property of equality   **d.** Substitution property of equality   **e.** Subtraction property of equality

27. Given: $m\angle M = m\angle P$
$\qquad m\angle N = m\angle P$
Prove: $m\angle M = m\angle N$

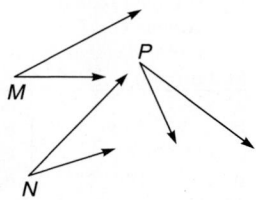

Statements	Reasons
a. $m\angle M = m\angle P$ $m\angle N = m\angle P$	**a.** Given
b. $m\angle M = m\angle N$	**b.** Transitive property of equality

29. Given: $m\angle ABC = 90$
$\qquad m\angle EDC = 90$
$\qquad m\angle 1 = m\angle 3$
Prove: $m\angle 2 = m\angle 4$

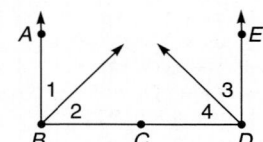

Statements	Reasons
a. $m\angle ABC = 90$ $m\angle EDC = 90$ $m\angle 1 = m\angle 3$	a. Given
b. $m\angle ABC = m\angle EDC$	b. Substitution property of equality
c. $m\angle ABC = m\angle 1 + m\angle 2$ $m\angle EDC = m\angle 3 + m\angle 4$	c. Angle addition postulate
d. $m\angle 1 + m\angle 2 = m\angle 3 + m\angle 4$	d. Substitution property of equality
e. $m\angle 1 + m\angle 2 = m\angle 1 + m\angle 4$	e. Substitution property of equality
f. $m\angle 2 = m\angle 4$	f. Subtraction property of equality

31. Given: $A = p + prt$

Prove: $p = \frac{A}{1 + rt}$

Statements	Reasons
a. $A = p + prt$	a. Given
b. $A = p(1 + rt)$	b. Distributive property
c. $\frac{A}{1 + rt} = p$	c. Division property of equality
d. $p = \frac{A}{1 + rt}$	d. Symmetric property of equality

34. $7 = 7$; detachment   **35.** $\frac{5}{9} = 0.\bar{5}$ **36.** $(3, \frac{11}{2})$

37.

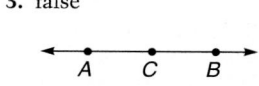

Page 94 Mid-Chapter Review

1. true, since a midpoint divides a segment into two congruent segments   **2.** True, since $x^3 = x \cdot x \cdot x$ and the reals are closed under multiplication.

3. false

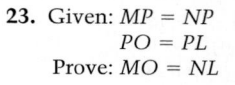

4. True, since all right angles have a measure of 90 and congruent angles are by definition angles with the same measure.

5. If two lines are perpendicular, then they form four right angles.   **6.** If a substance is ordinary table sugar, then its chemical formula is $C_{12}H_{22}O_{11}$.   **7.** If it is a non-leap year, then the month of February has 28 days.   **8.** no conclusion
9. The diagonals of $ABCD$ are congruent; detachment
10. If two angles are right angles, then they have the same measure; syllogism
11. Given: $x = 7$

Prove: $4x^2 = 196$

Statements	Reasons
a. $x = 7$	a. Given
b. $x \cdot x = 7 \cdot x$	b. Multiplication property of equality
c. $x^2 = 7 \cdot 7$	c. Substitution property of equality
d. $4x^2 = 196$	d. Multiplication property of equality

12. Given: $AC = AB$, $AC = 4x + 1$, $AB = 6x - 13$

Prove: $x = 7$

Statements	Reasons
a. $AC = AB$ $AC = 4x + 1$ $AB = 6x - 13$	a. Given
b. $4x + 1 = AB$	b. Substitution property of equality
c. $4x + 1 = 6x - 13$	c. Substitution property of equality
d. $1 = 2x - 13$	d. Subtraction property of equality
e. $14 = 2x$	e. Addition property of equality
f. $7 = x$	f. Division property of equality
g. $x = 7$	g. Symmetric property of equality

Pages 96–97 Lesson 2-5
3. 9th - Anthony, 10th - Erin, 11th - Brad, 12th - Lisa   **5.** 19
7. Umeko - Drama Club, delivery person; Jim - Spanish Club, tutor; Gwen - marching band, lifeguard   **9.** The jeans box contained T-shirts and jeans, the T-shirt box contained jeans, and the jeans and T-shirts box contained T-shirts.

Pages 100–104 Lesson 2-6
5. Theorem 2-1 (Congruence of segments is reflexive.)
7. Theorem 2-1 (Congruence of segments is symmetric.)
9. Substitution property of equality   **11.** Addition property of equality

13. Given: $\angle A$ is a right angle.
Prove: $m\angle A = 90$

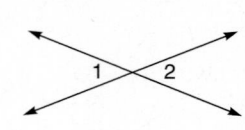

15. Given: $\angle 1$ and $\angle 2$ are vertical angles.
Prove: $\angle 1 \cong \angle 2$

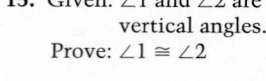

17. Given: $\triangle QED$ is a triangle.
Prove: $m\angle Q + m\angle E + m\angle D = 180$

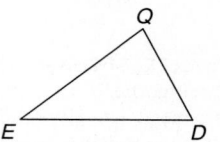

19a. $\overline{LE} \cong \overline{MR}$; $\overline{EG} \cong \overline{RA}$ **b.** Definition of congruent segments   **c.** Segment addition postulate   **e.** $LG = MA$ **f.** Definition of congruent segments   **21a.** Given
b. Definition of congruent segments   **c.** $AM = MB$; $CN = ND$ **d.** Segment addition postulate   **e.** Substitution property of equality   **f.** Substitution property of equality
h. Division property of equality   **i.** Definition of congruent segments

23. Given: $MP = NP$
$PO = PL$
Prove: $MO = NL$

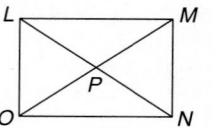

Statements	Reasons
1. $MP = NP$ $PO = PL$	1. Given
2. $MP + PO = NP + PL$	2. Addition property of equality
3. $MO = MP + PO$ $NL = NP + PL$	3. Segment addition postulate
4. $MO = NL$	4. Substitution property of equality

25. Given: $\overline{SA} \cong \overline{ND}$
Prove: $\overline{SN} \cong \overline{AD}$

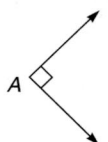

Statements	Reasons
1. $\overline{SA} \cong \overline{ND}$	1. Given
2. $SA = ND$	2. Definition of congruent segments
3. $SA + AN = AN + ND$	3. Addition property of equality
4. $SN = SA + AN$ $AD = AN + ND$	4. Segment addition postulate
5. $SN = AD$	5. Substitution property of equality
6. $\overline{SN} \cong \overline{AD}$	6. Definition of congruent segments

27. Given: $\overline{QT} \cong \overline{RT}$
$\overline{TS} \cong \overline{TP}$
Prove: $\overline{QS} \cong \overline{RP}$

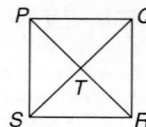

Statements	Reasons
1. $\overline{QT} \cong \overline{RT}$ $\overline{TS} \cong \overline{TP}$	1. Given
2. $QT = RT$ $TS = TP$	2. Definition of congruent segments
3. $QT + TS = RT + TP$	3. Addition property of equality
4. $QS = QT + TS$ $RP = RT + TP$	4. Segment addition postulate
5. $QS = RP$	5. Substitution property of equality
6. $\overline{QS} \cong \overline{RP}$	6. Definition of congruent segments

29. Given: $AB = CD$
M is the midpoint of $\overline{AB}$.
N is the midpoint of $\overline{CD}$.
Prove: $AM = MB = CN = ND$

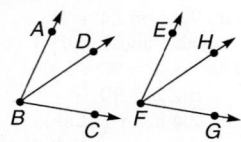

Statements	Reasons
1. $AB = CD$ M is the midpoint of $\overline{AB}$. N is the midpoint of $\overline{CD}$.	1. Given
2. $AB = AM + MB$ $CD = CN + ND$	2. Segment addition postulate
3. $AM = MB$ $CN = ND$	3. Definition of midpoint
4. $AB = AM + AM$ $CD = CN + CN$	4. Substitution property of equality
5. $2AM = 2CN$	5. Substitution property of equality
6. $AM = CN$	6. Division property of equality
7. $AM = ND$	7. Transitive property of equality
8. $AM = MB = CN = ND$	8. Transitive property of equality

31.

Statements	Reasons
1. The defendant drove through a red traffic light at the corner of Washington and Elm.	1. The defendant was seen.
2. The signal was not down.	2. The traffic computer shows no indication that the signal was down.
3. The defendant is subject to a $50 fine.	3. The law states that if a driver proceeds through a red traffic light that is in proper working order, that driver is subject to a $50 fine.

33. Jan. - Pablo, Feb. - Timothy, Aug. - Emma, Sept. - Amy
34. Division or multiplication property of equality **35.** If a student maintains a C average, then he or she is eligible to play a varsity sport. **36.** a satellite **37.** $m\angle AND = 72$, $m\angle NOR = 18$ **38a.** 5 units **b.** 2 units **c.** 7 units **d.** 8 units

3. sometimes **5.** sometimes **7.** sometimes **9.** always
11. $m\angle 1 = 112$, $m\angle 2 = 112$ **13.** $m\angle 1 = 140$, $m\angle 2 = 40$
15. (1) Given (4) $m\angle ABC = m\angle 1 + m\angle 2$ (5) Substitution property of equality (6) Definition of supplementary
17. $\angle MLN$ or $\angle PLQ$ **19.** 110 **21.** 30
23. Given: $\angle ABC \cong \angle EFG$
$\angle ABD \cong \angle EFH$
Prove: $\angle DBC \cong \angle HFG$

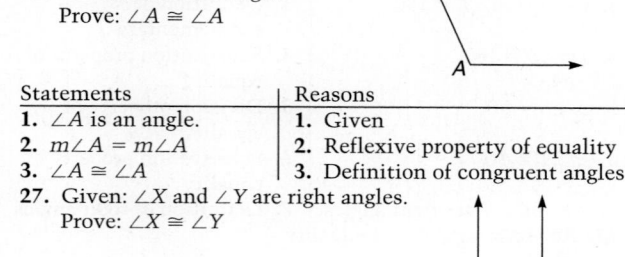

Statements	Reasons
1. $\angle ABC \cong \angle EFG$ $\angle ABD \cong \angle EFH$	1. Given
2. $m\angle ABC = m\angle EFG$ $m\angle ABD = m\angle EFH$	2. Definition of congruent angles
3. $m\angle ABC = m\angle ABD + m\angle DBC$ $m\angle EFG = m\angle EFH + m\angle HFG$	3. Angle addition postulate
4. $m\angle ABD + m\angle DBC =$ $m\angle EFH + m\angle HFG$	4. Substitution property of equality
5. $m\angle DBC = m\angle HFG$	5. Subtraction property of equality
6. $\angle DBC \cong \angle HFG$	6. Definition of congruent angles

25. Given: $\angle A$ is an angle.
Prove: $\angle A \cong \angle A$

Statements	Reasons
1. $\angle A$ is an angle.	1. Given
2. $m\angle A = m\angle A$	2. Reflexive property of equality
3. $\angle A \cong \angle A$	3. Definition of congruent angles

27. Given: $\angle X$ and $\angle Y$ are right angles.
Prove: $\angle X \cong \angle Y$

Statements	Reasons
1. $\angle X$ and $\angle Y$ are right angles.	1. Given
2. $m\angle X = 90$ $m\angle Y = 90$	2. Definition of right angle
3. $m\angle X = m\angle Y$	3. Substitution property of equality
4. $\angle X \cong \angle Y$	4. Definition of congruent angles

29. Given: $\ell \perp m$
Prove: $\angle 1$, $\angle 2$, and $\angle 3$, and $\angle 4$ are right angles.

Statements	Reasons
1. $\ell \perp m$	1. Given
2. $\angle 1$ is a right angle.	2. Definition of perpendicular lines
3. $m\angle 1 = 90$	3. Definition of right angle
4. $\angle 1 \cong \angle 3$	4. Vertical $\angle$s are $\cong$.
5. $m\angle 3 = 90$	5. Definition of congruent angles
6. $\angle 3$ is a right angle.	6. Definition of right angle

7. ∠1 and ∠4 form a linear pair.
∠1 and ∠2 form a linear pair.

7. Definition of linear pair

8. ∠1 and ∠4 are supplementary.
∠1 and ∠2 are supplementary.

8. If 2 ∠s form a linear pair, they are supp.

9. $m\angle 1 + m\angle 4 = 180$
$m\angle 1 + m\angle 2 = 180$

9. Definition of supplementary

10. $90 + m\angle 4 = 180$
$90 + m\angle 2 = 180$

10. Substitution property of equality

11. $m\angle 4 = 90$
$m\angle 2 = 90$

11. Subtraction property of equality

12. ∠4 is a right angle.
∠2 is a right angle.

12. Definition of right angle

31. Given: $\angle S \cong \angle T$
∠S and ∠T are supplementary.
Prove: ∠S and ∠T are right angles.

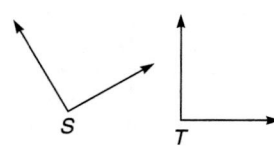

Statements	Reasons
1. $\angle S \cong \angle T$ ∠S and ∠T are supplementary.	**1.** Given
2. $m\angle S = m\angle T$	**2.** Definition of congruent angles
3. $m\angle S + m\angle T = 180$	**3.** Definition of supplementary
4. $2m\angle S = 180$	**4.** Substitution property of equality
5. $m\angle S = 90$	**5.** Division property of equality
6. $m\angle T = 90$	**6.** Substitution property of equality
7. ∠S and ∠T are right angles.	**7.** Definition of right angles

35. Reflexive property of equality

36. $F = \frac{9}{5}C + 32$ Given
$F - 32 = \frac{9}{5}C$ Subtraction property of equality
$\frac{5}{9}(F - 32) = C$ Multiplication property of equality

37. no conclusion   **38.** no complement, 21

Pages 110–113 Chapter 2 Summary and Review
1. true   **3.** If something is a cloud, then it has a silver lining.   **5.** If a rock is obsidian, then it is a glassy rock produced by a volcano.   **7.** ∠A and ∠B have measures with a sum of 90; detachment   **9.** The Sun is in constant motion; syllogism
11. Given: $MN = PN$
$NL = NO$
Prove: $ML = PO$

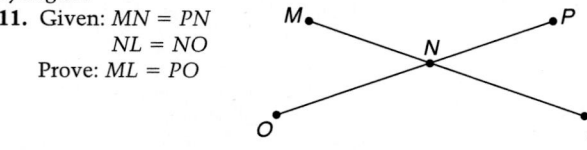

Statements	Reasons
1. $MN = PN$ $NL = NO$	**1.** Given
2. $MN + NL = PN + NO$	**2.** Addition property of equality
3. $ML = MN + NL$ $PO = PN + NO$	**3.** Segment addition postulate
4. $ML = PO$	**4.** Substitution property of equality

13. Given: $\overline{AM} \cong \overline{CN}$
$\overline{MB} \cong \overline{ND}$
Prove: $\overline{AB} \cong \overline{CD}$

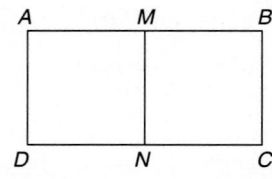

Statements	Reasons
1. $\overline{AM} \cong \overline{CN}$ $\overline{MB} \cong \overline{ND}$	**1.** Given
2. $AM = CN$ $MB = ND$	**2.** Definition of congruent segments
3. $AM + MB = CN + ND$	**3.** Addition property of equality
4. $AB = AM + MB$ $CD = CN + ND$	**4.** Segment addition postulate
5. $AB = CD$	**5.** Substitution property of equality
6. $\overline{AB} \cong \overline{CD}$	**6.** Definition of congruent segments

15. Given: ∠1 and ∠2 form a linear pair.
$\angle 1 \cong \angle 2$
Prove: ∠1 and ∠2 are right angles.

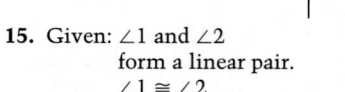

Statements	Reasons
1. ∠1 and ∠2 form a linear pair. $\angle 1 \cong \angle 2$	**1.** Given
2. $m\angle 1 = m\angle 2$	**2.** Definition of congruent angles
3. ∠1 and ∠2 are supplementary.	**3.** If 2 ∠s form a linear pair, they are supp.
4. $m\angle 1 + m\angle 2 = 180$	**4.** Definition of supplementary
5. $m\angle 1 + m\angle 1 = 180$	**5.** Substitution property of equality
6. $2m\angle 1 = 180$	**6.** Substitution property of equality
7. $m\angle 1 = 90$	**7.** Division property of equality
8. $m\angle 2 = 90$	**8.** Substitution property of equality
9. ∠1 and ∠2 are right angles.	**9.** Definition of right angle

17. A sponge remains permanently attached to a surface for all of its adult life; syllogism
19. $t = 35d + 20$ Given
$t - 20 = 35d$ Subtraction property of equality
$\frac{t-20}{35} = d$ Division property of equality

CHAPTER 3 PARALLELS

Pages 119–121 Lesson 3-1
5. 21
7. Given: ∠AED and ∠BEC are supplementary.
Prove: ∠AED is a right angle.
∠BEC is a right angle.

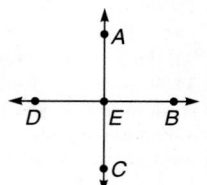

9. They are the same.   **11.** 1,111,088,889   **13.** 6   **17.** 11

Pages 124–127 Lesson 3-2
5. parallel   **7.** parallel, intersecting, skew   **9.** intersecting or parallel   **11.** false; could be skew   **13.** true   **15.** false   **17.** false   **19.** true   **21.** true   **23.** $\overrightarrow{RT}$; alternate interior angles   **25.** $\overrightarrow{RV}$; consecutive interior angles   **27.** m; corresponding angles   **29.** a; corresponding angles   **31.** ℓ; consecutive interior angles   **33.** parallel and intersecting   **35.** intersecting   **37.** intersecting

39. 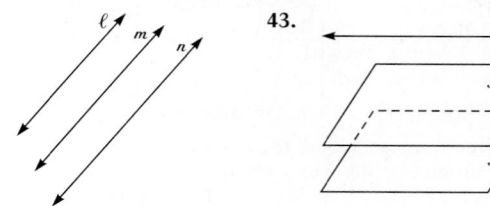   **43.**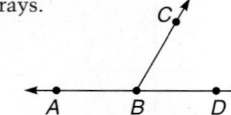

45. $\overline{CV}, \overline{BW}, \overline{ZX}, \overline{AY}, \overline{RU}$ **47.** plane BWX **49.** If plane $\mathcal{A}$ is parallel to plane $\mathcal{B}$ and plane $\mathcal{B}$ is parallel to plane $\mathcal{C}$, then plane $\mathcal{A}$ is parallel to plane $\mathcal{C}$. The basement floor is parallel to the ground-level floor and the ground-level floor is parallel to the upstairs floor, so the basement floor is parallel to the upstairs floor.   **51a.** 2,000 feet   **b.** easy to keep track of which airplanes are eastbound and which are westbound; less worry about collisions
52. Given: $\overrightarrow{BA}$ and $\overrightarrow{BD}$ are opposite rays.
Prove: $\angle ABC$ and $\angle CBD$ are supplementary.

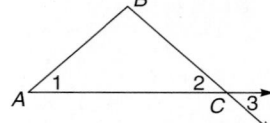

53. Given: $\angle 1 \cong \angle 2$
Prove: $\angle 1 \cong \angle 3$

Statements	Reasons
1. $\angle 1 \cong \angle 2$	**1.** Given
2. $\angle 2 \cong \angle 3$	**2.** Vertical $\angle$s are $\cong$.
3. $\angle 1 \cong \angle 3$	**3.** Congruence of angles is transitive.

54. Symmetric property of equality   **55.** If two lines lie in the same plane and do not intersect, then they are parallel.   **56.** $(2, -2)$ **57.** 13

Pages 130–134 Lesson 3-3
7. $\angle 5$ and $\angle 2$ are supplementary; $\angle 1$ and $\angle 4$ are supplementary; $\angle 3 \cong \angle 2$; $\angle 3$ and $\angle 5$ are supplementary.
9. 82   **11.** 82   **13.** 40   **15.** 140   **17.** $x = 16$, $y = 11$ **19.** 90   **21.** 125   **23.** 35   **25.** $x = 52$, $y = 13$ **27.** $x = 7$, $y = 16$ **29.** 77   **31.** 62   **33.** 103   **35.** $x = 16$, $y = 41$, $z = 42$ **37.** $x = 127$, $y = 5$, $z = 31$ **39.** 35   **41.** 125   **43.** 35
45. a. Given   **b.** $\perp$ lines form 4 rt. $\angle$s.   **c.** $m\angle 1 = 90$ **d.** If 2 $\parallel$ lines are cut by a trasversal, corr. $\angle$s are $\cong$.   **e.** $m\angle 2 = 90$ **f.** Definition of right angle   **g.** $m \perp p$

47. Given: $\ell \parallel m$
Prove: $\angle 3$ and $\angle 5$ are supplementary.
$\angle 4$ and $\angle 6$ are supplementary.

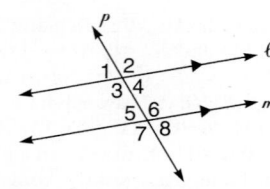

Proof: Since $\ell \parallel m$, $\angle 1 \cong \angle 5$ and $\angle 2 \cong \angle 6$ because they are corresponding angles. $\angle 1$ and $\angle 3$ form a linear pair, as do $\angle 2$ and $\angle 4$, by definition. Hence $\angle 1$ and $\angle 3$ are supplementary, as are $\angle 2$ and $\angle 4$, because if 2 $\angle$s form a linear pair, they are supplementary. By definition of supplementary $m\angle 1 + m\angle 3 = 180$ and $m\angle 2 + m\angle 4 = 180$. Then by substitution, $m\angle 5 + m\angle 3 = 180$ and $m\angle 6 + m\angle 4 = 180$. Hence $\angle 3$ and $\angle 5$ and $\angle 4$ and $\angle 6$ are supplementary by definition.

49. Given: $\overline{MQ} \parallel \overline{NP}$
$\angle 1 \cong \angle 5$
Prove: $\angle 4 \cong \angle 3$

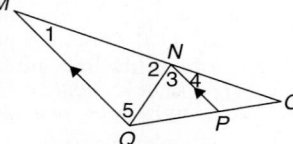

Statements	Reasons
1. $\overline{MQ} \parallel \overline{NP}$ $\angle 1 \cong \angle 5$	**1.** Given
2. $\angle 4 \cong \angle 1$	**2.** If 2 $\parallel$ lines are cut by a transversal, corr. $\angle$s are $\cong$.
3. $\angle 4 \cong \angle 5$	**3.** Congruence of angles is transitive.
4. $\angle 5 \cong \angle 3$	**4.** If 2 $\parallel$ lines are cut by a transversal, alt. int. $\angle$s are $\cong$.
5. $\angle 4 \cong \angle 3$	**5.** Congruence of angles is transitive.

53. parallel

54. Given: $\overline{AB} \cong \overline{FE}$
$\overline{BC} \cong \overline{ED}$
Prove: $\overline{AC} \cong \overline{FD}$

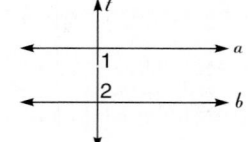

Statements	Reasons
1. $\overline{AB} \cong \overline{FE}$ $\overline{BC} \cong \overline{ED}$	**1.** Given
2. $AB = FE$ $BC = ED$	**2.** Definition of congruent segments
3. $AC = AB + BC$ $FD = FE + ED$	**3.** Segment addition postulate
4. $AB + BC = FE + ED$	**4.** Addition property of equality
5. $AC = FD$	**5.** Substitution property of equality
6. $\overline{AC} \cong \overline{FD}$	**6.** Definition of congruent segments

55. Lines p and q never meet; detachment   **56.** 7   **57.** -3 or 9   **58.** III

Page 134 Mid-Chapter Review
1. Given: $a \parallel b$
$\angle 1 \cong \angle 2$
Prove: $a \perp \ell$
$b \perp \ell$

2. $\overline{EF}$ **3.** $\overline{AC}, \overline{EF}$ **4.** plane DEF **5.** none **6.** 65 **7.** 65 **8.** 115 **9.** 65 **10.** 115 **11.** 115 **12.** 65

Pages 137–141 Lesson 3-4
7. 13 **9.** 10 **11.** 20 **13.** $\overline{AB} \parallel \overline{DC}$, Theorem 3-5
15. false; They must be in a plane. **17.** false; The alternate interior angles would be congruent. **19.** $\overleftrightarrow{GK} \parallel \overleftrightarrow{HL}$, corresponding angles congruent (Postulate 3-2) **21.** $\overleftrightarrow{FG} \parallel \overleftrightarrow{JK}$, alternate interior angles congruent (Theorem 3-5) **23.** none **25.** $c \parallel d$, corresponding angles congruent (Postulate 3-2)
27. none **29.** none **31.** $x = 7$, $y = 138$ **33.** $\angle 2$ and $\angle 3$; $\angle 6$ and $\angle 7$; $\angle 2$ and $\angle 8$; $\angle 6$ and $\angle 4$; $\angle 3$ and $\angle 5$; $\angle 7$ and $\angle 1$; $\angle 5$ and $\angle 8$; $\angle 1$ and $\angle 4$ **35.** $\overleftrightarrow{AE} \parallel \overleftrightarrow{DF}$ since in a plane, if 2 lines are $\perp$ to the same line they are $\parallel$. $\overleftrightarrow{EB} \parallel \overleftrightarrow{FH}$ since if 2 lines in a plane are cut by a transversal and alt. int. $\angle$s are $\cong$, then the lines are $\parallel$. **37. a.** Given **b.** $\angle 1$ and $\angle 2$ form a linear pair. **c.** If 2 $\angle$ form a linear pair, they are supp. **d.** $\angle 1 \cong \angle 3$ **e.** If 2 lines in a plane are cut by a transversal and corr. $\angle$ are $\cong$, the lines are $\parallel$.
39. Given: $\angle RQP \cong \angle PSR$
$\angle SRQ$ and $\angle PSR$ are supplementary.
Prove: $\overline{QP} \parallel \overline{RS}$

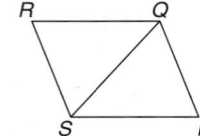

Statements	Reasons
1. $\angle RQP \cong \angle PSR$ $\angle SRQ$ and $\angle PSR$ are supplementary.	**1.** Given
2. $m\angle RQP = m\angle PSR$	**2.** Definition of congruent angles
3. $m\angle SRQ + m\angle PSR = 180$	**3.** Definition of supplementary
4. $m\angle SRQ + m\angle RQP = 180$	**4.** Substitution property of equality
5. $\angle SRQ$ and $\angle RQP$ are supplementary.	**5.** Definition of supplementary
6. $\overline{QP} \parallel \overline{RS}$	**6.** If 2 lines are cut by a transversal and consec. int. $\angle$ are supp., then the lines are $\parallel$.

41. Given: $\angle ABD \cong \angle BEF$
$\overrightarrow{BC}$ bisects $\angle ABD$.
$\overrightarrow{EH}$ bisects $\angle BEF$.
Prove: $\overrightarrow{BC} \parallel \overrightarrow{EH}$

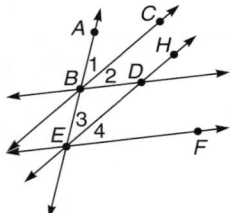

Statements	Reasons
1. $\angle ABD \cong \angle BEF$ $\overrightarrow{BC}$ bisects $\angle ABD$. $\overrightarrow{EH}$ bisects $\angle BEF$.	**1.** Given
2. $m\angle 1 + m\angle 2 = m\angle ABD$ $m\angle 3 + m\angle 4 = m\angle BEF$	**2.** Angle addition postulate
3. $m\angle 1 + m\angle 2 = m\angle 3 + m\angle 4$	**3.** Substitution property of equality
4. $m\angle 1 = m\angle 2$ $m\angle 3 = m\angle 4$	**4.** Definition of angle bisector
5. $m\angle 1 + m\angle 1 = m\angle 3 + m\angle 3$	**5.** Substitution property of equality

6. $2m\angle 1 = 2m\angle 3$

7. $m\angle 1 = m\angle 3$

8. $\overrightarrow{BC} \parallel \overrightarrow{EH}$

6. Substitution property of equality

7. Division property of equality

8. If 2 lines are cut by a transversal and corr. $\angle$s are $\cong$, then the lines are $\parallel$.

43. Postulate 3-2 **44.** true **45.** intersecting or skew

46. Statements	Reasons
1. $A = 2\pi r^2 + 2\pi rh$	**1.** Given
2. $A - 2\pi r^2 = 2\pi rh$	**2.** Subtraction property of equality
3. $\frac{A - 2\pi r^2}{2\pi r} = h$	**3.** Division property of equality

47. If something is a cloud, then it is composed of millions of water droplets. **48.** yes **49.** 6

Pages 144–147 Lesson 3-5
7. $-\frac{1}{2}$, falling **9.** 1, rising **11.** undefined, vertical
13. perpendicular **15.** $\frac{3}{4}$, $-\frac{4}{3}$ **17.** $-\frac{3}{2}$, $\frac{2}{3}$ **19.** $\frac{11}{3}$, $-\frac{3}{11}$ **21.** 2
23. $\frac{3}{2}$ **25.** undefined **27.** $-\frac{2}{3}$

29. 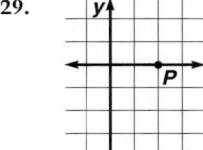 **33.**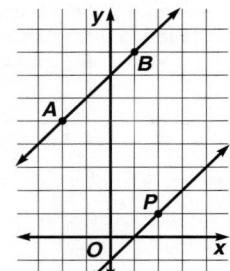

35. slope of $\overleftrightarrow{AB} = -\frac{1}{3}$; slope of $\overleftrightarrow{BC} = -\frac{1}{3}$ Either $\overleftrightarrow{AB} \parallel \overleftrightarrow{BC}$ or $\overleftrightarrow{AB}$ and $\overleftrightarrow{BC}$ are the same line. Since B is a common point, $\overleftrightarrow{AB}$ is not parallel to $\overleftrightarrow{BC}$. Thus $\overleftrightarrow{AB}$ and $\overleftrightarrow{BC}$ are the same line and A, B, and C are collinear. **37.** slope of $\overleftrightarrow{AB} = 3$; slope of $\overleftrightarrow{CD} = 3$. No, $\overleftrightarrow{AB}$ and $\overleftrightarrow{CD}$ are the same line since A, B, C, and D are collinear. **43.** (7, 5), (5, -1), or (-3, 3) **45.** slope between (5, 5) and (9, 1) = -1; slope between (5, 5) and (0, 10) = -1. So the lines between (5, 5) and (9,1) and (5, 5) and (0, 10) are either parallel or the same line. But the lines share the point (5, 5). So, they must be the same line. Therefore, the line through (5, 5) and (9, 1) crosses the y-axis at (0, 10).
47a. 7500 **b.** The rate of change is the slope of the line that relates population and time. **c.** 300,000

49a. **b.** 11,080 feet

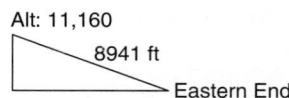

Alt: 11,160

8941 ft

Eastern End

51. Given: $\angle 1 \cong \angle 2$
$\overline{PQ} \perp \overline{QR}$
Prove: $\overline{ST} \perp \overline{PQ}$

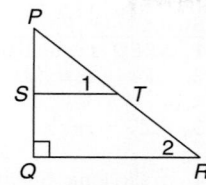

Statements	Reasons
1. $\angle 1 \cong \angle 2$ $\overline{PQ} \perp \overline{QR}$	1. Given
2. $\overline{ST} \parallel \overline{QR}$	2. If 2 lines in a plane are cut by a transversal and corr. $\angle$s are $\cong$, the lines are $\parallel$.
3. $\overline{ST} \perp \overline{PQ}$	3. In a plane, if a line is $\perp$ to one of 2 $\parallel$ lines, it is $\perp$ to the other.

52. Sample answers: $\angle 1$ and $\angle 2$ are supplementary; $\angle 1 \cong \angle 3$; $\angle 2$ and $\angle 3$ are supplementary; $\angle 4$ and $\angle 5$ are supplementary; $\angle 4 \cong \angle 6$; $\angle 5$ and $\angle 6$ are supplementary.

53.

Statements	Reasons
1. $5x - 7 = x + 1$	1. Given
2. $4x - 7 = 1$	2. Subtraction property of equality
3. $4x = 8$	3. Addition property of equality
4. $x = 2$	4. Division property of equality

54. $(\frac{1}{2})^2 = \frac{1}{4}$, and $\frac{1}{2} \not< \frac{1}{4}$ **55.** $(2, 9)$

56.

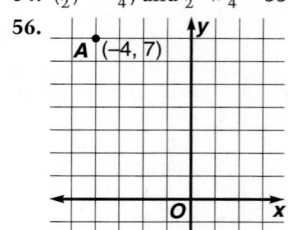

Pages 151–154 Lesson 3-6

5.

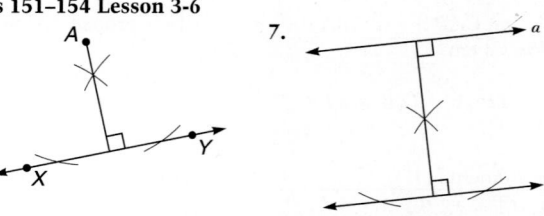

7.

9. true **11.** true **13.** yes; equidistant at all points

15.

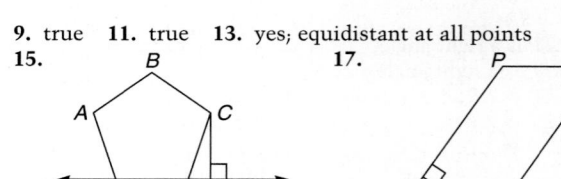

17.

19. $2\sqrt{10}$ **21.** 0 **23.** 5

25.

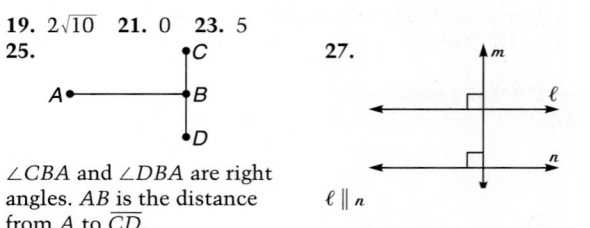

27.

$\angle CBA$ and $\angle DBA$ are right angles. AB is the distance from A to $\overline{CD}$.

$\ell \parallel n$

29. $\overline{PS}$ **31.** $\overline{QR}$ **33.** Not necessarily. The lines may be skew.

35. yes **37a.** E. 69th St.; it is the perpendicular from the point to the line. **b.** Sample answers: heavy traffic, one-way streets **39a.** 2.1 kilometers **b.** 2.7 kilometers **c.** 4.1 kilometers **d.** Riverboat; bird; bird is not restricted to traveling on the roads or in the rivers. **40.** $-\frac{2}{5}$

41.

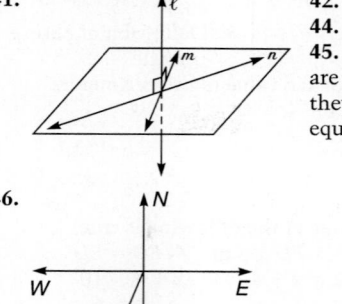

42. true **43.** 43
44. yes; detachment
45. Hypothesis—two lines are parallel; conclusion— they are everywhere equidistant.

46.

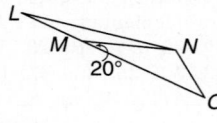

Pages 156–158 Chapter 3 Summary and Review

1. t, n **3.** t, n, ℓ **5.** t, m **7.** $\angle FAC, \angle ACD; \angle GAD, \angle ADC$
9. $\angle EBC$ **11.** $\overline{DE}$ is parallel to $\overline{CF}$; The alternate interior angles are congruent. **13.** 6 **15.** $-\frac{1}{3}$ **17.** $-\frac{9}{7}, \frac{7}{9}$
19. $\frac{1}{6}, -6$ **21.** $\overline{PS}$ **23.** $\overline{RQ}$ or $\overline{MP}$ **25.** 36 **27.** 65 mph

Pages 160–161 Algebra Review

1. 10 **3.** -18 **5.** 69 **7.** 18 **9.** 22 **11.** 16 **13.** 48
15. 87.5%
17.

-5 -4 -3 -2 -1 0 1 2

19. $\{n | n < 13\}$
21. $\{a | a \geq -5.5\}$

23. $\{x | x \leq 7\}$ **25.** y^8 **27.** $20a^5x^5$ **29.** $\frac{-y^2}{w}$ **31.** 4 **33.** 3
35. $2mr$ **37.** xyz^3 **39.** 3.7 hours **41.** 7 weeks

CHAPTER 4 CONGRUENT TRIANGLES

Pages 166–169 Lesson 4-1

13. $\triangle BCD, \triangle ABD$ **15.** $\triangle BCD$ **17.** $\overline{BD}, \overline{AD}$ **19.** 33 units
21. right isosceles **23.** scalene **25.** obtuse isosceles
27. $\angle R, \angle O, \angle M$ **29.** $\angle O, \angle M$ **31.** $\overline{RO}$ and $\overline{RM}$ **33.** true
35. true **37.** false **39.** equiangular, equilateral
41. equiangular, equilateral **43.** $\triangle OAT$ and $\triangle RYE$, and $\triangle WHT$ and $\triangle CAR$; $\triangle OAT$ and $\triangle RYE$ **45.** obtuse, isosceles
47. Given: $m\angle NMO = 20$
Prove: $\triangle LMN$ is an obtuse triangle.

Statements	Reasons
1. $m\angle NMO = 20$	1. Given
2. $\angle LMN$ and $\angle NMO$ form a linear pair.	2. Definition of linear pair
3. $\angle LMN$ and $\angle NMO$ are supplementary.	3. If 2 $\angle$s form a linear pair, they are supp.
4. $m\angle LMN + m\angle NMO = 180$	4. Definition of supplementary

5. $m\angle LMN + 20 = 180$ | **5.** Substitution property of equality
6. $m\angle LMN = 160$ | **6.** Subtraction property of equality
7. $\angle LMN$ is obtuse. | **7.** Definition of obtuse angle
8. ΔLMN is obtuse. | **8.** Definition of obtuse triangle

49. Write an inequality for the value of the perimeter.
$23 < 2x + 2 + 10 + x + 4 < 32$
$23 < 3x + 16 < 32$
$7 < 3x < 16$
$\frac{7}{3} < x < \frac{16}{3}$

Since ΔDEF is isosceles, one of the following is true.

$EF = ED$	or	$EF = FD$	or	$FD = ED$
$2x + 2 = 10$		$2x + 2 = x + 4$		$x + 4 = 10$
$2x = 8$		$x = 2$		$x = 6$
$x = 4$				

The only case that satisfies the inequality is $x = 4$, so $EF = ED$. The vertex angle is the angle between the congruent sides, so $\angle DEF$ is the vertex angle. **51.** Isosceles triangle; the segments from the vertex A to B, C, D, and E will be congruent.

55a. 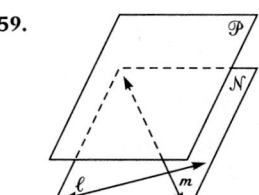 **b.** 36 **56.** Yes; the definition of parallel is that they are everywhere equidistant.

57. 0.1 or $\frac{1}{10}$ **58.** No; if they were parallel, $m\angle 1 = m\angle 5$.

59. 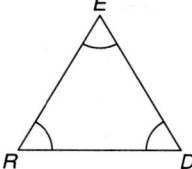 **60.** Substitution property of equality **61.** 17

Pages 174–176 Lesson 4-2
5. 42 **7.** 73 **9.** 65 **11.** 51
13.

exterior angle	remote interior angles
$\angle 1$	$\angle 3$ and $\angle 4$
$\angle 5$	$\angle 3$ and $\angle 4$
$\angle 6$	$\angle 2$ and $\angle 4$
$\angle 7$	$\angle 2$ and $\angle 4$
$\angle 8$	$\angle 2$ and $\angle 3$
$\angle 9$	$\angle 2$ and $\angle 3$

15. yes **17.** Sample answer: $\angle S$ and $\angle SUV$ are complementary and $\angle R$ and $\angle RUT$ are complementary.
19. 90 **21.** 70 **23.** 17 **25.** 55 **27.** 55 **29.** 55 **31.** 90 **33.** 30 **35.** 30 **37.** 15 **39.** $m\angle BTD = 140$, $m\angle CTD = 40$, $m\angle ATB = 40$, $m\angle B = 20$, $m\angle A = 120$, $m\angle D = 120$

41. Given: ΔRED is equiangular.
Prove: $M\angle R = m\angle E = m\angle D = 60$

Statements	Reasons
1. ΔRED is equiangular.	**1.** Given
2. $\angle R \cong \angle E \cong \angle D$	**2.** Definition of equiangular
3. $m\angle R = m\angle E = m\angle D$	**3.** Definition of congruent angles
4. $m\angle R + m\angle E + m\angle D = 180$	**4.** The sum of the ∡ in a Δ is 180.
5. $m\angle R + m\angle R + m\angle R = 180$	**5.** Substitution property of equality
6. $3m\angle R = 180$	**6.** Substitution property of equality
7. $m\angle R = 60$	**7.** Division property of equality
8. $m\angle R = m\angle E = m\angle D = 60$	**8.** Substitution property of equality

43. Given: ΔABC
Prove: $m\angle DCB = m\angle CAB + m\angle CBA$

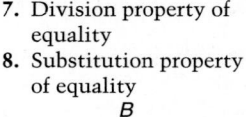

Statements	Reasons
1. ΔABC	**1.** Given
2. $\angle DCB$ and $\angle BCA$ form a linear pair.	**2.** Definition of linear pair
3. $\angle DCB$ and $\angle BCA$ are supplementary.	**3.** If 2 ∡ form a linear pair, they are supp.
4. $m\angle DCB + m\angle BCA = 180$	**4.** Definition of supplementary
5. $m\angle BCA + m\angle CAB + m\angle CBA = 180$	**5.** The sum of the ∡ in a Δ is 180.
6. $m\angle DCB + m\angle BCA = m\angle BCA + m\angle CAB + m\angle CBA$	**6.** Substitution property of equality
7. $m\angle DCB = m\angle CAB + m\angle CBA$	**7.** Subtraction property of equality

45. Given: $\overline{LT} \perp \overline{TS}$
$\overline{ST} \perp \overline{SR}$
Prove: $\angle TLR \cong \angle LRS$

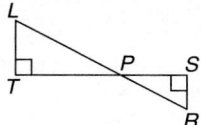

Statements	Reasons
1. $\overline{LT} \perp \overline{TS}$ $\overline{ST} \perp \overline{SR}$	**1.** Given
2. $\angle LTP$ is a right angle. $\angle RSP$ is a right angle.	**2.** $\perp$ lines form 4 rt. ∡
3. $\angle LTP \cong \angle RSP$	**3.** All rt. ∡ are $\cong$.
4. $\angle LPT \cong \angle RPS$	**4.** Vertical ∡ are $\cong$.
5. $\angle TLR \cong \angle LRS$	**5.** If 2 ∡ in a Δ are $\cong$ to 2 ∡ in another Δ, the third ∡ are $\cong$ also.

47. $\angle 2 \cong \angle 3$ **49.** 360 **53.** yes **54.** $-\frac{1}{9}$

55. Congruence of angles is reflexive.

56. 45 **57.** 2 or 8

Pages 179–182 Lesson 4-3
5. ΔPSK **7.** $\Delta WXY \cong \Delta WZY$

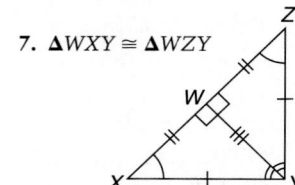

9. ΔEFD **11.** $\angle K$ **13.** $\overline{BR}$ **15.** $\Delta MIT \cong \Delta NIT$

17. The congruent parts are not corresponding.   **19.** ΔEAD
21. ΔABR ≅ ΔABS, ΔARO ≅ ΔASO ≅ ΔBRO ≅ ΔBSO,
ΔASR ≅ ΔBSR   **23.** 11   **25.** $\overline{BD} \cong \overline{AE}$ is true because the
segments are corresponding parts of congruent triangles.
27. $\overline{BC} \cong \overline{AC}$ is not necessarily true. They are not
corresponding parts of the triangles.   **29.** ∠CBA ≅ ∠CED is
true. The angles are corresponding parts of congruent
triangles.
35. Given: ΔXYZ
Prove: ΔXYZ ≅ ΔXYZ

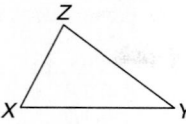

Statements	Reasons
1. ∠X ≅ ∠X ∠Y ≅ ∠Y ∠Z ≅ ∠Z	**1.** Congruence of angles is reflexive.
2. $\overline{XY} \cong \overline{XY}$ $\overline{YZ} \cong \overline{YZ}$ $\overline{XZ} \cong \overline{XZ}$	**2.** Congruence of segments is reflexive.
3. ΔXYZ ≅ ΔXYZ	**3.** Definition of congruent triangles

37. Given: ΔMNO ≅ ΔONM
Prove: ΔMNO is isosceles.

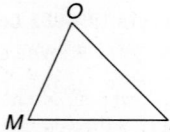

Statements	Reasons
1. ΔMNO ≅ ΔONM	**1.** Given
2. $\overline{MN} \cong \overline{ON}$	**2.** CPCTC
3. ΔMNO is isosceles.	**3.** Definition of isosceles triangle

42. 133   **43.** 105, 33, 42   **44.** true   **45.** -2   **46.** 12

Pages 187–191 Lesson 4-4
5. SSS   **7a.** Given   **b.** Definition of a midpoint   **c.** Given
d. If 2 ∥ lines are cut by a traversal, alt. int. ∠ are ≅.
e. Vertical ∠ are ≅.   **f.** ASA   **9.** SAS   **11.** true
13. could be true   **15.** could be true   **17.** could be true
19. SAS   **21.** SSS   **23.** ΔGHF; SSS
25. Given: ∠A ≅ ∠D
$AO \cong OD$
Prove: ΔAOB ≅ ΔDOC

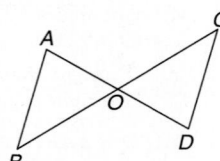

Statements	Reasons
1. ∠A ≅ ∠D $\overline{AO} \cong \overline{OD}$	**1.** Given
2. ∠AOB ≅ ∠DOC	**2.** Vertical ∠ are ≅.
3. ΔAOB ≅ ΔDOC	**3.** ASA

27. Given: $\overline{MO} \cong \overline{PO}$
$\overline{NO}$ bisects $\overline{MP}$.
Prove: ΔMNO ≅ ΔPNO

Statements	Reasons
1. $\overline{MO} \cong \overline{PO}$ $\overline{NO}$ bisects $\overline{MP}$.	**1.** Given

2. $\overline{MN} \cong \overline{PN}$	**2.** Definition of bisector
3. $\overline{NO} \cong \overline{NO}$	**3.** Congruence of segments is reflexive.
4. ΔMNO ≅ ΔPNO	**4.** SSS

29.

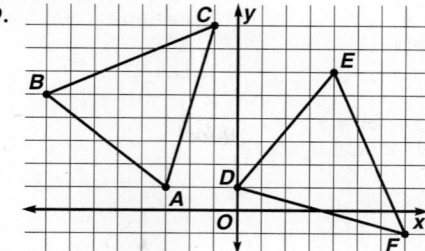

$AB = \sqrt{(-3 - (-8))^2 + (1 - 5)^2} = \sqrt{41}$
$DE = \sqrt{(0-4)^2 + (1 - 6)^2} = \sqrt{41}$
$BC = \sqrt{(-8 - (-1))^2 + (5 - 8)^2} = \sqrt{58}$
$EF = \sqrt{(4 - 7)^2 + (6 - (-1))^2} = \sqrt{58}$
$AC = \sqrt{(-3 - (-1))^2 + (1 - 8)^2} = \sqrt{53}$
$DF = \sqrt{(0 - 7)^2 + (1 - (-1))^2} = \sqrt{53}$
Since corresponding sides are congruent, the triangles are
congruent by SSS.
31. Given: ∠3 ≅ ∠4
$\overline{DC} \cong \overline{BA}$
Prove: ∠1 ≅ ∠6

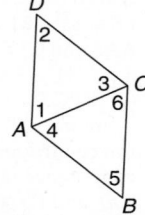

Statements	Reasons
1. ∠3 ≅ ∠4 $\overline{DC} \cong \overline{BA}$	**1.** Given
2. $\overline{AC} \cong \overline{AC}$	**2.** Congruence of segments is reflexive.
3. ΔADC ≅ ΔCBA	**3.** SAS
4. ∠1 ≅ ∠6	**4.** CPCTC

33a. ΔDCF   **b.** ΔEFC   **c.** ΔEDF   **d.** ΔFCG   **e.** ΔECG
f. ΔCGA   **34.** ∠B ≅ ∠T; ∠I ≅ ∠O; ∠G ≅ ∠P; $\overline{BI} \cong \overline{TO}$;
$\overline{IG} \cong \overline{OP}$; $\overline{BG} \cong \overline{TP}$ **35.** 12 units   **36.** Hypothesis: you
want a great pizza; Conclusion: go to Katie's   **37.** a straight
angle

Page 191 Mid-Chapter Review
1. False, the hypotenuse must be
longer than the legs.
2. true   **3.** true   **4.** true   **5.** yes   **6.** no   **7.** yes   **8.** yes

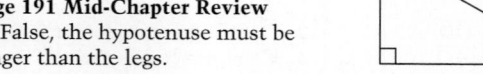

9. ∠O   **10.** $\overline{TP}$ **11.** ∠T

12. Given: $\overline{QP} \cong \overline{ST}$
∠P and ∠T are
right angles.
R is the midpoint
of $\overline{PT}$.
Prove: $\overline{QR} \cong \overline{SR}$

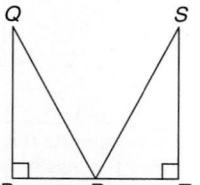

Statements	Reasons
1. $\overline{QP} \cong \overline{ST}$ $\angle P$ and $\angle T$ are right angles. R is the midpoint of PT.	1. Given
2. $\angle P \cong \angle T$	2. All rt. $\angle$s are $\cong$.
3. $\overline{PR} \cong \overline{TR}$	3. Definition of midpoint
4. $\triangle QPR \cong \triangle STR$	4. SAS
5. $\overline{QR} \cong \overline{SR}$	5. CPCTC

Pages 194–197 Lesson 4-5

7. $\overline{CE} \cong \overline{AB}$ **9.** $\angle ACB \cong \angle CAE$
11. Given: $\overline{AB} \cong \overline{CD}$
$\overline{AB} \parallel \overline{CD}$
Prove: $\triangle AOB \cong \triangle DOC$

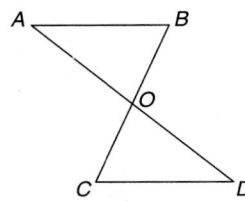

Proof: We are given that $\overline{AB} \cong \overline{CD}$ and $\overline{AB} \parallel \overline{CD}$. $\angle A \cong \angle D$ and $\angle B \cong \angle C$ since if parallel lines are cut by a transversal, alternate interior angles are congruent. Therefore, $\triangle AOB \cong \triangle DOC$ by ASA.
13. $\triangle ADO \cong \triangle CBO$ by AAS or ASA; $\triangle ADB \cong \triangle CBD$ by SAS; $\triangle ABD \cong \triangle CAD$ by SAS   **15.** $\triangle AOD \cong \triangle COB$ by SAS; $\triangle AOB \cong \triangle COD$ by SAS **17.** $\angle E \cong \angle S$ **19.** $\overline{DE} \cong \overline{RS}$ or $\overline{EF} \cong \overline{ST}$ **21.** $\triangle ABD \cong \triangle CDB$ by AAS; $\triangle AOD \cong \triangle CDB$ by AAS and CPCTC   **23.** One order of steps: 3, 1, 5, 9, 8, 2, 7, 6, 4. (1) $\perp$ lines form rt. $\angle$s.   (2) Given   (3) Given   (4) CPCTC   (5) Given   (6) ASA   (7) Given   (8) All rt. $\angle$s are $\cong$.   (9) $\perp$ lines form four rt. $\angle$s.   **25.** not valid because the conditions of the theorems or postulates that prove the congruence of triangles are not met   **27.** $\overline{ST} \cong \overline{QN}$, $\angle S \cong \angle Q$, and $\overline{PS} \cong \overline{PQ}$ is given. $\triangle TSP \cong \triangle NQP$ by SAS. $\overline{TP} \cong \overline{NP}$ by CPCTC. So $\triangle TPN$ is isosceles by the definition of isosceles triangle.

29. Given: $\overline{AB} \cong \overline{AC}$
D is the midpoint of $\overline{BC}$.
Prove: $\triangle ABD \cong \triangle ACD$

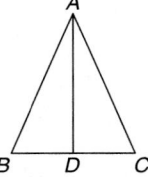

Statements	Reasons
1. $\overline{AB} \cong \overline{AC}$ D is the midpoint of $\overline{BC}$.	1. Given
2. $\overline{BD} \cong \overline{CD}$	2. Definition of midpoint
3. $\overline{AD} \cong \overline{AD}$	3. Congruence of segments is reflexive.
4. $\triangle ABD \cong \triangle ACD$	4. SSS

33.

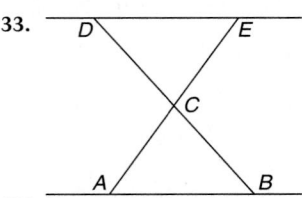

$\overline{DE}$ represents the ironing board and AB represents the floor. Since the legs bisect each other, $\overline{DC} \cong \overline{BC}$ and $\overline{CE} \cong \overline{CA}$. $\angle DCE \cong \angle BCA$ because vertical angles are congruent.

Therefore, $\triangle DCE \cong \triangle BCA$ by SAS. Since corresponding parts of congruent triangles are congruent, $\angle D \cong \angle B$. Since if two lines are cut by a transversal so that alt. int. $\angle$s are congruent, the lines are parallel, $\overline{DE} \parallel \overline{AB}$.
34. Given: $\overline{PR} \cong \overline{TR}$
$\angle 1 \cong \angle 2$
$\angle P$ and $\angle T$ are right angles.
Prove: $\overline{QR} \cong \overline{SR}$

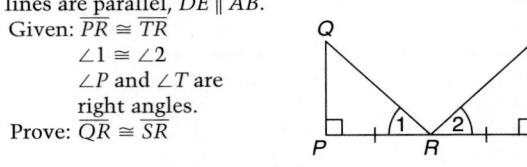

Statements	Reasons
1. $\overline{PR} \cong \overline{TR}$ $\angle 1 \cong \angle 2$ $\angle P$ and $\angle T$ are right angles.	1. Given
2. $\angle P \cong \angle T$	2. All rt. $\angle$s are $\cong$.
3. $\triangle QPR \cong \triangle STR$	3. ASA
4. $\overline{QR} \cong \overline{SR}$	4. CPCTC

35. $\angle ACK$ **36.** Alternate interior angles are congruent; corresponding angles are congruent; alternate exterior angles are congruent; consecutive interior angles are supplementary; two lines in a plane are perpendicular to a third line.
37. $2\sqrt{29}$; $(2, 6)$

Pages 199–201 Lesson 4-6

5. $2\frac{7}{12}$ **7.** $\triangle BCG \cong \triangle FCD$; $\overline{BG} \cong \overline{FD}$; $\triangle ABG \cong \triangle EFD$; $\angle A \cong \angle E$ **9.** $4624 = 68^2$

11. Subgoals: $\triangle ABD \cong \triangle ACB$, $\angle DAB \cong \angle CAB$
Proof:
Given: $\overrightarrow{AB} \perp$ plane BCD
$\overline{DB} \cong \overline{CB}$
Prove: $\angle DAB \cong \angle CAB$

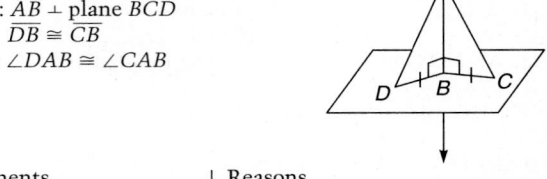

Statements	Reasons
1. $\overrightarrow{AB} \perp$ plane BCD	1. Given
2. $\overline{AB} \perp \overline{DB}$ $\overline{AB} \perp \overline{CB}$	2. Definition of perpendicular plane
3. $\angle ABD$ and $\angle ABC$ are right angles.	3. $\perp$ lines form four rt. $\angle$s.
4. $\angle ABD \cong \angle ABC$	4. All rt. $\angle$s are $\cong$.
5. $\overline{DB} \cong \overline{CB}$	5. Given
6. $\overline{AB} \cong \overline{AB}$	6. Congruence of segments is reflexive.
7. $\triangle ABD \cong \triangle ABC$	7. SAS
8. $\angle DAB \cong \angle CAB$	8. CPCTC

13. 3; 1 dog, 1 cat, and 1 hamster   **15.** 12

Pages 204–207 Lesson 4-7

5.

$\angle 1 \cong \angle 2$
$\overline{BD} \not\cong \overline{DC}$

7.

9. isosceles   **11.** $\angle EAB$ and $\angle 4$ **13.** $\angle 5$ and $\angle 6$ or $\angle EFA$ and $\angle BGA$ **15.** 67   **17.** 21

19. Given: $\overline{AB} \cong \overline{BC}$
Prove: $\angle 3 \cong \angle 5$

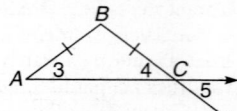

Statements	Reasons
1. $\overline{AB} \cong \overline{BC}$	1. Given
2. $\angle 3 \cong \angle 4$	2. If 2 sides of a $\triangle$ are $\cong$ the $\angle\!$s opp. the sides are $\cong$.
3. $\angle 4 \cong \angle 5$	3. Vertical $\angle\!$s are $\cong$.
4. $\angle 3 \cong \angle 5$	4. Congruence of angles is transitive.

21. 6 **23.** 3 **25.** 18 **27.** $\triangle TBR$ is isosceles—Definition of isosceles triangle; $\angle RQB \cong \angle BCR$—$\angle RQB$ and $\angle 1$ form a linear pair and so do $\angle BCR$ and $\angle 2$, so these pairs are supplementary. Since $\angle 1 \cong \angle 2$ $\angle RQB \cong \angle BCR$. $\triangle TQR \cong \triangle TCB$—AAS ($\angle 1 \cong \angle 2$, $\angle T \cong \angle T$, and $\overline{TB} \cong \overline{TR}$) $\angle TBR \cong \angle TRB$—If two sides of a $\triangle$ are $\cong$, then the $\angle\!$s opp. the sides are $\cong$.

29. Given: $\overline{PS} \cong \overline{QR}$
    $\angle 3 \cong \angle 4$
Prove: $\angle 1 \cong \angle 2$

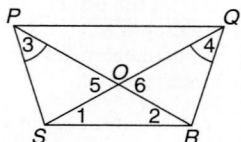

Statements	Reasons
1. $\overline{PS} \cong \overline{QR}$ $\angle 3 \cong \angle 4$	1. Given
2. $\angle 5 \cong \angle 6$	2. Vertical $\angle\!$s are $\cong$.
3. $\triangle POS \cong \triangle QOR$	3. AAS
4. $\overline{OS} \cong \overline{OR}$	4. CPCTC
5. $\angle 1 \cong \angle 2$	5. If 2 sides of a $\triangle$ are $\cong$, the $\angle\!$s opp. the sides are $\cong$.

31. Given: $\triangle ABC$ is isosceles.
    $\overline{DE} \parallel \overline{AB}$
    $\overline{AC} \cong \overline{BC}$

Prove: $\triangle DEC$ is isosceles.

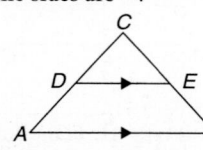

Statements	Reasons
1. $\overline{AC} \cong \overline{BC}$ $\overline{DE} \parallel \overline{AB}$	1. Given
2. $\angle A \cong \angle B$	2. If 2 sides of a $\triangle$ are $\cong$, the $\angle\!$s opp. the sides are $\cong$.
3. $\angle A \cong \angle EDC$ $\angle B \cong \angle DEC$	3. If 2 $\parallel$ lines are cut by a transversal, corr. $\angle\!$s are $\cong$.
4. $\angle EDC \cong \angle DEC$	4. Congruence of angles is transitive.
5. $\overline{CD} \cong \overline{CE}$	5. If 2 $\angle\!$s of a $\triangle$ are $\cong$, the sides opp. the $\angle\!$s are $\cong$.
6. $\triangle DEC$ is isosceles.	6. Definition of isosceles triangle

33. Given: $\overline{AB} \cong \overline{AC}$
    $\overline{BX}$ bisects $\angle ABC$.
    $\overline{CX}$ bisects $\angle ACB$.
Prove: $\overline{BX} \cong \overline{CX}$

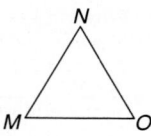

Statements	Reasons
1. $\overline{AB} \cong \overline{AC}$ $\overline{BX}$ bisects $\angle ABC$. $\overline{CX}$ bisects $\angle ACB$.	1. Given
2. $\angle ABX \cong \angle XBC$ $\angle ACX \cong \angle XCB$	2. Definition of angle bisector
3. $\angle ABC \cong \angle ACB$	3. If 2 sides of a $\triangle$ are $\cong$, the $\angle\!$s opp. the sides are $\cong$.
4. $m\angle ABX = m\angle XBC$ $m\angle ACX = m\angle XCB$ $m\angle ABC = m\angle ACB$	4. Definition of congruent angles
5. $m\angle ABC = m\angle ABX + \angle XBC$ $m\angle ACB = m\,\angle ACX + m\angle XCB$	5. Angle addition postulate
6. $m\angle ABC = 2m\angle XBC$ $m\angle ACB = 2m\angle XCB$	6. Substitution property of equality
7. $2m\angle XBC = 2m\angle XCB$	7. Substitution property of equality
8. $m\angle XBC = m\angle XCB$	8. Division property of equality
9. $\angle XBC = mXCB$	9. Definition of congruent angles
10. $\overline{BX} \cong \overline{CX}$	10. If 2 $\angle\!$s of a $\triangle$ are $\cong$, the sides opp. the $\angle\!$s are $\cong$.

35. $m\angle 1 = 20$, $m\angle 2 = 140$, $m\angle 3 = 20$, $m\angle 4 = 40$, $m\angle 5 = 100$, $m\angle 6 = 40$ $m\angle 7 = 140$

37. Given: $\triangle MNO$ is equilateral.
    Prove: $m\angle M$, $m\angle N$, and $m\angle O = 60$

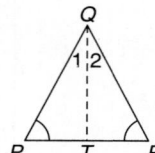

Statements	Reasons
1. $\triangle MNO$ is equilateral.	1. Given
2. $\triangle MNO$ is equiangular.	2. An equilateral $\triangle$ is equiangular.
3. $m\angle M = m\angle N = m\angle O$	3. Definition of equiangular
4. $m\angle M + m\angle N + m\angle O = 180$	4. The sum of the $\angle\!$s in a $\triangle$ is 180.
5. $3m\angle M = 180$	5. Substitution property of equality
6. $m\angle M = 60$	6. Division property of equality
7. $m\angle M$, $m\angle N$, $m\angle O = 60$	7. Substitution property of equality

39. Given: $\triangle PQR$
    $\angle P \cong \angle R$
Prove: $\overline{PQ} \cong \overline{RQ}$

Statements	Reasons
1. Let $\overline{QT}$ bisect $\angle PQR$.	1. Through any 2 pts. there is 1 line.
2. $\angle P \cong \angle R$	2. Given
3. $\angle 1 \cong \angle 2$	3. Definition of an angle bisector
4. $\overline{QT} \cong \overline{QT}$	4. Congruence of segments is reflexive.
5. $\triangle PQT \cong \triangle RQT$	5. AAS
6. $\overline{PQ} \cong \overline{RQ}$	6. CPCTC

41. 135 **43a.** 77 **b.** 30 **c.** 74 **d.** 51 **e.** 47.5 **f.** 39.5

44. $\triangle BLS \cong \triangle BES$; $\angle LBS \cong \angle EBS$; $\triangle LBU \cong \triangle EBU$; $\angle LUS \cong \angle EUS$ **45.** $\angle NTI \cong \angle NCA$, $\angle TIN \cong \angle CAN$, and $\overline{TN} \cong \overline{CN}$; $\angle NTI \cong \angle NCA$; $\angle TIN \cong \angle CAN$, and $\overline{IN} \cong \overline{AN}$; $\angle NTI \cong \angle NCA$, $\angle INT \cong \angle ANC$, and $\overline{TI} \cong \overline{CA}$; $\angle NTI \cong \angle NCA$, $\angle INT \cong \angle ANC$, and $\overline{IN} \cong \overline{AN}$; $\angle TIN \cong \angle CAN$, $\angle INT \cong \angle ANC$, and $\overline{TI} \cong \overline{CA}$; $\angle TIN \cong \angle CAN$, $\angle INT \cong \angle ANC$, and $\overline{TN} \cong \overline{CN}$
46. 31, 52, 97
47. $\angle 1 \cong \angle 4 \cong \angle 5 \cong \angle 8$; $\angle 2 \cong \angle 3 \cong \angle 6 \cong \angle 7$; Angles that are supplementary because the lines are parallel: $\angle 2$ and $\angle 5$, $\angle 4$ and $\angle 6$, $\angle 1$ and $\angle 7$, $\angle 3$ and $\angle 8$; Angles that are supplementary because they form linear pairs: $\angle 1$ and $\angle 2$, $\angle 2$ and $\angle 4$, $\angle 4$ and $\angle 3$, $\angle 3$ and $\angle 1$, $\angle 5$ and $\angle 7$, $\angle 7$ and $\angle 8$, $\angle 8$ and $\angle 6$, $\angle 6$ and $\angle 5$.
48. Don will receive an A on the Geometry test; detachment

Pages 208–210 Summary and Review
1. $\triangle ABE$, $\triangle DBE$ **3.** $\overline{BD}$ **5.** $\triangle ABF$, $\triangle BFD$, $\triangle DFE$, $\triangle AFE$, $\triangle BCD$ **7.** 53 **9.** 53 **11.** 120 **13.** 60 **15.** 55 **17.** 25
19. $\angle I$ **21.** $\overline{HG}$ **23.** $\overline{IG}$
25. Given: E is the midpoint of $\overline{AC}$.
$\angle 1 \cong \angle 2$
Prove: $\angle 3 \cong \angle 4$

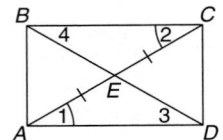

Statements	Reasons
1. E is the midpoint of $\overline{AC}$. $\angle 1 \cong \angle 2$	**1.** Given
2. $\overline{AE} \cong \overline{CE}$	**2.** Definition of midpoint
3. $\angle BEC \cong \angle DEA$	**3.** Vertical $\angle$s are $\cong$.
4. $\triangle BEC \cong \triangle DEA$	**4.** ASA
5. $\angle 3 \cong \angle 4$	**5.** CPCTC

27. We are given that $\overline{KL} \cong \overline{ML}$, $\angle J \cong \angle N$, and $\angle 1 \cong \angle 2$. Therefore, $\triangle JKL \cong \triangle NML$ by AAS. So, $\overline{JK} \cong \overline{NM}$ by CPCTC.
29. 12
31. Given: $\angle A \cong \angle D$
$\overline{AB} \cong \overline{DC}$
E is the midpoint of $\overline{AD}$.
Prove: $\angle 3 \cong \angle 4$

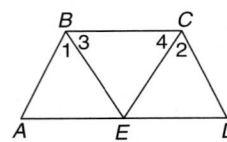

Statements	Reasons
1. $\angle A \cong \angle D$ $\overline{AB} \cong \overline{DC}$ E is the midpoint of $\overline{AD}$.	**1.** Given
2. $\overline{AE} \cong \overline{DE}$	**2.** Definition of midpoint
3. $\triangle ABE \cong \triangle DCE$	**3.** SAS
4. $\overline{BE} \cong \overline{CE}$	**4.** CPCTC
5. $\angle 3 \cong \angle 4$	**5.** If 2 sides of a $\triangle$ are $\cong$, the $\angle$s opp. the sides are $\cong$.

33. 729

CHAPTER 5 APPLYING CONGRUENT TRIANGLES

Pages 219–222 Lesson 5-1
5. $\overline{AD}$
7.

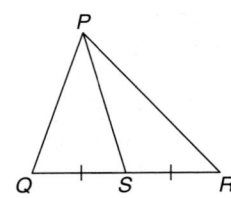

11.

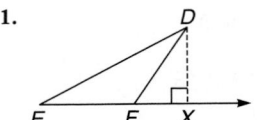

13. Given: $\overline{AB} \cong \overline{CB}$
$\overline{BD}$ is a median of $\triangle ABC$.
Prove: $\overline{BD}$ is an altitude of $\triangle ABC$.

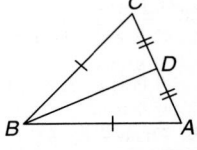
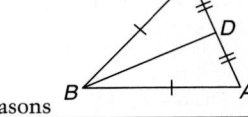

Statements	Reasons
1. $\overline{AB} \cong \overline{CB}$	**1.** Given
2. $\overline{BD}$ is a median of $\triangle ABC$.	**2.** Given
3. D is the midpoint of $\overline{CA}$.	**3.** Definition of median
4. $\overline{CD} \cong \overline{AD}$	**4.** Definition of midpoint
5. B is on the perpendicular bisector of $\overline{AC}$. D is on the perpendicular bisector of $\overline{AC}$.	**5.** A pt. equidistant from the endpts. of a segment lies on the $\perp$ bisector of the segment.
6. $\overline{BD}$ is the perpendicular bisector of $\overline{AC}$.	**6.** Through any 2 pts. there is 1 line.
7. $\overline{BD} \perp \overline{AC}$	**7.** Definition of perpendicular bisector
8. $\overline{BD}$ is an altitude of $\triangle ABC$.	**8.** Definition of altitude

15.

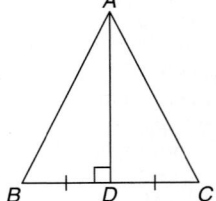

17.

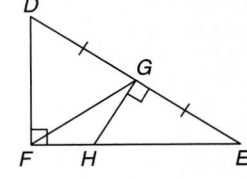

19. always **21.** sometimes **23a.** (7, 4) **b.** 3 **c.** yes **25.** 2

27. Given: $\overline{BD}$ is a median of $\triangle ABC$.
$\overline{BD}$ is an altitude of $\triangle ABC$.
Prove: $\triangle ABC$ is isosceles.

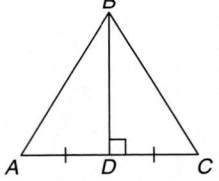

Statements	Reasons
1. $\overline{BD}$ is a median of $\triangle ABC$.	**1.** Given
2. D is the midpoint of $\overline{AC}$.	**2.** Definition of median
3. $\overline{AD} \cong \overline{CD}$	**3.** Definition of midpoint
4. $\overline{BD}$ is an altitude of $\triangle ABC$.	**4.** Given
5. $\overline{BD} \perp \overline{AC}$	**5.** Definition of altitude
6. $\angle BDA$ and $\angle BDC$ are right angles.	**6.** $\perp$ lines form 4 rt. $\angle$s.
7. $\angle BDA \cong \angle BDC$	**7.** All rt. $\angle$s are $\cong$.
8. $\overline{BD} \cong \overline{BD}$	**8.** Congruence of segments is reflexive.
9. $\triangle BDA \cong \triangle BDC$	**9.** SAS
10. $\overline{BA} \cong \overline{BC}$	**10.** CPCTC
11. $\triangle ABC$ is isosceles.	**11.** Definition of isosceles triangle

29. Given: C is equidistant from A and B.
   E is the midpoint of $\overline{AB}$.
   Prove: C lies on the perpendicular bisector of $\overline{AB}$.

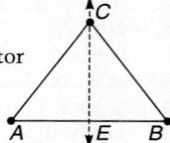

Statements	Reasons
1. C is equidistant from A and B. E is the midpoint of $\overline{AB}$.	1. Given
2. $\overline{CA} \cong \overline{CB}$	2. Definition of equidistant
3. Draw $\overleftrightarrow{CE}$.	3. Through any 2 pts. there is 1 line.
4. $\overline{CE} \cong \overline{CE}$	4. Congruence of segments is reflexive.
5. $\overline{AE} \cong \overline{BE}$	5. Definition of midpoint
6. $\triangle CAE \cong \triangle CBE$	6. SSS
7. $\angle CEA \cong \angle CEB$	7. CPCTC
8. $\angle CEA$ and $\angle CEB$ form a linear pair.	8. Definition of linear pair
9. $\angle CEA$ and $\angle CEB$ are supplementary.	9. If 2 $\angle$s form a linear pair, they are supp.
10. $m\angle CEA + m\angle CEB = 180$	10. Definition of supplementary
11. $m\angle CEA + m\angle CEA = 180$	11. Substitution property of equality
12. $2m\angle CEA = 180$	12. Substitution property of equality
13. $m\angle CEA = 90$	13. Division property of equality
14. $m\angle CEB = 90$	14. Substitution property of equality
15. $\angle CEA$ and $\angle CEB$ are right angles.	15. Definition of right angle
16. $\overline{CE} \perp \overline{AB}$	16. Definition of perpendicular
17. $\overleftrightarrow{CE}$ is the perpendicular bisector of $\overline{AB}$.	17. Definition of perpendicular bisector
18. C is on the perpendicular bisector of $\overline{AB}$.	18. A line contains at least 2 pts.

31. Given: $\overline{AB} \cong \overline{AC}$
   $\overline{AD}$ is an altitude of $\triangle ABC$.
   Prove: $\overline{AD}$ is a median of $\triangle ABC$.

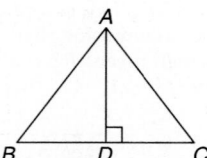

Statements	Reasons
1. $\overline{AD}$ is an altitude of $\triangle ABC$.	1. Given
2. $\overline{AD} \perp \overline{BC}$	2. Definition of altitude.
3. $\angle ADB$ and $\angle ADC$ are right angles.	3. $\perp$ lines form 4 rt. $\angle$s.
4. $\angle ADB \cong \angle ADC$	4. All rt. $\angle$s are $\cong$.
5. $\overline{AB} \cong \overline{AC}$	5. Given
6. $\angle ABD \cong \angle ACD$	6. If 2 sides of a $\triangle$ are $\cong$, the $\angle$s opp. the sides are $\cong$.
7. $\triangle ADB \cong \triangle ADC$	7. AAS
8. $\overline{BD} \cong \overline{CD}$	8. CPCTC
9. $\overline{AD}$ is a median of $\triangle ABC$.	9. Definition of median

33. Given: $\triangle ABC \cong \triangle DEF$
   $\overline{BG}$ is an angle bisector of $\triangle ABC$.
   $\overline{EH}$ is an angle bisector of $\triangle DEF$.
   Prove: $\overline{BG} \cong \overline{EH}$

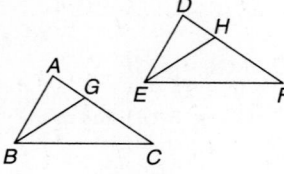

Statements	Reasons
1. $\triangle ABC \cong \triangle DEF$	1. Given
2. $\angle A \cong \angle D$ $\overline{AB} \cong \overline{DE}$ $\angle ABC \cong \angle DEF$	2. CPCTC
3. $\overline{BG}$ is an angle bisector of $\triangle ABC$. $\overline{EH}$ is an angle bisector of $\triangle DEF$.	3. Given
4. $\overline{BG}$ bisects $\angle ABC$. $\overline{EH}$ bisects $\angle DEF$.	4. Definition of angle bisector
5. $m\angle ABG = \frac{1}{2}m\angle ABC$ $m\angle DEH = \frac{1}{2}m\angle DEF$	5. Definition of bisect
6. $m\angle ABC = m\angle DEF$	6. Definition of congruent angles
7. $\frac{1}{2}m\angle ABC = \frac{1}{2}m\angle DEF$	7. Multiplication property of equality
8. $m\angle ABG = m\angle DEH$	8. Substitution property of equality
9. $\angle ABG \cong \angle DEH$	9. Definition of congruent angles
10. $\triangle ABG \cong \triangle DEH$	10. ASA
11. $\overline{BG} \cong \overline{EH}$	11. CPCTC

38. 7   **39.** 107   **40.** 8   **41.** yes; both have slope $-\frac{2}{3}$
42. $\overline{AX}$ is an altitude of $\triangle ABC$; detachment.

Pages 226–229 Lesson 5-2
5. none   **7.** yes, HA or AAS   **9.** none   **11.** $x = 6$
13. Given: $\angle Q$ and $\angle S$ are right angles.
   $\angle 1 \cong \angle 2$
   Prove: $\triangle PQR \cong \triangle RSP$

Statements	Reasons
1. $\angle Q$ and $\angle S$ are right angles. $\angle 1 \cong \angle 2$	1. Given
2. $\triangle QRP$ and $\triangle SPR$ are right triangles.	2. Definition of right triangle
3. $\overline{PR} \cong \overline{RP}$	3. Congruence of segments is reflexive.
4. $\triangle PQR \cong \triangle RSP$	4. HA

15. No; there is no AA or AAA congruence theorem.
17. Yes; HA   **19.** $x = 5$, $y = 3$ **21.** $x = 7$, $y = 20$
23. Given: $\overline{QP} \cong \overline{SR}$
   $\angle Q$ and $\angle S$ are right angles.
   Prove: $\angle 1 \cong \angle 2$

Statements	Reasons
1. $\overline{QP} \cong \overline{SR}$ $\angle Q$ and $\angle S$ are right angles.	1. Given
2. $\triangle RQP$ and $\triangle PSR$ are right triangles.	2. Definition of right triangle

3. $\overline{PR} \cong \overline{RP}$

4. $\triangle RQP \cong \triangle PSR$
5. $\angle 1 \cong \angle 2$
25. Given: $\triangle ABY$ and $\triangle CBY$
    are right
    triangles.
    $\overline{AB} \cong \overline{CB}$
    $\overline{YX} \perp \overline{AC}$
    Prove: $\overline{AX} \cong \overline{CX}$

3. Congruence of
    segments is reflexive.
4. HL
5. CPCTC

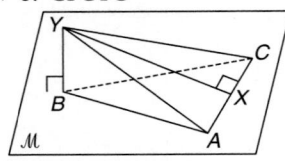

Statements	Reasons
1. $\triangle ABY$ and $\triangle CBY$ are right triangles. $\overline{AB} \cong \overline{CB}$	**1.** Given
2. $\overline{YB} \cong \overline{YB}$	**2.** Congruence of segments is reflexive.
3. $\triangle YBA \cong \triangle YBC$	**3.** LL
4. $\overline{YA} \cong \overline{YC}$	**4.** CPCTC
5. $\overline{YX} \perp \overline{AC}$	**5.** Given
6. $\angle YXA$ and $\angle YXC$ are right angles.	**6.** $\perp$ lines form four rt. $\angle$s.
7. $\triangle YXA$ and $\triangle YXC$ are right triangles.	**7.** Definition of right triangle
8. $\overline{YX} \cong \overline{YX}$	**8.** Congruence of segments is reflexive.
9. $\triangle YXA \cong \triangle YXC$	**9.** HL
10. $\overline{AX} \cong \overline{CX}$	**10.** CPCTC

27. Given: $\triangle ABC$ and $\triangle DEF$ are right
    triangles.
    $\overline{AB} \cong \overline{DE}$
    $\overline{BC} \cong \overline{EF}$
    Prove: $\triangle ABC \cong \triangle DEF$

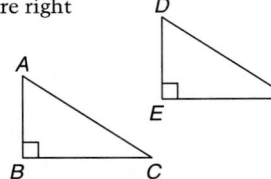

Statements	Reasons
1. $\triangle ABC$ and $\triangle DEF$ are right triangles.	**1.** Given
2. $\angle ABC$ and $\angle DEF$ are right angles.	**2.** Definition of right triangle
3. $\angle ABC \cong \angle DEF$	**3.** All rt. $\angle$s are $\cong$.
4. $\overline{AB} \cong \overline{DE}$ $\overline{BC} \cong \overline{EF}$	**4.** Given
5. $\triangle ABC \cong \triangle DEF$	**5.** SAS

29. Given: $\triangle ABC \cong \triangle DEF$
    $\overline{AG}$ is the
    altitude to $\overline{BC}$.
    $\overline{DH}$ is the
    altitude to $\overline{EF}$.
    Prove: $\overline{AG} \cong \overline{DH}$

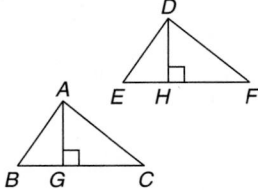

Statements	Reasons
1. $\triangle ABC \cong \triangle DEF$	**1.** Given
2. $\overline{AC} \cong \overline{DF}$ $\angle C \cong \angle F$	**2.** CPCTC
3. $\overline{AG}$ is the altitude to $\overline{BC}$. $\overline{DH}$ is the altitude to $\overline{EF}$.	**3.** Given
4. $\overline{AG} \perp \overline{BC}$ $\overline{DH} \perp \overline{EF}$	**4.** Definition of altitude
5. $\angle AGC$ is a right angle. $\angle DHF$ is a right angle.	**5.** $\perp$ lines form four rt. $\angle$s.
6. $\triangle AGC$ is a right triangle. $\triangle DHF$ is a right triangle.	**6.** Definition of right triangle

7. $\triangle AGC \cong \triangle DHE$
8. $\overline{AG} \cong \overline{DH}$

7. HA
8. CPCTC

33. The brace represents the hypotenuse of a right triangle as shown in the diagram, (assuming the deck will be attached at a right angle to the wall). If each brace is attached at the same distance from the wall, this distance represents a leg of the triangle. HL says that the four triangles will be congruent and hence all will be attached at the same distance on the wall since that distance represents the other leg of the triangle.

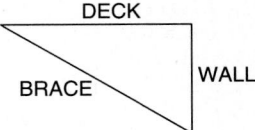

34. $\angle 6 \cong \angle 1$ **35.** $\angle 5$ and $\angle 4$; $\angle 1$ and $\angle 6$ **36.** $d = 11$
37. If a segment is a median of a triangle, then it bisects one side of the triangle.

Pages 231–232 Lesson 5-3
5. 61   **7.** 5   **9.** \$136   **11.** $O = 0, N = 5, G = 2$ or $O = 2, N = 3, G = 9$ **13.** 225 square units

Pages 235–239 Lesson 5-4
5. $\triangle ABC$ is right or obtuse.   **7.** If two parallel lines are cut by a transversal, then alternate exterior angles are not congruent.
9. $>$ **11.** $<$ **13.** division   **15.** transitive
17. Given: $\overline{PQ} \cong \overline{PR}$
         $\angle 1 \not\cong \angle 2$
    Prove: $\overline{PZ}$ is not a median of $\triangle PQR$.

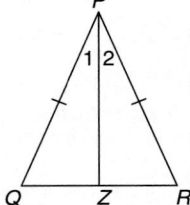

Proof: Assume that $\overline{PZ}$ is a median of $\triangle PQR$. We are given that $\overline{PQ} \cong \overline{PR}$ and that $\angle 1 \not\cong \angle 2$. Since $\overline{PZ}$ is a median of $\triangle PQR$, $\overline{QZ} \cong \overline{RZ}$ since Z is the midpoint of $\overline{QR}$ by the definition of median. If two sides of a triangle are congruent, then the angles opposite the sides are congruent, so $\angle Q \cong \angle R$. Therefore, $\triangle PZQ \cong \triangle PZR$ by SAS. Then $\angle 1 \cong \angle 2$ by CPCTC. This is a contradiction of a given fact. Therefore, our assumption that $\overline{PZ}$ is a median of $\triangle PQR$ must be false, which means $\overline{PZ}$ is not a median of $\triangle PQR$.
19. $>$ **21.** $<$

23. Given: $\triangle KNL$
         $\overline{NM} \cong \overline{OM}$
    Prove: $m\angle 1 > m\angle 2$

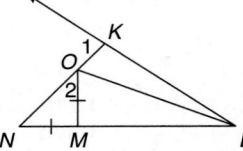

Statements	Reasons
1. $\overline{NM} \cong \overline{OM}$	**1.** Given
2. $\angle 2 \cong \angle N$	**2.** If 2 sides of a $\triangle$ are $\cong$, the $\angle$s opp. the sides are $\cong$.
3. $m\angle 1 > m\angle N$	**3.** If an $\angle$ is an ext. $\angle$ of a $\triangle$, then its measure is greater than the measure of either of its corr. remote int. $\angle$s.
4. $m\angle 2 = m\angle N$	**4.** Definition of congruent angles
5. $m\angle 1 > m\angle 2$	**5.** Substitution property of equality

25. Given: $\triangle ABC$
   $m\angle ABC = m\angle BCA$
   Prove: $x < y$

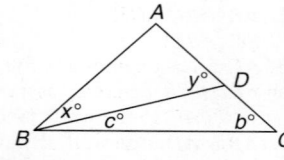

Statements	Reasons
1. $m\angle ABC = m\angle BCA$	**1.** Given
2. $m\angle ABC = x + c$	**2.** Angle addition postulate
3. $m\angle ABC > x$	**3.** Definition of inequality
4. $m\angle BCA > x$	**4.** Substitution property of equality
5. $m\angle ADB > m\angle BCA$	**5.** If an $\angle$ is an ext. $\angle$ of a $\triangle$, then its measure is greater than the measure of either of its curr. remote int. $\angle$s.
6. $m\angle ADB > x$	**6.** Transitive property of inequality
7. $y > x$	**7.** Substitution property of equality

27. Given: $\angle 2 \not\cong \angle 1$
   Prove: ℓ is not parallel to m.

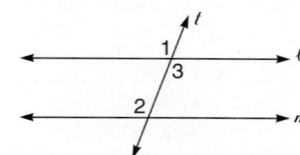

Proof: We are given that $\angle 2 \not\cong \angle 1$. We assume that ℓ is parallel to m. Since $\angle 1$ and $\angle 2$ are corresponding angles, the corresponding angles postulate says that $\angle 1 \cong \angle 2$. But this is a contradiction of our given fact. Therefore, our assumption that ℓ is parallel to m must be false, and hence ℓ is not parallel to m.

29. Given: Intersecting lines ℓ and m.
   Prove: ℓ and m intersect in no more than one point.

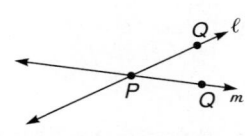

Proof: Assume lines ℓ and m intersect in more than one point. This means a point P is on both lines ℓ and m, and a point Q is on both lines ℓ and m. Therefore points P and Q determine both lines ℓ and m. But this contradicts our postulate that states through any two points there is exactly one line. So, our assumption must be false, which means lines ℓ and m intersect in no more than one point.

31. Given: $\overline{CD}$, $\overline{BE}$, and $\overline{AF}$
   are altitudes of $\triangle ABC$.
   $\overline{CD} \not\cong \overline{BE} \not\cong \overline{AF}$
   Prove: $\triangle ABC$ is scalene.

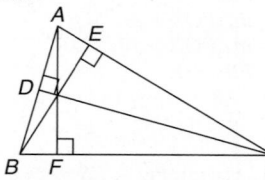

Proof: Assume $\triangle ABC$ is not scalene. Then at least two sides must be congruent by the definition. Say $\overline{AB} \cong \overline{AC}$. Now consider $\triangle ABE$ and $\triangle ACD$. Since $\overline{CD}$ and $\overline{BE}$ are altitudes and altitudes are perpendicular to the opposite side by definition, and perpendicular lines form right angles, we have that $\triangle ABE$ and $\triangle ACD$ are right triangles. By the reflexive property of congruent angles, $\angle BAC \cong \angle BAC$, and hence $\triangle ABE \cong \triangle ACD$ by HA. Then by CPCTC, $\overline{BE} \cong \overline{CD}$. But this contradicts our given statement and hence our assumption must be false. $\overline{AB} \not\cong \overline{BC}$ and $\overline{AC} \not\cong \overline{BC}$ can be proved in a similar manner. Therefore, $\triangle ABC$ is scalene.

33. Given: X is in the interior of $\triangle PQR$.
   Prove: $m\angle X > m\angle Q$

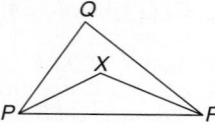

Statements	Reasons
1. $m\angle X + m\angle XPR + m\angle XRP = 180$ $m\angle Q + m\angle QPR + m\angle QRP = 180$	**1.** The sum of the $\angle$s in a $\triangle$ is 180.
2. $m\angle X + m\angle XPR + m\angle XRP = m\angle Q + m\angle QPR + m\angle QRP$	**2.** Substitution property of equality
3. $m\angle QPR = m\angle QPX + m\angle XPR$ $m\angle QRP = m\angle QRX + m\angle XRP$	**3.** Angle addition postulate
4. $m\angle X + m\angle XPR + m\angle XRP = m\angle Q + (m\angle QPX + m\angle XPR) + (m\angle QRX + m\angle XRP)$	**4.** Substitution property of equality
5. $m\angle X = m\angle Q + (m\angle QPX + m\angle QRX)$	**5.** Subtraction property of equality
6. $m\angle X > m\angle Q$	**6.** Definition of inequality

35. Mr. Sopher; Photos and Tebbe each have alibis and Bloom couldn't shoot an arrow with a sling on. **36.** S; $RS + ST = RT$ **37.** Distributive, Division **38.** $x = 4$; The figure is a square because the two triangles are congruent.
39. 3000 bacteria

Page 239 Mid-Chapter Review
1. 3 **2.** 9 **3.** yes by LL or SAS **4.** $\overline{XY} \cong \overline{XZ}$ **5.** $<$; Exterior angle inequality theorem **6.** $a > 2$ **7.** We are given that we have two lines that are noncoplanar and that do not intersect. Assume the lines are not skew. Then we have two possibilities for the lines.
Case I: The lines intersect. This contradicts the given statement that the lines do not intersect.
Case II: The lines are parallel. By the definition of parallel, this contradicts the given statement that the lines are noncoplanar.
In each case, we are led to a contradiction. Hence our assumption must be false and therefore the lines are skew.
8. Eric

Pages 242–245 Lesson 5-5
5. $\angle H$, $\angle G$, $\angle I$ **7.** $\overline{MN}$, $\overline{LN}$, $\overline{LM}$ **9.** $\overline{PQ}$, $\overline{RQ}$, $\overline{RP}$ **11.** $\overline{HT}$ **13.** $\overline{PA}$ **15.** $\angle CBA$; $\angle A$ **17.** $\overline{QT}$ **19.** $\angle EAD$, $\angle ADE$, $\angle DEA$ **21.** $\angle ADB$, $\angle ABD$, $\angle BAD$ **23.** $\overline{QR}$, $\overline{PQ}$, $\overline{PR}$
25. Given: $QR > QP$
   $\overline{PR} \cong \overline{PQ}$
   Prove: $m\angle P > m\angle Q$

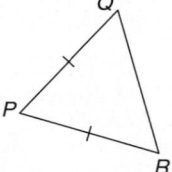

Statements	Reasons
1. $QR > QP$	**1.** Given
2. $m\angle P > m\angle R$	**2.** If one side of a $\triangle$ is longer than another side, then the $\angle$ opp. the longer side is greater than the $\angle$ opp. the shorter side.
3. $\overline{PR} \cong \overline{PQ}$	**3.** Given
4. $\angle Q \cong \angle R$	**4.** If 2 sides of a $\triangle$ are $\cong$, the $\angle$s opp. the sides are $\cong$.

5. $m\angle Q = m\angle R$ | **5.** Definition of congruent angles
6. $m\angle P > m\angle Q$ | **6.** Substitution property of equality
27. Given: $TE > AE$
  $m\angle P > m\angle PAE$
Prove: $TE > PE$

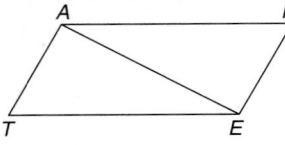

Statements	Reasons
1. $m\angle P > m\angle PAE$	1. Given
2. $AE > PE$	2. If one angle of a triangle is greater than another angle, then the side opp. the greater $\angle$ is longer than the side opp. the lesser $\angle$.
3. $TE > AE$	3. Given
4. $TE > PE$	4. Transitive property of inequality

29. Given: $\overline{PQ} \perp$ plane $\mathcal{M}$
  Prove: $\overline{PQ}$ is the shortest
    segment from P
    to plane $\mathcal{M}$.

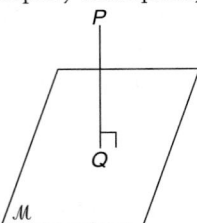

Proof: By definition, $\overline{PQ}$ is perpendicular to plane $\mathcal{M}$ if it is perpendicular to every line in $\mathcal{M}$ that intersects it. But by Theorem 5-11, that perpendicular segment is the shortest segment from the point to each of these lines. Therefore, $\overline{PQ}$ is the shortest segment from P to $\mathcal{M}$.

31. C; distance from C to line is greatest.

32. $-3 < x < \frac{21}{4}$ **33.** 5

34.

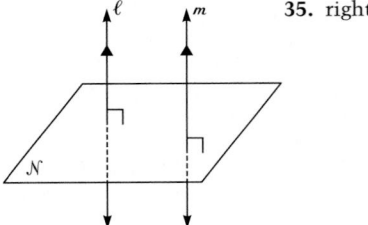

35. right

Pages 248–250 Lesson 5-6
5. no **7.** yes **9.** 9 and 17 **11.** no; the points are collinear. **13.** yes **15.** no **17.** no **19.** yes **21.** no
23. no **25.** yes **27.** no **29.** no **31.** yes

33. $\{x|x > \frac{8}{3}\}$ **35.** 1

37. Given: $\overline{AD}$, $\overline{BE}$, $\overline{CF}$
    are altitudes
    of $\triangle ABC$.
  Prove: $AB + BC + AC >$
      $AD + BE + CF$

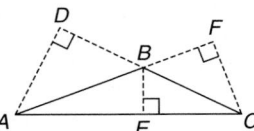

Statements	Reasons
1. $\overline{AD}$ is the altitude to $\overleftrightarrow{DC}$. $\overline{BE}$ is the altitude to $\overleftrightarrow{AC}$. $\overline{CF}$ is the altitude to $\overleftrightarrow{AB}$.	1. Given
2. $\overline{AD} \perp \overleftrightarrow{DC}$ $\overline{BE} \perp \overleftrightarrow{AC}$ $\overline{CF} \perp \overleftrightarrow{AB}$	2. Definition of altitude

---

3. $AB > AD$
  $BC > BE$
  $AC > CF$ | **3.** The perpendicular segment from a point to a line is the shortest segment from the point to the line.

4. $AB = AD + x$
  $BC = BE + y$
  $AC = CF + z$ | **4.** Definition of inequality

5. $AB + BC + AC = AD + BE + CF + x + y + z$ | **5.** Addition property of equality

6. $AB + BC + AC > AD + BE + CF$ | **6.** Definition of inequality

41a. 1 in., 4 in., 4 in.; 2 in., 3 in., 4 in.; 3 in., 3 in., 3 in.
b. The shortest side is 1 in. and the triangle is 1 in., 4 in., 4 in., an isosceles triangle **43.** $\overline{XZ}$ **44.** acute, isosceles
45. -10

46. Given: $\overline{PQ}$ bisects $\overline{AB}$.
    Prove: $\overline{AM} \cong \overline{MB}$

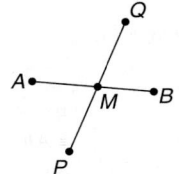

Statements	Reasons
1. $\overline{PQ}$ bisects $\overline{AB}$.	1. Given
2. M is the midpoint of $\overline{AB}$.	2. Definition of bisect
3. $AM = MB$	3. Definition of midpoint
4. $\overline{AM} \cong \overline{MB}$	4. Definition of congruent segments

47. 73, 17

Pages 254–257 Lesson 5-7
5. $m\angle ALK < m\angle NLO$ **7.** $m\angle KLO = m\angle ALN$ **9.** $m\angle B$

11. Given: $\overline{PQ} \cong \overline{SQ}$
    Prove: $PR > SR$

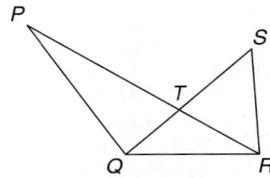

Statements	Reasons
1. $\overline{PQ} \cong \overline{SQ}$	1. Given
2. $\overline{QR} \cong \overline{QR}$	2. Congruence of segments is reflexive.
3. $m\angle PQR = m\angle PQS + m\angle SQR$	3. Angle addition postulate
4. $m\angle PQR > m\angle SQR$	4. Definition of inequality
5. $PR > SR$	5. SAS Inequality

13. $AB > AC$ **15.** $m\angle 1 < m\angle 2$ **17.** $m\angle DFE > m\angle DFG$
19. $x > 4$

21. Given: $\overline{PQ} \cong \overline{RS}$
    $QR < PS$
    Prove: $m\angle 3 < m\angle 1$

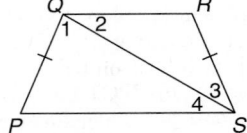

Statements	Reasons
1. $\overline{PQ} \cong \overline{RS}$	1. Given
2. $\overline{QS} \cong \overline{QS}$	2. Congruence of segments is reflexive.
3. $QR < PS$	3. Given
4. $m\angle 3 < m\angle 1$	4. SSS Inequality

23. Given: $\triangle TER$
$\overline{TR} \cong \overline{EU}$
Prove: $TE > RU$

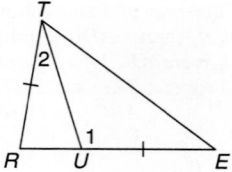

Statements	Reasons
1. $\overline{TR} \cong \overline{EU}$	1. Given
2. $\overline{TU} \cong \overline{TU}$	2. Congruence of segments is reflexive.
3. $m\angle 1 > m\angle 2$	3. If an $\angle$ is an ext. $\angle$ of a $\triangle$, then its measure is greater than the measure of either of its corr. remote int. $\angle$s.
4. $TE > RU$	4. SAS Inequality

25. Given: $\overline{ED} \cong \overline{DF}$
$m\angle 1 > m\angle 2$
D is the midpoint of CB.
$\overline{AE} \cong \overline{AF}$
Prove: $AC > AB$

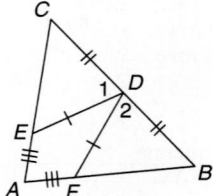

Statements	Reasons
1. $\overline{ED} \cong \overline{DF}$ D is the midpoint of $\overline{CB}$.	1. Given
2. $CD = BD$	2. Definition of midpoint
3. $\overline{CD} \cong \overline{BD}$	3. Definition of congruent segments
4. $m\angle 1 > m\angle 2$	4. Given
5. $CE > FB$	5. SAS Inequality
6. $AC = EA + CE$ $AB = AF + FB$	6. Segment addition postulate
7. $CE = AC - EA$ $FB = AB - AF$	7. Subtraction property of equality
8. $AC - EA > AB - AF$	8. Substitution property of equality
9. $\overline{AE} \cong \overline{AF}$	9. Given
10. $AE = AF$	10. Definition of congruent segments
11. $AC > AB$	11. Addition property of inequality

27. Given: $\overline{AC} \cong \overline{DF}$
$\overline{BC} \cong \overline{EF}$
$m\angle F > m\angle C$
Prove: $DE > AB$

We are given that $\overline{AC} \cong \overline{DF}$ and $\overline{BC} \cong \overline{EF}$. We also know that $m\angle F > m\angle C$. Now draw auxiliary ray $\overrightarrow{FZ}$ such that $m\angle DFZ = m\angle C$ and that $\overline{ZF} \cong \overline{BC}$. This leads to two cases.
Case I: If Z lies on $\overline{DE}$, then $\triangle FZD \cong \triangle CBA$ by SAS. Hence $ZD = BA$ by CPCTC and the definition of congruent segments. By the Segment Addition Postulate, $DE = EZ + ZD$ and hence $DE > ZD$ by the definition of inequality, then $DE > AB$ by substitution property of equality.

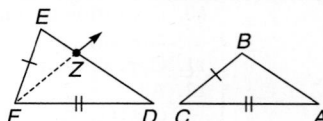

Case II: If Z does not lie on $\overline{DE}$, then let the intersection of $\overline{FZ}$ and $\overline{ED}$ be point T.

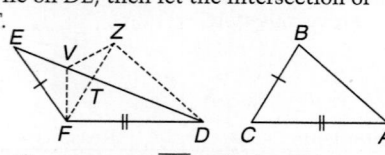

Now draw another auxiliary segment $\overline{FV}$ such that V is on $\overline{DE}$ and $\angle EFV \cong \angle VFZ$. Since $\overline{FZ} \cong \overline{BC}$ and $\overline{BC} \cong \overline{EF}$, we have $\overline{FZ} \cong \overline{EF}$ by the transitive theorem. Also $\overline{VF}$ is congruent to itself by the reflexive theorem. Hence, $\triangle EFV \cong \triangle ZFV$ by SAS. Then by CPCTC, $\overline{EV} \cong \overline{ZV}$. In $\triangle VZD$ the Triangle Inequality Theorem gives $VD + VZ > ZD$ and so by substitution $VD + EV > ZD$. By the Segment Addition Postulate $ED > ZD$. We also have $\triangle FZD \cong \triangle CBA$ by SAS which gives $\overline{ZD} \cong \overline{AB}$ by CPCTC. Making the substitution, we get $ED > BA$ or $DE > AB$.
31. yes; the measures satisfy the triangle inequality.

32. Given: $\overline{AC} \cong \overline{BD}$
$\overline{AD} \cong \overline{BC}$
Prove: $\triangle AXC \cong \triangle BXD$

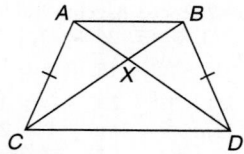

Statements	Reasons
1. $\overline{AC} \cong \overline{BD}$ $\overline{AD} \cong \overline{BC}$	1. Given
2. $\overline{AB} \cong \overline{BA}$	2. Congruence of segments is reflexive.
3. $\triangle ACB \cong \triangle BDA$	3. SSS
4. $\angle ACB \cong \angle BDA$	4. CPCTC
5. $\angle AXC \cong \angle BXD$	5. Vertical $\angle$s are $\cong$.
6. $\triangle AXC \cong \triangle BXD$	6. AAS

33. 9 **34.** $m\angle A = 36, m\angle B = 54$

Pages 258–260 Summary and Review
1. $m\angle BDC = m\angle BCD = 57, m\angle DBC = 66$ **3.** no; $m\angle AED \neq 90$ **5.** $x = 11, y = 26$ **7.** $x = 2, y = 1$

9. Given: $\triangle QXP \cong \triangle QXR$
Prove: $\overline{QX}$ is an altitude of $\triangle PQR$.

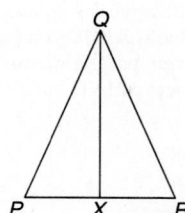

Proof: We assume $\overline{QX}$ is not an altitude of $\triangle PQR$. This means that $\overline{QX} \not\perp \overline{PR}$ by the definition of altitude. So, by the definition of perpendicular this means $\angle QXR$ is not a right angle. Therefore, $\angle QXR$ is either acute or obtuse. Since $\angle QXP$ and $\angle QXR$ form a linear pair, these two angles are supplementary. Hence, if $\angle QXP$ is acute, $\angle QXR$ is obtuse (or vice versa), by the definition of supplementary. In either case, $\angle QXP \not\cong \angle QXR$. But we are given that $\triangle QXP \cong \triangle QXR$ and by CPCTC this would mean $\angle QXP \cong \angle QXR$. This is a contradiction and hence our assumption must be false. Therefore $\overline{QX}$ is an altitude of $\triangle PQR$.
11. $>$ **13.** $<$ **15.** $\overline{SP}$ **17.** $\angle D, \angle CBD, \angle BCD$ **19.** 6 and 16 **21.** yes **23.** 3 **25.** $m\angle PSN < m\angle NQP$

27. Given: $AD = BC$
Prove: $DB < AC$

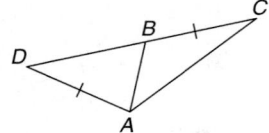

Statements	Reasons
1. $AD = BC$	1. Given
2. $\overline{AD} \cong \overline{BC}$	2. Definition of congruent segments
3. $\overline{BA} \cong \overline{BA}$	3. Congruence of segments is reflexive.
4. $m\angle CBA > m\angle DAB$	4. If an $\angle$ is an ext. $\angle$ of a Δ then its measure is greater than the measure of either of its corr. remote int. $\angle$s.
5. $AC > DB$	5. SAS Inequality

29. $(2, -1)$

Pages 262–263 Algebra Review
1. 7   **3.** 3   **5.** 25%   **7.** \$48   **9.** 15   **11.** $\{x|x \le -4\}$
13. $\{t|t > 1.2\}$ **15.** $\{k|k \ge \frac{1}{5}\}$ **17.** $64a^6b^3$ **19.** $-\frac{432d^{10}}{c^5}$
21. 2.4×10^5 **23.** 3.14×10^{-4} **25.** $-3x^3 + x^2 - 5x + 5$
27. $16m^2n^2 - 2mn + 11$ **29.** $(y + 3)(y + 4)$
31. $(a - b)(a - 9b)$ **33.** $(2x - 3)(3x + 2)$ **35.** 6.4 cm
37. 7 at \$2.99, 9 at \$2.79

CHAPTER 6 QUADRILATERALS

Pages 268–271 Lesson 6-1
5. $\overline{DC}$; definition of parallelogram
7. ΔCBA; SAS or SSS   **9.** $\overline{EB}$; Th. 6-4
11. $A(1, 1)$, $B(3, 6)$, $C(8, 8)$, and $D(6, 3)$
slope of $\overline{AB} = \frac{1-6}{1-3}$ or $\frac{5}{2}$
slope of $\overline{BC} = \frac{6-8}{3-8}$ or $\frac{2}{5}$
slope of $\overline{CD} = \frac{8-3}{8-6}$ or $\frac{5}{2}$
slope of $\overline{DA} = \frac{3-1}{6-1}$ or $\frac{2}{5}$
Since the opposite sides have the same slope, they are parallel and $ABCD$ is a parallelogram.
13. Given: parallelogram $MNOP$
Prove: $\Delta MNO \cong \Delta OPM$

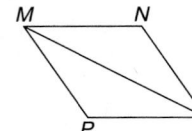

Statements	Reasons
1. $MNOP$ is a parallelogram.	1. Given
2. $\overline{MN} \cong \overline{OP}$ $\overline{NO} \cong \overline{PM}$	2. Opp. sides of a $\square$ are $\cong$.
3. $\angle MNO \cong \angle OPM$	3. Opp. $\angle$s of a $\square$ are $\cong$.
4. $\Delta MNO \cong \Delta OPM$	4. SAS

15. definition of parallelogram   **17.** Th. 6-2   **19.** 64
21. true; Th. 6-4; vertical angles are congruent and SAS
23. false   **25.** true; Th. 6-4   **27.** $x = 30$, $y = 45$, $z = 75$
29. $m\angle R = 32$, $m\angle S = 148$ **31.** $(9, 4), (5, -2), (-3, 4)$
33. yes; $\overline{JU} \parallel \overline{YL}$ and $\overline{JY} \parallel \overline{UL}$ since if two lines are cut by a tranversal so that corresponding angles are congruent, then the lines are parallel, so $JULY$ is a parallelogram by definition.   **35.** The opposite angles should be congruent.

37. The opposite sides should be parallel, and if they were parallel, then $\angle ADC$ would be congruent to $\angle BCE$.   **39.** 36
41. Given: $ABCD$ is a parallelogram.
Prove: $\angle BAD \cong \angle DCB$
$\angle ABC \cong \angle CDA$

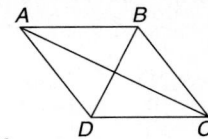

Statements	Reasons
1. $ABCD$ is a parallelogram.	1. Given
2. $\overline{AD} \cong \overline{BC}$ $\overline{AB} \cong \overline{CD}$	2. Opp. sides of a $\square$ are $\cong$.
3. $\overline{BD} \cong \overline{BD}$ $\overline{AC} \cong \overline{AC}$	3. Congruence of segments is reflexive.
4. $\Delta BAD \cong \Delta DCB$ $\Delta ABC \cong \Delta CDA$	4. SSS
5. $\angle BAD \cong \angle DCB$ $\angle ABC \cong \angle CDA$	5. CPCTC

43. Given: $\square EAST$
Prove: $\overline{ES}$ bisects $\overline{AT}$.
$\overline{AT}$ bisects $\overline{ES}$.

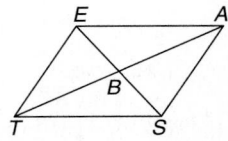

Statements	Reasons
1. $\square EAST$	1. Given
2. $\overline{EA} \cong \overline{ST}$	2. Opp. sides of a $\square$ are $\cong$.
3. $\overline{EA} \parallel \overline{ST}$	3. Definition of $\square$
4. $\angle AEB \cong \angle TSB$ $\angle EAB \cong \angle STB$	4. If 2 $\parallel$ lines are cut by a transversal, alt. int. $\angle$s are $\cong$.
5. $\Delta EBA \cong \Delta SBT$	5. ASA
6. $\overline{EB} \cong \overline{SB}$ $\overline{AB} \cong \overline{TB}$	6. CPCTC
7. $\overline{ES}$ bisects $\overline{AT}$. $\overline{AT}$ bisects $\overline{ES}$.	7. Definition of segment bisector

45. Given: $PQST$ is a parallelogram.
$\overline{RP}$ bisects $\angle QPT$.
$\overline{VS}$ bisects $\angle QST$.
Prove: $\overline{RP} \cong \overline{VS}$

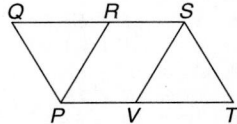

Statements	Reasons
1. $PQST$ is a parallelogram.	1. Given
2. $\angle Q \cong \angle T$ $\angle QST \cong \angle QPT$	2. Opp. $\angle$s of a $\square$ are $\cong$.
3. $m\angle QST = m\angle QPT$	3. Definition of congruent angles
4. $m\angle QST = m\angle QSV + m\angle VST$ $m\angle QPT = m\angle QPR + m\angle RPT$	4. Angle addition postulate
5. $\overline{RP}$ bisects $\angle QPT$. $\overline{VS}$ bisects $\angle QST$.	5. Given
6. $m\angle QSV = m\angle VST$ $m\angle QPR = m\angle RPT$	6. Definition of angle bisector
7. $m\angle QST = 2m\angle VST$ $m\angle QPT = 2m\angle QPR$	7. Substitution property of equality
8. $2m\angle VST = 2m\angle QPR$	8. Substitution property of equality
9. $m\angle VST = m\angle QPR$	9. Division property of equality
10. $\angle VST \cong \angle QPR$	10. Definition of congruent angles
11. $\overline{QP} \cong \overline{ST}$	11. Opp. sides of a $\square$ are $\cong$.
12. $\Delta QPR \cong \Delta TSV$	12. ASA
13. $\overline{RP} \cong \overline{VS}$	13. CPCTC

49. = ; > **50.** HA, LL, LA, and HL **51.** $\overline{TA}$ **52.** right;
yes; no **53.** $-\frac{8}{7}$ **54.** parallel **55.** If a quadrilateral has
opposite sides parallel, then it is a parallelogram.

Pages 273–274 Lesson 6-2
5. 29 **7.** 7 tables **9.** 56 pairs **11.** 47 **13.** 123, 454, 321

Pages 277-280 Lesson 6-3
7. No; the top and bottom segments are parallel, but the
other pair may not be.
9. Yes; both pairs of opposite angles are congruent.
11. $x = 8$ or -2, $y = 5$ or -5
13. midpoint A of $\overline{JK}$ = $(\frac{3+8}{2}, \frac{-2+(-2)}{2})$ or $(\frac{11}{2}, -2)$

midpoint B of $\overline{KL}$ = $(\frac{8+7}{2}, \frac{-2+(-4)}{2})$ or $(\frac{15}{2}, -3)$

midpoint C of $\overline{LM}$ = $(\frac{7+3}{2}, \frac{-4+(-6)}{2})$ or $(5, -5)$

midpoint D of $\overline{MJ}$ = $(\frac{3+3}{2}, \frac{-6+(-2)}{2})$ or $(3, -4)$

slope of $\overline{AB}$ = $\frac{-2-(-3)}{\frac{11}{2}-\frac{15}{2}}$ or $-\frac{1}{2}$

slope of $\overline{BC}$ = $\frac{-3-(-5)}{\frac{15}{2}-5}$ or $\frac{4}{5}$

slope of $\overline{CD}$ = $\frac{-5-(-4)}{5-3}$ or $-\frac{1}{2}$

slope of $\overline{DA}$ = $\frac{-4-(-2)}{3-\frac{11}{2}}$ or $\frac{4}{5}$

Since the opposite sides are parallel, $ABCD$ is a
parallelogram.

15. Given: $\square PQRS$
$\overline{XS} \cong \overline{QY}$
Prove: $PYRX$ is a
parallelogram.

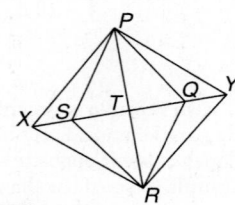

Statements	Reasons
1. $\square PQRS$ $\overline{XS} \cong \overline{QY}$	**1.** Given
2. $\overline{PT} \cong \overline{TR}$ $\overline{ST} \cong \overline{TQ}$	**2.** The diagonals of a $\square$ bisect each other.
3. $ST = TQ$ $XS = QY$	**3.** Definition of congruent segments
4. $XS + ST = TQ + QY$	**4.** Addition property of equality
5. $XT = XS + ST$ $TY = TQ + QY$	**5.** Segment addition postulate
6. $XT = TY$	**6.** Substitution property of equality
7. $\overline{XT} \cong \overline{TY}$	**7.** Definition of congruent segments
8. $\overline{XY}$ bisects $\overline{PR}$. $\overline{PR}$ bisects $\overline{XY}$.	**8.** Definition of bisector
9. $PYRX$ is a parallelogram.	**9.** If the diagonals of a quad. bisect, it is a $\square$.

17. Given: $\overline{SR} \cong \overline{TA}$
$\overline{SR} \parallel \overline{TA}$
Prove: $STAR$ is a
parallelogram.

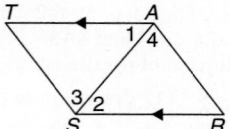

Statements	Reasons
1. $\overline{SR} \cong \overline{TA}$ $\overline{SR} \parallel \overline{TA}$	**1.** Given
2. $\angle 1 \cong \angle 2$	**2.** If 2 $\parallel$ lines are cut by a transversal, alt. int. $\angle$s are $\cong$.
3. $\overline{SA} \cong \overline{AS}$	**3.** Congruence of segments is reflexive.
4. $\triangle RSA \cong \triangle TAS$	**4.** SAS
5. $\angle 3 \cong \angle 4$	**5.** CPCTC
6. $\overline{ST} \parallel \overline{RA}$	**6.** If 2 lines are cut by a transversal and alt. int. $\angle$s are $\cong$, then the lines are $\parallel$.
7. $STAR$ is a parallelogram.	**7.** Definition of parallelogram

19. yes; Theorem 6-8 **21.** no **23.** 8 **25.** 3 **27.** 49
29. $x = 1$, $y = 4$

31. no; sample drawing:

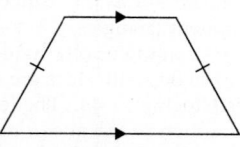

35. slope of $\overline{AB}$ = $\frac{6-8}{-2-2}$ = $\frac{-2}{-4}$ = $\frac{1}{2}$

slope of $\overline{BC}$ = $\frac{8-8}{2-3}$ = $\frac{0}{-1}$ = 0

slope of $\overline{CD}$ = $\frac{8-3}{3-(-1)}$ = $\frac{5}{4}$

slope of $\overline{DA}$ = $\frac{3-6}{-1-(-2)}$ = $\frac{-3}{1}$ = -3
This is not a parallelogram because
the opposite sides are not parallel.

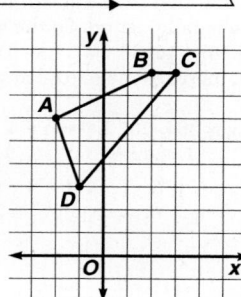

37.

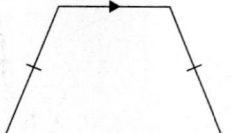

39. Given: $\triangle TWA$ is equilateral.
$TBWA$ is a
parallelogram.
$TWAI$ is a
parallelogram.
Prove: $\triangle IBM$ is equilateral.

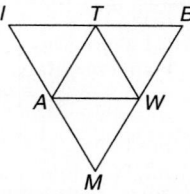

Statements	Reasons
1. $\triangle TWA$ is equilateral. $TBWA$ is a parallelogram. $TWAI$ is a parallelogram.	**1.** Given
2. $m\angle ATW = m\angle TWA$ $= m\angle WAT = 60$	**2.** Each $\angle$ of an equilateral triangle measures 60°.
3. $\angle TAW \cong \angle IBW$ $\angle TWA \cong \angle BIA$	**3.** Opp. $\angle$s of a $\square$ are $\cong$.
4. $m\angle TAW = m\angle IBW$ $m\angle TWA = m\angle BIA$	**4.** Definition of congruent angles
5. $m\angle IBW = 60$ $m\angle BIA = 60$	**5.** Substitution property of equality
6. $m\angle IBW + m\angle BIA$ $+ m\angle IMB = 180$	**6.** The sum of the $\angle$s in a $\triangle$ is 180.

7. $60 + 60 + m\angle IMB = 180$ **7.** Substitution property of equality

8. $m\angle IMB = 60$ **8.** Subtraction property of equality

9. $\triangle IBM$ is equiangular.   **9.** Definition of equiangular

10. $\triangle IBM$ is equilateral.   **10.** An equiangular $\triangle$ is equilateral.

11. $90 + m\angle WXY = 180$
$90 + m\angle YZW = 180$ **11.** Substitution property of equality

12. $m\angle WXY = 90$
$m\angle YZW = 90$ **12.** Subtraction property of equality

13. $\angle W$, $\angle Y$, $\angle WXY$, and $\angle YZW$ are right angles.   **13.** Definition of right angle

14. $WXYZ$ is a rectangle.   **14.** Definition of rectangle

13. 12   **15.** 6   **17.** 70

41. Given: $\overline{BD}$ bisects $\overline{AC}$.
$\overline{AC}$ bisects $\overline{BD}$.
Prove: $ABCD$ is a parallelogram.

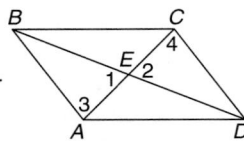

By definitions of segment bisector and midpoint, $\overline{AE} \cong \overline{CE}$ and $\overline{BE} \cong \overline{DE}$. Since they are vertical angles, $\angle 1 \cong \angle 2$. By SAS, $\triangle BEA \cong \triangle DEC$. Since they are corresponding parts in congruent triangles, $\angle 3 \cong \angle 4$ and $\overline{AB} \cong \overline{CD}$. Since $\angle 3$ and $\angle 4$ are congruent alternate interior angles, $\overline{AB} \parallel \overline{CD}$. So, since a pair of opposite sides are congruent and parallel, $ABCD$ is a parallelogram.   **43.** The legs are made so that they bisect each other, so the quadrilateral formed by the ends of the legs is a parallelogram. So the table top is parallel to the floor.
45. 37   **46.** 30   **47.** no; Triangle inequality $30 + 35 \not> 66$
48. obtuse; one obtuse angle   **49.** $0 < y < 5$

Pages 284–287 Lesson 6-4
5. 2   **7.** 2 or 5   **9.** no; sample drawing:

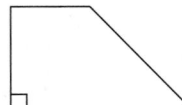

19.

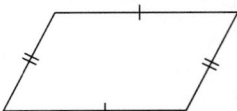

11. Given: $\square WXYZ$
$\angle 1$ and $\angle 2$ are complementary.
Prove: $WXYZ$ is a rectangle.

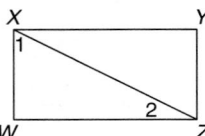

21.

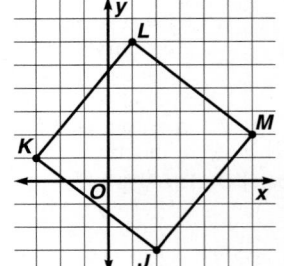

Statements	Reasons
1. $\square WXYZ$ $\angle 1$ and $\angle 2$ are complementary.	**1.** Given
2. $m\angle 1 + m\angle 2 = 90$	**2.** Definition of complementary
3. $m\angle 1 + m\angle 2 + m\angle W = 180$	**3.** The sum of the $\angle$s in a $\triangle$ is 180.
4. $90 + m\angle W = 180$	**4.** Substitution property of equality
5. $m\angle W = 90$	**5.** Subtraction property of equality
6. $\angle W \cong \angle Y$	**6.** Opp. $\angle$s of a $\square$ are $\cong$.
7. $m\angle W = m\angle Y$	**7.** Definition of congruent angles
8. $m\angle Y = 90$	**8.** Substitution property of equality
9. $\angle W$ and $\angle WXY$ are supplementary. $\angle W$ and $\angle YZW$ are supplementary.	**9.** Consec. int. $\angle$s in a $\square$ are supp.
10. $m\angle W + m\angle WXY = 180$ $m\angle W + m\angle YZW = 180$	**10.** Definition of supplementary

a. Two possible ways are to use slopes to see if opposite sides are parallel and adjacent sides are perpendicular, or to use slopes to see if opposite sides are parallel and the distance formula to see if the diagonals are congruent.
b. midpoint of $\overline{JL} = (\frac{2+1}{2}, \frac{-3+6}{2})$ or $(\frac{3}{2}, \frac{3}{2})$

midpoint of $\overline{KM} = (\frac{-3+6}{2}, \frac{1+2}{2})$ or $(\frac{3}{2}, \frac{3}{2})$

Since they have the same midpoint, $\overline{JL}$ and $\overline{KM}$ bisect each other. Therefore, $JKLM$ is a parallelogram.

$JL = \sqrt{(2-1)^2 + (-3-6)^2}$ or $\sqrt{82}$
$KM = \sqrt{(-3-6)^2 + (1-2)^2}$ or $\sqrt{82}$
Since the diagonals are congruent, $JKLM$ is a rectangle.
23. 3, 10   **25.** 32, 58, 58   **27.** 32, 58, 58   **29.** no; not all right angles   **31.** yes; opposite sides parallel and all right angles   **33.** yes   **35.** no   **37.** yes   **41.** Sample answer: Since all of the angles and the opposite sides are congruent, the bricks are interchangeable and can be installed in rows easily.   **43.** no   **44.** 58   **45.** 7   **46.** If a quadrilateral is a rectangle, then it is a parallelogram.   **47.** 16

Page 287 Mid-Chapter Review
1. $\overline{FE}$; definition of parallelogram
2. $\angle GFE$; Theorem 6-2   **3.** $\overline{HD}$; Theorem 6-4   **4.** $\triangle HDG$; Theorem 6-4 and SAS   **5.** $\overline{FG}$; Theorem 6-1   **6.** $\overline{HE}$; definition of parallelogram   **7.** 21   **8.** 125   **9.** 32
10. $-\frac{3}{2}$ **11.** definition of parallelogram   **12.** Theorem 6-6
13. Theorem 6-8   **14.** Theorem 6-7

15. Given: rectangle $JKLM$
$\overline{KF} \cong \overline{MH}$
$\overline{JE} \cong \overline{LG}$
Prove: $EFGH$ is a parallelogram.

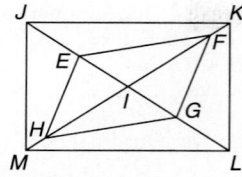

Statements	Reasons
1. rectangle $JKLM$ $\overline{KF} \cong \overline{MH}$ $\overline{JE} \cong \overline{LG}$	1. Given
2. $\overline{KI} \cong \overline{MI}$ $\overline{JI} \cong \overline{LI}$	2. Diagonals of a $\square$ bisect each other.
3. $KI = MI$ $JI = LI$ $KF = MH$ $JE = LG$	3. Definition of congruent segments
4. $KI = KF + FI$ $MI = MH + HI$ $JI = JE + EI$ $LI = LG + GI$	4. Segment addition postulate
5. $KF + FI = MH + HI$ $JE + EI = LG + GI$	5. Substitution property of equality
6. $FI = HI$ $EI = GI$	6. Subtraction property of equality
7. $\overline{FI} \cong \overline{HI}$ $\overline{EJ} \cong \overline{GI}$	7. Definition of congruent segments
8. $EFGH$ is a parallelogram.	8. If the diagonals of a quad bisect, it is a $\square$.

Pages 290–293 Lesson 6-5
5. parallelogram **7.** parallelogram

9.

Property	Parallelogram	Rectangle	Rhombus	Square
The diagonals bisect each other.	yes	yes	yes	yes
The diagonals are congruent.	no	yes	no	yes
Each diagonal bisects a pair of opposite angles.	no	no	yes	yes
The diagonals are perpendicular.	no	no	yes	yes

11. 51.8 **13.** 6 or -4 **15.** parallelogram, rectangle, rhombus, square **17.** parallelogram, rectangle, rhombus, square **19.** False; the diagonals of a rhombus are not congruent unless it is also a square. **21.** True; the diagonals of a rhombus are perpendicular. **23.** False; the consecutive angles of a rhombus are not congruent unless it is also a square. **25.** parallelogram, rectangle **27.** parallelogram, rectangle, rhombus, square **29.** 28, 62, 90 **31.** 14 **33.** 8 **35.** The diagonals are perpendicular.

Given: $KITE$
$\overline{KI} \cong \overline{KE}$
$\overline{IT} \cong \overline{ET}$
Prove: $\overline{KT} \perp \overline{IE}$

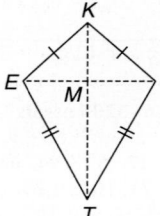

Statements	Reasons
1. $\overline{KI} \cong \overline{KE}$ $\overline{IT} \cong \overline{ET}$	1. Given
2. $\overline{KT} \cong \overline{KT}$	2. Congruence of segments is reflexive.
3. $\triangle KIT \cong \triangle KET$	3. SSS
4. $\angle IKM \cong \angle EKM$	4. CPCTC
5. $\overline{KM} \cong \overline{KM}$	5. Congruence of segments is reflexive.
6. $\triangle IKM \cong \triangle EKM$	6. SAS
7. $\angle IMK \cong \angle EMK$	7. CPCTC
8. $\angle IMK$ and $\angle EMK$ form a linear pair.	8. Definition of linear pair
9. $\angle IMK$ and $\angle EMK$ are supplementary.	9. If 2 $\angle$s form a linear pair, they are supp.
10. $m\angle IMK + m\angle EMK = 180$	10. Definition of supplementary
11. $m\angle IMK = m\angle EMK$	11. Definition of congruent angles
12. $2m\angle IMK = 180$	12. Substitution property of equality
13. $m\angle IMK = 90$	13. Division property of equality
14. $\angle IMK$ is a right angle.	14. Definition of right angle
15. $\overline{KT} \perp \overline{IE}$	15. Definition of perpendicular

37. Given: $ABCD$ is a rhombus.
$\overline{AF} \cong \overline{BG}$
$\overline{BG} \cong \overline{CH}$
$\overline{CH} \cong \overline{DE}$
$\overline{DE} \cong \overline{AF}$
Prove: $EFGH$ is a parallelogram.

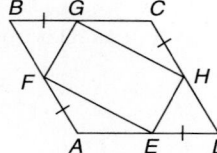

Statements	Reasons
1. $ABCD$ is a rhombus. $\overline{AF} \cong \overline{BG}$; $\overline{BG} \cong \overline{CH}$; $\overline{CH} \cong \overline{DE}$; $\overline{DE} \cong \overline{AF}$	1. Given
2. $\overline{AB} \cong \overline{BC}$; $\overline{BC} \cong \overline{CD}$; $\overline{CD} \cong \overline{AD}$; $\overline{AD} \cong \overline{AB}$	2. Definition of rhombus
3. $AF = BG, BG = CH,$ $CH = DE, DE = AF,$ $AB = BC, BC = CD,$ $CD = AD, AD = AB$	3. Definition of congruent segments
4. $AB = AF + FB,$ $BC = BG + GC,$ $CD = CH + HD,$ $AD = DE + EA$	4. Segment addition postulate
5. $AF + FB = BG + GC$ $BG + GC = CH + HD$ $CH + HD = DE + EA$ $DE + EA = AF + FB$	5. Substitution property of equality
6. $FB = GC, GC = HD,$ $HD = EA, EA = FB$	6. Subtraction property of equality
7. $\overline{FB} \cong \overline{GC}, \overline{GC} \cong \overline{HD}$ $\overline{HD} \cong \overline{EA}, \overline{EA} \cong \overline{FB}$	7. Definition of congruent segments
8. $\angle A \cong \angle C, \angle B \cong \angle D$	8. Opp. angles of a $\square$ are $\cong$.
9. $\overline{FB} \cong \overline{HD}, \overline{BG} \cong \overline{ED},$ $\overline{GC} \cong \overline{AE}, \overline{CH} \cong \overline{FA}$	9. Transitive property of equality
10. $\triangle FBG \cong \triangle HDE,$ $\triangle GCH \cong \triangle EAF$	10. SAS

11. $\overline{FG} \cong \overline{HE}$, $\overline{FE} \cong \overline{GH}$
12. Quad $EFGH$ is a parallelogram.

11. CPCTC
12. If opp. sides of a quad are $\cong$, it is a $\square$.

39a. $\overline{AC}$ becomes shorter and $\overline{BD}$ becomes longer.   **b.** The base of the jack and the plate that supports the car are parallel to the rod between points A and C and perpendicular to the diagonal $\overline{BD}$. The diagonals of a rhombus are perpendicular. Changing the lengths of the diagonals doesn't affect the level of the car.   **c.** Since the diagonals of other parallelograms are not perpendicular, the load would shift as the jack was raised.   **40.** 32, 58, 58   **41.** $AB = 31$, $BC = 35$, $CD = 31$, and $AD = 35$ **42.** no solution
43. yes, LA or AAS   **44.** Transitive property of equality
45. plane

Pages 296–299 Lesson 6-6

5. 21   **7.** 57   **9.** $\frac{9\sqrt{2}}{2} \approx 6.364$ units   **11.** $x = 11\frac{1}{2}$

13. 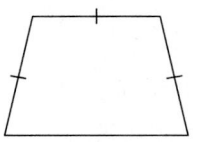   **17.**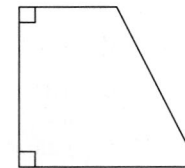

19. cannot be drawn; it would be a parallelogram   **21.** 32.1
23. 57   **25.** 1, 8; 2, 7; 3, 6; 4, 5   **27.** isosceles trapezoid

29. Given: Trapezoid $RSPT$ is isosceles.
Prove: $\triangle RSQ$ is isosceles.

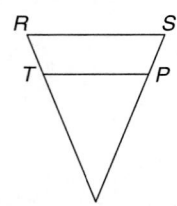

Statements	Reasons
1. Trapezoid $RSPT$ is isosceles.	1. Given
2. $\angle R \cong \angle S$	2. Base $\angle$s of an isos. trap. are $\cong$.
3. $\overline{RQ} \cong \overline{SQ}$	3. If 2 $\angle$s of a $\triangle$ are $\cong$, the sides opp. the $\angle$s are $\cong$.
4. $\triangle RSQ$ is isosceles.	4. Definition of isosceles triangle

31a. 3; $JKZX$, $IJXY$, $IKZY$ **b.** Yes; the bases and legs must be congruent if they are isosceles.

33a.

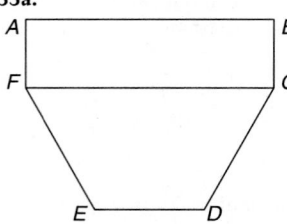   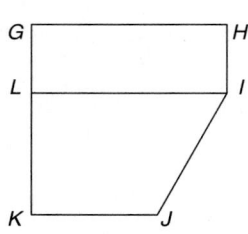

$ABCF$ - rectangle, $FCDE$ - trapezoid, $GHIL$ - rectangle, $LIKJ$ - trapezoid   **b.** Yes; $LIJK$ from the end view is congruent to the trapezoid on the other end of the box.   **35a.** 6.18
b. 4.74   **36.** false; any rhombus that is not a square   **37.** 30
38. yes; detachment   **39.** obtuse

Pages 300–302 Summary and Review
1. $\overline{ED}$; Th. 6-4   **3.** $\angle ABC$; Th. 6-2   **5.** $\triangle DAB$; SAS or SSS
7. $\overline{EA}$; Th. 6-4
9. Given: $\square PRSV$
        $\triangle PQR \cong \triangle STV$
Prove: Quadrilateral $PQST$ is a parallelogram.

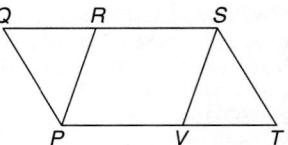

Statements	Reasons
1. $\square PRSV$ $\triangle PQR \cong \triangle STV$	1. Given
2. $\overline{RS} \cong \overline{PV}$	2. Opp. sides of a $\square$ are $\cong$.
3. $\overline{QS} \parallel \overline{PT}$	3. Definition of parallelogram
4. $\overline{QR} \cong \overline{VT}$	4. CPCTC
5. $QR + RS = QS$ $PV + VT = PT$	5. Segment addition postulate
6. $QR + RS = PV + VT$	6. Addition property of equality
7. $QS = PT$	7. Substitution property of equality
8. $\overline{QS} \cong \overline{PT}$	8. Definition of congruent segments
9. Quadrilateral $PQST$ is a parallelogram.	9. If a pair of opp. sides of a quad. are $\cong$ and $\parallel$, it is a $\square$.

11. 6   **13.** 2   **15.** 3 or -3   **17.** 46   **19.** 7   **21.** rectangle, parallelogram   **23.** 35   **25.** 47   **27.** 30   **29.** Yes; the corners will each have a 90° angle.

CHAPTER 7 SIMILARITY

Pages 310–313 Lesson 7-1
7. 0.542   **9.** 0.976   **11.** yes   **13.** yes   **15.** 4.5   **17.** 0.4
19. 0.50   **21.** 0.25   **23.** 11   **25.** 0.405   **27.** 12   **29.** $\frac{1}{1}$
31. $\frac{2}{3}$ **33.** 37.5%   **35.** 325%
37.
$$\frac{a-b}{b} = \frac{c-d}{d}$$
$$(a-b)d = (c-d)b$$
$$ad - bd = cb - db$$
$$ad - bd = cb - bd$$
$$ad - bd + bd = cb - bd + bd$$
$$ad = cb$$
$$\frac{a}{b} = \frac{c}{d}$$

39. $x = 1.25$ $y = 40$ **41.** Sample answer: $\frac{x}{2} = \frac{11}{y}$
45. 2984   **47.** about 1.3   **48.** yes; if it is a square   **49.** no; fails the triangle inequality
50.

51. If a quadrilateral is a trapezoid, then it has exactly two opposite sides parallel.

52.

Pages 316–320 Lesson 7-2
5. a   **7.** about 5.06   **9.** no   **11.** 487 soft drinks   **13.** yes
15. no   **17.** 5   **19a.** about 569 people   **b.** about 40,290 people   **21.** 10; 8   **23.** about 18.5 ft   **25.** $A(1, -1)$ and $T(1, 5)$ or $A(-5, -1)$ and $T(-5, 5)$ **27.** 50 points

31. $166.67 for CD component, $500 for a receiver, $333.33 for speakers **33.** 20.8 in. **35.** 25% **37a.** 1, 1, 2, 3, 5, 8, 13, 21, 34, 55, 89, 144, 233, 377, 610, 987, 1597, 2584, 4181, 6765 **b.** A term is the sum of the two previous terms. **c.** 1, 2, 1.5, 1.666, 1.6, 1.625, 1.61538, 1.619047, 1.617647, 1.6181818, 1.6179775, 1.618055556, 1.6180258, 1.618037135, 1.618032787, 1.618034448, 1.618033813, 1.618032056, 1.618033963; They are closer and closer approximations of the golden ratio. **38.** 15 **39.** 38, 38

40.

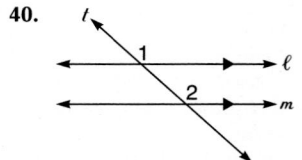

41.

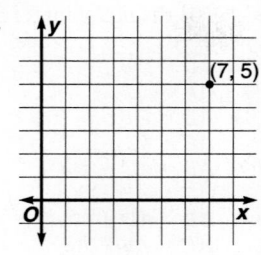

(7, 5)

Pages 323–326 Lesson 7-3
5. $\angle A \cong \angle D$, $\angle B \cong \angle E$, $\angle C \cong \angle F$, $\frac{AB}{DE} = \frac{BC}{EF} = \frac{AC}{DF}$ **7.** Yes; corresponding angles are congruent and $\frac{2.0}{3.0} = \frac{1.6}{2.4} = \frac{1.8}{2.7}$.

9. No; their two pairs of acute angles may not be congruent.
11. No; they may not have the same number of sides.

13. $\frac{2}{3}$ **15.** 15 **17a.** 43 **b.** 64.5 **c.** $\frac{43}{64.5} = \frac{2}{3}$ **19.** 12, 12

21. 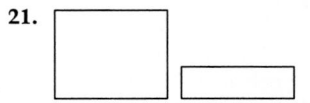 **25.**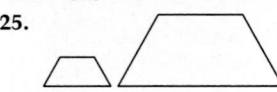

27. $\frac{6.2}{17.6}$ or $\frac{31}{88}$ or about 0.35

31. 6 times **33.** $M(0, -4)$, $N(3, -2)$ or $M(0,4)$, $N(3,2)$
39. 90 cm **41.** 3.75 in. **43.** 14 seniors **44.** trapezoid
45. It is less than 13 and greater than 3. **46.** intersecting, parallel, skew **47.** If it is cool, then I will wear a sweater.
48. the angle itself, the interior, the exterior

Pages 331–335 Lesson 7-4
5. $\overline{RA}$, $\overline{OF}$; $\overline{AT}$, $\overline{FT}$; $\overline{RT}$, $\overline{OT}$ **7.** no **9.** no **11.** yes; AA Similarity **13.** yes; AA Similarity; $x = 3\frac{1}{3}$, $y = 3$
15. yes; AA Similarity **17.** yes; SSS Similarity **19.** 11
21. $\triangle ABC \sim \triangle ADB$; AA Similarity; $\triangle ABC \sim \triangle BDC$; AA Similarity; $\triangle ADB \sim \triangle BDC$ (Th. 7-3) **23.** 12, 22.5, 7.5; $\triangle AEB \approx \triangle ADC$ by AA Similarity
25. Given: $\angle D$ is a right angle.
　　　$\overline{BE} \perp \overline{AC}$
　　Prove: $\triangle ADC \sim \triangle ABE$

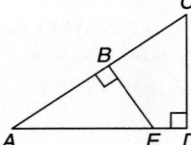

Statements	Reasons
1. $\angle D$ is a right angle. $\overline{BE} \perp \overline{AC}$	1. Given
2. $\angle EBA$ is a right angle.	2. ⊥ lines form 4 rt. ∡
3. $\angle D \cong \angle EBA$	3. All rt. ∡ are ≅.
4. $\angle A \cong \angle A$	4. Congruence of angles is reflexive.
5. $\triangle ADC \sim \triangle ABE$	5. AA Similarity

27. Given: $\angle B \cong \angle E$
　　　$\frac{AB}{DE} = \frac{BC}{EF}$
　　Prove: $\triangle ABC \sim \triangle DEF$

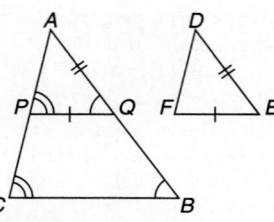

Statements	Reasons
1. Draw $\overline{QP} \parallel \overline{BC}$ so that $\overline{QP} \cong \overline{EF}$.	1. Parallel postulate
2. $\angle APQ \cong \angle C$ $\angle AQP \cong \angle B$	2. If 2 ∥ lines are cut by a transversal, corr. ∡ are ≅.
3. $\angle B \cong \angle E$	3. Given
4. $\angle AQP \cong \angle E$	4. Congruence of angles is transitive.
5. $\triangle ABC \sim \triangle AQP$	5. AA Similarity
6. $\frac{AB}{AQ} = \frac{BC}{QP}$	6. Definition of similar polygons
7. $\frac{AB}{DE} = \frac{BC}{EF}$	7. Given
8. $AB \cdot QP = AQ \cdot BC$; $AB \cdot EF = DE \cdot BC$	8. Equality of cross products
9. $QP = EF$	9. Definition of congruent segments
10. $AB \cdot EF = AQ \cdot BC$	10. Substitution property of equality
11. $AQ \cdot BC = DE \cdot BC$	11. Substitution property of equality
12. $AQ = DE$	12. Division property of equality
13. $\overline{AQ} \cong \overline{DE}$	13. Definition of congruent segments
14. $\triangle AQP \cong \triangle DEF$	14. SAS
15. $\angle APQ \cong \angle F$	15. CPCTC
16. $\angle C \cong \angle F$	16. Congruence of angles is transitive.
17. $\triangle ABC \sim \triangle DEF$	17. AA Similarity

29. Reflexive property
Given: $\triangle ABC$
Prove: $\triangle ABC \sim \triangle ABC$

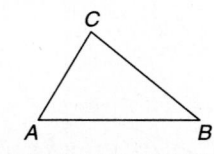

Statements	Reasons
1. $\triangle ABC$	1. Given
2. $\angle A \cong \angle A$ $\angle B \cong \angle B$	2. Congruence of angles is reflexive.
3. $\triangle ABC \sim \triangle ABC$	3. AA Similarity

Symmetric property
Given: $\triangle ABC \sim \triangle DEF$
Prove: $\triangle DEF \sim \triangle ABC$

Statements	Reasons
1. $\triangle ABC \sim \triangle DEF$	1. Given
2. $\angle A \cong \angle D$ $\angle B \cong \angle E$	2. Definition of similar polygons
3. $\angle D \cong \angle A$ $\angle E \cong \angle B$	3. Congruence of angles is symmetric.
4. $\triangle DEF \sim \triangle ABC$	4. AA Similarity

Transitive property
Given: $\triangle ABC \sim \triangle DEF$
$\qquad \triangle DEF \sim \triangle GHI$
Prove: $\triangle ABC \sim \triangle GHI$

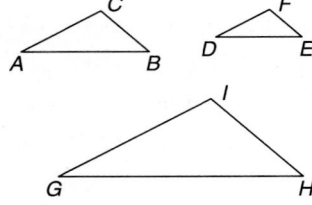

Statements	Reasons
1. $\triangle ABC \sim \triangle DEF$ $\triangle DEF \sim \triangle GHI$	1. Given
2. $\angle A \cong \angle D$ $\angle B \cong \angle E$ $\angle D \cong \angle G$ $\angle E \cong \angle H$	2. Definition of similar polygons
3. $\angle A \cong \angle G$ $\angle B \cong \angle H$	3. Congruence of angles is transitive.
4. $\triangle ABC \sim \triangle GHI$	4. AA Similarity

33. 12 m   **35.** false   **36.** true   **37.** true   **38.** true
39. false   **40.** true

Page 335 Mid-Chapter Review

1. $\frac{12}{16}$ or $\frac{3}{4}$ **2.** about \$2.22   **3.** about 93.1 gal   **4.** 2.5

5. Two polygons are similar if and only if their corresponding angles are congruent and the measures of their corresponding sides are proportional.   **6.** yes; AA Similarity   **7.** David; the right angles are congruent, but the other two pairs of angles may not be.

Pages 339–341 Lesson 7-5

7. true   **9.** true   **11.** no   **13.** no   **15.** 2

17.

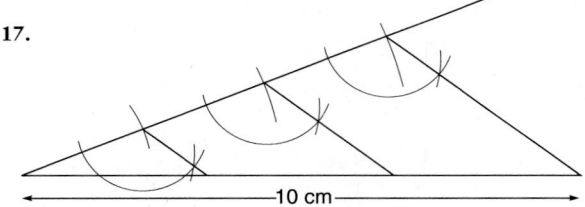
—10 cm—

19. AR **21.** AE **23.** DE **25.** 2, 12   **27.** 2.5   **29.** 3
31. 70; 1:2

33.

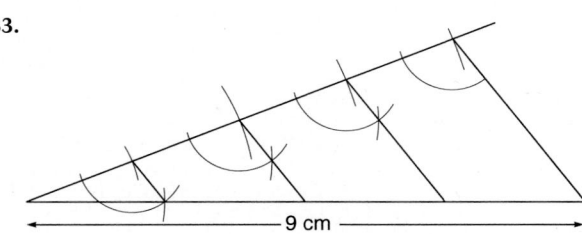
—9 cm—

35. Given: D is the midpoint of $\overline{AB}$.
E is the midpoint of $\overline{AC}$.
Prove: $\overline{DE} \parallel \overline{BC}$
$\qquad DE = \frac{1}{2}BC$

Statements	Reasons
1. D is the midpoint of $\overline{AB}$. E is the midpoint of $\overline{AC}$.	1. Given
2. $\overline{AD} \cong \overline{DB}$ $\overline{AE} \cong \overline{EC}$	2. Definition of midpoint
3. $AD = DB$ $AE = EC$	3. Definition of congruent segments
4. $AB = AD + DB$ $AC = AE + EC$	4. Segment addition postulate
5. $AB = AD + AD$ $AC = AE + AE$	5. Substitution property of equality
6. $AB = 2AD$ $AC = 2AE$	6. Substitution property of equality
7. $\frac{AB}{AD} = 2$ $\frac{AC}{AE} = 2$	7. Division property of equality
8. $\frac{AB}{AD} = \frac{AC}{AE}$	8. Transitive property of equality
9. $\angle A \cong \angle A$	9. Congruence of angles is reflexive.
10. $\triangle ADE \sim \triangle ABC$	10. SAS Similarity
11. $\angle ADE \cong \angle ABC$	11. Definition of similar polygons
12. $\overline{DE} \parallel \overline{BC}$	12. If 2 lines are cut by a transversal so that corr. $\angle$s are $\cong$, the lines are $\parallel$.
13. $\frac{BC}{DE} = \frac{AB}{AD}$	13. Definition of similar polygons
14. $\frac{BC}{DE} = 2$	14. Substitution property of equality
15. $2DE = BC$	15. Multiplication property of equality
16. $DE = \frac{1}{2}BC$	16. Division property of equality

37. (4, 6) or (6, 9)   **41.** $w = 74.1$ ft; $x = 80.2$ ft; $y = 86.4$ ft; $z = 92.6$ ft; $v = 98.7$ ft   **43.** 25 cm   **44.** $\angle R$, $\angle Q$, $\angle P$
45. obtuse   **46.** $-\frac{7}{6}$ **47.** Addition property of equality

Pages 345–348 Lesson 7-6

5. false   **7.** true   **9.** 6   **11.** true   **13.** false   **15.** true
17. $8\frac{1}{3}$ **19.** 6.75   **21.** 6   **23.** 3 or $\frac{1}{3}$ **25.** 8; 18.75   **27.** $\frac{1}{1}$

29. Given: $\triangle ABC \sim \triangle RST$
$\overline{AD}$ is a median of $\triangle ABC$.
$\overline{RU}$ is a median of $\triangle RST$.
Prove: $\frac{AD}{RU} = \frac{AB}{RS}$

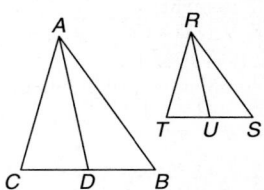

We are given that $\triangle ABC \sim \triangle RST$, $\overline{AD}$ is a median of $\triangle ABC$, and $\overline{RU}$ is a median of $\triangle RST$. So, by the definition of median, $CD = DB$ and $TU = US$. According to the definition of similar polygons, $\frac{AB}{RS} = \frac{CB}{TS}$. $CB = CD + DB$ and $TS = TU + US$ by the segment addition postulate.

Substituting, $\frac{AB}{RS} = \frac{CD + DB}{TU + US}$

$\frac{AB}{RS} = \frac{DB + DB}{US + US}$

$\frac{AB}{RS} = \frac{2DB}{2US}$

$\frac{AB}{RS} = \frac{DB}{US}$

$\angle B \cong \angle S$ by the definition of similar polygons, and $\triangle ABD \sim \triangle RSU$ using SAS Similarity. Therefore, $\frac{AD}{RU} = \frac{AB}{RS}$ by the definition of similar polygons.

31. It is a trapezoid.
Given: $\overline{SV}$ bisects $\angle RST$
$\overline{RA} \cong \overline{RV}$
$\overline{BT} \cong \overline{VT}$
Prove: $ABTR$ is a trapezoid.

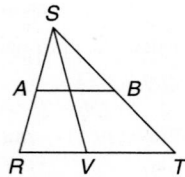

Statements	Reasons
1. $\overline{SV}$ bisects $\angle RST$. $\overline{RA} \cong \overline{RV}$ $\overline{BT} \cong \overline{VT}$	**1.** Given
2. $\frac{RV}{VT} = \frac{SR}{ST}$	**2.** An angle bisector in a triangle separates the opposite side into segments that have the same ratio as the other sides.
3. $\frac{ST}{VT} = \frac{SR}{RV}$	**3.** Property of proportions
4. $ST = SB + BT$ $SR = SA + AR$	**4.** Segment addition postulate
5. $\frac{SB + BT}{VT} = \frac{SA + AR}{RV}$	**5.** Substitution property of equality
6. $RA = RV$ $BT = VT$	**6.** Definition of congruent segments
7. $\frac{SB + BT}{BT} = \frac{SA + AR}{AR}$	**7.** Substitution property of equality
8. $\frac{SB}{BT} = \frac{SA}{AR}$	**8.** Property of proportions
9. $\overline{AB} \parallel \overline{RT}$	**9.** If a line intersects two sides of a triangle into corresponding segments of proportional lengths then the line is parallel to the third side.
10. $ABTR$ is a trapezoid.	**10.** Definition of trapezoid

33. 0.78 cm   **35.** 6 ft   **36.** 8   **37.** 5   **38.** $\angle 2 \cong \angle 1$, $\angle 2 \cong \angle N$, $\overline{PQ} \parallel \overline{LN}$, $\angle 1 \cong \angle L$, $\angle 3 \cong \angle 4$, $\angle L \cong \angle N$, $\angle 2 \cong \angle L$, $\triangle MPQ \sim \triangle MLN$, $\frac{MP}{ML} = \frac{PQ}{LN} = \frac{QM}{NM}$, $\triangle MPQ$ and $\triangle MLN$ are isosceles   **39.** $\overline{PQ} \perp \overline{QS}$, $\triangle RPQ$ and $\triangle RSQ$ are isosceles, $\overline{RP} \cong \overline{QP}$, $\overline{RS} \cong \overline{QS}$ **40.** $\triangle AEF$ and $\triangle BDC$ are right triangles, $\overline{CD} \perp \overline{AD}$, $\overline{AF} \perp \overline{AD}$, $\overline{CD} \parallel \overline{AF}$
41. $\overline{AB} \parallel \overline{DC}$, $\angle 1 \cong \angle 3$, $\triangle ADC \cong \triangle CBA$, $\angle 1$ and $\angle 2$ are complementary, $\angle 3$ and $\angle 4$ are complementary

Pages 350–351 Lesson 7-7
5. 9 socks   **7.** 1869   **9.** 24 guests

11. The series of fractions simplifies to $\frac{1}{2} + 1 + \frac{3}{2} + 2 \cdots + \frac{99}{2}$. So, find half of the sum of the series $1 + 2 + 3 + \cdots + 99$. $1 + 2 + 3 + \cdots + 99 = 49(100) + 50$ or 4950, since there are 49 pairs of addends with a sum of 100, and 50 has no match.
The sum of the series of fractions is $\frac{4950}{2}$ or 2475.

Pages 352–354 Summary and Review
1. 7.5   **3.** 1.25   **5.** false   **7.** $9\frac{1}{3}$ **9.** true   **11.** 8

13. Given: $\frac{RP}{QS} = \frac{RS}{QP}$
$\overline{QR} \parallel \overline{PS}$
isosceles trapezoid $PQRS$
Prove: $\triangle PQR \sim \triangle SRQ$

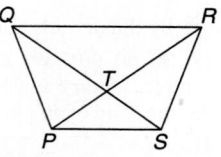

Statements	Reasons
1. isosceles trapezoid $PQRS$ $\overline{QR} \parallel \overline{PS}$	**1.** Given
2. $\overline{QP} \cong \overline{RS}$	**2.** Definition of isosceles trapezoid
3. $\overline{RQ} \cong \overline{RQ}$	**3.** Congruence of segments is reflexive.
4. $QP = RS$ $RQ = RQ$	**4.** Definition of congruent segments
5. $\frac{RQ}{RQ} = 1$, $\frac{QP}{RS} = 1$	**5.** Division property of equality
6. $\frac{RQ}{RQ} = \frac{QP}{RS}$	**6.** Substitution property of equality
7. $\frac{RP}{QS} = \frac{RS}{QP}$	**7.** Given
8. $\angle PQR \cong \angle SRQ$	**8.** Base $\angle$ of an iso. trap. are $\cong$.
9. $\triangle PQR \sim \triangle SRQ$	**9.** SAS Similarity

15. 4   **17.** $9\frac{1}{3}$ **19.** 29   **21.** $AT = TC = 4$ and $DT = TB = 7$ **23.** 2

Pages 356–357 Algebra Review
1. $7x^3y + 28x^2y^2 - 56xy^3$ **3.** $-2x^3 + 56x^2 - 9x$ **5.** $3x^2 + 13x - 10$ **7.** $6x^2 + 25xy - 9y^2$ **9.** $(x + 9)^2$
11. $\frac{1}{4}\left(n + \frac{3}{2}\right)\left(n - \frac{3}{2}\right)$ **13.** $(4p - 9r^2)(4p + 9r^2)$ **15.** $\frac{x}{4y^2z}$;
$x = 0, y = 0, z = 0$ **17.** $\frac{a-5}{a-2}$; $a = -5$ or 2   **19.** Domain: $\{-2, -1, 0\}$; Range: $\{-1, 0, 2\}$; Inverse: $\{(-1, -2), (0, -1), (2, 0)\}$
21. Domain: $\{4\}$; Range: $\{-2, -1, 1, 7\}$; Inverse: $\{(1,4), (-2, 4), (7, 4), (-1, 4)\}$ **23.** $\{y \mid y \leq -\frac{9}{2}\}$ **25.** $\{d \mid d \geq 20\}$ **27.** $\frac{245}{3}$ or 81.6   **29.** $cd - y$ **31.** $\frac{14b - 9}{a}$ **33.** $62.40   **35.** 14 in. by 11 in.

CHAPTER 8 RIGHT TRIANGLES AND TRIGONOMETRY

Pages 362–364 Lesson 8-1
5. $\sqrt{45} \approx 6.7$ **7.** $\sqrt{154} \approx 12.4$ **9.** $\sqrt{40} \approx 6.3$ **11.** $\sqrt{44} \approx 6.6$, $\sqrt{28} \approx 5.3$ **13.** $\sqrt{15} \approx 3.9$ **15.** $\frac{3}{2}$ **17.** 1   **19.** $\sqrt{45} \approx 6.7$
21. $\sqrt{30} \approx 5.5$ **23.** $\sqrt{32} \approx 5.7$ **25.** 4, 5   **27.** 8, $\sqrt{1280} \approx 35.8$ **29.** 5, $\sqrt{20} \approx 4.5$ **31.** $PQ = 9$, $PR = 13$, $PV = 3\sqrt{13}$, $VR = 2\sqrt{13}$

33. Given: $\triangle ADC$
$\angle ADC$ is a right angle.
$\overline{DB}$ is an altitude of $\triangle ADC$.
Prove: $\frac{AB}{DB} = \frac{DB}{CB}$

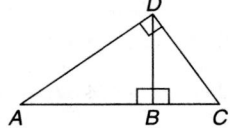

We are given that $\angle ADC$ is a right angle and $\overline{DB}$ is an altitude of $\triangle ADC$. $\triangle ADC$ is a right triangle by the definition of a right triangle. Therefore, $\triangle ADB \sim \triangle DCB$ since if the altitude is drawn from the vertex of the right angle to the hypotenuse of a right triangle, then the two triangles formed are similar to the given triangle and to each other. So $\frac{AB}{DB} =$ $\frac{DB}{CB}$ by the definition of similar polygons. **37.** 127 pages **38.** 30, 60, 90 **39.** Distributive property **40.** No; complementary angles have measures with a sum of 90 and the measure of an obtuse angle is greater than 90.

41. $AB + BC = AC$

Pages 367–370 Lesson 8-2
5. yes **7.** yes **9.** yes **11.** $\sqrt{27} \approx 5.2$ **13.** 3 **15.** 4.5 miles **17.** yes **19.** yes **21.** no **23.** 1 **25.** 13.6 **27.** 9.8 **29.** 68 cm **31.** $32 + 4\sqrt{241}$ units or about 94.1 units **33.** 19.2 ft **35.** 13 feet

37. Given: $\triangle ABC$ with sides of measure a, b, and c where $a^2 + b^2 = c^2$.
Prove: $\triangle ABC$ is a right triangle.

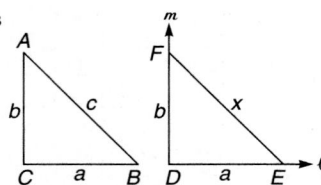

Draw $\overline{DE}$ on line ℓ with measure equal to a. At D, draw line $m \perp \overline{DE}$. Locate point F on m so that $DF = b$. Draw $\overline{FE}$ and call its measure x. Because $\triangle FED$ is a right triangle, $a^2 + b^2 = x^2$. But $a^2 + b^2 = c^2$, so $x^2 = c^2$ or $x = c$. Thus, $\triangle ABC \cong \triangle FED$ by SSS. This means $\angle C \cong \angle D$. Therefore, $\angle C$ must be a right angle, making $\triangle ABC$ a right triangle. **39.** 13 ft **41.** the area of a trapezoid **43a.** yes **b.** yes **c.** The conjecture is true. **d.** No; 1, 2, and 30 have a product of 60, but $1^2 + 2^2 \neq 30^2$. **44.** $3\sqrt{15}$ **45.** 15 m **46.** $\overleftrightarrow{XT} \| \overleftrightarrow{WY}$; $\overleftrightarrow{TZ} \| \overleftrightarrow{SY}$ **47.** 4 **48.** A duck-billed platypus is a mammal that lays eggs; syllogism

Pages 373–375 Lesson 8-3
5. 16, $8\sqrt{3}$ **7.** $31.2\sqrt{2} \approx 44.1$ m **9.** $2\sqrt{3} \approx 3.5$ ft **11.** $\frac{\sqrt{3}}{3} \approx$ 0.6 yd **13.** $3\sqrt{3} \approx 5.2$ **15.** $\frac{7\sqrt{2}}{2} \approx 4.9$ **17.** $7.5\sqrt{3} \approx 13$
19. $\sqrt{37} \approx 6.083$ **21.** 27 **23.** $12 + 12\sqrt{3}$ or about 32.8 units **25.** $\sqrt{147} \approx 12.1$ cm **27.** $\sqrt{3}$ **29.** $\sqrt{5}$ **31.** $\sqrt{7}$
33. $m\angle BFD = 60$ **37.** about 9.5 feet **38.** yes; SAS Similarity **39.** 78 in.

40. Given: $m\angle BAC = 90$,
$m\angle ABC = 30$,
$m\angle EDC = 60$
Prove: ℓ is parallel to m.

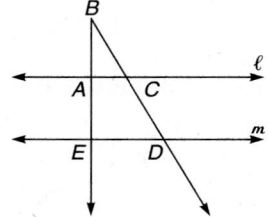

Proof: Since $m\angle BAC = 90$, $\triangle BAC$ is a right triangle. Thus, $m\angle BAC + m\angle ABC + m\angle ACB = 180$, and since $m\angle ABC = 30$, it follows that $90 + 30 + m\angle ACB = 180$. By subtraction, $m\angle ACB = 60$. Since $\angle ACB$ and $\angle EDC$ are congruent corresponding angles, ℓ is parallel to m.

Pages 378–382 Lesson 8-4
5. $\frac{15}{17} \approx 0.882$ **7.** $\frac{15}{8} \approx 1.875$ **9.** $\frac{15}{17} \approx 0.882$ **11.** $\tan Q$
13. $\sin P$ **15.** 0.174 **17.** 0.781 **19.** $m\angle S = 35$
21. about 15.4 miles **23.** $\frac{20}{29} \approx 0.690$ **25.** $\frac{21}{29} \approx 0.724$
27. $\frac{3}{4} \approx 0.750$ **29.** $\cos T$ **31.** $\tan T$ **33.** $\frac{1}{2}$ **35.** $\frac{1}{2}$
37. $\frac{\sqrt{3}}{3}$ **39.** 9.3 **41.** 42, 26.8 **43.** 30, 3.1 **45.** 12.9, 17.6 **47.** about 122 feet **49.** about 43.6 in. **53.** about 2733 feet **55.** 16 units; $8\sqrt{3}$ or about 13.9 units **56.** $x = \sqrt{104} \approx 10.2$, $y = \sqrt{65} \approx 8.1$ **57.** no; $\frac{AB}{AC} \neq \frac{AE}{AD}$ **58.** 16 in.
59. False; the diagonals of a rhombus bisect opposite angles.

60. Given: $\overline{GA} \cong \overline{AI}$
$GL < IL$
Prove: $m\angle 1 < m\angle 2$

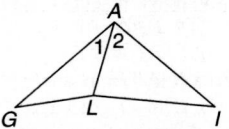

Proof: $\triangle GAL$ and $\triangle IAL$ satisfy the SSS inequality. That is, $\overline{GA} \cong \overline{AI}$, $\overline{AL} \cong \overline{AL}$, and $GL < IL$. It follows that $m\angle 1 < m\angle 2$. **61.** 100 **62.** 10

Page 382 Mid-Chapter Review
1. $\sqrt{112} \approx 10.6$ **2.** $\sqrt{135} \approx 11.6$ **3.** $\sqrt{77} \approx 8.8$ **4.** $\sqrt{128} \approx$ 11.3 **5.** yes **6.** no **7.** yes **8.** no **9.** yes **10.** yes
11. 72 units **12.** $8\sqrt{2} \approx 11.3$ cm **13.** 51°

Pages 386–388 Lesson 8-5
5. E: $\angle ZXY$; D: $\angle WYX$ **7.** E: $\angle KHJ$; D: $\angle IJH$ **9.** $\sin 47° = \frac{10}{PQ}$; 13.7 **11.** $\tan 72° = \frac{13}{QR}$; 4.2 **13.** $\cos 24° = \frac{43.7}{PQ}$; 47.8
15. 19 feet **17.** 27 **19.** 61 **21.** 2 **23.** 19 **25.** 132.63 meters **27.** 8° **29.** 31.07 meters **31.** 938.22 feet
35. 11.7 cm **37.** $\cos A = \frac{1}{3}$ or 0.333; $\sin A = \frac{2\sqrt{2}}{3}$ or 0.943; $\tan A = 2\sqrt{2}$ or 2.828 **38.** 254 miles **39.** 15.2

40. Given: $\overline{CI} \cong \overline{MI}$
$\overline{IT}$ is a median of $\triangle CIM$.
Prove: $\angle CIT \cong \angle MIT$

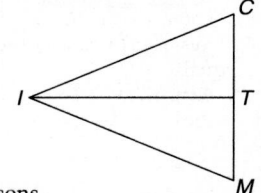

Statements	Reasons
1. $\overline{CI} \cong \overline{MI}$ $\overline{IT}$ is a median of $\triangle CIM$.	1. Given
2. $\overline{IT} \cong \overline{IT}$	2. Congruence of segments is reflexive.
3. $\overline{TC} \cong \overline{TM}$	3. Definition of median
4. $\triangle CTI \cong \triangle MTI$	4. SSS
5. $\angle CIT \cong \angle MIT$	5. CPCTC

Pages 391–393 Lesson 8-6
5.

$\frac{\sin 50°}{14} = \frac{\sin B}{10}$

7.

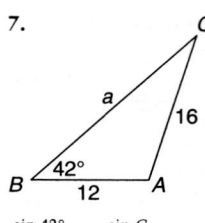

$\frac{\sin 42°}{16} = \frac{\sin C}{12}$

9. $m\angle B \approx 34$, $m\angle C \approx 40$, $c \approx 11.4$
11. $m\angle C \approx 80$, $a \approx 13.1$, $b \approx 17.6$
13. $\frac{\sin 53°}{a} = \frac{\sin 61°}{2.8}$; 2.6
15. $\frac{\sin 87°}{2.2} = \frac{\sin 70°}{a}$; 2.1
17. $m\angle B \approx 80$, $a \approx 4.3$, $b \approx 8.4$
19. $m\angle C \approx 89$, $a \approx 5.6$, $b \approx 10.2$
21. $a \approx 5.8$, $m\angle A \approx 25$, $c \approx 11.9$
23. $m\angle C \approx 27$, $m\angle A \approx 50$, $a \approx 15.7$
25. 536 feet **27.** 21.8 miles **31.** 109.6 feet **32.** 50.50 meters **33.** about 9.7

35. Given: $\overline{AB} \perp \overline{BD}$
$\overline{DE} \perp \overline{DB}$
$\overline{DB}$ bisects $\overline{AE}$.
Prove: $\angle A \cong \angle E$

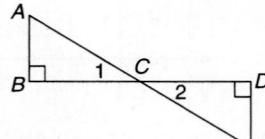

Statements	Reasons
1. $\overline{AB} \perp \overline{BD}$ $\overline{DE} \perp \overline{DB}$	1. Given
2. $\angle B$ is a right angle. $\angle D$ is a right angle.	2. $\perp$ lines form four rt. $\angle$s.
3. $\angle B \cong \angle D$	3. All rt. $\angle$s are $\cong$.
4. $\angle 1 \cong \angle 2$	4. Vertical $\angle$s are $\cong$.
5. $\overline{DB}$ bisects $\overline{AE}$.	5. Given
6. $\overline{AC} \cong \overline{EC}$	6. Definition of bisector
7. $\triangle ABC \cong \triangle EDC$	7. AAS
8. $\angle A \cong \angle E$	8. CPCTC

Pages 396–398 Lesson 8-7
5. law of cosines; $a \approx 6.1$, $m\angle B \approx 54$, $m\angle C \approx 71$ **7.** law of cosines; $m\angle A \approx 54$, $m\angle B \approx 59$, $m\angle C \approx 67$ **9.** law of cosines; $m\angle A \approx 44$, $m\angle B \approx 56$, $m\angle C \approx 80$ **11.** law of cosines; $c \approx 22.7$, $m\angle A \approx 68$, $m\angle B \approx 34$ **13.** law of cosines; $c \approx 6.5$, $m\angle A \approx 76$, $m\angle B \approx 69$ **15.** law of sines; $a \approx 23.1$, $m\angle B \approx 98$, $b \approx 27.6$ **17.** $m\angle A \approx 23$, $m\angle B \approx 67$, $m\angle C \approx 90$ **19.** $m\angle C \approx 81$, $a \approx 9.1$, $b \approx 12.1$ **21.** $a = 2.5$, $m\angle B \approx 76$, $m\angle C \approx 75$ **23.** $m\angle A \approx 103$, $m\angle B \approx 49$, $m\angle C \approx 28$ **25.** $m\angle A \approx 15$, $m\angle B \approx 131$, $m\angle C \approx 34$ **27.** 36 **29.** 26 cm **31.** 61.9 ft **35.** about 67 nautical miles **37.** about 74 yards **38.** 24.56 cm **39.** 12 **40.** 13 **41.** Yes; the lengths of the segments satisfy the triangle inequality.
42. Given: $\overline{AB} \cong \overline{BC}$
Prove: $\angle 3 \cong \angle 4$

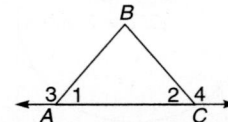

We are given that $\overline{AB} \cong \overline{BC}$. So $\angle 1 \cong \angle 2$ since if two sides of a triangle are congruent, then the angles opposite those sides are congruent. $\angle 1$ and $\angle 3$ and $\angle 2$ and $\angle 4$ form linear pairs. The angles in a linear pair are supplementary, so $\angle 1$ and $\angle 3$ are supplementary and $\angle 2$ and $\angle 4$ are supplementary. If two angles are supplementary to the same or congruent angles, then they are congruent. So $\angle 3$ and $\angle 4$ are congruent.

Pages 400–401 Lesson 8-8
3. look for a pattern, act it out, make a chart; 220 cans
5. 2730; multiply the previous term by 4 and add 2 **7.** Start both timers. When the 3-minute timer runs out, start boiling the spaghetti. When, after 4 minutes, the 7-minute timer runs out, start it over and cook for 7 more minutes.

9. $144,000 **11.** 2660 cm³ **13.** 70; It is the only number divisible by 5 ($20\% = \frac{1}{5}$) and 7 between 50 and 100.

Pages 402–404 Summary and Review
1. 18 **3.** $\sqrt{3120} \approx 55.9$ **5.** 2 **7.** $\sqrt{11,979} \approx 109.4$ **9.** $\sqrt{mn}$ **11.** $LM = \sqrt{24}$ or 4.9 **13.** $LM = \sqrt{30}$ or 5.5 **15.** $KM \approx 25.8$ **17.** 9.8 **19.** 17.0 **21.** no **23.** yes **25.** $1.55\sqrt{3} \approx 2.7$ **27.** $\frac{14.2}{\sqrt{2}} \approx 10.0$ **29.** $\frac{15}{17} \approx 0.882$ **31.** $\frac{15}{17} \approx 0.882$ **33.** $m\angle A = 51$, $c \approx 89.7$, $a \approx 70.2$ **35.** $m\angle A \approx 13$, $m\angle C \approx 145$, $c \approx 10.4$ **37.** $b \approx 30.6$, $m\angle A \approx 89$, $m\angle C \approx 47$ **39.** $m\angle A \approx 41$, $m\angle B \approx 79$, $m\angle C \approx 60$ **41.** about 4°
43. about 1675 km

CHAPTER 9 CIRCLES

Pages 413–415 Lesson 9-1
5. P **7.** $\overline{DB}$ **9.** $\overrightarrow{HB}$ **11.** G, P **13.** A, B, C, D, E
15. $(-2, -7)$, 9 **17.** true **19.** false **21.** false **23.** 7.6
25. x **27.** $x^2 + y^2 = 49$ **29.** $x^2 + y^2 = 14$

31.

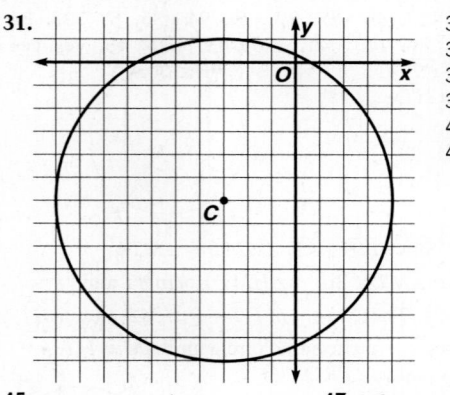

33. 15 units
35. QB
37. 15
39. $>$
41. exterior
43. on the circle

45. **47.**

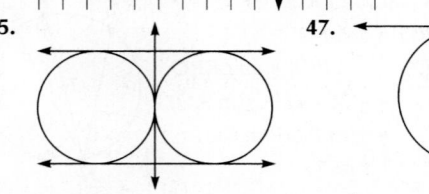

49. $(x + 2)^2 + (y - 11)^2 = 32$ **51.** $5\frac{1}{4}$ in. **53.** 16 **54.** true **55.** false **56.** true **57.** false **58.** false **59.** false

Pages 418–421 Lesson 9-2
7. major; 320 **9.** semicircle; 180 **11.** major; 270 **13.** minor; 40 **15.** minor; 130 **17.** minor; 90 **19.** 28 **21.** 246 **23.** 180 **25.** 152 **27.** 180 **29.** 114 **31.** 40 **33.** 85 **35.** 135 **37.** 85 **39.** 140 **41.** 320 **43.** false **45.** true **47.** false **49.** true **51.** 144 **53.** 32 **55.** 112 **57.** 216 **59.** 30 **61.** 13 **63.** 60 **65.** 46 **67.** $(x - 1)^2 + (y - 2)^2 = 9$ **68.** 4.5 **69.** -3, subtract 2 from the previous term **70.** 8 **71.** Obtuse triangles have one obtuse angle and all the angles in an acute triangle are acute. **72.** If circles are concentric, then they have the same center. **73.** $\sqrt{65} \approx 8.1$

Pages 425–427 Lesson 9-3
5. Theorem 9-2 **7.** Theorem 9-3 **9.** Theorem 9-1 **11.** Theorem 9-1 **13.** 75 **15.** $\overline{QV}$ **17.** V **19.** $\overarc{YT}$

21. $\overline{WA}$ **23.** no **25.** 16 **27.** Yes, because in a circle, if a diameter is perpendicular to a chord, then it bisects the chord and its arc. **29.** 13 in. **31.** 6 cm **33.** longer chord **35.** 31 **37.** Given: $\odot O$
$\overline{OS} \perp \overline{RT}$
$\overline{OV} \perp \overline{UW}$
$\overline{OS} \cong \overline{OV}$
Prove: $\overline{RT} \cong \overline{UW}$

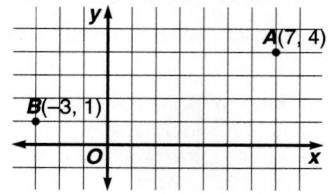

Proof: Draw radii $\overline{OT}$ and $\overline{OW}$. Since $\overline{OT} \cong \overline{OW}$ and $\overline{OS} \cong \overline{OV}$, $\triangle STO \cong \triangle VWO$ by HL. Then $\overline{ST} \cong \overline{VW}$ and $ST = VW$. Since a diameter perpendicular to a chord bisects a chord, $\overline{OS}$ bisects $\overline{RT}$ and $\overline{OV}$ bisects $\overline{UW}$. So $RT = 2ST$ and $UW = 2VW$. Therefore, $RT = UW$ and $\overline{RT} \cong \overline{UW}$. **39.** $20\sqrt{3}$ or about 34.6 units **43.** about 7.1 in. **45.** 57 **46.** $\sqrt{189} \approx 13.7$ **48.** Division or multiplication property of equality **49.** 5

Pages 431–433 Lesson 9-4
5. no **7.** no **9.** 60 **11.** 30 **13.** 40 **15.** 100 **19.** 47 **21.** 52 **23.** 99 **25.** 38 **27.** 99 **29.** 94 **31.** 68 **33.** 34 **35.** 47 **37.** 95 **39.** 105 **41.** 190 **43.** 150 **45.** yes; yes **47.** Given: $\overline{MH} \parallel \overline{AT}$
Prove: $\widehat{AM} \cong \widehat{HT}$

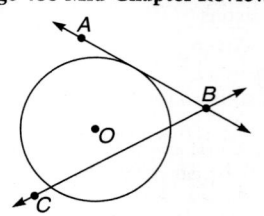

Proof: Draw $\overline{MT}$. Since $\overline{MH} \parallel \overline{AT}$, $\angle HMT \cong \angle MTA$ and $m\angle HMT = m\angle MTA$. But $m\angle HMT = \frac{1}{2}m\widehat{HT}$ and $m\angle MTA = \frac{1}{2}m\widehat{MA}$. Therefore, $\frac{1}{2}m\widehat{HT} = \frac{1}{2}m\widehat{MA}$ and $m\widehat{HT} = m\widehat{MA}$. The arcs are in the same circle and $\widehat{AM} \cong \widehat{HT}$.
49. Given: T lies inside $\angle PRQ$.
Prove: $m\angle PRQ = \frac{1}{2}m\widehat{PQ}$
Proof: $m\angle PRQ = m\angle PRK + m\angle KRQ$
$= \frac{1}{2}(m\widehat{PK}) + \frac{1}{2}(m\widehat{KQ})$
$= \frac{1}{2}(m\widehat{PK} + m\widehat{KQ})$
$= \frac{1}{2}m\widehat{PQ}$

51. Give: $\odot O$
$\widehat{MN} \cong \widehat{DC}$
Prove: $\angle MLN \cong \angle DEC$

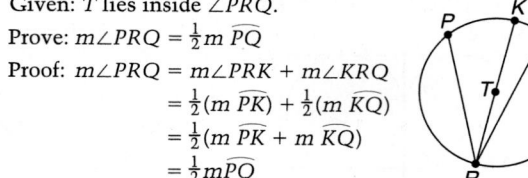

Proof: Since $\widehat{MN} \cong \widehat{DC}$, $m\widehat{MN} = m\widehat{DC}$ and $\frac{1}{2}m\widehat{MN} = \frac{1}{2}m\widehat{DC}$, $m\angle MLN = \frac{1}{2}m\widehat{MN}$ and $m\angle DEC = \frac{1}{2}m\widehat{DC}$. Therefore, $m\angle MLN = m\angle DEC$ and $\angle MLN \cong \angle DEC$.
53. Given: quadrilateral inscribed in $\odot O$.
Prove: $\angle DCB$ and $\angle DAB$ are supplementary.

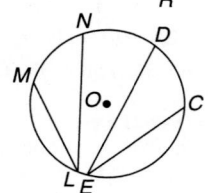

Proof: In $\odot O$ $m\widehat{DCB} + m\widehat{DAB} = 360$. Since $m\angle DAB =$

$\frac{1}{2}m\widehat{DCB}$ and $m\angle DCB = \frac{1}{2}m\widehat{DAB}$, $m\angle DAB + m\angle DCB = \frac{1}{2}m\widehat{DCB} + \frac{1}{2}m\widehat{DAB}$ or $m\angle DAB + m\angle DCB = \frac{1}{2}(m\widehat{DCB} + m\widehat{DAB}) = \frac{1}{2}(360)$ or 180. Since $m\angle DCB + m\angle DAB = 180$, the angles are supplementary by definition.
55a. 60 **b.** 120 **56.** 65 cm **57.** no, $6^2 + 9^2 \neq 11^2$ **58.** yes, all angles 90° and the sides are proportional **59.** 7 inches **60.** hypothesis: an angle is inscribed in a semicircle; conclusion: the angle is a right angle
61.

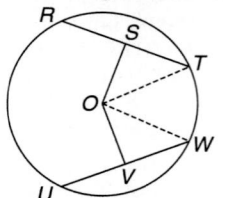

$AB = \sqrt{109} \approx 10.4$

Page 433 Mid-Chapter Review
1.

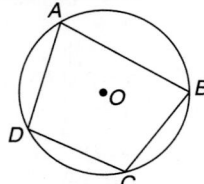

2. 12 **3.** 180 **4.** 64 **5.** 148 **6.** 116 **7.** 116 **8.** 3 cm **9.** 20.8 units **10.** 12 units **11.** 120

Pages 436-439 Lesson 9-5
5. neither **7.** 12 **9.** 14 **11.** 8 **13.** 45 **15.** 45 **17.** 90 **19.** 45 **21.** 5 **23.** 13 **25.** $5\sqrt{2} \approx 7.1$ **27.** $\sqrt{329} \approx 18.1$ **29.** $\triangle OKM \sim \triangle CLM$; Sample answer: A line parallel to a side of a triangle forms a triangle similar to the original triangle by AA Similarity. **31.** 15
33. Sample answer:
$TB = TS$
$TA = TR$
$TA - TB = TR - TS$
$AB = RS$

35.

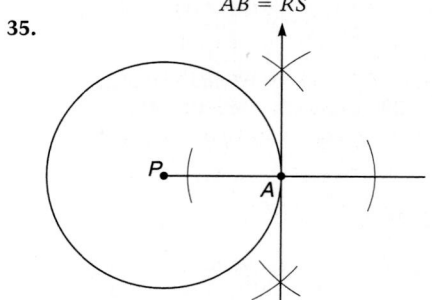

37. Given: $\overleftrightarrow{CA}$ is tangent to the circle at A.
Prove: $\overline{XA} \perp \overleftrightarrow{CA}$

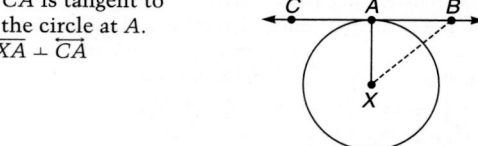

Proof: Pick any point on $\overleftrightarrow{CA}$ other than A and call it B. Now, draw $\overline{XB}$. From the definition of tangent, we know that $\overleftrightarrow{CA}$ intersects $\odot X$ at exactly one point, A, and that B lies in the exterior of $\odot X$. As a result, $XA < XB$. Thus, since $\overline{XA}$ is the shortest segment from X to $\overleftrightarrow{CA}$, it follows that $\overline{XA} \perp \overleftrightarrow{CA}$.

39. Given: $\ell \perp \overline{AB}$
$\overline{AB}$ is a radius of $\odot A$.
Prove: ℓ is tangent to $\odot A$.

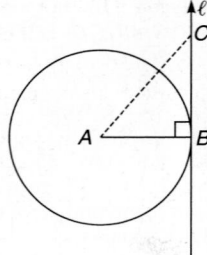

Proof: Assume that ℓ is not tangent to the circle. Since ℓ touches $\odot A$ at B, it must touch the circle in another point. Call this point C. Then $AB = AC$. But if $\overline{AB}$ is perpendicular to ℓ, AB must be the shortest distance between A and ℓ. There is a contradiction. Therefore, ℓ is tangent to $\odot A$.
44. 84 **45.** 68 in. **46.** yes; AA Similarity **47.** yes; isosceles **48.** -6

Pages 442–446 Lesson 9-6

5. 59 **7.** 105 **9.** 40 **11.** $35 = \frac{1}{2}[(360 - x) - x]$; 145
13. 114 **15.** 66 **17.** 138 **19.** 174 **21.** 49 **23.** 198
25. 236 **27.** 38 **29.** 44 **31.** 44 **33.** 200 **35.** 46
37. 134 **39.** 144 **41.** 160 **43.** 26 **45.** 144 **47.** 15
49. $x = 46$, $y = 64$, $z = 40$

51. Given: Secants $\overrightarrow{AC}$ and $\overrightarrow{BD}$ intersect at X in the interior of $\odot P$.
Prove: $m\angle AXB = \frac{1}{2}(m \widehat{AB} + m \widehat{CD})$.

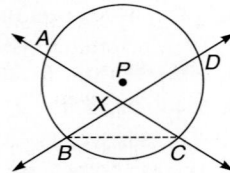

Proof: We are given that secants $\overrightarrow{AC}$ and $\overrightarrow{BD}$ intersect at X inside circle P. Draw $\overline{BC}$. Because an angle inscribed has the measure of $\frac{1}{2}$ the measure of its intercepted arc, $m\angle XBC = \frac{1}{2}m\widehat{CD}$ and $m\angle XCB = \frac{1}{2}m\widehat{AB}$. By the Exterior Angle Theorem, $m\angle AXB = m\angle XCB + m\angle XBC$. By substitution, $m\angle AXB = \frac{1}{2}m\widehat{AB} + \frac{1}{2}m\widehat{CD}$. Then by use of the distributive property, $m\angle AXB = \frac{1}{2}(m\widehat{AB} + m\widehat{CD})$.

53. Give: $\overrightarrow{DG}$ is a tangent to the circle.
$\overrightarrow{DF}$ is a secant to the circle.
Prove: $m\angle FDG = \frac{1}{2}(m \widehat{FG} - m \widehat{EG})$

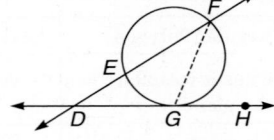

Proof: We are given that $\overrightarrow{DG}$ is a tangent to a circle, and $\overrightarrow{DF}$ is a secant to that circle. Draw $\overline{FG}$: $m\angle DFG = \frac{1}{2}m\widehat{EG}$; $m\angle FGH = \frac{1}{2}m\widehat{FG}$ because the measure of an inscribed angle equals $\frac{1}{2}$ the measure of the intercepted arc. By the Exterior Angle Theorem, $m\angle FGH = m\widehat{DFG} + m\angle FDG$. Then by substitution $\frac{1}{2}m\widehat{FG} = \frac{1}{2}m\widehat{EG} + m\angle FDG$, and by the subtraction property of equality $\frac{1}{2}m\widehat{FG} - \frac{1}{2}m\widehat{EG} = m\angle FDG$. Finally, by the distributive property of equality, $\frac{1}{2}(m\widehat{FG} - m\widehat{GE}) = m\angle FDG$).

55. Case I: The secant contains the center of the circle.
Given: Secant $\overline{AB}$ contains the center of the circle P. $\overrightarrow{CB}$ is tangent to $\odot P$ at B.
Prove: $m\angle CBA = \frac{1}{2}m \widehat{ADB}$

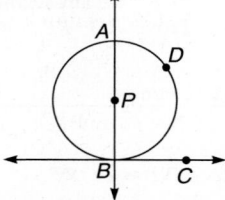

Proof: By Theorem 9-8, $\overline{BA} \perp \overline{BC}$. Thus $\angle CBA$ is a right angle and $m\angle CBA = 90$. $\widehat{ADB}$ is a semi-circle, thus $m\widehat{ADB} = 180$.
Substituting, $m\angle CBA = 90 = \frac{1}{2}(180) = m\widehat{ADB}$

Case II: The secant does not contain the center of the circle.
Given: Secant $\overline{AB}$; $\overrightarrow{CE}$ is tangent to $\odot P$ at B. D is a point on the major arc BFA.
Prove: $m\angle CBA = \frac{1}{2}m \widehat{AB}$
$m\angle EBA = \frac{1}{2}m \widehat{BDA}$

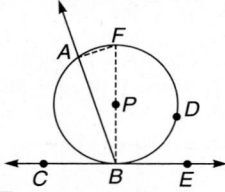

Proof: Draw diameter $\overline{BF}$ and chord $\overline{AF}$. $m\angle CBA + m\angle ABF = m\angle CBF$ by the Angle Addition Postulate and, subtracting, $m\angle CBA = m\angle CBF - m\angle ABF$. $m\angle ABF = \frac{1}{2}m\widehat{AF}$ by Theorem 9-4. $m\widehat{FAB} = 180$ as $\widehat{FAB}$ is a semi-circle. $\overline{BF} \perp \overline{CB}$ by Theorem 9-8, making $\angle CBF$ a right angle and $m\angle CBF = 90$. Substituting $m\angle CBA = 90 - \frac{1}{2}m\widehat{AF} = \frac{1}{2}(180) - \frac{1}{2}m\widehat{AF} = \frac{1}{2}(180 - m\widehat{AF}) = \frac{1}{2}(m\widehat{FAB} - m\widehat{AF})$. Using the Arc Addition Postulate, $m\widehat{BA} + m\widehat{AF} = m\widehat{FAB}$. Subtracting, $m\widehat{BA} = m\widehat{FAB} - m\widehat{AF}$. Substituting, $m\angle CBA = \frac{1}{2}m\widehat{AB}$. Using the Angle Addition Postulate, $m\angle EBA = m\angle EBF + m\angle FBA$. $m\angle FBA = \frac{1}{2}m\widehat{FA}$ by Theorem 9-4. $m\widehat{BDF} = 180$ as $\widehat{BDF}$ is a semi-circle. $\overline{BF} \perp \overline{CB}$ by Theorem 9-8 making $\angle EBF$ a right angle, thus $m\angle EBF = 90$. Substituting, $m\angle EBA = 90 + m\widehat{FA} = \frac{1}{2}(180) + \frac{1}{2}m\widehat{FA} = \frac{1}{2}(180 + m\widehat{FA}) = \frac{1}{2}(m\widehat{BDF} + m\widehat{FA})$. Using the Arc Addition Postulate, $m\widehat{BDA} = m\widehat{BDF} + m\widehat{FA}$. Therefore, $m\angle EBA = \frac{1}{2}m\widehat{BDA}$.

57a. yes **b.** no **58.** It is tangent to the circle. **59.** 17.5
60. yes **61.** 116 **62.** 50 **63.** Congruence of angles is reflexive.

64.

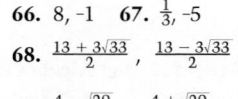

66. 8, -1 **67.** $\frac{1}{3}$, -5
68. $\frac{13 + 3\sqrt{33}}{2}$, $\frac{13 - 3\sqrt{33}}{2}$
69. $\frac{4 - \sqrt{29}}{2}$, $\frac{4 + \sqrt{29}}{2}$

Pages 450–453 Lesson 9-7
7. $3x = 7 \cdot 2$; $4\frac{2}{3}$ **9.** $4(x + 4) = 3 \cdot 8$; 2
11. $3x = 7 \cdot 3$; 7 **13.** $x^2 = 8 \cdot 16$; $8\sqrt{2} \approx 11.31$
15. $\frac{17}{8}$ **17.** 0.46 **19.** 1.2
21. $\frac{-5 + \sqrt{73}}{2} \approx 1.77$ **23.** $\frac{\sqrt{5}}{4} \approx 0.56$
25. 15.3 **27.** 26.3 **29.** 12.25 **31.** $\sqrt{51.25} \approx 7.16$

33. Given: $\overline{RP}$ and $\overline{RT}$ are secant segments.
Prove: $RQ \cdot RP = RS \cdot RT$

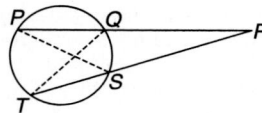

Statements	Reasons
1. Draw $\overline{PS}$ and $\overline{TQ}$.	1. Through any 2 pts there is 1 line.
2. $\angle SRP \cong \angle QRT$	2. Congruence of angles is reflexive.
3. $\angle RPS \cong \angle RTQ$	3. If 2 inscribed $\angle$ of a $\odot$ intercept the same arc, then the $\angle$ are $\cong$.
4. $\triangle PSR \approx \triangle TQR$	4. AA Similarity
5. $\frac{RQ}{RS} = \frac{RT}{RP}$	5. Definition of similar polygons
6. $RQ \cdot RP = RS \cdot RT$	6. Cross products

37. about 1106 mi **39.** 925 ft **41.** about 2.6 **43.** about 1
45. 25 **46.** 25 **47.** about 0.85 ft. or 10.2 in.

48. yes;

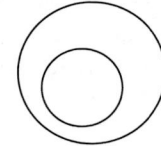

49. 2.5

Pages 456–457 Lesson 9-8
7.
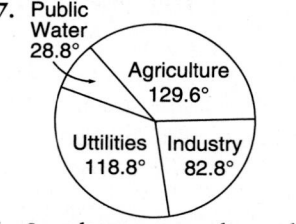

9a.
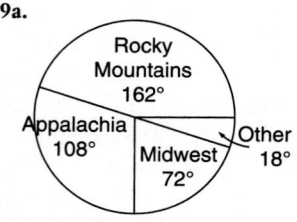

b. Sample answer: quality and price of coal **11.** 40; Dividing by 2, 3, 4, 5, . . . **13.** about 18.0%

Pages 458–460 Summary and Review
1. no
3.

(circle figure)

5. 180 **7.** 117 **9.** 123
11. 34.2 cm **13.** 144
15. 36 **17.** 12 **19.** 42
21. 18.5 **23.** 138 **25.** 6
27. $15\frac{1}{3}$ **29.** 36
31. 22.1 m

Pages 462–463 Algebra Review
1. $\{x \mid x < -1 \text{ or } x \geq 3\}$
3. $\{r \mid 7 < r \leq 11\}$ **5.** $\{0, -17\}$
7. $\{\frac{3}{2}, -8\}$ **9.** $\{0, -\frac{2}{5}\}$ **11.** $(3, 5)$ **13.** $6\sqrt{3}$ **15.** $\frac{\sqrt{11}}{11}$
17. $4x^2\sqrt{6}$ **19.** $\frac{3axy}{10}$ **21.** $b + 7$ **23.** $\frac{7ab(x + 9)}{3(x - 5)}$ **25.** 3
27. $\frac{3}{4}$ **29.** 36 ounces **31.** $16, $9 **33.** about 14.7 seconds

CHAPTER 10 POLYGONS AND AREA

Pages 469–472 Lesson 10-1
7. not a polygon **9.** concave polygon **11.** concave

polygon **13.** not a polygon **15.** faces: quadrilaterals $ABFE$, $FBCG$, $HGCD$, $EHDA$, $ABCD$, and $EFGH$; edges: $\overline{AE}$, $\overline{EF}$, $\overline{FB}$, $\overline{AB}$, $\overline{FG}$, $\overline{GC}$, $\overline{CB}$, $\overline{HG}$, $\overline{CD}$, $\overline{DH}$, $\overline{EH}$, and $\overline{AD}$; vertices: A, B, C, D, E, F, G, H **17.** triangle **19.** 20-gon **21.** hexagon
23. not a polygon **25.** convex pentagon **27.** not a polygon
29. M, N, O, P, Q **31.** $\overline{MN}, \overline{NO}, \overline{OP}, \overline{PQ}, \overline{QM}$
33. pentagon **35.** not regular; not all of the sides are congruent **37.** regular; It is convex, all the sides are congruent, and all of the angles are congruent.
39. a square
41. not possible **43a.** triangles **b.** squares **c.** triangles **d.** pentagons **e.** triangles
45a. 4, 4, 6 **b.** 6, 8, 12 **c.** 8, 6, 12 **d.** 12, 20, 30 **e.** 20, 12, 30

(square figure)

49.
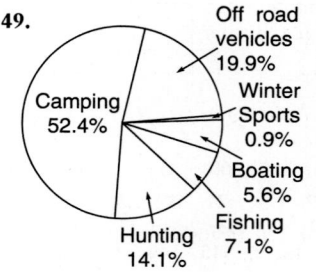

50. 6.9 **51.** not enough information **52.** undefined **53.** If a polygon is regular, then it is convex and has all sides congruent.

Pages 476–479 Lesson 10-2
5. 720 **7.** 4140 **9.** $180(x - 2)$ **11.** $128\frac{4}{7}$
13. $\frac{180x - 360}{x}$ **15.** 5 **17.** $\frac{360}{n}$ **19.** 10 **21.** 20
23. 3240 **25.** 2340 **27.** $360t - 360$ **29.** 6 **31.** 24
33. 360 **35.** 135, 45 **37.** 162, 18 **39.** $\frac{180(x - 2)}{x}$, $\frac{360}{x}$
41. 21 **43.** 26; 36 **45.** 36 **47a.** 43 **b.** 7380 **49a.** 1010
b. 110 **c.** They don't always work; no
51a.

Regular Polygon	triangle	square	pentagon
Does it tessellate the plane?	yes	yes	no
Measure, m, of one interior angle	60	90	108
Is m a factor of 360?	yes	yes	no

Regular Polygon	hexagon	heptagon	octagon
Does it tessellate the plane?	yes	no	no
Measure, m, of one interior angle	120	$128\frac{4}{7}$	135
Is m a factor of 360?	yes	no	no

b. If the measure of an interior angle of a regular polygon is a factor of 360, the polygon will tessellate the plane.
52. concave polygon; heptagon **53.** 13 in. **54.** 45 feet
55. yes **56.** 46 **57.** 61

Pages 481–482 Lesson 10-3
3. 120

5. Sample answer:

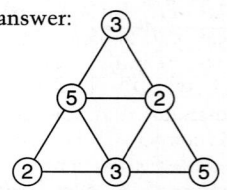

7. 35
9. 0.1; 4, 5; 12, 13; 24, 25; 40, 41

Pages 486–488 Lesson 10-4
5. 56 in^2 **7.** 100 mm^2 **9.** 56 ft^2 **11.** 4 m **13.** 31.75 mm
15.

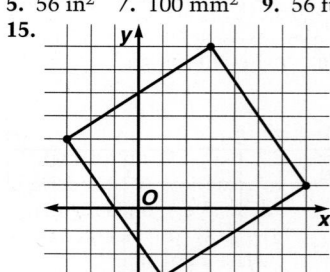

square; 52 square units

17.

rectangle; 20 square units

19. $x + 4$ cm **21.** 11 in. **23.** The triangles can be assembled to form a square that is congruent to *MNOP*. So the area of the new square = the area of *MNOP*. Since the area of *ABCD* is the sum of these two areas, it is twice the area of *MNOP*. **25.** 1577.8 pounds per square inch
27. $4 \cdot (5 - 2) + 7 = 19$ **28.** 18
29. Given: $\overline{AB} \parallel \overline{DC}$
Prove: $\angle A$ and $\angle D$ are supplementary.

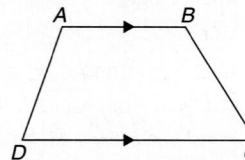

Statements	Reasons
1. $\overline{AB} \parallel \overline{DC}$	1. Given
2. $\angle A$ and $\angle D$ are supplementary.	2. If 2 $\parallel$ lines are cut by a transversal, consec. int. $\angle$s are supp.

Page 488 Mid-Chapter Review
1. concave; pentagon **2.** not a polygon **3.** convex; quadrilateral **4.** not a polygon **5.** 120, 60 **6.** 157.5, 22.5
7. 168, 12 **8.** 727 **9.** Yes, the area is 650 sq yd.

Pages 492–494 Lesson 10-5
5. 52.5 ft^2 **7.** 24 ft^2 **9.** $9\sqrt{3}$ or about 15.6 m^2 **11.** 30 in^2
13. 114 cm^2 **15.** 148.5 m^2 **17.** 120 square units
19. 3.5 in. **21.** 4 cm **23.** The base of the triangle is twice as long as the base of the parallelogram.

25. The diagonals of a rhombus are perpendicular, so $\overline{AE} \perp \overline{BD}$ and $\overline{CE} \perp \overline{DB}$. Therefore $\overline{AE}$ is an altitude of $\triangle ABD$ and $\overline{CE}$ is an altitude of $\triangle BCD$. Since the diagonals of a rhombus bisect each other, $\overline{AE} \cong \overline{EC}$.

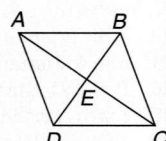

So $AE = \frac{1}{2}AC$ and $EC = \frac{1}{2}AC$.
area of $ABCD$ = area of $\triangle ABD$ + area of $\triangle BCD$
area of $ABCD = \frac{1}{2}(BD)(AE) + \frac{1}{2}(BD)(EC)$
area of $ABCD = \frac{1}{2}(BD)(\frac{1}{2}AC) + \frac{1}{2}(BD)(\frac{1}{2}AC)$
area of $ABCD = \frac{1}{4}(BD)(AC) + \frac{1}{4}(BD)(AC)$
area of $ABCD = \frac{1}{2}(BD)(AC)$
The area is one-half the product of the diagonals.

29a. 35 sq units **b.** 27.125 sq units **30.** $288\sqrt{2}$ or about 407.3 square inches **31.** $\sqrt{98}$ or about 9.9 **32.** $\frac{2}{27}$
33. No; $4 + 9 < 21$; it fails the triangle inequality.

Pages 498–500 Lesson 10-6
5. 30 cm **7.** $30° - 60° - 90°$; Central angle COA would measure 120; $\overline{OT}$ bisects $\angle COA$, so $m\angle TOA = 60$.
9. $OT, \frac{5}{\sqrt{3}}$ or about 2.89 cm; $OA, \frac{10}{\sqrt{3}}$ or about 5.77 cm
11. 18 cm; 120; $\sqrt{3}$ cm; $9\sqrt{3}$ or about 15.6 cm^2
13. 10 m; 72; 1.4 m; 7m^2 **15.** 256 in^2 **17.** 289.3 mi^2
19. 186 ft^2 **21.** 88 units^2 **23.** $12 + 4\sqrt{3} \approx 18.9$ units^2
25. $108\sqrt{3} \approx 187.1$ units^2 **27.** 60 cm; $5\sqrt{3}$; $150\sqrt{3}$ cm^2
29. $4\sqrt{3}$ in. **31.** $P = 24.72$ ft, $A = 47.02$ ft^2 **33a.** square
b. 2.91 in^2 **c.** 1.91 in^2 **35a.** 54 ft **b.** 140.3 ft^2
37. 204 ft^2 **38.** no; $18 + 32 \le 67$ so these lengths fail the triangle inequality. **39.** If two figures are congruent, then they have equal areas; two figures are congruent; they have equal areas.

Pages 504–506 Lesson 10-7
5. $r = 2.4$ km; $C = 4.8\pi$ km; $A = 5.76\pi$ km^2 **7.** $r = 9$ ft; $d = 18$ ft; $C = 18\pi$ ft **9.** 62.8 m **11.** 44.0 yd **13.** 6.9 mm
15. 1017.9 in^2 **17.** 295.6 km^2 **19.** 34.9 yd^2 **21.** 11; 121π
23. $\sqrt{11}$; 11π **25.** 25; 625π **27.** 6π m; 9π m^2 **29.** $18\pi - 36$ units^2; 2055 units^2 **31.** $12.25\pi - 2.25\sqrt{3}$ units^2; 34.59 units^2 **33.** 50π units^2; 157.08 units^2 **35.** 150π units^2; 471.24 units^2 **37.** $56.25\pi - 108$ units^2; 68.71 units^2
41. about 7 square miles **43.** about 7.7 ounces **45.** 259.81 in^2 **46.** 10 cm **47.** 10.3 feet; 31, 46 **48.** acute **49.** 6

Pages 509–511 Lesson 10-8
5. $\frac{8}{10} = \frac{4}{5}$ **7.** $\frac{2}{10} = \frac{1}{5}$ **9.** $\frac{7}{10}$ **11.** 0.57 **13.** 0.625
15b. 0.08 **c.** No; as long as the dart is randomly thrown and the cards do not overlap, the area of the board and the cards is always the same. **17.** $\frac{2}{3}$ **21.** 0.0625 **22.** 5.0 in., 2.0 in^2 **23.** $\sqrt{1144} \approx 33.8$

Pages 514–517 Lesson 10-9
5. $A - 1, M - 1, C - 0$ **7.** $A - 1, B - 2, C - 2, D - 2, E - 2, F - 1$ **9.** no **11.** Not complete; add edges between I and T and between C and M. **13.** complete **15.** $A - 3, B - 2, C - 3, D - 2, E - 5, F - 2, G - 3$ **17.** edges between: P and E, E and N, P and N **19.** edges between: R and U, R and N, R and K, E and U, E and N, and K and U **21.** traceable
23. traceable

25. Sample answer:

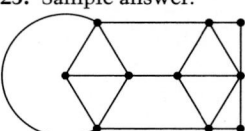

27a. yes **b.** no **c.** No; if a network has an Euler circuit, each node has an even degree, so any path will return to its starting node.

29a.

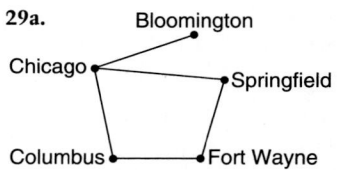

b. yes; through Chicago or Fort Wayne

31a. complete **b.** 21 **32.** 0.21
33. Given: Lines ℓ and m intersect at P.
    Prove: Plane $\mathcal{R}$ contains both ℓ and m.
    Assume: Plane $\mathcal{R}$ does not contain both ℓ and m.

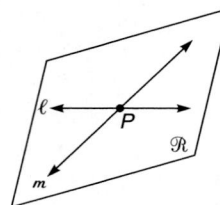

34. reflexive
35.

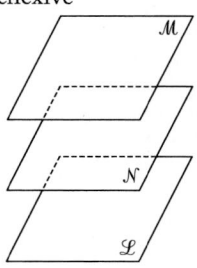

Pages 518–520 Summary and Review
1. $L, M, N, O, P; \overline{LM}, \overline{LP}, \overline{LN}, \overline{LO}, \overline{OP}, \overline{PM}, \overline{MN}$, and $\overline{NO}$
3. No; all of the faces are not congruent. **5.** 13 **7.** 20.3 ft^2
9. 9 m **11.** 27.09 cm^2 **13.** 411.6 in^2 **15.** 10,641.7 mm^2
17. 44.0 mm; 153.9 mm^2 **19.** 5.7 ft; 2.5 ft^2 **21.** A, B, C, $D, E; \overline{AB}, \overline{BC}, \overline{BE}, \overline{CD}, \overline{BD}$ **23.** Edges need to be drawn between A and C, A and D, A and E, C and E, and D and E
25. Yes; the total area is 272 ft^2.

CHAPTER 11 SURFACE AREA AND VOLUME

Pages 527–528 Lesson 11-1
5. 31 games **7.** $12 - 34 + 56 - 7 + 89 = 116$ **9.** 25 bacteria **11.** 15

13.

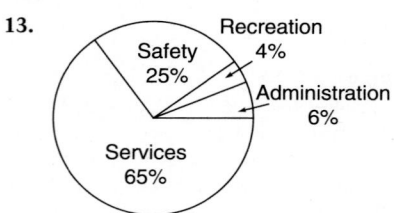

15. 7¢, 12¢, 16¢, 27¢, 31¢, 36¢, 40¢

Pages 531–534 Lesson 11-2
5.

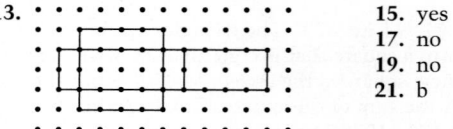

7.

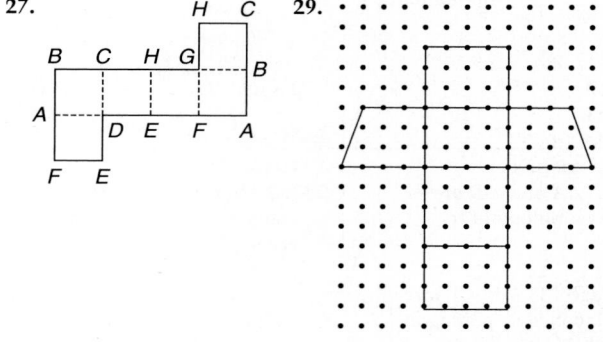

9. 2 pentagons, 5 rectangles **11.** c
13.

15. yes
17. no
19. no
21. b

23. 2 pentagons, 5 rectangles
25. 2 hexagons, 6 rectangles

27.   **29.**

31. yes **33.** yes **35.** yes **39.** Wright brothers': 1.41, Four-passenger: 9.83, Supersonic: 97.40 **40.** 1656 in^2
41. 12π or 37.7 in. **42.** 7ft^2 **43a.** < **b.** >

Pages 539–541 Lesson 11-3
7. 569.5 cm^2 **9.** about 412.7 cm^2 **11.** about 1016.9 cm^2
13. right prism **15.** 42 units **17.** 6π cm **19.** 9π cm^2
21. $L = 432$ in^2; $T = 432 + 108\sqrt{3} \approx 619.1$ in^2
23. $L = 150 + 50\sqrt{3} \approx 236.6$ ft^2; $T = 150 + 150\sqrt{3} \approx$ 409.8 ft^2 **25.** 384 units^2 **27.** 96π or about 301.6 m^2
29. about 559.8 in^2 **33.** about 2010.6 ft^2

35.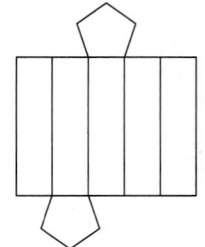

36. 7.5
37. 10
38. 2.5
39. 13.5

Pages 545–547 Lesson 11-4
5. pyramid **7.** prism **9.** 27 cm² **11.** 143.5 cm²
13. 736 cm² **15.** prism **17.** neither **19.** pyramid
21. about 144.5 units² **23.** about 1154.0 units²
25. 144 cm² **27.** about 282.7 cm² **29.** 420 ft²
31. 864 in² **33.** about 1382.3 m² **35.** about 255,161.7 ft²
37. about 46 ft **38.** false **39.** 4π or about 12.6 yd²
40. The measure of the inscribed angle is half the measure of the central angle. **41.** They are perpendicular.

Page 547 Mid-Chapter Review
1. T **2.** $\overline{TO}$ **3.** 6
4.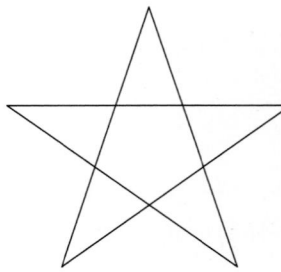

5. 108π in²
6. 176π cm²
7. 720 units²

Pages 550–553 Lesson 11-5
5. 48 m³ **7.** about 77.0 in³ **9.** 32π or about 100.5 m³
11. about 1950.9 ft³ **13.** 272 cm³ **15.** 18.5 cm
17. 67.2 ft³ **19.** 9π or about 28.3 ft³ **21.** about 754.0 cm³
23. 600 m³ **25.** about 2598.1 cm³ **27a.** about 1011.5 mm³
b. about 9 grams **29.** 360 cm³ **31.** no **33.** 6 units
37. almost 3 cords **39a.** 84 feet **b.** 139 ft³ or about
5.15 yd³ **c.** $368.55 **40.** 52.3 mm² **41.** 3 cm **42.** 9
43. 12 **44.** 42

Pages 556–559 Lesson 11-6
5. about 314.2 in³ **7.** about 536.2 in³ **9.** about 1322.3
units³ **11.** 35 ft³ **13.** 190.3 m³ **15.** about 1407.4 units³
17. about 134.0 cm³ **19.** about 5178.8 m³ **21.** 192 units³
23a. 108 units³ **b.** 1 to 6 **25.** 58.9 in³ **27.** about 48.9
units³ **29.** about 5730.3 units³ **33.** 90,187,500 ft³
35. The formula for the volume of a cone rounded to the
nearest unit. **38.** 120 ft³ **39.** 0.82 **40.** They are
complementary. **41.** $\sqrt{73} \approx 8.5$

Pages 562–565 Lesson 11-7
5. true **7.** true **9.** 5 **11.** $T \approx 200.96$ cm²; $V \approx 267.9$ cm³
13. about 448.9 in³ **15.** circle **17.** circle **19.** circle
21. neither **23.** neither **25.** true **27.** true **29.** true
31. true **33.** 12 **35.** $T \approx 50,265,482$ ft²;
$V \approx 33,510,321,640$ ft³ **37.** 2 in. **39.** 2:1 **41.** about 4701
cm³ **43.** Sample answer: Labrador Sea, Glasgow, Scotland;
Essen, Germany **45.** about 620,561.5 yd³

47. about 10,053.1 ft² **49.** about 418.9 ft³ **50.** 60.35 ft²
51. no; $2.7^2 + 3.0^2 \neq 5.3^2$ **52.** no **53.** 10

Pages 566–568 Summary and Review
1. c **3.** b **5.** $L = 264$ in²; $T = 312$ in² **7.** $L \approx 197.9$ ft²;
$T \approx 325.2$ ft² **9.** $L = 48$ in²; $T = 84$ in² **11.** $L \approx 52.3$ mm²;
$T \approx 84.4$ mm² **13.** about 6283.2 cm³
15. about 175.4 cm³ **17.** about 1570.8 mm³ **19.** about
14,657,415 mi² **21.** 64 blocks **23.** 2145 lb

Pages 570–571 Algebra Review
1. $\{y \mid -4 \le y \le 6\}$ **3.** $\{p \mid p < -2 \text{ or } p > \frac{5}{2}\}$ **5.** $\frac{1}{x+2}$
7. $\frac{x^2 - 7x - 15}{x^2 + x - 6}$ **9.** (4, 2) **11.** (0,2) **13.** $\frac{11}{20}$ or 0.55
15. 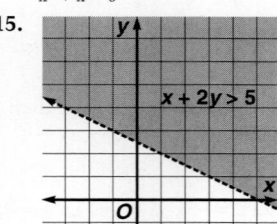 **17.**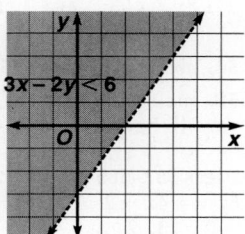

19. $5\sqrt{13} + 5\sqrt{15}$ **21.** $-6\sqrt{2} - 12\sqrt{7}$ **23.** 10, 2
25. $\frac{2 \pm \sqrt{5}}{3}$; 1.41, -0.08 **27.** $2000 at 6%, $8000 at 8%
29. $y = 1.65x + 3$; $4.65

CHAPTER 12 MORE COORDINATE GEOMETRY

Pages 576–579 Lesson 12-1
7. No; y is squared. **9.** yes **11.** yes **13.** 1; -4 **15.** 4; no
y-intercept **17.** 2; -1 **19.** neither; 1, $\frac{1}{2}$ **21.** parallel; 0, 0
23. parallel; -1, -1
25.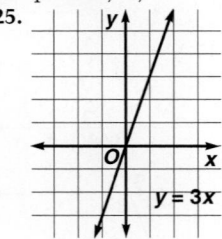

29.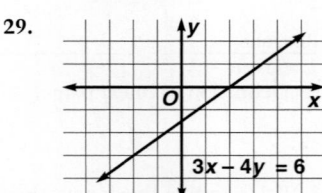

31. parallel **33.** $m = 1, b = 0$ **35.** $m = -\frac{3}{4}, b = 2$
37. m is undefined, no y-intercept **39.** $y = -\frac{1}{3}x + 2$
41. $y = 4x - 3$ **43.** $y = 2x + 3$ **45.** $y = \frac{1}{3}x + 4$
47. $x = 2$ **49.** All are of the form $y = mx + 3$, but all have
a different value for m.

53a. 200 **b.** 1400 **c.**

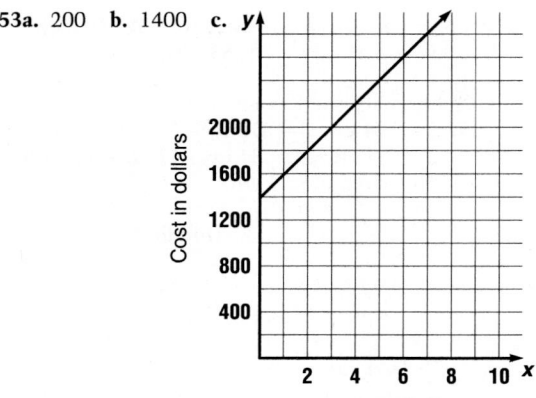

Cost in dollars (y-axis), number of days (x-axis)

54. about 523.6 in³ **55.** about 113.1 ft² **56.** $-\frac{2}{5}$

58. $m\angle 1 = 49$, $m\angle 2 = 131$ **59.** If it snows Saturday, then we will have to rent skis; law of syllogism

Pages 582–585 Lesson 12-2
5. $y = 4x + 2$ **7.** $y = 5x + 8$ **9.** $y = -5x - 31$ **11.** $y = 3x - 2$ **13.** $2, -3; y = 2x - 3$ **15.** $1, -1; y = x - 1$
17. $y = \frac{1}{6}x - 5$ **19.** $y = -4x - 14$ **21.** $y = 7$
23. $y = -2x + 1$ **25.** $y = -\frac{1}{2}x + \frac{11}{2}$ **27.** $y = -4x - 11$
29. $y = 2$ **31.** $y = -x + 5$ **33.** $y = -5x + 4$
35. $y = \frac{3}{4}x + 8$ **39.** $y = 12x + 900$

41.

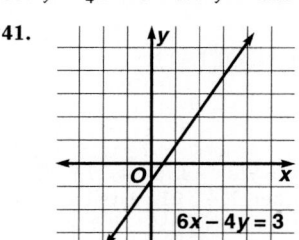

$\frac{3}{2}; -\frac{3}{4}$

$6x - 4y = 3$

42. $m\angle C \approx 23.9$, $m\angle A \approx 40.4$, $AC \approx 11.1$

43. Given: $\angle 4 \cong \angle 6$
Prove: $\angle 3 \cong \angle 5$

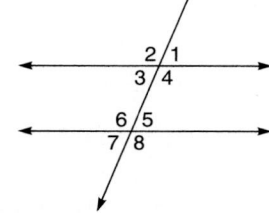

Statements	Reasons
1. $\angle 4 \cong \angle 6$	1. Given
2. $\angle 3$ and $\angle 4$ form a linear pair. $\angle 5$ and $\angle 6$ form a linear pair.	2. Definition of linear pair
3. $\angle 3$ and $\angle 4$ are supplementary. $\angle 5$ and $\angle 6$ are supplementary.	3. If 2 $\angle$s form a linear pair, they are supp.
4. $m\angle 3 + m\angle 4 = 180$ $m\angle 5 + m\angle 6 = 180$	4. Definition of supplementary
5. $m\angle 3 + m\angle 4 = m\angle 5 + m\angle 6$	5. Substitution property of equality
6. $m\angle 3 = m\angle 5$	6. Subtraction property of equality
7. $\angle 3 \cong \angle 5$	7. Definition of congruent angles

44. $\sqrt{74} \cong 8.6$ **45.** $(-1.5, 1)$

Pages 588–591 Lesson 12-3
5. $y = -x - 1$, $y = 3x + 7$, $y = 1$ **7.** no **9.** yes
11b. Sample answer: $y = 0.15x + 3$ **c.** Answer based on equation in 11b: $1950.30 **13.** $y = -2$, $y = -2x + 6$, $y = 2x + 6$ **15.** $y = \frac{1}{9}x + \frac{44}{9}$ **17.** $y = x - 2$, $y = -\frac{1}{2}x + 7$, $x = -6$ **19.** $y = -x + 4$, $y = 2x + 4$, $y = 4$
21. $(3 + 1)^2 + (5 - 2)^2 \stackrel{?}{=} 25$
$(4)^2 + (3)^2 \stackrel{?}{=} 25$
$16 + 9 \stackrel{?}{=} 25$
$25 = 25$ ✔

25b. Sample answer: $y = -\frac{5}{6}x + 142$ **c.** Answer based on equation in 25b: about 126 **26.** $428 **27.** 248 cm²
28. $RS > QR$; SAS Inequality

Pages 593–594 Lesson 12-4
5. 3 hours **7.** 8 adult tickets and 12 student tickets
9. $10\pi \approx 31.4$ feet **11.** 89 mph and 99 mph **13.** 46

Pages 597–600 Lesson 12-5
5. $E(d - f, r)$
7. Midpoint A of $\overline{TS}$ is $\left(\frac{2d + 2a}{2}, \frac{2e + 2c}{2}\right)$ or $(d + a, e + c)$.
Midpoint B of $\overline{SR}$ is $\left(\frac{2a + 2b}{2}, \frac{2c + 0}{2}\right)$ or $(a + b, c)$.
Midpoint C of $\overline{VR}$ is $\left(\frac{0 + 2b}{2}, \frac{0 + 0}{2}\right)$ or $(b, 0)$.
Midpoint D of $\overline{TV}$ is $\left(\frac{0 + 2d}{2}, \frac{0 + 2e}{2}\right)$ or (d, e).
Slope of $\overline{AB}$ is $\frac{e + c - c}{d + a - (a + b)}$ or $\frac{e}{d - b}$.
Slope of $\overline{DC}$ is $\frac{e - 0}{d - b}$ or $\frac{e}{d - b}$.
Slope of $\overline{DA}$ is $\frac{e + c - e}{d + a - d}$ or $\frac{c}{a}$.
Slope of $\overline{CB}$ is $\frac{c - 0}{a + b - b}$ or $\frac{c}{a}$.
Since opposite sides are parallel, $ABCD$ is a parallelogram.

9.

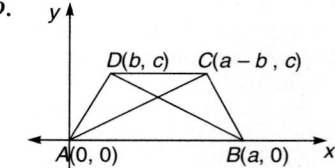

$DB = \sqrt{(a - b)^2 + (0 - c)^2} = \sqrt{(a - b)^2 + c^2}$
$AC = \sqrt{((a - b) - 0)^2 + (c - 0)^2} = \sqrt{(a - b)^2 + c^2}$
$DB = AC$ and $\overline{DB} \cong \overline{AC}$

11. $A(0, 0)$, $Y(b, 0)$ **13.** $R(-b, 2b)$
15. $AB = \sqrt{(a - 0)^2 + (b - 0)^2} = \sqrt{a^2 + b^2}$
$BC = \sqrt{(2a - a)^2 + (0 - b)^2} = \sqrt{a^2 + b^2}$
$AB = BC$ and $\triangle ABC$ is isosceles.

17. $DE = \sqrt{(a-0)^2 + (a\sqrt{3}-0)^2} = \sqrt{a^2 + 3a^2} = \sqrt{4a^2} = 2a$

$EF = \sqrt{(2a-a)^2 + (0-a\sqrt{3})^2} = \sqrt{a^2 + 3a^2} = \sqrt{4a^2} = 2a$

$DF = \sqrt{(2a-0)^2 + (0-0)^2} = \sqrt{4a^2} = 2a$

$DE = EF = DF$ and $\overline{DE} \cong \overline{EF} \cong \overline{DF}$

$\Delta\, DEF$ is equilateral.

19.

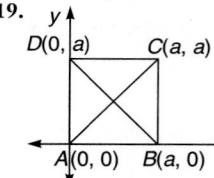

Slope of $\overline{AC}$ is $\frac{a-0}{a-0}$ or $\frac{a}{a}$ or 1.

Slope of $\overline{BD}$ is $\frac{a-0}{0-a}$ or $\frac{a}{-a}$ or -1.

$\overline{AC} \perp \overline{BD}$

21.

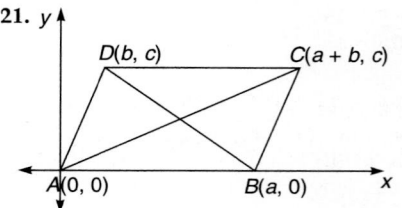

Midpoint of $\overline{AC}$ is $\left(\frac{(a+b)+0}{2}, \frac{c+0}{2}\right)$ or $\left(\frac{a+b}{2}, \frac{c}{2}\right)$.

Midpoint of $\overline{DB}$ is $\left(\frac{a+b}{2}, \frac{0+c}{2}\right)$ or $\left(\frac{a+b}{2}, \frac{c}{2}\right)$.

$\overline{AC}$ and $\overline{DB}$ bisect each other.

23.

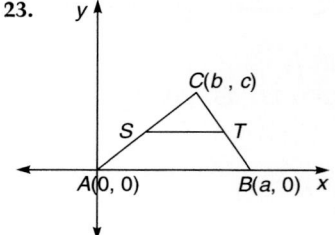

Midpoint S is $\left(\frac{b+0}{2}, \frac{c+0}{2}\right)$ or $\left(\frac{b}{2}, \frac{c}{2}\right)$.

Midpoint T is $\left(\frac{a+b}{2}, \frac{0+c}{2}\right)$ or $\left(\frac{a+b}{2}, \frac{c}{2}\right)$.

Slope of $\overline{ST}$ is $\dfrac{\frac{c}{2} - \frac{c}{2}}{\frac{a+b}{2} - \frac{b}{2}}$ or $\frac{0}{\frac{a}{2}}$ or 0.

Slope of $\overline{AB}$ is $\frac{0-0}{a-0}$ or $\frac{0}{a}$ or 0.

$\overline{ST} \parallel \overline{AB}$

27.

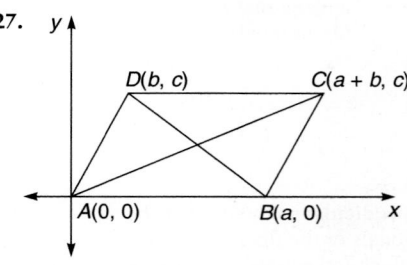

Slope of $\overline{BD}$ is $\frac{c-0}{b-a}$ or $\frac{c}{b-a}$.

Slope of $\overline{AC}$ is $\frac{c-0}{(a+b)-0}$ or $\frac{c}{a+b}$.

But $\overline{BD} \perp \overline{AC}$ and $\frac{c}{b-a} = -\frac{a+b}{c} \cdot \frac{c}{b-a} = \frac{a+b}{-c}$

$-c^2 = b^2 - a^2$

$a^2 = b^2 + c^2$ and $\sqrt{a^2} = \sqrt{b^2 + c^2}$

$AD = \sqrt{(b-0)^2 + (c-0)^2} = \sqrt{b^2 + c^2}$

$DC = \sqrt{((a+b)-b)^2 + (c-c)^2} = \sqrt{a^2}$

$BC = \sqrt{((a+b)-a)^2 + (c-0)^2} = \sqrt{b^2 + c^2}$

$AB = \sqrt{(a-0)^2 + (0-0)^2} = \sqrt{a^2}$

$AD = DC = BC = AB$ and $\overline{AD} \cong \overline{DC} \cong \overline{BC} \cong \overline{AB}$

$ABCD$ is a rhombus.

29. $x = 20$ **31.** $\sqrt{58} \cong 7.6$ km **32.** false **33.** false
34. true **35.** true **36.** true **37.** false **38.** false
39. false

Page 600 Mid-Chapter Review

1. 3; -4 **2.** no x-intercept; 15 **3.** $y = -\frac{2}{3}x + \frac{10}{3}$

4. $y = 3x$ **5.** $y = -\frac{1}{2}x + 3$ **6.** yes **7.** no **8.** 10:33

9. $A(-b, 0)$, $C(b, 2b)$, $D(-b, 2b)$ **10.** $E(0, 0)$, $G(a, b+c)$

11.

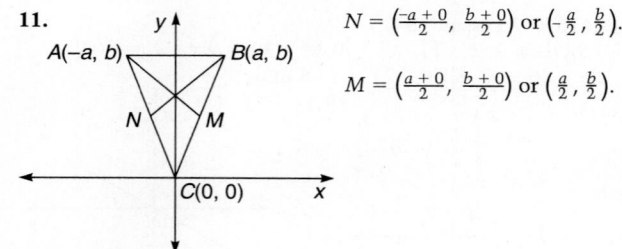

$N = \left(\frac{-a+0}{2}, \frac{b+0}{2}\right)$ or $\left(-\frac{a}{2}, \frac{b}{2}\right)$.

$M = \left(\frac{a+0}{2}, \frac{b+0}{2}\right)$ or $\left(\frac{a}{2}, \frac{b}{2}\right)$.

$BN = \sqrt{\left(-\frac{a}{2} - a\right)^2 + \left(\frac{b}{2} - b\right)^2}$ $AM = \sqrt{\left(-a - \frac{a}{2}\right)^2 + \left(b - \frac{b}{2}\right)^2}$

$= \sqrt{\left(\frac{-3a}{2}\right)^2 + \left(\frac{-b}{2}\right)^2}$ $= \sqrt{\left(\frac{-3a}{2}\right)^2 + \left(\frac{b}{2}\right)^2}$

$= \sqrt{\frac{9a^2}{4} + \frac{b^2}{4}}$ or $\frac{\sqrt{9a^2 + b^2}}{2}$ $= \sqrt{\frac{9a^2}{4} + \frac{b^2}{4}}$ or $\frac{\sqrt{9a^2 + b^2}}{2}$

Therefore, $\overline{BN} \cong \overline{AM}$.

Pages 604–606 Lesson 12-6

9. $\sqrt{73} \cong 8.5$, 69° **11.** $\overrightarrow{AB}$ and $\overrightarrow{DC}$ **13.** $\overrightarrow{AB}$ and $\overrightarrow{BC}$

15.

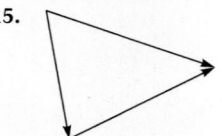

17.

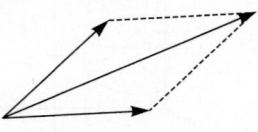

19. (1, 10) **21.** (-1, 9) **23.** $6\sqrt{2} \approx 8.5$ units **25.** $4\sqrt{2} \approx 5.7$
units, 45° **27.** $\overrightarrow{BC}$ and $\overrightarrow{AD}$ **29.** $\overrightarrow{RT}$ **31.** $\overrightarrow{PR}$ **33.** (9, 6)
35. (20, 17) **37.** 11 **39.** $\overrightarrow{AB}$ and $2\overrightarrow{AB}$, $\overrightarrow{AB} + \overrightarrow{BL}$ and $\overrightarrow{SR}$
41. $\vec{v}$ and $\vec{w}$, $\vec{v}$ and $\vec{t}$ **43.** The resulting speed is 250 km/h
and the direction is about 16° south of west. **45.** about 86
newtons, about 54° west of north

46.

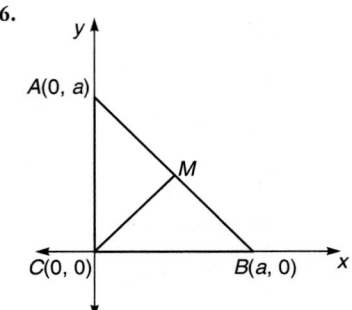

Midpoint M is $\left(\frac{0+a}{2}, \frac{a+0}{2}\right)$ or $\left(\frac{a}{2}, \frac{a}{2}\right)$.

Slope of $\overline{AB}$ is $\frac{0-a}{a-0}$ or $\frac{-a}{a}$ or -1.

Slope of $\overline{CM}$ is $\dfrac{\frac{a}{2}-0}{\frac{a}{2}-0}$ or $\dfrac{\frac{a}{2}}{\frac{a}{2}}$ or 1.

Since $-1 \cdot 1 = -1$, $\overline{CM} \perp \overline{AB}$.
47. about 157.1 m^2 **48.** about 50.3 in. **49.** 18, 22

Pages 610–612 Lesson 12-7
7. 5 **9.** (1.5, -2, 2) **11.** (0, 3, 4), 9 **13.** $(x-4)^2 + (y-1)^2 + (z+2)^2 = 36$ **15.** $11 + \sqrt{21} \approx 15.6$ units
17.

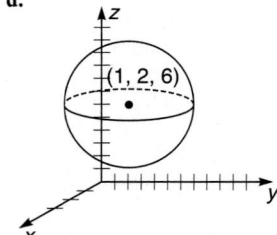

(0, 0, 5)

19.

(3, 1, −4)

21. $\sqrt{94} \approx 9.7$ units **23.** $\sqrt{134} \approx 11.6$ units **25.** (0, 0, 0)
27. (11, 1, 2.5) **29.** (-2, -3, 2), 10 **31.** (-8, 0, -4), $\sqrt{18} \approx 4.2$
33. $(x-6)^2 + (y+1)^2 + (z-3)^2 = 144$ **35.** $(x+2)^2 + (y-4)^2 + (z-1)^2 = 13$

37a. (1, 2, 6)
  b. $\sqrt{26} \approx 5.1$ units
  c. $(x-1)^2 + (y-2)^2 + (z-6)^2 = 26$
  d.

(1, 2, 6)

  e. about 326.7 units^2
  f. about 555.3 units^3

39. 2 or $\frac{4}{13}$ **41.** 3 to 5 **43.** 27 to 125 **45.** $\sqrt{147} \approx 12.1$ miles **47.** (-2, -8) **48.** about 78.5 cm^2 **49.** 110 cm^2
50. 10.5 in^2 **51.** Two lines intersect and more that one plane contains them. **52.** 100

Pages 614–616 Summary and Review
1.

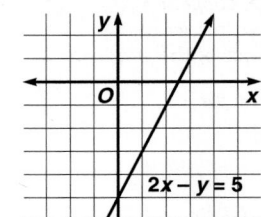

2x − y = 5

3. perpendicular
5. $y = x + 8$
7. $y = 2$
9. $y = \frac{1}{2}x - 2$, $y = \frac{2}{3}x - 3$, $y = x - 3$
11. $y = -2x - 3$, $y = -\frac{3}{2}x + 2$, $y = -x + 7$

13.

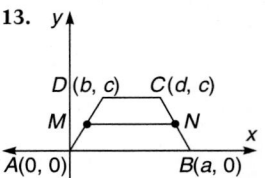

$D(b, c)$ $C(d, c)$
M N
$A(0, 0)$ $B(a, 0)$

Midpoint M is $\left(\frac{b+0}{2}, \frac{c+0}{2}\right)$ or $\left(\frac{b}{2}, \frac{c}{2}\right)$.
Midpoint N is $\left(\frac{a+d}{2}, \frac{c+0}{2}\right)$ or $\left(\frac{2a+d}{2}, \frac{c}{2}\right)$.
Slope of $\overline{DC}$ is $\frac{c-c}{d-b}$ or $\frac{0}{d-b}$ or 0.

Slope of $\overline{MN}$ is $\dfrac{\frac{c}{2}-\frac{c}{2}}{\frac{a+d}{2}-\frac{b}{2}}$ or $\dfrac{0}{\frac{a+d-b}{2}}$ or 0.

Slope of $\overline{AB}$ is $\frac{0-0}{a-0}$ or $\frac{0}{a}$ or 0.

$\overline{DC} \parallel \overline{MN} \parallel \overline{AB}$
15. $\sqrt{50} \approx 7.1$ units; about 8.1° **17.** (7, 1) **19.** $4\sqrt{2} \approx 5.7$ units; (5, -3, 3) **21.** $x^2 + y^2 + z^2 = 25$ **25.** (20, 20)

CHAPTER 13 LOCUS AND TRANSFORMATIONS

Pages 624–627 Lesson 13-1
7.

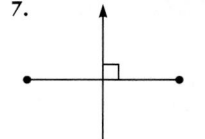

The perpendicular bisector of the line segment

11.

a plane that is the perpendicular bisector of the given line segment

15. a line segment perpendicular to the floor at the intersection of the diagonals of the floor of the classroom with endpoints on the floor and ceiling **17.** the 50-yard line of the football field **19.** a cylindrical surface with line ℓ as the axis and a radius of 4 inches

21. 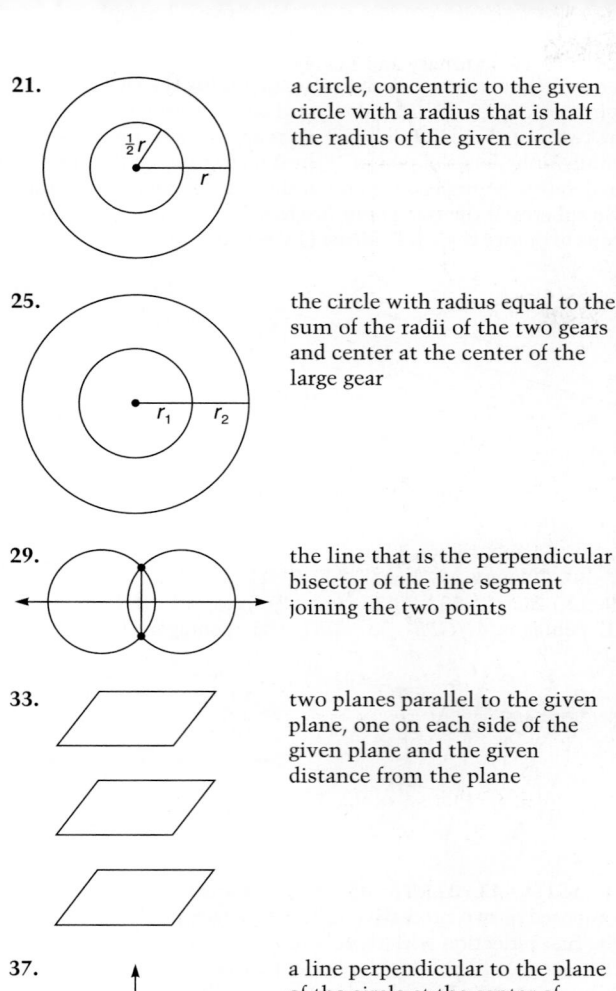 a circle, concentric to the given circle with a radius that is half the radius of the given circle

25. the circle with radius equal to the sum of the radii of the two gears and center at the center of the large gear

29. the line that is the perpendicular bisector of the line segment joining the two points

33. two planes parallel to the given plane, one on each side of the given plane and the given distance from the plane

37. a line perpendicular to the plane of the circle at the center of the circle

39. a line perpendicular to $\mathcal{R}$ at the point of intersection of the diagonals of the square   **41.** two planes perpendicular to $\mathcal{R}$ and passing through two perpendicular lines, one parallel to $\overline{AB}$ and $\overline{DC}$ and the other parallel to $\overline{AD}$ and $\overline{BC}$ and intersecting at the center of the square   **43.** all points on a circle with center at the vertex and radius half the length of the hypotenuse except the points on the given line and the points on the line perpendicular to the given line at the vertex   **45.** a curve which repeats itself every time the wheel makes one complete rotation

49. a great circle crossing the great circle passing through Chicago and London such that their tangents at the point of intersection are perpendicular to each other   **51.** the points on the perpendicular bisector of the line segment between the two students   **52.** slope   **53.** about 1256.6 cm^2
54. 90   **55.** diameters   **56.** right triangle   **57.** skew

Pages 631–633 Lesson 13-2
5. (6, 5)   **7.** (-3, -9)   **9.** (0, 4)   **11.** (-2, 2)   **13.** (6, 2)
15. (0, -1)   **17.** a, c, d   **19.** a, b, d   **21.** (1, 3)
23. $(5\frac{1}{2}, -\frac{1}{2})$ **25.** (-1, -1)   **27.** (14, 4)   **29.** (-9, -7)
31. (-1, -1)   **33.** (7, 4)   **35a.** (2, 2), (12, 2), (6, 6)   **b.** 20 units^2
37. (-1, -1) and (4, 4)   **39.** $\frac{9\sqrt{10}}{10} \approx 2.8$ **41.** about 5.58 years or 5 years 7 months   **43.** yes; their areas of coverage overlap
45. two circles, concentric to the given circle, one with radius of 2 inches and the other with a radius of 8 inches
46. $x = \sqrt{76}$ or 8.7, $y = \sqrt{92}$ or 9.6, $z = \sqrt{437}$ or 20.9
48. If three points lie in the same plane, then they are coplanar.   **49.** 36

Pages 636–639 Lesson 13-3
5. a sphere with radius 7 and center (2, -6, 5)
7. a cylinder with radius 3 and an axis passing through (5, 7, z)
9. They may have no points of intersection; the plane may be tangent to the sphere or it may intersect the sphere in a circle; numbers of possible points of intersection: 0, 1, infinite   **11.** They may have no points of intersection; one or both lines may be tangent to the outer circle; one or both lines may be tangent to the inner circle and intersect the outer circle in 2 places; one or both lines may be secants of just the outer circle; one or both lines may be secants of both circles; numbers of possible points of intersection: 0, 1, 2, 3, 4, 5, 6, 7, or 8

15. 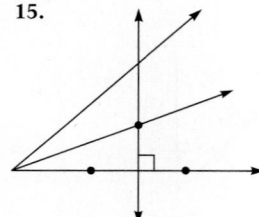 the point inside the angle where the ray that bisects the angle intersects the line that is the perpendicular bisector of the segment that has the given points as endpoints

17. a cylinder with radius 6 whose axis is perpendicular to the xy-plane through the point (2, -4, 0)   **19.** a sphere with radius 4 and center (3, 4, 5)   **21.** $(x + 1)^2 + (y + 6)^2 = 16$
23. They may have no points of intersection; the line may be tangent to either circle; the line may be secant of the outer circle; the line may be secant of both circles; numbers of possible points of intersection: 0, 1, 2, 3, or 4   **25.** They may have no points of intersection; one or both lines may be tangent to the sphere; one or both lines may be secants of the sphere; numbers of possible points of intersection: 0, 1, 2, 3, or 4   **27.** They may have no points of intersection; one or both planes may be tangent to the sphere; one or both planes may intersect the sphere in a circle; numbers of possible points of intersection 0, 1, 2, or infinite

33.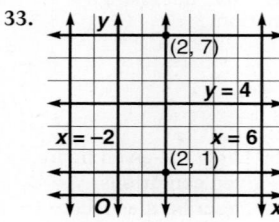

points (2, 1) and (2, 7)

37.

39. ∅   **41.** 5 points   **43.** 0 points
47.

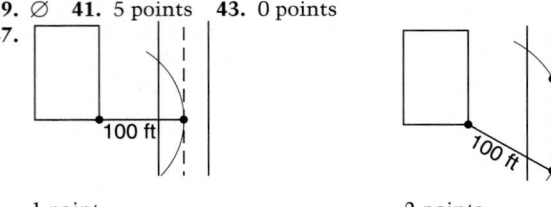

1 point   2 points

49. sometimes   **50.** never   **51.** always   **52.** never
53. always   **54.** sometimes   **55.** sometimes   **56.** always

Pages 641–643 Lesson 13-4
5. $\overline{DC}$ **7.** ∠S   **9.** $\overline{RS}$ **11.** B   **13.** ∠DEB   **15.** $\overline{ED}$
17. B   **19.** $\overline{BA}$ **21.** ∠CBA   **23.** ∠T   **25.** ∠B   **27.** ∆RQS
29. ∆NMW   **31.** ∆XZY   **33.** CDAB   **35.** $\overline{WY}$
37. ∆XYW → ∆ZYW   **41.** Angel D is rotated or reflected
to form angel C.   **43.** For each frame of the cartoon, the
picture of the ball slides just slightly in one direction.   **44.** a
circle   **45.** 315 cm²   **46.** 5   **47.** $\sqrt{558} \approx 23.6$ **48.** If a
mapping is a transformation, then it is one-to-one.

Pages 647–651 Lesson 13-5
7. C   **9.**

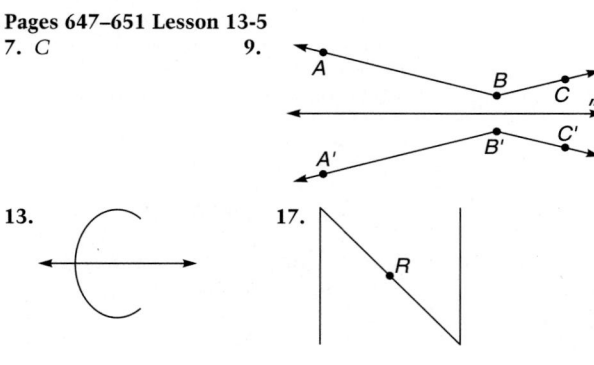

13.   **17.**

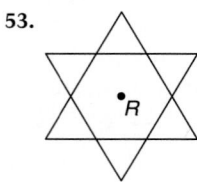

19. J   **21.** ∠IHG   **23.** ∆CXA   **25.** $\overline{IH}$ **27.** no   **29.** yes
31. yes   **33.** both
39.   **43.**

47. none   **49.** none   **51.** none

53.   **57.** 168 cm   **58.** ∠S   **59.** $\overline{CD}$
60. HA   **61.** SSS   **62.** AAS
63. not enough information
64. HL   **65.** not enough
information

Page 651 Mid-Chapter Review
1.a. Read the problem carefully.   **b.** Draw the given figure.
c. Locate the points that satisfy the given conditions.
d. Draw a smooth curve or line.   **e.** Describe the locus.
2. a line which is the perpendicular bisector of the segment
joining the two given points   **3.** a plane which is the

perpendicular bisector of the segment joining the two given
points   **4.** a   **5.** b   **6.** a doughnut shape 6 cm wide   **7.** If
the two points are more than 8 units apart, there are no
points in the locus of points. If the 2 points are 8 units apart,
the locus of points is one point at the point of tangency of the
two spheres. If the two points are less than 8 units apart, the
locus of points is a circle formed by the intersection of the
two spheres.
8.   **9.** $\overline{BC}$
                                             10. ∠B

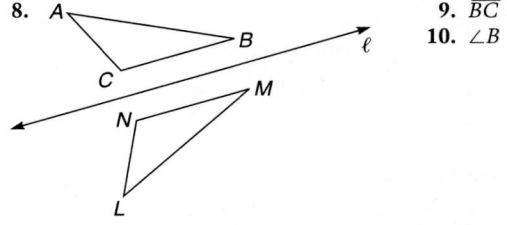

Pages 654–658 Lesson 13-6
5. no   **7.** none   **9.** none   **13.** F   **15.** C   **17.** P
19. Q   **21.** C   **23.** P   **25.** yes   **27.** yes   **29.** ∆HGI
31. pentagon AHGFE   **33.** ∆JKL   **35.** pentagon IJKLM

37.   **39.**

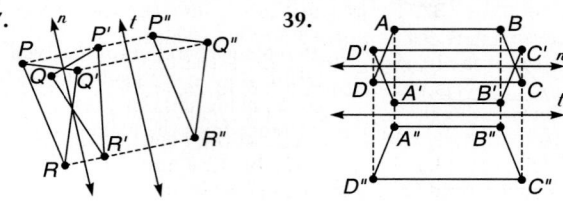

41. ∆STU   **43.** ∆LMN   **45.** Plan: A translation is
composed of two successive reflections over parallel lines.
The first reflection with respect to ℓ preserves collinearity.
The second reflection with respect to m preserves
collinearity. Therefore, by transitivity, collinearity is
preserved from preimage to image.   **47.** Plan: A translation
is composed of two successive reflections over parallel lines.
The first reflection with respect to ℓ preserves angle and
distance measure. The second reflection with respect to m
preserves angle and distance measure. Therefore, by
transitivity, angle and distance measure is preserved from
preimage to image.
49.

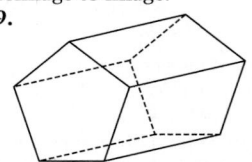

53.   **54.** 72 ft²
                            55. about 166.3 cm²
                            56. 6 in²
                            57. ∠P
                            58. 56.5

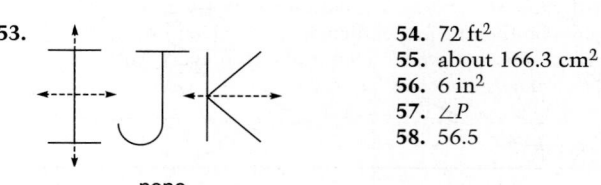

Pages 661–664 Lesson 13-7
5. quadrilateral EFCD   **7.** quadrilateral HGJK
9. quadrilateral CDAB   **11.** 140   **13.** 140   **15.** $\overline{GK}$

17.

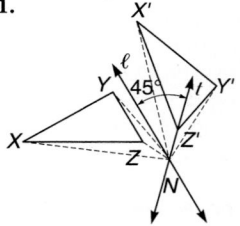

19. yes **21.** 90° **23.** 74°
25. yes **27.** yes

31.

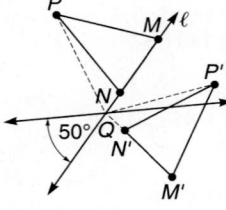

33.

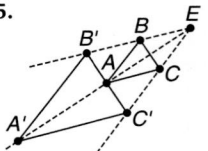

35. rotation **37.** Sample answer: It preserves orientation, because if vertices of the preimage are in clockwise order, the vertices of the image will be in clockwise order.
39. $m\angle AOC$ is 120 so the measure of the angle of intersecting lines will be 60. **41a.** right circular cone
b. right cylinder with hollowed out right cone. **43.** 108
45. 75 **46.** 37.5 **47.** 65 **48.** No; the sum of their measures would have to be both 90 and 180.

Pages 667–670 Lesson 13-8
5. similar **7.** 4 **9.** 2; enlargement **11.** $\frac{1}{4}$; reduction
13.

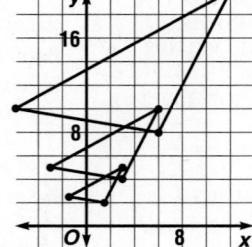

15. enlargement
17. reduction
19. reduction
21. congruence
23. 30
25. 24 **27.** 3
29. A **31.** T
33. S **35.** F

37. 2; enlargement **39.** $\frac{1}{3}$; reduction **41.** $\frac{1}{4}$; reduction

45.

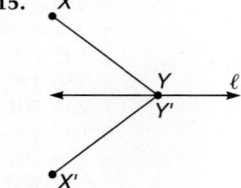

49.

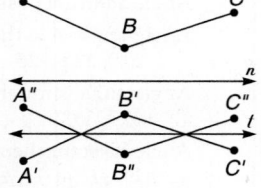

53.

55a. The perimeter of the dilation image will be 4 times the perimeter of the preimage. **b.** The area of the dilation image will be 16 times the area of the preimage.

57. Given: Dilation with center C and scale factor k.
Prove: $ED = k(AB)$

$CE = k(CA)$ and $CD = k(CB)$ by the definition of a dilation.
$\frac{CE}{CA} = k$ and $\frac{CD}{CB} = k$ so, $\frac{CE}{CA} = \frac{CD}{CB}$ by substitution.
$\angle ACB \cong \angle ECD$ since congruence of angles is reflexive. Therefore, by SAS Similarity, $\triangle ACB \approx \triangle ECD$. The corresponding sides of similar triangles are proportional, so $\frac{ED}{AB} = \frac{CE}{CA}$. We know that $\frac{CE}{CA} = k$, so $\frac{ED}{AB} = k$ by substitution. Therefore, $ED = k(AB)$ by the multiplication property of equality. **59.** Sample answer: The fish are dilations of each other. **61.** $\frac{3}{5}$ **63.** 6 **64.** $\sqrt{74} \approx 8.6$ **65.** 21.4
67. a triangle with one obtuse angle; no **68.** 25

Pages 672–673 Lesson 13-9
5. AAADF, AABCF, AABDD, AACCD, ABBBF, ABBCD, ABCCC, BBBBD, BBBCC **7.** 2, 3, 6 **9.** 28
13. 90 **15.** 2550

Pages 674–676 Summary and Review
1. a circle in the plane with the given point as its center and radius 11 inches **3.** (5, 3) **5.** (1,1) **7.** They may have no points of intersection; the line may be tangent to the circle; the line may intersect the circle at two points; numbers of possible points of intersection: 0, 1, or 2 **9.** They may have no points of intersection; the plane may be tangent to the outside circle; the plane may intersect the outside circle at two points and not touch the inside circle; the plane may be tangent to the inside circle and intersect the outside circle at two points; the plane may intersect both circles at two points; the circles may lie in the plane; numbers of possible points of intersection: 0, 1, 2, 3, 4, or infinite **11.** E **13.** B

15.

17.

19. 140
23. Imagine the reflection of the 5 ball with respect to the line formed by one side of the billiard table and aim for the reflection.

Pages 678–679 Algebra Review
1. $-\frac{14}{3}$ **3.** $-\frac{23}{2}$ **5.** (5, 1) **7.** (2, -1) **9.** $x^2 + 7x - 8 = 0$
11. $6x^2 + 13x + 6 = 0$ **13.** 12 **15.** 3
21. 7; 6; no mode **23.** 4; 3; 2 **25.** 22:8 or 11:4
27. No; it would skid 240 ft at 60 mph. **29.** 30

INDEX

constructing, 57–58, 149
slopes of, 143–145, 157, 217

Perpendicular transversal theorem, 130

Perpendicular vectors, 606

Peruvians, 410

Planes, 13–18, 77–80
coordinate, 8–12, 14
horizontal, 17
intersecting, 78, 123
lines perpendicular to, 58
parallel, 122–123, 156
vertical, 17

Plato, 468

Platonic solids, 468

Points, 13–18, 77–80
betweenness, 23, 36, 59, 71–72, 645, 654, 671
collinear, 9–11, 14–16, 59, 70, 587, 644, 654, 671
on coordinate planes, 8–11, 14, 62
coplanar, 14–17, 59
distance between, 23–26, 63, 166, 185
incenters, 436
locus of, 622–639, 674–675
midpoints, 30–34, 63, 216–217, 295, 338, 582, 596–599, 608, 616, 644, 647
nodes, 512–516, 520
noncollinear, 9–10, 13
origin, 8, 601
power of, 454
of reflections, 644, 646
of symmetry, 646
of tangency, 434

Point-slope form, 581–582, 586–588, 614

Point symmetry, 646–651

Polygons, 164, 266, 466–479, 512, 518–519
angles of, 473–479, 518, 590
area of, 483–502, 519–520
circumscribed, 436–438
concave, 466–467
convex, 466–479, 518
decagons, 467
diagonals of, 350
dodecagons, 467
heptagons, 467, 473–474
hexagons, 467, 473, 475, 495–496, 519
inscribed, 430–432
n-gons, 467, 475
nonogons, 467
octagons, 467, 473–474
pentagons, 467, 473, 475, 497–499

quadrilaterals, 264–271, 275–303, 430–432, 467, 473, 483–494, 519
regular, 467–469, 474–478, 495–502, 519
sides of, 164, 266, 466–467, 473
similar, 321–348, 353–354, 360–362, 376
triangles, 163–197, 199–210, 217–229, 233–261, 327–348, 353–354, 360–398, 403–404, 467, 473, 489–493, 496–500, 519
vertices of, 164–165, 266

Polyhedra, 468–472, 529–537, 542–559, 566–568
dodecahedra, 468, 471
hexahedra, 468, 471
icosahedra, 468, 471
octahedra, 468, 471
prisms, 17, 121, 123, 126, 359, 529–537, 548–556, 566–567, 607, 609, 654
pyramids, 17, 169, 525, 529–531, 542–547, 554–559, 562, 567–568
regular, 468–469
rhombohedra, 539
tetrahedra, 468, 471

Polynesians, 127

Postulates, 24, 77–78, 98
angle addition, 38–39, 57
angle-angle similarity, 329, 353
angle-side-angle, 186–187, 192, 225
arc addition, 417–418
area probability, 508, 520
corresponding angles, 128
hypotenuse-leg, 226–227
length probability, 507, 520
parallel, 136
protractor, 38
ruler, 24
segment addition, 25, 38
side-angle-side, 186–188, 194, 209, 223
side-side-side, 184–185

Power of points, 454

Preimages, 640–643, 665, 675

Primitive triples, 370

Prisms, 17, 121, 123, 126, 359, 529–537, 548–556, 607, 609, 654
lateral area of, 537, 567
oblique, 536, 552, 555–556
right, 536, 548–556, 567
surface area of, 537, 567
volume of, 548–556, 567

Probability, 507–511, 520

Problem-solving strategies
decision making, 399–401
draw a diagram, 118–121
guess and check, 480–482
identify subgoals, 198–201
list the possibilities, 19–22
look for a pattern, 272–274
make a model, 526–528
make a table, 671–673
process of elimination, 95–97
solve a simpler problem, 349–351
using graphs, 455–457
work backward, 230–232, 364, 399
write an equation, 592–594

Projections, 613

Proofs, 89
coordinate, 595–600, 615
indirect, 233–239, 253, 259
paragraph, 129, 193, 240–241, 267, 283, 422, 424, 429
two column, 89–94, 98–103, 106–109, 111–112, 129, 150, 186–188, 192–194, 199, 204, 242–244, 253, 275, 288, 447

Properties
addition, 88–92, 235
comparison, 234–235
distributive, 88–90, 537
division, 88–92, 235
multiplication, 88–89, 235
reflexive, 88–91, 98–101, 106, 111, 178, 331
substitution, 88–91
subtraction, 88, 235
symmetric, 88–92, 98–99, 106, 111, 178, 331
transitive, 88–90, 98–101, 106, 111, 129, 178, 235, 331

Proportional perimeters theorem, 342

Proportions, 308–346, 352–354, 360–362, 365

Protractor postulate, 38

Ptolemy, 29

Pyramids, 17, 169, 525, 529–531, 542–547
lateral area of, 543–547, 567
oblique, 556
regular, 542–547, 567
right, 554–559
surface area of, 543–546, 567
volume of, 554–559, 568

Pythagoras, 365

Pythagorean Theorem, 365–372, 403, 423–424, 434–435, 491, 607

Pythagorean triples, 369–370

Photo Credits

Cover, J. A. Krawlis/Masterfile; vii, Pictures Unlimited; x(t), NASA, (ct), Tom Mareschal/The Image Bank, (cb), Frank A. Cezus/FPG, (b), Art Montes De Oca/FPG; xii, Aaron Haupt; xiv, (t, b) Aaron Haupt, (tc) Ted Horowitz/The Stock Market, (bc) Bryan Peterson/The Stock Market; 6, Adrian Baker/FPG, (inset), Courtesy Benoit Mandelbrot; 7, A. M. Rosario/The Image Bank; 8, Todd Gray/LGI Photo Agency; 9,12(t), Pictures Unlimited, 12(b), David Frazier; 13, Jerry Schad/Photo Researchers; 16, Bob Peterson/FPG; 18, Steve Lissau; 19, William H. Allen, Jr.; 20,21, Elaine Shay; 23(t), E. A. McGee/ FPG, (b),24, PEANUTS reprinted by permission of UFS, Inc; 28, Michel Tcherevkoff/The Image Bank; 30, Ken Frick; 34, Pictures Unlimited; 36, Courtesy United Airlines; 41, Pictures Unlimited; 42, Larry West/FPG; 43(l), Phillip Hayson/Photo Researchers, (r), William Rivelli/The Image Bank; 45,50, Pictures Unlimited; 55, T. Zimmerman/FPG; 56, Pictures Unlimited; 67, Elaine Shay; 68, Marc Romanelli/The Image Bank, (inset), The Western Reserve Historical Society Library; 69, James Westwater; 70, Drawing by Ed Fisher, ©1966 Saturday Review, Inc; 73, Crown Studio; 74(t), Robert A. Isaacs/Photo Researchers, (b), Historical Pictures Service, Chicago; 76(t), D. Halstead/Gamma Liaison, (b), Elaine Shay; 78, United Negro College Fund; 79, The White House; 80(t), Courtesy Chrysler Corporation, (b), Alan Carey; 82(l), Crown Studio, (r), Larry Hamill; 83(t), Elaine Shay, (b), Crown Studio; 84, Pictures Unlimited; 85(t), Elaine Shay, (b), Richard Dole/DUOMO; 86, MAK-1, 87, William Weber; 88, By permission of Johnny Hart and NAS, Inc; 93, Courtesy of Kennywood; 94,95,96, Crown Studio; 103, Doug Martin; 104, Crown Studios; 105, L. D. Franga; 109, Ruth Dixon; 113, Randy Scheiber; 116,117, Courtesy Kenzo Tange Associates; 118, Studiohio; 119, C. J. Zimmerman/FPG; 120, Pictures Unlimited; 120, Tom Campbell/FPG; 121, Bob Winsett/Tom Stack & Assoc; 122, Charles Feil/FPG; 123, Jim Pickerell/FPG; 125,126, Pictures Unlimited; 128, By permission of Johnny Hart and NAS, Inc; 129,133, Pictures Unlimited; 135, D & P Valenti/H. Armstrong Roberts; 137, Doug Martin; 140, Pictures Unlimited; 141, ©1960 M. C. Escher/Cordon Art-Baarn, Holland; 142, Historical Pictures Service, Chicago; 146, First Image; 147, Tom Stack/Tom Stack & Assoc; 151,153,154, Pictures Unlimited; 162, Scala/Art Resource; 163, David Lyle Millard, STILL LIFE PAINTING TECHNIQUES, Watson-Guptill Publications; 164, Benn Mitchell/The Image Bank; 165, Studiohio; 166,168, Pictures Unlimited; 170, Doug Martin; 171,172, Pictures Unlimited; 177, Courtesy Ford Motor Company; 178, Pictures Unlimited; 182(t), First Image, (b), Museum of Modern Art/Rosenthal Art Slides; 184, Pictures Unlimited/Glencoe; 186, Allen Zak; 191, Pictures Unlimited; 192,193, Doug Martin; 200,201, First Image; 202(t), Doug Martin, (b), Larry Hamill; 206, Frank Cezus; 213, Pictures Unlimited; 214, Courtesy U.S. Embassy, Tokyo, Japan, (inset), Courtesy Norma Sklarek; 215(t), Robert Frerck/Odyssey/Chicago, (b), file photo; 216, Janet Adams; 223,225, Leo Mason/The Image Bank; 229(t), Steve Dunwell/The Image Bank, (b), Historical Pictures Service, Chicago; 230, Doug Martin; 231, First Image; 232,233,235, Pictures Unlimited; 239, file photo; 245, Aaron Haupt/Glencoe; 246,247,249, Pictures Unlimited; 250, R. Krubner/H. Armstrong Roberts; 252,254, Pictures Unlimited; 257, Zefa/H. Armstrong Roberts; 264, David Heald © Solomon R. Guggenheim Foundation, New York, (inset), Philadelphia Museum of Art/Rosenthal Art Slides; 265, David Heald © Solomon R. Guggenheim Foundation, New York; 266,271,272,273, Pictures Unlimited; 274(t), James Westwater, (b), Pictures Unlimited; 275,277, Pictures Unlimited; 278, Lee E. Yunker; 280(t), Anne Van DerVaeren/The Image Bank, (b), Pictures Unlimited; 282(t), Ken Frick, (top inset), Andrea Pistolesi/The Image Bank, (b), Studiohio, (bottom inset), Steve Proehl/The Image Bank; 283, Pictures Unlimited; 286, Mark Gibson; 287, Tim Courlas; 288, Denise morris Curt/The Connecticut Limner; 291, Pictures Unlimited; 292, Doug Martin; 293, Jean Kugler/FPG; 294, Hedrich-Blessing, Ltd; 298, H. Armstrong Roberts; 302, Pictures Unlimited; 306, Art Resource/Giraudon; (inset), Art Resource/Prado, Madrid; 307, The Bettmann Archive; 308,309, Pictures Unlimited; 310(l), Richard Kane/Sportschrome East/West, (r),311,312, Pictures Unlimited; 313(t), Mark Godfrey, (b), NOAO; 314, Don C. Nieman; 315, Frank A. Cezus/FPG; 316,317, Pictures Unlimited; 318, David Hiser/The Image Bank; 319, Doug Martin; 320, Pictures Unlimited; 321(l), Doug Martin, (r), Eric Grave/Science Source/Photo Researchers; 325, Pictures Unlimited; 334, M. Thonig/H. Armstrong Roberts; 335, Pictures Unlimited; 336, Tim Courlas; 337, Folger Shakespeare Library; 350, Pictures Unlimited; 351, Mak-1; 358,359, Robert Frerck/Odyssey/Chicago; 360, Craig Kramer; 364, Susan Snyder; 366, Pictures Unlimited; 367, Mark Gibson; 369, Doug Martin; 370, Animals Animals/Hans & Judy Beste; 371, Lindsay Gerard/Glencoe; 375,376, file photo; 377, Courtesy Carnival Cruise Line; 378, William Weber; 381, Tim Slattery/Harbor Reflections; 384, Ed & Chris Kumler; 387, Aaron Haupt/Glencoe; 388, Susan Snyder; 391, Joseph DiChello; 392, Gary Gay/The Image Bank; 393,394, Pictures Unlimited; 396, Metro Dade Tourism/Walter Marks; 397, Jeff Smith/The Image Bank; 398, Ken Frick; 400, Pictures Unlimited; 408, Nyina Warwinu/Picture Group, (inset), Jerry Sinkovec/Artwerks; 409, Nyina Warwinu/Picture Group; 410, David Frazier; 415(l), Doug Martin; (r),417,418,420, Pictures Unlimited; 421, Perez Siquier/Spanish Tourist Office, Chicago; 427,430, Pictures Unlimited; 433, Mazda of America, Inc; 436, Doug Martin; 439, Tim Courlas; 440, file photo; 442, Doug Martin; 445, David Frazier; 447(l), Gerard Photography, (r), Pictures Unlimited; 452, NASA; 455, Pictures Unlimited; 456, Aaron Haupt/Glencoe; 460, David L. Perry; 464, Paul Warchol, (inset), Serge Hambourg; 465, Paul Warchol; 466, Matt Meadows; 467, George Matchneer; 468, Bob Mullenix; 472, Kathleen O'Donnell/Stockphotos/The Image Bank; 473, Mak-1; 475, Department of Defense; 478, Pictures Unlimited; 479, John Shaw/Tom Stack & Assoc; 482, Pictures Unlimited; 483,484, John Colwell from Grant Heilman; 487, Matt

Meadows/OSU, Department of Engineering Mechanics; **488**, First Image; **489,494**, Bob Mullenix; **495,496**, Pictures Unlimited; **501**, Crown Studio; **502**, Matt Meadows; **503**, Crown Studios; **504**, John Banagan/The Image Bank; **506**, Bob Mullenix; **507**, Blair Seitz/Photo Researchers; **508**, Crown Studios; **510**, Comstock, Inc/Bonnie Camin; **511**, Crown Studios; **512**, W. Cody/Westlight; **517**, Crown Studios; **520(t)**, David Germon, **(b)**, Paul Brown; **524**, Eugene G. Schulz, **525**, Farrell Grehan/FPG; **526**, Doug Martin; **527**, Chris Michaels/FPG; **528**, Visual Horizons/FPG; **529**, Harald Sund/The Image Bank; **534**, Crown Studios; **534**, Matt Meadows; **536**, Bob Mullenix; **538**, Bill Ross/Westlight; **541,542(t)**, Lee Yunker, **(b)**, Salt Institute; **546**, Bob Mullenix; **547**, Mark Stephensen/Westlight; **548(l)**, Pictures Unlimited, **(r)**, Robert Winslow/Tom Stack & Assoc; **549**, Pictures Unlimited; **552**, Bob Mullenix; **553**, Alex Bartel/FPG; **553**, Pictures Unlimited; **554**, ©1989 Tully/Ballenger; **554**, Neal & Mary Jane Mishler/FPG; **555**, Crown Studios; **559**, Tom Tracy/FPG; **560**, Sportschrome East/West; **561**, Doug Martin; **563**, NASA; **564**, Studiohio; **572,573**, Robert Frerck/Odyssey/Chicago; **574(t)**, Aaron Haupt/Glencoe, **(b)**, Thomas Kitchin/Tom Stack & Assoc; **575**, Pictures Unlimited; **578**, Ken Frick; **579**, Courtesy Navy Research Laboratory, Washington DC; **580,581**, Mak-1; **584**, Pictures Unlimited; **585**, Mak-1; **586**, Norbert Wu/TSW; **587**, Pictures Unlimited; **588**, George Obremski/The Image Bank; **589**, Pictures Unlimited; **590**, Rich Buzzelli/Tom Stack & Assoc; **591**, The Bettmann Archive; **592**, Comstock, Inc/Billy Brown; **593**, Mak-1; **594,595**, Pictures Unlimited; **599**, Mak-1; **601**, Pictures Unlimited; **602**, Bill Ross/Westlight; **606**, Don & Pat Valenti/Tom Stack & Assoc; **607**, F. Stuart Westmorland/Tom Stack & Assoc; **608**, William Rivelli/The Image Bank; **616**, Jim Zuckerman/Westlight; **620**, Star Trek II: The Wrath of Kahn, Paramount, 1982; **621**, Stock Imagery; **622(t)**, NASA, **(b)**, Pete Turner/The Image Bank; **624**, Melchior Digiacomo/The Image Bank; **625(t)**, Steve Proehl/The Image Bank, **(b)**, Murray Alcosser/The Image Bank; **626**, Greg Vaughn/Tom Stack & Assoc; **627**, Courtesy Christine M. Darden/Advanced Vehicles Division/NASA; **628**, Harald Sund/The Image Bank; **629**, Andrea Pistolesi/The Image Bank; **633**, Travelpix/FPG; **634**, Eddie Hironaica/The Image Bank; **639**, Pictures Unlimited; **640**, ©1938 M. C. Escher/Cordon Art-Baarn, Holland; **643**, ©1941 M. C. Escher/Cordon Art-Baarn, Holland; **644**, Cradoc Bagshaw/Westlight; **646(t)**, Pictures Unlimited, **(bl)**, Geoffrey Gove/The Image Bank, **(br)**, Runk/Schoenberger from Grant Heilman; **650**, Pictures Unlimited; **653**, Stock Imagery; **654**, Pictures Unlimited; **657**, Robin Smith/FPG; **658**, Doug Martin; **665**, Elaine Shay; **667**, Pictures Unlimited; **670**, ©1959 M. C. Escher/Cordon Art-Baarn, Holland; **672(t)**, Paul J. Sutton/ DUOMO, **(b)**, Jim Cummins/ALLSTOCK; **679**, Pictures Unlimited; **680**, Courtesy Benoit Mandelbrot, IBM, Watson Research Center; **681,682**, Images by H. JÜrgens, H.-O. Peitgen, D. Saupe, from: THE BEAUTY OF FRACTALS by H.-O. Peitgen, P. Richter. Springer-Verlag, Heidelberg, 1986, and FRACTALS FOR THE CLASSROOM, H.-O.Peitgen, H. JÜrgens, D. Saupe. Springer-Verlag, New York, 1991; **683,684**, Michael D. McGuire; **685**, Image by Manfred Kage, Institut fur wissenschaftliche Fotografie; from FRACTALS FOR THE CLASSROOM, H.-O. Peitgen, H. JÜrgens, D. Saupe. Springer-Verlag, New York, 1991; **686**, Michael D. McGuire; **687**, Dr. Vehrenberg KG, from FRACTALS FOR THE CLASSROOM, H.-O. Peitgen, H. JÜrgens, D. Saupe. Springer-Verlag, New York 1991; **688**, FRACTALS FOR THE CLASSROOM by H.-O. Peitgen, H. JÜrgens, D. Saupe. Springer-Verlag, New York, 1991; **689**, Images by H. JÜrgens, H.-O. Peitgen from FRACTELE: GEZAHMTES CHAOS, Carl Freidrich Von Siemens Stiftung, 1988; **690,691**, Images by H. JÜrgens, H.-O. Peitgen, D. Saupe, from: THE BEAUTY OF FRACTALS by H.-O. Peitgen, P. Richter. Springer-Verlag, Heidelberg, 1986, and FRACTALS FOR THE CLASSROOM, H.-O.Peitgen, H. JÜrgens, D. Saupe. Springer-Verlag, New York, 1991; **A1**, Aaron Haput; **B1**, Paul Avis/Gamma-Liaison Network; **B2**, StudiOhio; **B3**, Matt Meadows; **B4, B5**, StudiOhio; **B6**, Aaron Haupt; **B7(t)** Doug Martin, **(c1)** StudiOhio, **(cr)** Bachman/Uniphoto, **(b1)** Ed Young/The Stock Market, **(br)** George Anderson; **B8-B9**, StudiOhio; **B10**, Henley & Savage/The Stock Market; **B11(t1)** M. Howell/Superstock Inc., **(tr)** Chuck O'Rear/Westlight, **(c)** Pictor/Uniphoto, **(b)** David L. Brown/The Stock Market; **B12-B13**, StudiOhio; **B14(t)** StudiOhio, **(b)** Larry Hamill; **B16(t)** Randy Trine, **(c)** David Pollack/The Stock Market, **(b1)** Wernher Krutein/Gamma-Liaison Network, **(br)** Aaron Haupt.

Teacher's Wraparound Edition:

T1, Ross Hickson; **T2(t)** file photo, **(b)**, **T3**, **T6-T7**, **T8**, BLT Productions; **T9**, **T10-11**, Robert Mullenix; **T12**, BLT Productions; **T13**, Robert Mullenix; **T14-15**, Eugene G. Schulz; **T16-17**, file photo; **T18**, **T20**, **T21**, **T23**, BLT Productions.

MORE INVESTIGATIONS IN GEOMETRY

for Merrill Geometry

UNDERSTANDING THROUGH HANDS-ON EXPERIENCES

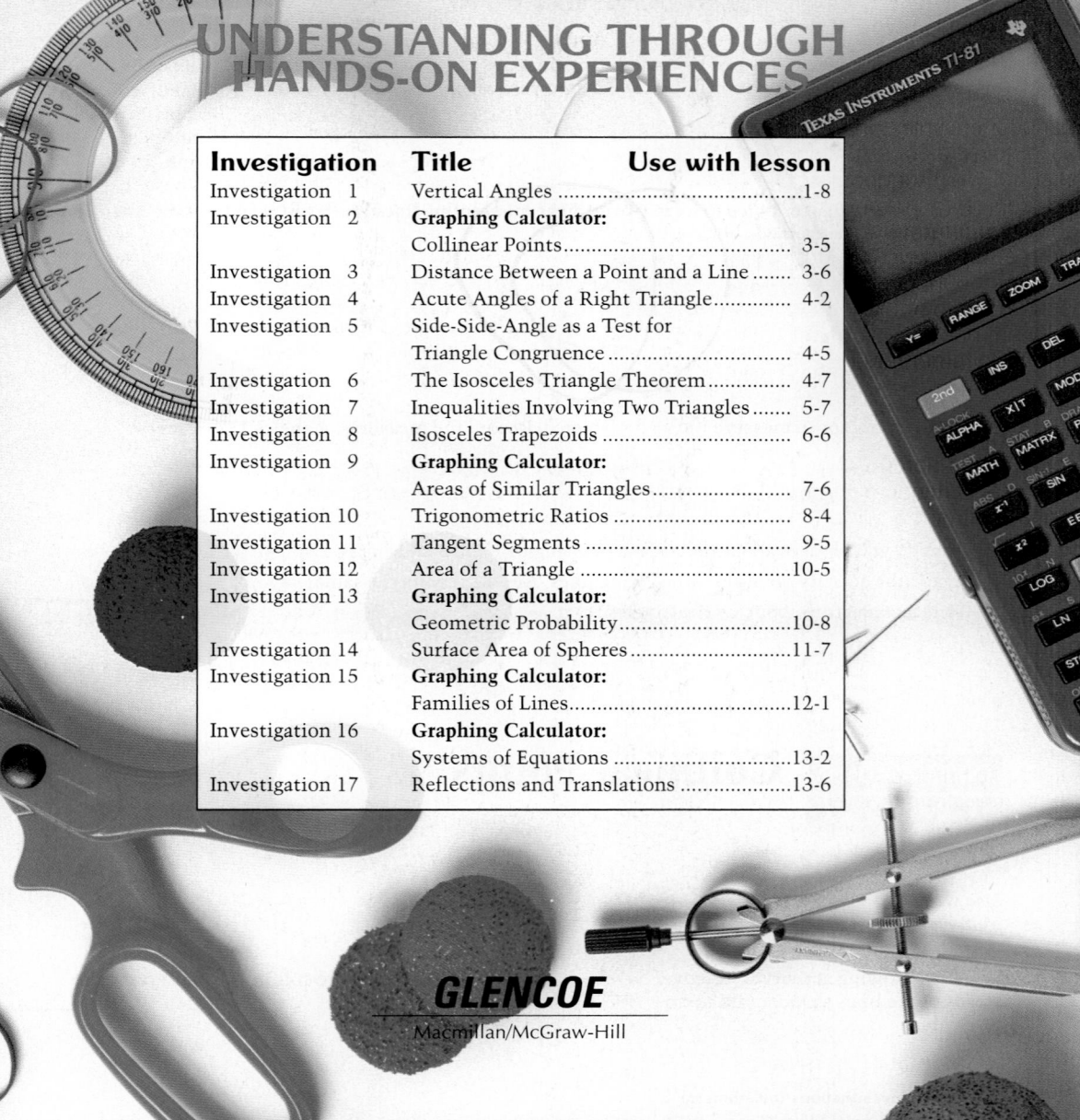

GLENCOE
Macmillan/McGraw-Hill

Using Investigations

Using hands-on investigation activities in your geometry classroom allows students to discover the principles of geometry by using inductive reasoning.

Using Cooperative Learning

The Investigations on the following pages offer an excellent opportunity for using cooperative learning groups. For more information on cooperative learning strategies and group management, see *Cooperative Learning in the Mathematics Classroom,* one of the titles in the Glencoe Mathematics Professional Series.

Management Tips

Some helpful hints on managing manipulatives can help make the use of activities in the classroom an easier task for the teacher.

- Put the manipulatives for each student or group into self-locking plastic bags.
- If you are doing more than one activity with groups, label the bags with group numbers and put them in boxes or baskets, one box per group.
- When the activity is completed, have students return all manipulatives to the proper bags. Assigning one member of each group as inventory controller helps when cleaning up.

Assessment

Observing students working in cooperative groups is an excellent method of assessment. You may wish to ask a student at random from each group to explain the group's solution. Also, look for students helping others to understand the concept being taught.

Investigation 1 Notes

Vertical Angles

Objective Discover that vertical angles are congruent.

Time Required 15 minutes

TEACHING SUGGESTIONS

- Use the Investigation at the beginning of Lesson 1-8, after explaining the definition of adjacent angles.
- If it is available, waxed paper works well for paper folding activities like this one where students need to see the lines formed by their folds. If unlined paper is used, make sure students crease the paper well enough for the lines to be visible.

Answers

1. $m\angle 1 = m\angle 3$ and $m\angle 2 = m\angle 4$
2. Yes, the results are the same.
3. Vertical angles are congruent.

Investigation 2 Notes

Collinear Points

Objective Discover a method for determining if three points are collinear.

Time Required 30 minutes

TEACHING SUGGESTIONS

- Use the Investigation after discussing Example 3 in Lesson 3-5.

 # Vertical Angles

Use with: Lesson 1-8, pages 50–55
Materials: paper, protractor, pencil

The nonadjacent angles formed by intersecting lines are called *vertical angles*. Use the following activity to discover the relationship between two vertical angles.

Activity

▶ Fold a sheet of paper twice to form two straight intersecting lines like lines *m* and *n*. Label the angles as shown below.

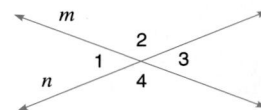

▶ Use a protractor to measure the angles formed. Record the measures of angles 1, 2, 3, and 4.

Write About It See margin.

1. What do you observe about the measures of angles 1 and 3 and angles 2 and 4?
2. Repeat the activity on other intersecting lines. Are the results the same? yes
3. Write a conjecture about vertical angles.

 # Collinear Points

Use with: Lesson 3-5, pages 142–147
Materials: graphing calculator

Use the following activity to discover how to determine if three points are collinear by observing the slopes of the lines that contain them.

Activity

▶ Draw $\overline{AB}$ and $\overline{BC}$ for each set of points on your graphing calculator. Are the segments collinear?

1. $A(3, 6)$, $B(5, 7)$, $C(7, 8)$ **1–5. See margin.**
2. $A(5, 9)$, $B(7, 12)$, $C(11, 17)$
3. $A(0, 1.5)$, $B(5, 8.2)$, $C(11, 15.4)$
4. $A(2.2, -2.1)$, $B(0.6, -1.3)$, $C(-3.8, 0.9)$
5. $A(-11.1, 9.1)$, $B(-14.9, -0.4)$, $C(-15.4, -1.65)$

▶ Use the program to find the slopes of $\overline{AB}$ and $\overline{BC}$ for each set of points.

Write About It See margin.

1. Compare the slopes of $\overline{AB}$ and $\overline{BC}$ for each set of points. When are the slopes the same and when are they different?
2. Write a conjecture about when three points A, B, and C are collinear. Justify your conjecture.

```
Prgm1 SLOPE
:Disp "ENTER X AND Y FOR
 POINT 1"
:Input A
:Input B
:Disp "ENTER X AND Y FOR
 POINT 2"
:Input C
:Input D
:If (C-A) = 0
:Goto 1
:(D-B)/(C-A) → M
:Disp "THE SLOPE IS "
:Disp M
:End
:Lbl 1
:Disp "THE SLOPE IS
 UNDEFINED"
:End
```

The program is written for use on a TI-81 graphing calculator. If you have a different type of programmable calculator, consult your user's guide to adapt the program for use on your calculator.

 **INVESTIGATION 3**

Distance Between a Line and a Point

Use with: Lesson 3-6, pages 148–154
Materials: *lined notebook paper, cardboard, pencil, pin, straightedge, scissors*

You can draw many line segments from a line to a point not on the line. But which one of the segments is the shortest one? Use the following activity to make a conjecture about the shortest segment from a line to a point.

Activity

▶ Cut a vertical strip from a sheet of lined notebook paper. Then number the lines from the top to the bottom.

▶ Draw a horizontal line on a different piece of paper or cardboard. Use a pin to attach the strip of paper at a point above the horizontal line so that the strip moves freely.

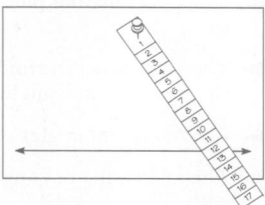

(continued on the next page)

APPENDIX A3

Activity Answers

1. yes; slopes are both 0.5
2. no; slope of $\overline{AB}$ = 1.5, slope of $\overline{BC}$ = 1.25
3. no; slope of $\overline{AB}$ = 1.34, slope of $\overline{BC}$ = 1.2
4. yes; slopes are both -0.5
5. yes; slopes are both 2.5

Investigation 3 Notes

Distance Between a Line and a Point

Objective Discover that the shortest segment between a line and a point not on the line is the segment that passes through the point and is perpendicular to the line.

Time Required 15 minutes

Write About It Answers

1. When the line segments are collinear, their slopes are the same.
2. Three points A, B, and C are collinear if the slopes of $\overline{AB}$ and $\overline{BC}$ are the same. Two lines are parallel if they have the same slope. Since two segments $\overline{AB}$ and $\overline{BC}$ that have the same slope have a point B in common, they must be the same line. Thus, the three points A, B, and C must be collinear.

- Use the Investigation at the beginning of Lesson 3-6 before discussing the introductory application.
- If students use pins to fasten their strips to the paper, it may be helpful to place cardboard behind the paper to make the pin more secure. If cardboard is not available, paper fasteners may be used in place of the pins and cardboard.

Answers

1. Answers will vary.
2. They appear to be perpendicular.
3. The shortest segment between a line and a point not on the line is the segment that passes through the point and is perpendicular to the line.

Investigation 4 Notes

Acute Angles of a Right Triangle

Objective Discover that the sum of the measures of the acute angles of a right triangle is 90.

Time Required 15 minutes

TEACHING SUGGESTIONS

- Use this Investigation after discussing Example 2 in Lesson 4-2.
- Make sure that students fold and cut their rectangle along a straight line so that a right triangle is formed.
- Remind students that angle B is a right angle, so it measures 90.

▶ Move the strip to the far right. Using the numbers on the strip as a scale, record the measure from the pin to the horizontal line.

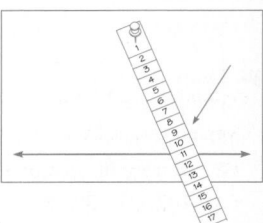

▶ Move the strip a little to the left and remeasure. Record this measure.

▶ Continue moving the strip and measuring the distance to the horizontal line. Stop when the strip is on the far left.

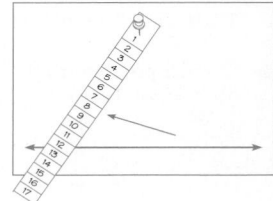

Write About It See margin.

1. Find the least measure in the list of measures that you made. Return the strip to the position of the least measure. Can you find another position that will give an even smaller measure? If you can, move the strip to that position.

2. The strip of paper in exercise 1 represents the shortest segment from the line to the point. What seems true about the strip of paper and the horizontal line?

3. Make a conjecture about the shortest segment from a line to a point not on the line.

INVESTIGATION 4 — Acute Angles of a Right Triangle

Use with: Lesson 4-2, pages 170–176
Materials: paper, scissors

The acute angles of a right triangle are related. Use the following activity to discover this relationship.

Activity

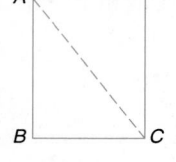
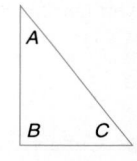

▶ Fold a rectangular piece of paper along a diagonal from A to C.

▶ Then cut along the fold to form a right triangle ABC. Write the name of each angle on the inside of the triangle.

▶ Cut or tear off angles A and C.

▶ Then place the cut angles at $\angle B$.

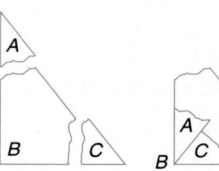

A4   More Investigations In Geometry

Write About It 1, 3–4. See margin.

1. What seems to be true about the measures of the three angles?

2. Repeat the activity on other right triangles. Are the results the same? **yes**

3. Write a conjecture about the sum of the measures of the acute angles in a right triangle.

4. Prove your conjecture.

Side-Side-Angle as a Test for Triangle Congruence

Use with: *Lesson 4-5, pages 192–197*
Materials: *two straws, scissors, straight pin, tape, straightedge, protractor, paper, pencil*

You have studied different methods for proving that two triangles are congruent. Is proving that two sides and a non-included angle of two triangles are congruent, or SSA, sufficient for proving the triangles congruent?

Activity

▶ Using a straightedge, draw a horizontal line on your paper.

▶ Connect two straws of unequal length with a pin, then position the straws so that the two straws form a triangle with the segment. Anchor one of the straws with tape, and label the vertices of the triangle *A*, *B*, and *C*.

▶ Measure ∠*BAC* and ∠*BCA*.

▶ Now swing the straw representing $\overline{BC}$ so that the end of the straw touches the segment again. Label this point *D*.

▶ Measure ∠*BAC* and ∠*ADB*.

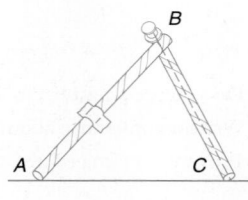

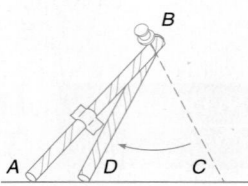

Write About It See margin.

1. List the corresponding parts of Δ*ABC* and Δ*ABD* that are congruent.

2. If SSA is a test for triangle congruence, would you be able to say that Δ*ABC* ≅ Δ*ABD*?

3. Tell whether you think that SSA is a valid test for triangle congruence and justify your answer.

APPENDIX A5

Answers
1. $\overline{AB} \cong \overline{AB}$, $\overline{BC} \cong \overline{BD}$, ∠*BAC* ≅ ∠*BAD*
2. Yes, if SSA was a test for triangle congruence we could conclude that Δ*ABC* ≅ Δ*ABD*.
3. No, SSA is not a valid test for triangle congruence. Δ*ABC* and Δ*ABD* are a counterexample that disproves the conjecture that SSA is a test for triangle congruence.

Answers
1. It appears that
   m∠*A* + m∠*C* = m∠*B*.
2. The results of the activity are the same with any right triangle.
3. Conjecture: The sum of the measures of the acute angles of a right triangle is 90.
4. Given: Δ*XYZ* with right angle at *X*
   Prove: m∠*Y* + m∠*Z* = 90

   By the angle sum theorem, m∠*X* + m∠*Y* + m∠*Z* = 180. m∠*X* = 90 by the definition of a right angle. Thus, 90 + m∠*Y* + m∠*Z* = 180 by the substitution property of equality. Therefore, m∠*Y* + m∠*Z* = 90 by the Subtraction property of equality.

Investigation 5 Notes

Side-Side-Angle as a Test for Triangle Congruence

Objective   Discover that Side-Side-Angle, or SSA, is not a valid test for triangle congruence.

Time Required   15 minutes

TEACHING SUGGESTIONS

• Use the Investigation after discussing Theorem 4-5, AAS, in Lesson 4-5.
• It may be helpful for students to pin the straws to cardboard for stability.
• If students have trouble listing the congruent parts of the two triangles, you may wish to have them measure all of the sides and angles of each triangle. Then they will be able to make a list of the corresponding parts of the triangles that are congruent.

Investigation 6 Notes

The Isosceles Triangle Theorem

Objective Discover that the base angles of an isosceles triangle are congruent.

Time Required 15 minutes

TEACHING SUGGESTIONS

- Use the Investigation at the beginning of Lesson 4-7 before discussing the introductory application.
- Make sure that students connect their straws so that the segments are congruent.
- You may wish to have students work in pairs to complete this investigation. One student could hold the straws in place while the other measures the angles. Make sure both students measure angles.

Activity Answers

1. $m\angle A = 45$, $m\angle B = 45$
2. $m\angle A = 60$, $m\angle B = 60$
3. $m\angle A = 65$, $m\angle B = 65$
4. $m\angle A = 30$, $m\angle B = 30$

Write About It Answers

1. In each triangle, $m\angle A = m\angle B$.
2. The measures of the angles opposite two congruent sides of a triangle are congruent.
3. The proof of this theorem appears on page 202 of Lesson 4-7.

Investigation 7 Notes

Inequalities Involving Two Triangles

Objective Discover SAS Inequality.

Time Required 15 minutes

 **INVESTIGATION 6** # The Isosceles Triangle Theorem

Use with: Lesson 4-7, pages 202–207
Materials: two straws, straight pin, protractor

Isoceles triangles have at least two sides congruent. Compete the following activity to discover an important property of isosceles triangles.

Activity

▶ Connect two straws of the same length with a pin so that they form an angle. Think of the angle as $\angle C$ and the straws as sides $\overline{AC}$ and $\overline{BC}$ in $\triangle ABC$.

▶ Lay the straws on your desk and position them so that the edge of the desk represents line AB.

▶ Use the protractor to position the straws so that $\angle C$ has each of the measures listed below. For each measure of $\angle C$, find the measures of $\angle A$ and $\angle B$. **See margin.**

1. $m\angle C = 90$ 2. $m\angle C = 60$
3. $m\angle C = 50$ 4. $m\angle C = 120$

Write About It See margin.

1. Do you see a pattern in the measures of angles A and B for each measure of $\angle C$?
2. Write a conjecture about the measure of the angles opposite congruent sides of a triangle.
3. Prove your conjecture.

 **INVESTIGATION 7** # Inequalities Involving Two Triangles

Use with: Lesson 5-7, pages 252–257
Materials: rubber band, ball bearing compass, centimeter ruler, protractor

You know that if two sides and an included angle of one triangle are congruent to the corresponding parts of a second triangle then the triangles are congruent. Use the following activity to determine the relationship between two triangles if two pairs of corresponding sides are congruent, but the included angles are not congruent.

Activity

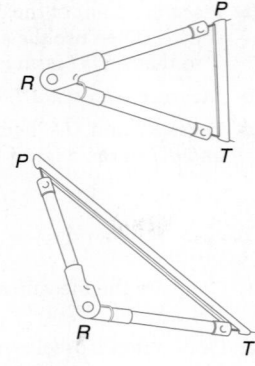

▶ Place a rubber band over the tips of a ball bearing compass as shown. Imagine that the sides of the compass and the rubber band form a triangle which we will call △*PRT*.

▶ Measure ∠*R* and $\overline{PT}$.

▶ Spread the compass arms farther apart to form a different triangle.

Write About It 1. See margin.

1. What happened to *m*∠*R* and *PT* after you moved the arms of the compass?
2. Measure ∠*R* and $\overline{PT}$. Change the position of the compass arms again and repeat the measurements. **See students' work.**
3. Suppose $\overline{AB} \cong \overline{DE}$ and $\overline{BC} \cong \overline{EF}$ in △*ABC* and △*DEF*. If *m*∠*B* > *m*∠*E*, how are *AC* and *DF* related? ***AC* > *DF***

Isosceles Trapezoids

Use with: Lesson 6-6, pages 294–299
Materials: *lined notebook paper, centimeter ruler, pencil, compass, protractor*

A trapezoid *ABCD* is a quadrilateral with exactly one pair of sides parallel. The parallel sides $\overline{AB}$ and $\overline{CD}$ are called *bases* and the nonparallel sides are called *legs*. The pairs of angles ∠*A* and ∠*D* and ∠*B* and ∠*C* are *base angles*. In an *isosceles trapezoid,* the legs are congruent. Use the following activity to discover properties of trapezoids.

Activity

▶ Darken two lines on a piece of lined notebook paper to show two parallel lines.

▶ Place the point of the compass on a point *R* on one of the lines and draw an arc that intersects the second line. Label the point where the arc intersects the line as point *S*. Draw $\overline{RS}$.

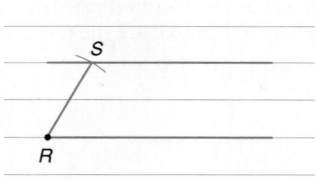

(continued on the next page)

● Use the Investigation at the beginning of Lesson 5-7 before discussing the introductory application.
● You may wish to have students work in pairs on the Investigation. Have one student hold the compass and rubber band while the other measures the angle or side.

Answer

1. Both *m*∠*R* and *PT* appear to be greater.

Investigation 8 Notes

Isosceles Trapezoids

Objective   Discover that in an isosceles trapezoid the base angles are congruent and the diagonals are congruent.

Time Required   20 minutes

TEACHING SUGGESTIONS

● Use the Investigation at the beginning of Lesson 6-6 before discussing the introductory application.
● Ask students to explain why the trapezoid they construct is isosceles.

Answers

3. Answers may vary. A sample answer is that the base angles of an isosceles trapezoid are congruent. This is Theorem 6-12 and is proved on page 294 of Lesson 6-6.

A8   More Investigations in Geometry

4. Answers may vary. A sample answer is that the diagonals of an isosceles trapezoid are congruent. This is Theorem 6-13. Students will prove this theorem in Exercise 28 of Lesson 6-6.

Investigation 9 Notes

Areas of Similar Triangles

Objective Discover the relationship between the areas of similar triangles.

Time Required   30 minutes

TEACHING SUGGESTIONS

- Use the Investigation after discussing Theorem 7-10 in Lesson 7-6, which describes the relationship between corresponding medians of similar triangles.
- If students have had little experience with graphing calculators, they will need help in entering the program into the memory. Explain that many of the TI-81 programming commands are found in the menus. Consult the User's Guide for the locations of specific commands.

▶ Place the point of the compass on another point U as shown. Then use the same compass setting to mark a point T so that $RSTU$ is an isosceles trapezoid. Draw $\overline{TU}$.

▶ Measure $\angle R$, $\angle S$, $\angle T$, and $\angle U$ of trapezoid $RSTU$.

▶ Draw $\overline{RT}$ and $\overline{SU}$. Then use a centimeter ruler to find RT and SU to the nearest millimeter.

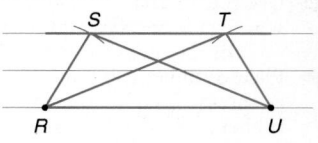

Write About It 3–4. See margin.

1. Compare the measures of the pairs of base angles of isosceles trapezoid $RSTU$, $\angle R$ and $\angle U$, and $\angle S$ and $\angle T$. $m\angle R = m\angle U$, $m\angle S = m\angle T$

2. Draw a non-isosceles trapezoid $LMNO$ and measure the base angles. Are the base angles of $LMNO$ related in the same way that the base angles of $RSTU$ are? **no**

3. Make a conjecture about the base angles of trapezoids based on your observations. Then prove your conjecture.

4. Draw and measure the diagonals for trapezoid $LMNO$. Write a conjecture about the diagonals of a trapezoid based on the measures of $\overline{RT}$ and $\overline{SU}$ and the measures of $\overline{LN}$ and $\overline{MO}$.

 **Areas of Similar Triangles**

Use with: *Lesson 7-6, pages 342–348*
Materials: *graphing or other programmable calculator*

If two triangles are similar, you can draw conclusions about many of the corresponding parts of the triangle. Corresponding sides, altitudes, and perimeters are proportional. Complete the following activity to draw a conclusion about the areas of similar triangles.

The program at the right uses Hero's formula to find the area of a triangle. Hero's formula is $A = \sqrt{s(s-a)(s-b)(s-c)}$, where a, b, and c are the measures of the sides of the triangle, and $s = \frac{1}{2}(a+b+c)$.

```
Prgm2: HEROS
:ClrHome
:Disp "SIDE 1 ="
:Input A
:Disp "SIDE 2 ="
:Input B
:Disp "SIDE 3 ="
:Input C
:If A + B ≤ C
:Goto 1
:If A + C ≤ B
:Goto 1
:If B + C ≤ A
:Goto 1
:(A+B+C)/2 → S
```

Activity

▶ Write a conjecture about the relationship between the areas of two similar triangles.

A8   More Investigations In Geometry

- Use the program to find the areas of similar triangles whose sides have the given measures. Then find the ratio of the measure of the sides and the ratio of the areas of the triangles. **See margin.**

  1. 3, 4, 5 and 6, 8, 10

  2. 8, 11, 17 and 24, 33, 51

  3. 5.1, 6.3, 8.1 and 30.6, 37.8, 48.6

Write About It See margin.

1. Do you need to revise your conjecture based on the examples?

2. If necessary, write a new conjecture and then justify your conclusion.

```
:√(S(S-A)(S-B)(S-C)) → K
:Disp "AREA ="
:Disp K
:Goto 2
:Lbl 1
:Disp "NO TRIANGLE"
:Lbl 2
:End
```

The program is written for use on a TI-81 graphing calculator. If you have a different type of programmable calculator, consult your user's guide to adapt the program for use on your calculator.

Trigonometric Ratios

Use with: *Lesson 8-4, pages 376–382*
Materials: *centimeter ruler, paper*

Trigonometry has been used in fields like construction for centuries. Use the following activity to explore the basic trigonometric ratios.

Activity

- Fold a rectangular piece of paper along a diagonal from A to C.

- Then cut along the fold to form a right triangle ABC. Write the name of each angle on the inside of the triangle.

- Fold two more segments perpendicular to $\overline{AB}$. Label points D, E, F, and G as shown.

- Find each of the measures AC, AB, BC, AF, AG, FG, AD, AE, and DE.

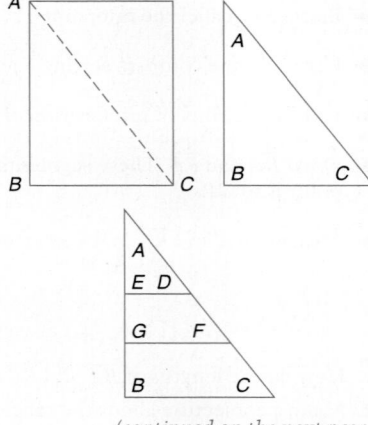

(continued on the next page)

APPENDIX A9

Activity Answers

Conjectures may vary. A sample answer is that if two triangles are similar, then the areas are proportional to the measures of corresponding sides.

1. 6; 24; 2; 4
2. 35.5; 319.5; 3; 9
3. 16.1; 578.3; 6; 36

Write About It Answer

1. Answers may vary. A sample answer is that the new conjecture is *If the ratio of the measures of the sides of two similar triangles is k, then ratio of the areas of the triangles is k^2.* A proof of this conjecture follows.

   Given: $\triangle ABC \sim \triangle DEF$
   $$\frac{a}{d} = \frac{b}{e} = \frac{c}{f} = k$$

   Prove: $\dfrac{area\ of\ \triangle ABC}{area\ of\ \triangle DEF} = k^2$

   See bottom margin for proof.

Investigation 10 Notes

Trigonometry

Objective Investigate the sine, cosine, and tangent ratios.

Time Required 20 minutes

TEACHING SUGGESTIONS

- Use the Investigation before the definitions of the trigonometric ratios in Lesson 8-4.
- Remind students that to fold a line perpendicular to a AB, fold the edge so that A falls on AB and make a crease.

Answers

1. Measures will vary. Students should find that the fractions are equivalent.
2. $\triangle ABC \sim \triangle AGF \sim \triangle AED$ so the ratios of the sides are equivalent.

$$\frac{area\ of\ \triangle ABC}{area\ of\ \triangle DEF} = \frac{\sqrt{\frac{a+b+c}{2}\left(\frac{a+b+c}{2}-a\right)\left(\frac{a+b+c}{2}-b\right)\left(\frac{a+b+c}{2}-c\right)}}{\sqrt{\frac{d+e+f}{2}\left(\frac{d+e+f}{2}-d\right)\left(\frac{d+e+f}{2}-e\right)\left(\frac{d+e+f}{2}-f\right)}}$$

$$= \frac{\sqrt{\frac{dk+ek+fk}{2}\left(\frac{dk+ek+fk}{2}-dk\right)\left(\frac{dk+ek+fk}{2}-ek\right)\left(\frac{dk+ek+fk}{2}-fk\right)}}{\sqrt{\frac{d+e+f}{2}\left(\frac{d+e+f}{2}-d\right)\left(\frac{d+e+f}{2}-e\right)\left(\frac{d+e+f}{2}-f\right)}}$$

$$= \frac{\sqrt{k^4\left(\frac{d+e+f}{2}\right)\left(\frac{d+e+f}{2}-d\right)\left(\frac{d+e+f}{2}-e\right)\left(\frac{d+e+f}{2}-f\right)}}{\sqrt{\frac{d+e+f}{2}\left(\frac{d+e+f}{2}-d\right)\left(\frac{d+e+f}{2}-e\right)\left(\frac{d+e+f}{2}-f\right)}}$$

$$= k^2$$

3. Measurements will vary. The fractions should be $\frac{AE}{AD}$, $\frac{AG}{AF}$, and $\frac{AB}{AC}$. The fractions should be equivalent.

Investigation 11 Notes

Tangent Segments

Objective   Discover that the two tangent segments to a circle from a point outside of the circle are congruent.

Time Required   15 minutes

TEACHING SUGGESTIONS

- Use the Investigation before discussing Theorem 9-10 in Lesson 9-5.
- Students may need to refresh their memories on how to construct a perpendicular bisector. This construction appears on page 31 of Lesson 1-5.
- You may wish to have students extend segments RA and RB to verify that the segments are tangent to $\odot P$.

Answers

2. The tangent segments to a circle from a point outside of the circle are congruent.
3. Given: circles $\odot P$ and $\odot T$
   Prove: $\overline{RA} \cong \overline{RB}$
   Draw $\overline{PA}$ and $\overline{PB}$. $\overline{PA} \cong \overline{PB}$ since both are radii of $\odot P$. Thus, $\overline{PA} \perp \overline{RA}$ and $\overline{PB} \perp \overline{RB}$ since a tangent segment is perpendicular to the radius drawn to the point of tangency. $\triangle RAP$ and $\triangle RBP$ are right triangles by definition. $\overline{RP} \cong \overline{RP}$ since congruence of segments is reflexive. Therefore by HL, $\triangle RAP \cong \triangle RBP$. $\overline{RA} \cong \overline{RB}$ by CPCTC.

Write About It   See margin.

1. The sine of an angle in a right triangle is the ratio of the measure of the side opposite the angle to the measure of the hypotenuse. For angle A, the sine could be expressed as $\frac{DE}{AD}$ for $\triangle ADE$, $\frac{FG}{AF}$ for $\triangle AFG$, and $\frac{BC}{AC}$ for $\triangle ACB$. How do these fractions compare?
2. Use similar triangles to explain your findings in Exercise 1.
3. The cosine of an angle in a right triangle is the ratio of the measure of the side adjacent to the angle to the measure of the hypotenuse. Use your measurements to write three fractions for the cosine of angle A. How do these fractions compare?

INVESTIGATION 11

Tangent Segments

Use with: Lesson 9-5, pages 434–439
Materials: compass, pencil, paper, centimeter ruler

Complete the following activity to discover an important property of two segments that are tangent to a circle from a point outside the circle.

Activity

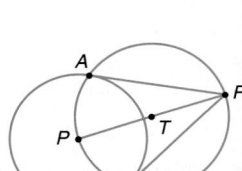

▶ Construct a circle P. Then label a point R in the exterior of $\odot P$ as shown.

▶ Use a straightedge to draw $\overline{PR}$.

▶ Bisect $\overline{PR}$. Label the midpoint T.

▶ Using a same compass setting equal to PT, construct $\odot T$.

▶ Label the points of intersection of $\odot P$ and $\odot T$ as A and B.

▶ Draw $\overline{RA}$ and $\overline{RB}$. These segments are the tangents from point R to $\odot P$.

▶ Measure $\overline{RA}$ and $\overline{RB}$ to the nearest millimeter.

Write About It   2–3. See margin.

1. How do the lengths of $\overline{RA}$ and $\overline{RB}$ compare?   **They are equal.**
2. Make a conjecture about the tangent segments to a circle from a point outside of the circle.
3. Write a proof for your conjecture. *Hint: You may need to draw segments PA and PB.*

A10   More Investigations In Geometry

INVESTIGATION 12

Area of a Triangle

Use with: Lesson 10-5, pages 489–494
Materials: pencil, grid paper, scissors, straightedge

Area of a Triangle
Objective Discover the formula for the area of a triangle.

Time Required 15 minutes

You know formulas for the areas of squares and rectangles. Use the following activity to discover the formula for the area of a triangle.

Activity

▶ Draw a triangle on grid paper so that one edge is along a horizontal line as shown at the right. Label the vertices of the triangle A, B, and C.

▶ Draw a line perpendicular to $\overline{AC}$ through A.

▶ Draw a line perpendicular to $\overline{AC}$ through C.

▶ Draw a line parallel to $\overline{AC}$ through B.

▶ Label the points of intersection of the lines drawn as D and E as shown.

▶ Find the area of rectangle ACDE in square units.

▶ Cut out rectangle ACDE. Then cut out △ABC. Place the two smaller pieces over △ABC to completely cover the triangle.

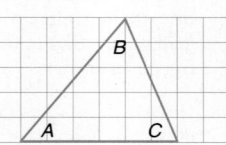

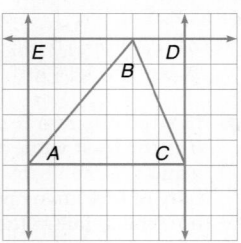

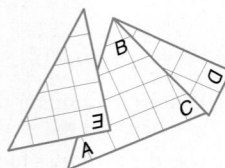

TEACHING SUGGESTIONS

- Use the Investigation at the beginning of Lesson 10-5, before discussing the introductory application.
- Suggest that students place vertices A and C on grid marks so that the perpendicular lines they need to construct will be easy to find.

Answers
1. area of △ABC = area of △ABE + area of △BCD
2. area of △ABC = $\frac{1}{2}$ (area of rectangle ABDE); the bases are congruent and the heights are congruent
3. $A = \frac{1}{2}bh$

Write About It See margin.

1. Write a sentence comparing the area of △ABC and the sum of the areas of △ABE and △BCD.

2. How does the area of △ABC compare to the area of rectangle ACDE? How are the bases and the heights of △ABC and rectangle ACDE related?

3. Write a formula for the area of a triangle, A, in terms of the lengths of its base, b, and height, h.

Geometric Probability

Objective Investigate geometric probability.

Time Required 30 minutes

TEACHING SUGGESTIONS

- Use the Investigation at the beginning of Lesson 10-8, before discussing the introductory application.
- Explain that the calculator program will generate ordered pairs within the large square.
- If students have had little experience with graphing calculators, they will need help in entering the program into the memory. Explain that many of the TI-81 programming commands are found in the menus. Consult the User's Guide for the locations of specific commands.
- Instruct students to count points that fall on the outside edge of the large square or unshaded square as inside the particular square.
- You may wish to have students work in pairs on this Investigation. Have one student graph while the other uses the calculator.
- As an extension activity, you may wish to use the calculator program to explore the Monte Carlo method of finding the area of an irregular figure.

Answers

1. Answers will vary.
2. $\frac{1}{2}$
3. Answers will vary. The fractions should be close.
4. Answers will vary. The fractions should be closer than the fractions compared in Exercise 3.

 **INVESTIGATION 13**

Geometric Probability

Use with: *Lesson 10-8, pages 507–511*
Materials: *pencil, grid paper, graphing calculator, straightedge*

Geometric probability involves using area and length to find the probability of an event. Use the following activity to explore the principles of geometric probability.

Activity

▶ Use a straightedge to draw a figure like the one at the right on grid paper. Shade the figure as shown.

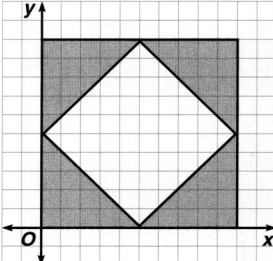

▶ Use the program to generate 50 ordered pairs. Enter the 0 as the least value and 10 as the greatest value for both x and y. Graph each pair on the grid paper. Keep a tally of how many points fall in the shaded areas and how many fall in the unshaded area.

Write About It See margin.

1. Write a fraction for the number of points that were graphed that fell in the shaded area.
2. Use the formulas for the area of a triangle and the area of a square to find the fraction of the large square that is shaded.
3. How do the two fractions you have written compare?
4. Generate and graph 50 more ordered pairs. Add the results to your previous results. What fraction of the 100 points generated fell in the shaded area? How does this fraction compare to the fraction of the square that is shaded?

```
Prgm3 RAND.PRS
:ClrHome
:Fix 1
:Disp "LEAST INTEGER FOR
 X"
:Input A
:Disp "GREATEST INTEGER
 FOR X"
:Input B
:Disp "LEAST INTEGER
 FOR Y"
:Input C
:Disp "GREATEST INTEGER
 FOR Y"
:Input D
:Disp "NUMBER OF PAIRS"
:Input P
:Disp "SEED NUMBER"
:Input N
:N → Rand
:0 → I
:Lbl 1
:I+1 → I
:(B-A)Rand+A → X
:Disp X
:(D-C)Rand+C → Y
:Disp Y
:Disp " "
:Pause
:If I ≠ P
:Goto 1
:End
```

The program is written for use on a TI-81 graphing calculator. If you have a different type of programmable calculator, consult your user's guide to adapt the program for use on your calculator.

A12   More Investigations In Geometry

INVESTIGATION 14

Surface Area of Spheres

Use with: Lesson 11-7, pages 560–565
Materials: styrofoam ball, scissors, tape, straight pins, paper, pencil

A styrofoam ball is a model of a sphere. Use the following activity to find a formula for the surface area of a sphere.

Activity

▶ Cut the styrofoam ball in half. Trace around the edge to draw a circle. Then cut out the circle.

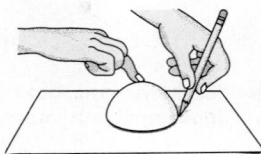

▶ Fold the circle into eighths. Then unfold and cut the eight pieces apart. Tape the pieces back together in the arrangement shown at the right.

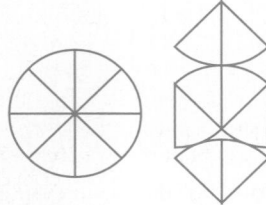

▶ Use tape or a straight pin to put the two pieces of the sphere back together. Then use pins to attach the pattern to the sphere.

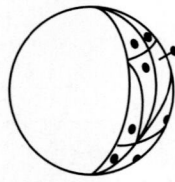

Write About It See margin.

1. How much of the surface of the sphere was covered by the pattern?
2. What is the area of the pattern in terms of the radius of the sphere, r?
3. Write a formula for the surface area of the sphere.

Surface Area of Spheres

Objective Discover the formula for the surface area of a sphere.

Time Required 20 minutes

TEACHING SUGGESTIONS

- Use the Investigation after discussing the parts of a sphere in Lesson 11-7.
- You may wish to cut the styrofoam balls in advance to save time and avoid accidents while cutting. A kitchen knife is an effective cutting tool, or the industrial technology teacher in your school may be able to offer some suggestions for cutting the balls safely.
- If supplies are limited, you may wish to have students work in pairs.
- If students have trouble determining what fraction of the sphere is covered by the pattern, have students make a second pattern and attach it to the sphere as well.

Answers

1. one-fourth of the sphere
2. $A = \pi r^2$
3. $A = 4\pi r^2$

Families of Lines

Objective Investigate the differences and similarities among families of linear functions.

Time Required 20 minutes

TEACHING SUGGESTIONS

- Use the Investigation before discussing Theorem 12-1 in Lesson 12-1.
- If students have had little experience with graphing calculators, they will need help in graphing the functions. If necessary, have students consult the User's Guide for their calculator.
- You may wish to have students graph additional families of linear equations before drawing a conclusion.

Answers

1. In the first set, all of the lines passed through the point (0, 1). But, the lines all had different slopes. In the second set, all of the lines were parallel. No two lines had a common point.
2. In the first set, all of the values of *b* were 1. All of the values of *m* were different. In the second set, all of the values of *m* were 3 and all of the values of *b* were different.
3. All graphs are parallel lines.
4. All graphs are lines that pass through the point (0, *a*).

Families of Lines

Use with: *Lesson 12-1, pages 574–579*
Materials: *graphing calculator*

A family of graphs is a group of graphs that displays one or more similar characteristics. Use Investigation 15 to observe some of the families of lines.

Activity

▶ Set the viewing window of your calculator to the standard viewing window, which has a domain of $\{x \mid -10 \le x \le 10\}$ and a range of $\{y \mid -10 \le y \le 10\}$.

▶ Graph the following functions on the same screen. Observe the similarities and differences among the graphs.

$y = x + 1$
$y = 3x + 1$
$y = 5x + 1$
$y = 0.5x + 1$

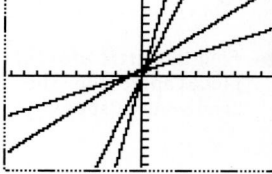

▶ Clear the viewing window. Then graph the following functions on the same screen. Observe the similarities and differences among these graphs.

$y = 3x$
$y = 3x + 1$
$y = 3x - 2$
$y = 3x + 5$

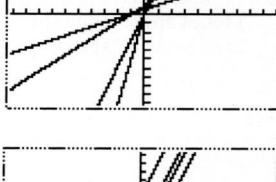

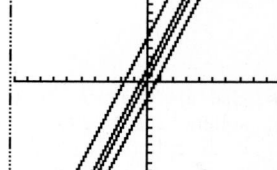

Write About It See margin.

1. Describe the similarities and differences among the graphs of each set of functions.
2. Using the slope-intercept form of a linear equation, $y = mx + b$, explain the similarities and differences among the equations of each set of functions.
3. If a is a constant, describe the family of graphs $y = ax + b$.
4. If a is a constant, describe the family of graphs $y = mx + a$.

A14   More Investigations In Geometry

Systems of Equations

Use with: Lesson 13-2, pages 628–633
Materials: graphing calculator

Since you can graph several functions on the screen at one time, you can use a graphing calculator to solve systems of equations. Use the following activity to explore how to solve a system of equations using a graphing calculator.

Activity

Find the locus of points that satisfy both $y = 3.4x + 2.1$ and $y = -5.1x + 8.3$.

▶ Set the viewing window of your calculator to the standard viewing window of [-10, 10] by [-10, 10].

▶ Graph both functions.

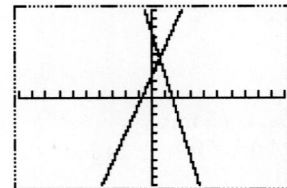

▶ Use the trace function to place the cursor at the point of intersection and read the coordinates.

▶ Use the zoom feature of the calculator to find the coordinates of the intersection point more accurately. Repeatedly tracing and zooming allows you to find very accurate coordinates.

Write About It 3. See margin.

1. According to your explorations on the graphing calculator, what are the coordinates of the point of intersection to the nearest hundredth? **(0.73, 4.58)**

2. Solve the system of equations algebraically. Is your solution close to the results found on the graphing calculator? **Answers will vary.**

3. When do you think finding a solution to a system of equations with a graphing calculator is appropriate? Does this method of solution always give an accurate solution?

APPENDIX   A15

Investigation 16 Notes

Systems of Equations
Objective   Investigate solving systems of equations with a graphing calculator.

Time Required   15 minutes

TEACHING SUGGESTIONS

- Use the Investigation after discussing Example 1 of Lesson 13-2.
- If students have had little experience with graphing calculators, you may wish to have them work in pairs. Have students consult the User's Guide for their calculator for the keystrokes for entering equations and accessing the trace and zoom features.
- The TI-82 calculator has a special function on the CALC menu that will identify the point of intersection of two graphs. When "5: intersect" is selected from the CALC menu, a prompt saying "First Curve?" appears. Have students use the ▲ or ▼ to select the first function and press ENTER. Use the same keys to answer the "Second curve?" prompt and press ENTER. The cursor automatically moves to the intersection, and the coordinates of that point are displayed at the bottom of the screen.

Answer
3. Answers may vary. A sample answer is that a graphing calculator can be used when an approximate answer is needed. It may also be used to estimate an answer before or after an algebraic solution is found.

Investigation 17 Notes

Reflections and Translations

Objective Investigate translations as reflections over two parallel lines.

Time Required 20 minutes

TEACHING SUGGESTIONS

- Use the Investigation at the beginning of Lesson 13-6 before discussing the introductory application.
- Students may have never used a mira™ before. Instruct them to position the mira so that the words at the top are legible and so that the drawing edge is flat on the desk. Working on one sheet of paper with a sharp pencil gives the best results.

Answers

3. Answers may vary. Sample answer: Slide or translate $\triangle ABC$ onto $\triangle A''B''C''$.
4. $AA'' = BB'' = CC'' = \frac{1}{2}$ (distance from ℓ to m)

Reflections and Translations

Use with: Lesson 13-6, pages 653–658
Materials: paper, pencil, straightedge, mira™

A *mira*™ is a construction instrument that allows you to find the reflection image of a figure. Use a mira™ with the following activity to investigate translations.

Activity

▶ Draw two parallel lines ℓ and m and a triangle *ABC*.

▶ Place the mira so that the edge is aligned with line ℓ. Look into the mira to see the reflection image of $\triangle ABC$.

▶ Use a straightedge to draw the image of $\triangle ABC$. Label the vertices A', B', and C'.

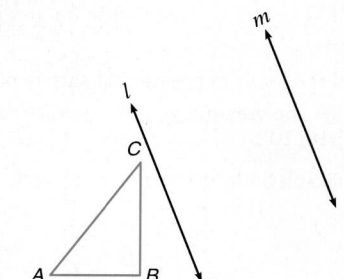

▶ Align the edge of the mira with line *m.* Look into the mira to see the reflection image of $\triangle A'B'C'$.

▶ Draw the image of $\triangle A'B'C'$. Label the vertices A'', B'', and C''.

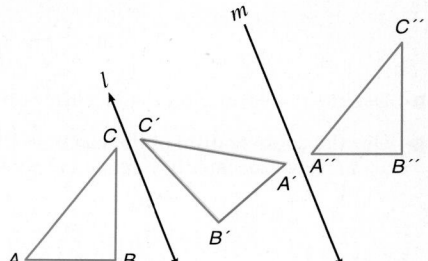

Write About It 3–4. See margin.

1. You know that a reflection changes the orientation of its image. What happens when a figure is reflected twice? **Its orientation is not changed.**
2. Are the points A, A', and A'' collinear? How about B, B', and B'' and C, C', and C''? Use a straightedge to verify your answer. **Yes, each of the sets of three points are collinear.**
3. Describe how you could map $\triangle ABC$ onto $\triangle A''B''C''$ in one motion instead of two reflections.
4. Compare the lengths of $\overline{AA''}$, $\overline{BB''}$, $\overline{CC''}$, and the distance between ℓ, and m.

GLENCOE

EXTENDED PROJECTS

for Merrill Geometry

PROJECTS

THE GEOMETRY OF MINIATURE GOLF

Objectives

- Understand angles.
- Analyze angles of incidence and reflection.
- Design a miniature golf hole that illustrates students' discoveries about angles.

Overview

A ball approaches an obstruction, strikes it, and deflects in another direction. This simple and familiar action, central to many sports and games, is a common thread that links many popular pastimes. Behind it lies the law of physics which states that for any such action, the angle of incidence is congruent to the angle of reflection.

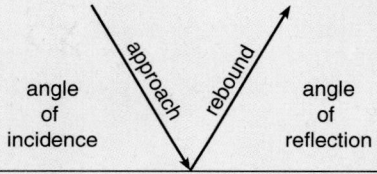

angle   approach rebound   angle
of   of
incidence   reflection

In miniature golf, a ball might strike and rebound from several reflective surfaces. Analyzing how to play a hole off the tee becomes a complex, but interesting, matter. In this project, students will undertake such an analysis, attempting to determine the initial angle of incidence by studying the design of the hole. They then will construct a miniature golf hole that illustrates their findings.

Mathematical Content

Students should incorporate ideas from Chapters 1-3 in their work, possibly including, but not limited to, lines, planes, rays, angles, supplementary angles, congruent angles, and perpendicular lines.

The Geometry of Miniature Golf

"Follow the bouncing ball!"

That old saying originally applied to a ball on a movie screen that guided viewers, word by word, through song lyrics printed on the screen. But it could apply equally well to sports.

Think of examples of bouncing balls in sports—a baseball rebounding off a bat or careening off an outfield wall, a tennis ball flying off a racquet, a basketball banking off a backboard into a basket. In each case, the ball hits an obstruction and flies off at an angle. Players who are successful in these sports must understand angles and must learn to control the angles at which balls hit and reflect off of the obstructions that lie in their paths.

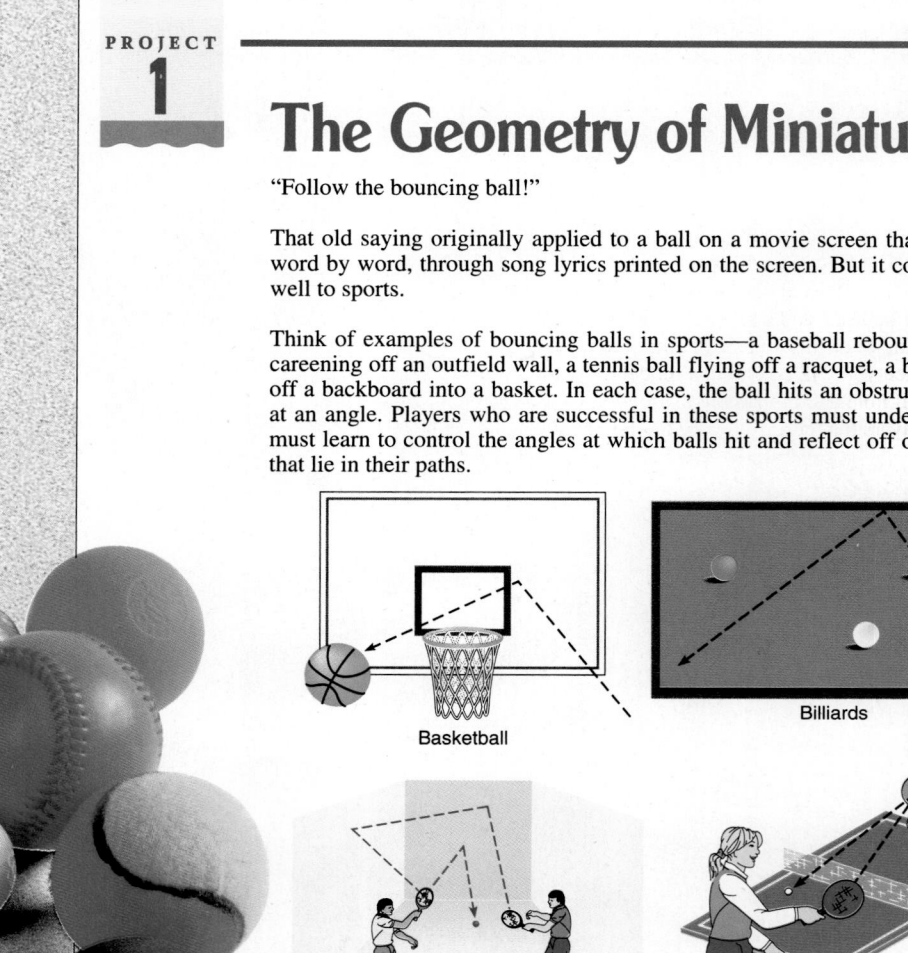

Basketball

Billiards

Raquetball

Table Tennis

Miniature golf is designed around the idea of a ball bouncing off an obstruction. The fun of the game lies in analyzing angles and hitting the ball so it ends up exactly where the player wants—in the cup!

B2

Analyzing Miniature Golf

In this project, your group will investigate how a ball bounces in miniature golf. You will work out strategies to determine the angle at which the ball should be hit so it will bounce off one or more obstructions and drop into the cup. Then you will construct a model of a miniature golf hole and prepare an instruction guide for players that describes how to play the hole.

B3

Project Description

Students will construct reflective surfaces and analyze the behavior of balls reflecting off those surfaces. After studying simple single-wall reflections, students will study two-wall, and perhaps three-wall, reflections. After they have thoroughly analyzed these situations, they will design and construct a "world-class" miniature golf hole and prepare a guide on how to play the hole, based on their findings.

Group Size

Students should work in groups of three to five.

Time

Students will need four to six weeks to complete the project.

Materials Needed

Students will need golf balls and putters. (Reasonable substitutes, such as rubber balls and putters constructed of wood, might also be used.) Short sections of 2-by-4s, stacks of books, weighted down pasteboard cartons, and similar materials can serve as reflecting surfaces. Materials for the hole students construct will depend on the designs and sizes of the holes. Space requirements might limit sizes to desktop-size models. However, if an area of the school grounds can be made available, groups might be able to construct full-size miniature golf holes.

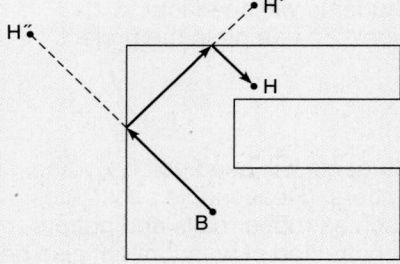
Getting Started

Have your group follow these steps.

1. Discuss the game of miniature golf. Ask individuals who have played the game to describe their strategies for playing.
2. Obtain several golf balls and putters.
3. Arrange an area where you can bounce balls off walls, 2-by-4s, or other obstructions you set up for the purpose. Use a cardboard circle to represent the cup.
4. Work together to learn how and where a golf ball should be hit so it ends up in the cup. You might use protractors or other measuring devices. Design situations like those shown below to test your theories. For each situation, ask yourself: At what angle should I hit the ball to make a hole-in-one?

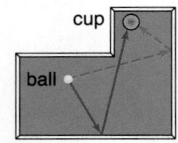
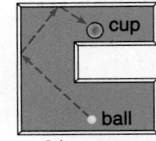
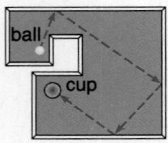

| 1 bounce (2 methods) | 2 bounces | 3 bounces |

As you analyze angles, keep in mind the importance of the stroke of the golf club. How does the way that you hold the club and the speed at which you hit the ball affect the way the ball bounces off each obstruction?

5. Discuss your results with your group. Then list conclusions your group has reached as a result of your investigation.
6. Work with your group to design the final, most challenging hole for next year's "World Championship of Miniature Golf." Decide on the shape of the green, the obstructions you will place in the ball's path, the placement of the tee and the cup, and so on. Discuss interesting miniature golf course features you have seen. For example, some courses place a windmill in the middle of one of the greens. The blades of the windmill turn continually, nearly touching the ground. A player must time their stroke so that the ball reaches the windmill when a blade is not obstructing the path. When creating your design, don't overlook such artistic matters as the landscaping of the hole, the color scheme you will use, and the overall attractiveness of the hole for players.
7. Build a model of the hole. Try to make the model look as much like an actual miniature golf course hole as possible.
8. Finally, prepare a guide for people who will play your hole in the championship. Suggest strategies for playing the hole. Describe ways to analyze the angles so that a player can figure out how to put the ball in the cup from the tee or anywhere else.

B4

Extensions

1. Billiards players use diamonds printed on the cushions of a billiards table to determine where to hit the cue ball so that it strikes the other balls.

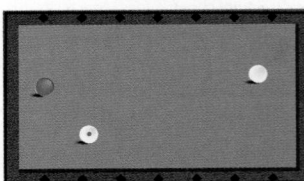

   Research the "diamond system" and report on how the diamonds are used to analyze the angle of a shot.

2. Choose a sport that interests you. Describe the importance of angles in the sport and explain how a player who understands how to play the angles has an advantage over players who do not.

3. Research and report on the law of physics which states that the angle of incidence is congruent to the angle of reflection.

Culminating Activities

Show what you have learned in this project by completing one of these activities.

1. Participate in a class model miniature golf tournament. Each group gives an oral presentation, displays and describes the design of its golf hole, points out special or unique features of the hole, and outlines methods for playing it. Each group might also prepare and distribute copies of its guidelines for playing the hole it designed. Students can then move from hole to hole to inspect each design and, if designs permit, to play the holes.

2. Prepare a handbook entitled "How to Win at Miniature Golf". In your handbook, explain the rules for playing the angles that you have discovered in your investigation.

B5

Assessment

Students should not be penalized for not discovering the reflection method described under "Tips for Groups." Praise any common sense or thoughtfully worked-out rule that students propose for striking the ball. In assessing student-designed holes, look for imagination, creative application of discoveries about angles, and interesting design and placement of obstructions.

Additional Notes

Be sure groups work on their projects regularly throughout the project period, rather than rush completion as the deadline approaches. You might provide regular times in class for groups to work on their projects.

Scoring Rubric

Top Level: Complete work. Clear, coherent, unambiguous explanation. Effective communication. Strong arguments. Understanding of math ideas and processes. Goes beyond requirements of problem.
Second Level: Solid work, but less complete than above. Does not go beyond requirements of problem.
Third Level: Complete response, but unclear explanation. Incomplete arguments. Some understanding of math, but vague or unclear responses.
Fourth Level: Omits significant parts. Major errors.

Objectives

- Research a career of interest.
- Search for applications of geometry in the career.
- Write a profile of the career highlighting geometry connections and applications

Overview

At the center of any study of Euclidean plane geometry is deductive logic. Formal proofs are precise applications of deduction. Theorems are "true" in the same sense that the assumptions on which they are based are true. The system is unmatched as a means of teaching careful, step-by-step deductive reasoning.

Because of its educational value as an abstract, self-contained system, geometry traditionally has been taught with little or no reference to its practicality. In recent years that has begun to change out of recognition that doing so does not harm the purity of the system, but adds considerable interest and motivation to the study itself. In this project, students will turn their attentions to practicality by researching applications of geometry in various careers.

Mathematical Content

Students can incorporate ideas from anywhere in the text in their work, depending on the careers they choose. Among geometric concepts with widespread application are deduction, congruence, measure, similarity, proportion, right triangles and the Pythagorean Theorem, area, volume, coordinate geometry, loci, and transformations.

PROJECT 2

Geometry in the Workplace

- A rough diamond will be worth $50,000 if the diamond cutter measures the angles and cuts the diamond precisely. However, it will be nearly worthless if she makes an error in measurement.

- A trial lawyer uses deductive reasoning to lead the jury step by step through the lawyer's argument. From hypothesis—that the defendant did not commit the crime—to conclusion, the lawyer contends that the jury should find the defendant innocent.

- A product engineer for a sporting goods manufacturer uses his knowledge of surface area and volume to design a strong yet light motorcross helmet.

Not long ago, geometry was taught as "pure" or abstract mathematics— mathematics that had little or no relationship to the real world. Students studied the subject solely to learn about the deductive system employed in Euclidean geometry and to study the principles of logic.

There was merit in that approach, and the abstractions of geometry still comprise the core of a modern geometry course. But educators now know the value in including everyday applications of geometry in their texts, and relating the subject to life outside the classroom. That is why this text emphasizes applications in addition to theory. Today's geometry courses demonstrate that geometry has theoretical importance and, as you will show in this project, importance in everyday life.

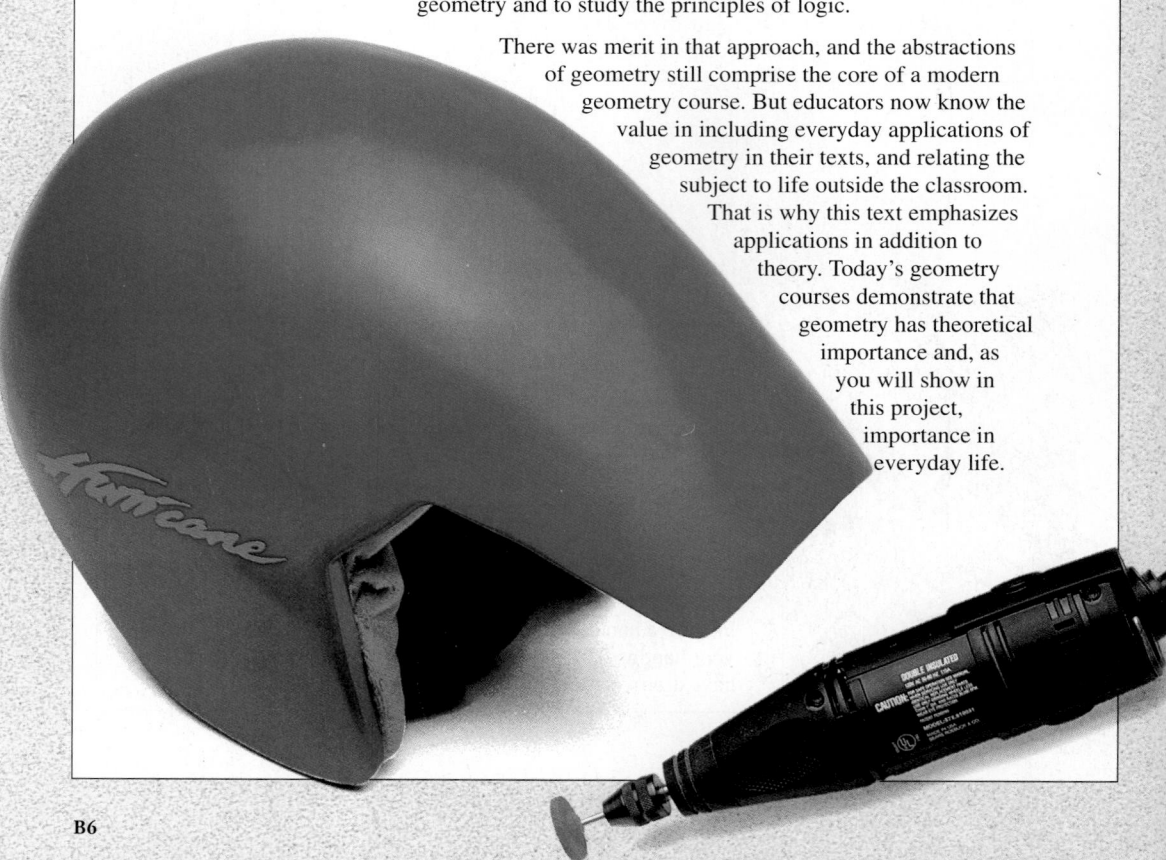

B6

Write a Career Profile

In this project, you will conduct research into a profession that interests you. Your goal is to find connections between that profession and geometry. Finally, you will write a career profile that highlights the connections and applications you have uncovered.

Project Description

Students begin by choosing careers which they would like to find out more about. They will research the careers and talk to people actively involved in them, with the goal of finding applications of geometry to each career. In some fields, geometry will play a central role. In others it might be of minor importance. In any case, students will document as many connections as they can find. Finally, students will demonstrate their understanding of their findings.

Group Size

Students might work alone or in groups of two to four students.

Time

Students will need four to six weeks to complete the project.

Materials Needed

Have available books, articles, and/or pamphlets relating to careers.

Resources

Encourage students to discuss careers with people who are pursuing them. While one of the objectives of this project is to demonstrate that geometry is all around us, students might find it difficult to find meaningful connections in some professions. If a student suspects this after talking to several people in the field, or if you suspect this when a student first discusses a project with you, you might suggest that the student choose another career.

B7

Tips for Groups

This will be a good group project if groups choose professions that are heavily involved with geometrical ideas, such as architecture or surveying. In such a case, a group might divide the work, assigning one aspect of the profession to each member. Students then can work as individuals, discussing their findings at periodic group meetings. When all have completed their assignments, students can meet again to compile their findings.

Assessment

Students should not be penalized for not finding large numbers of connections between geometry and the careers they choose. Instead, look for clear and precise descriptions of the connections they do find. Also check that students understand the relevance of each connection to the chosen profession.

Additional Notes

Be sure students work on their projects at a regular pace throughout the project period, rather than to attempt to complete them quickly as the deadline approaches. You might provide regular times in class for students to work on their projects.

Getting Started

Follow these steps to carry out your project.

1. Choose a career that interests you. You might already have an idea of the career path you would like to pursue. If not, spend some time thinking about a career. For now, consider a career solely from the standpoint of what you think might be an enjoyable and fulfilling line of work a few years from now. (There is nothing wrong with not knowing at this point what you want to do after you graduate. Some very successful people did not make their ultimate career choices until they were in their twenties or thirties, or even later.)

   You might ask yourself:
   - Which occupation(s) would enable me to do what I like to do most?
   - Which occupation(s) might provide the opportunity to best fulfill my potential?
   - Which occupation(s) would allow me time to spend with the kind of people I enjoy being with? to work with the kinds of things I like to work with?
   - Which occupation(s) offers benefits I might enjoy, such as travel or the opportunity to make a significant contribution to society?

   If you are still baffled, you might get some ideas by studying this list compiled by the U.S. Department of Labor. It lists occupations expected to grow more than 40% (in number of job openings) during the 1990s.

Medical assistants	Radiologic technicians
Home health aides	Data processing equipment repairers
Medical secretaries	Operations research analysts
Physical therapists	Surgical technicians
Travel agents	Computer systems analysts
Occupational therapists	Paralegals
Computer programmers	Child-care workers

2. Talk to people in the profession you have decided to research. Ask them about ways they might use geometry in their work. (Listen for even vague applications of geometry; they might lead to more fully developed ideas later on.) Before you meet with someone, prepare a list of ideas they might not think of as "geometrical," but that might help them find geometrical content in their work. Do they ever need to make logical deductions? Do they use measurements or proportions in their work? With reasonable effort, you should be able to uncover applications of geometry in nearly every profession.

3. Review the applications exercises in your text. They are listed at the bottom of each page in the table of contents. These problems will give you ideas about ways geometry is used in everyday life.

4. Read about the profession. Check the library for books about the profession or related professions. Your local or state employment office also might have booklets or statistics that relate to the occupation.

B8

Extensions

1. Consult the *U.S. Statistical Abstract,* a government publication that is produced annually. (Your public library should have a copy.) Find statistics on changes in earnings and numbers of jobs in major areas of employment in recent years. Prepare a visual that summarizes your findings.
2. Sherlock Holmes is perhaps the most famous literary character who used geometry—in the form of deductive logic—in his work. Read a Sherlock Holmes mystery (written by Arthur Conan Doyle) and report to the class on Holmes' use of deductive reasoning and logic.

Culminating Activities

Show what you have learned in this project by completing one of these activities.

1. Write a career profile entitled "Geometry and _____." Fill in the blank with the name of the profession you have investigated. In your profile, describe the kind of work that is done in the profession. Detail the educational background necessary to enter the field. Include the amount of mathematics that people in the profession typically have studied. Then describe your findings on relationships between geometry and the profession.
2. Participate in a "Career Day" with classmates. Prepare an exhibit that highlights interesting aspects of the profession you have researched, illustrating connections between the profession and geometry. During Career Day, visit the exhibits of other students and be prepared to answer questions about your exhibit. Discuss both the career itself and applications of geometry to the career.

Scoring Rubric

Top Level: Complete work. Clear, coherent, unambiguous explanation. Effective communication. Strong arguments. Understanding of math ideas and processes. Goes beyond requirements of problem.

Second Level: Solid work, but less complete than above. Does not go beyond requirements of problem.

Third Level: Complete response, but muddled explanation. Incomplete arguments. Some understanding of math, but vague or unclear responses.

Fourth Level: Omits significant parts. Major errors.

THE GEOMETRY OF NETWORKS

Objectives

- Analyze the factors involved in the creation of a transportation network and design such a network.
- Understand that compromise might be necessary to achieve objectives.

Overview

Few large-scale projects undertaken by government or industry can hope to satisfy everyone. As plans for a project proceed, new factors affecting the outcome arise every day. Compromises must be made. Changes may have to be made to save money. The introduction to this Extended Project points out the importance of cost in any significant undertaking, but there are many other factors. In this project, students will encounter some of those factors as they attempt to design a complex transportation network.

Mathematical Content

Students should incorporate ideas from Chapters 1-10 in their work, possibly including line segments, angles, graphs, and polygons. Students should study Lesson 10-9, "Polygons as Networks," as a prerequisite to the project.

PROJECT
3

The Geometry of Networks

Two engineers were each asked to design a fiber optics phone network that would connect five towns in the Colorado mountains. The phone company would choose the better of the designs for a new communications network to link the towns with the rest of the world.

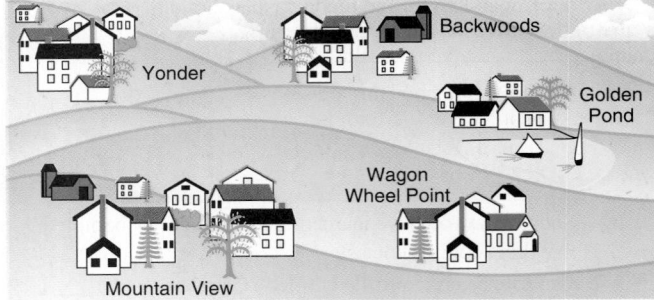

Study these drawings of the networks created by the two engineers.

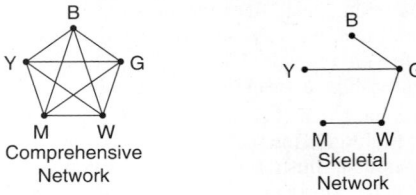

Comprehensive Network

Skeletal Network

The comprehensive network linked each town with every other town. Two hundred years ago, the comprehensive network might have served nicely for a pony express route. Each town would get the latest news no later than one day after any other town in the network.

However, fiber optic signals move at the speed of light, considerably faster than horses. No matter what the design of the network, a signal would reach the towns practically instantaneously. In addition, the critical factor for the phone company was cost, not speed. Laying fiber optics lines to these remote towns promised to be expensive. The shorter the total length of the lines, the cheaper the projected cost. The company chose the skeletal network.

Designing the best network to meet its goals is a critical matter for many organizations. As this example illustrates, cost is one factor that must be considered. But for a city designing a garbage collection network, customer convenience might also be a factor. When choosing a home-delivery network for postal carriers, speed and safety might be most important. Exactly what is "best" is likely to change from situation to situation.

B10

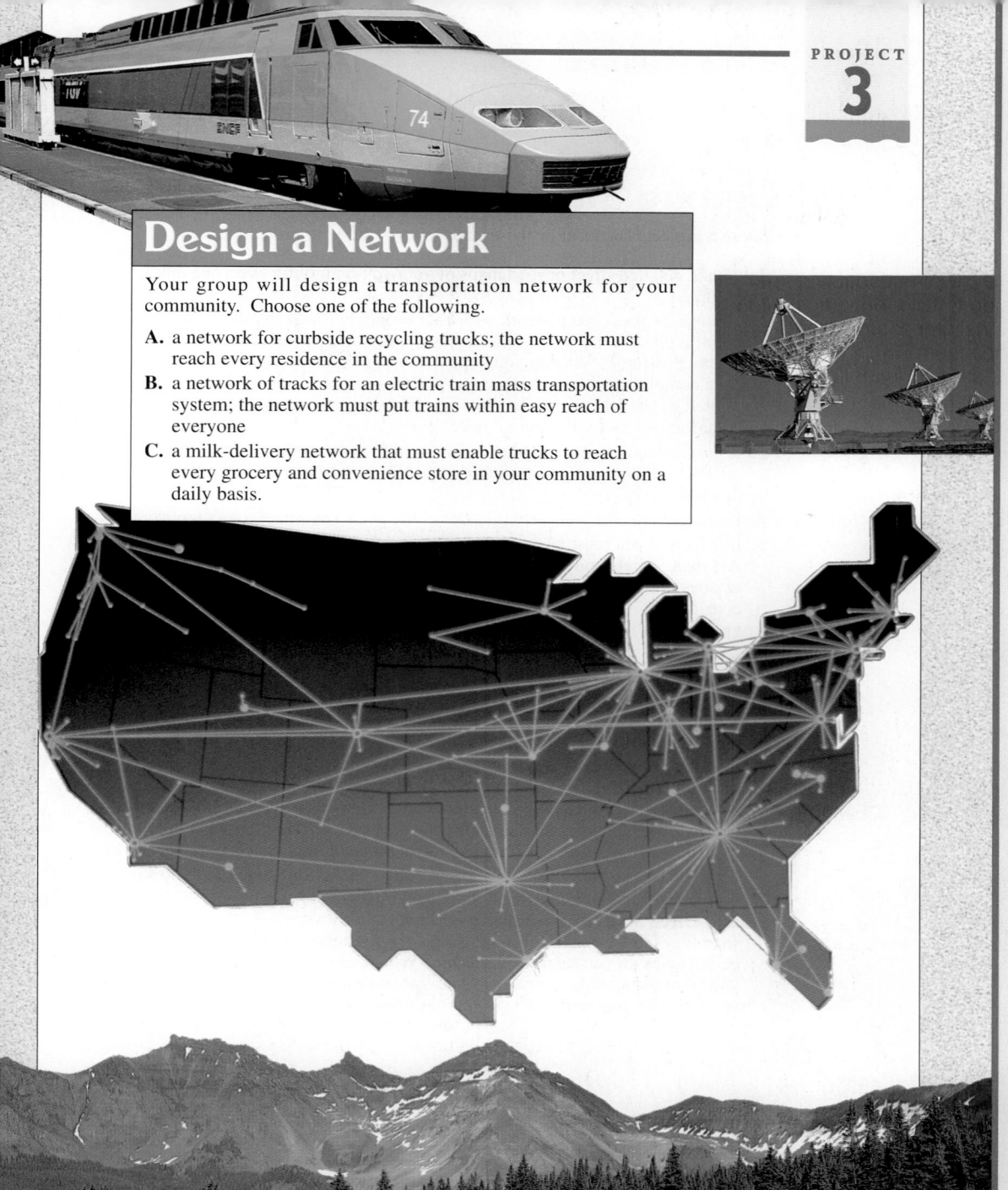

Design a Network

Your group will design a transportation network for your community. Choose one of the following.

A. a network for curbside recycling trucks; the network must reach every residence in the community

B. a network of tracks for an electric train mass transportation system; the network must put trains within easy reach of everyone

C. a milk-delivery network that must enable trucks to reach every grocery and convenience store in your community on a daily basis.

Project Description

Students will choose one of three projects to design transportation networks for their towns. The complexity of the networks range from a short public transportation system to a curbside recycling network that will reach every residence in town. Groups will compose a list of objectives they hope to accomplish and a list of factors they must consider in planning their networks. They will draw up master plans that describe their networks and how they intend to proceed. Then they will design the networks. At the completion of the projects, students will estimate the cost and time of setting up their networks, and critique their work.

Group Size

Students should work in groups of three to five.

Time

Students will need four to six weeks to complete the project.

Materials Needed

Each student will need a detailed map of their community.

Resources

Depending on the project they choose, groups might get help from an appropriate professional in the field. For Project A, a representative of the city's solid waste disposal or recycling agency might be of assistance. For Project B, a representative of the city's public transportation department might be able to help. For Project C, a representative of the sales or marketing divisions of any manufacturer might offer advice on planning delivery routes.

Tips for Groups

Suggest that groups begin by considering very small networks. Sketch an array of four or five points, a few streets, and several local landmarks on the board. Then ask students to consider the many networks which take in all of the points. Which network is shortest in distance? Which involves the fewest street crossings? Which ones finish at the opposite end from where they started? Which finish at the same end? Which would be most enjoyable or safest to walk on foot? (Answers will depend upon the network drawn. Accept all reasonable answers.)

Assessment

Consider how well groups met their objectives and how well they handled compromises they had to make. Students do not have to succeed completely at either task. However, as they proceed with their projects, they should do so with the objectives and considerations they identified in their master plans in view.

Additional Notes

At the conclusion of the project, discuss the projects with the class. Use these questions as springboards for discussion.

- Who will be most satisfied with your network?
- Who will be least satisfied?

Be sure groups work on their projects at a regular pace throughout the project period, rather than attempt to complete them quickly as the deadline approaches. You might provide regular times in class for groups to work on their projects.

Getting Started

Choose a project. Then follow these steps to carry out your project.

1. Obtain detailed street or road maps of your community for everyone in your group.
2. Discuss the proposed network with your group. For now, avoid making specific plans or suggestions regarding the network. Instead, concentrate on the "big picture." What do you hope to accomplish with the network? Do you have complete freedom to choose a "perfect" system, or are your choices limited by the realities of the situation? Who do you intend to serve? What compromises will you have to make?
3. If possible, talk to people who are involved in network design or in fields related to the system you are setting up. Ask their advice on how you might proceed.
4. List objectives for your network. Detail the goals you hope to accomplish.
5. List factors you must take into consideration in your plan. Is cost a factor? Are there streets you will be unable to use because of heavy traffic or other reasons? Are there special community groups whose needs must be considered?
6. Using your two lists as guides, prepare a description of the network as you see it at this stage of the project. Also prepare an outline of your group's ideas for implementing the network. (This step is similar to the "business plan" that a person who intends to go into business must write.)
7. You might conduct a survey of other students or adults to gather their opinions on the proposed network.
8. Design your network. You might begin by having each group member work out a "draft" network. The group can discuss the advantages and disadvantages of each network, and then work together to design the final network. Prepare a detailed map of your final network. Include a key that explains anything that someone looking at the map might need to know.
9. Estimate the cost of setting up your network and the time required to do so.
10. Remember that few projects on the scale of the network you have designed are perfect. Most large projects are completed only after numerous, and sometimes unpleasant, compromises have been made. What deficiencies do you see in your design? What factors might prevent you from completing your network as you envision it? How might you improve your network?

B12

Extensions

1. You can learn the fundamentals of the mathematics of networks in Lesson 10-9 of your text. Among related topics in this field are *loops, walks, shortest paths,* and *trees*. Research one or more of these topics and report your findings to the class.
2. Talk to a representative of your local phone company to find out about phone networks. How are the networks designed? What are the phone company's goals? What compromises must be made in order to reach those goals?
3. Companies that offer overnight delivery service can speed a package between any two points in the United States overnight. Find out how their delivery networks are designed.

Culminating Activities

Show what you have learned in this project by completing one of these activities.

1. Prepare a report for your community's government leaders or, if you chose the delivery network, your company's president. Summarize your work on the project. Outline your objectives, detail factors your group took into consideration, and explain the reasoning behind the principal decisions you made. Make whatever recommendations regarding the network you feel are necessary. Include a map of the network and an explanation of its features with your report.
2. Imagine you are a city council member or the company president and make an oral presentation to your classmates. Maintain that your network is the one that should be implemented. Include in your presentation elements listed in Culminating Activity 1. You might include graphs, displays, survey results, or any other visual materials that might help you make your case.

B13

Scoring Rubric

Top Level: Complete work. Clear, coherent, unambiguous explanation. Effective communication. Strong arguments. Understanding of math ideas and processes. Goes beyond requirements of problem.

Second Level: Solid work, but less complete than above. Does not go beyond requirements of problem.

Third Level: Complete response, but muddled explanation. Incomplete arguments. Some understanding of math, but vague or unclear responses.

Fourth Level: Omits significant parts. Major errors.

Extended Project 4

STRING ART DESIGNS

Objectives

Understand how mathematics is involved in the creation of pieces of art.

Construct a string art picture.

Overview

Students often feel that their work in mathematics is isolated and unrelated to other fields, especially the arts. However, geometry is and has been used in creating many different styles of paintings and sculpture. In string art creations, the mathematical structure is especially evident.

Mathematical Content

Students can incorporate geometric figures that are discussed anywhere in the book into their designs. Parallel, perpendicular, and intersecting lines, triangles, squares, rhombi, regular polygons, and circles are among the figures that students can use as the basis for many different-looking designs.

Project Description

Students will investigate different ways of using string to make a design for a string art picture. They will research the techniques artists use to create different feelings and effects in a painting. Using the techniques they discover, students will plan and complete a string art picture.

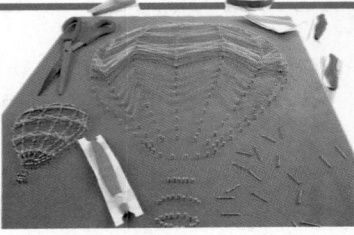

String Art Designs

It may seem like art is as far from mathematics as you can get. But, geometry is actually the basis for many artistic pieces. From the way people are rendered in Renaissance paintings to the form and support for a modern sculpture, art and mathematics are intertwined.

String art is a technique that uses geometry to create colorful and interesting designs. The designs may be recognizable objects or abstract images. In abstract designs, color and geometric shapes are useful tools for conveying motion or feelings. Two-dimensional pictures can be made on a wooden board with string or wire and three-dimensional pieces use string or wire on wooden or metal rods. String art designs have been created for homes, art museums, and public places like office buildings.

Create a String Art Picture

In this project, you will design and create a two-dimensional string art picture. You will draw designs, select colors and materials, and then construct the picture.

B14

Getting Started

Follow these steps to carry out your project.

1. Investigate the technique involved in string art design. Most designs are formed by placing equally-spaced nails around the edges of a figure. The basic angle is formed by numbering the nails along each side as shown below. Tie your string to nail 1 and loop the string to nail 1 on the other ray of the angle. Then loop your string to nail 2 on the same side of the angle, and loop it to nail 2 on the first side. Continue the pattern with nail 3.

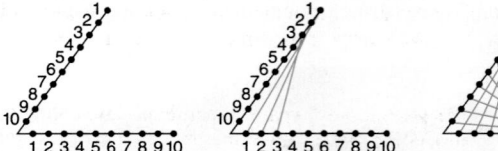

Explore the method of creating the designs shown below. Use a centimeter ruler to draw each shape and make equally-spaced marks on each side. Then determine how the string was looped to complete the design.

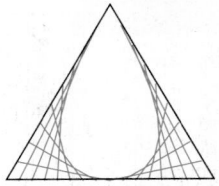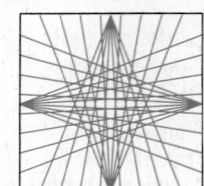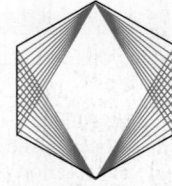

2. Research how artists use color and shape to convey motion and emotion in their creations. Determine what you would like your string design to look like. Will you make a recognizable object like a ship? Will you make an abstract design to convey a feeling like joy or sadness or an action like discovery or destruction?

3. Make a plan for your string art piece. Try combining figures to create the effect you are looking for. Pay attention to symmetry as well. If you plan to use more than one color of thread or to make layered designs, it may be helpful to use colored pencils as you draw. Drawing each layer or color of the design on tracing paper may also be used to show the variations in the design. Choose the colors of the string and a fabric for the background. Solid-colored backgrounds show the detail of string art designs well.

4. When you have decided on your plan, make a pattern for the nails you will need to string the art piece. Measure carefully to make the pattern as accurate as possible.

5. Have a teacher assist you in stretching a piece of opaque fabric over a piece of plywood and stapling it in the back. Then secure your pattern to the board and begin driving the nails. Small brads or brass nails will work best. Make sure that all of the nails are driven straight and to the same height.

6. Once the nailing is completed, use your plan to string the design. Strong cotton string like button thread or bedspread crochet thread will make the best designs. Start a string by tying it firmly to the first nail. Snip the thread as close to the knot as possible to avoid having a loose end showing. Be sure to pull the string taut as you complete the design, slack threads will detract from the finished piece.

B15

Group Size
Students should work alone or in pairs.

Time
Students will need four to six weeks to complete the project.

Materials Needed
Students will need a ruler, a compass, a protractor, colored pencils, and tracing paper to create their string art plans. To complete the picture, students will need opaque fabric, a piece of plywood, a staple gun, a hammer, small nails, and strong colored thread.

Resources
Students will need to refer to books on art and design. Books on technique as well as books on notable art pieces would be helpful as students make their designs. You might also invite a local artist or the art teacher in your school to talk to students on art techniques.

Tips for Groups
This project is best completed individually. However, if students work in pairs on this project, suggest that they each work on every stage of the project. Each student should have input as they make a plan for the picture. At certain points in the project it will be difficult for two people to work at once. Suggest that students take turns working. When stringing, each student can complete the work in one color.

Assessment

Some students will have more artistic designs than others. Look for careful planning, accurate nailing and stringing, creativity, and an interesting design.

Additional Notes

Be sure students work on their projects at a steady pace throughout the project period, rather than rush completion as the deadline approaches. You might provide regular times in each week for students to work on their projects.

Scoring Rubric

Top Level: Complete work. Well made picture with interesting design. Understanding of symmetry and mathematical and artistic elements. Goes beyond requirements of problem.

Second Level: Solid work, but less complete than above. Does not go beyond requirements of problem.

Third Level: Completed project, but not well done. Some understanding of math and art involved, but not well designed or executed.

Fourth Level: Omits significant parts.

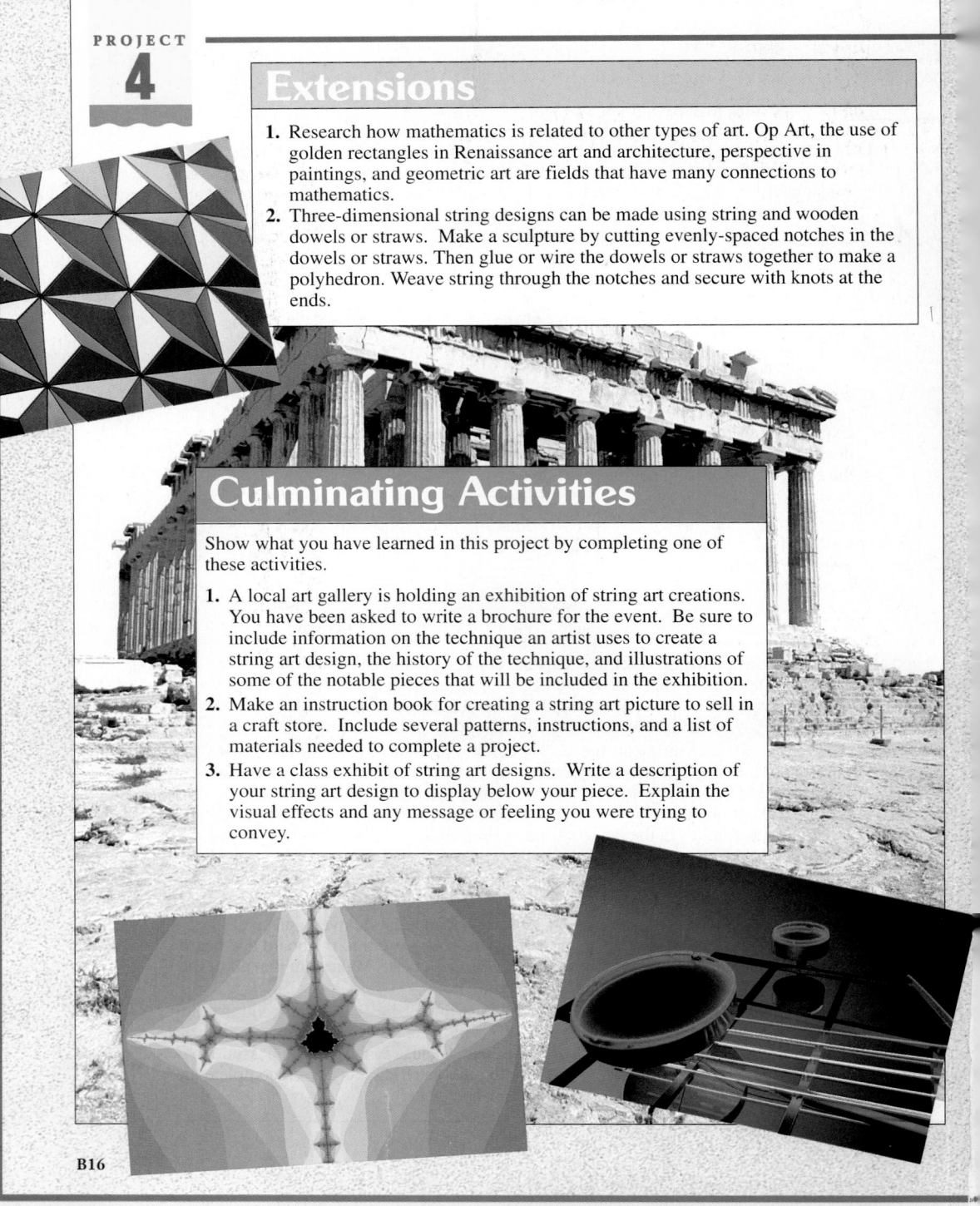

Extensions

1. Research how mathematics is related to other types of art. Op Art, the use of golden rectangles in Renaissance art and architecture, perspective in paintings, and geometric art are fields that have many connections to mathematics.
2. Three-dimensional string designs can be made using string and wooden dowels or straws. Make a sculpture by cutting evenly-spaced notches in the dowels or straws. Then glue or wire the dowels or straws together to make a polyhedron. Weave string through the notches and secure with knots at the ends.

Culminating Activities

Show what you have learned in this project by completing one of these activities.

1. A local art gallery is holding an exhibition of string art creations. You have been asked to write a brochure for the event. Be sure to include information on the technique an artist uses to create a string art design, the history of the technique, and illustrations of some of the notable pieces that will be included in the exhibition.
2. Make an instruction book for creating a string art picture to sell in a craft store. Include several patterns, instructions, and a list of materials needed to complete a project.
3. Have a class exhibit of string art designs. Write a description of your string art design to display below your piece. Explain the visual effects and any message or feeling you were trying to convey.

B16